MECHANICS OF MATERIALS

By

Dr. B.C. PUNMIA

Formerly,
Professor and Head, Deptt. of Civil Engineering, &
Dean, Faculty of Engineering
M.B.M. Engineering College,
Jodhpur

Er. ASHOK KUMAR JAIN
Director,
Arihant Consultants,
Jodhpur

Dr. ARUN KUMAR JAIN
Assistant Professor
M.B.M. Engineering College,
Jodhpur

CONTAINING 27 CHAPTERS

(ENTIRELY IN SI UNITS)

LAXMI PUBLICATIONS (P) LTD

**BANGALORE ● CHENNAI ● COCHIN ● GUWAHATI ● HYDERABAD
JALANDHAR ● KOLKATA ● LUCKNOW ● MUMBAI ● RANCHI
NEW DELHI ● BOSTON, USA**

Published by :
LAXMI PUBLICATIONS (P) LTD
113, Golden House, Daryaganj,
New Delhi-110002

Phone : 011-43 53 25 00
Fax : 011-43 53 25 28

www.laxmipublications.com
info@laxmipublications.com

© 2001, 2007   B.C. Punmia, Ashok Kumar Jain and Arun Kumar Jain

---

Price : ₹ **595.00** *Only.*

First Edition : 2001
Reprints : Jan. 2002, Aug. 2003, Sept. 2004, Aug. 2005, Sept. 2006, Aug. 2007
June 2008, Sept. 2008, May 2009, Sept. 2009, Dec. 2009, Aug. 2010, Sept. 2011, April 2012, Oct. 2012

OFFICES

© **Bangalore**	080-26 75 69 30		© **Chennai**	044-24 34 47 26	
© **Cochin**	0484-237 70 04, 405 13 03		© **Guwahati**	0361-251 36 69, 251 38 81	
© **Hyderabad**	040-24 65 23 33		© **Jalandhar**	0181-222 12 72	
© **Kolkata**	033-22 27 43 84		© **Lucknow**	0522-220 99 16	
© **Mumbai**	022-24 91 54 15, 24 92 78 69		© **Ranchi**	0651-220 44 64	

EMM-0577-595-MECHANICS OF MATERIALS-JAI   C—5711/012/10
Typeset at : Arihant Consultants, Jodhpur.   *Printed at* : Printman India, Delhi.

Preface

For an efficient, critical and competitive design of a machine or a structure, a thorough knowledge of Strength or Mechanics of Materials is essential. Consequently, the modern engineering curriculum lays greater emphasis on the comprehensive study of the fundamentals as well as advanced concepts of Mechanics of Materials. The book, through its twenty seven chapters, covers almost all the standard topics of strength or mechanics of materials. Each chapter includes topics of both the elementary as well as advanced and specialised nature. Hence it can be used both as a standard text as well as the reference for professional/field designs. Through their long teaching, design and professional experience, the Authors have made an attempt to present the subject matter which lays emphasis on fundamentals, keeping in view the difficulties confronted by the students. Permissible stresses have been adopted as per the latest recommendations contained in various Standards published by the Bureau of Indian Standards (formerly, Indian Standards Institution), New Delhi.

Starting with an introductory chapter on *mechanical properties of materials*, chapters 2 to 5 are devoted on *stress and strain,* with chapter 5 dealing with more advanced topics on *analysis of strain.* Chapter 6 is on *strain energy*, while chapter 7 includes advanced material on *theories of failure.* Most of chapters use the *properties of area* of a plane lamina; hence these properties have been discussed thoroughly in chapter 8. Chapters 9 to 17 deal with *bending aspects of beams*, incorporating bending moment, shear force, bending stresses, shearing stresses, slope and deflection of various types of beams. The effects of *axial loads,* with or without eccentricity, as well as *lateral loads,* have been dealt with in chapters 18 to 20, along with the *design aspects.* Chapters 21 and 22 deals with *torsion of shafts and springs. Pressure vessels*, both thin and thick, have been included in chapters 23 and 24, incorporating both the analysis as well as the design aspects. Chapter 25 includes the analysis of *perfect frames.* Lastly, chapters 26 and 27 deal with the analysis and design of *riveted and welded joints.*

Each chapter, starting with assumptions and theory, is complete in itself and is built up logically to cover all aspects of the particular theory, and in some cases, designs also. Both worked examples and unsolved problems are given in the text, and all these are treated in SI units. Some examples are based on questions set up by various examining bodies, and thankful acknowledgement is recorded here. Though utmost care has been taken to eliminate errors, some may still remain, and we would be thankful if these are pointed out. The Authors are thankful to Shri M.S. Gahlot for Laser Type Setting and to Shri Kanhya Lal for tracing the diagrams. Finally, the Authors are thankful to Shri R.K. Gupta of Laxmi Publications (P) Ltd. for good printing and excellent get up to the book and that too in a record short period.

Jodhpur
Gandhi Jayanti,
2-10-2001

B.C. PUNMIA
ASHOK K. JAIN
ARUN K. JAIN

Contents

Mechanical Properties of Materials

1.1. IMPORTANT MECHANICAL PROPERTIES

The following are the most important *mechanical properties* of *engineering materials:*

(i)	Elasticity	(ii)	Plasticity
(iii)	Ductility	(iv)	Brittleness
(v)	Malleability	(vi)	Toughness
(vii)	Hardness, and	(viii)	Strength

Some of the above properties can not be mutually reconciled; hence no material can possess them all simultaneously. The criteria of suitability (or otherwise) of an engineering material, forming part of either a machine or a structure, is dependent upon the possession of one or more of the above properties. The above properties are assessed, with a fair degree of accuracy, by resorting to *mechanical tests.*

1.2. ELASTICITY

When external forces are applied on a body, made of engineering materials, the external forces tend to deform the body while the molecular forces acting between the molecules offer resistance against *deformation.* The deformation or displacement of the particles continues till full resistance to the external forces is setup. If the forces are now gradually diminished, the body will return, wholly or partly to its original shape. *Elasticity is the property by virtue of which a material deformed under the load is enabled to return to its original dimension when the load is removed.* If a body regains completely its original shape, it is said to be *perfectly elastic.* For any particular material, a critical value of the load, known as the *elastic limit* marks the partial break down of elasticity beyond which removal of load results in a degree of *permanent deformation* or *permanent set* (Fig. 1.1). Steel, aluminium, copper, stone, concrete etc. may be considered to be perfectly elastic, within certain limits.

Stress-Strain relationship : The load per unit area, normal to the applied load is known as *stress (p).* Similarly, the deformation per unit length in the direction of deformation is known as *strain (ε).* The elastic properties of materials used in engineering are determined by tests performed on small specimens of material. The tests are conducted in materials-testing-laboratories equipped with testing machines capable of loading the specimens in gradually applied increments, and the resulting stresses and strains are measured at all such load increments, till the specimen fails. Fig. 1.1 shows one such stress-strain diagram (schematic). In Fig. 1.1(*a*), the specimen is loaded only upto point *A*, well within the elastic limit *E*. When the load, corresponding to point *A*, is gradually removed the curve follows the same path *AO* and the strain completely disappears. Such a behaviour is known as the *elastic behaviour.* In Fig. 1.1(*b*), the specimen

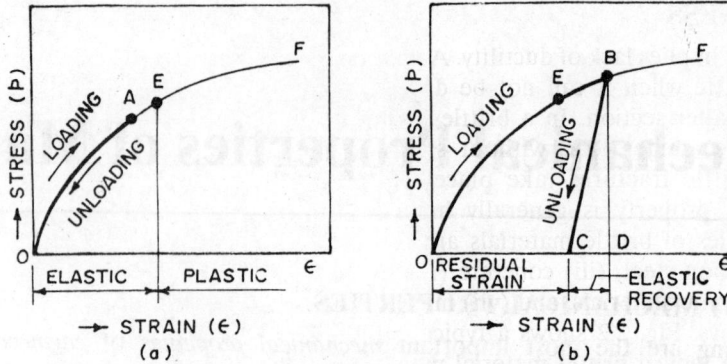

FIG. 1.1. ELASTICITY AND PLASTICITY

is loaded upto point B, beyond the elastic limit E. When the specimen is gradually *unloaded*, the curve follows path BC, resulting in a *residual strain* (OC) or permanent strain. Such a behaviour of the material, loaded beyond the elastic limit, is known as partially elastic behaviour. A more detailed discussion of stress-strain curve is given in § 2.4.

Homogeneity and Isotropy : A material is homogeneous if it has *same composition* throughout the body. For such a material, the *elastic properties* are the same at each and every point in the body. It is interesting to note that for a homogeneous material, the elastic properties need not be the same in all the directions. If a material is equally elastic in all the directions, it is said to be *isotropic*. If, however, it is not equally elastic in all directions, *i.e.* it possesses different elastic properties in different directions, it is called *anisotropic*. A *theoretically ideal material* could be equally elastic in all directions, *i.e.* isotropic. Many structural materials meet the requirements of homogeneity and isotropy. We shall be dealing with only the homogeneous and isotropic materials in this book.

1.3. PLASTICITY

Plasticity is the converse of elasticity. A material in *plastic state* is permanently deformed by the application of load, and it has no tendency to recover. Every elastic material possesses the property of plasticity. Under the action of large forces, most engineering materials become *plastic* and behave in a manner similar to a *viscous liquid*. The characteristic of the material by which it undergoes *inelastic strains* beyond those at the *elastic limit* is known as *plasticity*. When large deformations occur in a ductile material loaded in the *plastic region*, the material is said to undergo *plastic flow*. The property is particularly useful in the operations of *pressing* and *forging*. 'Plasticity' is also useful in the design of structural members, utilising its *ultimate strength*.

1.4. DUCTILITY

Ductility is the characteristic which permits a material to be drawn out longitudinally to a reduced section, under the action of a tensile force. In a ductile material, therefore, large deformation is possible before *absolute failure* or *rupture* takes place. A ductile material must, of necessity, possess a high degree of *plasticity* and *strength*. During ductile extension, a material shows a certain degree of elasticity, together with a considerable degree of plasticity. Ductility is measured in the tensile test of specimen of the material, either in terms of percentage elongation or in terms of percentage reduction in the cross-sectional area of the test specimen. The property of ductility is utilised in wire drawing.

1.5. BRITTLENESS

Brittleness implies lack of ductility. A material is said to be brittle when it can not be drawn out by tension to smaller section. In a brittle material, failure takes place under load without significant deformation. Brittle fractures take place without warning and the property is generally highly undesirable. Examples of brittle materials are (i) cast iron (ii) high carbon steel, (iii) concrete (iv) stone, (v) glass, (vi) ceramic materials, and (vii) many common metallic alloys. Fig. 2.2 shows a typical stress-strain curve for a typical brittle material which fail with only little elongation after proportional limit (point A) is exceeded, and the fracture stress (point F) is the same as ultimate stress. Ordinary glass is a nearly ideal brittle material in which the stress-

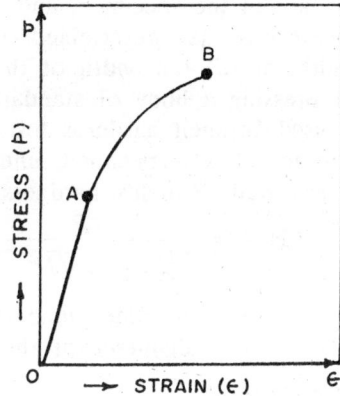

FIG. 1.2. STRESS STRAIN CURVE FOR A BRITTLE MATERIAL

strain curve in tension is essentially a straight line, with failure occurring before any yielding takes place. Thus, glass exhibits almost no ductility whatsoever.

1.6. MALLEABILITY

Malleability is a property of a material which permits the materials to be extended in all directions without rupture. *A malleable material possesses a high degree of plasticity, but not necessarily great strength.* This property is utilised in many operations such as forging, hot rolling, drop-stamping etc.

1.7. TOUGHNESS

Toughness is the property of a material which enables it to absorb energy without fracture. This property is very desirable in components subject to cyclic or shock loading. Toughness is measured in terms of energy required per unit volume of the material, to cause rupture under the action of gradually increasing tensile load. This energy includes the work done upto the elastic limit which is small in comparison with the energy subsequently expanded. Fig. 1.3 shows the stress-strain curves, both for mild steel as well as high carbon steel. The toughness is represented by the area under the stress-strain curve for the material. A common comparative test for toughness is the bend test in which a material is expected to sustain angular bending without failure.

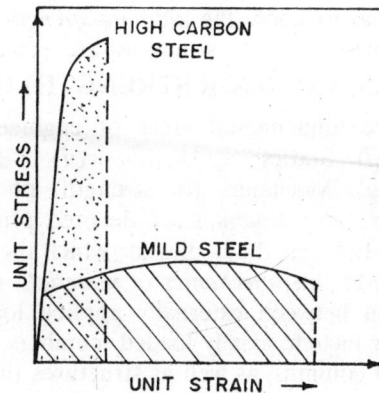

FIG. 1.3. MEASURE OF TOUGHNESS.

1.8. HARDNESS

Hardness is the ability of a material to resist indentation or surface abrasion. Since these resistances are not necessarily synonymous, it is usual to base the estimation of the hardness of a material on resistance to indentation only. Tests on hardness may be classified into (i) scratch test, and (ii) indentation test. The scratch test consists of pressing a loaded diamond into the surface of the specimen, and then pulling the diamond so as to make a scratch. The *hardness number* is then determined on the basis of (i) load required to make a scratch of a given width, or (ii) the width of the scratch made with a given load. The *indentation test* consists of pressing a body of standard shape into the surface of the test specimen. In the commonly used Brinnell hardness test a hardened steel ball of a given diameter is squeezed into the surface of test specimen, under a fixed standard load and then surface area of the indent is measured. Brinell's hardness number (B.H.N.) is then given by :

$$\text{B.H.N.} = \frac{P}{\frac{\pi D}{2}[D - \sqrt{D^2 - d^2}]}$$

where P = Standard load (N) ; D = diameter of steel ball (mm)
d = diameter of the indent (mm)

1.9. STRENGTH

This is the most important property of a material, from design point of view. *The strength of a material enables it to resist fracture under load.* The load required to cause fracture, divided by the area of the test specimen, is termed as the *ultimate strength* of the material, and is expressed in the unit of stress. An important consideration in engineering design is the capacity of the object (such as building structure, machine, air craft, vehicle, ship etc.), usually referred to as *structure*, to support or transmit loads. If structural failure is to be avoided, the loads that a structure actually can support must be greater than the loads it will be required to sustain when in service. Since the ability of a *structure* to resist loads is called *strength*, the governing criterion is that the *actual strength* of a structure must exceed the required strength. The ratio of the actual strength to the required strength is called the *factor of safety*. However, failure may occur under the action of tensile load, compressive load or shear load. Hence it is essential to know the *ultimate strength* of the material in each of these three conditions, and the three ultimate strengths are separately determined experimentally.

1.10. MECHANICS (OR STRENGTH) OF MATERIALS

Three fundamental areas of engineering mechanics (or applied mechanics) are
(i) Statics   (ii) Dynamics
and   (iii) Mechanics (or strength) of materials.

Statics and dynamics are devoted primarily to the study of the *extended effects* of forces on rigid bodies, *i.e.* the bodies for which the change in shape (or deformations) can be neglected. In contrast to this, *mechanics of materials,* commonly known as *strength of materials* deals with the relation between externally applied loads and their *internal effects* on solid bodies. The *solid bodies* include axially loaded members, shaft in torsion, thin and thick cylinders and shells, beams, and columns, as well as structures that are assemblies of these components. These bodies are no longer assumed to be rigid ; the deformation, however small, are of major interest. In actual design, the engineer must consider both dimensions and material properties to satisfy the requirements of *strength* and *rigidity*. A machine part or structure should neither break nor deform excessively. The purpose of studying *strength of materials* is to ensure that the structure used will be safe against maximum internal effects that may be produced by any combination of loading.

Simple Stresses and Strains

2.1. SIMPLE STRESSES

When a body (*i.e.* structural element) is acted upon by external force or load, internal resisting force is set up. Such a body is then said to be in a *state of stress*, where *stress is the resistance offered by the body to deformation.* For further understanding of this internal resistance, consider a *prismatic bar AB* subjected to axial forces at the ends as shown in Fig. 2.1 (*a*). A *prismatic bar* is a straight structural member of uniform cross-section (*A*) throughout its length (*L*). In order to know the *internal stresses* produced in the prismatic bar, take a section *mn* normal to the longitudinal axis of the bar ; such a section is known as

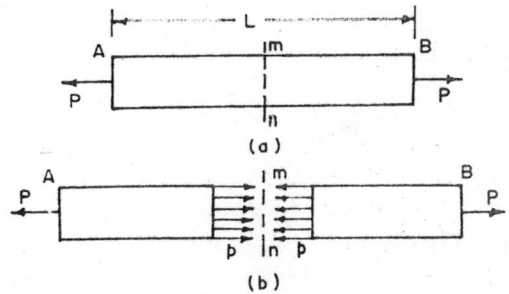

FIG. 2.1. STATE OF STRESS

a *cross-section*. If we consider the equilibrium of either the left part or the right part at section *mn*, taken as a free body, the *internal resistance* or the stress (*p*) offered by the molecules against the external force may be assumed to be uniformly distributed over the whole area of cross-section. Then

$$p = \frac{P}{A} \qquad \qquad ...(2.1)$$

where p = Internal resistance = stress = intensity of force.
         A = Area of cross-section normal to the axis.

As the stress p acts in a direction perpendicular to the cut surface, it is referred to as a *normal stress*. Since the normal stress p is obtained by dividing the axial force by the cross-sectional area, it has the units of force per unit area, such as kN/m^2 or N/mm^2

Saint Venant's principle

We have assumed above that the distribution of stress over the cross-section *mn* is *uniform*. This assumption is based on Saint Venant's principle. This principle states that except in the region of extreme ends of a bar carrying direct loading, the stress distribution over the cross-section is *uniform*.

(5)

Consider a square bar (Fig. 2.2a) of section $b \times b$, subjected to axial force P. The stress distribution at section $m_1 n_1$, distant $b/2$ from the end is shown in Fig. 2.2 (b), where the maximum normal stress (p_{max}) is found to be equal to 1.387 times the average stress (p_{av}). The stress distribution at section $m_2 n_2$, distant b from the end is shown in Fig. 2.2 (c), where p_{max} is found to be 1.027 p_{av}. Lastly, at section $m_3 n_3$, distant $3b/2$ from the end (Fig. 2.2 d), p_{max} is found to be equal to p_{av}. This illustrates Saint Venant's famous principal of *rapid dissipation of localised stresses*. Hence in all practical cases of stress analysis, St. Venant's principle can be safely followed, and the normal stress distribution given by Eq. 2.1 can be assumed.

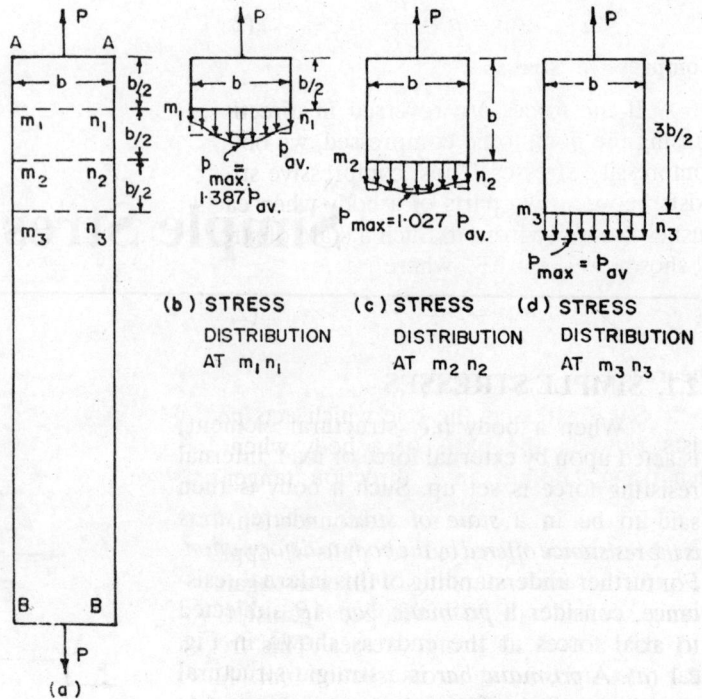

FIG. 2.2. St. VENANT'S PRINCIPLE

2.2. KINDS OF STRESSES

There are the following kinds of stresses

(1) Normal stresses

  (i) Tensile stress

  (ii) Compressive stress

(2) Shear stress or tangential stress

(3) Bending stress

(4) Twisting or torsional stress

(5) Bearing stress

Normal stresses

When a stress acts in a direction perpendicular to the cut surface, it is known as *normal stress* or *direct stress*. Normal stresses are of two types : (i) tensile stress, and (ii) compressive stress.

Tensile stress

When a body is stretched by the force P, as shown in Fig. 2.1, the resulting stresses are tensile stresses. Thus tensile stress exists between two parts of a body when each draws the other towards itself. Such a state of stress is shown in Fig. 2.1 where

$$p_{av} = p = \frac{P}{A} \qquad ...(2.1)$$

Compressive stress

If the forces are reversed in direction, causing the body to be compressed, we obtain compressive stresses. Thus, compressive stress exists between two parts of a body when each pushes the other from it. Such a state of stress is shown in Fig. 2.3. where

$$p_{av} = p = \frac{P}{A} \qquad ...(2.2)$$

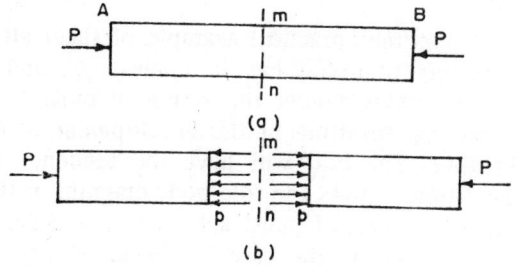

FIG. 2.3. COMPRESSIVE STRESS

Shear stress

Shear stress is the one which acts *parallel* or *tangential* to the surface. Thus, shear stress exists between the parts of a body when the two parts exert equal and opposite forces on each other laterally in a direction tangential to their surface in contact.

Fig. 2.4 (a) shows a riveted connection, where the rivet resists the shear across its cross-sectional area (A), when subjected to pulls P applied to the plates so jointed. Under the action of the pulls P, the two plates will press against the rivet in *bearing*, and contact stresses, called *bearing stresses* will be developed against the rivet. A free-body diagram of the rivet (Fig. 2.4 a ii) shows these bearing stresses. This free body diagram shows that there is a tendency to shear the rivet along cross section *mn*. From the free body diagram of the section *mn* of the rivet (Fig. 2.4 a iii), we see that shear force V acts over the cut surface. In this particular case (known as the case of *single shear*), the shear force V is equal to P. This shear force is, infact, the resultant of the shear stresses distributed over the cross-sectional area of the rivet, shown in Fig. 2.4 (a iv).

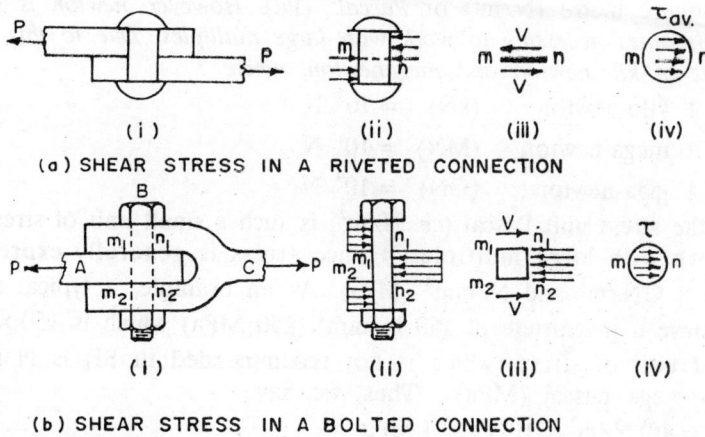

(i)   (ii)   (iii)   (iv)

(a) SHEAR STRESS IN A RIVETED CONNECTION

(i)   (ii)   (iii)   (iv)

(b) SHEAR STRESS IN A BOLTED CONNECTION

FIG. 2.4. EXAMPLES OF DIRECT SHEAR OR SIMPLE SHEAR

The average shear stress on the cross-section of the rivet is obtained by dividing the shear force V by the area of cross-section (A) of the rivet :

$$\tau_{av} = \frac{V}{A} = \frac{P}{A} \qquad\qquad ...(2.3)$$

Another practical example of shear stress is the bolted connection shown in Fig. 2.4(*b*), consisting of a flat bar *A*, a clevis *C*, and a bolt *B* that passes through holes in the bar and the clevis. Under the action of pulls *P*, the bar and the clevis will press against the bolt in *bearing*, resulting in the development of *bearing stresses* against the bolt, as shown in Fig. 2.4 (*bii*). The bolt will have the tendency to get sheared across sections $m_1 n_1$ and $m_2 n_2$. Fig 2.4(*biii*) shows the free body diagram of the portion $m_1 n_1 - m_2 n_2$ of the bolt, which suggests that shear forces *V* must act over the cut surfaces $m_1 n_1$ and $m_2 n_2$ of the bolt. In this particular case (known as the case of *double shear*), each shear force is equal to *P*/2 . These shear forces are in fact the resultants of the shear stresses distributed over the cross-sectional area of the bolt, at sections $m_1 n_1$ and $m_2 n_2$ (Fig. 2.4 *b iv*).

The average shear stress on the cross-section of the bolt is obtained by dividing the shear force *V* by the area of the cross-section (*A*) of the bolt :

$$\tau_{av} = \frac{V}{A} = \frac{P}{2A} \qquad\qquad ...(2.3\ a)$$

The examples shown in Fig. 2.4 are the examples of *direct shear* or *simple shear*. Such direct stresses arise in bolted, pinned, riveted, welded or glued joints, wherein the shear stresses are caused by a direct action of the force trying to act through the material. Shear stresses are also developed in an *indirect* manner when members are subjected to bending or torsion.

Bending stresses, torsional stresses and bearing stresses have been discussed in later chapters.

Units of stress

(*i*) *SI system* : Since normal stress *p* is obtained by dividing the axial force by the cross-sectional area, it has *units* of force per unit of area. In S.I. units, the unit of force is *newton* expressed by the symbol N, and the area is expressed in square metres (m^2) . Hence the unit of stress is newtons per square metre (N/m^2) or *Pascals* (Pa). *However, newton is such a small unit of stress that it becomes necessary to work with large multiples. Due to this, force is generally expressed in terms of kilo-newton and meganewton, where :*

$$1 \text{ kilo-newton} \quad (kN) \quad = 10^3 \text{ N}$$
$$1 \text{ mega-newton} \quad (MN) \quad = 10^6 \text{ N}$$
$$1 \text{ giga-newton} \quad (GN) \quad = 10^9 \text{ N}$$

Similarly, the stress unit Pascal (*i.e.* N/m^2) is such a small unit of stress that it becomes necessary to work with large multiples. Hence stress is generally expressed in terms of kN/m^2, MN/m^2, GN/m^2 and N/mm^2 (MPa). As an example, a typical tensile stress in a steel bar might have a magnitude of 150 N/mm^2 (150 MPa) which is 150×10^6 Pa . A more common form of unit of stress (which is not recommended in SI) is N/mm^2, which is a unit identical to mega pascal (MPa)   Thus, we have

$$1 \, N/mm^2 = 10^6 \, N/m^2 = 10^6 \, Pa = 1 \, MPa$$

(*ii*) *M.K.S. system* : In M.K.S. system, the unit of force is in the *gravitational unit, i.e.* kilogram force kg(f), commonly expressed by kg only. When force is large, it is expressed by tonnes, where 1 t = 1000 kg . The unit of stress´ is usually expressed as kg/cm^2.

The following relationships exist :

$$1 \ kg(f) = g \ \text{newtons}$$

Taking $\qquad g = 9.807,$

$$1 \ kg(f) = 9.807 \ N \approx 10 \ N$$

Also, $\qquad 1 \ \text{tonne} = 9.807 \ kN \approx 10 \ kN$

Hence $\qquad 1 \ kg/cm^2 \approx \dfrac{10 \ N}{10^{-4} \ m^2} \approx 10^5 \ N/m^2 \approx 10^5 \ Pa$

or $\qquad 1 \ kg/cm^2 \approx \dfrac{10^5 \ N}{10^6 \ mm^2} \approx 0.1 \ N/mm^2$

2.3. STRAIN

When a prismatic bar is subjected to axial load, it undergoes a change in length, as indicated in Fig. 2.5. This change in length is usually called *deformation*. If the axial force is tensile, the length of the bar is increased, while if the axial force is compressive, there is shortening of the length of the bar. This *elongation* (or shortening), as the case may be, is the cumulative result of the stretching (or compressing) of the material throughout the length L of the bar. The deformation (*i.e.* elongation or shortening) per unit length of the bar is termed as strain (ε or e). In general, *strain* is the *measure* of the deformation caused due to external loading.

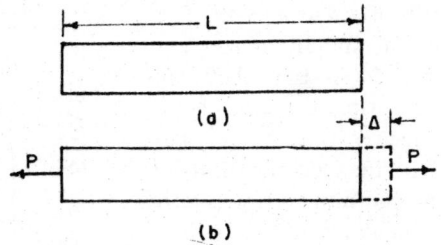

FIG. 2.5. DEFORMATION AND STRAIN

If the bar is in tension, the resulting strain is known as *tensile strain*. Similarly, the strain resulting from a compressive force is known as *compressive strain*. In general, strains associated with *normal stresses* are known as *normal strains*. Similarly, the strain associated with shear stress is known as *shear strain*.

Since strain is the deformation per unit length, it is a *dimensionless quantity*. Thus, it has no units, and therefore, it is expressed as pure number. For example, if the deformation of a bar of 1.6 m length is 1.2 mm, the strain $\varepsilon = \Delta/L = 1.2 \ mm/1.6 \times 1000 \ mm = 0.00075 = 750 \times 10^{-6}$. Some times, in practice, strain is recorded in forms such as mm/m or μ m/m etc. Thus, strain of the above example is 0.75 mm/m or 750 μ m/m.

Example 2.1. A prismatic bar has a cross-section of 25 mm × 50 mm and a length of 2 m. Under an axial tensile force of 90 kN, the measured elongation of the bar is 1.5 mm. Compute the tensile stress and strain in the bar.

Solution

Stress $p = \dfrac{P}{A} = \dfrac{90 \times 1000}{25 \times 50}$

$\qquad = 72 \ N/mm^2$ (or MPa)

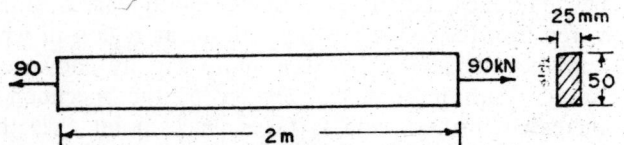

FIG. 2.6

Strain $$\varepsilon = \frac{\Delta}{L} = \frac{1.5 \text{ mm}}{(2 \times 1000) \text{ mm}} = 0.00075 = 750 \times 10^{-6}$$

2.4 . STRESS - STRAIN DIAGRAM

The mechanical properties of a material, discussed in chapter 1, are determined in the laboratory by performing tests on small specimens of the material, in the *materials testing laboratory*. The most common materials test is the *tension test* performed on a cylindrical specimen of the material. The loads are measured on the main dial of the machine while the elongations are measured with the help of *extensometers*. The cylindrical specimen has enlarged ends so that they can fit in the grips of the machine. This ensures that failure will occur in the central uniform region, where the stress is easy to be calculated rather than at or near ends where the stress distribution is not uniform. When such a specimen of a ductile material is subjected to a gradually increasing pull in a tension test machine, it is found that the resultant strain

A = Proportional Limit	Oa = Linear Deformation
B = Elastic Limit	Ob = Elastic Deformation
C = Yield Point	bd = Perfect Plastic Yielding
C' = Lower Yield Point	de = Strain Hardening
E = Ultimate Strength	ef = Necking
F = Rupture Strength	

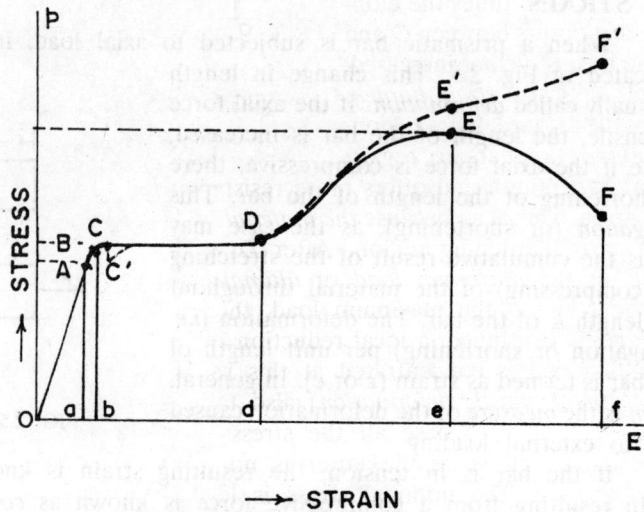

FIG. 2.7. TENSILE TEST DIAGRAM (NOT TO SCALE)

is proportional to the corresponding stress upto a limit only and beyond that, the relation is not linear. In investigating the mechanical properties of the material beyond this limit, the relationship between the strain and the corresponding stress is usually represented graphically by a *tensile test diagram* or *stress strain diagram*.

A stress-strain diagram for a typical structural steel in tension is shown in Fig. 2.7 (not to scale), where the strain is plotted along the horizontal axis while stress is plotted on the vertical axis. The diagram begins with a straight line O to A, in which the stress strain relationship is *linear, i.e.* stress and strain are directly proportional. Point A marks the *limit of proportionality* beyond which the curve becomes slightly curved, until point B, the *elastic limit* of the material, is reached. Region AB is the non-linear region in which the stress is not proportional to strain, and the elongation increases more rapidly. However, upto the point B, the removal of load would result in *complete recovery* by the specimen of its original dimensions. If the load is increased further, yielding takes place; point C is the point of sudden large extension, known as the *yield point*. After the yield point stress is reached, the *ductile extensions* take place, the strains increasing at an accelerating rate as represented by C to D.

During the ductile extension, the area of cross-section decreases in practically the same proportion that the length increases, and hence this is the region of *perfect plasticity* or *yielding*. In this region, there is no noticeable increase in the tensile force. The material becomes *perfectly plastic* in this region (*C* to *D*), which means that it can deform without an increase in the applied load. For mild steel, the elongation in this region is 10 to 15 times the elongation that occurs between *O* and *A*. If the load is further increased, the steel begins to *strain harden*. During strain hardening region, the material appears to regain

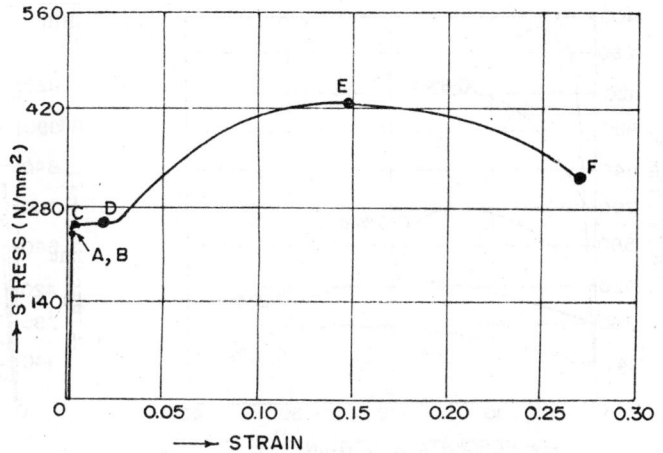

FIG. 2.8. TENSILE TEST DIAGRAM FOR MILD STEEL (DRAWN TO SCALE)

some of its strength and offers more resistance, thus requiring increased tensile load for further deformation. This is so because *the material undergoes changes in its atomic and crystalline structure* in the strain hardening region. After *D*, with further increases in loads and extensions, the point *E* of the *maximum load* or *ultimate stress* (commonly known as the *ultimate strength*) is reached. Up to the maximum load, the bar extends *uniformly* over its parallel length but, if straining is continued, a local reduction in cross-sectional area occurs (*i.e.* formation of waist) and as the load is concentrated at this reduced area, a considerable local extension (known as *concentrated plastic deformation*) also takes place, till the failure or rupture takes place at *F*. It is customary to base all the stress calculations on the original cross-sectional area of the specimen, and since the latter is not constant, the stresses so calculated are known as *nominal stresses*. The nominal stress is less at rupture load than at the maximum load, as indicated by points *F* and *E* respectively. The diagram of *real stresses* (*i.e.* load divided by reduced area of cross-section) would be as shown by the dotted curve in Fig. 2.7. The breaking load divided by the reduced area of section (*i.e. actual stress intensity*) is greater than at the maximum load.

Fig. 2.8 shows a stress-strain curve in tension for mild steel drawn to scale. The strains that occur from *C* to *D* are 15 times more than the strains that occur from *O* to *A*, and further the strains from *D* to *F* are many times greater than those from *C* to *D*. Hence, in this diagram, the linear part of the diagram appears to be vertical, with the points *A*, *B* and *C* over lapping.

Stress-strain curves for other materials

Fig. 2.9 shows stress strain curves for steels having carbon contents varying from 0.12 to 1 percent. From these curves, we notice that with increasing carbon content, the curves approach the form characteristic of brittle materials such as cast iron, though the ultimate stress is many times greater.

Fig. 2.10 shows typical stress-strain diagrams for several common materials such as high carbon steel, nickel-chrome steel, mild steel, wrought iron, cast iron, copper and cast aluminium. From these we observe that for steels and wrought irons, proportionality exists almost until

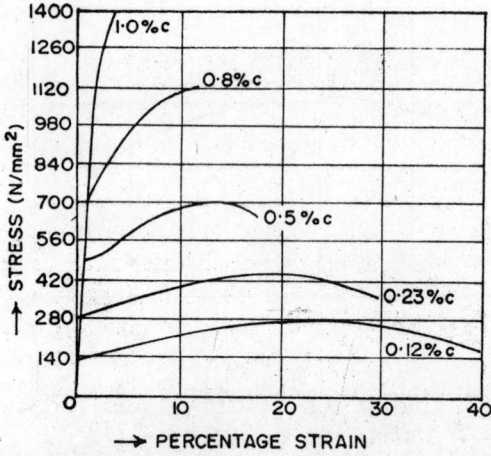

FIG. 2.9. STRESS-STRAIN DIAGRAMS FOR STEELS
WITH VARYING PERCENTAGE OF CARBON

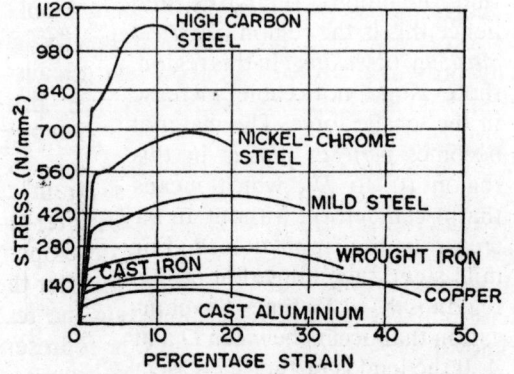

FIG. 2.10. STRESS STRAIN DIAGRAMS FOR
SOME COMMON MATERIALS

yielding takes place. However, for copper, cast aluminium and high alloys, no clearly defined limit of proportionality, elastic limit or yield point are exhibited. Cast iron behaves like a brittle material which fails without any visible elongation or reduction in area.

Fig. 2.11 shows typical stress-strain diagram for aluminium alloy, exhibiting considerable ductility, though they do not have clearly definable yield point. Fig. 2.12 shows stress-strain diagrams for hard rubber and soft rubber. The curve for rubber is linear upto very large strains in the vicinity of 0.1 or 0.2. Soft rubber usually continue to stretch enormously without failure, and after that if offers increasing resistance to the load with the result that the curve turns markedly upward prior to failure.

Typical stress-strain curve for brittle material is shown in Fig. 1.2 wherein the material fails in tension at relatively low value of strain. Examples of brittle materials are concrete, stone, cast iron, glass, ceramic materials and many common metallic alloys. Ordinary glass is

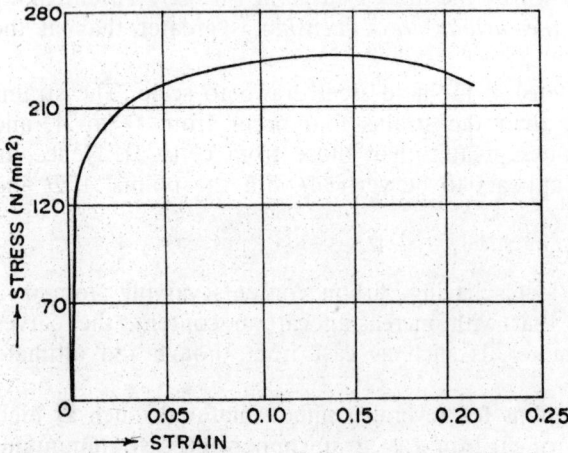

FIG. 2.11. STRESS STRAIN DIAGRAM FOR
ALUMINIUM ALLOY

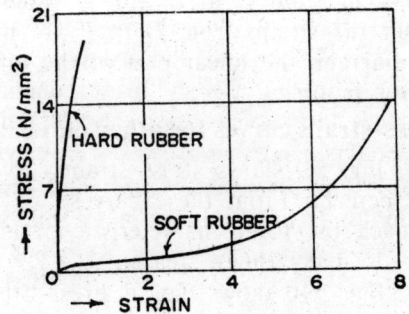

FIG. 2.12. STRESS-STRAIN DIAGRAM FOR RUBBER

a nearly ideal brittle material, exhibiting almost no ductility whatsoever.

Limit of proportionality

Limit of proportionality is the stress at which the stress-strain curve ceases to be a straight line; it is the stress at which extensions cease to be proportional to strain. In Fig. 2.7, point *A* corresponds to this limit. Robert Hooke's famous law "Ut tensio sic vis", *i.e.* 'As strain, so force' related strain to stress linearly, and did not recognise limit to this proportionality. The proportional limit is important because all subsequent theory involving the behaviour of elastic bodies is based on stress-strain proportionality.

Elastic limit

It is that point in the stress-strain curve upto which the material remains elastic, *i.e.* the material regains its original shape after the removal of the load. Thus, elastic limit represents the *maximum stress* that may be developed during a simple tension test such that there is no permanent or residual deformation after the removal of the load. Its value can be approximately determined by loading and unloading the test specimen till *permanent set* is found on complete removal of the load. This point is represented by point *B* in stress-strain curve of Fig. 2.7. However, for many materials, elastic limit and proportional limit are almost numerically the same, and the terms are sometimes used synonymously. In cases (such as in Fig. 2.7), where the two are different, elastic limit is always greater than the proportional limit.

Elastic range

This is the region of the stress-strain curve between the origin and the elastic limit. Thus in Fig. 2.7, *ob* is the *elastic range* in which only elastic deformations take place. These deformations disappear on the removal of the load.

Plastic range

This is the region of the stress-strain curve between the elastic limit (*B*) and point of rupture (*F*). Thus, in Fig. 2.7, *bf* is the plastic range, in which plastic deformations take place. These deformations are permanent deformations which do not disappear even after the removal of the load. The plastic range consists of three regions : (*i*) region *bd* in which perfect plastic yielding takes place, (*ii*) region *de*, usually called *strain hardening range,* and (*iii*) region *ef* in which non-uniform or concentrated plastic deformation takes place giving rise to *necking* of the specimen. Region *bd* and *de* taken together mark the *uniformly distributed plastic deformation.*

Yield point

Yield point is the point just beyond the elastic limit, at which the specimen undergoes an *appreciable* increase in length without further increase in the load. The phenomenon of yielding is more peculiar to structural steel; other materials do not possess well defined yield point. Careful testing of more ductile materials (like annealed low carbon steel) indicates that there is, in reality, a slight load reduction giving two yield points *C* and *C'* (Fig. 2.7), known respectively as *upper* and *lower* yield points. It is possible to obtain yield point in mild steel of the order of 100% greater than the lower yield stress. M.M. Hutchinson obtained upper yield point at 73000 1b/sq in. (486 N/mm^2) and lower yield point at 37000 1b/sq in. (247 N/mm^2) from a tensile test on a 0.038 in. diameter mild steel wire after proper annealing and careful preparation of the test piece. In a tensile test, it is usual to remove the *extensometer* from the specimen at this stage (*i.e.* at yield point) so that the instrument is not damaged by the ensuing large plastic extensions which thereafter are measured by means of dividers and a steel rule or similar other device.

Yield strength

The yield strength of a material is closely associated with the yield point. *Yield strength* is defined as the lowest stress at which extension of the test piece increases without further increase in load. It is indicated by careful testing of the specimen. Many materials do not have well defined yield point. For such cases, yield strength is determined by *off-set method*. As illustrated in Fig. 2.13 (*a*), a line offset of an arbitrary strain of 0.2% (*i.e.* 0.002 m/m), is drawn parallel to the straight line portion of the original stress-strain diagram. Where there is no specific straight line portion (the diagram being continuously curved), the 0.2% offset is drawn parallel to the *initial tangent* of the stress strain curve (Fig. 2.13 *b*). In both the cases, the intersection of the offset line with the curve (*i.e.* point *C*) *defines the yield stress*, some times also known as the *offset yield stress*.

Ultimate strength

The *ultimate stress* or *ultimate strength*, as it is more commonly called, is the highest point (such as point *E* in Fig. 2.7) on the stress-strain curve. At this highest point, concentrated plastic deformation takes place, resulting in the formation of *neck* or *waist* in the specimen, resulting in decrease in the load.

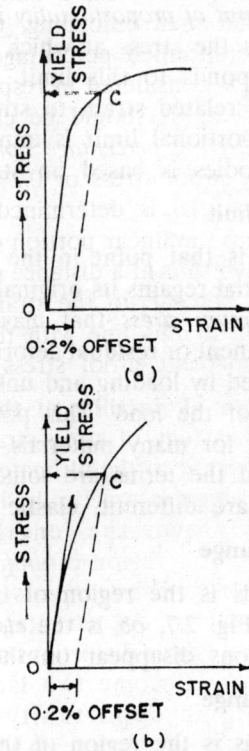

FIG. 2.13. OFFSET METHOD

$$\text{Thus, Ultimate strength} = \frac{\text{Maximum load}}{\text{Original area of cross–section}}$$

$$...(2.5)$$

Rupture strength

The *rupture strength* is the stress corresponding to the failure point *F* of the stress-strain curve. For structural steel, it is some what lower than the ultimate strength. This is so because the rupture stress is computed by dividing the rupture load by the original cross-sectional area, while the actual area is very much less because of *necking*. The *actual rupture strength* (point *F′*) obtained by dividing the rupture load by the cross-sectional area at the time of rupture, is very much higher than the *actual ultimate strength* (point *E′*). Although actual rupture strength is considerably higher than the ultimate strength, *the ultimate strength is commonly taken as the maximum stress of the material.*

Proof stress

Proof stress is the stress necessary to cause a non-proportional or permanent extension equal to a *defined percentage* (say 0.1 or 0.2%) of gauge length. Alternatively, proof stress can be expressed as the stress at which the stress-strain diagram departs by a specified percentage of the gauge length from the produced straight line of proportionality. If the specified percentage is 0.1% of the gauge length, the corresponding proof stress is designated as 0.1% *proof stress*. If a certain value for proof stress is specified for a material, and, after loading to that stress and then unloading, the permanent extension is less than the specified percentage of the gauge length, then the material is considered in respect of the minimum proof stress requirement. It should be clearly noted that *proof stress is prefixed by the percentage non-proportional strain it produces*, *i.e.* 0.1% proof stress or 0.2% proof stress. The proof stress for a material is determined (Fig. 2.14) by drawing a line parallel to the linear portion of the stress-strain diagram from a point which is at a distance equal to the specified percentage (say, 0.1 percent) of the strain on the gauge length. The intersection of this line with the stress-strain curve represents the 0.1 percent proof stress for the material.

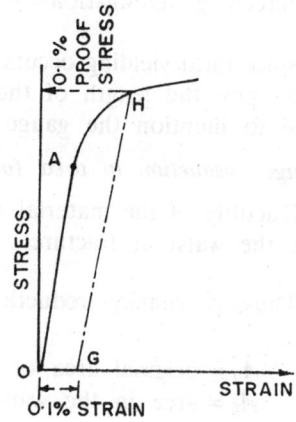

FIG. 2.14. DETERMINATION OF PROOF STRESS

Estimation of ductility of the material

The study of stress-strain diagram indicates that from the yield point to the ultimate strength, the elongation is practically distributed uniformly over the length of the specimen. This region of *uniformly distributed plastic deformation* is typical of ductile material. An advantage of ductility is that visible distortions may occur if the loads become two large, thus providing an opportunity to take remedial measures before an actual fracture takes place. Also, ductile materials are capable of absorbing large amounts of energy prior to fracture. The presence of a pronounced yield point followed by large plastic strains is an important characteristic of mild steel that is some times used in practical design. Other duc-

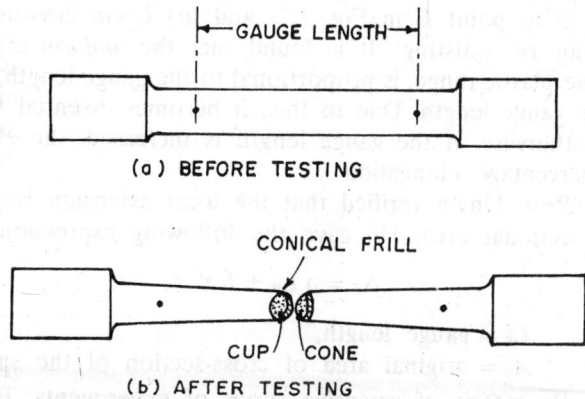

FIG. 2.15. TEST SPECIMEN BEFORE AND AFTER TESTING

tile materials include aluminum and some of its alloys, copper, magnesium, lead, molybdenum, nickel, brass, bronze, monel metal, nylon, teflon etc.

Ductility of a material is estimated by two methods.

(*i*) Percentage elongation method

(*ii*) Percentage reduction in area or percentage contraction

The second method is considered to be a better measure of ductility, being independent of gauge length.

Percentage elongation

The percentage elongation is the percentage increase in the length of the gauge length. If L_0 is the original gauge length and L_f the final length between the gauge marks, measured after fracture,

$$\text{Percentage elongation} = \frac{L_f - L_0}{L_0} = \frac{\Delta L_0}{L_0} \times 100 \qquad ...(2.6)$$

Since local yielding occurs before the fracture of the specimen, the percentage elongation depends upon the length of the specimen, (*i.e.*, upon the gauge length). Hence it is always essential to mention the gauge length over which percentage elongation is computed

Percentage reduction in area (or percentage contraction)

Ductility of the material can also be estimated in terms of percentage reduction in the area in the waist at fracture.

$$\text{Thus, percentage reduction in area} = \frac{A_0 - A_f}{A_f} \times 100 \qquad ...(2.7)$$

Where A_0 = original area of test specimen
A_f = area in the waist at fracture

For ductile materials, this reduction is about 50%.

Gauge length : Barba's law

From the study of the tensile test diagram (Fig. 2.7) we observe that the total elongation of a specimen of a given gauge length is equal to the sum of (*i*) *uniform extension* (*i.e.* from point O to point E in Fig. 2.7) and (*ii*) *Local extension* (From point E to point F) due to 'necking' or 'waisting'. It is found that the *uniform extension*, taking place during the elastic and the plastic range, is proportional to the gauge length, while the *local extension* is independent of the gauge length. Due to this, it becomes essential to specify the *gauge length* in a tension test; otherwise, if the gauge length is increased, the effect of local extension would decrease the percentage elongation.

Prof. Unvin verified that the local extension is proportional to the square root of the cross-sectional area. He gave the following expression for the total extension (Δ_T) :

$$\Delta_T = a\, L_0 + b\, \sqrt{A_0} \qquad ...(2.9)$$

where L_0 = gauge length,
A_0 = original area of cross-section of the specimen and a, b are constants,

By means of extensive series of experiments, Barba gave the following law :

Geometrically similar specimens of the same material deform similarly if they are so proportioned that $L_0/\sqrt{A_0}$ is constant.

The following values are given for mild steel :

$$a = 0.2 \text{ and } b = 0.7$$

In order to eliminate any error in comparison of elongation figures, it is recommended in B.S. 18 that the gauge length (L_0) should be equal to $4\sqrt{A}$.

Working stress and factor of safety

The *working stress*, also called the *allowable stress*, is the *maximum safe stress* the material may carry. In design, the working stress should be limited to a value not exceeding the proportional limit of the material so that Hooke's law, on which all subsequent theories are based, is not invalidated. Working stress is based either on the yield point stress or on ultimate strength, by dividing these by suitable factors of safety (*n*).

Thus, $\text{Working stress} = \dfrac{\text{Ultimate strength}}{\text{Factor of safety}} = \dfrac{p_u}{n}$ ...(2.8 *a*)

or $\text{Working stress} = \dfrac{\text{Yield stress}}{\text{Factor of safety}} = \dfrac{p_y}{n'}$ ...(2.8)

For structural steel and other similar ductile materials having definite yield stress, working stress is based on yield strength. For brittle materials, where there is no definite yield point, working stress is based on ultimate strength of the material.

While selecting the factor of safety and hence the working stress for a particular material, the following points are taken into consideration :

(1) *Nature of loading*

    (*i*) Whether it is *dead load* or *live load*

    (*ii*) Whether the load is applied *gradually* or *suddenly*

    (*iii*) Whether the load is *constant* in type or *alternating*

    (*iv*) Whether the load is for *short duration* or for *long duration*

(2) *Nature of the material*

    (*i*) Whether the material is homogeneous and isotropic or not

    (*ii*) Whether there are likely to be any weaknesses (such as internal flaws etc.) or not.

(3) *Environmental factors*

    (*i*) Effects of salt water and humidity

    (*ii*) Effects of corrosion

    (*iii*) Effects of wear

(4) *Previous case histories* : Possible results of any failure

(5) *Workman-ship* : The possibility of errors occurring in manufacture or fabrication.

As a rule, the factors of safety are not directly specified; working stresses are set for different materials under different conditions of use. Generally, *codes of practice* for different materials are prepared by the Bureau of Standards, specifying the working stresses which are to be used by the designers.

2.5. LINEAR ELASTICITY : HOOKE'S LAW

In Fig. 2.7, we observe that the initial portion (*OA*) of the stress-strain diagram is straight. The *slope* of this line is the *ratio* of stress to strain, and is constant for a material. In this range, the material also remains elastic. When a material behaves elastically and also exhibits a linear relationship between stress and strain, it is called *linearly elastic*. *Linear elasticity is a property of many solid materials, including metals, wood, concrete, plastics and ceramics.*

The slope of stress-strain curve is called the *modulus of elasticity* (*E*):

$$\text{Slope of stress-strain curve} = E = \frac{p}{\varepsilon} \qquad \qquad ...(2.10)$$

In other words, the linear relationship between stress and strain is expressed by the equation

$$p = E \cdot \varepsilon \qquad \qquad ...(2.10\ a)$$

Thus, the *modulus of elasticity* (*E*) is the constant of proportionality which is defined as the *intensity of stress that causes unit strain*. Thus, modulus of elasticity *E* has the units same as units of stress.

The equation $p = E . \varepsilon$ is commonly known as *Hooke's law*, named after the famous English scientist Robert Hooke (1635-1703) who was the first person to investigate the elastic properties of various materials such as metals, wood, stone, bones etc. Robert Hooke's famous law *"Ut tensio sic vis"*, i.e. *"As strain, so force"* related strain to stress and did not recognise a limit to this proportionality.

Originally, Hooke's law specified merely that stress was proportional to strain. It was Thomas Young in 1807, who introduced a constant of proportionality, which later came to be known as *Young's modulus of elasticity*.

A common variation of Hooke's law is obtained by replacing stress p by its equivalent P/A and replacing ε by Δ/L , in Eq. 2.10. Thus,

$$\frac{p}{\varepsilon} = E$$

or

$$\frac{P/A}{\Delta/L} = E$$

which gives

$$\Delta = \frac{PL}{AE} = \frac{pL}{E} \qquad \qquad ...(2.11)$$

Eq. 2.11 is the most commonly used version of Hooke's law applied for direct stress (tensile or compressive).

Most metals have high value of E and hence the strains are always very small. For example, mild steel has a value of E approximately 2.05×10^5 N/mm^2 under normal working conditions. At this value, strain $\varepsilon = p/E = 150/2.05 \times 10^5 = 0.00073$, when $p = 150$ N/mm^2. This means that a bar of 1 m length will change in length by 0.73 mm only. On the other hand, rubber, though it does not obey Hooke's law accurately, has a low value of E and will undergo considerable deformation at moderate stress values, as is evident from Fig. 2.12.

2.6. PRINCIPLE OF SUPERPOSITION

Many times, a structural member is subjected to a number of forces acting, not only at the ends, but also at intermediate points along its length. Such a member can be analysed by the application of principle of superposition. According to the principle of superposition, the resulting strain will be equal to the algebraic sum of the strains caused by the individual forces acting along the length of the member. Thus, if a member of uniform section is subjected to a number of forces, the resulting deformation (Δ) is given by

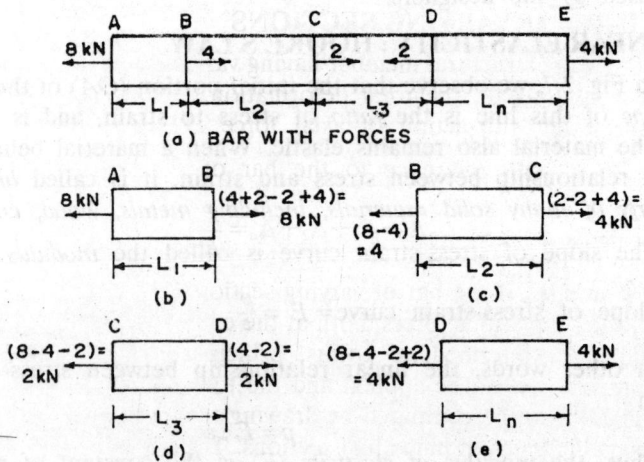

FIG. 2.16. USE OF FREE BODY DIAGRAMS.

$$\Delta = \Sigma \frac{PL}{AE} = \frac{1}{AE} \left[P_1 L_1 + P_2 L_2 + \ldots + P_n L_n \right] \qquad \ldots(2.12)$$

where P_n = force acting on section n

L_n = length of section n

The computations are conveniently done by the use of free body diagrams. Fig. 2.16 (a) shows a bar AE with four different sections of lengths L_1, L_2, L_3 and $L_n (= L_4)$ and acted upon by several forces. The free body diagrams shown in Figs. 2.16 (b), (c), (d) and (e) for the four sections of length.

For the first section AB of length L_1, the net force to the left end = 8 kN (tensile), while the net force acting to the right end = (4+2−2+4) = 8 kN. Thus the first section of length L_1, is subjected to a tensile force of 8 kN. Hence its extension will be $\Delta_1 = \dfrac{8 L_1}{AE}$.

For the second section BC of length L_2, the net force at end B = (8 − 4) = 4 kN while the net force at end C = (2 − 2 + 4) = 4 kN. Thus the second section of length L_2 is subjected to a tensile force of 4 kN, and its extension will be $\Delta_2 = \dfrac{4 L_2}{AE}$.

Similarly, for the third section CD of length L_3, the net force at end $C = (8 − 4 − 2) = 2$ kN while the net force at end $D = (4 − 2) = 2$ kN. Thus, the third section of length L_3 is subjected to a tensile force of 2 kN and its extension will be $\Delta_3 = \dfrac{2 L_3}{AE}$.

Like wise, the last section DE of length L_n is subjected to a tensile force of 4 kN and its extension will be $\Delta_n = \dfrac{4 L_n}{AE}$.

According to the principle of superposition, the total extension of the bar is given by

$$\Delta = \Delta_1 + \Delta_2 + \Delta_3 + \Delta_n = \frac{8 L_1}{AE} + \frac{4 L_2}{AE} + \frac{2 L_3}{AE} + \frac{4 L_n}{AE}$$

2.7. BARS OF VARYING SECTIONS

When a structural member having varying areas of cross-section along its length is subjected to an axial force P, the total deformation will be equal to sum of deformations of individual sections under the action of axial force P.

Thus, with reference to the bar of Fig. 2.17, the total elongation is

$$\Delta = \Delta_1 + \Delta_2 + \Delta_n = \frac{P}{E} \left(\frac{L_1}{A_1} + \frac{L_2}{A_2} + \frac{L_n}{A_n} \right) \qquad \ldots(2.12)$$

Similarly, if the bar of varying sections is subjected to various forces, both at the ends as well as at intermediate points, principle of superposition can be applied and the total deformation can be computed by drawing the free body diagrams of individual sections. The total deformation for such a bar is given by

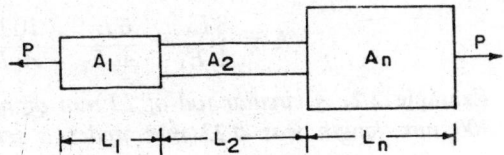

FIG. 2.17. BAR OF VARYING SECTIONS

$$\Delta = \Sigma \Delta = \frac{1}{E}\left(\frac{P_1 L_1}{A_1} + \frac{P_2 L_2}{A_2} + \dots \frac{P_n L_n}{A_n}\right) = \frac{1}{E}\Sigma \frac{PL}{A} \qquad \dots(2.14)$$

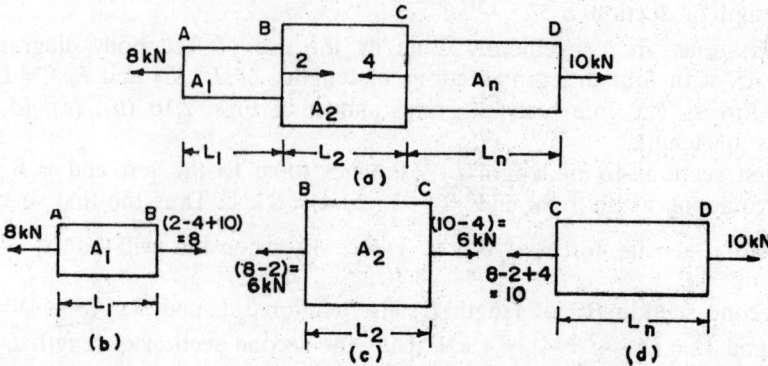

FIG. 2.18. BARS OF VARYING SECTIONS WITH MULTIPLE LOADS

Thus with reference to the free body diagrams of bar of Fig. 2.18(a), we have

$$\Delta = \Sigma \Delta = \frac{1}{E}\Sigma \frac{PL}{A} = \frac{1}{E}\left(\frac{8 L_1}{A_1} + \frac{6 L_2}{A_2} + \frac{10 L_3}{A_3}\right)$$

2.8. BARS OF VARYING SECTIONS OF DIFFERENT MATERIALS

If, however, a bar of varying section is composed of different materials for its different sections, the final deformation under the action of various forces acting at different sections can be computed by drawing free body diagrams of individual sections and then applying the principle of superposition.

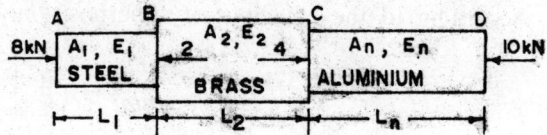

FIG. 2.19. BAR OF VARYING SECTIONS OF DIFFERENT MATERIALS

The total deformation for such a bar is given by

$$\Delta = \Sigma \Delta = \Sigma \frac{PL}{AE} = \frac{P_1 L_1}{A_1 E_1} + \frac{P_2 L_2}{A_2 E_2} + \dots \frac{P_n L_n}{A_n E_n} \qquad \dots(2.15)$$

With reference to the bar of Fig. 2.19 made of different materials, the total contraction is given by

$$\Delta = \frac{8 L_1}{A_1 E_1} + \frac{6 L_2}{A_2 E_2} + \frac{10 L_3}{A_3 E_3}$$

Example 2.2. *A circular rod of 12 mm diameter was tested for tension. The total elongation on a 300 mm length was 0.22 mm under a tensile load of 17 kN. Find the value of E.*

Solution

Stress $\qquad p = \dfrac{P}{A} = \dfrac{17 \times 10^3}{\dfrac{\pi}{4}(12)^2} = 150.31 \text{ N/mm}^2$

Strain $\qquad \varepsilon = \dfrac{\Delta L}{L} = \dfrac{0.22}{300} = 7.333 \times 10^{-4}$

$\therefore \qquad E = \dfrac{\text{Stress}}{\text{Strain}} = \dfrac{150.31}{7.333 \times 10^{-4}} = 2.05 \times 10^5 \text{ N/mm}^2 = 210 \text{ kN/mm}^2$

Example 2.3. *A rod of variable sections, shown in Fig. 2.20 is subjected to a pull of 1000 kN at the ends. Find the extension of the rod, taking $E = 2 \times 10^5 \text{ N/mm}^2$.*

Solution

From Eq. 2.13, $\Delta = \dfrac{P}{E}\left[\dfrac{L_1}{A_1} + \dfrac{L_2}{A_2} + \dfrac{L_3}{A_3} + \ldots\right]$

Here, $\quad A_1 = \dfrac{\pi}{4}(100)^2 = 7854 \text{ mm}^2$

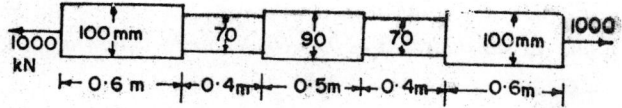

$A_2 = \dfrac{\pi}{4}(70)^2 = 3848.5 \text{ mm}^2$

$A_3 = \dfrac{\pi}{4}(90)^2 = 6361.7 \text{ mm}^2$

FIG. 2.20

$\therefore \qquad \Delta = \dfrac{1000 \times 10^3}{2 \times 10^5}\left[\dfrac{600+600}{7854} + \dfrac{400+400}{3848.5} + \dfrac{500}{6361.7}\right] = 5\,[0.1528 + 0.2079 + 0.0786]$

$\qquad = \textbf{2.196 mm}$

Example 2.4. *A steel bar of variable section is subjected to forces as shown in Fig. 2.21. Taking $E = 205 \text{ kN/m}^2$, determine the total elongation of the bar.*

Solution

$A_1 = \dfrac{\pi}{4}(30)^2 = 706.86 \text{ mm}^2 \; ; \; L_1 = 1000 \text{ mm}$

$A_2 = \dfrac{\pi}{4}(35)^2 = 962.11 \text{ mm}^2 \; ; \; L_2 = 1200 \text{ mm}$

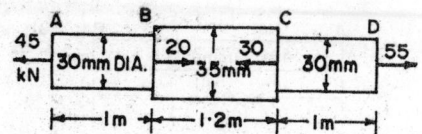

FIG. 2.21

$A_3 = \dfrac{\pi}{10}(30)^2 = 706.86 \text{ mm}^2 \; L_3 = 100 \text{ mm}$

The free body diagrams of the three sections are shown is Fig. 2.22.

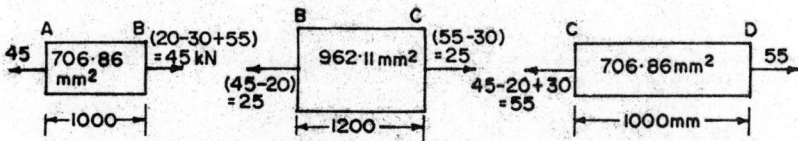

FIG. 2.22. FREE BODY DIAGRAMS

$$\therefore \qquad \Delta_1 = \frac{P_1 L_1}{A_1 E} = \frac{45 \times 1000 \times 1000}{706.86 \times 205 \times 1000} = 0.311 \text{ mm}$$

$$\Delta_2 = \frac{P_2 L_2}{A_2 E} = \frac{25 \times 1000 \times 1200}{962.11 \times 205 \times 1000} = 0.152 \text{ mm}$$

$$\Delta_3 = \frac{P_3 L_3}{A_3 E} = \frac{55 \times 1000 \times 1000}{706.86 \times 205 \times 1000} = 0.380$$

Total $\qquad \Delta = \Delta_1 + \Delta_2 + \Delta_3 = 0.311 + 0.152 + 0.380 = \textbf{0.843 mm}$

Example 2.5. *A member ABCD is subjected to point loads P_1, P_2, P_3 and P_4 as shown in Fig. 2.23.*

Calculate the force P_2 necessary for equilibrium if $P_1 = 10\,kN$, $P_3 = 40\,kN$ and $P_4 = 16\,kN$. Taking modulus of elasticity as $2.05 \times 10^5 N/mm^2$, determine the total elongation of the member.

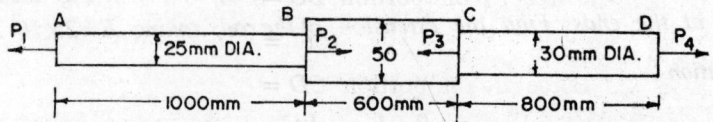

FIG. 2.23

(Based on Jadhavpur University, 1976)

Solution

For the equilibrium of the bar,
$$P_1 + P_3 = P_2 + P_4$$

or $\qquad 10 + 40 = P_2 + 16$, From which $P_2 = \textbf{34 kN} (\rightarrow)$

Now from Eq. 2.14, $\Delta = \dfrac{1}{E} \Sigma \dfrac{PL}{A}$

The free body diagrams for the three portions of the bar are shown in Fig. 2.24.

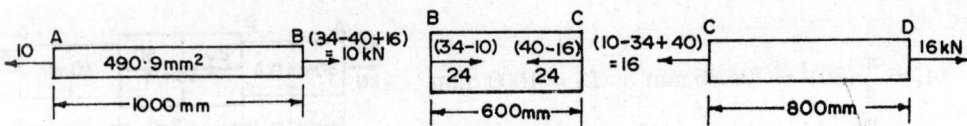

FIG. 2.24. FREE BODY DIAGRAMS

$$A_1 = \frac{\pi}{4}(25)^2 = 490.9 \text{ mm}^2 \; ; \; A_2 = \frac{\pi}{4}(50)^2 = 1963.5 \text{ mm}^2 \; ; \; A_3 = \frac{\pi}{4}(30)^2 = 706.9 \text{ mm}^2$$

$$\Delta_1 = \frac{10 \times 1000 \times 1000}{490.9 \times 2.05 \times 10^5} = 0.099 \text{ (elongation)}$$

$$\Delta_2 = \frac{24 \times 1000 \times 600}{1963.5 \times 2.05 \times 10^5} = 0.036 \text{ (contraction)}$$

$$\Delta_3 = \frac{16 \times 1000 \times 800}{706.9 \times 2.05 \times 10^5} = 0.088 \text{ (elongation)}$$

Total $\Delta = \Delta_1 - \Delta_2 + \Delta_3 = 0.099 - 0.036 + 0.088 = \textbf{0.151 mm}$.

Example 2.6. *A steel bar of 2 m length and uniform section of 600 sq. mm is suspended vertically and loaded as shown in Fig. 2.25. Taking $E = 2.05 \times 10^5 N/mm^2$, determine the total elongation of the bar.*

Solution

$$\text{Reaction} \quad R = 20 + 30 + 40 = 90 \text{ kN}$$

Hence force P_1 on portion $AB = 90$ kN (tensile)

$$\text{Force } P_2 \text{ on portion } BC = 30 + 40 = 70 \text{ kN (tensile)}$$

$$(\text{or } = 90 - 20 = 70 \text{ kN})$$

$$\text{Force } P_3 \text{ on portion } CD = 40 \text{ kN (tensile)}$$

From Eq. 2.12, total deformation $\Delta = \dfrac{1}{AE} \left[P_1 L_1 + P_2 L_2 + P_3 L_3 \right]$

$\therefore \Delta = \dfrac{1}{600 \times 2.05 \times 10^5} \left[90 \times 10^3 \times 750 + 70 \times 10^3 \times 500 + 40 \times 10^3 \times 750 \right]$

$= \dfrac{1}{1230 \times 10^5} \left[675 \times 10^5 + 350 \times 10^5 + 300 \times 10^5 \right] = \textbf{1.077 mm}$

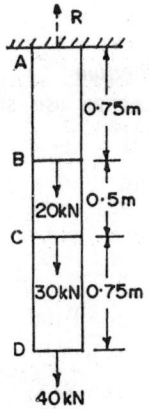

FIG. 2.25

Example 2.7. *A member ABC is formed by connecting a steel bar of 20 mm diameter to an aluminium bar of 30 mm diameter, and is subjected to forces as shown in Fig. 2.26. Determine the total deformation of the bar, taking E for aluminium as $0.7 \times 10^5 N/mm^2$ and that for steel as $2 \times 10^5 N/mm^2$.*

Solution

From Eq. 2.15, $\Delta = \Sigma \dfrac{PL}{AE} = \dfrac{P_1 L_1}{A_1 E_1} + \dfrac{P_2 L_2}{A_2 E_2}$

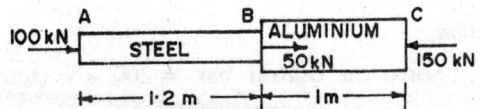

FIG. 2.26

Portion AB

Force $P_1 = 100$ kN (or $150 - 50 = 100$ kN), compressive;

$L_1 = 1200$ mm

$A_1 = \dfrac{\pi}{4}(20)^2 = 314.16 \text{ mm}^2$

$E_1 = 2 \times 10^5 \text{ N/mm}^2$

$\therefore \quad \Delta_1 = \dfrac{100 \times 10^3 \times 1200}{314.16 \times 2 \times 10^5} \approx 1.91 \text{ mm (contraction)}$

Portion BC

Force $\quad P_2 = 100 + 50 = 150 \text{ kN}; \quad L_2 = 1000 \text{ mm}$

$A_2 = \dfrac{\pi}{4}(30)^2 = 706.86 \; ; \quad E_2 = 0.7 \times 10^5 \text{ N/mm}^2$

$\therefore \quad \Delta_2 = \dfrac{150 \times 10^3 \times 1000}{706.86 \times 0.7 \times 10^5} = 0.303 \text{ mm (contraction)}$

∴ Total $\qquad \Delta = \Delta_1 + \Delta_2 = 1.91 + 0.303 = \mathbf{2.213\ mm}$ (contraction)

Example 2.8. *A member formed by connecting a steel bar to an aluminium bar is shown in Fig. 2.27. Assuming that the bars are prevented from buckling sidewise, calculate the magnitude of force P, that will cause the total length of the member to decrease 0.20 mm. The values of elastic modulus for steel and aluminium are 210 kN/mm^2 and 70 kN/mm^2 respectively.*

(Based on Oxford University)

Solution

Let us use suffix 1 for steel bar and suffix 2 for aluminium bar.

∴ $\qquad A_1 = 40 \times 40 = 1600\ mm^2$

and $\qquad A_2 = 80 \times 80 = 6400\ mm^2$

$\qquad L_1 = 500$ mm; $L_2 = 600$ mm; $E_1 = 210 \times 10^3\ N/mm^2$;

$\qquad E_2 = 70 \times 10^3\ N/mm^2$

Total $\qquad \Delta = P \left[\dfrac{L_1}{A_1 E_1} + \dfrac{L_2}{A_2 E_2} \right]$, where $\Delta = 0.2$ mm

∴ $\qquad 0.2 = P \left[\dfrac{500}{1600 \times 210 \times 10^3} + \dfrac{600}{6400 \times 70 \times 10^3} \right]$

$\qquad\qquad = P \left[1.488 \times 10^{-6} + 1.339 + 10^{-6} \right]$

From which $\qquad P = 70737\ N = \mathbf{70.737\ kN}$

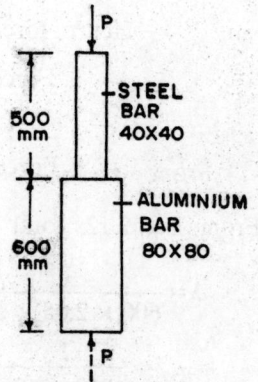

FIG. 2.27

Example 2.9. *A bar, shown in Fig. 2.28 is subjected to a tensile force of 200 kN at each end. Find (a) the diameter of middle portion if the stress in the middle portion is limited to 150 N/mm^2 , and (b) the length of the individual portions if the total elongation of the bar is limited to 0.30 mm. Take E = 200 kN/mm^2.*

Solution

Force on central bar $= 200$ kN (tensile)

Let the diameter of central portion be d_2.

∴ $\qquad A_2 = \dfrac{\pi}{4} d_2^2$

∴ $\qquad$ Stress $= \dfrac{200 \times 10^3}{\dfrac{\pi}{4} d_2^2}$

$\qquad\qquad = \dfrac{254648}{d_2^2}\ N/mm^2$

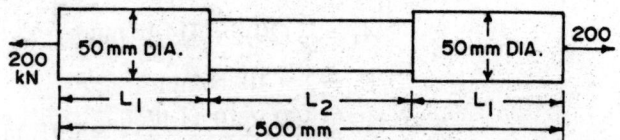

FIG. 2.28

But this should not exceed 150 N/mm^2.

∴ $\qquad 150 = \dfrac{254648}{d_2^2}$

From which $d_2 = \mathbf{41.2\ mm}$. Hence $A_2 = \dfrac{\pi}{4} (41.2)^2 = 1333.3\ mm^2$

Also, $$A_1 = \frac{\pi}{4}(50)^2 = 1963.5 \text{ mm}^2$$

Let the length of middle portion be L_2 mm

Hence total length of the two end portions $= 2L_1 = (500 - L_2)$ mm.

$$\therefore \quad \Delta = \frac{P}{E}\left[\frac{2L_1}{A_1} + \frac{L_2}{A_2}\right] = \frac{200 \times 10^3}{200 \times 10^3}\left[\frac{500 - L_2}{1963.5} + \frac{L_2}{1333.3}\right]$$

But Δ is limited to 0.3 mm.

$$\therefore \quad 0.3 = \frac{500 - L_2}{1963.5} + \frac{L_2}{1333.3} = 0.2546 - 5.093 \times 10^{-4} L_2 + 7.5 \times 10^{-4} L_2$$

or $\quad 2.407 L_2 \times 10^{-4} = 0.0454$

From which $\quad L_2 = \mathbf{188.62}$ **mm**

$\therefore \quad L_1 = \frac{1}{2}(500 - 188.62) = \mathbf{155.69}$ **mm**

Example 2.10. *A tensile load of 50 kN is acting on rod of 50 mm diameter and length of 5 m. Determine the length of a bore of 25 mm that can be made central in the rod, if the total extension is not to exceed by 25 percent under the same tensile load. Take $E = 2.05 \times 10^5 \, N/mm^2$.*

Solution

(a) Rod without bore

$$A = \frac{\pi}{4}(50)^2 = 1963.5 \text{ mm}^2$$

$$L = 5 \times 1000 = 5000 \text{ mm}$$

$$\therefore \quad \Delta = \frac{50 \times 10^3 \times 5000}{1963.5 \times 2.05 \times 10^5}$$

$$= 0.621 \text{ mm}$$

(b) Rod with bore (Fig. 2.29 b)

Let the length of the bore be L_b mm.

Hence length of unbored rod $= (5000 - L_b)$ mm.

Area of bored tube, $A_b = \frac{\pi}{4}(25)^2 = 490.87 \text{ mm}^2$

Permissible total extension $= (1 + 0.25)\,0.621 = 0.7763$ mm.

But $$\Delta = \frac{P}{E}\left[\frac{L}{A} + \frac{L_b}{A_b}\right]$$

$$\therefore \quad 0.7763 = \frac{50 \times 10^3}{2.05 \times 10^5}\left[\frac{5000 - L_b}{1963.5} + \frac{L_b}{490.87}\right]$$

or $$0.7763 = 0.2439\left[2.5465 - 5.0929 \times 10^{-4} L_b + 20.372 \times 10^{-4} L_b\right]$$

or $$15.2791 \times 10^{-4} L_b = 0.6363$$

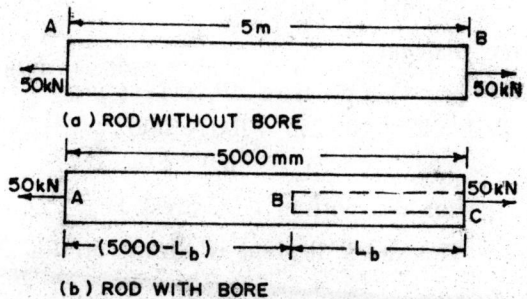

FIG. 2.29

From which $L_b = 416.5$ mm

Example 2.11. *For the steel bar shown in Fig. 2.30 (a), determine the longitudinal force P and stress p at all cross-sections. Determine also the vertical displacement Δ of all cross-sections of the bar. Represent the result graphically by plotting P, p and Δ diagrams. Take E = $2 \times 10^5 N/mm^2$. Also, locate the section of zero displacement.*

Solution

Considering the overall equilibrium of the bar, we get

$$R - 50 + 25 = 0$$

or $R = 25$ kN $(\downarrow)$

Force diagram

For the portion *AB*, force $P = R = 25$ kN (comp.)

For the portion *BC*, force $P = 50 - R = 50 - 25 = 25$ kN (tensile)

The force diagram is shown in Fig. 2.30 (*b*).

Stress diagram

For the portion *AB*, stress $p = P/A = 25 \times 10^3/250 = 100 N/mm^2$.
(compressive)

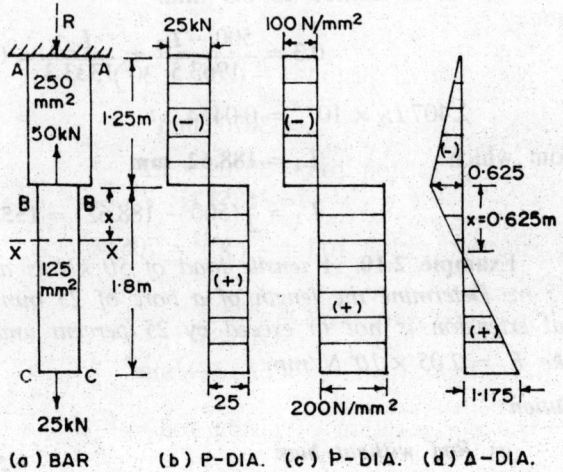

(a) BAR   (b) P-DIA.   (c) P-DIA.   (d) Δ-DIA.

FIG. 2.30

For the portion *CD*, stress $p = P/A = 25 \times 10^3/1250 = 200 N/mm^2$ (tensile)

The stress diagram is shown in Fig. 2.30 (*c*).

Δ diagram

Point *A* is fixed in position. Hence $\Delta_A = 0$

Bar *AB* is subjected to a compressive force $P = 25$ kN

∴ $$\Delta_B = \frac{P_{AB} \cdot L_{AB}}{A_{AB} \cdot E} = -\frac{(25 \times 10^3)(1.25 \times 1000)}{250 \times 2 \times 10^5} = -0.625 \text{ mm}$$

Bar *BC* is subjected a tensile force $P = 25$ kN

∴ $$\Delta_C = \Delta_{AB} + \Delta_{BC} = \frac{P_{AB} \cdot L_{AB}}{A_{AB} \cdot E} + \frac{P_{BC} \cdot L_{BC}}{A_{BC} \cdot E}$$

$$= -\frac{(25 \times 10^3)(1.25 \times 1000)}{250 \times 2 \times 10^5} + \frac{(25 \times 10^3)(1.8 \times 1000)}{125 \times 2 \times 10^5}$$

$$= -0.625 + 1.8 = +1.175 \text{ mm}$$

The displacement diagram is shown in Fig. 2.30 (*d*). Let the section of zero displacement be section X-X, located at distance *x* m from *BB*.

$$\therefore \qquad \Delta_{xx} = -\,0.625 + \frac{P_{xx} \cdot L_{xx}}{A_{xx} \cdot E} = -\,0.625 + \frac{(25 \times 1000)\,(x \times 1000)}{125 \times 2 \times 10^{5}} = 0$$

or $\qquad -\,0.625 + 1\,x = 0$, From which $x = \mathbf{0.625\ m}$

Example 2.12. *The piston of a steam engine is 200 mm diameter and the piston rod is of 30 mm diameter. The steam pressure is 1.2 N/mm². Find the stress in the piston rod and the elongation of a length of 750 mm, taking $E = 2 \times 10^{5} N/mm^{2}$, when the piston is on the in stroke.*

Solution

Net area of piston $= \dfrac{\pi}{4}\,(200^{2} - 30^{2})$

$\qquad\qquad\qquad\quad = 30709\ \text{mm}^{2}$

Load on piston rod $= 30709 \times 1.2$

$\qquad\qquad\qquad\quad = 36851\ \text{N}$

Area of piston rod $= \dfrac{\pi}{4}\,(30)^{2} = 706.86\ \text{mm}^{2}$

$\therefore$ Stress in piston rod $= \dfrac{36851}{706.86}$

$\qquad\qquad\qquad\qquad = \mathbf{52.13\ N/mm^{2}}$

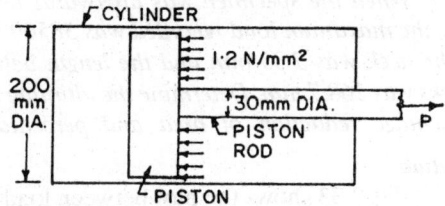

FIG. 2.31

Also, elongation of piston rod $= \dfrac{p\,L}{E} = \dfrac{52.13 \times 750}{2 \times 10^{5}} = \mathbf{0.196\ mm}$

Example 2.13. *A signal is being worked by steel wire 600 m long and 6.25 mm is diameter. Find the movement which must be given to the signal box end of wire, at a pull of 1.5 kN, if the movement of the signal end is to be 180 mm. Take $E = 2.05 \times 10^{5} N/mm^{2}$.*

Solution (Fig. 2.32)

$AB\,(= 600\,\text{m})$ is the initial position of the wire, where A is the signal box end and B is the signal end. If the wire were rigid (*i.e.* stretch proof), the movement at end A at the

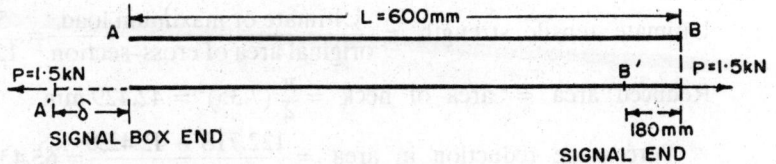

FIG. 2.32

signal box would have been the required movement of 180 mm at the signal end. But the wire extends by an amount Δ under a tensile force $P = 1.5$ kN. Hence the required movement δ at A will be equal to $(180 + \Delta)$, to move the signal end by 180 mm.

Thus, $\qquad\qquad\qquad\qquad \delta = 180 + \Delta$

Now, from Hooke's Law, $\Delta = \dfrac{P\,L}{A\,E} = \dfrac{1.5 \times 10^{3} \times 600 \times 10^{3}}{\dfrac{\pi}{4}\,(6.25)^{2} \times 2.05 \times 10^{5}} = 143.1\ \text{mm}$

Total movement $\delta = 180 + \Delta = 180 + 143.1 = \mathbf{323.1\ mm}$

Example 2.14. *In a tensile test on a specimen of mild steel, 12.5 mm diameter and gauge length 200 mm, the following results were recorded :*

Load (N)	5000	10000	15000	20000	25000	30000	35000	40000
Extension (mm)	0.040	0.080	0.121	0.161	0.201	0.242	0.282	0.322

Determine the value of Young's modulus of elasticity.

When the specimen was afterwards tested to destruction, the maximum load recorded was 58500 N, the diameter of the neck was 7.35 mm and the length between the gauge marks was 268.7 mm. Determine the ultimate tensile strength, percentage reduction of area and percentage elongation.

Solution

Fig. 2.33 shows the plot between load and extension.

Slope of the graph

$$= \frac{P}{\Delta} = \frac{35000}{0.282} = 124113 \text{ N/mm}$$

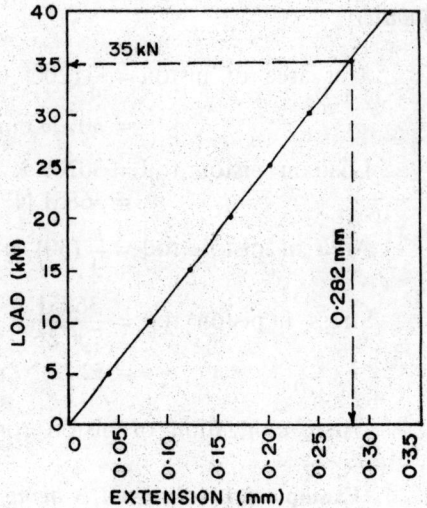

Original $\qquad A = \frac{\pi}{4}(12.5)^2 = 122.718 \text{ mm}^2$

Original length $\quad L = 200 \text{ mm}$

Now $\qquad E = \frac{PL}{A\Delta} = \frac{L}{A}$ (slope of graph)

$$= \frac{200}{122.718} \times 124113$$

$$= 2.023 \times 10^5 \text{ N/mm}^2$$

$$= 202.3 \text{ kN/mm}^2$$

FIG. 2.33

Ultimate tensile strength $= \dfrac{\text{Ultimate or maximum load}}{\text{original area of cross–section}} = \dfrac{58500}{122.718} = \mathbf{476.7 \text{ N/mm}^2}$

Reduced area $=$ area of neck $= \dfrac{\pi}{4}(7.35)^2 = 42.429 \text{ mm}^2$

∴ Percentage reduction in area $= \dfrac{122.718 - 42.429}{122.718} = \mathbf{65.43\%}$

Percentage elongation $= \dfrac{L_f - L_0}{L_f} = \dfrac{268.7 - 200}{200} = \mathbf{34.35\%}$

Example 2.15. *A tensile test on a bar having a cross-sectional area of 161.3 mm^2 and gauge length of 50.8 mm, gave the following results :*

Load (kN)	2.5	5.00	7.5	10.0	12.5	15.0	17.5	20.0	22.5
Extension (mm)	0.013	0.025	0.038	0.051	0.064	0.082	0.102	0.128	0.162
Load (kN)	25.0	27.5	30.0						
Extension	0.203	0.263	0.383						

Calculate for the material (i) the limit of proportionality stress (ii) the 0.1 percent proof stress.

Solution

Fig. 2.34 shows the graph between load and extension.

From the graph, we get

Load at limit of proportionality

= 12.5 kN

∴ Limit of proportionality stress

$$= \frac{12.5 \times 10^3}{161.3} = 77.5 \text{ N/mm}^2$$

0.1 percent of gauge length

$$= \frac{0.1}{100} \times 50.8 = 0.0508 \text{ mm}$$

By drawing a line parallel to the linear portion of the graph from the offset of 0.0508 mm, the intersection with the graph gives a proof load = 22.4 kN

∴ 0.1 percent proof stress

$$= \frac{22.4 \times 10^3}{161.3} = 138.9 \text{ N/mm}^2$$

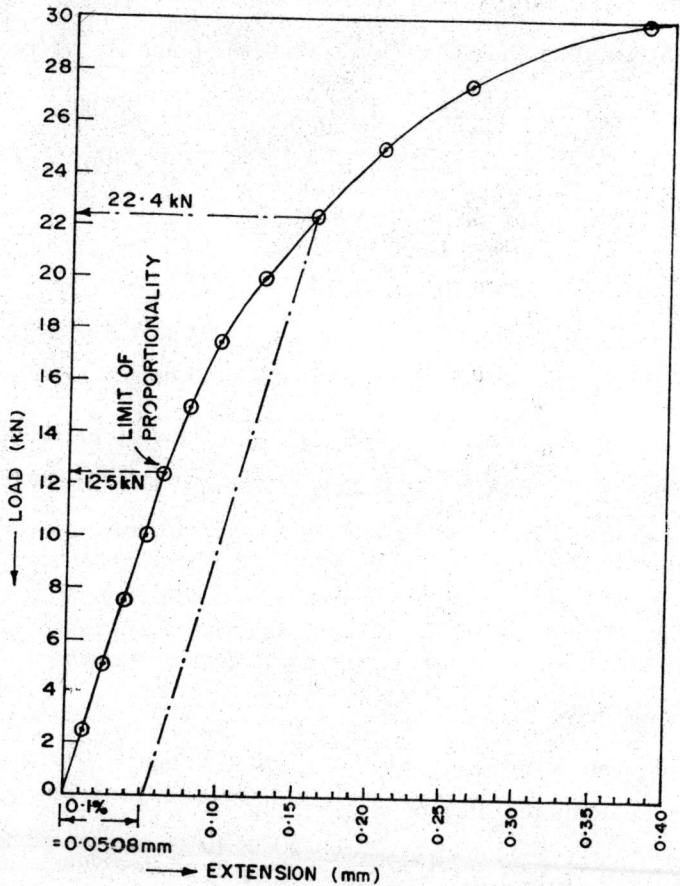

FIG. 2.34

Example 2.16. *A tensile test to destruction was conducted on two specimens A and B of the same material, and the following data was obtained*

Specimen	Gauge length (mm)	Thickness (mm)	Width (mm)	% elongation
A	200	7.5	40	28
B	250	9	65	30

Estimate the percentage elongation of a third specimen C of the same material, having a gauge length of 150 mm and a diameter of 20 mm.

Solution

From Unwin's formula,

Total elongation = Uniform elongation + Local extension

i.e.
$$\Delta_T = a L_0 + b \sqrt{A_0} \qquad \qquad ...(2.9)$$

or
$$\% \text{ elongation} = \frac{\Delta_T}{L_0} \times 100 = \left(a + \frac{b}{L_0}\sqrt{A_0}\right) 100$$

Substituting the values for specimens A and B, we get

$$28 = \left\{ a + \frac{b}{200}\sqrt{7.5 \times 40} \right\} \times 100 \qquad \qquad ...(a)$$

and
$$30 = \left\{ a + \frac{b}{250}\sqrt{9 \times 65} \right\} \times 100 \qquad \qquad ...(b)$$

After simplifying these, we get

$$a + 0.0866\, b = 0.28 \qquad \qquad ...(i)$$

and
$$a + 0.09675\, b = 0.30 \qquad \qquad ...(ii)$$

Solving (i) and (ii), we get $a = 0.1094$ and $b = 1.97$

Hence for the third specimen C, percentage elongation

$$= \left(a + \frac{b}{L_0}\sqrt{A_0}\right) 100 = \left[0.1094 + \frac{1.97}{150}\sqrt{\frac{\pi}{4}(20)^2} \right] 100$$
$$= \mathbf{34.22\,\%}$$

Example 2.17. *A short, hollow, circular, cast iron cylinder, shown in Fig. 2.35 is to support an axial compressive load of $P = 500$ kN. The ultimate stress in compression for the material is $p_u = 240 \text{ N/mm}^2$. Determine the minimum required outside diameter d of the cylinder of 25 mm wall thickness, if the factor of safety is to be 3.0 with respect to ultimate strength.*

Solution:

Allowable stress $p_{allow.} = \dfrac{p_u}{F} = \dfrac{240}{3} = 80 \text{ N/mm}^2$

$\therefore$ Required area of cross-section,

$$A = \frac{P}{p_{allow}} = \frac{500 \times 10^3}{80} = 6250 \text{ mm}^2$$

Now, for a hollow cylinder of outside diameter d and thickness t

$$A = \frac{\pi}{4}d^2 - \frac{\pi}{4}(d - 2t)^2 = \pi t (d - t)$$

or
$$d = t + \frac{A}{\pi t} = 25 + \frac{6250}{\pi (25)}$$
$$= 104.58 \text{ mm} \approx \mathbf{105 \text{ mm}}$$

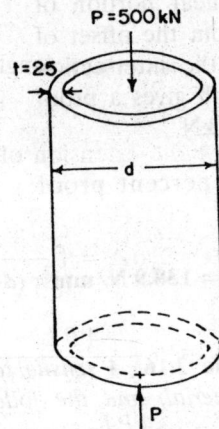

FIG. 2.35

Example 2.18. *A steel bar of rectangular cross-section (12.5 × 50 mm) carries a load P and is attached to a support by means of round pin of 16 mm diameter, as shown in Fig. 2.36. Determine the maximum permissible value of load P if the allowable stresses for the bar in tension and the pin in shear are 140 N/mm² and 70 N/mm² respectively.*

Solution : Since a hole of 16 mm diameter has been made in the steel bar, to let the pin pass through it, the net area (A_{net}) will carry the tensile load P in the bar.

$$A_{net} = (b - d) t = (50 - 16) \; 12.5 = 425 \text{ mm}^2$$

Hence allowable load P_1 based on tension in the bar is

$$P_1 = A_{net} \cdot p_{allow} = 425 \times 140 \times 10^{-3} = 59.5 \text{ kN}$$

Again the pin tends to shear in two cross-sections (*i.e.* the pin is in double shear). Hence, allowable load P_2 based on shear in pin is

$$P_2 = (2 A_p) \, \tau_{allow} = 2 \times \frac{\pi}{4} (16)^2 \times 70 \times 10^{-3} = 28.1 \text{ kN}$$

Comparing P_1 and P_2, we find that the pin governs the allowable load P.

$$\therefore \qquad P_{allow} = \textbf{28.1 kN}$$

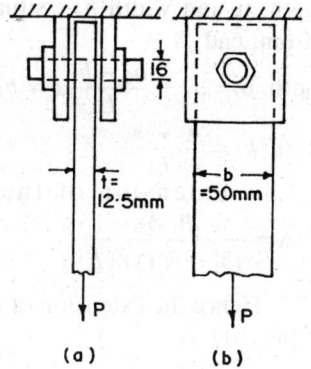

2.9. UNIFORMLY TAPERING CIRCULAR BARS

Let us now consider a *uniformly tapering* circular bar, subjected to an axial force P, as shown in Fig. 2.37. The bar of length L has a diameter d_1 at one end and d_2 at the other end $(d_2 > d_1)$.

Consider a very short section XX of length δx and diameter d_x, situated at a distance x from end A.

$$\text{Diameter } d_x = d_1 + \frac{d_2 - d_1}{L} x = d_1 + kx \text{ where}$$

$$k = \frac{d_2 - d_1}{L}.$$

Extension of the short length $= \delta\Delta = \dfrac{P \cdot \delta x}{\dfrac{\pi}{4} d_x^2 E}$

Hence the extension of the whole length of the rod is

$$\Delta = \sum_{x=0}^{x=L} \delta\Delta = \int_0^L \frac{4 P \, dx}{\pi \, (d_1 + kx)^2 E} = -\frac{4P}{\pi E} \frac{1}{k} \left\{ \frac{1}{d_1 + kx} \right\}_0^L$$

or $\qquad \Delta = -\dfrac{4PL}{\pi E (d_2 - d_1)} \left(\dfrac{1}{d_1 + d_2 - d_1} - \dfrac{1}{d_1} \right) = \dfrac{4PL}{\pi E (d_2 - d_1)} \left\{ \dfrac{1}{d_1} - \dfrac{1}{d_2} \right\}$

or $\qquad \Delta = \dfrac{4PL}{\pi E d_1 d_2}$ ...(2.16)

When $\quad d_1 = d_2 = d$, $\Delta = \dfrac{4PL}{\pi E d^2} = \dfrac{PL}{AE}$, which is the same as Eq. 2.11.

2.10. UNIFORMLY TAPERING RECTANGULAR BARS

Fig. 2.38 shows a uniformly tapering bar of rectangular cross-section, length L and thickness t. The width of the bar at one end is b_1 and the width at the other end is b_2, where $b_2 > b_1$. The bar is subjected to an axial force P.

FIG. 2.36

FIG. 2.37

Consider a very short section XX of length δx and width b_x , situated at distance x from end A.

Width $b_x = b_1 + \dfrac{b_2 - b_1}{L} x = b_1 + k x$

where $k = \dfrac{b_2 - b_1}{L}$

∴ Extension of the short length

$= \delta \Delta = \dfrac{P \cdot \delta x}{(b_1 + k x) \, t \cdot E}$

Hence the extension of the whole length of the rod is

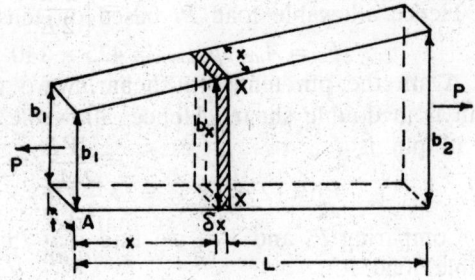

FIG. 2.38

$$\Delta = \overset{x=L}{\underset{x=0}{\Sigma}} \delta \Delta = \int_0^L \dfrac{P \, dx}{(b_1 + k x) \, t \, E} = \dfrac{P}{t E} \cdot \dfrac{1}{k} \left[\log_e (b_1 + k x) \right]_0^L$$

or $\qquad \Delta = \dfrac{P}{k \, t \, E} \log_e \dfrac{b_1 + k L}{b_1} = \dfrac{P}{k \, t \, E} \log_e \dfrac{b_2}{b_1}$

or $\qquad \Delta = \dfrac{P L}{(b_2 - b_1) \, t \, E} \log_e \dfrac{b_2}{b_1}$ $\hfill$ ...(2.17)

2.11. ELONGATION OF BAR OF UNIFORM SECTION DUE TO SELF WEIGHT

Fig. 2.39 shows a bar of uniform section, hanging freely under its own weight. The bar is either of circular section (Fig. 2.37a) or of rectangular section (Fig. 2.37 b). In each case, the area of cross-section, A, is constant along its whole length L. Let λ be the *specific weight* or *unit weight* of the material. In MKS units, λ is expressed in kg(f)/m^3, while in SI units, $\lambda = \rho \, g$ where ρ is the *specific mass* or *unit mass* or *density* of the material (expressed in kg/m^3) and g is the acceleration due to gravity which may be taken as 9.81 m/sec^2. In SI units λ is expressed in N/cm^3 or kN/m^3 since it is the gravitational weight developed by the body per unit volume.

Consider a small section of length δx , at a distance x from the free end. The deformation $\delta \Delta$ is given by

$$\delta \Delta = \dfrac{W_x \cdot \delta x}{A \cdot E}$$

where $W_x =$ weight of portion below the section
$$= A \cdot x \cdot \lambda$$

∴ $\qquad \delta \Delta = \dfrac{(A x \lambda) \, \delta x}{A \cdot E} = \dfrac{x \lambda \, \delta x}{E}$

∴ Total deformation of the rod,

$$\Delta = \overset{x=L}{\underset{x=0}{\Sigma}} \delta \Delta = \int_0^L \dfrac{x \lambda}{E} \, dx$$

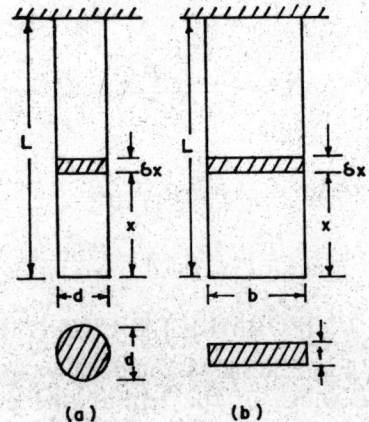

FIG. 2.39

or
$$\Delta = \left[\frac{x^2 \lambda}{2E} \right]_0^L = \frac{\lambda L^2}{2E} = \frac{\rho g L^2}{2E} \qquad ...(2.18)$$

If W = total weight of the bar, we have $\lambda = \dfrac{W}{AL}$

Hence
$$\Delta = \frac{WL}{2AE} \qquad ...(2.19)$$

From Eq. 2.19, it is clear that *the deformation of the bar of uniform section, under its own weight is equal to half the deformation of the bar under the axial load equal to the weight of the body.*

2.12. ELONGATION OF BAR OF UNIFORMLY TAPERING SECTION

Fig. 2.40 shows a bar of uniformly tapering section of length L, hanging freely under its own weight.

Consider an elementary section of length δx, at a distance x from the free end. Let A_x be the area of cross section of the elementary section. The extension of this elementary section is given by

$$\delta \Delta = \frac{W_x . \delta x}{A_x . E}$$

where W_x = weight of the portion below the section = $\dfrac{1}{3} A_x . x . \lambda$

(where λ is the specific weight or unit weight of the material)

$$\therefore \quad \delta \Delta = \frac{1}{3} \frac{A_x . x . \lambda \, \delta x}{A_x . E} = \frac{x \lambda \, \delta x}{3E}$$

Hence total extension of the bar, $\Delta = \sum_{x=0}^{x=L} \delta \Delta = \int_0^L \dfrac{x \lambda \, \delta x}{3E}$

which gives
$$\Delta = \frac{\lambda L^2}{6E} = \frac{\rho g L^2}{6E} \qquad ...(2.20)$$

If d is the diameter of bar at its uppermost section (*i.e.* at the support) total weight of the bar = $W = \dfrac{1}{3} \left(\dfrac{\pi}{4} d^2 \right) L \lambda$

or
$$\lambda = \frac{12 W}{\pi d^2 L}$$

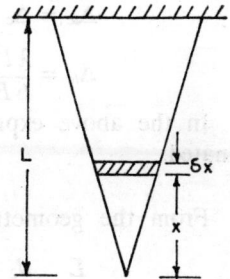

FIG. 2.40

Substituting this value of λ in Eq. 2.20, we get

$$\Delta = \frac{2WL}{\pi d^2 E} = \frac{WL}{2AE} \qquad ...(2.21)$$

where A = area of cross-section of the bar at its support.

2.13. ELONGATION OF TRUNCATED CONE SHAPED BAR

Fig. 2.41 shows a solid bar in the form of a truncated cone, having a diameter d_1 at the free end and diameter d_2 at the support. The length of the bar is L and it is hanging freely.

Prolong AD and BC to meet at O. Let l' be the length of cone DCO and l be the length of the full cone ABO.

From Eq. 2.20, the extension of the cone ABO under its own weight is given by

$$\Delta_c = \frac{\lambda\, l^2}{6\,E} \qquad\qquad ...(1)$$

Similarly, the extension of cone DCO, under its own weight is

$$\Delta_c' = \frac{\lambda\, l'^2}{6\,E} \qquad\qquad ...(2)$$

The weight of cone $DCO = W' = \frac{1}{3}\left(\frac{\pi}{4}d_1^2\right)l'\,\lambda = \frac{\pi}{12}d_1^2\,l'\,\lambda$

Again, from Eq. 2.16, the extension of a tapering circular bar of length L, under an axial pull W' is given by

$$\Delta_{tc}' = \frac{4\,W'\,L}{\pi\,E\,d_1\,d_2} = \frac{4\,L}{\pi\,E\,d_1\,d_2}\left[\frac{\pi}{12}d_1^2\,l'\,\lambda\right]$$

or $\qquad\qquad \Delta_{tc}' = \frac{\lambda}{3}\frac{L\,l'}{E}\cdot\frac{d_1}{d_2} \qquad\qquad ...(3)$

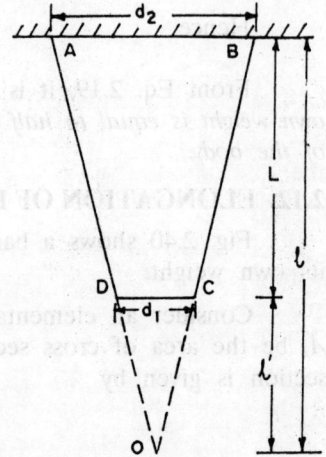

FIG. 2.41

Now extension of $ABCD$ = Extension of ABO − extension of DCO − extension of $ABCD$ under weight W'

or $\qquad\qquad \Delta_{tc} = \Delta_c - \Delta_c' - \Delta_{tc}'$

or $\qquad\qquad \Delta_{tc} = \frac{\lambda\,l^2}{6E} - \frac{\lambda\,l'^2}{6E} - \frac{\lambda}{3}\frac{L\,l'}{E}\cdot\frac{d_1}{d_2} \qquad\qquad ...(4)$

In the above expression, l and l' are not directly known and hence these are to be eliminated.

From the geometry of the cone, $\dfrac{d_2}{d_1} = \dfrac{l}{l'} = \dfrac{L+l'}{l'} = \dfrac{L}{l'}+1$

Hence $\qquad\qquad \frac{L}{l'} = \frac{d_2 - d_1}{d_1}$, from which $l' = \frac{d_1\,L}{d_2 - d_1} \qquad\qquad ...(i)$

and $\qquad\qquad l = \frac{d_2}{d_1}l' = \frac{d_2}{d_1}\times\frac{d_1\,L}{d_2 - d_1} = \frac{d_2\,L}{d_2 - d_1} \qquad\qquad ...(ii)$

Substituting these values in (4), we get

$$\Delta_{tc} = \frac{\lambda}{6\,E}\left(\frac{d_2\,L}{d_2 - d_1}\right)^2 - \frac{\lambda}{6\,E}\left(\frac{d_1\,L}{d_2 - d_1}\right)^2 - \frac{\lambda}{3\,E\,d_2}\frac{L^2\,d_1^2}{d_2 - d_1}$$

or $\qquad\qquad \Delta_{tc} = \frac{\lambda\,L^2}{6\,E}\left[\frac{d_2^3 - d_1^2\,d_2 - 2\,d_1^2\,(d_2 - d_1)}{d_2\,(d_2 - d_1)^2}\right]$

or $$\Delta_{tc} = \frac{\lambda L^2}{6E}\left[\frac{d_2^3 + 2d_1^3 - 3d_1^2 d_2}{a_2(d_2 - d_1)^2}\right] \qquad \dots(2.22)$$

This is the required expression.

When $d_1 = 0$ and $d_2 = d$ (*i.e.* case of § 2.12, Fig. 2.40), we get

$$\Delta = \frac{\lambda L^2}{6E}\left[\frac{d^3}{d^3}\right] = \frac{\lambda L^2}{6E} \quad \text{which is the same as Eq. 2.20.}$$

2.14. DEFORMATION OF BAR OF UNIFORM STRENGTH

For a bar to have *constant strength*, the stress at any section, due to external load P and the weight of the portion below it should be constant.

Consider an elementary section of a length δx, at a distance x from the lower end. The bar is subjected to a pull P at its free end. Let A be the area of cross-section of the free end (section CC). Let A_x be the area of cross-section of the bar at the lower end of the elementary section and $A_x + \delta A_x$ be the area of cross-section at the upper end of the elementary section.

For a bar of uniform section, $f = f_x = $ constant

Now $$f = \frac{P}{A} \; ; \; f_x = \frac{W_x}{A_x} \text{ and } f_{x+\delta x} = \frac{W_x'}{A_x + \delta A_x}$$

FIG. 2.42

Hence $$f = \frac{P}{A} = \frac{W_x}{A_x} = \frac{W_x'}{A_x + \delta A_x} \qquad \dots(1)$$

where $W_x = P + $ weight of bar below the elementary section $= P + W_1$ (say)

$$W_x' = P + W_1 + A_x . \lambda . \delta x$$

From (1), we get

$$f.A = P \qquad \dots(i)$$

$$fA_x = P + W_1 \qquad \dots(ii)$$

and $$f(A_x + \delta A_x) = P + W_1 + A_x . \lambda . \delta x \qquad \dots(iii)$$

where $\lambda = $ specific weight (or unit weight) of the material $= \rho \, g$

$\rho = $ specific mass (or unit mass) of the material

Subtracting (*ii*) from (*iii*), we get

$$f.\delta A_x = A_x . \lambda . \delta x$$

or $$\frac{\delta A_x}{A_x} = \frac{\lambda}{f} . \delta x$$

Integrating, we get $$\int_A^{A_x} \frac{dA_x}{A_x} = \int_0^x \frac{\lambda}{f} \, dx$$

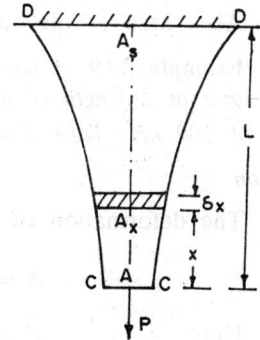

or $\qquad \log_e \dfrac{A_x}{A} = \dfrac{\lambda}{f} x$

From which $\qquad \dfrac{A_x}{A} = e^{\lambda x/f}$

or $\qquad A_x = A \cdot e^{\lambda x/f} = A e^{\rho g x/f}$ $\qquad\qquad$ ...(2.23)

The above expression gives the area of cross-section (A_x) of the bar at a distance x from the free end. Knowing the values of A, λ and f, the shape of the bar can be determined from Eq. 2.22.

Also, area at the support, $A_s = A e^{\lambda L/f}$ $\qquad\qquad$ ...(2.23 a)

Example 2.19. *A conical bar tapers uniformly from a diameter of 15 mm to a diameter of 40 mm in a length of 400 mm. Determine the elongation of the bar under an axial tensile force of 100 kN. Take $E = 2 \times 10^5 N/mm^2$.*

Solution

The deformation of a tapering conical bar is given by Eq. 2.16.

$$\Delta = \frac{4 P L}{\pi E d_1 d_2}$$

Here $\qquad P = 100$ kN $= 100 \times 10^3$ N ; $L = 400$ mm; $d_1 = 15$ mm; $d_2 = 40$ mm

$\therefore \qquad \Delta = \dfrac{4 \times 100 \times 10^3 \times 400}{\pi \times 2 \times 10^5 \times 15 \times 40} = \mathbf{0.424\ mm}$

Example 2.20. *A flat steel plate is of trapezoidal form. The thickness of the plate is 15 mm and it tapers uniformly from a width of 60 mm to a width of 10 mm in a length of 300 mm. Determine the elongation of the plate under an axial force of 120 kN.*
Take $E = 2.04 \times 10^5 N/mm^2$.

Solution

The deformation of uniformly tapering rectangular bar is given by Eq. 2.17.

$$\Delta = \frac{P L}{(b_2 - b_1) t E} \log_e \frac{b_2}{b_1}$$

Here $\qquad P = 120$ kN $= 120 \times 10^3$ N; $L = 300$ mm

$\qquad b_1 = 10$ mm; $b_2 = 60$ mm; $t = 15$ mm

$\therefore \qquad \Delta = \dfrac{120 \times 10^3 \times 300}{(60 - 10)\, 15 \times 2.04 \times 10^5} \log_e \dfrac{60}{10} = \mathbf{0.422\ mm}$

Example 2.21. *A solid conical bar tapers uniformly from a diameter of 60 mm at the support to 20 mm at the end, in a length of 1 m. It is suspended vertically. Calculate the elongation of the bar due to self weight. Take unit weight of bar material as 78.5 $k N/m^3$ and E as 204 $k N/mm^2$.*

Solution

The extension of a truncated shaped bar is given by Eq. 2.22.

$$\Delta_{tc} = \frac{\lambda L^2}{6 E} \left[\frac{d_2^3 + 2 d_1^3 - 3 d_1^2 d_2}{d_2 (d_2 - d_1)^2} \right]$$

Solution

Here $\quad d_1 = 20$ mm; $d_2 = 60$ mm; $L = 1000$ mm

$$\lambda = 78.5 \text{ kN/m}^3 = 78.5 \times 10^3/10^9 \text{ N/mm}^3 = 7.85 \times 10^{-5} \text{ N/mm}^3$$

$$E = 204 \text{ kN/mm}^2 = 204 \times 10^3 \text{ N/mm}^2$$

$\therefore \qquad \Delta_{tc} = \dfrac{7.85 \times 10^{-5} (1000)^2}{6 \times 204 \times 10^3} \left[\dfrac{60^3 + 2 \times 20^3 - 3 (20)^2 60}{60 (60 - 20)^2} \right]$

$$= 1.07 \times 10^{-4} \text{ mm}$$

Example 2.22. *If a tension test bar is found to taper from $(D + a)$ diameter to $(D - a)$ diameter, prove that the error involved in using the mean diameter to calculate the Young's modulus is $\left(\dfrac{10 \, a}{D} \right)^2$ percent.* (U.L.)

Solution

Smaller diameter, $d_1 = D - a$ and larger diameter, $d_2 = D + a$

Let $\qquad E_0 = $ modulus of elasticity computed by mean diameter

$\qquad E = $ actual Young's modulus

From Eq. 2.16, we get $E = \dfrac{4 P L}{\pi d_1 d_2 \Delta}$

$\therefore \qquad E = \dfrac{4 P L}{\pi (D - a)(D + a) \Delta} = \dfrac{K}{D^2 - a^2} \quad$ where $K = \dfrac{4 P L}{\pi \Delta}$ ...(i)

Also, based on the basis of mean diameter, we get

$$E_0 = \dfrac{P L}{A \Delta} = \dfrac{P L}{\dfrac{\pi}{4} D^2 \Delta} = \dfrac{4 P L}{\pi \Delta D^2} = \dfrac{K}{D^2} \qquad \text{...(ii)}$$

Hence % error $= \dfrac{E - E_0}{E} \times 100 = \dfrac{\dfrac{K}{D^2 - a^2} - \dfrac{K}{D^2}}{\dfrac{K}{D^2 - a^2}} \times 100$

$$= \dfrac{D^2 - (D^2 - a^2)}{D^2} \times 100 = \dfrac{100 \, a^2}{D^2}$$

$$= \left(\dfrac{10 \, a}{D} \right)^2 \text{ percent}$$

Example 2.23. *A steel wire of 10 mm diameter and length 150 m is used to lift a weight of 2.5 kN at its lowest end. Calculate the total elongation of the wire if the unit mass (or mass density) of the wire is 7.95 kg/m³ and $E = 2.04 \times 10^5$ N/mm².*

Solution

Area of cross-section of wire, $A = \dfrac{\pi}{4} (10)^2 = 78.54 \text{ mm}^2$

Extension of wire due to the load, $\Delta_1 = \dfrac{P L}{A E}$

$$= \dfrac{2.5 \times 10^3 \times 150 \times 10^3}{78.54 \times 2.04 \times 10^5} = 23.41 \text{ mm}$$

Extension of wire due to self weight, $\Delta_2 = \dfrac{\lambda L^2}{2E}$

Here, $\lambda = \rho g = 7.95 \times 9.81 = 77.99 \text{ kN/m}^3$

$= 77.99 \times 10^3 / 10^9 \text{ N/mm}^3 = 7.799 \times 10^{-5} \text{ N/mm}^3$

$\therefore$ $\Delta_2 = \dfrac{7.799 \times 10^{-5} (150 \times 1000)^2}{2 \times 2.04 \times 10^5} = 4.30 \text{ mm}$

$\therefore$ Total elongation $= \Delta_1 + \Delta_2 = 23.41 + 4.30 = \mathbf{27.71\ mm}$

Example 2.24. *A vertical tie of uniform strength is 10 m long and hangs from a ceiling. The area of the bar at the lower end is 400 mm^2. Find the area at the upper end when the tie is to carry a load of 60 kN. The material of the tie weighs 78 kN/m^3.*

Solution

Area of the tie at the bottom $= A = 400 \text{ mm}^2$

$\therefore$ Intensity of stress at the bottom $= f = \dfrac{60 \times 10^3}{400} = 150 \text{ N/mm}^2$

The area at any section is given by Eq. 2.23

$A_x = A\, e^{\lambda x/f}$ where $\lambda = 78 \text{ kN/m}^3 = 78 \times 10^3/10^9 \text{ N/mm}^3 = 7.8 \times 10^{-5} \text{ N/mm}^3$

At $x = 10 \times 10^3 \text{ mm},\ A_S = 400\, e^{\frac{7.8 \times 10^{-5} \times 10 \times 10^3}{150}}$

or $A_S = 400\, e^{5.2 \times 10^{-3}} = \mathbf{402.09\ mm^2}$

2.15. COMPOUND BARS : COMPOSITE SECTIONS

A structural member, composed of two or more elements of different materials rigidly connected together at their ends to form a parallel arrangement and subjected to axial loading is termed a *compound bar*. Such a section is also known as *composite section*. Such a problem is *statically indeterminate*, since equation of statics alone based on conditions of equilibrium, will provide only one equation for the stresses in the individual sections. Other equation can be obtained from the consideration of the deformation of the whole structure.

Consider the effect of a compressive load P upon a composite bar consisting of a rod and enveloping tube having the same length, but made of different material. Let the end collars be rigid. Let us use suffix 1 for the rod and 2 for the tube.

From the conditions of equilibrium,

$P_1 + P_2 = P$ ...(i)

Since the members are of the same initial length and are shortened by the same amount under load, we have

$\Delta_1 = \Delta_2$

or $\dfrac{P_1 L_1}{A_1 E_1} = \dfrac{P_2 L_2}{A_2 E_2}$ ...(ii)

The second equation is known as the *equation of compatibility*.

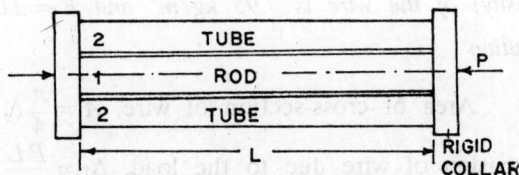

FIG. 2.43

Now from (ii),
$$P_1 = P_2 \cdot \frac{A_1 E_1}{A_2 E_2} \qquad \qquad ...(iii)$$

Substituting in (i), we get
$$P_2 \left[\frac{A_1 E_1}{A_2 E_2} + 1 \right] = P$$

From which
$$P_2 = \frac{P}{1 + \dfrac{A_1 E_1}{A_2 E_2}} \qquad \qquad ...(2.24)$$

Hence from (iii),
$$P_1 = \frac{P}{1 + \dfrac{A_2 E_2}{A_1 E_1}} \qquad \qquad ...(2.24\ a)$$

Example 2.25. *A mild steel rod of 25 mm diameter and 400 mm long is encased centrally inside a hollow copper tube of external diameter 35 mm and inside diameter 30 mm. The ends of the rod and tube are rigidly attached, and the composite bar is subjected to an axial pull of 40 kN.*

If E for steel and copper is 200 GN/m² and 100 GN/m² respectively, find the stress developed in the rod and the tube. Find also the extension of the rod.

(Based on Cambridge University)

Solution

Let us use suffix 1 for the steel rod and suffix 2 for the copper tube.

$$A_1 = \frac{\pi}{4} (25)^2 = 490.87 \text{ mm}^2$$

$$A_2 = \frac{\pi}{4} \left[(35)^2 - (30)^2 \right] = 255.25 \text{ mm}^2$$

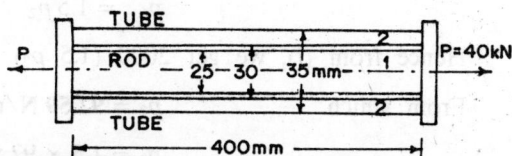

FIG. 2.44

From the equilibrium of the bar
$$p_1 A_1 + p_2 A_2 = P = 40 \times 10^3 \qquad \qquad ...(i)$$

Also, from compatibility, $\dfrac{p_1 L}{E_1} = \dfrac{p_2 L}{E_2}$

or
$$p_1 = p_2 \frac{E_1}{E_2} = p_2 \times \frac{200}{100} = 2 p_2 \qquad \qquad ...(ii)$$

Substituting the value of p_1 in (i), we get
$$2 p_2 A_1 + p_2 A_2 = 40 \times 10^3$$

or
$$2 p_2 (490.87) + p_2 (255.25) = 40 \times 10^3$$

From which,
$$p_2 = \textbf{32.34 N/mm}^2$$

Hence
$$p_1 = 2 p_2 = \textbf{64.68 N/mm}^2$$

Also, extension of rod $= \dfrac{p_1 L}{E} = \dfrac{64.88 \times 4000}{2 \times 10^5} = \mathbf{1.294\ mm}$

Example 2.26. *A steel rod of cross-sectional area 2000 mm² and two brass rods each of cross-sectional area of 1200 mm² together support a load of 60 kN, as shown in Fig. 2.45. Find the stresses in the rods. Take E for steel $=2\times10^5\ N/mm^2$ and E for brass $=1\times10^5\ N/mm^2$.*

Solution

Let us use suffix 1 for steel rod and suffix 2 for brass rods.

Given : $A_1 = 2000\ mm^2$ and $L_1 = 400\ mm$

$A_2 = 1200\ mm^2$ and $L_2 = 300\ mm$

From the equilibrium of the system,

$$p_1 A_1 + 2 p_2 A_2 = P$$

or $2000\,p_1 + 2400\,p_2 = 500 \times 10^3$ ...(i)

Also, $\Delta_1 = \Delta_2$

∴ $\dfrac{p_1 L_1}{E_1} = \dfrac{p_2 L_2}{E_2}$

or $\dfrac{p_1 \times 400}{2 \times 10^5} = \dfrac{p_2 \times 300}{1 \times 10^5}$

∴ $p_1 = 1.5\,p_2$ ...(ii)

Hence from (i), we get $2000\ (1.5\ p_2)\ + 2400\,p_2 = 500 \times 10^3$

From which $p_2 = \mathbf{92.59\ N/mm^2}$

∴ $p_1 = 1.5 \times 92.59 \approx \mathbf{138.89\ N/mm^2}$

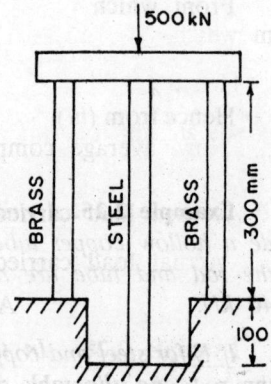

FIG. 2.45

Example 2.27. *A reinforced concrete column 450 mm × 450 mm has four steel rods of 25 mm diameter embedded in it. Find the stresses in steel and concrete when the total load on the column is 1000 kN. Find also the adhesive force between the steel and concrete. Take $E_s = 205\ N/mm^2$ and $E_c = 13.6\ kN/mm^2$.*

Solution

Total area of column $= 450 \times 450$

$= 202500\ mm^2$

Area of steel rods $= 4 \left(\dfrac{\pi}{4} 25^2 \right)$

$= 1963.5\ mm^2$

∴   Area of concrete, $A_c = 202500 - 1963.5$

$= 200536.5\ mm^2$

From equilibrium, $p_s A_s + p_c A_c = 1000 \times 10^3$ ...(i)

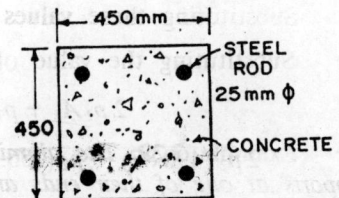

FIG. 2.46

From compatibility, $\dfrac{p_s}{E_s} = \dfrac{p_c}{E_c}$

or $\qquad\qquad p_s = p_c \cdot \dfrac{E_s}{E_c} = p_c \dfrac{205}{13.6} = 15.074\,p_c$ ...(2)

Substituting this value of p_s in (1) we get

$15.074\,p_c\,(1963.5) + p_c\,(200536.5) = 1000 \times 10^3$

From which, $\qquad\qquad\qquad p_c = \textbf{4.345 N/mm}^2$

Hence $\qquad\qquad\qquad p_s = 15.074 \times 4.345 = \textbf{65.501 N/mm}^2$

Now, average compressive stress $= \dfrac{1000 \times 10^3}{202500} = 4.938 \text{ N/mm}^2$

∴ Average load carried by concrete $= 4.938 \times 200536.5 \times 10^{-3} = 990.3$ kN

Actual load carried by concrete $= 4.345 \times 200536.5 \times 10^{-3} = 871.3$ kN

Adhesive force $= 990.3 - 871.3 = \textbf{119 kN}$

Example 2.28. *In the preceding example, compute the maximum safe load P that may be applied if the allowable stresses in steel and concrete are 140 N/mm² and 5 N/mm² respectively.*

Solution

An unwary student may find the value of P by substituting the values of allowable stresses only in the equation of static equilibrium. This would give wrong result, since it would not be on the consideration of equal deformations of the two materials.

From consideration of equal deformations, we have $p_s = 15.074\,p_c$

Hence, if concrete were to be stressed to $6\,\text{N/mm}^2$, we get

$$p_s = 15.074 \times 6 = 90.444 \text{ N/mm}^2$$

On the contrary, if steel were to be stressed to 140 N/mm², we get

$$p_c = p_s/15.074 = 140/15.074 = 9.288 \text{ N/mm}^2$$

Thus, concrete will be overstressed if p_s is taken as 140 N/mm². Therefore, steel could not be stressed to 140 N/mm² without over stressing the concrete.

The actual *working stresses* could therefore be $p_c = 6\,\text{N/mm}^2$ and $p_s = 90.444\,\text{N/mm}^2$.

Substituting these values in the equation of static equilibrium, we get

$$P = p_s A_s + p_c A_c = (90.444 \times 1963.5 + 6 \times 200536.5)\,10^{-3}$$
$$= \textbf{1380.81 kN}$$

Example 2.29. *The aluminium and steel pipes shown in Fig. 2.47 are fastened to rigid supports at one of their ends and to a rigid plate C at the other ends. Derive expressions for axial stresses in the two pipes. Hence find the numerical values if P = 30 kN, $A_a = 4000\,mm^2$, $A_s = 400\,mm^2$, $E_a = 0.7 \times 10^5 N/mm^2$ and $E_s = 2 \times 10^5\,N/mm^2$.*

Solution

From the inspection of Fig. 2.47, we observe that steel pipe will carry tensile stress (p_s) while aluminium pipe will carry compressive stress (p_a) . If R_s and R_a are the reactions at the two ends, as marked in Fig. 2.47, we get from static equilibrium :

$$R_s + R_a = 2P$$

Since R_s causes tensile stress in steel pipe, $R_s = p_s . A_s$. Similarly, R_a causes compressive stress in aluminium pipe and hence $R_a = p_a A_a$.

$$p_s A_s + p_a A_a = 2P \qquad \qquad ...(i)$$

Also, extension of steel pipe = contraction of aluminium pipe

or
$$\frac{p_s L}{E_s} = \frac{p_a (2L)}{E_a}$$

or
$$p_s = p_a \frac{2L}{L} . \frac{E_s}{E_a} = 2p_a . \frac{E_s}{E_a} \qquad ...(ii)$$

Substituting in (i), we get

$$2 p_a \frac{E_s}{E_a} A_s + p_a A_a = 2P$$

From which
$$p_a = \frac{2P}{2A_s . \dfrac{E_s}{E_a} + A_a}$$

Hence
$$p_s = 4P . \frac{E_s/E_a}{2A_s \dfrac{E_s}{E_a} + A_a} = \frac{4P}{2A_s + A_a . \dfrac{E_a}{E_s}}$$

These are the required expressions.

Here, $E_s/E_a = 2 \times 10^5 / 0.7 \times 10^5 = 2.857$

and $E_a/E_s = 0.7 \times 10^5 / 2 \times 10^5 = 0.35$

FIG. 2.47

$\therefore$
$$p_a = \frac{2 \times 30 \times 10^3}{2 \times 400 \times 2.857 + 4000} = \textbf{9.55 N/mm}^2 \text{ (compressive)}$$

and
$$p_s = \frac{4 \times 30 \times 10^3}{2 \times 400 + 4000 \times 0.35} = \textbf{54.44 N/mm}^2 \textbf{(tensile)}$$

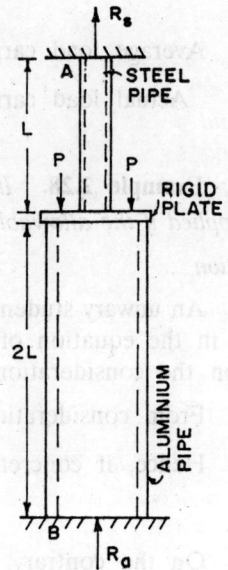

Example 2.30. *A rigid bar ABC is supported by three rods of the same material and of equal diameter as shown in Fig. 2.48. Calculate the forces in the bars due to an applied force P, if the bar ABC remains horizontal after the load has been applied. Neglect the weight of the rigid bar.*

Solution

Let us use suffix 1 for outer bars and suffix 2 for the inner bar.

From statical equilibrium,

$$2P_1 + P_2 = P \qquad ...(i)$$

From compatibility, $\Delta_1 = \Delta_2$

or

$$\frac{P_1 L}{A E} = \frac{P_2 (2L)}{A E},$$

from which $\qquad P_1 = 2 P_2 \qquad ...(ii)$

Substituting in (i), we get

$$2(2P_2) + P_2 = P \ , \ \text{from which} \ P_2 = \mathbf{0.2\, P}$$

Hence $\qquad P_1 = 2 \times 0.2\, P = \mathbf{0.4\, P}$

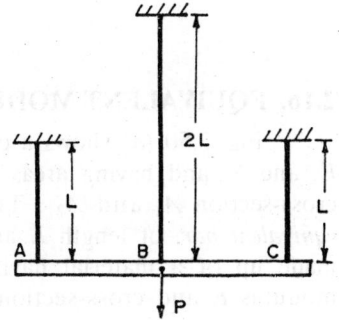

FIG. 2.48

Example 2.31. *Two horizontal rigid bars AB and CD are connected by two wires of aluminium and copper as shown in Fig. 2.49. Both the wires have length L. Vertical loads P are applied at mid points E and F of the two bars. Compute the increase Δ in the distance between points E and F when the loads are applied.*

Solution

Let us use suffix 1 for aluminium wire and suffix 2 for copper wire.

The extensions Δ_1 and Δ_2 of the two wires will be different. Hence the displacement Δ between points E and F is given by

$$\Delta = \tfrac{1}{2} (\Delta_1 + \Delta_2) \qquad ...(i)$$

Also, from statical equilibrium, by taking moments about plane AC, we get

$$P_2 \times AB = P \times AE$$

$\therefore \qquad P_2 = P \dfrac{AE}{AB} = \dfrac{1}{2} P \qquad ...(ii)$

Hence $\qquad P_1 = \dfrac{1}{2} P$

Now $\qquad \Delta_1 = \dfrac{P_1 L}{A_1 E_1} = \dfrac{\left(\dfrac{P}{2}\right) L}{\dfrac{\pi}{4} d_1^2 E_1} = \dfrac{2 P L}{\pi\, d_1^2 E_1}$

and $\qquad \Delta_2 = \dfrac{P_2 L}{A_2 E_2} = \dfrac{(P/2) L}{\dfrac{\pi}{4} d_2^2 E_2} = \dfrac{2 P L}{\pi\, d_2^2 E_2}$

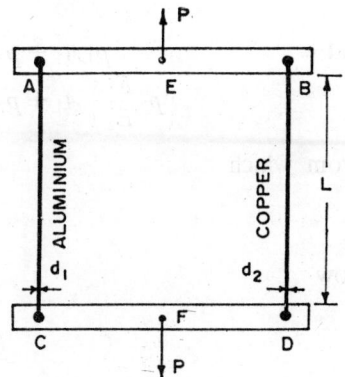

FIG. 2.49

$\therefore \qquad \Delta = \tfrac{1}{2} (\Delta_1 + \Delta_2) = \dfrac{1}{2} \left[\dfrac{2 P L}{\pi\, d_1^2 E_1} + \dfrac{2 P L}{\pi\, d_2^2 E_2} \right]$

or $\qquad \Delta = \dfrac{P L}{\pi} \left[\dfrac{1}{d_1^2 E_1} + \dfrac{1}{d_2^2 E_2} \right] ,$ which is the required expression.

If, however, both the wires are of the same material, $E_1 = E_2 = E$

$$\therefore \qquad \Delta = \frac{PL}{\pi E}\left[\frac{1}{d_1^2} + \frac{1}{d_2^2}\right]$$

2.16. EQUIVALENT MODULUS OF A COMPOUND BAR

Fig. 2.50 (a) shows a compound bar of length L, consisting of two materials of modulus E_1 and E_2 and having areas of cross-section A_1 and A_2. The *equivalent bar*, of length L and made up of a material having modulus E and cross-sectional area $A = A_1 + A_2$, is shown in Fig. 2.50 (b). Such equivalent bar should have the same deformation under the load as that of the compound bar.

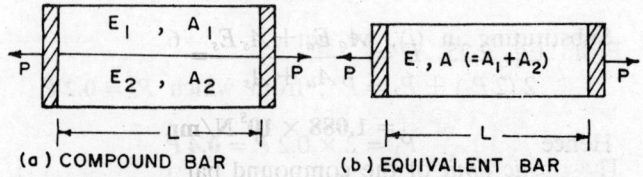

(a) COMPOUND BAR   (b) EQUIVALENT BAR

FIG. 2.50

For the equivalent bar,

Extension $\qquad \Delta = \frac{PL}{AE} = \frac{PL}{(A_1 + A_2)E}$

$$\therefore \qquad \frac{PL}{\Delta} = (A_1 + A_2)E \qquad \qquad ...(i)$$

For the compound bar

$$\frac{p_1}{E_1} = \frac{p_2}{E_2} \qquad \text{or} \qquad p_1 = p_2 \cdot \frac{E_1}{E_2}$$

and $\qquad p_1 A_1 + p_2 A_2 = P$

or $\qquad \left(p_2 \frac{E_1}{E_2}\right)A_1 + p_2 A_2 = P$

From which $\qquad p_2 = \dfrac{P}{\dfrac{E_1}{E_2}\cdot A_1 + A_2}$

Now $\qquad \Delta = \dfrac{p_2 L}{E_2} = \dfrac{PL}{A_1 E_1 + A_2 E_2}$

or $\qquad \dfrac{PL}{\Delta} = A_1 E_1 + A_2 E_2 \qquad \qquad ...(ii)$

Equating (i) and (ii), we get

$$(A_1 + A_2)E = A_1 E_1 + A_2 E_2$$

From which $\qquad E = \dfrac{A_1 E_1 + A_2 E_2}{A_1 + A_2} \qquad \qquad ...(2.25)$

Example 2.32. *A compound bar is made by fastening one flat bar of steel between two similar bars of aluminium alloy. The dimensions of each bar are 40 mm wide × 8 mm thick, so that the cross-section of the composite bar measures 40 mm × 24 mm. If E for steel*

$= 2.04 \times 10^5 \ N/mm^2$ and E for alloy $= 0.612 \times 10^5 \ N/mm^2$, find the apparent value of E for the composite bar loaded in tension. If the respective elastic limits are 230 N/mm^2 and 50 N/mm^2, find the elastic limit of the compound bar.

Solution

Let us use suffix s for steel and a for aluminium alloy.

$\therefore \qquad A_s = (40 \times 8) = 320 \ mm^2$ and $A_a = 2 \times 40 \times 8 = 640 \ mm^2$

$\therefore$ Total area $\quad A = A_s + A_a = 320 + 640 = 960 \ mm^2$

From Eq. 2.25, $E = \dfrac{A_a E_a + A_s E_s}{A_a + A_s} = \dfrac{640 \times 0.612 \times 10^5 + 320 \times 2.04 \times 10^5}{640 + 320}$

$$= 1.088 \times 10^5 \ N/mm^2$$

The *elastic limit* of the compound bar is the stress at which one of the members, either steel or aluminium alloy, is stressed to its elastic limit.

Let P be the load at elastic limit of the compound bar, and p_a and p_s be the corresponding stresses in the two materials at the elastic limit of the compound bar.

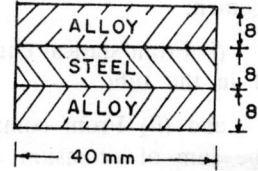

Since the strains in the two materials are equal,

FIG. 2.51

$$\frac{p_s}{E_s} = \frac{p_a}{E_a} \ , \ \text{from which} \ p_s = p_a \frac{E_s}{E_a} = p_a \frac{2.04}{0.612} = 3.333 \, p_a \qquad \ldots(i)$$

Also, $\qquad p_s A_s + p_a A_a = P$

$\therefore \qquad 3.333 \, p_a A_s + p_a A_a = P$

$\therefore \qquad p_a \left[3.333 \times 320 + 640 \right] = P$

$$p_a = \frac{P}{1706.7} \ ; \ \text{Hence} \ p_s = \frac{P}{512} \qquad \ldots(ii)$$

Let $\qquad p = $ elastic limit of the compound bar.

Hence $\qquad p (A_a + A_s) = P$,

or $\qquad 960 \, p = P \qquad \ldots(iii)$

But $\qquad P = 1706.7 \, p_a$, from (ii)

Hence $\qquad 960 \, p = 1706.7 \, p_a$

From which $\qquad p = \dfrac{1706.7}{960} \, p_a = 1.778 \, p_a = 1.778 \times 50 = 88.89 \ N/mm^2 \qquad \ldots(I)$

Also, from Eq. (ii), $\qquad p = 512 \, p_s$

Hence from (iii), $\qquad 960 \, p = 512 \, p_s$

or $\qquad p = \dfrac{512}{960} \, p_s = \dfrac{512}{960} \times 230 = 122.67 \ N/mm^2 \qquad \ldots(II)$

The elastic limit (p) is the lower of the two values of p given by Eqs (I) and (II). Hence the elastic limit of the compound bar will be **88.89 N/mm²**.

2.17. STRESSES IN BOLTS AND NUTS

Fig. 2.52 shows a bolt passing through a tube. The bolt is tightened by turning the nut. When the nut is tightened by placing washers as shown, the nut will be easily turned initially, till the space between the two washers is exactly equal to the body of the bolt (and hence length of the tube) between the them. If the bolt is tightened further, the bolt will be subjected to tension while the washers and the tube will be subjected to compression. The following criteria apply to such an arrangement.

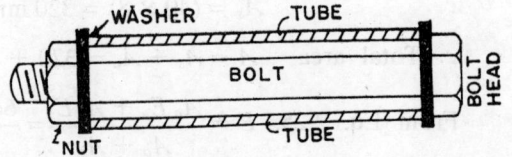

FIG. 2.52

(i) From statical equilibrium, the tensile load in the bolt will be equal to the compressive load in the tube

and (ii) From compatibility point of view, the *axial advancement* of the nut is equal to be sum of extension of the bolt and the contraction of the tube.

Example 2.33. *A steel bolt 650 mm² cross-sectional area passes centrally through a copper tube to 1200 mm² cross-sectional area. The tube is 500 mm long and is closed by rigid washers, which are fastened by the threads on the steel bolt.*

The nut is now tightened by 1/4 of a turn. Find the stress in the bolt and the tube if the pitch of the thread is 3 mm. Take $E_s = 2.05 \times 10^5 \, N/mm^2$ and $E_c = 1.1 \times 10^5 \, N/mm^2$.

(Based on Oxford University)

Solution

Let us use suffix s for steel bolt and c for copper tube.

$$\therefore \qquad p_s A_s = p_c A_c$$

or $\qquad p_s (650) = p_c (1200)$, which gives $p_s = 1.846 \, p_c$ $\qquad\qquad$ ...(i)

Since the final length of the bolt and tube is the same, we have

$$\Delta_s + \Delta_c = \text{movement of the nut}$$

$$\therefore \qquad \frac{p_s L}{E_s} + \frac{p_c L}{E_c} = \frac{1}{4} \times 3$$

or $\qquad \dfrac{p_s \times 500}{2.05 \times 10^5} + \dfrac{p_c \times 500}{1.1 \times 10^5} = 0.75$ $\qquad\qquad$ ...(ii)

Substituting the value of p_s from (i) we get

$$(1.846 \, p_c) \, 243.9 + p_c \times 454.5 = 0.75 \times 10^5$$

which gives $p_c = $ **82.89 N/mm²** and $p_s = 1.846 \times 82.89 = $ **153 N/mm²**

Example 2.34. *Two steel plugs fit freely into the ends of a steel tubular distance piece 400 mm long and are drawn together by a steel bolt (500 mm long) and nut, the nut being tight fit in the beginning. The nut is further tightened by $\frac{1}{4}$ turn to draw the pieces together, the pitch of the bolt thread being 2 mm. The pieces are then subjected to forces of 50 kN tending to pull them apart. Calculate the stresses in the bolt and the tube. The area of cross-section of the bolt is 700 sq. mm and that of the tube is 500 sq. mm. Take E for steel as 200 GN/m².*

Solution

Let us consider both the effects separately.

(a) Effect of tightening the nut

Due to tightening of the nut, tensile stress will be induced in the bolt and compressive stress will be induced in the tube. Let us use suffix 1 for the bolt and suffix 2 for the tube.

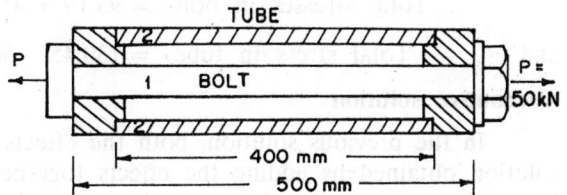

FIG. 2.53

From statical equilibrium, $p_1 A_1 = p_2 A_2$ ...(i)

Also, $\Delta_1 + \Delta_2 = $ movement of the nut

$\therefore \qquad \dfrac{p_1 L_1}{E} + \dfrac{p_2 L_2}{E} = \dfrac{1}{4} \times 2 = 0.5$

or $\qquad p_1 = \left(0.5 - \dfrac{p_2 L_2}{E} \right) \dfrac{E}{L_1}$ ...(ii)

Substituting this value of p_1 is (i), we get

$$p_2 = \left(0.5 - \frac{p_2 L_2}{E} \right) \frac{E}{L_1} \times \frac{A_1}{A_2}$$

or $\qquad p_2 \left(1 + \dfrac{L_2}{L_1} \times \dfrac{A_1}{A_2} \right) = 0.5 \dfrac{E}{L_1} \times \dfrac{A_1}{A_2}$

Substituting the numerical values and noting that
$E = 205 \text{ GN/m}^2 = 205 \times 10^9 \text{ N/m}^2 = 2.05 \times 10^5 \text{ N/mm}^2$, we get

$$p_2 \left(1 + \frac{500}{400} \times \frac{700}{500} \right) = 0.5 \times \frac{2.05 \times 10^5}{400} \times \frac{700}{500}$$

From which $\qquad p_2 = 130.45 \text{ N/mm}^2$ (Compressive)

Hence $\qquad p_1 = \left(0.5 - \dfrac{130.45 \times 500}{2.05 \times 10^5} \right) \dfrac{2.05 \times 10^5}{400} = 93.19 \text{ N/mm}^2$ (tensile)

(b) Effect of external load

Let p_1' and p_2' be the additional stresses, both tensile, due to external tensile load of 50 kN.

$\therefore \qquad p_1' A_1 + p_2' A_2 = 50000$ ...(iii)

Also, from compatibility, $\dfrac{p_1' L_1}{E} = \dfrac{p_2' L_2}{E}$

or $\qquad\qquad\qquad p_1' = p_2' \dfrac{L_2}{L_1} = \dfrac{500}{400} p_2' = 1.25 \, p_2'$ ...(iv)

Hence from (iii) $1.25 \, p_2' \, (700) + p_2' \, (500) = 50000$

From which $p_2' = 36.36 \, \text{N/mm}^2$ (tensile), and $p_1' = 1.25 \times 36.36 = 45.45 \, \text{N/mm}^2$ (tensile)

(c) *Final stresses*

Total stresses in bolt $= 93.19 + 45.45 = \textbf{138.64 N/mm}^2$ (tensile)

and Total stress in tube $= 130.45 - 36.36 = \textbf{94.09 N/mm}^2$ (comp.)

Alternative solution

In the previous solution, both the effects have been considered separately and the final solution obtained by adding the effects together. This is a long and cumbersome procedure. However, the solution can be obtained directly, and in short, by considering both the effects together.

Let p_1(tensile) and p_2 (compressive) be the final stresses in the bolt and the tube respectively.

From static equilibrium, we have :

$\therefore \qquad\qquad\qquad p_1 A_1 - p_2 A_2 = 50,000$

or $\qquad\qquad\qquad 700 \, p_1 - 500 \, p_2 = 50000$

or $\qquad\qquad\qquad p_1 - 0.714 \, p_2 = 71.43$ ...(1)

Also, from compatibility,

(Total extension of bolt) + (total compression of tube) = movement of nut

$\therefore \qquad\qquad \dfrac{p_1 L_1}{E} + \dfrac{p_2 L_2}{E} = \dfrac{1}{4} \times 2 = 0.5$

or $\qquad\quad p_1 \times 400 + p_2 \times 500 = 0.5 \times 2.05 \times 10^5$

$\therefore \qquad\qquad\qquad p_1 + 1.25 \, p_2 = 256.25$ ...(2)

Subtracting (1) from (2), we get $1.964 \, p_2 = 184.82$

From which $\qquad\qquad p_2 = \textbf{94.1 N/mm}^2$ (comp.)

Hence $\qquad\qquad p_1 = 71.43 + 0.714 \times 94.1 = \textbf{138.62 N/mm}^2$ (tensile)

2.18. TEMPERATURE STRESSES IN UNIFORM BARS

When the temperature of an object changes, its dimensions are changed. Let us consider a block of homogeneous and isotropic material that is *free* to expand in all the directions. If this block is subjected to *uniform* changes in temperature (t, increase), the sides of the block will increase, and will take the shape shown by the dotted lines, with corner C taken as the reference point. If α is the *coefficient of thermal expansion* (or contraction), the *uniform thermal strain* (ε_t) is given by

$$\varepsilon_t = \alpha\,(t) \qquad\qquad ...(2.26)$$

The coefficient α is a property of the material and has a unit reciprocal of temperature change. In SI units, α has the dimensions of either $1/K$ (the reciprocal of kelvins) or $1/C$ (the reciprocal of degree Celsius), because the change in temperature is numerically the same in both kelvins and degrees Celsius. Common values of α are : 10×10^{-6} to $18 \times 10^{-6}/^{\circ}C$ for steel, $17 \times 10^{-6}/^{\circ}C$ for copper and $23 \times 10^{-6}/^{\circ}C$ for aluminium and aluminium alloys. Ordinary materials expand when heated and contract

FIG. 2.54

when cooled. Increase in temperature produces a positive thermal strain while decrease in temperature cause negative thermal strains. Also, thermal strains are reversible in nature, meaning thereby that the member returns to its original shape when the temperature returns to its original value. However, there are some special materials, recently developed which do not behave in customary manner; these special metals decrease in the dimensions when heated and increase when cooled, over certain temperature range. Another example of *unusual material* is water which *expands* when heated above $4^{\circ}C$ and also *expands* when cooled at temperature below $4^{\circ}C$, thus attaining its maximum density at $4^{\circ}C$.

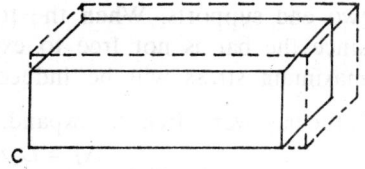

Consider a bar of length L (Fig. 2.55 *a*), subjected to uniform temperature increase t, the bar being *free* to expand. Then the increase in the length of bar will be

$$\Delta_t = \varepsilon_t \cdot L = \alpha t L \qquad ...(2.26\ a)$$

It should be clearly noted that since the bar is free to expand, there will be no *thermal stress* in the bar.

In contrast to this, consider a bar (Fig. 2.55 *b*) of length L, fixed at both ends between rigid supports. If the supports do not yield, the bar is not free to expand by the amount Δ_t and hence it will be subjected to *thermal stress* p_t given by

$$p_t = \frac{\Delta_t E}{L} = L\,\alpha\,t \cdot \frac{E}{L} = E\,\alpha\,t \quad ...(2.27)$$

This stress will be *compressive* when the change in temperature (t) is positive (*i.e.* increase) and *tensile* when the change in temperature is negative (*i.e.* decrease). *Note that the thermal stress p_t does not depend upon the cross-sectional area.*

(a) BAR FREE TO EXPAND

(b) BAR CONSTRAINED

(c) YIELDING OF SUPPORT

FIG. 2.55

Lastly, consider the case shown in Fig. 2.55 (*c*), in which one of the support *yields* by an amount a. In this case, the total amount of expansion *checked* will be $(\Delta_t - a)$. Hence the resulting temperature stress is

$$p_t = (\Delta_t - a)\frac{E}{L} = (L\,\alpha\,t - a)\frac{E}{L} \qquad\qquad ...(2.28)$$

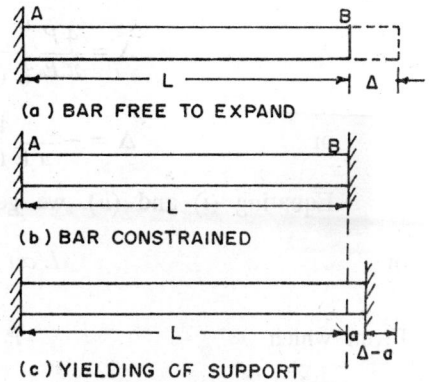

2.19. TEMPERATURE STRESSES IN BARS OF TAPERING SECTION

Consider a bar of uniformly tapering section, shown in Fig. 2.25, rigidly fixed between two end supports. When the temperature is raised by t, compressive force P will be induced since the bar is not free to expand. This force is the same for all cross-sections, and hence maximum stress will be induced at section AA where diameter is d_1.

If the bar were free to expand, we have
$$\Delta_t = L \alpha t \qquad ...(i)$$

The force induced in the bar will be a compressive force P which is required to prevent free expansion of Δ given by (i).

Now, for an element of length dx, the deformation due to P is

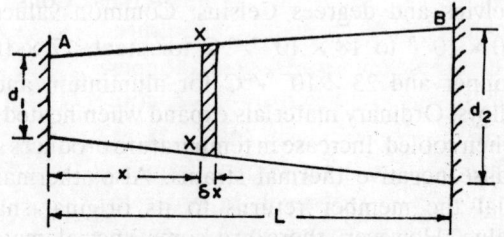

$$\delta\Delta = \frac{P \cdot dx}{A_x E}$$

$\therefore$ Total deformation $\Delta = \int\limits_0^L \frac{P \, dx}{A_x E}$

FIG. 2.56

But
$$A_x = \frac{\pi}{4}\left(d_1 + \frac{d_2 - d_1}{L}x\right)^2 = \frac{\pi}{4}(d_1 + kx)^2 \text{ where } x = \frac{d_2 - d_1}{L}$$

$\therefore$
$$\Delta = \frac{4P}{\pi E}\int\limits_0^L \frac{dx}{(d_1 + bx)^2} = -\frac{4P}{\pi k E}\left[\frac{1}{d_1 + kx}\right]_0^L$$

or
$$\Delta = -\frac{4PL}{\pi E(d_2 - d_1)}\left[\frac{1}{d_1 + d_2 - d_1} - \frac{1}{d_1}\right] = \frac{4PL}{\pi E d_1 d_2} \qquad ...(ii)$$

Equating (i) and (ii), we get, $\Delta_t = \Delta$

or
$$L\alpha t = \frac{4PL}{\pi E d_1 d_2} \qquad\qquad\qquad ...(iii)$$

From which
$$P = \frac{\pi E}{4} d_1 d_2 . \alpha t \qquad\qquad ...(2.29)$$

Maximum stress induced at section AA is given by

$$p_{t,\,max} = \left(\frac{\pi E}{4} d_1 d_2 \alpha t\right) \div \left(\frac{\pi}{4} d_1^2\right) = E \alpha t \frac{d_2}{d_1} \qquad ...(2.30)$$

If $d_1 = d_2$, $p_t = E\alpha t$, which is the same as Eq. 2.27.

Again, if the support yields by an amount a, the amount of expansion *checked* will be $(\Delta_t - a)$. Hence

$$\Delta_t - a = \Delta$$

or
$$(L\alpha t - a) = \frac{4PL}{\pi E d_1 d_2}$$

From which $\qquad P = \dfrac{\pi E}{4} d_1 d_2 \left(\dfrac{L \alpha t - a}{L} \right)$ $\hspace{2cm}$ ...(2.31)

2.20. TEMPERATURE STRESSES IN COMPOSITE BAR

When a composite bar, consisting of two materials having different coefficients of thermal expansion, is subjected to temperature change, opposite kinds of stresses (*i.e.* tensile and compressive) will be set up in the two materials. Consider a composite bar of steel (*S*) and copper (*C*), subjected to increase in temperature.

The free expansion (Δ_c^t) of copper due to temperature rise will be more than the free expansion (Δ_s^t) of steel, since α ($= \alpha_c$) for copper is more than $\alpha(= \alpha_s$) of steel. In order to have common expansion (Δ), tensile stress will be developed in steel and compressive stress in copper. From statics, we get :

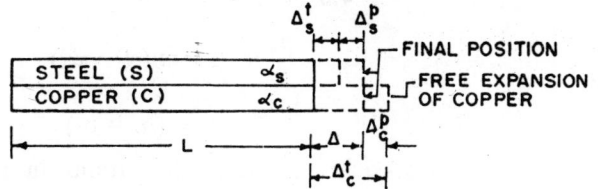

FIG. 2.57

Tensile force in steel = compressive force in copper

$\therefore \qquad P_s = P_c = P$ (say) $\hspace{4cm}$ ...(*i*)

From compatibility equation,

Final extension of copper = Final extension of steel

$\therefore \qquad \Delta_c = \Delta_s = \Delta$ (say) $\hspace{4cm}$ ...(*ii*)

Also, from geometry of Fig. 2.57, we get

$\qquad \Delta_s = \Delta_s^t + \Delta_s^p$ and $\Delta_c = \Delta_c^t - \Delta_c^p$ $\hspace{2cm}$ ...(*iii*)

where $\qquad \Delta_s = \Delta_c = \Delta$ = Final expansion

$\qquad \Delta_s^t$ = Free expansion of steel, due to temperature rise

$\qquad \Delta_c^t$ = Free expansion of copper, due to temperature rise

$\qquad \Delta_s^p$ = Expansion of steel due to temperature stress (tensile)

$\qquad \Delta_c^p$ = Compression of copper due to Temperature stress (comp.)

From (*ii*), we get

$\qquad \Delta_s^t + \Delta_s^p = \Delta_c^t - \Delta_c^p$

or $\qquad \Delta_s^p + \Delta_c^p = \Delta_c^t - \Delta_s^t$

or $\qquad \Delta_s^p + \Delta_c^p = L t (\alpha_c - \alpha_s)$ $\hspace{3cm}$ ...(*iv*)

But $\qquad \Delta_s^p = \dfrac{PL}{A_s E_s}$ and $\Delta_c^p = \dfrac{PL}{A_c E_c}$, where P is the final force in the bar.

$\therefore \quad PL \left(\dfrac{1}{A_s E_s} + \dfrac{1}{A_s E_s} \right) = L t (\alpha_c - \alpha_s)$ $\hspace{3cm}$ ...(*v*)

From which
$$P = \frac{t(\alpha_c - \alpha_s)}{\dfrac{1}{A_s E_s} + \dfrac{1}{A_c E_c}} \qquad \qquad ...(2.32)$$

Knowing the value of P, the individual stresses in steel and copper are :
$$p_s = P/A_s \text{ and } p_c = P/A_c$$

Eq. (v) can also be written as
$$\frac{P}{A_s E_s} + \frac{P}{A_c E_c} = t(\alpha_c - \alpha_s)$$

or
$$\frac{p_s}{E_s} + \frac{p_c}{E_c} = t(\alpha_c - \alpha_s) \qquad \qquad ...(2.33\ a)$$

or
$$e_s + e_c = (\alpha_c - \alpha_s)\ t \qquad \qquad ...(2.33)$$

The above equation relates the strains in the two materials.

Also, from Eqs. (ii) and (iii), the final elongation of the composite bar is given by
$$\Delta = \Delta_s = \Delta_s^t + \Delta_s^p$$

or
$$\Delta = L\,\alpha_s t + \frac{PL}{A_s E_s}$$

Substituting the value of P from Eq. 2.32.
$$\Delta = L\,\alpha_s t + \frac{L}{A_s E_s}\left[\frac{t(\alpha_c - \alpha_s)}{\dfrac{1}{A_s E_s} + \dfrac{1}{A_c E_c}}\right]$$

From which
$$\Delta = \frac{(\alpha_s A_s E_s + \alpha_c A_c E_c)\,L\,t}{A_s E_s + A_c E_c} \qquad \qquad ...(2.34)$$

Example 2.35. *Two parallel walls, 8 m apart, are stayed together by a steel rod of 20 mm diameter passing through metal plates and nuts at each end. The nuts are screwed upto the plates while the bar is at a temperature of 400 K. Find the pull exerted by the bar after it has cooled to 300 K, (a) if the ends do not yield (b) if the total yielding at the two ends is 5 mm. Take α for steel $= 12 \times 10^{-6}$ per K and $E = 2 \times 10^5\,N/mm^2$.*

Solution

Change in temperature (fall) $= 400 - 300 = 100$ K

Area of cross-section of rod $= \dfrac{\pi}{4}(20)^2 = 314.16\ mm^2$

(a) *Non-yielding walls*
$$p_t = \alpha\,t\,E = 12 \times 10^{-6} \times 100 \times 2 \times 10^5 = 240\ N/mm^2$$

∴   Pull $P = p_t\,.\,A = 240 \times 314.16 = 75398$ N $= \mathbf{75.398\ kN}$

(b) *Walls yielding by 5 mm*
$$\frac{p_t L}{E} = \Delta = (L\,\alpha t - a) \text{ where } a = 5 \text{ mm}$$

$$\therefore \qquad p_t = \frac{E}{L}(L\,\alpha t - 5) = E\,\alpha t - \frac{5E}{L}$$

$$= 240 - \frac{5 \times 2 \times 10^5}{8000} = 240 - 125 = 115 \text{ N/mm}^2$$

$$\therefore \qquad \text{Pull} \quad P = p_t \cdot A = 115 \times 314.16 = 36128 \text{ N} = \mathbf{36.128 \ kN}$$

Example 2.36. *A railway is laid so that there is no stress in the rails at 8°C. Calculate (a) the stress on the rails at 50°C if there is no allowance for expansion, (b) the stress in the rails at 50°C if there is an expansion allowance of 8 mm per rail. (c) the expansion allowance if the stress in the rail is to be zero when the temperature is 50° C (d) the maximum temperature to have no stress in the rails if the expansion allowance is 12 mm per rail. The rails are 30 m long. Take $\alpha = 12 \times 10^{-6}$ per °C and $E = 2 \times 10^5 \text{ N/mm}^2$.*
Solution

Change in temperature (rise) $= 50 - 8 = 42°C$

(a) *No expansion allowance*

$$\text{Stress } p_t = \alpha\,t\,E = 12 \times 10^{-6} \times 42 \times 2 \times 10^5 = 100.8 \text{ N/mm}^2$$

(b) *Expansion allowance of 8 mm*

$$\frac{p_t \cdot L}{E} = \Delta = (L\,\alpha t - a)$$

$$\therefore \qquad p_t = E\,\alpha t - \frac{aE}{L} = 100.8 - \frac{5 \times 2 \times 10^5}{30000} = 67.5 \text{ N/mm}^2$$

(c) *Value of a if p_t is to be zero*

$$p_t = E\,\alpha t - \frac{aE}{L}$$

For p_t to be zero, $\qquad a = L\,\alpha\,t = 30000 \times 12 \times 10^{-6} \times 42 = \mathbf{15.12 \ mm}$

(d) *Value of temperature for p_t to be zero*

$$p_t = \frac{E}{L}(L\,\alpha t - a) = 0$$

$$\therefore \qquad L\,\alpha\,t = a$$

Hence $\qquad t = \dfrac{a}{L\,\alpha} = \dfrac{12}{30000 \times 12 \times 10^{-6}} = 33.33°$

$\therefore \qquad$ Allowable temperature $= 8 + 33.33 = \mathbf{41.33°}$

Example 2.37. *A circular section tapering bar is rigidly fixed at both the ends. The diameter change from 75 mm at one end to 150 mm at the other end, in a length of 1.2 m. Compute the maximum stress in the bar if the temperature is raised by 32°C. Take $E = 2 \times 10^5 \text{ N/mm}^2$ and $\alpha = 12 \times 10^{-6}$ per 1°C.*
Solution

For Eq. 2.30, $\qquad p_{t,\,\max} = E\,\alpha\,t \cdot \dfrac{d_2}{d_1} = 2 \times 10^5 \times 12 \times 10^{-6} \times 32 \times \dfrac{150}{75}$

$$= \mathbf{153.6 \ N/mm^2}$$

Example 2.38. *A gun metal rod screwed at the ends passes through a steel tube. The tube has 25 mm external diameter and 20 mm internal diameter. The diameter of the rod is 16 mm. The assembly is heated to 400 K and the nuts on the rod are then screwed tightly home on the ends of the tube. Find the intensity of stress in the rod and in the tube when the common temperature falls to 300 K.*

Coefficient of expansion per K for steel $= 12 \times 10^{-6}$

Coefficient of expansion per K for gun metal $= 20 \times 10^{-6}$

Young's modulus for gun metal $= 0.91 \times 10^5 \, N/mm^2$

Young's modulus for steel $= 2 \times 10^5 \, N/mm^2$

Solution

Let us use suffix s for steel and g for gun metal. From statics, we get

$$p_s A_s = p_g . A_g \qquad \qquad ...(i)$$

Also $\qquad \qquad \Delta_s = \Delta_g = \Delta = $ net reduction in length.

Fall in temperature $= 400 - 300 = 100$ K.

Since $\alpha_g > \alpha_s$, gun metal will shrink more than steel. Hence compressive stress will induced in steel and tensile stress will be induced in gun metal.

Also, From Eq. 2.33(a), $\dfrac{p_s}{E_s} + \dfrac{p_g}{E_g} = (\alpha_g - \alpha_s) t \qquad \qquad ...(ii)$

Now $\qquad \qquad A_s = \dfrac{\pi}{4}(25^2 - 20^2) = 176.7 \, mm^2$ and $A_g = \dfrac{\pi}{4}(16)^2 = 201.06 \, mm^2$

Hence from (i), $\qquad p_g = p_s \dfrac{A_s}{A_g} = p_s \times \dfrac{176.71}{201.06} = 0.879 \, p_s$

Substituting in (ii), we get

$$p_s \left[\dfrac{1}{E_s} + \dfrac{0.879}{E_g} \right] = (20 - 12) \, 10^{-6} \times 100$$

or $\qquad p_s \left[\dfrac{1}{2 \times 10^5} + \dfrac{0.879}{0.91 \times 10^5} \right] = 800 \times 10^{-6}$

or $\qquad p_s \, (\, 0.5 + 0.966 \,) \, \dfrac{1}{10^5} = 800 \times 10^{-6}$

From which $\qquad p_s = $ **54.57 N/mm²** (tension)

Hence $\qquad p_g = 0.879 \times 54.57 = $ **47.97 N/mm²** (comp.)

Example 2.39. *A copper bar 25 mm diameter is completely enclosed in a steel tube, 25 mm internal diameter and 40 mm external diameter. A pin, 10 mm in diameter is fitted transversely to the axis of the bar near each end, to secure the bar to the tube. Calculate the intensity of shear stress induced in the pin when the temperature of the whole is raised by 40 K.*

Take $\qquad E_c = 1 \times 10^5 \, N/mm^2 \, ; E_s = 2 \times 10^5 \, N/mm^2.$

$$\alpha_c = 18 \times 10^{-6} \; per \; K \, ; \, \alpha_s = 12 \times 10^{-6} \; per \; K.$$

Solution

Area of cross-section of copper bar, $A_c = \frac{\pi}{4}(25)^2 = 490.87 \text{ mm}^2$

Area of cross-section of steel tube, $A_s = \frac{\pi}{4}(40^2 - 25^2) = 765.76 \text{ mm}^2$

From compatibility, $\quad \dfrac{p_s}{E_s} + \dfrac{p_c}{E_c} = (\alpha_c - \alpha_s)\,t$

or $\quad \dfrac{p_s}{2 \times 10^5} + \dfrac{p_c}{1 \times 10^5} = (18 - 12)\,10^{-6} \times 40 = 240 \times 10^{-6}$

or $\quad p_s + 2\,p_c = 240 \times 10^{-6} \times 2 \times 10^5 = 48 \qquad \qquad ...(i)$

From statics, $\quad p_s A_s = p_c A_c$

$\therefore \qquad\qquad p_s = p_c \cdot \dfrac{A_c}{A_c} = p_c \times \dfrac{490.87}{765.76} = 0.641\,p_c \qquad\qquad ...(ii)$

Substituting in (i), we get

$$0.651\,p_c + 2\,p_c = 48$$

From which $\qquad p_c = 18.17 \text{ N/mm}^2$

$\therefore$ Force P between steel tube and copper bar $= p_c A_c = 18.17 \times 490.87 = 8921$ N

Area of cross-section of pin $= \dfrac{\pi}{4}(10)^2 = 78.54 \text{ mm}^2$

Since the pin is fitted transversely, and passes through the tube and the rod, it will be in *double shear*.

$\therefore$ Shear stress in pin $= \dfrac{8921}{2 \times 78.54} = \mathbf{56.79 \text{ N/mm}^2}$

Example 2.40. *A composite bar made up of aluminium and steel is held between two supports as shown in Fig. 2.58. The bars are stress free at a temperature of 42°C. What will be the stresses in the two bars when the temperature drops to 24°C, if (a) the supports are un-yielding, (b) the supports come nearer to each other by 0.1 mm. The cross-sectional area of steel bar is 160 mm^2 and that of aluminium bar is 240 mm^2.*

Take E for aluminium as 0.7×10^5 N/mm^2 and that for steel as 2×10^5 N/mm^2. The coefficients of thermal expansion for aluminium and steel are 24×10^{-6} per °C and 12×10^{-6} per °C respectively.

Solution

Using suffix s for steel and a for aluminium, the free contraction due to drop of temperature

$(t = 42 - 24 = 18°C)$ is given by:

$$\Delta = (L_s \alpha_s + L_a \alpha_a)\,t = (500 \times 12 \times 10^{-6} + 250 \times 24 \times 10^{-6})\,18 = 0.216 \text{ mm} \qquad ...(i)$$

However, the above free contraction is checked by the supports, either fully or partially. Hence tensile stresses will be set up in both steel and aluminium bars. However, force in steel bar and aluminium bars will be the same. Hence

$$A_s p_s = A_a p_a$$

or

$$160 p_s = 240 p_a$$

From which

$$p_s = 1.5 p_a \qquad \qquad ...(ii)$$

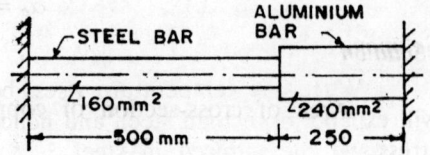

FIG. 2.58

Let

$$\Delta_s^p = \text{elongation of steel bar due to temperature stress}$$

$$= \frac{p_s}{E_s} L_s \; = \frac{500}{2 \times 10^5} \times p_s = 250 \times 10^{-5} p_s \qquad \qquad ...(ii)$$

and

$$\Delta_a^p = \text{elongation of aluminium bar due to temperature stress}$$

$$= \frac{p_a}{E_a} L_a = \frac{250}{0.7 \times 10^5} \times p_a = 357.1 \times 10^{-5} p_a \qquad \qquad ...(iv)$$

Case (a) : Supports non-yielding

$$\Delta_s^p + \Delta_a^p = \text{Free contraction } \Delta \qquad \qquad ...(v)$$

$\therefore \qquad 250 \times 10^{-5} p_s + 357.1 \times 10^{-5} p_a = 0.216$

But $\qquad\qquad\qquad\qquad\qquad p_s = 1.5 p_a$ from (ii)

Hence $250 \times 10^{-5} \times 1.5 p_a + 357.1 \times 10^{-5} p_a = 0.216$

From which $\qquad\qquad\qquad p_a = \mathbf{29.50 \ N/mm^2}$ (tensile)

Hence $\qquad\qquad\qquad p_s = 1.5 \times 29.5 = \mathbf{44.26 \ N/mm^2} \ (\textbf{tensile})$

Case (b) : Supports yielding by a = 0.1 mm

$$\Delta_s^p + \Delta_a^p = \Delta - a \quad (vi)$$

$\therefore \qquad 250 \times 10^{-5} p_s + 357.1 \times 10^{-5} p_a = 0.216 - 0.1$

Substituting $\qquad\qquad p_s = 1.5 p_a$ from (ii), we get

$250 \times 10^{-5} \times 1.5 p_a + 357.1 \times 10^{-5} p_a = 0.116$

From which, $\qquad\qquad p_a = \mathbf{15.84 \ N/mm^2}$ (tensile)

Hence $\qquad\qquad\qquad p_s = 1.5 \times 15.84 = \mathbf{23.77 \ N/mm^2}$ (tensile)

Example 2.41. *A composite bar is made up by connecting a steel member and a copper member rigidly fixed at their ends as shown in Fig. 2.59. The cross-sectional area of steel member is A mm^2 while that of the copper member is 2A mm^2 for half the length and A mm^2 for the other half of the length. The coefficients of expansion of steel and copper are α and 1.25 α respectively while the elastic moduli are E and 0.5 E respectively. Estimate the stresses induced in the members due to a temperature rise of t degrees.* (Based on U.L.)

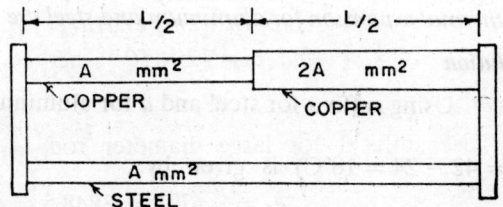

FIG. 2.59

Solution

When the temperature rises, both copper and steel bars will expand. However, copper will expand more than steel, and hence compressive stress will be induced in copper and tensile stress will be induced in steel.

Let p_c = compressive stress in copper bar of A mm^2 area of cross-section

$\therefore$ Stress in copper bar of $2A$ mm^2 area $= \dfrac{p_c A}{2A} = 0.5 p_c$

Hence, compression of copper bar due to temperature stress is given by

$$\Delta_c^p = \frac{(p_c)}{E_c} \cdot \frac{L}{2} + \frac{(0.5 p_c)}{E_c} \cdot \frac{L}{2} = \frac{3}{4} \frac{p_c L}{E_c} = \frac{3}{2} \frac{p_c L}{E} \qquad \qquad \dots(i)$$

Also, expansion of steel bar due to temperature stress $= \Delta_s^p = \dfrac{p_s L}{E}$ $\qquad \dots(ii)$

Now, from compatibility, $\Delta_s^p + \Delta_c^p = L\,t\,(\alpha_c - \alpha_s)$

$\therefore \qquad\qquad \dfrac{3}{2}\dfrac{p_c L}{E} + \dfrac{p_s L}{E} = L\,t\,(1.25\,\alpha - \alpha)$

or $\qquad\qquad\qquad p_s + 1.5\,p_c = 0.25\,E\,\alpha\,t$ $\qquad\qquad\qquad\qquad \dots(a)$

Since there is no external force acting,

$$p_c A = p_s A$$

or $\qquad\qquad\qquad\qquad p_c = p_s$ $\qquad\qquad\qquad\qquad\qquad \dots(b)$

Hence from (a) and (b), we get.

$$p_c = p_s = \textbf{0.1}\,\boldsymbol{E\,\alpha\,t}$$

Example 2.42. *Two steel rods, one of 70 mm diameter and the other of 50 mm diameter and joined end to end by means of a turn buckle, as shown in Fig. 2.60. The other end of each rod is rigidly fixed and there is initially a little tension in the rods. The effective length of each rod is 4 m. Calculate the increase in the tension* when the turn buckle is tightened by one quarter of a turn if there are 2 threads per cm on the bigger diameter and 3 threads per cm on the other end. Neglect the extension of turn buckle. *Also, find what rise in temperature could nullify the increase in tension. Take $E = 2 \times 10^5 \, N/mm^2$ and $\alpha = 12 \times 10^{-6}$ per °C.*

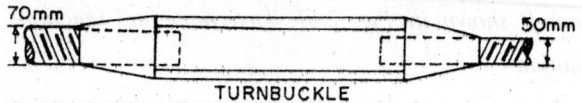

FIG. 2.60

Solution

Use suffix 1 for large diameter rod and 2 for smaller diameter rod.

$\therefore \qquad\qquad A_1 = \dfrac{\pi}{4}(70)^2 = 3848.5 \text{ mm}^2$ and $A_2 = \dfrac{\pi}{2}(50)^2 = 3927 \text{ mm}^2$

When the turn-buckle is turned by one quarter of a turn,

Extension of larger diameter rod, $\Delta_1 = \dfrac{1}{4} \cdot \dfrac{10}{3} = 0.833$ mm

Extension of smaller diameter rod $\Delta_2 = \dfrac{1}{4} \cdot \dfrac{10}{2} = 1.25$ mm.

Total extension of both the rods, $\Delta = \Delta_1 + \Delta_2 = 0.833 + 1.25 = 2.083$ mm   ...(i)

Let P Newtons be the tensile force in each bar when the turn buckle is tightened.

Hence from Hooke's law, $\Delta = \dfrac{Pl_1}{A_1 E} + \dfrac{Pl_2}{A_2 E} = \dfrac{P \times 4000}{2 \times 10^5} \left[\dfrac{1}{3848.5} + \dfrac{1}{3927} \right]$

$= 1.029 \times 10^{-5} P$ mm   ...(ii)

Equating (i) and (ii), we get $P = 202434$ N $= \mathbf{202.434\ kN}$

Now, in order to nullify this tension, the rise of temperature of the two rods must be such that the total thermal expansion of the two rods is equal to 2.083 mm.

$\therefore$ $l\alpha\, t = 2.083$

or $(2 \times 4000)\, t \times 12 \times 10^{-6}\, t = 2.083$

From which $t = \mathbf{21.7°C}$

2.21. STATICALLY INDETERMINATE PROBLEMS

In the preceding articles, we considered axially loaded bars and other *simple* structures which could be analysed by the simple equations of statics by considering static equilibrium. The axial forces in the members and the reactions at the supports could be found by drawing the free body diagrams and solving equilibrium equations. Such problems are usually called *statically determinate problems*. Now we shall consider some simple *statically indeterminate* problems which can not be solved by the simple equations of statics *alone*. To solve such problems, the deformation characteristics of the structure will have to be taken into account, in addition to the equations of statical equilibrium. We shall illustrate the solution of several such problems through solved examples.

Example 2.43. *A bar of uniform section is fixed at both the ends and is loaded with a force P shown in Fig. 2.61. Determine the reactions at both the ends and the extension of AC.*

Solution

Let R_1 and R_2 be the two reactions, obviously in the directions shown.

From statics, $R_1 + R_1 = P$ ...(1)

Since the ends are fixed in position,

Extension of AB = compression of BC

$\therefore$ $\dfrac{R_1 a}{AE} = \dfrac{R_2 b}{AE}$ ...(2)

or $a R_1 = b R_2$

$\therefore$ $R_1 = \dfrac{b}{a} R_2$

Substituting in (1), we get

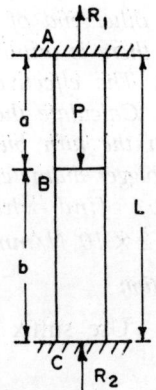
FIG. 2.61

$$R_2 \left(\frac{b}{a} + 1 \right) = P$$

From which

$$R_2 = \frac{Pa}{a+b} = \frac{Pa}{L}$$

Hence

$$R_1 = \frac{b}{a} \cdot \frac{Pa}{a+b} = \frac{Pb}{L}$$

These are thus the values of reactions R_1 and R_2

Now extension of $AB = \Delta_1 = \dfrac{R_1 a}{AE} = \dfrac{Pab}{LAE}$

Example 2.44. *A rigid bar AB is supported by three equidistant rods in the same vertical plane, and is loaded as shown in Fig. 2.62. All the three rods have the same area of cross-section. Determine the forces in the three rods, if the bars 1 and 3 are of steel and bar 2 is of brass. Take $E_s/E_b = 2$.*

Solution

From statics, $P_1 + P_2 + P_3 = P$ ...(1)

Also, taking moments about B, $P_3(2a) + P_2(a) = P \times 1.5a$

or $2P_3 + P_2 = 1.5P$ ...(2)

There are three unknown forces (*i.e.* P_1, P_2 and P_3), while we have only two equations obtained from statical equilibrium.

The third equation is obtained from the deformation pattern of the structure. The dotted lines show the *deformed position* of the structure, where Δ_1, Δ_2 and Δ_3 are the extensions of the three rods. From compatibility, we obtain

$$\Delta_2 = \frac{\Delta_1 + \Delta_3}{2}$$

or

$$\frac{P_2}{A_2 E_2} = \frac{P_1}{2A_1 E_1} + \frac{P_3}{2A_3 E_3}$$

Here, $A_1 = A_2 = A_3$.

Also, $E_1 = E_3 = 2E_2 = 2E$ (say)

$\therefore$

$$\frac{P_2}{E} = \frac{P_1}{2(2E)} + \frac{P_3}{2(2E)}$$

or $4P_2 = P_1 + P_3$ ...(3)

Substituting this value of $(P_1 + P_3)$ in (1), we get

$$4P_2 + P_2 = P$$

From which $P_2 = \dfrac{P}{5} = \mathbf{0.2\,P}$

Hence from (2), $2P_3 + 0.2P = 1.5P$

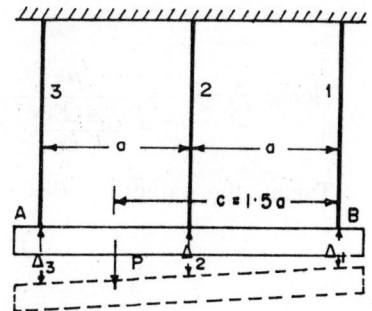

FIG. 2.62

From which $\qquad P_3 = \mathbf{0.65\,P}$

Substituting these values of P_2 and P_3 in (1), we get

$$P_1 + 0.2\,P + 0.65\,P = P$$

From which $\qquad P_1 = \mathbf{0.15\,P}$

Example 2.45. *A load P is supported by a system of three rods shown in Fig. 2.63. The outer rods are identical and are of the same material while the inner rod is of different material, Determine the forces in the rods. Hence if P = 30 kN and θ = 30°, determine value of these forces when the outer bars are of steel and the central bar is of brass. Take the ratio of moduli of elasticity of steel and brass as 2.*

Solution

From statics, $2\,P_1 \cos\theta + P_2 = P$ $\qquad ...(1)$

The dotted lines show the deformed shape of the structure, in which point O takes the position O'. Assuming that θ does not change appreciably, we get.

$$\Delta_1 = \Delta_2 \cos\theta$$

or $\qquad \dfrac{P_1 L_1}{A_1 E_1} = \dfrac{P_2 L_2}{A_2 E_2} \cos\theta \qquad ...(2)$

But, from geometry, $L_2/L_1 = \cos\theta$.

Hence, from (2),

$$P_1 = P_2 \cdot \frac{A_1 E_1}{A_2 E_2} \cdot \frac{L_2}{L_1} \cos\theta = P_2 \cdot \frac{A_1 E_1}{A_2 E_2} \cos^2\theta \quad ...(a)$$

Substituting this value of P_1 in (2), we get

$$2\,P_2 \frac{A_1 E_1}{A_2 E_2} \cos^3\theta + P_2 = P$$

From which $\qquad P_2 = \dfrac{P}{1 + \dfrac{2 A_1 E_1}{A_2 E_2} \cos^3\theta} \qquad\qquad\qquad ...(i)$

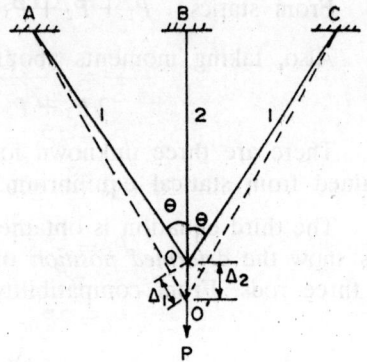

FIG. 2.63

Hence $P_1 = \left(\dfrac{P}{1 + \dfrac{2 A_1 E_1}{A_2 E_2} \cos^3\theta} \right) \cdot \dfrac{A_1 E_1}{A_2 E_2} \cos^2\theta = \dfrac{P}{\dfrac{A_2 E_2}{A_1 E_1 \cos^2\theta} + 2\cos\theta} \qquad ...(ii)$

Taking the values : $P = 30$ kN, $\theta = 30°$, $A_1 = A_2$, $E_1/E_2 = 2$, we get

$$P_2 = \frac{P}{1 + 2 \times 2 \cos^3 30°} = 0.278\,P = \mathbf{8.34\ kN}$$

and $\qquad P_1 = \dfrac{P}{\dfrac{1}{2\cos^2 30°} + 2\cos 30°} = 0.417\,P = \mathbf{12.5\ kN}$

Example 2.46. *Three identical pin-connected bars are arranged as shown in Fig. 2.64, and support a load P. Find the axial force in each bar and also the vertical displacement of the point of application of load. Neglect any possibility of lateral buckling of the bar. All the bars are of the same length and same areas of cross-section.*

Solution

Let us use suffix 1 for bars AO and BO and suffix 2 for CO. Obviously, force P_1 in bars AO and BO will be tensile while force P_2 in bar OC will be compressive.

From statics, $2P_1 \cos 60° + P_2 = P$

From which $P_1 + P_2 = P$ ...(i)

The dotted lines show the deformed position of the structure. Assuming that the angles between the rods do not change appreciably, we get

$$\Delta_1 = \Delta_2 \cos 60° = \frac{1}{2}\Delta_2$$

or $\dfrac{P_1 L}{A E} = \dfrac{1}{2}\dfrac{P_2 L}{AE}$

From which $P_2 = 2P_1$ ...(ii)

Substituting in (i), we get $P_1 + 2P_1 = P$

From which $P_1 = \dfrac{P}{3}$.

Hence $P_2 = 2P_1 = \dfrac{2P}{3}$

Also, $\Delta_2 = \dfrac{P_2 L}{AE} = \dfrac{2PL}{3AE}$

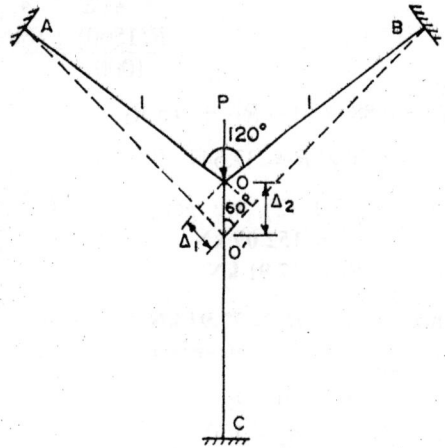

FIG. 2.64

Example 2.47. *A circular bar ABCD is rigidly fixed at A and D and is subjected to axial forces as shown in Fig. 2.65. Determine the reactions, the forces in each portion of the bar and the displacement of point B and C. Take $E = 200\,kN/mm^2$.*

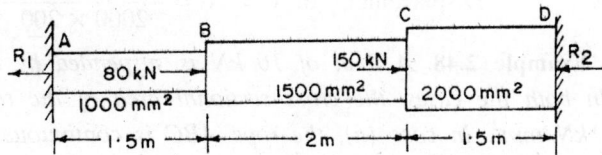

FIG. 2.65

Solution

Let R_1 and R_2 be the end reactions, obviously in the directions shown in Fig. 2.65. The free body diagrams for the three portions AB, BC and CD of the bar are shown in Fig. 2.66. Obviously portion AB will be in tension while portions BC and CD will be in compression.

For AB, force $P_1 = R_1$; $L_1 = 1500$ mm ; $A_1 = 1000\,mm^2$

For BC, force $P_2 = 80 - R_1 = R_2 - 150$; $L_2 = 2000$ mm; $A_2 = 1500$ mm^2

For CD, force $P_3 = R_2$; $L_3 = 1500$ mm ; $A_3 = 2000$ mm^2

From statics, $R_1 + R_2 = 80 + 150 = 230$ kN   ...(1)

From compatibility, extension of AB = compression of BC and CD

$\therefore$

$$\Delta_1 = \Delta_2 + \Delta_3$$

$$\frac{P_1 L_1}{A_1 E} = \frac{P_2 L_2}{A_2 E} + \frac{P_3 L_3}{A_3 E}$$

$$\frac{R(1500)}{1000} = \frac{(80 - R_1)2000}{1500} + \frac{R_2(1500)}{2000}$$

or $R_1 = 0.889 (80 - R_1) + 0.5 R_2$

or $R_1 - 0.2647 R_2 = 37.647$...(2)

From (1) and (2), we get

$R_2 = $ **152.09 kN**

and $R_1 = $ **77.91 kN**

Hence $P_1 = R_1 = $ **77.91 kN**

(tension)

$P_2 = 80 - R_1$

$= R_2 - 150$

$= $ **2.09 kN**

(compression)

$P_3 = R_2 = $ **152.09 kN**

(compression)

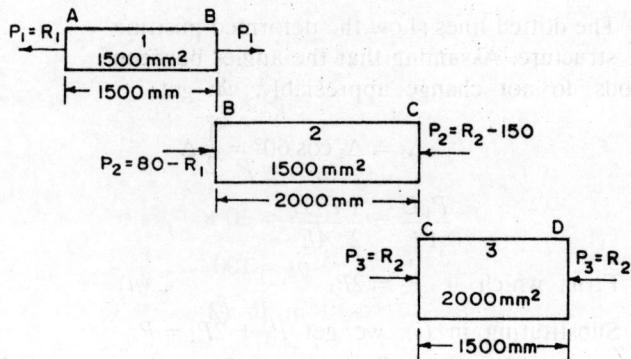

FIG. 2.66

Displacement of $B = \Delta_1 = \dfrac{P_1 L_1}{A_1 E} = \dfrac{77.91 \times 1500}{1000 \times 200} = $ **0.584 mm** $(\rightarrow)$

Displacement of $C = \Delta_1 + \Delta_2$ (where $\Delta_2 = \dfrac{2.09 \times 2000}{1500 \times 200} = 0.014$ mm$\leftarrow$)

$= 0.584 - 0.014 = $ **0.570 mm** $(\rightarrow)$

Check :   Displacement of $C = \Delta_3 = \dfrac{152.09 \times 1500}{2000 \times 200} = $ **0.570** $(\rightarrow)$

Example 2.48. *A load of 10 kN is suspended by the ropes shown in Fig. 2.67 (a) and (b). In both the cases, the cross sectional area of the ropes is 100 mm^2 and the values of E is 200 kN/mm^2. In case (a), the rope ABC is continuous over a smooth pulley from which the load is suspended. In case (b), the ropes AB and CB are separate ropes joined by a rigid block from which the load is suspended in such a way that both the ropes are stretched by the same amount. Determine, for both the cases, the stresses in the ropes and the deflections of the pulley and the block due to the load.*   *(Based on U.L.)*

Solution : Let us use suffix 1 for rope AB and 2 for rope CB. Load = 10 kN ; length of $AB = l_1 = 6$ m; length of $CB = l_2 = 8$ m. Area of rope = 200 mm^2.

Case (a): Since the load is applied on a smooth pulley, the external load ($=10$ kN) is shared *equally* by both the ropes.

$\therefore$ P in each rope $= \dfrac{10}{2} = 5$ kN.

(Note that reactions at A and C, each are equal to 5 kN)

Hence stress $\quad p = \dfrac{5 \times 1000}{200} = 25$ N/mm^2

Also, $\Delta = \dfrac{Pl}{AE} = \dfrac{P(l_1 + l_2)}{AE} = \dfrac{5(6000 + 8000)}{100 \times 200} = 3.50$ mm

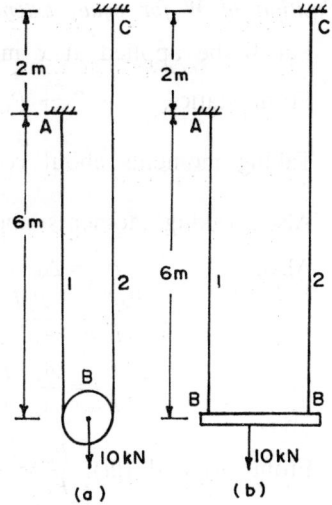

FIG. 2.67.

Case (b): Load is suspended is such a way that :

$$\Delta_1 = \Delta_2$$

or $\qquad \dfrac{p_1 l_1}{E} = \dfrac{p_2 l_2}{E}$

or $\qquad p_1 = p_2 \dfrac{l_2}{l_1} = p_2 \times \dfrac{8}{6} = \dfrac{4}{3} p_2 \quad$ ...(1)

Also, from statics, $\quad p_1 A_1 + p_2 A_2 = P$

or $\qquad 100(p_1 + p_2) = 10 \times 1000$

or $\qquad p_1 + p_2 = 100 \qquad\qquad$ ...(2)

Substituting the value of p_1 in (2), we get

$$\dfrac{4}{3} p_2 + p_2 = 100$$

From which $\qquad p_2 = \textbf{42.86 N/mm}^2$

Hence, $\qquad p_1 = 42.86 \times \dfrac{4}{3} = \textbf{57.14 N/mm}^2$

Also, $\qquad \Delta = \dfrac{p_1 l_1}{E} = \dfrac{57.14 \times 6000}{200 \times 1000} = \textbf{1.71 mm}$

Example 2.49. *Two vertical wires are suspended at a distance of 500 mm apart as shown in Fig. 2.68. Their upper ends are firmly secured and their lower ends support a rigid horizontal bar, which carries a load W. The left hand wire has a diameter of 1.6 mm and is made of copper, and the right hand wire has a diameter of 0.8 mm and is made of steel. Both the wires, initially, are 4 m long. Determine : (a) The position of line of action of W, if due to W both the wires extend by the same amount. (b) The slope of the wire if a load of 500 N is hung at the centre of the bar.*

Neglect the weight of the bar and take E for steel $= 2 \times 10^5$ N/mm^2 and E for copper $= 1.2 \times 10^5$ N/mm^2.

Solution

Let us use suffix c for copper wire and s for steel wire.

$$A_c = \frac{\pi}{4}(1.6)^2 = 2.011 \text{ mm}^2; \quad A_s = \frac{\pi}{4}(0.8)^2 = 0.503 \text{ mm}^2$$

(a) Position of W for equal extension

Let W be applied at x mm from the copper wire.

From statics, $\qquad P_c + P_s = W$ ...(i)

Taking moments about copper wire, $P_s = \dfrac{Wx}{500}$ ...(ii)

Also, Taking moments about steel wire, $P_c = \dfrac{W(500-x)}{500}$ ...(iii)

Also, $\qquad\qquad \Delta_c = \Delta_s$

or $\qquad\qquad \dfrac{P_c l}{A_c E_c} = \dfrac{P_s l}{A_s E_s}$

or $\qquad\qquad \dfrac{P_c}{P_s} = \dfrac{A_c}{A_s} \cdot \dfrac{E_c}{E_s} = \dfrac{2.011}{0.503} \times \dfrac{1.2 \times 10^5}{2 \times 10^5} = 2.399$ ...(iv)

From (ii) and (iii), $\dfrac{P_c}{P_s} = \dfrac{500-x}{x}$ ...(v)

Hence from (iv) and (v), we get $\quad \dfrac{500-x}{x} = 2.399$

From which $\qquad\qquad\qquad x = 147.11 \text{ mm}$

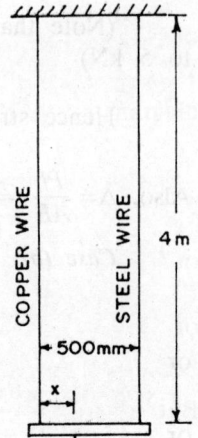

FIG. 2.68.

(b) Slope of wire if W is hung in the middle of bar

Since W is hung in the middle (i.e. $x = 250$ mm), $P_s = P_c = \dfrac{W}{2} = 250$ N

Now $\qquad\qquad \Delta_c = \dfrac{P_c l}{A_c E_c} = \dfrac{250 \times 4000}{2.011 \times 1.2 \times 10^5} = 4.144$ mm

and $\qquad\qquad \Delta_s = \dfrac{P_s \cdot l}{A_s E_s} = \dfrac{250 \times 4000}{0.503 \times 2 \times 10^5} = 9.940$ mm

If θ is the slope of the bar, we get

$$\tan \theta = \frac{9.940 - 4.144}{500} = 0.011592$$

From which $\qquad\qquad \theta = 0.6641° = 0° 39.85'$ (clockwise)

Example 2.50. A rigid bar AB is hinged at A and supported by a bronze rod GD of length 2L and a steel rod FC of length L. A load P is applied at the end B as shown in Fig. 2.69. Calculate the load carried by each rod and the reaction at A. Area of steel rod is equal to 1.5 times the area of bronze rod. The modulus of elasticity for steel is 2.5 times that of bronze.

Solution :

Let us use suffix s for steel and b for bronze. There are three unknown forces : (i) force P_s in steel rod, (ii) force P_b in bronze rod and (iii) reaction R at A. Hence from statics, we get

$$R + P_s + P_b = P \qquad\qquad ...(i)$$

Taking moments about A,

$$P_s \cdot L + P_b (3L) = P \cdot (4L)$$

or $\qquad P_s + 3 P_b = 4 P \qquad ...(ii)$

Fig. 2.69 (b) shows the deformation diagram, from which we get

$$\frac{\Delta_b}{\Delta_s} = \frac{3L}{L} = 3 \quad \text{or} \quad \Delta_b = 3 \Delta_s$$

or $\qquad \dfrac{P_b (2L)}{A_b E_b} = 3 \dfrac{P_s (L)}{A_s E_s}$

or $\qquad P_b = \dfrac{3}{2} P_s \cdot \dfrac{A_b}{A_s} \cdot \dfrac{E_b}{E_s}$

But $\qquad \dfrac{A_b}{A_s} = \dfrac{1}{1.5}$ and $\dfrac{E_b}{E_s} = \dfrac{1}{2.5}$

$\therefore \qquad P_b = \dfrac{3}{2} P_s \left(\dfrac{1}{1.5} \right) \left(\dfrac{1}{2.5} \right) = \dfrac{P_s}{2.5} = \dfrac{2}{5} P_s \qquad ...(iii)$

Substituting in (ii), $P_s + 3 \left(\dfrac{2}{5} P_s \right) = 4 P$

From which $\qquad P_s = \dfrac{20}{11} P$

Hence $\qquad P_b = \dfrac{2}{5} P_s = \dfrac{2}{5} \times \dfrac{20}{11} P = \dfrac{8}{11} P$

Substituting the values of P_s and P_b in (i),

$$R = P - (P_s + P_b) = P \left[1 - \frac{20}{11} - \frac{8}{11} \right] = -\frac{17}{11} P$$

Hence $\qquad R = \dfrac{17}{11} P \; (\downarrow)$

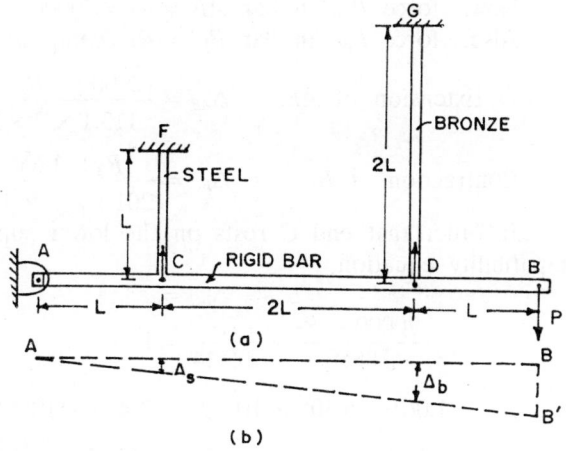

FIG. 2.69

Example 2.51. *A composite bar ABC, rigidly fixed at upper support at A and hanging 1 mm above the lower support D, is loaded as shown in Fig. 2.70. Determine the reaction at the two supports and stresses in the two sections. Take $E = 2 \times 10^5 \, N/mm^2$. The diameter of upper portion AB is 12 mm and that of lower portion BC is 16 mm.*

Solution :

Let R_1 be the reaction at the upper support A. Similarly, let R_2 be the reaction at the lower support D when the bar touches it.

Area $A_{AB} = \dfrac{\pi}{4} (12)^2 = 113.1 \text{ mm}^2$ and $A_{BC} = \dfrac{\pi}{4} (16)^2 = 201.1 \text{ mm}^2$

When the bar finally touches the lower support, we have

$$R_1 + R_2 = 20,000 \qquad ...(i)$$

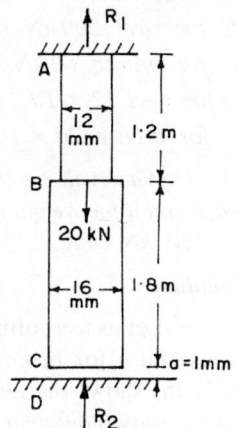

FIG. 2.70

Now, force P_{AB} in bar $AB = R_1 = 20000 - R_2$ (tensile)

Also, force P_{BC} in bar $BC = R_2$ (compressive)

∴ Extension of AB, $\Delta_{AB} = \dfrac{(20000 - R_2)\,1200}{113.1 \times 2 \times 10^5} = \dfrac{20000 - R_2}{18850}$ mm

Contraction of BC, $\Delta_{BC} = \dfrac{R_2 \times 1800}{201.1 \times 2 \times 10^5} = \dfrac{R_2}{22344}$ mm

In order that end C rests on the lower support to induce a reaction R_2, we have the compatibility equation :

$$\Delta_{AB} - \Delta_{BC} = a$$

or $\dfrac{20000 - R_2}{18850} - \dfrac{R_2}{22344} = 1$

or $1.061 - 5.305 \times 10^{-5}\,R_2 - 4.475 \times 10^{-5}\,R_2 = 1$

From which $R_2 = 6238\,N = \textbf{6.238 kN}$

∴ $R_1 = 20000 - 6238 = 13762\,N = \textbf{13.762 kN}$

∴   Stress in bar $AB = p_{AB} = \dfrac{R_1}{A_{AB}} = \dfrac{13762}{113.1} = \textbf{121.7 N/mm}^2$ (tensile)

Stress in bar $BC = p_{BC} = \dfrac{R_2}{A_{BC}} = \dfrac{6238}{201.1} = \textbf{31 N/mm}^2$ (comp.)

Example 2.52. *A rigid block ABC, weighing 180 kN is supported by three rods symmetrically placed as shown in Fig. 2.71 (a). Assuming the block to remain horizontal, determine the stress in each rod after a temperature rise of 25° C. The lower ends of the rods are assumed to have been at the same level before the block was attached and the temperature changed. Given :*

Area of steel rod 800 mm²;

Area of bronze rod 1400 mm²;

E for steel 200 kN/mm² ;

E for bronze 80 kN/mm²;

α for steel 12×10^{-6} per °C and

α for bronze 20×10^{-6} per °C.

What will be the stress in each rod if the weight of the block is 120 kN only ?

Solution :

Let us use suffix s for steel rods and b for bronze rod. Fig. 2.71 (b) shows the deformations of the rods at *different stages*. The ends of three rods are at the same level before the increase

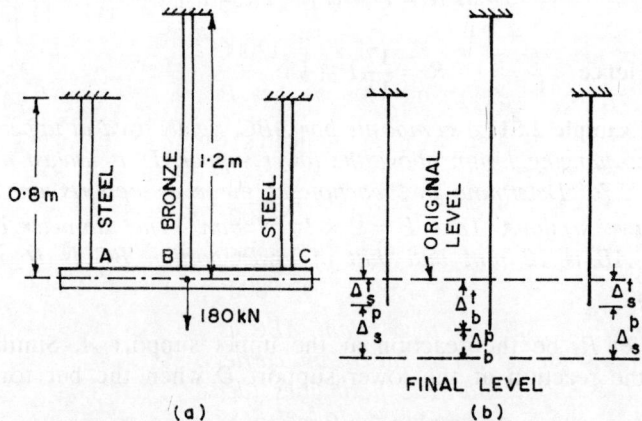

FIG. 2.71

in temperature and attachment of the block. Let the temperature rise, with the block *detached*. Then the ends of the rods will be free to expand and the extensions of steel and bronze bars due to this temperature rise t will be Δ_s^t and Δ_b^t respectively, where $\Delta_b^t > \Delta_s^t$. Now, after the temperature is increased, let us attach the block weighing 160 kN to the three rods. In doing so, the expanded ends of the three rods will be pulled further through load deformations Δ_s^p and Δ_b^p, so that finally all the ends are at the same level. From the study of Fig. 2.71 (b), it is clear that the sum of the two deformations of steel rod is equal to the sum of the two deformations of the bronze rod.

$$\therefore \qquad \Delta_s^t + \Delta_s^p = \Delta_b^t + \Delta_b^p$$

or
$$L_s \alpha_s t + \frac{P_s L_s}{A_s E_s} = L_b \alpha_b t + \frac{P_b.L_b}{A_b E_b}$$

where P_s is the load carried by each steel rod, and P_b is the load carried by the bronze rod.

Substituting the numerical values, we get

$$800 \times 12 \times 10^{-6} \times 25 + \frac{P_s \times 800}{800 \times 2 \times 10^5} = 1200 \times 20 \times 10^{-6} \times 25 + \frac{P_b (1200)}{1400 \times 0.8 \times 10^5}$$

or
$$P_s - 2.143\, P_b = 72000 \qquad \qquad ...(1)$$

Also, from statics, $2\,P_s + P_b = 180000 \qquad \qquad ...(2)$

From (1) and (2), we get $\quad P_b = 6810\,\text{N}$ and $P_s = 86595$ N

Hence the stresses are : $p_b = \dfrac{6810}{1400} = \mathbf{4.86\,N/mm^2}$ (tension)

and
$$p_s = \frac{86595}{800} = \mathbf{108.24\,N/mm^2} \text{ (tension)}$$

(b) If the weight of the block is 120 kN only, we have

$$2\,P_s + P_b = 120000 \qquad \qquad ...(3)$$

Hence from (1) and (3), we get $P_s = 62260$ N and $P_b = -4520$ N

The minus sign with P_b indicates that the bronze bar will be in compression.

The stresses are : $p_b = \dfrac{4520}{1400} = \mathbf{3.23\,N/mm^2}$ (compression)

and
$$p_s = \frac{62260}{800} = \mathbf{77.83\,N/mm^2} \text{ (tension)}$$

Example 2.53. *A rigid beam ABC is hinged at D and supported by two springs A and B as shows in Fig. 2.72. The beam carries a vertical load W at a point C at a distance of b from the hinged end. The flexibilities (deflection/unit load) of the springs at A and B are d_1 and d_2 respectively. Determine the forces in the springs and also the reaction at the hinged support.*

Solution :

The dotted line in Fig. 2.72 shows the deformed shape of the rigid beam. Let P_A and P_s be the loads carried by springs A and B.

For spring A, extension $\Delta_A = P_A \cdot d_1$

For spring B, extension $\Delta_B = P_B \cdot d_2$

Now, from compatibility, $\dfrac{\Delta_A}{b + 2b} = \dfrac{\Delta_B}{2b}$

or $\qquad \Delta_A = \dfrac{3}{2} \Delta_B$

Substituting the values of Δ_A and Δ_B,

$$P_A \cdot d_1 = \frac{3}{2} P_B \cdot d_2$$

or $\qquad P_A = \dfrac{3}{2} \dfrac{d_2}{d_1} \cdot P_B$ ...(1)

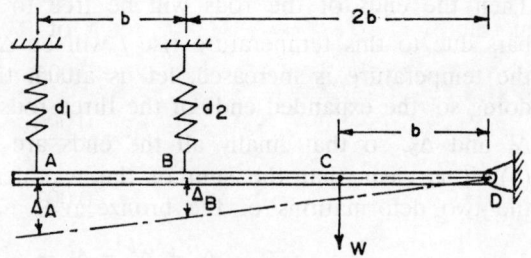

FIG. 2.72

Also, by taking moments about hinge D, we get

$$P_A \times 3b + P_B \times 2b = W \cdot b$$

or $\qquad\qquad 3 P_A + 2 P_B = W$ ...(2)

Substituting the value of P_A from (1) in (2), we get

$$3 \left(\frac{3}{2} \frac{d_2}{d_1} P_B \right) + 2 P_B = W$$

From which $\qquad\qquad P_B = \dfrac{2 d_1}{4 d_1 + 9 d_2} W$

and $\qquad\qquad\qquad P_A = \dfrac{3 d_2}{4 d_1 + 9 d_2} W$

Example 2.54. *Three wires, each of 6 mm diameter are used to lift a load W=6900 N, as shown in Fig. 2.73. Their unstressed lengths are 19.994 m, 19.997 m and 20.000 m.*

(a) What stress exists in the longest wire ?

(b) Determine the stress in the shortest wire if W=2200 N.

Take $\qquad\qquad\qquad E = 2 \times 10^5 \, N/mm^2.$

Solution :

Area of cross section of each wire $= \dfrac{\pi}{4} (6)^2 = 28.27 \text{ mm}^2$

The difference in length between the shortest wire (first wire) and the second wire $= 19.997 - 19.994 = 0.003$ m. Hence when the stretching of the shortest wire reaches value of 0.003 m, load taken by it is

$$P_1 = \frac{\Delta A E}{L} = \frac{0.003 \times 28.27 \times 2 \times 10^5}{19.994} = 848.5 \ \text{N} \ < \ 6900 \text{ N}.$$

Hence the second wire will also be stretched. The difference in the length of second wire and the third (i.e. longest) wire

FIG. 2.73

$= 20.000 - 19.997 = 0.003$ m. Hence when the second wire gets stretched by an amount 0.003 m, the first wire gets a total stretch of $0.003 + 0.003 = 0.006$ m.

Thus, $\Delta_1 = 0.006$ m and $\Delta_2 = 0.003$ m.

$\therefore$ $$P_1 = \frac{0.006 \times 28.27 \times 2 \times 10^5}{19.994} = 1696.7 \text{ N}$$

and $$P_2 = \frac{0.003 \times 28.27 \times 2 \times 10^5}{19.997} = 848.2 \text{ N}$$

$\therefore$ Total $P = P_1 + P_2 = 1696.7 + 848.2 = 2544.9 \text{ N} < 6900 \text{ N}.$

Hence the third wire will also get stretched.

Now, at the equilibrium position, we get the following relations :

$$P_1 + P_2 + P_3 = P = 6900 \qquad \ldots(i)$$

$$\Delta_2 = \Delta_3 + 0.003 \qquad \ldots(ii)$$

and $$\Delta_1 = \Delta_3 + 0.006 \qquad \ldots(iii)$$

From (ii), we get $\dfrac{P_2 L_2}{AE} = \dfrac{P_3 L_3}{AE} + 0.003$

or $$\frac{P_2 \times 19.997}{28.27 \times 2 \times 10^5} = \frac{P_3 \times 20.000}{28.27 \times 2 \times 10^5} + 0.003$$

or $$P_2 \approx P_3 + 848.23 \qquad \ldots(iv)$$

Similarly, from (iii), $\dfrac{P_1 L_1}{AE} = \dfrac{P_3 L_3}{AE} + 0.006$

or $$\frac{P_1 \times 19.994}{28.27 \times 2 \times 10^5} = \frac{P_3 \times 20.000}{28.27 \times 2 \times 10^5} + 0.006$$

$$P_1 \approx P_3 + 1696.71 \qquad \ldots(v)$$

Substituting these values of P_1 and P_2 in (i), we get

$$(P_3 + 1696.71) + (P_3 + 848.23) + P_3 = 6900$$

From which $P_3 = 4355.1$ kN. Hence $P_3 = \dfrac{4355.1}{28.27} = \mathbf{154.05 \text{ N/mm}^2}$

(b) When $W = 2200$ N, then as the second wire gets stretched by an amount of 0.003 m,

$$P_1 + P_2 = 2544.9 \, N > 2200 \, N$$

Hence the second wire does not get fully stretched. The final equilibrium equations are:

$$P_1 + P_2 = 2200 \, N \qquad \ldots(a)$$

and $$\Delta_1 = \Delta_2 + 0.003 \text{ m} \qquad \ldots(b)$$

From Eq. (b), $$\frac{P_1 \times 19.994}{28.27 \times 2 \times 10^5} = \frac{P_2 \times 19.997}{28.27 \times 2 \times 10^5} + 0.003$$

or $\qquad\qquad\qquad P_2 \approx P_1 - 861.1 \qquad\qquad\qquad\qquad\qquad$ ...(c)

Substituting in Eq.(a), we get $P_1 + P_1 - 861.1 = 2200$

From which $\qquad\qquad\qquad P_1 = 1530.6$ N

$\therefore \qquad\qquad\qquad p_1 = \dfrac{1530.6}{28.27} = \mathbf{54.14\ N/mm^2}$

2.22. STRESSES DUE TO LACK OF FIT OR PRE-STRAIN

A framed structure consists of an assemblage of a number of individual members; these individual members are to be of definite length as per the requirements of the geometry of structure. If, however, any one member of the structure is not of correct length, stresses will be set up in all the members of the structure when that member is fitted into the structure. Such a stress is known as *stress due to lack of fit*, and the strain set up in the member is known as *pre-strain*.

To analyse such cases, let us take the case of a simple structure consisting of an assemblage of three bars shown in Fig. 2.74, in which the central member *BO* is excess in length by an amount λ (say). When this member is fitted, compressive stress is set up in *OB* while tensile stresses are setup in *OA* and *OC*. The dotted lines show the deformed shape of the structure when the central member having a lack of fit (λ) is fitted.

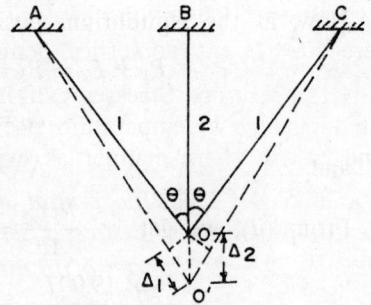

FIG. 2.74

Let us use suffix 1 for outer bars and 2 for central bar. From statics, we have :
$$2 P_1 \cos \theta = P_2 \qquad\qquad\qquad\qquad ...(i)$$

From compatibility, we have $\quad \Delta_1 = \Delta_2 \cos \theta \qquad\qquad\qquad\qquad ...(ii)$

where $\qquad\qquad\qquad \Delta_1 = \dfrac{P_1 L_1}{A_1 E_1} = \dfrac{P_1 L_2}{A_1 E_1 \cos \theta}$

and $\qquad\qquad\qquad \Delta_2 = \lambda - \dfrac{P_2 L_2}{A_2 E_2}$

Hence from (ii), $\dfrac{P_1 L_2}{A_1 E_1 \cos \theta} = \left(\lambda - \dfrac{P_2 L_2}{A_2 E_2} \right) \cos \theta$

From which $\qquad\qquad P_1 = \dfrac{A_1 E_1}{L_2} \left(\lambda - \dfrac{P_2 L_2}{A_2 E_2} \right) \cos^2 \theta \qquad\qquad ...(iii)$

Substituting in (i), we get $2 \dfrac{A_1 E_1}{L_2} \left(\lambda - \dfrac{P_2 L_2}{A_2 E_2} \right) \cos^3 \theta = P_2$

From which $\qquad\qquad P_2 = \dfrac{2 A_1 E_1 \lambda \cos^3 \theta}{L_2 \left(1 + \dfrac{2 A_1 E_1}{A_2 E_2} \cos^3 \theta \right)} \qquad\qquad ...(2.35\ a)$

Substituting this value of P_2 Eq. (i), we get

$$P_1 = \frac{P_2}{2 \cos \theta} = \frac{A_1 E_1 \lambda \cos^2 \theta}{L_2 \left(1 + \dfrac{2 A_1 E_1}{A_2 E_2} \cos^3 \theta \right)} \qquad ...(2.35 \ b)$$

If, however, all the bars have the same area of cross-section (A) and are of the same material, we have :

$$P_2 = \frac{2 AE \lambda \cos^3 \theta}{L (1 + 2 \cos^3 \theta)} \qquad ...(2.35 \ c)$$

and

$$P_1 = \frac{AE \lambda \cos^2 \theta}{L (1 + 2 \cos^3 \theta)} \qquad ...(2.35 \ d)$$

where $L = L_2 = $ geometrical length of the central bar.

Temperature Stresses : If instead of a lack of fit λ, the central bar of the system is heated through a temperature rise t, the temperature stresses set up in the members can be found in the same manner as explained above, by substituting $\lambda = L \alpha t$.

Example 2.55. *The central member of the system shown in Fig. 2.74 is 1.5 mm excess in length. Determine the stresses set up in all the members, if all the members are of the same material and have diameter of 10 mm. Take $\theta = 30°$ and $E = 200 \, kN/mm^2$. The geometrical length of central member is 900 mm.*

Solution :

All the bars have the same area of cross-section, and are of the same material. Hence from Eq. 2.35 (c)

$$P_2 = \frac{2 AE \lambda \cos^3 \theta}{L (1 + 2 \cos^3 \theta)}$$

Here $A = \dfrac{\pi}{4} (10)^2 = 78.54 \, mm^2$; $\lambda = 1.5$ mm , $L = 300$ mm and $\theta = 30°$

$\therefore \qquad P_2 = \dfrac{2 \times 78.54 \times 200 \times 1.5 \times \cos^3 30°}{900 (1 + 2 \cos^3 30)} = 14.793$ kN

Hence $\qquad p_2 = \dfrac{14.793 \times 10^3}{78.54} = \mathbf{188.4 \, N/mm^2}$ **(comp.)**

Also, $\qquad P_1 = \dfrac{P_2}{2 \cos \theta} = \dfrac{14.793}{2 \cos 30°} = 8.54$ kN

$\therefore \qquad p_1 = \dfrac{8.54 \times 10^3}{78.54} = \mathbf{108.7 \, N/mm^2}$ **(tension)**

Example 2.56. *In the system of bars shown in Fig. 2.74, the temperature of central bar is reduced by 80° F. Compute the stresses set up in the three rods if the outer rods are 150 mm² in area and of steel, and the central rod is of brass having area of cross-section of 200 mm². The length of central bar is 800 mm and angle $\theta = 30°$.*

Take $E_s = 2 \times 10^5 \, N/mm^2$, $E_b = 1 \times 10^5 \, N/mm^2$ and $\alpha = 10 \times 10^{-6}$ per F.

Solution :

Decrease in length of central bar, $\lambda = L \alpha t = 800 \times 10 \times 10^{-6} \times 80 = 0.64$ mm

Now, from Eq. 2.35 (a) $P_2 = \dfrac{2 A_1 E_1 \lambda \cos^3 \theta}{L_2 \left(1 + \dfrac{2 A_1 E_1}{A_2 E_2} \cos^3 \theta \right)}$

Here, $A_1 = 150$ mm^2; $A_2 = 200$ mm^2; $E_1 = 2 \times 10^5$ and $E_2 = 1 \times 10^5$ N/mm^2

$\therefore$ $P_2 = \dfrac{2 \times 150 \times 2 \times 10^5 \times 0.64 \cos^3 30°}{800 \left(1 + \dfrac{2 \times 150 \times 2 \times 10^5}{200 \times 1 \times 10^5} \cos^3 30° \right)} = 10574$ N (tension)

and $P_1 = \dfrac{P_2}{2 \cos 30} = 6105$ N (Compression)

Hence $p_1 = \dfrac{6105}{150} = \textbf{40.7 N/mm}^2$ (comp.)

and $p_2 = \dfrac{10574}{200} = \textbf{52.87 N/mm}^2$ (tensile)

2.33. STRESS DUE TO SHRINKING ON

Some times, tyre of steel (or other metal) is shrunk on a wheel. In such cases, the diameter of the tyre is kept slightly smaller than that of wheel so that it does not come out easily. While putting on the tyre to the wheel, the tyre is heated up so that it expands. On cooling, the tyre shrinks and gets fitted tightly on to the wheel.

Let D be the diameter of the wheel and d be the diameter of the tyre $(D > d)$. Let us increase the temperature of the tyre by $t°$ so that its diameter increases from d to D. When the tyre is slipped on to the wheel and the temperature falls, the metal tyre will try to come to its original diameter, and in doing so hoop stress (tensile) will be set up in it.

Tensile strain induced in tyre $= e = \dfrac{\pi D - \pi d}{\pi d} = \dfrac{D - d}{d}$

$\therefore$ Circumferential tensile stress or hoop stress induced $= eE = \left(\dfrac{D - d}{d} \right) E$ ...(2.36)

Example 2.57. *A thin tyre of steel is to be shrunk on to a rigid wheel of 900 mm diameter. Compute (a) internal diameter of the tyre if the hoop stress is limited to 120 N/mm^2, and (b) the least temperature to which the tyre must be heated above that of the wheel before it could be slipped on. For the tyre, take $\alpha = 12 \times 10^{-6}$ per °C and $E = 2 \times 10^5$ N/mm^2.*

Solution :

Hoop stress $p = \dfrac{E (D - d)}{d} = 120$ (given)

$\therefore$ $\dfrac{D - d}{d} = \dfrac{120}{2 \times 10^5} = 6 \times 10^{-4}$

or $\dfrac{D}{d} = (1 + 6 \times 10^{-4})$

$$\therefore \qquad \frac{d}{D} = (1 + 6 \times 10^{-4})^{-1} \approx (1 - 6 \times 10^{-4})$$

$$\therefore \qquad d = 900\,(1 - 6 \times 10^{-4}) = 900 - 0.54 = \mathbf{899.46\ mm}$$

Also, $\qquad \pi D = \pi d\,(1 + \alpha t)$ or $\alpha t = \dfrac{D - d}{d} = 6 \times 10^{-4}$

$$\therefore \qquad t = \frac{6 \times 10^{-4}}{12 \times 10^{-6}} = \mathbf{50°C}$$

2.24. ADDITIONAL ILLUSTRATIVE EXAMPLES*

Some additional illustrative examples of advanced nature, extremely useful for *competitive examinations* are given here, with short solutions.

Example 2.58. *Fig. 2.75 shows a deep well pump rod operated by a crank. The pump rod made of steel having specific weight of 78 kN/m³ has a diameter of 15 mm and length of 100 m. The resistance encountered by the piston during the downstroke is 1 kN and during the upstroke is 10 kN. Considering only the resistance forces and the weight of the rod, determine the maximum tensile and compressive stresses in the pump rod.*

Solution :

(*i*) During down stroke, the resistance of piston creates a compressive force (*C*) of 1 kN, uniform throughout the length of the rod.

(*ii*) During upstroke, the resistance of piston creates a tensile force (*T*) of 10 kN, uniform throughout the length of the rod.

(*iii*) The weight of the rod produces a tensile force which varies from zero at the lower end to a maximum weight force *W* at the upper end.

Area of cross-section of piston rod,
$A = \dfrac{\pi}{4}\,(15)^2 = 176.71\ mm^2$

Max. weight force
$W = \gamma L A = 78 \times 100 \times (176.71 \times 10^{-6}) = 1.378\ kN$

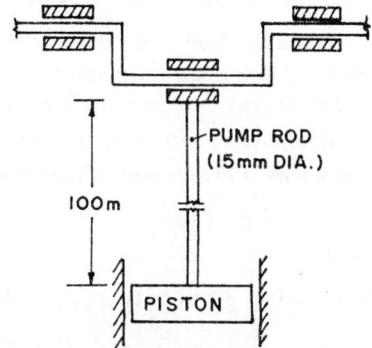

FIG. 2.75

Maximum tensile force occurs at the upper end of piston rod, during the upstroke, and its value is equal to $(T + W) = 10 + 1.378 = 11.378\ kN$

$\therefore$ Max. tensile stress, $p_t = \dfrac{11.378 \times 10^3}{176.71} = \mathbf{64.38\ N/mm^2}$

Maximum compressive force occurs at the lower end of piston rod, during the down stroke, its value being equal to $C = 1\ kN$

$\therefore$ Max compressive stress, $p_c = \dfrac{1 \times 10^3}{176.71} = \mathbf{5.66\ N/mm^2}$

---

* CAN BE LEFT OUT BY JUNIOR STUDENTS.

Example 2.59. *A steel bar of uniform cross-sectional area is loaded as shown in Fig. 2.76. Find the magnitude of force P_1 so that the lower end D does not move vertically when the load are applied.*

Solution :

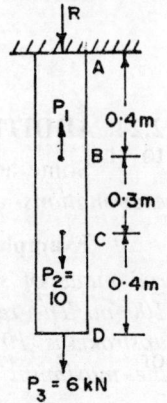

Given $\Delta_D = 0$

But $\Delta_D = \Sigma \dfrac{PL}{AE} = \dfrac{1}{AE} \Sigma PL$

In order that point D does not move vertically, $P_1 > (P_2 + P_3)$, so that AB is subjected to compressive load. Evidently, AB is subjected to a compressive force equal to R ($= P_1 - 10$), BC will be subjected to a tensile force equal to $10 + 6 = 16$ kN ($= P_1 - R$) while CD is subjected to a tensile load of 6 kN.

$\therefore$ $\Delta_D = \dfrac{1}{AE} \left[-(P_1 - 16) \times 0.4 + 16 \times 0.3 + 6 \times 0.4 \right] = 0$

or $0.4\,(P_1 - 16) = 4.8 + 2.4 = 7.2$

From which $P_1 = \mathbf{34\ kN}$

FIG. 2.76

Example 2.60. *A copper bar AB, carrying a tensile load of 400 kN hangs from a pin supported by two steel pillars, as shown in Fig. 2.77. The copper bar has a diameter of 100 mm and each steel pillar has a diameter of 50 mm. Taking E for steel $= 200\,kN/mm^2$ and E for copper as $105\,kN/mm^2$, determine the vertical displacement of point B.*

Solution :

Area of cross section of copper bar $= \dfrac{\pi}{4}\,(100)^2 \approx 7854\ \text{mm}^2$

Area of cross-section of each steel pillar $= \dfrac{\pi}{4}\,(50)^2 = 1963.5\ \text{mm}^2$

Tensile force in copper bar $= 400$ kN, while compressive force in each steel pillar $= 400/2 = 200$ kN.

Now $\Delta_B =$ Extension of copper bar + compression of steel pillars.

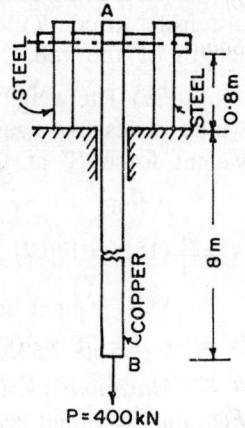

$\therefore$ $\Delta_B = \Delta_C + \Delta_S = \dfrac{400 \times 8800}{7854 \times 105} + \dfrac{200 \times 800}{1963.5 \times 200}$

$= 4.268 + 0.407 = \mathbf{4.675\ mm}$

FIG. 2.77

Example 2.61. *A steel rod, having a diameter of 40 mm is loaded as shown in Fig. 2.78. Taking E $= 200\,kN/mm^2$, determine (a) the deformation of the free end (b) the distance x from the left hand support to a point at which the deformation is zero.*

Solution :

$$A = \dfrac{\pi}{4}\,(40)^2 = 1256.6\ \text{mm}^2$$

Reaction $R = 12 + 10 - 10 = 12$ kN ($\leftarrow$)

A little consideration will show that portion AB is subjected to a tensile load $= R$ ($= 12$ kN), portion BC is subjected to a load $= 10 - 10 = 0$ (or $= R - 12 = 0$), while CD is subjected to a compressive load of 10 kN.

$$\Delta_D = \Sigma \frac{PL}{AE} = \frac{1}{AE} \left[P_{AB} L_{AB} + P_{BC} . L_{BC} + P_{CD} . L_{CD} \right]$$

$$= \frac{1}{1256.6 \times 200} \left[12 \times 1000 + 0 - 10 \times 200 \right] = \mathbf{-0.0318\ mm}$$

Minus sign shows that point D moves to the left.

Again $\Delta_x = \frac{1}{AE} [P_{AB} L_{AB} + P_{BC} L_{BC}$

$+ P_{CD} (x - 2000)] = 0$

$\therefore \quad 12 \times 1000 + 0 - 10 (x - 2000) = 0$

or $\qquad\qquad x - 2000 = 1200$

which gives $\qquad x = 3200$ mm $= \mathbf{3.2\ m}$

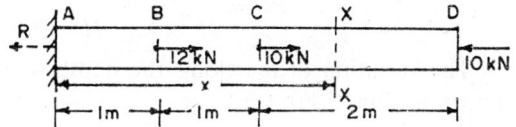

FIG. 2.78

Example 2.62. *A sample of a metal is tested in tension, and it is found that there is a strain of 0.0080 at a corresponding stress of 450 N/mm². On the removal of the load a permanent strain of 0.0015 is found to be present. Compute the value of modulus of elasticity for the metal.*

Solution :

Fig. 2.79 shows the loading and unloading diagram.

Elastic recovery $= 0.0080 - 0.0015 = 0.0065$

Stress $= 450$ N/mm²

$\therefore \qquad E = \frac{\text{Stress}}{\text{elastic recovery}}$

$$= \frac{450}{0.0065} = \mathbf{0.692 \times 10^5\ N/mm^2}$$

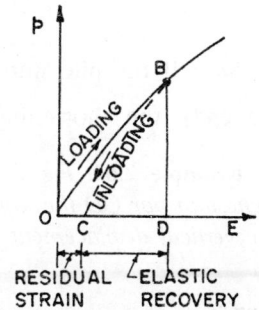

FIG. 2.79

Example 2.63. *A pile of uniform section is embedded in soil by a depth H. The pile supports a structural load P at its top which is transferred to the soil entirely by friction as shown in Fig. 2.80 (a). The variation of friction (f) along the depth of the pile is given by $f_y = k y^2$, where y is the elevation above the bottom of the pile. Determine the total shortening of the pile.*

Solution :

The variation of frictional resistance (f) along the depth is shown in Fig. 2.80 (b).

Total frictional resistance,

$$F = \int_0^H f_y . dy = \int_0^H k y^2 . dy = \frac{k H^3}{3}$$

$\therefore \qquad\qquad F = P = \frac{k H^3}{3}$, from which $k = \frac{3 P}{H^3}$ ...(i)

The compressive force on pile varies with the depth. At any height y above the bottom of the pile, the total compressive force will be equal to the frictional resistance (F_y) of clay for the bottom height y.

$\therefore$ Total compression,

$$P_{cy} = \int_0^y f_y \cdot dy = \int_0^y k y^2 \cdot dy = \frac{k y^3}{3}$$

or

$$P_{cy} = \frac{3P}{H^3} \cdot \frac{y^3}{3} = \frac{P y^3}{H^3} \qquad \ldots (ii)$$

The variation of P_{cy} along the depth of the pile is shown in Fig. 2.80 (c),

Now, shortening of small length dy of the pile

$$= \frac{P_{cy} \cdot dy}{A E}$$

$\therefore$ Total shortening of pile $= \sum_{y=H}^{y=0} \frac{P_{cy} \, dy}{A E} = \int_0^H \frac{P y^3}{H^3} \cdot \frac{dy}{A E}$

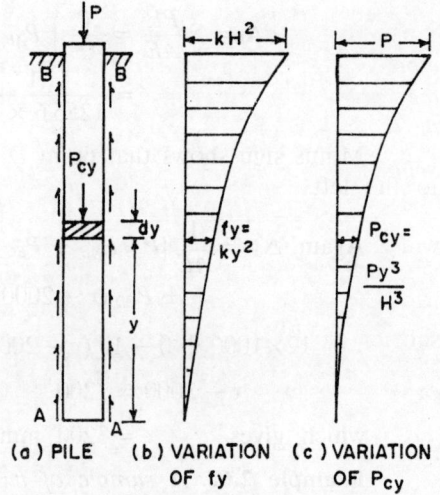

(a) PILE   (b) VARIATION   (c) VARIATION
            OF fy   OF P_{cy}

FIG. 2.80

$$= \frac{P}{A E H^3} \int_0^H y^3 \, dy = \frac{P}{AEH^3} \left(\frac{H^4}{4} \right) = \frac{PH}{4\,AE}$$

Note: If the pile were a point bearing pile (*i.e.* transferring the load to the solid strata at the end), the shortening of the pile would have been equal to $\dfrac{PH}{AE}$.

Example 2.64. *Fig. 2.81 shows a bimetallic thermometer, made of a tungsten bar AB and a magnesium bar CD the upper ends of which are attached to a pointer BDP. Derive an expression for the vertical displacement of the pointer in terms of a temperature increase t and the dimension shown.*

Solution :

The coefficient of thermal expansion of magnesium is more than that of tungsten. Hence the pointer P will move up (*i.e.* +ve vertical displacement) for rise of temperature and vice-versa.

Now $\qquad \Delta_B = L_1 \alpha_T t$ and $\Delta_D = L_1 \alpha_M t$

$\therefore \qquad \left(\Delta_D - \Delta_B \right) = L_1 t \left(\alpha_M - \alpha_T \right)$

Fig. 2.81 (b) shows the displacement diagram, from which :

$$\Delta_P = \Delta_B + \frac{\Delta_D - \Delta_B}{L_1} (L_2 + L_3)$$

$$= L_1 \alpha_T t + \frac{L_1 \alpha_M t - L_1 \alpha_T t}{L_2} (L_2 + L_3)$$

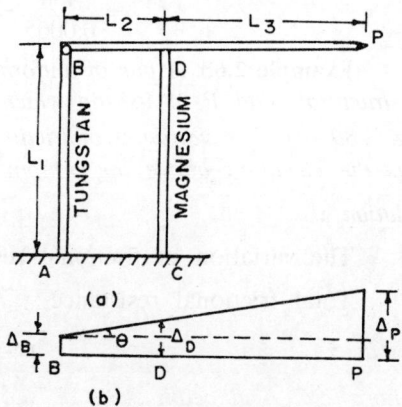

FIG. 2.81

or
$$\Delta_P = L_1 \alpha_T t + L_1 t (\alpha_M - \alpha_T) \left(1 + \frac{L_3}{L_2}\right)$$

or
$$\Delta_P = L_1 t \left[\alpha_M + (\alpha_M - \alpha_T)\frac{L_3}{L_2}\right]$$

Example 2.65. *A solid cylinder of steel is placed inside a copper tube. The assembly is compressed between rigid plates by forces P. Find the value of increase in temperature so that all the load is carried by the copper tube.*

Solution :

Let the increase in temperature be t. Due to this increase, copper will expand more than steel.

Difference between the two expansions $= \Delta_t = L(\alpha_c - \alpha_s) t$

If the load P is to be borne entirely by the copper tube, the shortening (Δ_c) of the copper tube due to P should be equal to Δ_t

$$\therefore \qquad \Delta_c = \Delta_t$$

or
$$\frac{PL}{A_c E_c} = L(\alpha_c - \alpha_s) t$$

or
$$t = \frac{P}{A_c E_c (\alpha_c - \alpha_s)}$$

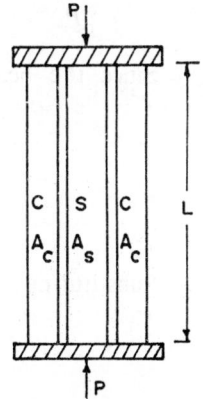

FIG. 2.82

Example 2.66. *A steel bar AB of length L is fixed at the ends and is subjected to a non-uniform increase in temperature represented by the expression $t_x = t \cdot \dfrac{x^2}{L^2}$, as shown in Fig. 2.83. Determine the value of compressive stress set up in the bar.*

Solution :

Consider a short length dx, at a distance x from end A.

Temperature $\qquad t_x = t\dfrac{x^2}{L^2}$

$\therefore$ Increase in length of dx due to temp. rise

$$= \Delta_{tx} = dx \cdot \alpha\, t_x = \alpha\, t\frac{x^2}{L^2} dx$$

Hence total increase in length $= \Delta_t$

$$= \Sigma\Delta_{tx} = \int_0^L \alpha t \frac{x^2}{L^2} dx = \frac{\alpha t}{L^2} \cdot \frac{L^3}{3} = \frac{\alpha t L}{3}$$

(a) THE BAR

(b) TEMPERATURE VARIATION

FIG. 2.83

Since this increase in length is restricted by end supports, compressive stress will be set up in the bar, the value of which is given by.

$$p_c = \Delta_t \cdot \frac{E}{L} = \frac{\alpha t L}{3}\left(\frac{E}{L}\right) = \frac{E \alpha t}{3}$$

Example 2.67. *Three steel bars A, B and C, having the same axial rigidity EA support a horizontal rigid beam ABC as shown in Fig. 2.84. Determine the distance a between bars A and B in order that the rigid beam will remain horizontal when a load P is applied at its mid-point.*

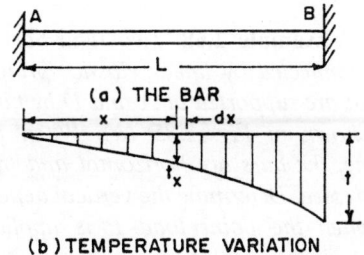

Solution :

Let us use suffix 1, 2 and 3 for bars A, B and C respectively.

From statics, $P_1 + P_2 + P_3 = P$ ....(1)

Taking moments about A,

$$P_2 . a + P_3 L = P . \frac{L}{2} \qquad ...(2)$$

Since the beam ABC remains horizontal,

$$\Delta_1 = \Delta_2 = \Delta_3$$

or

$$\frac{P_1 (2b)}{AE} = \frac{P_2 (1.5\, b)}{AE} = \frac{P_3 . b}{AE}$$

or

$$2 P_1 = \frac{3}{2} P_2 = P_3 \qquad ...(3)$$

Substituting in (1), we get

$$P_1 + \frac{4}{3} P_1 + 2 P_1 = P \ , \text{ from which } P_1 = \frac{3}{13} P \qquad ...(4)$$

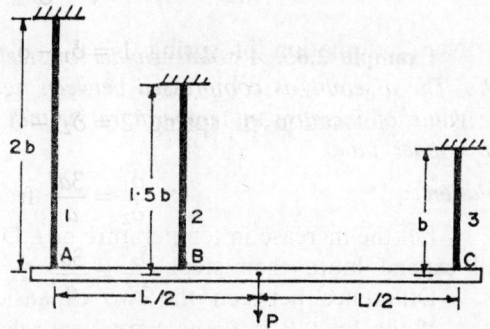

FIG. 2.84

Also, from (2), $\left(\dfrac{4}{3} P_1\right) a + 2 P_1 L = P . \dfrac{L}{2}$

or $\left(\dfrac{4}{3} a + 2 L\right) P_1 = P . \dfrac{L}{2}$

or $\left(\dfrac{4}{3} a + 2 L\right) \dfrac{3}{13} P = \dfrac{PL}{2}$

From which we get $a = \dfrac{L}{8}$

Example 2.68. *Two rigid bars AB and CD are connected by linear elastic springs of stiffness k and are supported at A and D by hinged supports as shown in Fig. 2.85 (a). When no loads are acting, the bars are horizontal and the springs are unstressed. Determine the vertical deflection at point C when the point load P is applied.*

Solution :

Let P_1 be the force in spring 1 at C and P_2 be the force in spring 2. Fig. 2.85 (b) shows the deformation diagram while Fig. 2.85 (c) shows the free body diagrams for bars AB and CD. A careful study of these diagrams will reveal that spring 1 (at C) carries a tensile force (P_1) and spring 2 (at B) carries a compressive force P_2.

Taking moments about A (Fig. 2.85 c), we get $P_1 = 3 P_2$

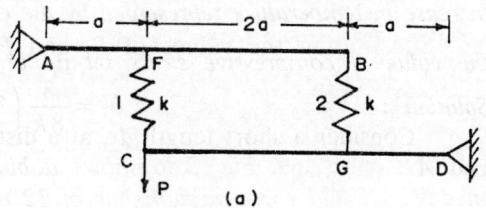

(a)

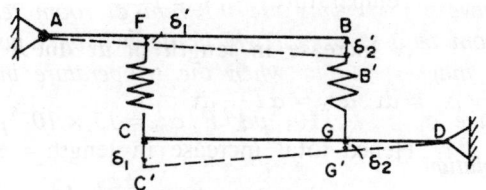

(b) DEFORMATION DIAGRAM

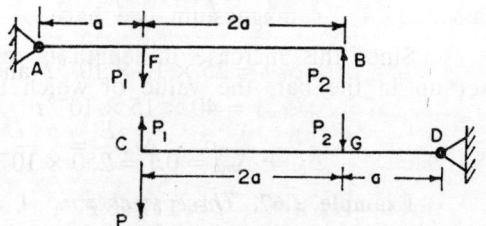

(c) FREE BODY DIAGRAMS

FIG. 2.85

Taking moments about D (Fig. 2.85 c), we get $(P_1 - P) 3a = P_2 a$

or $(P_1 - P) 3 = \dfrac{P_1}{3}$, from which $P_1 = \dfrac{9}{8} P$ and $P_2 = \dfrac{3}{8} P$

Net deformation of spring $1 = \delta_1 - \delta_1' = \Delta_1 = \dfrac{P_1}{k}$ (extension)

Net deformation of spring $2 = \delta_2' - \delta_2 = \Delta_2 = \dfrac{P_2}{k}$ (compression)

But $\dfrac{\delta_1}{\delta_2} = \dfrac{3a}{a}$, from which $\delta_1 = 3 \delta_2$ ...(i)

Also, $\dfrac{\delta_2'}{\delta_1'} = \dfrac{3a}{a}$, from which $\delta_2' = 3 \delta_1'$ ...(ii)

Now $\dfrac{P_1}{k} = \delta_1 - \delta_1' = \delta_1 - \dfrac{\delta_2'}{3}$

or $\dfrac{3 P_1}{k} = 3 \delta_1 - \delta_2'$ ...(a)

and $\dfrac{P_2}{k} = \delta_2' - \delta_2 = \delta_2' - \dfrac{\delta_1}{3}$

or $\dfrac{P_2}{k} = -\dfrac{\delta_1}{3} + \delta_2'$ ...(b)

Eliminating δ_2' from (a) and (b), we get $\delta_1 = \dfrac{3}{8k} (3 P_1 + P_2)$ ...(I)

Substituting the values of P_1 and P_2, we get

$$\delta_1 = \dfrac{3}{8k} \left(3 \times \dfrac{9}{8} P + \dfrac{3}{8} P \right) = \dfrac{45 P}{32 k}$$

Example 2.69. *Fig. 2.86 shows a bimetallic thermal control, made of a brass bar of 8 mm diameter and a magnesium bar of 12 mm diameter. The bars are so arranged that the gap between their ends are 0.1 mm at room temperature. Find the temperature increase above the room temperature at which the two bars just come in contact. Also find the compressive stress in magnesium bar when the temperature increase in 320° F.*

Take $\alpha_b = 10 \times 10^{-6}$ per° F, $\alpha_m = 15 \times 10^{-6}$ per ° F; $E_b = 100 \, kN/mm^2$ and $E_m = 40 \, kN/mm^2$.

Solution :

Let t be the rise in temperature. Using suffix b for brass and m for magnesium, we have

$\Delta_{bt} = L_b \, \alpha_b \, t = 25 \times 10 \times 10^{-6} t$ and

$\Delta_{mt} = L_m \, \alpha_m \, t = 40 \times 15 \times 10^{-6} t$

Hence $\Delta_{bt} + \Delta_{mt} = 0.1 = 250 \times 10^{-6} t + 600 \times 10^{-6} t$

From which $t = \mathbf{117.65°F}$

$$A_b = \dfrac{\pi}{4} (8)^2 = 50.27 \text{ mm}^2 \text{ and } A_m = \dfrac{\pi}{4} (12)^2 = 113.1 \text{ mm}^2$$

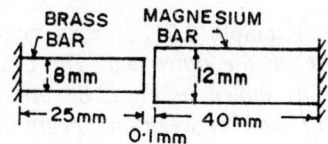

BRASS BAR   MAGNESIUM BAR

8mm   12mm

25mm   40mm

0·1mm

FIG. 2.86

When $\qquad t = 320°\,F$, $\Delta_{bt} = 25 \times 10 \times 10^{-6} \times 320 = 0.08$ mm

and $\qquad\qquad \Delta_{mt} = 40 \times 15 \times 10^{-6} \times 320 = 0.192$ mm

Now expansion restricted, $\Delta_t = \left(\Delta_{bt} + \Delta_{mt} \right) - 0.1 = (0.08 + 0.192) - 0.1 = 0.172$ mm ..(i)

If P is the compressive force induced, compression (Δ_c) of the two bars is

$$\Delta_c = \frac{P\,L_b}{A_b\,E_b} + \frac{P\,L_m}{A_m\,E_m} = P\left[\frac{25}{50.27 \times 100} + \frac{40}{113.1 \times 40} \right] = 0.0138\,P \quad ...(ii)$$

Equating (i) and (ii), we get $0.0138\,P = 0.172$ from which $P = 12.45$ kN

$\therefore \qquad\qquad p_m = \frac{P}{A_m} = \frac{12.45}{113.1} \times 1000 = \mathbf{110.1\ N/mm^2}$ (comp.)

Example 2.70. *A vertical bar ABC is attached to a rigid bar BDF, as shown in Fig. 2.87(a). Find the ratio of loads P_2 and P_1 so that the vertical deflection of point C is zero.*

Solution :

From the moment equilibrium of the rigid bar *BDF*, we find that a vertical force P (thrust)

$= P_2 \times \dfrac{1.5\,L}{L} = 1.5\,P_2$ is transmitted to the vertical

bar, through pin B. Hence the vertical bar ABC is subjected to forces as shown in Fig. 2.87 (b). The reaction $R_A = P - P_1$. Thus, the portion AB is subjected to a compressive force $= R_A\ (= P - P_1)$ and portion BC is subjected to a tensile force P_1.

Hence $\delta_c = \Sigma\,\dfrac{PL}{AE} = \dfrac{P_1\,(L)}{aE} - \dfrac{(P - P_1)\,(2\,L)}{2\,a\,E}$

Substituting the value of P and noting that δ_c has to be zero, we have

$$\frac{P_1\,L}{a\,E} - \frac{(1.5\,P_2 - P_1)\,2\,L}{2\,a\,E} = 0$$

or $\qquad P_1 - 1.5\,P_2 + P_1 = 0$ or $2\,P_1 = \dfrac{3}{2}\,P_2$

From which $\qquad\qquad \dfrac{P_2}{P_1} = \dfrac{4}{3}$

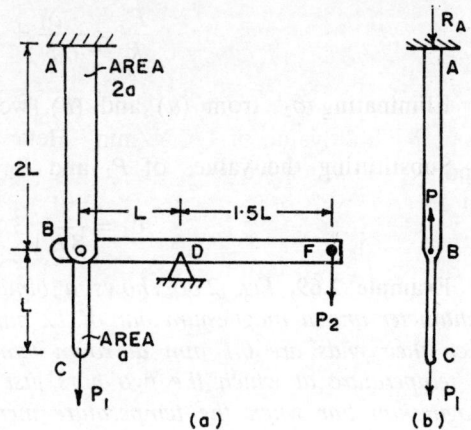

FIG. 2.87

Example 2.71. *A rigid beam AB is hinged at A and is connected to an aluminium alloy bar BC at the other end. The beam is also supported on a steel post DE through a rigid bearing at D, as shown in Fig .2.88. At no load, the beam is horizontal and there is an initial clearance $\delta = 0.1$ mm between the beam and rigid bearing. Determine the maximum permissible load W which may be applied at B if the axial stresses are not to exceed $120\,N/mm^2$ for steel and $140\,N/mm^2$ for the aluminium alloy. All the connections may be treated as smooth pins. Take $E = 2 \times 10^5\,N/mm^2$ for steel and $E = 0.8 \times 10^5\,N/mm^2$ for aluminium alloy.*

Solution :

Let us use suffix *a* for aluminium and suffix *s* for steel. There are four unknowns R_A, P_s, P_a and W as shown in Fig. 2.89 (*a*). Let p_s be the axial stress (comp.) in steel post and p_a be the axial stress (tensile) in aluminium bar. One of these axial stresses will be equal to permissible value (given) while the other one will be lesser than the allowable value.

Fig. 2.89 (*b*) shows the deformed position of the bars, from which we have :

$$\frac{\Delta_s + \delta}{0.1} = \frac{\Delta_a}{0.4}$$

or
$$4(\Delta_s + \delta) = \Delta_a$$

or
$$4\left[\frac{p_s \times 200}{2 \times 10^5} + 0.1\right] = \frac{p_a \times 400}{0.8 \times 10^5}$$

From which we get

$$p_a = 0.8 \, p_s + 80 \quad ...(1)$$

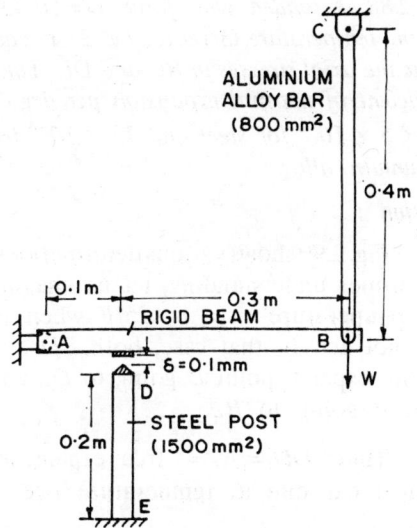

FIG. 2.88

If we have $p_s = 120 \text{ N/mm}^2$, we get $p_a = 0.8 \times 120 + 80 = 176 \text{ N/mm}^2$ which is more than the permissible value of 140 N/mm^2. Hence adopt $p_a = 140 \text{ N/mm}^2$ (the permissible value), corresponding to which, we obtain from (1)

$$p_s = \frac{1}{0.8}(p_a - 80)$$

$$= \frac{1}{0.8}(140 - 80)$$

$$= 75 \text{ N/mm}^2$$

$$\therefore P_a = 140 \times 800 \times 10^{-3}$$

$$= 112 \text{ kN and}$$

$$P_s = 75 \times 1500 \times 10^{-3}$$

$$= 112.5 \text{ kN}$$

Now, taking moments about *A* (Fig. 2.89 *a*), we get

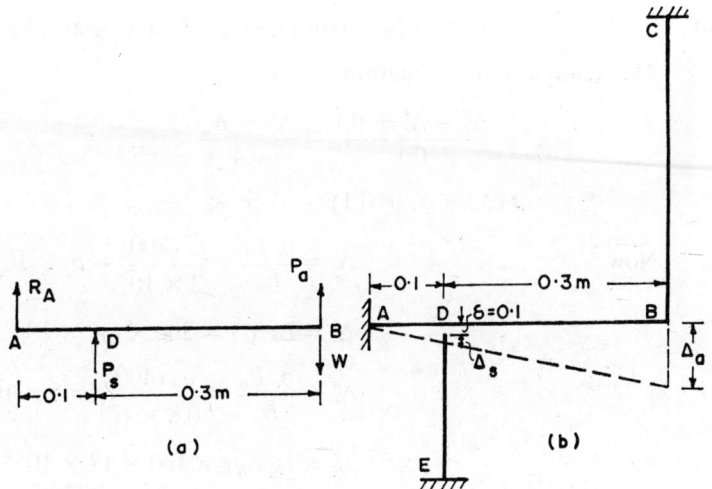

FIG. 2.89

$$112 \times 0.4 + 112.5 \times 0.1 = 0.4 \, W$$

From which we get $W = \textbf{140.125 kN}$

Example 2.72. *If the mechanism of Fig. 2.88 is loaded with force W=50 kN and the temperature increases by 25°F, calculate the axial stresses in BC and DE. Take coefficient of thermal expansion per degree F is 6.5×10^{-6} for steel and 13×10^{-6} for aluminium alloy.*

Solution :

Fig. 2.90 shows various deformations. For proper understanding, let us imagine that temperature rises by 25°F when W does not act. In that case, both ED and CB will expand, point D going to D_1, and point B going to B_1.

Thus, $DD_1 = \Delta_s^t =$ free expansion of steel bar due to temperature rise

and $BB_1 = \Delta_a^t =$ free expansion of aluminium bar due to temperature rise.

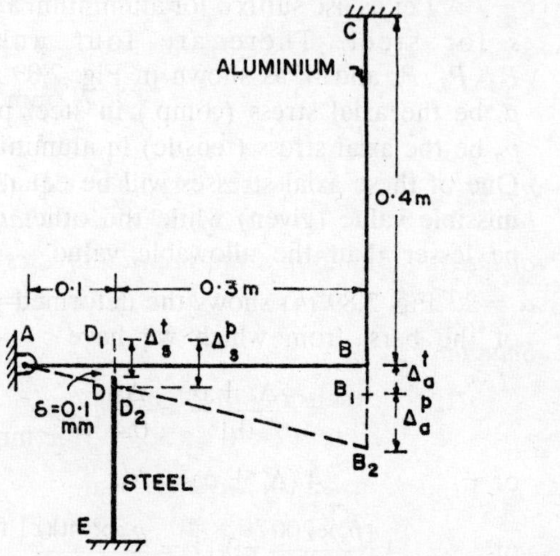

FIG. 2.90

Now, when the load W is applied at B, the rod CB extends further from B_1 to B_2 while the bar DE is *compressed* from D_1 to D_2 such that AD_2B_2 is the final position of the rigid bar.

Thus $B_1 B_2 = \Delta_a^p =$ expansion of aluminium bar due to external load.

and $D_1 D_2 = \Delta_s^p =$ contraction of steel bar, due to external load

The compatibility equation is

$$\frac{\Delta_s^p - \Delta_s^t + 0.1}{0.1} = \frac{\Delta_a^t + \Delta_a^p}{0.4}$$

or $\qquad 4\,(\Delta_s^p - \Delta_s^t + 0.1) = \Delta_a^t + \Delta_a^p$ $\qquad\qquad$ ...(*i*)

Now $\qquad\qquad \Delta_s^p = \dfrac{p_s L_s}{E_s} = \dfrac{p_s\,(200)}{2 \times 10^5} = p_s \times 10^{-3}$

$$\Delta_s^t = L_s \alpha_s t = 200 \times 6.5 \times 10^{-6} \times 25 = 0.0325 \text{ mm}$$

$$\Delta_a^p = \frac{p_a L_a}{E_a} = \frac{p_a\,(400)}{0.8 \times 10^5} = 5 \times 10^{-3} p_a$$

$$\Delta_a^t = L_a \alpha_a t = 400 \times 13 \times 10^{-6} \times 25 = 0.13 \text{ mm}$$

Hence from (*i*), $4\,(p_s \times 10^{-3} - 0.0325 + 0.1) = 5 \times 10^{-3} p_a + 0.13$

From which $\qquad\qquad p_s = 1.25\,p_a - 35$ $\qquad\qquad$ ...(*a*)

Also, taking moments about A (Fig. 2.89 *a*), $0.1\,P_s + 0.4\,P_a = 0.4\,W$

or $\qquad 0.1 \times 1500\,p_s + 0.4 \times 800\,p_a = 0.4 \times 50000$

which gives $\qquad p_s + 2.133\,p_a = 133.33$ ...(b)

From (a) and (b) we get

$$p_a = \textbf{49.76 N/mm}^2 \text{ (tensile)} \quad \text{and} \quad p_s = \textbf{27.20 N/mm}^2 \text{ (compressive)}$$

Example 2.73. *A rigid bar ABC is hinged at A and attached to brass bar BF (length 0.2 m, area 4000 mm^2) and steel bar CD (length 0.3 m and area 250 mm^2). The temperature of brass bar BF is lowered by 30 K and that of bar CD is raised by 30 K. Neglecting any possibility of lateral bucking, find the normal stresses in the brass and steel. Take E = 0.9 × 10^5 N/mm^2 and α = 20 × 10^{-6} per K for brass, and E = 2 × 10^5 N/mm^2 and α = 12 × 10^{-6} per K for steel.*

Solution :

Free expansion of steel bar
$= \Delta_S^t = 300 \times 12 \times 10^{-6} \times 30 = 0.108$ mm

Free contraction of brass bar
$= \Delta_B^t = 350 \times 20 \times 10^{-6} \times 30 = 0.21$ mm

For no temperature stresses to be developed, $\dfrac{\Delta_B^t}{AB} = \dfrac{\Delta_S^t}{AC}$

$\therefore \ \Delta_B^t = \Delta_S^t \cdot \dfrac{AB}{AC} = \Delta_S^t \times \dfrac{300}{700} = 0.4286\,\Delta_S^t$

$\qquad\qquad = 0.4286 \times 0.108 = 0.0463$ mm

But $\qquad\qquad \Delta_B^t = 0.21$ mm

Hence in the equilibrium position at- tained due to rigidity of bar *ABC*, tensile stress will be developed in the brass bar, and consequently, tensile stress will also be developed in steel bar.

FIG. 2.91

If Δ_B and Δ_S are the *final deformations* in the two bars at the *equilibrium position*, we have

$$\frac{\Delta_B}{AB} = \frac{\Delta_S}{AC}$$

$\therefore \qquad \Delta_B = \Delta_S \dfrac{AB}{AC} = \dfrac{0.3}{0.7}\Delta_S = 0.4286\,\Delta_S$ ...(i)

Now $\qquad \Delta_B = \Delta_B^t - \Delta_B^p = L_B\,\alpha_B\,t_B - \dfrac{p_B L_B}{E_B} = 0.21 - \dfrac{360\,p_B}{0.9 \times 10^5}$

an $\qquad \Delta_S = \Delta_S^t + \Delta_S^p = L_S\,\alpha_S t_S + \dfrac{p_s L_S}{E_S} = 0.108 + \dfrac{300\,p_s}{2 \times 10^5}$

Hence from (i), $0.21 - \dfrac{350\,p_B}{0.9 \times 10^5} = 0.4286\left(0.108 + \dfrac{300\,p_s}{2 \times 10^5}\right)$

which on simplification gives $p_s + 6.049\,p_B = 254.64$ ...(a)

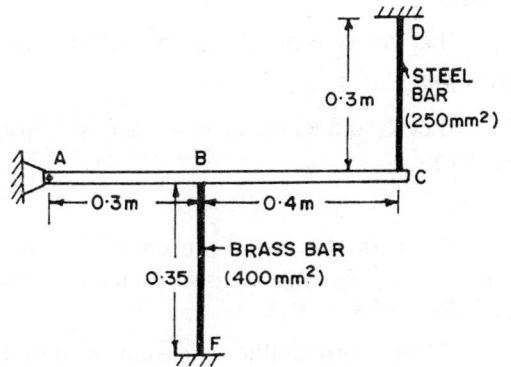

Also, taking moments about A, $p_B . A_B \times 350 - p_s A_s \times 700 = 0$

or　　　　$p_B \times 400 \times 350 = p_s \times 250 \times 700$

which gives　　　$p_B = 1.25 \, p_s$　　　　　　　　　　　　　...(b)

Hence from (a) and (b), we get

$$p_s = 29.74 \, \text{N/mm}^2 \text{ (tension) and } p_B = 37.18 \, \text{N/mm}^2 \text{ (tension)}$$

Example 2.74. *A composite bar made up of aluminium bar and steel bar is firmly held between two unyielding supports as shown in Fig. 2.92. An axial load of 200 kN is applied at B at 20°C. Find the stresses in each material, when the temperature is 70°C. Take E for aluminium and steel as $0.7 \times 10^5 \, N/mm^2$ and $2 \times 10^5 \, N/mm^2$ respectively and coefficients of expansions for aluminium and steel as 24×10^{-6} per °C and 12×10^{-6} per °C respectively.*

Solution :

Let us consider both the effects *separately*.

(a)　Effect of 200 kN load

Let R_A and R_B be the two reactions. From statics, we have

$$R_A = 200 - R_B \qquad ...(i)$$

Portion AB is subjected to a tensile load $= R_A = 200 - R_B$ while BC is subjected to a compressive load $R_B \, (= 200 - R_A)$.

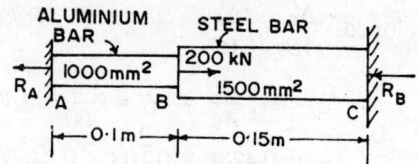

FIG. 2.92

From compatibility, extension (Δ_{AB}) of $AB =$ contraction (Δ_{BC}) of BC.

$$\therefore \quad \frac{(200 - R_B) \times 1000 \times 100}{1000 \times 0.7 \times 10^5} = \frac{R_B \times 1000 \times 150}{1500 \times 2 \times 10^5}$$

From which　　　　$R_B = 148.15 \, \text{kN}$

Hence force in AB,　　$P_{AB} = 200 - R_B = 200 - 148.15 = 51.85 \, \text{kN (tension)}$

and force in BC,　　$P_{BC} = R_B = 148.15 \, \text{kN (compression)}$

(b)　Effect of temperature rise : $t = 70 - 20 = 50° C$

Since the temperature strain in restricted, both the bars will be subjected to equal temperature force P_t of compressive nature.

Free expansion of $AB = \Delta_{AB,t} = 100 \times 24 \times 10^{-6} \times 50 = 0.12$ mm

Free expansion of $BC = \Delta_{BC,t} = 150 \times 12 \times 10^{-6} \times 50 = 0.09$ mm

$\therefore$　　　Total expansion, $\Delta_t = 0.12 + 0.09 = 0.21$ mm

Since this expansion is completely restricted, we have

$$\Delta_t = P_t \left[\frac{L_{AB}}{A_{AB} E_{AB}} + \frac{L_{BC}}{A_{BC} E_{BC}} \right]$$

or
$$0.21 = P_t \left[\frac{100}{1000 \times 0.7 \times 10^5} + \frac{150}{1500 \times 2 \times 10^5} \right] = 0.1929 \times 10^{-5} P_t$$

From which $\quad\quad P_t = 1.08889 \times 10^5 \text{ N} = 108.89 \text{ kN (compression)}$

(c) Final Stresses

Final force in $AB = 108.89 - 51.85 = 57.04$ kN (compression)

and Final force in $BC = 108.89 + 148.15 = 257.04$ kN (compression)

$\therefore$ Stress in AB, $\quad p_{AB} = \dfrac{57.04 \times 1000}{1000} = \textbf{57.04 N/mm}^2$ (compression)

Stress in BC, $\quad p_{BC} = \dfrac{257.04 \times 1000}{1500} = \textbf{171.36 N/mm}^2$ (compression)

Example 2.75. *A steel bar is sandwiched between two copper bars each having the same area and length as the steel bar, at an initial temperature of 10°C. These are rigidly connected together at both the ends. When the temperature is raised to 260°C, the length of the bars increases by 1.0 mm. Determine the original length and the final stresses in the bars. Take the following values :*

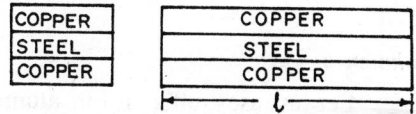

FIG. 2.93

$$E_s = 2 \times 10^5 \, N/mm^2; \; E_c = 1 \times 10^5 \, N/mm^2$$
$$\alpha_s = 12 \times 10^{-6} \; per \; °C \; ; \; \alpha_c = 18 \times 10^{-6} \; per \; °C$$

Solution :

Let A (mm^2) be the cross-sectional area of steel component. Hence cross-sectional area of copper component will be $= 2A$ (mm^2)

If δ is the actual expansion of the composite bar, we have $\alpha_s t l < \delta < \alpha_c t l$. Hence steel will be in tension and copper will be in compression.

For equilibrium, $\quad f_c A = f_c (2A)$

or $\quad\quad\quad\quad f_s = 2 f_c$ ...(1)

Also, final expansion of steel = final expansion of copper.

$\therefore \quad\quad\quad \alpha_s t l + \dfrac{f_s}{E_s} l = \alpha_c t l - \dfrac{f_c}{E_c} l$

Here $\quad\quad\quad t = 260 - 10 = 250° \, C$

$\therefore \quad 12 \times 10^{-6} \times 250 + \dfrac{f_s}{2 \times 10^5} = 18 \times 10^{-6} \times 250 - \dfrac{f_c}{1 \times 10^5}$ ...(2)

But $f_s = 2 f_c$. Hence from (2), we get.

$$3000 \times 10^{-6} + \frac{2 f_c}{2 \times 10^5} = 4500 \times 10^{-6} - \frac{f_c}{1 \times 10^5}$$

From which we get $\quad f_c = \textbf{75 N/mm}^2$ (compression)

$$\therefore \qquad f_s = 2 \times 75 = 150 \text{ N/mm}^2 \text{ (tension)}$$

Now $\qquad \Delta_s = \alpha_s t\, l + \dfrac{f_s}{E_s} l$ (where $\Delta_s = 1.0$ mm, given)

$$\therefore \qquad 1.0 = l\left(12 \times 10^{-6} \times 250 + \frac{150}{2 \times 10^5}\right) = 3.75 \times 10^{-3} l$$

From which $\qquad l = \mathbf{266.7 \ mm}$

Example 2.76. *A flat bar of aluminium alloy, 30 mm wide and 8 mm thick is placed between two steel bars each 30 mm wide and 10 mm thick, to form a composite bar 30 mm × 28 mm, as shown in Fig. 2.94. The three bars are fastened together at their ends when the temperature is 12°C. Find the stress in each of the material when the temperature of the whole assembly is raised to 42°C. If, at the new temperature, a compressive load of 30 kN is applied to the composite bar, what are the final stresses in steel and aluminium ?*
Take $E_s = 2 \times 10^5 \, N/mm^2$, $E_a = 0.7 \times 10^5 \, N/mm^2$; $\alpha_s = 12 \times 10^{-6}$ *per* °C *and* $\alpha_a = 23 \times 10^{-6}$ *per* °C.

Solution :

Let us use suffix a for aluminium and s for steel.

$A_s = 20 \times 30 = 600 \text{ mm}^2$ and $A_a = 8 \times 30 = 240 \text{ mm}^2$

We shall consider both the effects separately.

(a) Effect of temperature rise :

Due to temperature rise, steel will expand lesser than aluminium. Hence steel bar will be in tension and aluminium bar will be in compression.

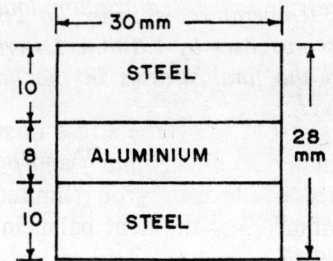

FIG. 2.94

For equilibrium,

$$p_s A_s = p_a A_a$$

or $\qquad p_s \times 600 = p_a \times 240$ from which $p_a = 2.5 p_s$ \qquad ...(1)

Also, $\qquad \Delta_s = \Delta_a$

or $\qquad \alpha_s t\, l + \dfrac{p_s}{E_s} l = \alpha_a t\, l - \dfrac{p_a l}{E_a}$

$$\therefore \quad 12 \times 10^{-6} \times 30 + \frac{p_s}{2 \times 10^5} = 23 \times 10^{-6} \times 30 - \frac{p_a}{0.7 \times 10^5}$$

or $\qquad 3.6 \times 10^{-4} + \dfrac{p_s}{2 \times 10^5} = 6.9 \times 10^{-4} - \dfrac{2.5 p_s}{0.7 \times 10^5}$

From which $p_s = 42 \text{ N/mm}^2$ (tension) and $p_a = 105 \text{ N/mm}^2$ (comp.)

(b) Effect of external load of 30 kN

$$f_s A_s + f_a A_a = P$$

$$\therefore \qquad f_s \times 600 + f_a \times 240 = 30000 \qquad\qquad\qquad ...(i)$$

Also, $$\frac{f_s}{E_s} = \frac{f_a}{E_a}$$

$\therefore$ $$f_s = f_a \frac{E_s}{E_a} = \frac{2}{0.7} f_a = 2.857 f_a \qquad \qquad ...(ii)$$

Substituting in (1) we get

$$600 \,(2.857 f_a) + 240 f_a = 30000$$

From which $f_a = 15.4 \text{ N/mm}^2$ (comp.)

Hence $f_s = 43.9 \text{ N/mm}^2$ (comp.)

(c) Final Stresses

Stress in aluminium $= 105 + 15.4 = \mathbf{120.4 \text{ N/mm}^2}$ (comp.)

Stress in steel $= -42 + 43.9 = \mathbf{1.9 \text{ N/mm}^2}$ (tension)

Example 2.77. *A rigid bar ABCD of negligible mass is pinned at B and is attached to two vertical rods CF and DG. Rod CF is of steel having L = 0.8 m and A = 800 mm², while rod DG is of bronze have L = 1 m and A = 250 mm². Assuming that the rods were initially stress free, what maximum load P can be applied without exceeding stresses of 160 N/mm² in steel rod and 80 mm² in bronze bar. Take $E_s = 2 \times 10^5 \text{ N/mm}^2$ and $E_b = 0.83 \times 10^5 \text{ N/mm}^2$.*

Solution :

Let p_s be the stress in steel rod (limited to 160 N/mm²) and p_b be the stress in bronze rod (limited to 80 N/mm²). For moment balancing about B,

$$P \times 1 = p_s A_s \times 0.75 + p_b A_b \times 1.5 \qquad ...(1)$$

Also, from compatibility,

FIG. 2.95

$$\frac{\Delta_s}{0.75} = \frac{\Delta_b}{1.5}$$

or $$\Delta_s = \frac{0.75}{1.5} \Delta_b = 0.5 \, \Delta_b$$

or $$\frac{p_s l_s}{E_s} = 0.5 \frac{p_b l_b}{E_b}$$

$\therefore$ $$p_s = 0.5 \frac{l_b}{l_s} \cdot \frac{E_s}{E_b} p_b = 0.5 \times \frac{1}{0.8} \times \frac{2}{0.83} p_b = 1.506 \, p_b \qquad ...(2)$$

or $$p_b = 0.664 \, p_s \qquad ...(3)$$

If p_b is kept equal to its maximum permissible value of 80 N/mm², we get $p_s = 1.506 \times 80 = 120.48 \text{ N/mm}^2$, which is less than its maximum permissible value of 160 N/mm². On the other hand, if p_s is kept equal to its maximum permissible value of 160 N/m m², we get $p_b = 0.664 \times 160 = 106.24 \text{ N/mm}^2$ which exceeds the permissible value of 80 N/mm².

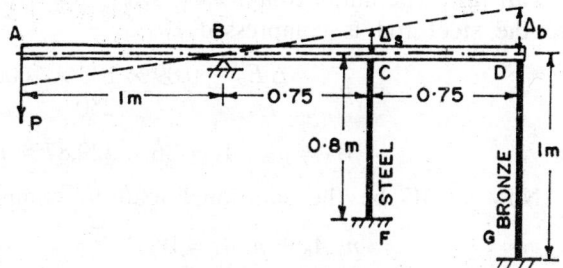

Hence the governing values of the stress is $p_b = 80\,\text{N/mm}^2$,   corresponding to which $p_s = 120.48\,\text{N/mm}^2$. Substituting these values in Eq. (1) we get

$$P = 120.48 \times 800 \times 0.75 + 80 \times 250 \times 1.5 = 102288\,N \approx \mathbf{102.288}\ \mathbf{kN.}$$

Example 2.78. *Fig. 2.96 shows a round steel rod supported in a recess and surrounded by a co-axial brass tube. The upper end of the rod is 0.1 mm below that of the tube and an axial load is applied to a rigid plate resting on the top of the tube.*

(a) Determine the magnitude of the maximum permissible load if the compressive stress in rod is not to exceed $120\,N/mm^2$ and that in the tube is not to exceed $90\,N/mm^2$.

(b) Find the amount by which the tube will be shortened by the load if the compressive stress in the tube is the same as that in the rod.

Take $E_s = 200\,kN/mm^2$ and $E_b = 100\,kN/mm^2$.

Solution :

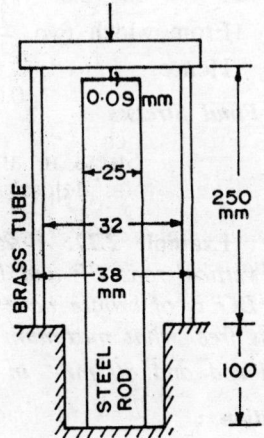

FIG. 2.96

$$A_s = \frac{\pi}{4}(25)^2 = 490.87\ \text{mm}^2 \ ; \ A_b = \frac{\pi}{4}(38^2 - 32^2) = 329.87\ \text{mm}^2$$

Part (a) : The initial compressive stress $\left(p_{bi}\right)$ in the tube, before the steel rod is compressed is

$$p_{bi} = \frac{\Delta E_b}{L_b} = \frac{0.09 \times 100 \times 1000}{250} = 36\ \text{N/mm}^2 < 90 \ .$$

$$\therefore \qquad\qquad W_1 = p_{bi}.A_b = 36 \times 329.87 \approx \mathbf{11875}\ \mathbf{N}$$

Now let W_2 be the additional load to compress further both the bar and the tube.

$$\therefore \qquad\qquad p_b A_b + p_s A_s = W_2 \qquad\qquad\qquad\qquad ...(i)$$

Also, $\qquad\qquad\qquad\qquad \Delta_b = \Delta_s$

or $\qquad\qquad\qquad\qquad \dfrac{p_b \times 250}{E_b} = \dfrac{p_s \times 350}{E_s}$

$$\therefore \qquad\qquad\qquad p_s = p_b \cdot \frac{E_s}{E_b} \cdot \frac{250}{350} = p_b \frac{200}{100} \times \frac{250}{350} = 1.4286\,p_b \qquad\qquad ...(ii)$$

Now limiting the stress in brass to $90\,\text{N/mm}^2$, we have

$$p_b = 90 - p_{bi} = 90 - 36 = 54\ \text{N/mm}^2$$

and   corresponding $\qquad\qquad p_s = 1.4286 \times 54 = 77.14\ \text{N/mm}^2 < 120\ \text{N/mm}^2$

Hence the governing value are : $p_b = 54\,\text{N/mm}^2$ and $p_s = 77.14\,\text{N/mm}^2$

Hence from (ii), $\qquad\qquad W_2 = 54 \times 329.87 + 77.14 \times 490.87 \approx 55679\ \text{N}$

$$\therefore \ \text{Total max. load} = W_1 + W_2 = 11875 + 55679 = 67554\,\text{N} = \mathbf{67.554\ kN}$$

Part a : Let the *additional* shortening be $= \Delta_b = \Delta_s$

∴ Total shortening of the tube $= (\Delta_b + 0.09)$ mm

Hence stress in brass $= \dfrac{E_b (\Delta_b + 0.09)}{L_b} = \dfrac{100 \times 10^3}{250} (0.09 + \Delta_b)$ ...(a)

and stress in steel $= \dfrac{E_s \Delta_s}{L_s} = \dfrac{200 \times 10^3}{350} \Delta_b$ ...(b)

Equating the two, $\dfrac{100 \times 10^3}{250} (0.09 + \Delta_b) = \dfrac{200 \times 10^3}{350} \Delta_b$

or $0.09 + \Delta_b = 1.4286 \Delta_b$

From which $\Delta_b = 0.21$ mm

Hence total deformation of brass tube $= 0.09 + 0.21 = \mathbf{0.3}$ **mm**

Example 2.79. *A rigid member AD of length 2L is supported at ends A and C and at its mid-point B by three vertical wires DA, EB and FC, as shown in Fig 2.97. The wires DA, EB and FC extend α_1, α_2 and α_3 respectively under unit load. Calculate the load in each wire if the member AC weighs w per unit length.*

Solution :

Total downward load $= 2 w L$

Let the loads in the three bars be P_1, P_2 and P_3 respectively.

∴ $P_1 + P_2 + P_3 = 2 w L$ ...(1)

Taking moments about AD,

$P_2 L + P_3 2 L = 2 w L \times L$

or $P_2 + 2 P_3 = 2 w L$ ...(2a)

Also, by taking moments about FC,

$P_1 \times 2 L + P_2 L = 2 w L . L$

or $2 P_1 + P_2 = 2 w L$ ...(2b)

From 2 (a) and 2 (b), we observe that $P_1 = P_3$ ...(2)

From compatibility, $\Delta_2 = \dfrac{\Delta_1 + \Delta_3}{2}$

or $P_2 \alpha_2 = \dfrac{1}{2} \left(P_1 \alpha_1 + P_3 \alpha_3 \right)$

or $P_2 \alpha_2 = \dfrac{1}{2} \left(P_1 \alpha_1 + P_1 \alpha_3 \right) = \dfrac{P_1}{2} \left(\alpha_1 + \alpha_3 \right)$

Hence $P_2 = \dfrac{P_1}{2 \alpha_2} \left(\alpha_1 + \alpha_3 \right)$ ...(3)

Substituting in (1), we get

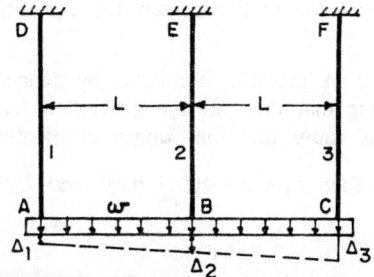

FIG. 2.97

$$P_1 + \frac{P_1}{2\,\alpha_2}\left(\alpha_1 + \alpha_3\right) + P_1 = 2\,w\,L$$

or
$$P_1\left[2 + \frac{\alpha_1 + \alpha_3}{2\,\alpha_2}\right] = 2\,w\,L$$

or
$$P_1\left[\frac{4\,\alpha_2 + (\alpha_1 + \alpha_3)}{2\,\alpha_2}\right] = 2\,w\,L$$

From which
$$P_1 = \frac{4\,w\,L\,\alpha_2}{\alpha_1 + 4\,\alpha_2 + \alpha_3} = P_3 \text{ Ans.}$$

Hence from (3),
$$P_2 = \frac{\alpha_1 + \alpha_3}{2\,\alpha_2}\left[\frac{4\,w\,L\,\alpha_2}{\alpha_1 + 4\,\alpha_2 + \alpha_3}\right]$$

or
$$P_2 = \frac{2\,w\,L\,(\alpha_1 + \alpha_3)}{\alpha_1 + 4\,\alpha_2 + \alpha_3} \textbf{ Ans.}$$

PROBLEMS

1. A steel bar $ABCD$ of varying sections is subjected to the axial forces as shown in Fig. 2.98. Find the value of P necessary for equilibrium. If $E = 210\,\text{kN/mm}^2$, determine the total elongation of the bar.

2. A member is formed by connecting a steel bar to an aluminium bar as shown in Fig. 2.99. Assuming that the bars are prevented from buckling sideways, calculate the magnitude of axial force P that will cause the total length of member to decrease by 0.3 mm.

Take $E_s = 2 \times 10^5\,\text{N/mm}^2$ and $E_a = 0.7 \times 10^5\,\text{N/mm}^2$.

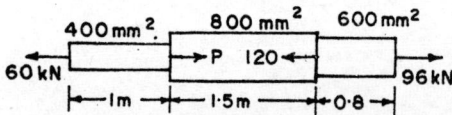

FIG. 2.98

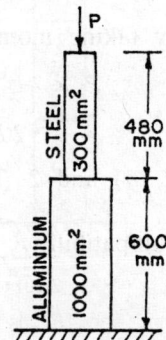

FIG. 2.99

3. A steel wire of 10 mm diameter is used for lifting a load of 1 kN at its lowest end, the length of the wire hanging vertically being 200 m.

Taking the unit weight of steel $= 78\,\text{kN/m}^3$ and $E = 2 \times 10^5\,\text{N/mm}^2$, calculate the total elongation of the wire.

4. The bar shown in Fig. 2.100 is subjected to a tensile load of 100 kN. Find diameter of the middle portion if the stress there is to be limited to 150 N/mm². Find also the length of the middle portion if the elongation of the bar is limited to 0.2 mm. Take $E = 2 \times 10^5$ N/mm².

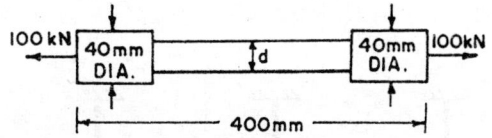

FIG. 2.100

5. A steel flat plate of 10 mm thickness tapers uniformly from 100 mm to 50 mm width in a length of 400 mm. From first principles, determine the elongation of the plate if the axial tensile force is 100 kN. Take $E = 2 \times 10^5$ N/mm².

6. A mild steel rod of 20 mm diameter and 300 mm long is enclosed centrally inside a hollow copper tube of external diameter 30 mm and internal diameter 25 mm. The ends of the rod and tube are brazed together, and the composite bar is subjected to an axial pull of 50 kN.

If E for steel and copper is 200 GN/m² and 100 GN/m² respectively, find the stresses developed in the rod and the tube. Also find the extension of the rod.

7. A reinforced concrete column 500 mm diameter has four steel rods of 30 mm diameter embedded in it and carries a load of 680 kN. Find the stresses in steel and concrete. Take E for steel $= 2.04 \times 10^5$ N/mm² and E for concrete $= 0.136 \times 10^5$ N/mm². Find also the adhesive force between steel and concrete.

8. A vertical rod of uniform section fixed at both its ends is axially loaded at intermediate sections by forces as shown in Fig. 2.101. Find the end reactions.

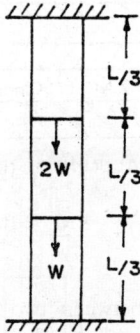

FIG. 2.101

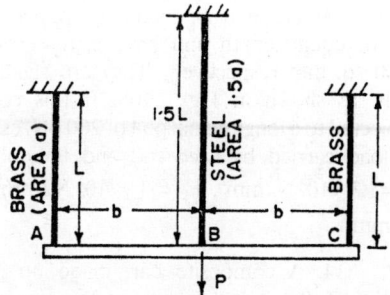

FIG. 2.102

9. A rigid bar ABC is supported by three rods in the same vertical plane and equidistant, as shown in Fig. 2.102. The outer rods are of brass and of length L and area a. The central rod is of steel of length $1.5 L$ and area $1.5 a$. Calculate the forces in the bars due to an applied force of P, if the bar AC remains horizontal after the load has been applied. Take $\dfrac{E_s}{E_b} = 2$.

10. A rigid beam carrying a load of W is supported by three bars as shown in Fig. 2.103. All the bars have the same length and same area of cross-section. Taking $E_s = 2E_b$, find the load carried by each bar.

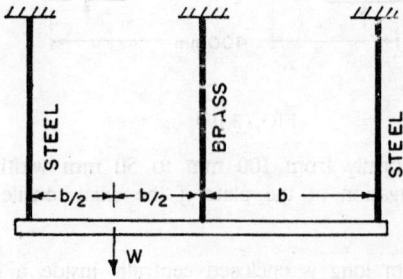

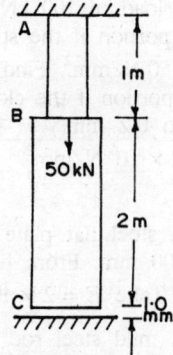

FIG. 2.103   FIG. 2.104

11. A composite bar ABC, rigidly fixed at A and 1 mm above the lower support is loaded as shown in Fig. 2.104. If the cross- sectional area of section AB is 100 mm^2 and that of section BC is 200 mm^2, find the reactions at the ends, and the stresses in the two sections. Take $E = 2 \times 10^5$ N/mm^2.

12. A compound bar consists of a central steel strip 20 mm wide and 5 mm thick placed between two strips of brass each 20 mm wide and t mm thick. The strips are firmly fixed together to form a compound bar of rectangular section 20 mm wide and $(2t+5)$ mm thick. Determine (a) the thickness of the brass strips which will make the apparent modulus of elasticity of compound bar 1.6×10^5 N/mm^2, and (b) the maximum axial pull the bar can then carry if the stress is not to exceed 150 N/mm^2, in either brass or steel. Take the values of E for steel and brass as 2×10^5 N/mm^2 and 1×10^5 N/mm^2.

13. Three bars, made of copper, zinc and aluminium are of equal length and have cross-section of 500, 750 and 1000 sq. mm respectively. They are rigidly connected at their ends, as shown in Fig. 2.105. If this compound member is subjected to a longitudinal pull of 200 kN, estimate the proportion of load carried by each rod and the induced stresses. Take $E_c = 1.3 \times 10^5$ N/mm^2, $E_z = 1 \times 10^5$ N/mm^2 and $E_a = 0.8 \times 10^5$ N/mm^2.

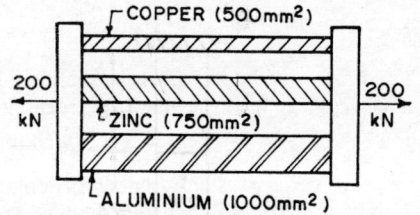

FIG. 2.105

14. A composite bar, made up of aluminium and steel, is held between two supports as shown in Fig. 2.106. The bars are stress free at a temperature of 40°C. What will be the stresses in the two bars when the temperature is 23°C, if (a) the supports are non-yielding, and (b) the supports come nearer to each other by 0.1 mm.

Take $E_s = 200$ kN/mm^2, $E_a = 70$ kN/mm^2, $\alpha_s = 12 \times 10^{-6}$ per °C and $\alpha_a = 24 \times 10^{-6}$ per °C

(Based on Oxford University)

15. A composite bar is made up by connecting a steel member and a copper member, rigidly fixed at their ends as shown in Fig. 2.107. The cross sectional area of steel member is A mm^2 for half of the length and $2A$ mm^2 for the other half of the length; while that for the copper member is A mm^2. The coefficient of expansion for steel and copper are α and $1.3\,\alpha$, while elastic moduli are E and $0.5\,E$ respectively. Determine the stresses induced in both the members when the composite bar is subjected to a rise of temperature of t degrees.

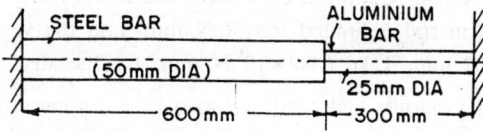

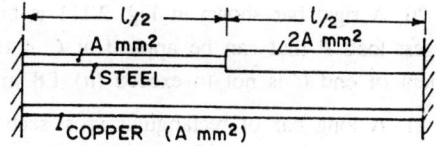

FIG. 2.106

FIG. 2.107

16. Fig. 2.108 shows a bar of varying sections, rigidly fixed at A and D and subjected axial forces. Determine the force in each portion of the bar and the displacements of point B and C. Portion AB, of length 1 m has area of cross-section of 2000 mm^2, portion BC, of length 1.5 m has area of cross-section of 3000 mm^2, while portion CD has a length of 2 m and area of cross-section of 4000 mm^2. Take $E = 200$ kN/mm^2.

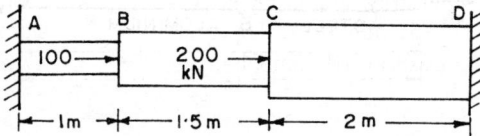

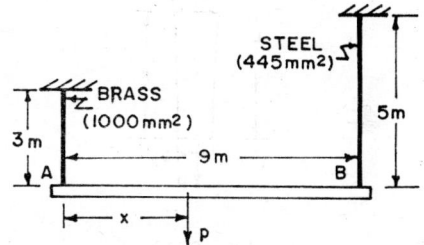

FIG. 2.108

FIG. 2.109

17. A rigid bar AB is suspended by two vertical rods at A and B, as shown in Fig. 2.109. At what distance x from A may a vertical load P be applied if the bar is to remain horizontal after the load is applied ? Take $E_s = 2 \times 10^5$ N/mm^2 and $E_b = 1 \times 10^5$ N/mm^2.

18. A hollow steel cylinder of length 300 mm, inside diameter 150 mm and uniform wall thickness of 3 mm is filled with concrete and compressed between two rigid parallel plates at the ends by a load of 600 kN. Find the compressive stress in each material and the total shortening of the cylinder. Take $E_s = 2 \times 10^5$ N/mm^2 and $E_c = 0.2 \times 10^5$ N/mm^2.

19. A rigid bean $ABCD$ is hinged at D and supported by two springs A and B as shown in Fig. 2.110. The beam carries a vertical load W at the point C at a distance of c from the hinged end. The

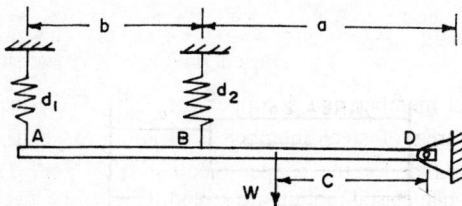

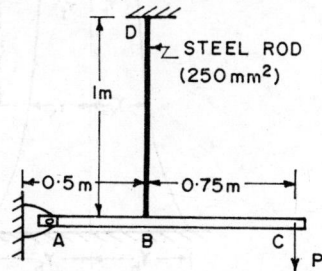

FIG. 2.110

FIG. 2.111

flexibilities (deflection/unit load) of the springs at A and B are d_1 and d_2 respectively. Determine the forces in the springs and also the reaction at the hinged support.

20. A rigid bar shown in Fig. 2.111 is hinged at A and supported by a steel rod at B. Determine the largest load P that can be applied at C if the stress in rod is limited to 150 N/mm^2 and the vertical movement of end C is not to exceed (a) 1.8 mm (b) 2.2 mm. Take $E=2\times10^5 \text{ N/mm}^2$ for the steel rod.

21. A long bar of rectangular cross-section hangs vertically and carries a load P at its lower end, in addition of its own weight, as shown in Fig. 2.112. The bar has constant thickness, but its width b varies along its length in such a way that the tensile stress σ_t is constant throughout. Find an expression of width b_x at x from the free end. Also find the width b_1 and b_2 and the volume V of the bar. Take γ as the specific weight.

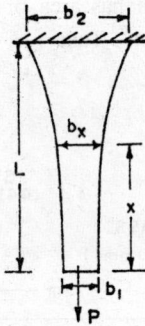

FIG. 2.112

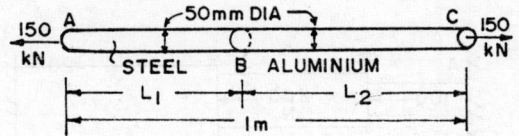

FIG. 2.113

22. A bar ABC, of 1000 mm length and 50 mm diameter is composed of two materials : part AB of steel and part BC of aluminium. If it is subjected to a tensile force of 150 kN, determine the lengths L_1 and L_2 for the steel and aluminium parts, respectively, in order that both the parts have the same elongation.

Also, determine the total elongation of the bar. Take $E_s = 210 \text{ kN/mm}^2$ and $E = 70 \text{ kN/mm}^2$.

23. Determine the radius r_x of a pillar of circular cross-section and height H in order that the volume of the pillar will be a minimum , if the pillar supports a compressive load P at the top, in addition

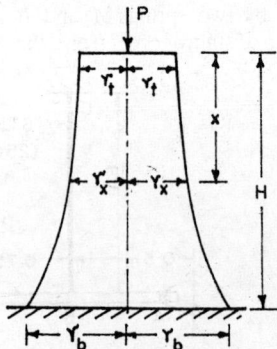

FIG. 2.114

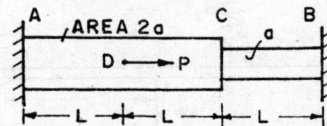

FIG. 2.115

to its own weight. Take f_c as the allowable stress in compression and γ as the specific weight of the material. Also determine the volume of the pillar.

24. An axially loaded bar AB, shown in Fig. 2.115 is held between rigid supports. The bar has cross-sectional area $2a$ from A to C and a from C to B. Determine the displacement δ_d of point D where the load P acts. Also determine the reactions at A and B.

25. A light rigid bar $ABCD$ pinned at B and connected to two vertical rods, is shown in Fig. 2.116. Assuming that the bar was initially horizontal and the rods stress free, determine the stress in each rod after the load $P=20$ kN is applied.

Take E for steel $= 200$ kN/mm^2 and E for aluminium $= 100$ kN/mm^2.

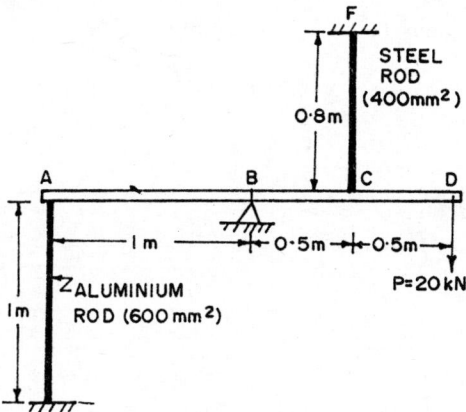

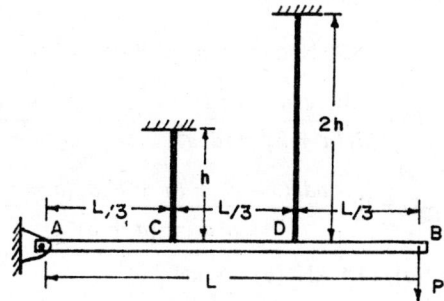

FIG. 2.116   FIG. 2.117

26. A rigid bar AB of length L is hinged to a wall at A and supported by two vertical wires attached at point C and D, as shown in Fig. 2.117. Both the wires have the same area of cross-section and are made of the same material. Determine the forces in the wires.

ANSWERS

1. $P = 84$ kN ; 1.11 mm

2.   196.875 kN

3.   20.53 mm

4.   29.13 mm ; 116 mm

5.   0.28 mm

6. $p_s = 118.44$ N/mm^2 ; 59.22 N/mm^2 ; 0.178 mm

7. $p_s = 43.24$ N/mm^2 ; $p_c = 2.88$ N/mm^2 ; 112.475 kN

8. $\dfrac{5}{3}W ; \dfrac{4}{3}W$

9. $P_b = \dfrac{1}{4}P ; P_s = \dfrac{1}{2}P$

10.   0.65 W ; 0.20 W ; 0.15 W

11. $R_A = 35$ kN ; $R_C = 15$ kN ; $p_{AB} = 350$ N/mm^2 (tension); $p_{BC} = 75$ N/mm^2 (comp.)

12.   (a) 2.5 mm (b) 22.5 kN

13. $P_c = 59.091$ kN ; $P_z = 68.178$ kN ; $P_a = 72.729$ kN

       $p_c = 118.18$ N/mm^2 ; $p_z = 90.90$ N/mm^2 ; $p_a = 72.729$ N/mm^2

14.   (a) $p_a = 48.61$ N/mm^2; $p_s = 12.15$ N/mm^2 (b) $p_a = 28.75$ N/mm^2 ; $p_s = 7.19$ N/mm^2

15. $p_s = \dfrac{6}{55}\,\alpha\,t\,E$; $p_s{'} = \dfrac{3}{55}\,\alpha\,t\,E$; $p_c = \dfrac{6}{55}\,\alpha\,t\,E$

16. $P_{AB} = 133.33$ kN (tension); $P_{BC} = 33.33$ kN (comp.) ; $P_{CD} = 166.67$ kN (comp.)

$$\Delta_B = 0.333 \text{ mm } (\rightarrow) \quad ; \quad \Delta_c = 0.417 \text{ mm } (\rightarrow)$$

17.   3.133 m

18. $p_c = 18.70$ N/mm^2 ; $p_s = 186.97$ N/mm^2 ; 0.28 mm

19. $F_A = \dfrac{W\,.\,c\,(a+b)\,d_2}{d_1\,(a+b)^2 + d_1\,a^2}$; $F_B = \dfrac{W\,.\,c\,.\,a\,.\,d_1}{d_2\,(a+b)^2 + d_1\,d^2}$

       $R_D = W\left[\dfrac{a d_1\,(a-c) + (a+b)\,d_2\,(a+b-c)}{a^2\,d_1 + (a+b)^2\,d_2}\right]$

20.   (a) 14.4 kN (b) 15 kN

21. $b_x = \dfrac{P}{\sigma_t\,.\,t}\,e^{\gamma\,x/\sigma_t}$

22. $L_1 = 750$ mm ; $L_2 = 250$ mm ; $\Delta = 0.546$ mm

23. $r_x = \left(\dfrac{P\,.\,e^{\gamma\,x/f_c}}{f_c\,.\,\pi}\right)^{1/2}$; $V = \dfrac{P}{\gamma}\left(e^{\gamma\,h/f_c} - 1\right)$

24. $\Delta_d = \dfrac{3\,PL}{8\,aE}$; $R_A = \dfrac{3}{4}P$; $R_B = \dfrac{1}{4}P$

25. $p_s = 29.41$ N/mm^2 ; $p_a = 23.53$ N/mm^2

26. $P_c = P_D = P$

Elastic Constants

3.1. ELASTIC CONSTANTS

Elastic constants are those *factors* which determine the deformations produced by a given *stress system* acting on a material. These factors (i.e. elastic constants) are *constant* within the limits for which Hooke's laws are obeyed. Various elastic constants are :

   (*i*) Modulus of elasticity (*E*)

   (*ii*) Poisson's ratio (μ or $1/m$)

   (*iii*) Modulus of rigidity (*G* or *N*)

and   (*iv*) Bulk modulus (*K*)

3.2. LONGITUDINAL STRAIN : MODULUS OF ELASTICITY

As stated in §2.3, when an axial stress *p* (say, tensile) is applied along the longitudinal axis of a bar, the length of the bar will be increased. This change in the length (usually called deformation) per unit length of the bar, is termed as *longitudinal strain* (ε) or *primary strain*. The ratio of stress to strain, within elastic limits, is called the *modulus of elasticity* (*E*):

Thus, modulus of elasticity $E = \dfrac{p}{\varepsilon}$ ...(3.1)

The modulus of elasticity (also called Young's modulus of elasticity) is the *constant of proportionality* which is defined as the intensity of stress that causes unit strain.

Table 3.1. gives the values of *modulus of elasticity* (*E*) for some common materials.

3.3. LATERAL STRAIN : POISSON'S RATIO

When an axial force (say, tensile) is applied along the longitudinal axis of a bar, the length of the bar will *increase*, but at the same time its lateral dimensions (i.e. either the width and breadth or the diameter) will be *decreased*. This phenomenon is shown by dotted lines in Fig. 3.1.

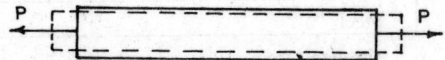

FIG. 3.1

TABLE 3.1. VALUES OF MODULUS OF ELASTICITY

S.No	Material	Modulus of elasticity E (kN/mm² or GPa)
1.	Aluminium (Pure)	70
2.	Aluminium alloys	70 – 79
3.	Brass	96 – 110
4.	Bronze	96 – 120
5.	Cast iron	83 – 170
6.	Concrete (compression)	18 – 30
7.	Copper (Pure)	110 – 120
8.	Rubber	0.0007 – 0.004
9.	Steel	190 – 210
10.	Wrought iron	190

Thus, any direct stress produces a strain in its own direction (called longitudinal strain) and an opposite kind of strain (called lateral strain) in every direction at right angles to this. The ratio of the lateral strain to the longitudinal strain is constant for a given material. This constant is known as Poisson's ratio.

Thus, $\dfrac{\text{Lateral strain}}{\text{Longitudinal strain}} = \text{constant} = \dfrac{1}{m} = \mu$ ...(3.2)

The *constant* is named after French mathematician Poisson, who first predicted its existence and found its value for many isotropic materials. The value of Poisson's ratio varies from 0.25 to 0.42 for most of metals. For rubber, its value range from 0.45 to 0.50. Table 3.2 gives the value of Poisson's ratio for some common materials. The value of Poisson's ratio is the same in tension and compression.

TABLE 3.2. VALUES OF POISSON'S RATIO

S.No	Material	Poisson's Ratio $\dfrac{1}{m}$ or μ
1.	Aluminium (Pure)	0.33
2.	Aluminium alloys	0.33
3.	Brass	0.34
4.	Bronze	0.34
5.	Cast iron	0.2 – 0.3
6.	Concrete (compression)	0.1 – 0.2
7.	Copper (Pure)	0.33 – 0.36
8.	Rubber	0.45 – 0.50
9.	Steel	0.27 – 0.30
10.	Wrought iron	0.3

3.4. VOLUMETRIC STRAIN DUE TO SINGLE DIRECT STRESS

Fig 3.2 shows a rectangular bar of length L, width b and thickness t subjected to single direct stress (p) acting along its longitudinal axis. Let this stress be tensile in nature.

Then longitudinal strain, $e_1 = \dfrac{p}{E}$ (tensile)

Lateral strain, $e_2 = -\dfrac{1}{m}e_1 = -\dfrac{1}{m}\dfrac{p}{E} = \dfrac{p}{mE}$

(compressive) ...(3.3)

Now, for the *rectangular bar*, $V = L \cdot b \cdot t$

...(i)

If δL, δb and δt denote the *change* in the corresponding dimension, the final volume $(V + \delta V)$ is given by

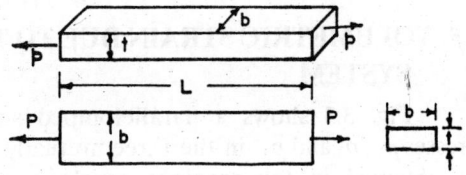

FIG. 3.2

$$(V + \delta V) = (L + \delta L)(b + \delta b)(t + \delta t)$$

or $$(V + \delta V) = Lbt\left(1 + \frac{\delta L}{L}\right)\left(1 + \frac{\delta b}{b}\right)\left(1 + \frac{\delta t}{t}\right)$$

or $$(V + \delta V) = V\left[1 + \frac{\delta L}{L} + \frac{\delta b}{b} + \frac{\delta t}{t} + \frac{\delta L}{L}\cdot\frac{\delta b}{b} + \frac{\delta L}{L}\frac{\delta t}{t} + \frac{\delta b}{b}\cdot\frac{\delta t}{t} + \frac{\delta L}{L}\cdot\frac{\delta b}{b}\cdot\frac{\delta t}{t}\right]$$

Ignoring the *products* of small quantities, we have

$$(V + \delta V) \approx V\left[1 + \frac{\delta L}{L} + \frac{\delta b}{b} + \frac{\delta t}{t}\right]$$

or $$\delta V \approx V\left(\frac{\delta L}{L} + \frac{\delta b}{b} + \frac{\delta t}{t}\right)$$

or $$\frac{\delta V}{V} = \frac{\delta L}{L} + \frac{\delta b}{b} + \frac{\delta t}{t} \qquad ...(ii)$$

or $$\frac{\delta V}{V} = e_v = e_1 + e_2 + e_3 = e_x + e_y + e_z \qquad ...(3.4)$$

The above equation could also be obtained directly by taking logarithm and partially differentiating both the sides of Eq. (i). Thus $\log V = \log L + \log b + \log t$

$\therefore$ $$\frac{\delta V}{V} = \frac{\delta L}{L} + \frac{\delta b}{L} + \frac{\delta t}{t} = e_1 + e_2 + e_3 \qquad ...(3.4)$$

Now, $$\frac{\delta L}{L} = e_1 = \frac{p}{E}\,;\, \frac{\delta b}{b} = e_2 = -\frac{p}{mE} \text{ and } \frac{\delta t}{t} = e_3 = -\frac{p}{mE}$$

$\therefore$ Volumetric strain, $$e_v = \frac{\delta V}{V} = \frac{p}{E} - \frac{p}{mE} - \frac{p}{mE} = \frac{p}{E}\left(1 - \frac{2}{m}\right) \qquad ...(3.5)$$

$\therefore$ Again, for the *circular bar* of diameter d, we have

$$V = \frac{\pi}{4}d^2 L$$

Hence $$\frac{\delta V}{V} = \frac{\delta L}{L} + \frac{2\,\delta d}{d}$$

Here, $$\frac{\delta L}{L} = e_1 = \frac{p}{E} \qquad \text{and} \qquad \frac{\delta d}{d} = e_2 = -\frac{p}{mE}$$

$\therefore$ Volumetric strain, $\quad e_v = \dfrac{\delta V}{V} = \dfrac{p}{E} - \dfrac{2p}{m} = \dfrac{p}{E}\left(1 - \dfrac{2}{m}\right)$ ...(3.5)

3.5. VOLUMETRIC STRAIN DUE TO THREE MUTUALLY PERPENDICULAR STRESS SYSTEM

Fig. 3.3 shows a parallelopiped subjected to three tensile stresses p_1, p_2 and p_3 in the three mutually perpendicular directions. As obtained in the previous article,

$$\frac{\delta V}{V} = e_1 + e_2 + e_3$$

Since any direct stress produces a strain in its own direction and an opposite kind of strain in every direction at right angles to this we have,

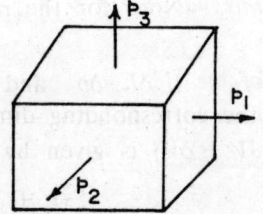

FIG. 3.3

Longitudinal strain $\qquad e_1 = \dfrac{p_1}{E} - \dfrac{p_2}{mE} - \dfrac{p_3}{mE} = \dfrac{p_1}{E} - \dfrac{p_2 + p_3}{mE}$ ...(3.7 a)

Similarly, $\qquad\qquad e_2 = \dfrac{p_2}{E} - \dfrac{p_3}{mE} - \dfrac{p_1}{mE} = \dfrac{p_2}{E} - \dfrac{p_3 + p_1}{mE}$ ...(3.7 b)

and $\qquad\qquad e_3 = \dfrac{p_3}{E} - \dfrac{p_1}{mE} - \dfrac{p_2}{mE} = \dfrac{p_3}{E} - \dfrac{p_1 + p_2}{mE}$ ...(3.7 c)

Eqs. 3.7 are known as *general equations of Hooke's law* or *generalised Hooke's law*.

Adding the three expressions of Eqs. 3.7, we get.

$$e_v = \frac{\delta V}{V} = e_1 + e_2 + e_3 = \left(1 - \frac{2}{m}\right)\left(\frac{p_1 + p_2 + p_3}{E}\right) \qquad ...(3.8)$$

The sum of three strains (e_1, e_2, e_3) is known as *dilatation* and, for small strains, it represents change in volume per unit volume.

If some of the stresses are of opposite sign (i.e., compressive) necessary changes in the algebraic signs of the above expressions will have to be made.

3.6. UPPER LIMIT OF POISSON'S RATIO

From Eq. 3.8 we have

$$e_1 + e_2 + e_3 = \left(1 - \frac{2}{m}\right)\left(\frac{p_1 + p_2 + p_3}{E}\right)$$

For the case of hydrostatic tension, we have $p_1 = p_2 = p_3 = p$ and the resulting strains are $e_1 = e_2 = e_3 = e$.

Hence $\qquad\qquad 3e = \left(1 - \dfrac{2}{m}\right)\left(\dfrac{3p}{E}\right)$

or $\qquad\qquad Ee = p\left(1 - \dfrac{2}{m}\right)$ ...(3.9)

Since Ee and p in the above expression are positive numbers, $\left(1 - \dfrac{2}{m}\right)$ must also be positive. This limits $\dfrac{2}{m}$ to a maximum of 1 or the Poisson's ratio $\dfrac{1}{m}$ to 0.5. *No material is known to have a higher value for Poisson's ratio although $\dfrac{1}{m}$ for materials like rubber approaches this value.*

Example 3.1. *A bar of steel has rectangular cross-section 30 mm × 20 mm. Find the dimensions of the sides and percentage decrease of area of cross-section, when it is subjected to a tensile force of 120 kN in the direction of its length. Take $E = 2 \times 10^5 \, N/mm^2$ and $m = 10/3$.*

Solution

Strain in the direction of pull $e_1 = \dfrac{P}{AE} = \dfrac{120 \times 10^3}{30 \times 20 \times 2 \times 10^5} = 10 \times 10^{-4}$

Lateral strain $= -\dfrac{e_1}{m} = -\dfrac{3}{10} \times 10 \times 10^{-4} = 3 \times 10^{-4}$

Hence 30 mm side is decreased by $30 \times 3 \times 10^{-4} = 0.009$ mm

and 20 mm side is decreased by $20 \times 3 \times 10^{-4} = 0.006$ mm

Hence dimension of 30 mm side $= 30 - 0.009 \approx 29.991$ mm

and dimension of 20 mm side $= 20 - 0.006 = 19.994$ mm.

New area of cross-section $= (30 - 0.009)(20 - 0.006) \approx 600 - 0.36$

% decrease of area of cross-section $= \dfrac{0.36}{600} \times 100 = \mathbf{0.06\%}$

Example 3.2. *A steel bar, 300 mm long and 30 mm × 30 mm cross-section, is subjected to a tensile force of 150 kN in the direction of its length. Determine the change in volume, taking $E = 2 \times 10^5 \, N/mm^2$ and $1/m = 0.3$.*

Solution :

Longitudinal strain $e_1 = \dfrac{150 \times 10^3}{30 \times 30 \times 2 \times 10^5} = 8.333 \times 10^{-4}$

∴ Lateral strain $e_2 = e_3 = -\dfrac{1}{m} e_1 = -0.3 \times 8.333 \times 10^{-4} = -2.5 \times 10^{-4}$

Now $\dfrac{\delta V}{V} = e_1 + e_2 + e_3 = [8.333 - 2 \times 2.5] \, 10^{-4} = 3.333 \times 10^{-4}$

$V = 300 \times 30 \times 30 = 270000 \, mm^3 = 27 \times 10^4 \, mm^3$

∴ $\delta V = (27 \times 10^4) \times (3.333 \times 10^{-4}) = \mathbf{90 \, mm^3}$

Example 3.3. *A metal bar, 40 mm × 40 mm section, is subjected to a tensile load of 320 kN. The extension of a 200 mm gauge length is found to be 0.2 mm and the decrease in thickness 0.012 mm. Find the value of Young's modulus and Poisson's ratio.*

Solution :

$A = 40 \times 40 = 1600 \, mm^2 \; ; \; \delta L = 0.2$ mm; $\delta b = 0.012$ mm

Linear strain, $\quad e_1 = \dfrac{\delta L}{L} = \dfrac{0.2}{200} = 10 \times 10^{-4}$

Lateral strain $\quad e_2 = \dfrac{\delta b}{b} = \dfrac{0.012}{40} = 3 \times 10^{-4}$

From Hooke's law, $\quad \delta L = \dfrac{PL}{AE}$

$\therefore \qquad E = \dfrac{PL}{A.\delta L} = \dfrac{320 \times 10^3 \times 200}{40 \times 40 \times 0.2} = 2 \times 10^5 \, \text{N/mm}^2$

Now, $\qquad \dfrac{1}{m} = \dfrac{\text{Lateral strain}}{\text{linear strain}} = \dfrac{e_2}{e_1} = \dfrac{3 \times 10^{-4}}{10 \times 10^{-4}} = 0.3$

Example 3.4. *A steel cube block of 50 mm side is subjected to a force of 10 kN (tension), 12.5 kN (compression) and 7.5 kN (tension) along x, y and z directions respectively. Determine the change in the volume of the block. Take $E = 200\,kN/mm^2$ and $1/m = 0.3$.*

Solution $\qquad$ Area of each side $= 50 \times 50 = 2500 \, \text{mm}^2$

Stress in x direction $= p_x = \dfrac{10 \times 10^3}{2500} = 4 \, \text{N/mm}^2$ (tensile)

Stress in y direction $= p_y = \dfrac{12.5 \times 10^3}{2500}$

$\qquad\qquad\qquad\qquad\qquad = 5 \, \text{N/mm}^2$ (comp.)

Taking tension as positive and compression as negative, we have

$e_x = \dfrac{p_x}{E} + \dfrac{p_y}{mE} - \dfrac{p_z}{mE} = \dfrac{4}{E} + \dfrac{5 \times 0.3}{E} - \dfrac{3 \times 0.3}{E} = \dfrac{4.6}{E}$

$e_y = -\dfrac{p_y}{E} - \dfrac{p_z}{mE} - \dfrac{p_x}{mE} = -\dfrac{5}{E} - \dfrac{3 \times 0.3}{E} - \dfrac{4 \times 0.3}{E} = -\dfrac{7.1}{E}$

$e_z = \dfrac{p_z}{E} - \dfrac{p_x}{mE} + \dfrac{p_y}{mE} = \dfrac{3}{E} - \dfrac{4 \times 0.3}{E} + \dfrac{5 \times 0.3}{E} = \dfrac{3.3}{E}$

Now $\qquad \dfrac{\delta V}{V} = e_x + e_y + e_z$

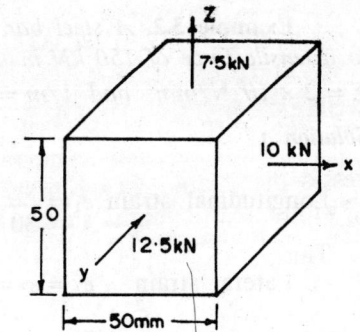

FIG. 3.4

$\therefore \qquad \dfrac{\delta V}{(50)^3} = \dfrac{4.6}{E} - \dfrac{7.1}{E} + \dfrac{3.3}{E} = \dfrac{0.8}{E}$

$\therefore \qquad \delta V = \dfrac{0.8}{2 \times 10^5} \times (50)^3 = \mathbf{0.5 \, mm^3}$

Example 3.5. *The plates of a cylindrical boiler, 1.6 metre diameter and 2.5 m long are subjected to a tensile stress of 70 N/mm^2 in the direction of circumference and tensile stress of*

35 N/mm² in the axial direction. Neglecting the compressive stress due to steam pressure on the inner surface, determine the increase in the internal capacity.

Take $E = 2 \times 10^5$ N/mm² and $1/m = 0.3$.

Solution

Let us use suffix x for axial direction and suffix y for circumferential direction.

$$\therefore \quad e_x = \frac{p_x}{E} - \frac{p_y}{mE} = \frac{35}{E} - \frac{0.3 \times 70}{E} = +\frac{14}{E}$$

and

$$e_y = \frac{p_y}{E} - \frac{p_x}{mE} = \frac{70}{E} - \frac{0.3 \times 35}{E} = +\frac{59.5}{E}$$

Since the diameter of the boiler increases or decreases in direct proportion to its circumference, also denotes the *diametrical strain*. Hence the strains are : $e_1 = +\frac{14}{E}$ parallel to the axis and $e_2 = e_3 = +\frac{59.5}{E}$ along any two perpendicular radii.

$$\therefore \quad \frac{\delta V}{V} = e_1 + e_2 + e_3 = \frac{14}{E} + \frac{59.5}{E} + \frac{59.5}{E} = \frac{133}{E}$$

Now

$$V = \frac{\pi}{4} d^2 L = \frac{\pi}{4} (1.6)^2 \times 2.5 = 5.0265 \text{ m}^3 = 5.0265 \times 10^9 \text{ mm}^3$$

$$\therefore \quad \delta V = \frac{133}{E} \times V = \frac{133}{2 \times 10^5} \times 5.0265 \times 10^9 = 3343 \times 10^3 \text{ mm}^3$$

$$= 3343 \text{ cm}^3 = \textbf{3.343 litres}$$

'. SHEAR MODULUS OR MODULUS OF RIGIDITY

The shear modules or modulus of rigidity (also called the *modulus of transverse elasticity*) presses the relation between shear stress and shear strain. It has been found experimentally t, within elastic limit, shear stress (q) is proportional to the shear strain (φ)

Thus,

$$q \propto \varphi \qquad \qquad \qquad \text{...(3.10 a)}$$

$$q = N\varphi \qquad \qquad \qquad \text{...(3.10 b)}$$

$$\frac{q}{\varphi} = N \qquad \qquad \qquad \text{...(3.10)}$$

e N = modulus of rigidity

(also sometimes denoted by symbol C or G)

φ = Shear strain (in radians)

(also sometimes denoted by the symbol γ)

Table 3.3 gives the values of *modulus of rigidity* for some common engineering materials.

TABLE 3.3. VALUES OF MODULUS OF RIGIDITY

S.No	Material	Modulus of Rigidity N (kN/mm^2 or GPa)
1.	Aluminium (Pure)	26
2.	Aluminium alloys	26 – 30
3.	Brass	36 – 41
4.	Bronze	36 – 44
5.	Cast iron	32 – 69
6.	Copper (Pure)	40 – 47
7.	Rubber	0.0002 – 0.001
8.	Steel	75 – 80
9.	Wrought iron	75

3.8. COMPLIMENTARY SHEAR STRESS

Fig. 3.5 (*a*) shows an infinitely small block *ABCD*, under shear stress intensity q. Such a state of shear will have a tendency to rotate the block in the clockwise direction. Since there is no other force acting on the block, there will be no equilibrium. The block can, however, attain equilibrium only if a couple is applied in such a way that it has the tendency to rotate the block in the counter-clockwise direction. This can be achieved by having a shear stress intensity q' on faces *AD* and *BC* in the direction shown in Fig. 3.5 (*b*). Considering unit thickness of the block perpendicular to the Fig., we have

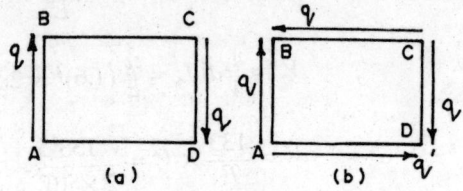

FIG. 3.5

Moment of given couple = Force × lever arm $= (q . AB) AD$

Moment of balancing couple $= (q' . AD) AB$.

Equating the two to attain equilibrium, we have

$$(q' AD) AB = (q . AB) AD.$$

From which $q' = q$ ...(3.11)

The stress q' is known as the *complimentary shear stress* and consequently, we have the following *rule* of complimentary shear stress:

"*A shear stress in a given direction cannot exist without a balancing shear stress of equal intensity in a direction at right angles to it*".

3.9. STATE OF SIMPLE SHEAR

The state of stress indicated in Fig. 3.5 (*b*) is known as the *state of simple shear*, in which no other stresses are acting. In order to study the effect of such a state of simple shear, let us consider a square block under the state of simple shear (Fig. 3.6 *a*).

Let $AB = BC = CD = DA = b$

∴ Length of diagonals $AC = BD = b\sqrt{2}$.
Consider unit thickness of the block, perpendicular to the Fig.

Consider the equilibrium of the triangular portion ABC (Fig. 3.6 b). Resolved sum of q perpendicular to the diagonal

$$= 2\,(q \times b \times 1)\cos 45° = \frac{2qb}{\sqrt{2}} = \sqrt{2}.qb$$

If p is the tensile stress so induced on the diagonal, we have

FIG. 3.6. STATE OF SIMPLE SHEAR

$$p\,(AC \times 1) = \sqrt{2}\,q\,.\,b$$

or

$$p\left(\sqrt{2}\,b\right) = \sqrt{2}\,q\,b$$

From which $\qquad p = q$ (tensile) $\qquad\qquad ...(3.12)$

Resolving the shear stresses q along the diagonal AC, the resultant is zero.

Similarly, it can be shown that the intensity of *compressive stress p* on plane BD is numerically equal to q. Hence we have the following rule :

"A state of simple shear produces pure tensile and compressive stresses across planes inclined at 45° to those of pure shear, and the intensities of these direct stresses are each equal to the intensity of the pure shear stress".

3.10. LINEAR STRAIN OF DIAGONAL DUE TO SHEAR

Fig. 3.7 (a) shows a square block $ABCD$ subjected to a state of simple shear q. Fig. 3.7 (b) shows the resulting distorted shape of the block, wherein the total change in each corner angles is $\pm\left(\dfrac{\varphi}{2} + \dfrac{\varphi}{2}\right) = \pm\,\varphi$. For the purpose of convenience in computations, Fig. 3.7 (c) shows the distorted shape of the block in which the direction of one side

FIG. 3.7. LINEAR STRAIN DUE TO SHEAR

AD has been kept fixed, while keeping the shearing strain φ still the same.

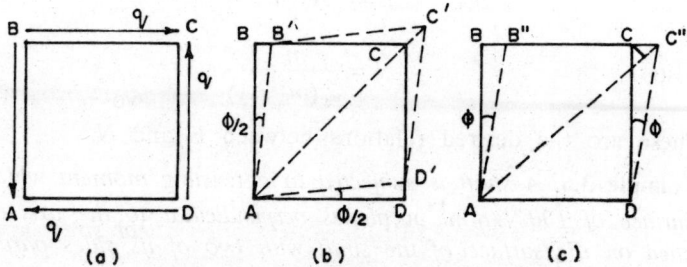

The shearing strain φ is extremely small. Hence we can assume BB'' as an arc with A as centre and AB as radius.

Then $\qquad\qquad \varphi = \dfrac{BB''}{AB} = \dfrac{CC''}{CD} \qquad\qquad ...(i)$

Draw CF perpendicular to AC''. Considering CF also an arc with A as centre and AC as radius, the elongation of diagonal AC can be nearly taken equal to FC''.

$$\therefore \text{ Linear strain } (e) \text{ of diagonal} = \frac{FC''}{AC} = \frac{CC'' \cos 45°}{CD \sec 45°} \qquad ...(ii)$$

$$\therefore \qquad\qquad e = \frac{1}{2}\frac{CC''}{CD} = \frac{1}{2}\varphi = \frac{q}{2N} \qquad ...(3.13)$$

Hence linear strain of the diagonal is equal to half the shear strain φ.

3.11. RELATION BETWEEN E AND N

From Eq. 3.13, we have seen that linear strain of a diagonal is given by

$$e = \frac{1}{2}\varphi = \frac{q}{2N} \qquad ...(i)$$

Also, from § 3.9, we find that state of simple shear produces tensile and compressive stresses along the diagonal planes, and the value of each such direct stress is numerically equal to q. Thus, along diagonal AC (Fig. 3.7 c), there is a tensile stress $p\ (= q)$ and along diagonal BD, there is compressive stress $p\ (= q)$.

Hence, the linear strain e of the diagonal AC, due to two mutually perpendicular direct stresses is given by.

$$e = \frac{p}{E} - \left(-\frac{p}{mE}\right) = \frac{p}{E}\left(1 + \frac{1}{m}\right) = \frac{q}{E}\left(1 + \frac{1}{m}\right) \qquad ...(ii)$$

Equating (i) and (ii), we get

$$\frac{q}{2N} = \frac{q}{E}\left(1 + \frac{1}{m}\right)$$

or $$\qquad\qquad E = 2N\left(1 + \frac{1}{m}\right) \qquad ...(3.14)$$

Also, $$\qquad\qquad N = \frac{mE}{2(m+1)} \qquad ...(3.14\ a)$$

These are the desired relations between E and N.

Example 3.6. *A shaft is subjected to a twisting moment which produces a shearing stress at the surface of $100\,N/mm^2$ in planes perpendicular to the axis of the shaft. A small square is scratched on the surface of the shaft with two of its sides parallel to the axis of the shaft. Find the change in the angle of the corners of the square. Take $N = 80\,N/mm^2$.*

Solution :

Let us assume that limit of proportionality is not exceeded.

$$\therefore \qquad\qquad q = N\varphi$$

or $$\qquad \varphi = \frac{q}{N} = \frac{100}{80 \times 1000} = 1.25 \times 10^{-3} \text{ radian}$$

But 1 radian = 206265 seconds.

$$\therefore \qquad \varphi \text{ (in seconds)} = 1.25 \times 10^{-3} \times 206265 \approx 258''$$

∴   Change in angle $\varphi = 4' \, 18''$

Example 3.7. *A hole is to be punched through a steel plate of 8 mm thickness. Find the least diameter of hole which can be punched, if (i) steel punch can be worked to a compressive stress of 800 N/mm² and (ii) the ultimate shear strength is 300 N/mm².*

Solution :

Let d be the diameter of the hole, t be the thickness of the plate, q be the shear stress and p be the compressive stress.

$$\text{Compressive force exerted} = \frac{\pi}{4} d^2 p \qquad \qquad ...(i)$$

$$\text{Shear force required} = (\pi \, d \, . \, t) \, q \qquad \qquad ...(ii)$$

Equating the two, $\dfrac{\pi}{4} d^2 p = \pi \, d \, t \, q$

∴ $d = \dfrac{4 \, t \, q}{p} = \dfrac{4 \times 8 \times 300}{800} = \mathbf{12 \, mm}$

Example 3.8. *A lever is keyed to a shaft of 100 mm diameter. The width of the key is 12 mm and the length is 50 mm. Find the load that can be applied at a radius of 1.2 m, if the shear stress in the key is not to exceed 100 N/mm².*

Solution :

Let W (in N) be the load, applied at a lever arm of 1.2 m.

∴ Torque (T) produced at the shaft = 1200 W N-mm.

Shear force in the plane AB

$$= \frac{T}{r} = \frac{1200 \, W}{50} = 24 \, W$$

Area of key = 12 × 50 = 600 mm²

Shear stress in key = $\dfrac{24 \, W}{600} = 0.04 \, W$ N/mm².

But this is not to exceed 100 N/mm².

∴   0.04 W = 100

or $W = \dfrac{100}{0.04} = 2500 \, \text{N} = \mathbf{2.5 \, kN}$

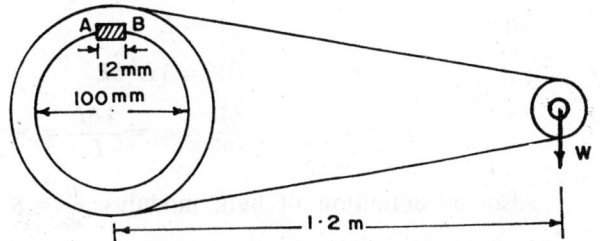

FIG. 3.8

Example 3.9. *A bronze specimen has a modulus of elasticity of 1.1 × 10⁵ N/mm² and modulus of rigidity of 0.41 × 10⁵ N/mm². Determine the Poisson's ratio for the material.*

Solution :

Given : $E = 1.1 \times 10^5$ N/mm² and $N = 0.41 \times 10^5$ N/mm².

From Eq. 3.14, $E = 2N \left(1 + \dfrac{1}{m} \right)$

$\therefore$ $\dfrac{1}{m} = \dfrac{E}{2N} - 1 = \dfrac{1.1 \times 10^5}{2 \times 0.41 \times 10^5} - 1 = \mathbf{0.341}$

3.12. BULK MODULUS

When a body is subjected to three mutually perpendicular like stresses of equal intensity (p), the ratio of direct stress (p) to the corresponding volumetric strain (e_v) is defined as the *bulk modulus K* for the material of the body.

Thus $K = \dfrac{\text{Direct stress}}{\text{Volumetric strain}} = \dfrac{p}{e_v}$ ...(3.15)

3.13. RELATION BETWEEN E AND K

Let a cube of side L be subjected to three mutually perpendicular like compressive stresses of equal intensity q (Fig. 3.9).

Total linear strain of each side $= e = \dfrac{p}{E} - \dfrac{p}{mE} - \dfrac{p}{mE}$

FIG. 3.9

Hence $\dfrac{\delta L}{L} = e = \dfrac{p}{E} \left(1 - \dfrac{2}{m} \right)$ ...(i)

Now $V = L^3$

or $\delta V = 3 L^2 \delta L$

$\therefore$ $\dfrac{\delta V}{V} = e_v = \dfrac{3 \delta L}{L} = 3e = \dfrac{3p}{E} \left(1 - \dfrac{2}{m} \right)$ ...(ii)

Also, by definition of bulk modulus, $\dfrac{p}{e_v} = K$

or $e_v = \dfrac{\delta V}{V} = \dfrac{p}{K}$ ...(iii)

Equating (ii) and (iii)

$\dfrac{p}{K} = \dfrac{3p}{E} \left(1 - \dfrac{2}{m} \right)$

or $E = 3K \left(1 - \dfrac{2}{m} \right)$ ...(3.16)

or $K = \dfrac{mE}{3(m-2)}$ ...(3.16 a)

This is the desired relation between E and K in terms of m.

3.14. RELATION BETWEEN E, N, K AND m

Equating Eq. 3.14 and 3.16

$E = 2N \left(1 + \dfrac{1}{m} \right) = 3K \left(1 - \dfrac{2}{m} \right)$ ...(3.17)

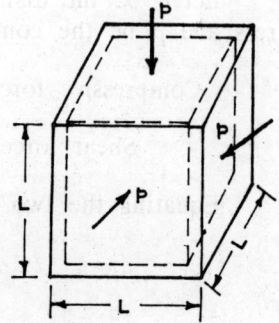

Eliminating E from Eq. 3.17, we get $\dfrac{1}{m} = \dfrac{3K - 2N}{6K + 2N}$ ...(3.18)

Eliminating m from Eq. 3.17, we get $E = \dfrac{9KN}{N + 3K}$ ...(3.19)

Example 3.10. *A bar of 25 mm diameter is subjected to a pull of 40 kN. The measured extension on gauge length of 200 mm is 0.085 mm and the change in diameter is 0.003 mm. Calculate the Poisson's ratio and the values of the three moduli.*

Solution :

$$A = \frac{\pi}{4}(25)^2 = 490.87 \text{ mm}^2.$$

(a) Value of E

Linear strain $\quad e_1 = \dfrac{P}{AE} = \dfrac{40 \times 10^3}{490.87 \times E} = \dfrac{81.49}{E}$ ...(i)

But linear strain $\quad e_1 = \dfrac{\delta L}{L} = \dfrac{0.085}{200} = 4.25 \times 10^{-4}$ ...(ii)

Equating the two, $\quad \dfrac{81.49}{E} = 4.25 \times 10^{-4}$

From which $\quad E = \mathbf{1.917 \times 10^5 \, N/mm^2}$

(b) Value of m

Lateral strain $= e_2 = \dfrac{\delta d}{d} = \dfrac{0.003}{25} = 1.2 \times 10^{-4}$

Now $\quad \dfrac{\text{Lateral strain}}{\text{Longitudinal strain}} = \dfrac{1}{m}$

∴ Poisson's ratio $\quad \dfrac{1}{m} = \dfrac{1.2 \times 10^{-4}}{4.25 \times 10^{-4}} = \dfrac{1}{\mathbf{3.542}}$

or $\quad m = \mathbf{3.542}$

(c) Value of N

Now, from Eq. 3.14 (a), $N = \dfrac{mE}{2(m+1)}$

∴ $\quad N = \dfrac{3.542 \times 1.917 \times 10^5}{2(3.542 + 1)} = \mathbf{0.748 \times 10^5 \, N/mm^2}$

(d) Value of K

From Eq. 3.16 (a), $\quad K = \dfrac{mE}{3(m-2)}$

∴ $\quad K = \dfrac{3.542 \times 1.917 \times 10^5}{3(3.542 - 2)} = \mathbf{1.468 \times 10^5 \, N/mm^2}$

Example 3.11. *Calculate the modulus of rigidity and bulk modulus of a cylindrical bar of diameter 25 mm and of length 1.2 m if the longitudinal strain in a bar during a tensile test is four times the lateral strain. Find the change in volume when the bar is subjected to a hydrostatic pressure of 120 N/mm². Take E = 1.2 × 10⁵ N/mm².*

Solution :

Volume of bar, $V = \dfrac{\pi}{4} d^2 L = \dfrac{\pi}{4} (25)^2 \times 1200 = 589049 \text{ mm}^3$.

(a) Value of m

Given : Longitudinal strain = 4 × Lateral strain.

∴ $\dfrac{1}{m} = \dfrac{\text{lateral strain}}{\text{longitudinal strain}} = \dfrac{1}{4} = 0.25$

and $m = 4$

(b) Value of N

From Eq. 3.14 (a), $N = \dfrac{mE}{2(m+1)} = \dfrac{4 \times 1.2 \times 10^5}{2(4+1)} = \mathbf{0.48 \times 10^5 \text{ N/mm}^2}$

(c) Value of K

From Eq. 3.16 (a), $K = \dfrac{mE}{3(m-2)} = \dfrac{4 \times 1.2 \times 10^5}{3(4-2)} = \mathbf{0.8 \times 10^5 \text{ N/mm}^2}$

(d) Change in volume of bar

By definition $K = \dfrac{p}{e_v}$

∴ $e_v = \dfrac{\delta V}{V} = \dfrac{p}{K} = \dfrac{120}{0.8 \times 10^5}$

Hence $\delta V = \dfrac{120}{0.8 \times 10^5} \times 589049 = \mathbf{884 \text{ mm}^3}$

Example 3.12 (a). *Determine the percentage change in volume of a steel bar 40 mm square in section and 1 m long when subjected to an axial compressive load of 15 kN. (b) What change in volume would a 100 mm cube of steel suffer at a depth of 4 km in sea water ?*

Take E = 2 × 10⁵ N/mm² and N = 0.81 × 10⁵ N/mm².

Solution :

(a) Volume of bar, $V = b^2 . L$

∴ $\dfrac{\delta V}{V} = 2 \dfrac{\delta b}{b} + \dfrac{\delta L}{L} = 2 e_b + e_L$

or $\dfrac{\delta V}{V} = -\dfrac{2p}{mE} + \dfrac{p}{E} = \dfrac{p}{E}\left(1 - \dfrac{2}{m}\right)$ ...(1)

Now, $E = 2N\left(1 + \dfrac{1}{m}\right)$ ...Eq. 3.14

∴ $\dfrac{1}{m} = \dfrac{E}{2N} - 1 = \dfrac{2 \times 10^5}{2 \times 0.81 \times 10^5} - 1 = 0.2346$

or $$m = 4.263$$

Hence from (1), $\frac{\delta V}{V} = \frac{p}{E}(1 - 2 \times 0.2346) = \frac{15000}{1600\,(2 \times 10^5)} \times 0.5309 = 2.488 \times 10^{-5}$

$\therefore$ % reduction in volume $= \frac{\delta V}{V} \times 100 = 2.488 \times 10^{-5} \times 100 = \mathbf{0.00249}$

(b) On the cube, $p = wh$

Here, $w = 10080\ \text{N/mm}^3$ (for sea water) and $h = 4\ \text{km} = 4000\ \text{m}$.

$\therefore$ $$p = 10080 \times 4000 = 40.32 \times 10^6\ \text{N/m}^2 = 40.32\ \text{N/mm}^2.$$

Now, from Eq. 3.16 (a) $K = \frac{mE}{3\,(m-2)} = \frac{4.263 \times 2 \times 10^5}{3\,(4.263 - 2)} = 1.256 \times 10^5\ \text{N/mm}^2$

Now $$e_v = \frac{\delta V}{V} = \frac{p}{K} \quad \text{(by definition)}$$

$\therefore$ $$\delta V = \frac{p}{K} \times V = \frac{40.32}{1.256 \times 10^5} \times (100)^3 = \mathbf{321\ mm^3}$$

Example 3.13. *The modulus of rigidity for a material is $0.5 \times 10^5\ N/mm^2$. A 12 mm diameter rod of the material was subjected to an axial pull of 14 kN and the change in diameter was observed to be 3.6×10^{-3} mm. Calculate Poisson's ratio and the modulus of elasticity.*

Solution :

$$A = \frac{\pi}{4}(12)^2 = 113.1\ \text{mm}^2$$

$$p = \frac{14 \times 10^3}{113.1} = 123.79\ \text{N/mm}^2$$

Now, lateral strain $= \frac{\delta d}{d} = \frac{3.6 \times 10^{-3}}{12} = 3 \times 10^{-4}$

But lateral strain $= \frac{p}{mE}$

$\therefore$ $$\frac{p}{mE} = 3 \times 10^{-4}$$

or $$mE = \frac{p}{3 \times 10^{-4}} = \frac{123.79}{3 \times 10^{-4}} = 41.26 \times 10^4 \qquad ...(i)$$

Now $$E = 2N\left(1 + \frac{1}{m}\right)$$

or $$mE = 2N\,(m + 1)$$

or $$41.26 \times 10^4 = 2 \times 0.5 \times 10^5\,(m + 1)$$

From which $$m = 3.126 \text{ and } \frac{1}{m} \approx \mathbf{0.32}$$

$$\therefore \qquad E = \frac{41.26 \times 10^4}{m} = \frac{41.26 \times 10^4}{3.126} = \textbf{1.32} \times \textbf{10}^5 \, \textbf{N/mm}^2$$

Also, $\qquad K = \dfrac{E}{3\left(1 - \dfrac{2}{m}\right)} = \dfrac{1.32 \times 10^5}{3\left(1 - \dfrac{2}{3.126}\right)} = \textbf{1.22} \times \textbf{10}^5 \, \textbf{N/mm}^2$

Alternatively, from Eq. 3.17, $\qquad K = \dfrac{2N\left(1 + \dfrac{1}{m}\right)}{3\left(1 - \dfrac{2}{m}\right)} = \dfrac{2 \times 0.5 \times 10^5 (1 + 0.32)}{3\,(1 - 2 \times 0.32)}$

$$= 1.22 \times 10^5 \, \text{N/mm}^2$$

Example 3.14. *A rectangular block* $250 \, mm \times 100 \, mm \times 80 \, mm$ *is subjected to axial loads as follows :*

480 kN tensile in the direction of its length,

1000 kN compressive on the 250 mm × 100 mm faces, *and*

900 kN tensile on 250 × 80 mm faces.

Assuming Poisson's ratio as 0.25, find in terms of modulus of elasticity of the material E, the strains in the direction of each force.

If $E = 2 \times 10^5 \, N/mm^2$, *find the values of the modulus of rigidity and bulk modulus for the material of the block. Also, calculate the change in volume of the block due to loading specified above.*

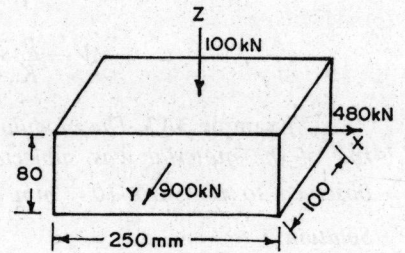

FIG. 3.10

(Based on Cambridge University)

Solution :

Volume $V = 250 \times 100 \times 80 = 2 \times 10^6 \, \text{mm}^3 \, ; \dfrac{1}{m} = 0.25 \, ; \, m = 4$

(a) Strains in each direction

Stress in x-direction, $\qquad p_x = \dfrac{P_x}{A_x} = \dfrac{480 \times 10^3}{100 \times 80} = 60 \, \text{N/mm}^2$ (tension)

Stress in y-direction, $\qquad p_y = \dfrac{P_y}{A_y} = \dfrac{900 \times 10^3}{250 \times 80} = 45 \, \text{N/mm}^2$ (tension)

Stress in z-direction, $\qquad p_z = \dfrac{P_z}{A_z} = \dfrac{1000 \times 10^3}{250 \times 100} = 40 \, \text{N/mm}^2$ (comp.)

Taking tension as +ve and compression as negative, we have

$$e_x = \frac{p_x}{E} - \frac{p_y}{mE} + \frac{p_z}{mE} = \frac{60}{E} - \frac{45}{4E} + \frac{40}{4E} = \frac{\textbf{58.75}}{E}$$

$$= \frac{58.75}{2 \times 10^5} = \textbf{2.9375} \times \textbf{10}^{-4}$$

$$e_y = \frac{p_y}{E} + \frac{p_z}{mE} - \frac{p_x}{mE} = \frac{45}{E} + \frac{40}{4E} - \frac{60}{4E} = \frac{40}{E}$$

$$= \frac{40}{2 \times 10^5} = 2 \times 10^{-4}$$

and $$e_z = -\frac{p_z}{E} - \frac{p_x}{mE} - \frac{p_y}{mE} = -\frac{40}{E} - \frac{60}{4E} - \frac{45}{4E} = -\frac{66.25}{E}$$

$$= -\frac{66.25}{2 \times 10^5} = -3.3125 \times 10^{-4}$$

(b) Change in volume

$$\frac{\delta V}{V} = e_x + e_y + e_z = 2.9375 \times 10^{-4} + 2 \times 10^{-4} - 3.3125 \times 10^{-4} = 1.625 \times 10^{-4}$$

$$\therefore \qquad \delta V = 1.625 \times 10^{-4} \times (2 \times 10^6) = 325 \text{ mm}^3$$

(c) Modulus of rigidity

$$N = \frac{mE}{2(m+1)} = \frac{4 \times 2 \times 10^5}{2(4+1)} = 0.8 \times 10^5 \text{ N/mm}^2$$

(d) Bulk Modulus

$$K = \frac{mE}{3(m-2)} = \frac{4 \times 2 \times 10^5}{3(4-2)} = 1.333 \times 10^5 \text{ N/mm}^2$$

Example 3.15. *A metallic bar 250 mm × 100 mm × 50 mm is loaded as shown in Fig. 3.11.*

Find the change in volume. Take E = 200 kN/mm² and Poisson's ratio = 0.25. Also find the change that should be made in the 4000 kN load, in order that there should be no change in the volume of the bar. *(Based in U.L.)*

Solution :

$$V = 250 \times 100 \times 50 = 1250 \times 10^3 \text{ mm}^3;$$

$$\frac{1}{m} = 0.25 \, ; m = 4$$

(a) Change in volume

$$p_x = \frac{P_x}{A_x} = \frac{400 \times 10^3}{100 \times 50} = 80 \text{ N/mm}^2 \text{ (tension)}$$

$$p_y = \frac{P_y}{A_y} = \frac{2000 \times 10^3}{250 \times 50} = 160 \text{ N/mm}^2 \text{ (tension)}$$

$$p_z = \frac{P_z}{A_z} = \frac{4000 \times 10^3}{250 \times 100} = 160 \text{ N/mm}^2 \text{ (comp.)}$$

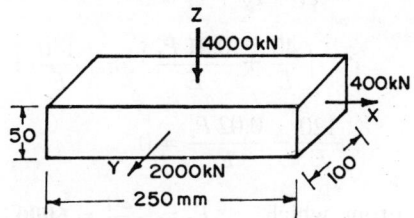

FIG. 3.11

Considering tension as positive and compression as negative, we have

$$e_x = \frac{p_x}{E} - \frac{p_y}{mE} + \frac{p_z}{mE} = \frac{80}{E} - \frac{160}{4E} + \frac{160}{4E} = \frac{80}{E}$$

$$e_y = \frac{p_y}{E} + \frac{p_z}{mE} - \frac{p_x}{mE} = \frac{160}{E} + \frac{160}{4E} - \frac{80}{4E} = \frac{180}{E}$$

$$e_z = -\frac{p_z}{E} - \frac{p_x}{mE} - \frac{p_y}{mE} = -\frac{160}{E} - \frac{80}{4E} - \frac{160}{4E} = -\frac{220}{E}$$

Now

$$\frac{\delta V}{V} = e_x + e_y + e_z = \frac{80}{E} + \frac{180}{E} - \frac{220}{E} = \frac{40}{E}$$

∴

$$\delta V = \frac{40}{E} \times V = \frac{40}{200 \times 1000} \times 1250 \times 10^3 = \textbf{250 mm}^3$$

(b) Change in 4000 kN load

Let P_z kN be the load, in place of 4000 kN load.

∴

$$p_z = \frac{P_z \times 10^3}{250 \times 100} = 0.04\, P_z \, \text{N/mm}^2 \text{ (comp.)}$$

Hence

$$e_x = \frac{p_x}{E} - \frac{p_y}{mE} + \frac{p_z}{mE} = \frac{80}{E} - \frac{160}{4E} + \frac{0.04\, P_z}{4E} = \frac{40}{E} + \frac{0.01\, P_z}{E}$$

$$e_y = \frac{p_y}{E} + \frac{p_z}{mE} - \frac{p_x}{mE} = \frac{160}{E} + \frac{0.04\, P_z}{4E} - \frac{80}{4E} = \frac{140}{E} + \frac{0.01\, P_z}{E}$$

and

$$e_z = -\frac{p_z}{E} - \frac{p_x}{mE} - \frac{p_y}{mE} = -\frac{0.04\, P_z}{E} - \frac{80}{4E} - \frac{160}{4E} = -\frac{0.04\, P_z}{E} - \frac{60}{E}$$

In order that $\dfrac{\delta V}{V} = e_x + e_y + e_z$ should be equal to zero, we have

$$e_x + e_y + e_z = 0$$

∴

$$\left(\frac{40}{E} + \frac{0.01\, P_z}{E}\right) + \left(\frac{140}{E} + \frac{0.01\, P_z}{E}\right) - \left(\frac{0.04\, P_z}{E} + \frac{60}{E}\right) = 0$$

or

$$\frac{120}{E} - \frac{0.02\, P_z}{E} = 0$$

From which

$$P_z = \frac{120}{0.02} = \textbf{6000 kN}$$

Hence P_z should be increased from its present value of 4000 kN to a new value of 6000 kN, in order that volumetric strain is zero.

Example 3.16. *A bar of steel is 40 mm in diameter and 500 mm long. A tensile load of 120 kN is found to stretch the bar by 0.24 mm. The same bar, when subjected to a torque of 1.3 kN-m is found to twist through 1.92°. Find the values of the four elastic constants.*

Solution :

(a) Value of E

As a bar, $\Delta = \dfrac{PL}{AE} = \dfrac{4\,PL}{\pi\,d^2\,E}$

$\therefore$ $E = \dfrac{4\,PL}{\pi\,d^2\,\Delta} = \dfrac{4 \times 120 \times 10^3 \times 500}{\pi\,(40)^2 \times 0.24} = \mathbf{1.989 \times 10^5\ N/mm^2}$

(b) Value of N

As a shaft, $N = \dfrac{TL}{J\theta} = \dfrac{32\,TL}{\pi\,d^4\,\theta}$

where $\theta = \dfrac{\pi}{180} \times 1.92 = 0.0335$ radian, and $T = 1.3$ kN-m $= 1.3 \times 10^6$ N-mm

$\therefore$ $N = \dfrac{32 \times 1.3 \times 10^6 \times 500}{\pi\,(40)^4 \times 0.0335} = \mathbf{0.772 \times 10^5\ N/mm^2}$

(c) Value of $\dfrac{1}{m}$

Again $E = 2N\left(1 + \dfrac{1}{m}\right)$

$\therefore$ $\dfrac{1}{m} = \dfrac{E}{2N} - 1 = \dfrac{1.989 \times 10^5}{2 \times 0.772 \times 10^5} - 1 = \mathbf{0.288}$

(d) Value of K

$K = \dfrac{E}{3\left(1 - \dfrac{2}{m}\right)} = \dfrac{1.989 \times 10^5}{3\,(1 - 2 \times 0.288)} = \mathbf{1.565 \times 10^5\ N/mm^2}$

3.15. ADDITIONAL ILLUSTRATIVE EXAMPLES*

Some additional illustrative examples of advanced nature extremely useful for *competitive examinations* are given here with short solutions.

Example 3.17. *A bar is stretched in such a manner that all the lateral strain is prevented. Determine the modified value of modulus of elasticity and modified value of Poisson's ratio in terms of original values of E and μ respectively.*

Solution :

Let p_1 be the applied axial stress. In order to have e_2 and e_3 zero, corresponding stresses p_2 and p_3, each of the same sign as that of p_1, will be induced is the two lateral directions.

Hence $e_1 = \dfrac{p_1}{E} - \dfrac{\mu}{E}\left(p_2 + p_3\right)$ ...(i)

$e_2 = \dfrac{p_2}{E} - \dfrac{\mu}{E}\left(p_3 + p_1\right) = 0$ ...(ii) and $\qquad e_3 = \dfrac{p_3}{E} - \dfrac{\mu}{E}\left(p_1 + p_2\right) = 0$ $\qquad\qquad\qquad\qquad$ ...(iii)

Adding (ii) and (iii), $p_2 + p_3 = 2\,p_1\dfrac{\mu}{1-\mu}$

Substituting in (i), we get

$$e_1 = \frac{p_1}{E} - \frac{\mu}{E}\cdot\frac{2\,p_1\mu}{1-\mu} = \frac{p_1}{E}\left(1 - \frac{2\mu^2}{1-\mu}\right)$$

$$= \frac{p_1}{E}\left(\frac{1-\mu-2\mu^2}{1-\mu}\right) = \frac{p_1}{E}\,\frac{(1+\mu)\,(1-2\mu)}{1-\mu}$$

$\therefore$ Modified modulus, $E' = \dfrac{p_1}{e_1} = \dfrac{E\,(1-\mu)}{(1+\mu)\,(1-2\mu)}$

Also, modified Poisson's ratio, $\mu' = \dfrac{e_3}{e_1} = \mathbf{0}$

Example 3.18. *A bar of rectangular section is subjected to an axial stress of p_1. No constraint is exerted on one pair of sides but on the other, external pressure restrict the lateral strain to one-half of what it would be if there were no restraint. Determine the modified value of modulus of elasticity.*

Solution :

Let us represent axial direction by suffix 1 and the two lateral directions by suffix 2 and 3. Let stress p_3, of the same sign as that of p_1, be the induced stress in the direction of restraint. Here p_2 will be zero since there is no restraint in the second direction.

Hence $\qquad\qquad\qquad\qquad e_1 = \dfrac{p_1}{E} - \dfrac{\mu}{E}p_3$ $\qquad\qquad\qquad\qquad$ ...(i)

$$e_2 = -\frac{\mu}{E}\left(p_1 + p_3\right) \qquad\qquad\qquad\qquad \text{...(ii)}$$

$$e_3 = \frac{p_3}{E} - \frac{\mu}{E}p_1 \qquad\qquad\qquad\qquad \text{...(iii)}$$

If there were no restraint in the third direction, $e_3{}' = -\dfrac{\mu}{E}p_1$

As per given condition, $\qquad\qquad e_3 = \dfrac{1}{2}e_3{}'$

Hence $\qquad\qquad\qquad \dfrac{p_3}{E} - \dfrac{\mu}{E}p_1 = -\dfrac{1}{2}\dfrac{\mu}{E}p_1$

From which $\qquad\qquad\qquad p_3 = \dfrac{1}{2}\mu\,p_1$

Substituting in (i), we get $e_1 = \dfrac{p_1}{E} - \dfrac{\mu}{E}\left(\dfrac{1}{2}\mu\,p_1\right) = \dfrac{p_1}{E}\left(1 - \dfrac{\mu^2}{2}\right) = \dfrac{p_1}{2E}\left(2 - \mu^2\right)$

$\therefore$ Modified modulus of elasticity, $E' = \dfrac{p_1}{e_1} = \dfrac{2E}{2-\mu^2}$

Example 3.19. *If two pieces of materials A and B have the same bulk modulus, but the value of E for B is 1% greater than that for A, find the value of N for the material B in terms of E and N for material A.*

Solution :

Given $\qquad K_A = K_B = K; \ E_B = 1.01 \, E_A$

From Eq. 3.19, we have $E = \dfrac{9 \, KN}{N + 3 \, K}$

or $\qquad EN + 3 \, EK = 9 \, KN$

or $\qquad 3 \, K \, (3 \, N - E) = EN,$ from which $K = \dfrac{E \, N}{3 \, (3 \, N - E)}$

Hence $\qquad \dfrac{E_A \, N_A}{3 \, (3 \, N_A - E_A)} = K = \dfrac{E_B \, N_B}{3 \, (3 \, N_B - E_B)}$

$\therefore \qquad E_A \, N_A \, (3 \, N_B - E_B) = E_B \, N_B \, (3 \, N_A - E_A)$

or $\qquad 3 \, E_A \, N_A \, N_B - E_A \, N_A \, E_B = 3 \, E_B \, N_B \, N_A - E_A \, E_B \, N_B$

or $\ N_B \, (\, 3 \, E_A \, N_A - 3 \, E_B \, N_A + E_A \, E_B) = E_A \, N_A \, E_B$

From which $\qquad N_B = \dfrac{E_A \, N_A \, E_B}{3 \, E_A \, N_A - 3 \, E_B \, N_A + E_A \, E_B} = \dfrac{1.01 \, E_A \, N_A \, E_A}{3 \, E_A \, N_A - 3 \times 1.01 \, E_A \, N_A + 1.01 \, E_A.E_A}$

or $\qquad N_B = \dfrac{1.01 \, E_A \, N_A}{1.01 \, E_A - 3 \, (1.01 - 1) \, N_A} = \dfrac{101 \, E_A \, N_A}{101 \, E_A - 3 \, N_A}$

Example 3.20. *Show that if E is assumed to be correct, an error of 1.5% in the determination of N will involve an error of about 6.5% in the calculation of Poisson's ratio when its correct value is 0.3.*

Solution :

Let E, N and μ be the correct values of the constants and μ' be the calculated value of Poisson's ratio.

From Eq. 3.14 $\qquad E = 2 \, N \, (1 + \mu)$ $\qquad\qquad$ ...(i)

If, due to an error of 1.5%, N is increased to 1.015 N, the calculated value μ' of Poisson's ratio is given by

$$E = 2 \times 1.015 \, N \, (1 + \mu') \qquad\qquad ...(ii)$$

Equating (i) and (ii), $2 \, N \, (1 + \mu) = 2 \times 1.015 \, N \, (1 + \mu')$

or $\qquad 1 + \mu = 1.015 + 1.015 \, \mu'$

or $\qquad \mu' - \mu = - 0.015 - 0.015 \, \mu' \ = - 0.015 \, (1 + \mu')$

Hence % error is μ is

$$\dfrac{\mu' - \mu}{\mu} \times 100 = - 0.015 \, \dfrac{1 + \mu'}{\mu} \times 100 \approx - 1.5 \, \dfrac{1 + \mu}{\mu}$$

(Taking $\mu' \approx \mu$)

$$\therefore \quad \frac{\mu' - \mu}{\mu} \times 100 \approx -1.5 \left(\frac{1 + 0.3}{0.3} \right) \approx -6.5\%$$

Alternative Solution :

$$E = 2N(1 + \mu)$$

Differentiating partially and noting that $\delta E = 0$ since E does not vary,

$$\delta E = 0 = 2\,\delta N(1 + \mu) + 2N\delta\mu$$

or

$$\delta\mu = -\frac{\delta N}{N}(1 + \mu)$$

$$\therefore \quad \% \text{ error} = \frac{\delta\mu}{\mu} \times 100 = -\frac{\delta N}{N} \cdot \frac{1 + \mu}{\mu} \times 100$$

$$= -\frac{1.5}{100} \times \frac{1 + 0.3}{0.3} \times 100 = -6.5\%$$

Example 3.21. *The values of E and N, determined experimentally were found to be $1.9 \times 10^5 \, N/mm^2$ and $0.75 \times 10^5 \, N/mm^2$. Calculate Poisson's ratio and the bulk modulus. If both the moduli are liable for an error of ± 1 percent, find the maximum percentage error in the derived value of Poisson's ratio.*

Solution :

We have $\qquad E = 2N(1 + \mu)$

From which $\qquad \mu = \dfrac{E}{2N} - 1 = \dfrac{1.9 \times 10^5}{2 \times 0.75 \times 10^5} - 1 = 0.267$

Also, $\qquad K = \dfrac{E}{3(1 - 2\mu)} = \dfrac{1.9 \times 10^5}{3(1 - 2 \times 0.267)} = 1.357 \times 10^5 \, N/mm^2$

For maximum percentage error in the derived value of μ, the error in the values of E and N should be of different sign. Let $\%$ error in E be $+1$ and that in N be -1.

Now $\qquad \mu = \dfrac{E}{2N} - 1$

Hence $\qquad \mu' = \dfrac{E'}{2N'} - 1,$

where $\quad E' = $ incorrect value of $E = (1.9 \times 10^5) \times 1.01$

$\qquad N' = $ incorrect value of $N = (0.75 \times 10^5) \times 0.99$

and $\qquad \mu' = $ computed incorrect value of μ.

$$\therefore \quad \mu' = \frac{1.9 \times 10^5 \times 1.01}{2(0.75 \times 10^5 \times 0.99)} - 1 = 0.2923$$

$$\therefore \quad \% \text{ error in } \mu = \frac{\mu' - \mu}{\mu} \times 100 = \frac{0.2923 - 0.267}{0.267} \times 100 = 9.46\%$$

Example 3.22. *A bar of elastic material is subjected to a direct compressive stress of p_1 in the longitudinal direction. Suitable lateral compressive stress p_2 is applied along the other two lateral directions to limit the net strain in each of the lateral directions to one third the magnitude that could be under p_1 acting alone. Find the magnitude of p_2 and the net strain in the longitudinal direction.*

Solution : When p_2 is applied along the two lateral directions,

$$e_2' = e_3' = \frac{p_2}{E} - \frac{\mu p_2}{E} - \frac{\mu p_1}{E}$$

However, if p_2 is not applied,

$$e_2 = -\frac{\mu p_1}{E}$$

$\therefore \qquad \dfrac{p_2}{E} - \dfrac{\mu p_2}{E} - \dfrac{\mu p_1}{E} = -\dfrac{1}{3}\dfrac{\mu p_1}{E}$

Hence $\qquad\qquad p_2 = \dfrac{2}{3}\dfrac{\mu}{1-\mu}p_1$ **(Ans.)**

Net strain in the longitudinal direction :

$$e_1' = \frac{p_1}{E} - \frac{\mu p_2}{E} - \frac{\mu p_2}{E} = \frac{p_1}{E}\left[1 - 2\mu \times \frac{2}{3}\frac{\mu}{1-\mu}\right]$$

or $\qquad\qquad e_1' = \dfrac{p_1}{E}\left[\dfrac{3 - 3\mu - 4\mu^2}{3(1-\mu)}\right]$ compressive.

Substituting $\qquad\qquad \mu = \dfrac{1}{m}$, the above expression reduces to

$$e_1' = \frac{p_1}{E}\left[\frac{3m^2 - 3m - 4}{3m(m-1)}\right]$$

Example 3.23. *A vertical rod of length L and diameter d is fixed at its upper end and carries a load W at its lower end. The extension of the rod due to W is δ. If a torque T_1, applied in a horizontal plane at the lower end of the rod, gives an angle of twist θ radians, show that Poisson's ratio is given by*

$$\mu = \left(\frac{W d^2 \theta}{16 \times T\delta} - 1\right)$$

Solution :

As a vertical rod under the action of W, the extension δ is given by

$$\delta = \frac{WL}{AE} = \frac{WL}{\frac{\pi}{4}d^2 E} = \frac{4WL}{\pi d^2 E}$$

or $\qquad\qquad E = \dfrac{4WL}{\pi d^2 \delta}$ \qquad\qquad\qquad ...(i)

As a shaft under the action of torque T, we have

$$\frac{T}{J} = \frac{N\theta}{L}$$

or $$N = \frac{TL}{J\theta} = \frac{TL}{\frac{\pi}{32}d^4\theta} = \frac{32\,TL}{\pi d^4\theta} \qquad \qquad ...(2)$$

$$\text{(where } J = \text{Polar moment of inertia} = \frac{\pi d^4}{32})$$

Now $$E = 2N(1+\mu)$$

From which $$1+\mu = \frac{E}{2N} = \frac{4\,WL}{\pi d^2 \delta}\cdot\frac{1}{2}\times\frac{\pi d^4\theta}{32\,TL} = \frac{Wd^2\theta}{16\,T\delta}$$

Hence $$\mu = \left(\frac{Wd^2\theta}{16\,T\delta} - 1\right)$$

Example 3.24. *A square frame ABCD consisting of five steel bars of 400 mm² cross-sectional area is subjected to the action of two forces P = 40 kN in the direction of the diagonal, as shown in Fig. 3.12. Determine the changes of the angles at A and C due to the deformation of the frame. Take E = 2 × 10⁵ N/mm².*

Solution :

Since loads P are applied at pin joints D and B, the diagonal DB will take *completely* these loads.

Assuming hinges D and the direction of diagonal DB as fixed, point B will move to point B_1 through a distance δ given by

$\delta = \dfrac{PL}{AE}$, where L is the length and A is the area of DB.

Due to the distortion of the frame, hinge C will move to its new position C_1. Draw C_1C' and CC' parallel to DC and DB respectively. The small triangle CC_1C' is right angled at C_1, wherein $CC_1 = \dfrac{\delta}{\sqrt{2}}$. The angle of rotation of the bar DC due to the deformation of the frame is

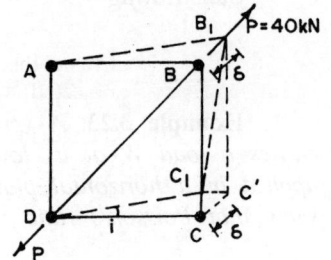

FIG. 3.12

$$i = \frac{CC_1}{DC} = \frac{\delta}{\sqrt{2}} \div \frac{L}{\sqrt{2}} = \frac{\delta}{L}$$

Substituting the value of δ, we get

$$i = \frac{PL}{AE}\cdot\frac{1}{L} = \frac{P}{AE} = \frac{40\times10^3}{400\times2\times10^5} = \frac{1}{2000} \text{ radian.}$$

Hence increase in the angle at C (or decrease in angle at A) will be

$$= 2\times\frac{1}{2000} = \frac{1}{1000} \text{ radian}$$

Example 3.25. *A rectangular parallelopiped is subjected to tension in two perpendicular directions as shown in Fig. 3.13. Find the unit elongation ε in direction OĊ.*

Solution :

Let a and b be the co-ordinates of point C. If ε_x and ε_y are the *unit elongations* in x and y directions, these co-ordinates of C, after deformation will be $a(1 + \varepsilon_x)$ and $b(1 + \varepsilon_y)$. Hence the length (L) of OC will become equal to L' after deformation, the value of which is given by

$$L' = \sqrt{a^2(1 + \varepsilon_x)^2 + b^2(1 + \varepsilon_y)^2} \approx \sqrt{a^2(1 + 2\varepsilon_x) + b^2(1 + 2\varepsilon_y)}$$

$$\approx \sqrt{a^2 + b^2}\left(1 + \frac{a^2\varepsilon_x}{a^2 + b^2} + \frac{b^2\varepsilon_y}{a^2 + b^2}\right)$$

Initial length $\qquad L = \sqrt{a^2 + b^2}$

Unit elongation $\quad \dfrac{L' - L}{L} = \varepsilon = \dfrac{a^2\varepsilon_x}{a^2 + b^2} + \dfrac{b^2\varepsilon_y}{a^2 + b^2}$

But $\qquad \dfrac{a^2}{a^2 + b^2} = \cos^2\alpha \ \text{ and } \ \dfrac{b^2}{a^2 + b^2} = \sin^2\alpha$

$\therefore \qquad\qquad \varepsilon = \varepsilon_x\cos^2\alpha + \varepsilon_y\sin^2\alpha$

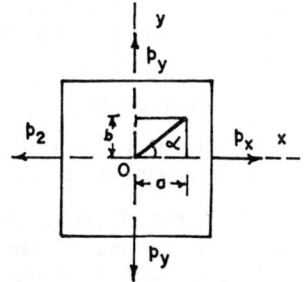

FIG. 3.13

PROBLEMS

1. (a) Determine the percentage change in volume of a steel bar 50 mm square in section and 1 m long when subjected to an axial compressive load of 20 kN.

(b) What change in volume would a 100 mm cube of steel suffer at a depth of 5 km in sea water ?

Take $E = 2.05 \times 10^5$ N/mm^2 and $N = 0.82 \times 10^5$ N/mm^2.

2. A bar 30 mm in diameter was subjected to a tensile load if 54 kN and the measured extension on 300 mm gauge length was 0.112 mm and change in diameter was 0.00366 mm. Calculate Poisson's ratio and values of three moduli.

3. For a given material, Young's modulus is 1.0×10^5 N/mm^2 and modulus of rigidity 0.4×10^5 N/mm^2. Find the bulk modulus and lateral contraction of a round bar of 50 mm diameter and 2.5 m long, when stretched 2.5 mm. Take Poisson's ratio as $\dfrac{1}{4}$.

4. A rectangular bar is subjected to axial stresses p_1, p_2 and p_3 on its sides. Show that the volumetric strain

$$\frac{\delta V}{V} = \left(p_1 + p_2 + p_3\right) \times \frac{1}{E}\left(1 - \frac{2}{m}\right)$$

5. A metal specimen is compressed in the direction of its axis and means are employed to reduce lateral expansion to one third of what it would be if free to expand. Calculate the modified value of the elastic constant. Prove that its value will be $\dfrac{9}{8}E$ if $m=4$.

6. Tensile stresses f_1 and f_2 act at right angles to one another on an element of isotropic elastic material. The strain in the direction of f_1 is twice that in the direction of f_2. Find the value of the ratio $\dfrac{f_1}{f_2}$. If E for the material is $120 \, kN/mm^2$ and $\mu = 0.3$, find the value of $\dfrac{f_1}{f_2}$.

7. A bar of elastic material is subjected to direct stress in a longitudinal direction, and its strains in the two directions at right angles are reduced to one-half and one-third respectively to those which normally occur in an ordinary tension member. Find the value of modified elastic constant. If $E = 200 \, kN/mm^2$ and $m = 4$, what is the value of the elastic constant ?

8. A determination of E and N gives values of $2 \times 10^5 \, N/mm^2$ and $0.79 \times 10^5 \, N/mm^2$. Calculate Poisson's ratio and the bulk modulus.

If both moduli are liable to an error of $\pm 2 \%$, find the maximum percentage error in the derived value of Poisson's value.

9. Show that if E is assumed to be correct, an error of 1% in the determination of N will involve an error of about 5% in the calculation of Poisson's ratio when its correct value is 0.25.

10. A bar of steel is 38 mm in diameter and 450 mm long. A tensile load of 100 kN is found to stretch the bar by 0.20 mm. The same bar, when subjected to a torque of 1.24 kN-m is found to twist through 1.982°. Find the values of the four elastic constants.

11. A bar of elastic material is subjected to a direct compressive stress of p_1 in the longitudinal direction. Suitable lateral compressive stress p_2 is applied along the other two lateral directions to limit the net strain in each of the lateral directions to half the magnitude that could be under p_1 acting alone. Find the magnitude of p_2 and the net strain in the longitudinal direction.

12. Derive the relationship between modulus of elasticity, modulus of rigidity and Poisson's ratio of an elastic body. A bronze specimen has a modulus of elasticity of $120 \, kN/mm^2$ and a modulus of rigidity of $47 \, kN/mm^2$. Determine Poisson's ratio of the material.

ANSWERS

1. (a) 0.00195 (b) 369 mm^3
2. 0.327 ; $E = 2.046 \times 10^5 \, N/mm^2$; $N = 0.771 \times 10^5 \, N/mm^2$; $K = 1.971 \times 10^5 \, N/mm^2$
3. $0.667 \times 10^5 \, N/mm^2$; 0.125 mm
5. $\dfrac{3m\,(m-1)}{3m^2 - 3m - 4} E$

6. $\dfrac{2+\mu}{1+2\mu}$; 1.438

7. $\dfrac{6m\,(m^2-1)}{6m^3 - 13m - 7} E$; 221.54 kN/mm^2

8. 0.266 ; $1.423 \times 10^5 \, N/mm^2$; 19.44%
10. $E = 1.984 \times 10^5 \, N/mm^2$; $N = 0.788 \times 10^5 \, N/mm^2$
    $\mu = 0.259$; $K = 1.372 \times 10^5 \, N/mm^2$

11. $\dfrac{1}{2}\left(\dfrac{\mu}{1-\mu}\right) p_1$; $\dfrac{p_1}{E}\left(\dfrac{1-\mu-\mu^2}{1-\mu}\right)$

12. 0.277

Analysis of Stress : Principal Stresses

4.1. INTRODUCTION

In Chapter 2, we have considered only the normal stresses acting on cross-sections, such as on cross-section mn of a bar AB (Fig 4.1a) when the bar is subjected to either a tensile force or a compressive force acting along the axis of the bar. In this chapter, we shall analyse the stresses induced on inclined sections such as section pq (Fig 4.1a). In actual practice, all the three types of stresses (*i.e.* tension, compression and shear) may act simultaneously on appropriate planes passing through a point in the strained material. We shall therefore, analyse such a general stress system (Fig 4.1b) and find the *resultant stress* on *critical inclined planes* which may carry greater stresses than the applied ones.

Sign Conventions. We shall follow the following sign conventions :

(*i*) Tensile stress is considered positive and compressive stress is considered negative.

(*ii*) Angle θ is considered positive when it is in the anticlockwise direction.

(*iii*) *Sign Convention for Shear :* A shear stress acting on a positive face of an element is considered positive if it acts in the positive direction of one of the coordinate axes and negative if it acts in the negative direction of the axes. Similarly a shear stress acting

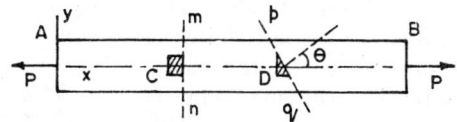

(a) BAR SUBJECT TO UNIAXIAL STRESS

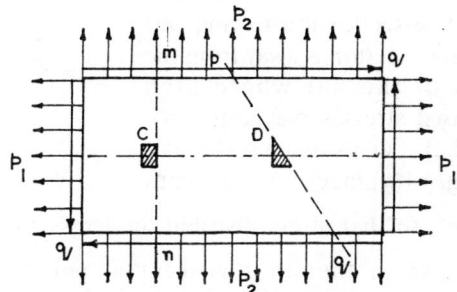

(b) BODY SUBJECT TO GENERAL STRESS SYSTEM

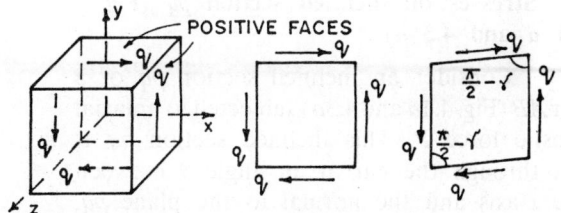

(c) POSITIVE SHEAR STRESSES

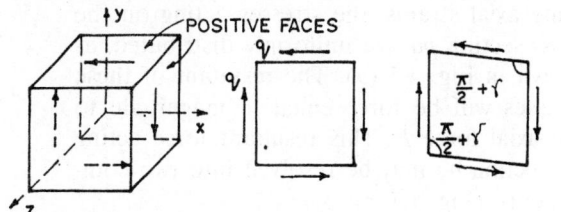

(d) NEGATIVE SHEAR STRESSES

FIG. 4.1

on a negative face of an element is positive if it acts in the negative direction of the axis and negative if it acts in the positive direction. Thus, all the shear stresses shown in Fig. 4.1(c) are positive. Such positive shear stresses tend to reduce the angle between two positive (or negative) faces. Similarly all shear stresses shown in Fig. 4.1(d) are negative.

4.2. STRESSES INDUCED DUE TO UNIAXIAL STRESS

(a) Stresses on normal cross-section mn (Fig 4.1 a)

Consider cross-section mn of a bar AB (Fig. 4.1 a) subjected to uniaxial tensile force P. Let us assume that the stress distribution is uniform over the entire cross-sectional area. This is possible when the following conditions exist : (i) the bar is prismatic, (ii) the material is homogeneous and isotropic (iii) the force acts at the centroid of the cross-sectional area and (iv) the cross-section is away from the ends of the bar where high localised stresses may exist (see Fig 2.2). Let us assume that bar of Fig. 4.1(a) meets all these con-

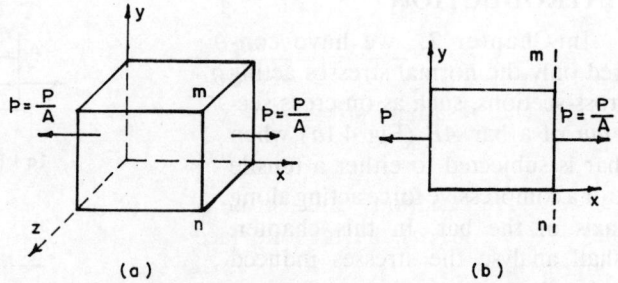

FIG. 4.2. STRESS ELEMENT AT POINT C

ditions, so that stress distribution across the section mn is uniform. In that case, stress $p = \dfrac{P}{A}$, as shown in the stress element at point C (Fig 4.2) which has the shape of a rectangular parallelopiped the right hand face of which is in cross section mn. The dimensions of such an element are assumed to be infinitesimally small.

(b) Stresses on inclined section pq (Fig 4.1 a and 4.3 a)

Consider an inclined section pq of a bar AB (Fig. 4.1a and 4.3a) subjected to uniaxial tensile force P. This inclined section pq is cut through the bar at an angle θ between the x-axis and the normal to the plane pq.

Since all the parts of the bar have the same axial strains, the stresses acting on the cross-section pq are uniformly distributed, as shown in Fig. 4.3 (b). The resultant of these stresses will be force equal in magnitude to the axial force P. This resultant force acting on section pq may be resolved into two components (Fig 4.3 c):

(i) a normal force N acting normal to the plane pq

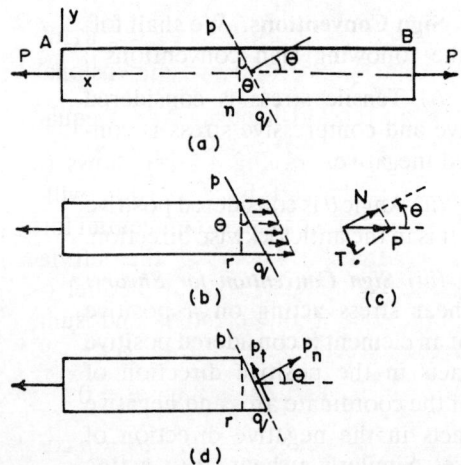

FIG. 4.3. STRESSES ON INCLINED SECTION pq

and   (ii) a tangential force T acting tangential to the plane pq.

Obviously, $N = P \cos \theta$ and $T = P \sin \theta$ ...(4.1)

These force components N and T give rise to normal stress p_n and tangential stress p_t respectively (Fig. 4.3d) which are uniformly distributed over the inclined section pq. These stresses are shown acting in the positive directions (Fig. 4.3d), that is, p_n is positive in tension and p_t is positive when it tends to produce counterclockwise rotation of the material.

The area of section (A_1) of pq is $A/\cos \theta$ ($= A \sec \theta$) where A is the area of cross-section of the normal section mn.

Hence $p_n = \dfrac{N}{A_1} = \dfrac{P \cos \theta}{A \sec \theta} = \dfrac{P}{A} \cos^2 \theta = p \cos^2 \theta$ ...(4.2 a)

and $p_t = -\dfrac{T}{A_1} = -\dfrac{P \sin \theta}{A \sec \theta} = -\dfrac{P}{A} \sin \theta \cos \theta = -p \sin \theta \cos \theta = -\dfrac{p}{2} \sin 2\theta$ ...(4.2 b)

The resultant stress $p_r = \sqrt{p_n^2 + p_t^2} = \sqrt{p^2 \cos^4 \theta + p^2 \sin^2 \theta \cos^2 \theta}$

$= p \cos \theta \sqrt{\cos^2 \theta + \sin^2 \theta} = p \cos \theta$ ...(4.2 c)

The above equations can also be derived by considering the wedge shaped stress element at point D (Fig. 4.1 a), having one face along the inclined section pq, as shown in Fig. 4.4.

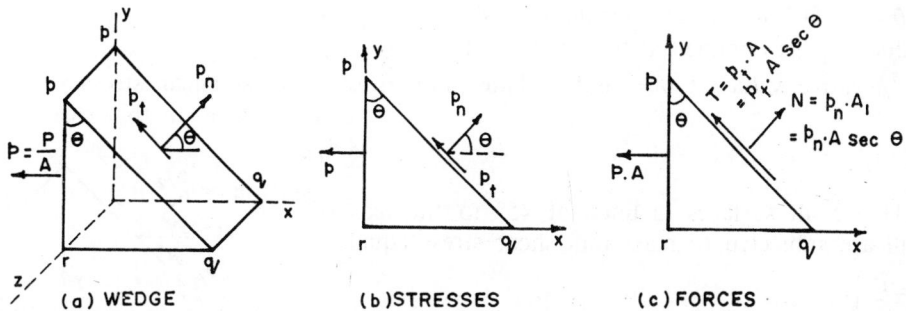

FIG. 4.4. STRESS ELEMENT AT POINT D

In Fig. 4.4 (b), the two dimensional view of the wedge shaped element is shown, where the stress on the left hand face pr is equal to stress p $\left(= \dfrac{P}{A} \right)$ while the stresses on the inclined face pq are p_n and p_t. Fig 4.4 (c) shows the forces on the two dimensional triangular element. The force on the left hand portion will be equal to $p.A$. The area of the inclined face is $A \sec \theta$. Hence the normal and tangential forces on this face are $p_n A \sec \theta$ and $p_t A \sec \theta$ respectively. Again the force $P (= pA)$ on the left face can be resolved into perpendicular (or normal) component $N(= pA \cos \theta)$ and parallel or tangential component $T(= pA \sin \theta)$. Considering the equilibrium of the element and summing the forces perpendicular to the inclined face (i.e. in the direction of p_n), we get

$p_n A \sec \theta - pA \cos \theta = 0$

or $p_n = p \cos^2 \theta$ ...(4.2 a)

Similarly, summing up the forces in tangential direction

$$p_t A \sec\theta + p A \sin\theta = 0$$

or
$$p_t = -p\sin\theta\cos\theta = -\frac{p}{2}\sin 2\theta \qquad ...(4.2\ a)$$

which are the same as obtained earlier.

Variation of p_n, p_t and p_r with θ

Fig 4.5 shows the variation of p_n, p_t and p_r, as θ varies from a value $-90°$ to $+90°$. When $\theta = 0°$, plane pq becomes a cross-section mn and hence the graph gives $p_n = p$, as expected. As θ increases, p_n decreases; when $\theta = 90°$, $p_n = 0$, indicating that there are no normal stresses on a plane cut parallel to the longitudinal axis. Hence

$$\left(p_n\right)_{max} = p = \frac{P}{A} \qquad ...(4.3)$$

Similarly, at cross-sections, where $\theta = 0$, $p_t = 0$. Also, on longitudinal sections, where $\theta = \pm 90°$, $p_t = 0$. The maximum positive value of p_t is obtained at $\theta = -45°$ and

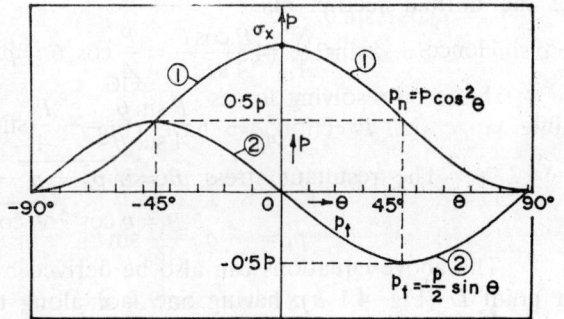

FIG. 4.5. VARIATION OF p_n, p_t AND p_r WITH θ.

largest negative value at $\theta = +45°$. Thus numerically, largest shear stresses are

$$\left(p_t\right)_{max} = \frac{P}{A} \qquad ...(4.4)$$

Hence all surfaces inclined at 45° to the axis of the pull are subjected to maximum shear stress equal to $\frac{P}{2A}\left(=\frac{p}{2}\right)$.

The complete state of stress on sections cut at 45° to axis of the pull is represented by the stress element shown in Fig. 4.6.

Thus in the uniaxial stress system, where the bar is subjected only to simple tension or compression, the two most important orientations of stress elements are $\theta = 0$ and 45°; the former orientation has maximum normal stress $p_{n,\,max}$ (Fig. 4.2) and the latter orientation has maximum shear stress $p_{t,\,max}$ (Fig. 4.6).

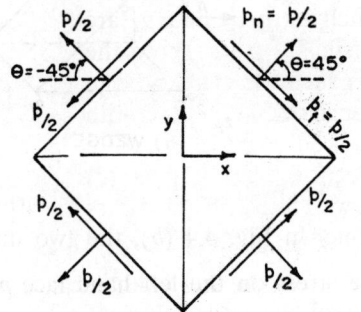

FIG. 4.6. STRESS ELEMENT AT $\theta = 45°$ FOR BAR IN TENSION

4.3. STRESSES INDUCED BY STATE OF SIMPLE SHEAR

Fig 4.7 (a) shows the state of simple shear or pure shear (see §3.8). Fig. 4.7 (b) and 4.7 (c) show wedge shaped stress element. It is required to find stresses p_n and p_t on inclined plane. Both the stresses p_n and p_t have been shown in their positive directions. Let the area of AB be A. Then area of $AC = A \sec\theta$.

Considering unit thickness of the element and balancing forces in direction normal to AC, we have (Fig 4.7 c) :

$$p_n . AC = q.AB \sin \theta + q\, BC \cos \theta$$

or $p_n = q.\dfrac{AB}{AC} \sin \theta + q\dfrac{BC}{AC} \cos \theta$

or $p_n = q \cos \theta \sin \theta$
$+ q \sin \theta \cos \theta + q \sin 2\theta ...(4.5)$

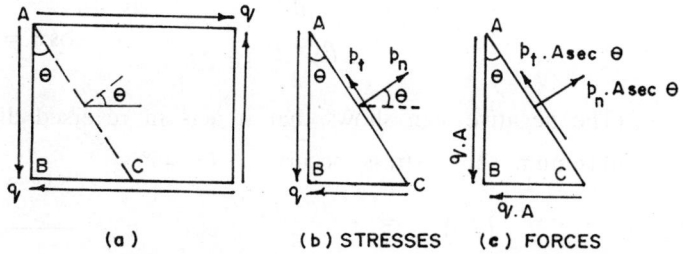

(a)   (b) STRESSES   (c) FORCES

FIG. 4.7. STRESSES DUE TO STATE OF SIMPLE SHEAR

Similarly, resolving forces along tangential direction, we have (Fig. 4.7 c)

$$p_t . AC = -q . BC \sin \theta + q\, AB \cos \theta$$

or
$$p_t = -q . \frac{BC}{AC} \sin \theta + q\frac{AB}{AC} \cos \theta = -q \sin^2 \theta + q \cos^2 \theta$$

or
$$p_t = q \left(\cos^2 \theta - \sin^2 \theta \right) = q \cos 2\theta \qquad ...(4.6)$$

From Eq. 4.5, we observe that $\left(p_n \right)_{max} = q$ when $\theta = 45°$, and for this position of the plane, p_t is zero.

4.4. STRESSES DUE TO STATE OF BIAXIAL STRESS

Fig. 4.8 (a) shows the state of biaxial stress, in which both p_1 and p_2 are tensile. Fig 4.8(b) shows the stresses on the wedge shaped stress element (both marked in the positive direction) while Fig 4.8 (c) shows forces on the stress element.

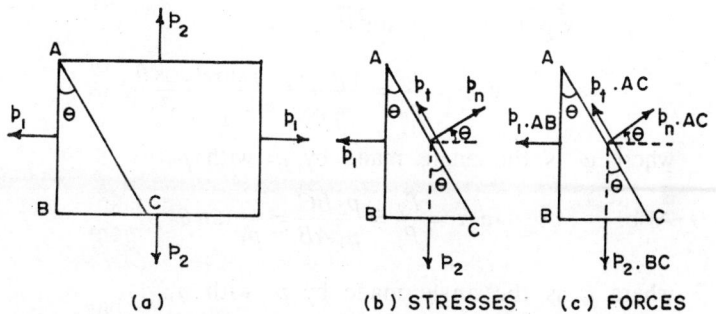

(a)   (b) STRESSES   (c) FORCES

FIG. 4.8. STATE OF BIAXIAL STRESS

Taking unit thickness of the stress element and resolving the forces perpendicular to AC, we have

$$p_n . AC = p_1 AB \cos \theta + p_2 BC \sin \theta$$

or
$$p_n = p_1 \frac{AB}{AC} \cos \theta + p_2 \frac{BC}{AC} \sin \theta = p_1 \cos^2 \theta + p_2 \sin^2 \theta \qquad ...(4.7)$$

Similarly, resolving the forces along AC, we have

$$p_t . AC = -p_1 AB \sin \theta + p_2 BC \cos \theta$$

or $$p_t = -p_1 \frac{AB}{AC} \sin\theta + p_2 \frac{BC}{AC} \cos\theta = -p_1 \cos\theta \sin\theta + p_2 \sin\theta \cos\theta$$

or $$p_t = -\frac{p_1 - p_2}{2} \sin 2\theta \qquad\qquad ...(4 \;)$$

(The negative sign shows that it acts in reversed direction than shown in Fig 4.8(c))
Maximum shear stress occurs at $\theta = 45°$:

$$\left(p_t\right)_{max} = -\frac{p_1 - p_2}{2} \qquad (4.9)$$

For this value of θ, normal stress is given by

$$p_n = p_1 \cos^2 45° + p_2 \sin^2 45° = \frac{p_1 + p_2}{2} \qquad ...(4.10)$$

The resultant stress p_r is given by

$$p_r = \sqrt{p_n^2 + p_t^2}$$

FIG. 4.9.

$$= \sqrt{\left(p_1 \cos^2\theta + p_2 \sin^2\theta\right)^2 + \left(-p_1 \cos\theta \sin\theta + p_2 \sin\theta \cos\theta\right)^2}$$

$$= \sqrt{p_1^2 \cos^4\theta + p_2^2 \sin^4\theta + 2p_1 p_2 \sin^2\theta \cos^2\theta + \left(p_1^2 + p_2^2 - 2p_1 p_2\right)\sin^2\theta \cos^2\theta}$$

$$= \sqrt{p_1^2 \cos^2\theta \left(\cos^2\theta + \sin^2\theta\right) + p_2^2 \sin^2\theta \left(\sin^2\theta + \cos^2\theta\right)}$$

or $$p_r = \sqrt{p_1^2 \cos^2\theta + p_2^2 \sin^2\theta} \qquad ...(4.11)$$

$$\tan\varphi = \frac{p_t}{p_n} = \frac{(p_1 - p_2)\sin\theta\cos\theta}{p_1 \cos^2\theta + p_2 \sin^2\theta} \qquad ...(4.12)$$

where φ is the angle made by p_r with p_n

Also, $$\tan\alpha = \frac{P_2}{P_1} = \frac{p_2 BC}{p_1 AB} = \frac{p_2}{p_1} \tan\theta \qquad ...(4.13)$$

where α is the angle made by p_r with p_1.

When stresses are not alike

A special case of biaxial stresses may arise when p_1 and p_2 may not be like, *i.e.* when p_1 may be tensile and p_2 may be compressive. In that case, p_n, p_t and p_r may be obtained by changing the sign of p_2 :

Thus, $$p_n = p_1 \cos^2\theta - p_2 \sin^2\theta \qquad ...(4.7\ a)$$

$$p_t = -\frac{p_1 + p_2}{2} \sin 2\theta \qquad ...(4.8\ a)$$

$$\left(p_t\right)_{max} = -\frac{p_1 + p_2}{2} \qquad ...(4.9\ a)$$

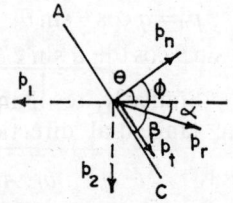

4.5. TWO PERPENDICULAR NORMAL STRESSES ACCOMPANIED WITH STATE OF SIMPLE SHEAR

Let us now consider a state of plane stress in which two perpendicular normal stresses are accompanied by the state of simple shear, as shown in Fig. 4.10 (a), (b). Such stress conditions are commonly encountered in axially loaded bars, shafts in torsion and beams is bending.

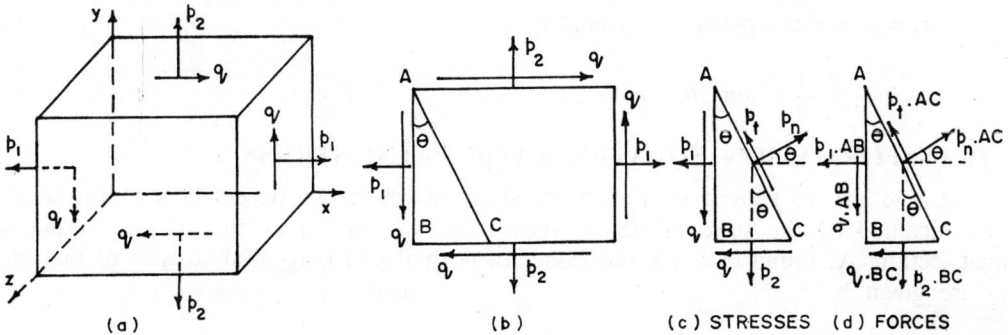

(a)   (b)   (c) STRESSES   (d) FORCES

FIG. 4.10. GENERALISED CASE OF PLANE STRESS

Fig. 4.10 (c) and (d) show the wedge shaped stress elements in terms of stresses and forces respectively. Considering unit thickness and resolving forces perpendicular to AC, we get

$$p_n\,AC = p_1 . AB \cos \theta + p_2 . BC \sin \theta + q\,AB \sin \theta + q . BC \cos \theta$$

or $\quad p_n = p_1 . \dfrac{AB}{AC} \cos \theta + p_2 . \dfrac{BC}{AC} \sin \theta + q . \dfrac{AB}{AC} \sin \theta + q . \dfrac{BC}{AC} \cos \theta$

or $\quad p_n = p_1 \cos^2 \theta + p_2 \sin^2 \theta + q \cos \theta \sin \theta + q \sin \theta \cos \theta$

or $\quad p_n = p_1 \cos^2 \theta + p_2 \sin^2 \theta + q \sin 2 \theta$ ...(4.14)

Eq. 4.14 can be expressed in an useful alternative form by using the following trigonometrical identities :

$$\cos^2 \theta = \frac{1}{2}\left(1 + \cos 2\theta\right) \; ; \sin^2 \theta = \frac{1}{2}\left(1 - \cos 2\theta\right) \text{ and } \sin \theta \cos \theta = \frac{1}{2}\sin 2\theta.$$

Then, Eq. 4.14 is reduced to the following form :

$$p_n = \frac{1}{2}\left(p_1 + p_2\right) + \frac{1}{2}\left(p_1 - p_2\right)\cos 2\theta + q \sin 2\theta$$ ...(4.15)

Similarly, resolving the forces along AC, are get

$$p_t . AC = - p_1 . AB \sin \theta + p_2 . BC \cos \theta + q . AB \cos \theta - q . BC \sin \theta$$

or $\qquad p_t = -p_1 . \dfrac{AB}{AC} \sin\theta + p_2 \dfrac{BC}{AC} \cos\theta + q . \dfrac{AB}{AC} \cos\theta - q . \dfrac{BC}{AC} \sin\theta$

or $\qquad p_t = -p_1 \cos\theta \sin\theta + p_2 \sin\theta \cos\theta + q . \cos^2\theta - q . \sin^2\theta$

or $\qquad p_t = -\dfrac{p_1 - p_2}{2} \sin 2\theta + q \cos 2\theta$ \hfill ...(4.15)

If p_1 and p_2 are unlike (*i.e.* p_1 tensile and p_2 compressive), similar expressions for p_n and p_t can be obtained, by simply changing the sign of p_2. Thus, we have

$$p_n = p_1 \cos^2\theta - p_2 \sin^2\theta + q \sin 2\theta \qquad ...(4.14a)$$

and $\qquad p_t = -\dfrac{p_1 + p_2}{2} \sin 2\theta + q \cos 2\theta$ \hfill ...(4.16 a)

4.6. TRANSFORMATION EQUATIONS FOR PLANE STRESS*

Fig. 4.11 (*a*) (*b*) show a state of plane stress in which two perpendicular normal stresses are accompanied by the state of simple shear. Fig. 4.11 (*c*) show the stresses acting on an inclined section. As found in § 4.5, the values of normal and tangential stresses of this inclined plane are given by :

$$p_n = p_1' = \frac{1}{2}\left(p_1 + p_2\right) + \frac{1}{2}\left(p_1 - p_2\right)\cos 2\theta + q \sin 2\theta \qquad ...(4.15)$$

and $\qquad p_t = q' = -\dfrac{p_1 - p_2}{2} \sin 2\theta + q \cos 2\theta$ \hfill ...(4.16)

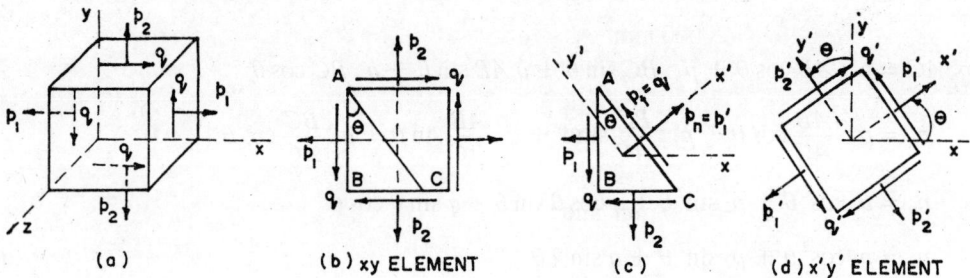

(a)   (b) xy ELEMENT   (c)   (d) x'y' ELEMENT

FIG. 4.11. ROTATION OF PLANE STRESS ELEMENT

The above equations for p_1' and q' are known as the transformation equations for plane stress because they transform the stress components from one set of axes (say x, y axes) to another set of axes (say x', y' axes) rotated through an angle θ. However, the intrinsic state of stress at the point under consideration is the same whether represented by the stresses on the xy element (Fig 4.11 *a*) or by the rotated $x'y'$ element (Fig. 4.11 *d*).

In a similar way, the normal stress p_2' acting on the y' face of the rotated element (Fig 4.11 *d*) can be obtained by Eq. 4.15 by substituting $\theta + 90°$ for θ. Thus, we have

$$\left(p_n\right)_{90+\theta} = p_2' = \frac{1}{2}\left(p_1 + p_2\right) - \frac{1}{2}\left(p - p_2\right)\cos 2\theta - q \sin 2\theta \qquad ...(4.15\ a)$$

Summing Eqs. 4.15 and 4.15 (a), we have

$$p_1' + p_2' = p_1 + p_2$$

Hence the sum of normal stresses acting on perpendicular faces of a plane stress elements is constant and independent of the angle θ.

Example 4.1. A tie bar is subjected to a uniform tensile stress of 100 N/mm². Find the intensity of normal stress, shear stress and resultant stress on a plane the normal to which is inclined 30° to the axis of the bar. Also estimate the maximum shear stress in the bar.

Solution

$$p_n = p \cos^2 \theta = 100 \cos^2 30° = \textbf{75 N/mm}^2$$

$$p_t = -\frac{p}{2} \sin 2\theta = -\frac{100}{2} \sin 60° = \textbf{- 43.3 N/mm}^2 \ (i.e. \ \text{in the clockwise direction})$$

$$p_r = \sqrt{p_n^2 + p_t^2} = \sqrt{(75)^2 + (43.3)^2} = \textbf{86.6 N/mm}^2$$

$$\left(p_t\right)_{max} = -\frac{p}{2} = -\frac{100}{2} = \textbf{- 50 N/mm}^2 \ \text{at} \ \theta = \textbf{+ 45°}$$

Example 4.2. A tension member is formed by connecting with glue two wooden scantlings each 100 mm × 200 mm at their ends which are cut at an angle of 60° as shown is Fig 4.12. The member is subjected to a pull P. Calculate the safe value of P if the permissible normal and shear stress in the glue are 2 N/mm² and 1 N/mm² respectively.

Solution

Area $\qquad A = 100 \times 200 = 20000 \ \text{mm}^2$

Angle of cut with horizontal $= 60°$

$\therefore$ Angle of cut (θ) with the vertical
$= 90° - 60° = 30°$

Given : Permissible $p_n = 2$ N/mm² and

permissible $p_t = 4$ N/mm².

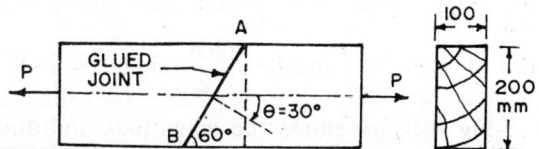

FIG. 4.12

But $\qquad\qquad p_n = p \cos^2 \theta$

From which $\qquad p = p_n \sec^2 \theta = 2 \sec^2 30° = 2.667 \ \text{N/mm}^2 \qquad\qquad ...(i)$

Also, $\qquad\qquad p_t = \frac{p}{2} \sin 2\theta$

From which $\qquad p = \frac{2 \, p_t}{\sin 2\theta} = \frac{2 \times 1}{\sin 60°} = 2.309 \ \text{N/mm}^2 \qquad\qquad ...(ii)$

The safe stress p will be the lesser of the two values.

$\therefore \qquad\qquad p = 2.309 \ \text{N/mm}^2$

$\therefore \qquad\qquad P = p \cdot A = 2.309 \times 20000 \times 10^{-3} = \textbf{46.18 kN}$

Example 4.3. *A prismatic bar in compression has a cross-sectional area $A = 900\ mm^2$ and carries a load of 60 kN (Fig. 4.13 a). Determine the stresses acting on a plane cut through the bar at $\theta = 30°$. Then show the complete state of stress for $\theta = 30°$ by determining the stresses on all faces of a stress element.*

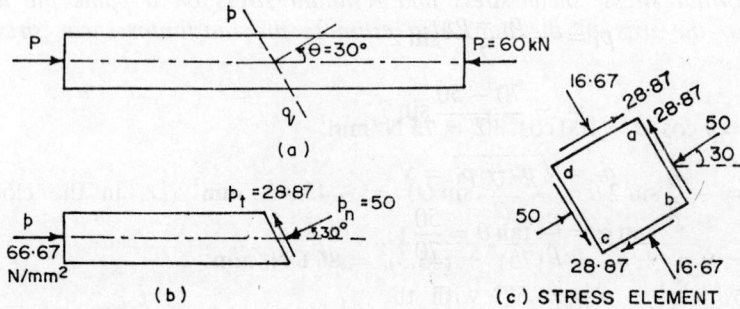

FIG. 4.13

Solution

$$p = \frac{P}{A} = \frac{60 \times 10^3}{900} = 66.67\ \text{N/mm}^2 \text{ (compression)}$$

Now $p_n = p \cos^2 \theta = (-66.67) \cos^2 30° = -50\ \text{N/mm}^2$ (i.e. comp.)

and $p_t = -\dfrac{p}{2} \sin 2\theta = \dfrac{66.67}{2} \sin 60° = 28.87\ \text{N/mm}^2$

Fig. 4.13 (a) shows the magnitude and direction of both p_n and p_t on the inclined plane. Fig. 4.13 (c) shows the stresses on all the four faces of the stress element. Since face ab has the same orientation as the inclined plane pq, the stresses are the same.

For stresses of face cd, substitute $\theta = 30° + 180° = 210°$ in Eqs. 4.2a and 4.2b,

Thus, $p_n = -66.67 \cos^2 210° = -50\ \text{N/mm}^2$

and $p_t = \dfrac{66.67}{2} \sin(2 \times 210°) = 28.87\ \text{N/mm}^2$

Similarly, for face ad, we have $\theta = 30° + 90° = 120°$

Hence $p_n = -66.67 \cos^2 120° = 16.67\ \text{N/mm}^2$

and $p_t = \dfrac{66.67}{2} \sin(2 \times 120°) = -28.87\ \text{N/mm}^2$

Lastly, the values of p_n and p_t for face cd can be obtained by substituting $\theta = -60°$. The stresses on all the four faces of the stress element are shown in Fig. 4.13(c).

Example 4.4. *A piece of material is subjected to tensile stresses of 70 N/mm^2 and 50 N/mm^2 at right angles to each other. Find fully the stresses on a plane the normal of which makes an angle of 35° with the 70 N/mm^2 stress.*

Solution

$$p_n = p_1 \cos^2 \theta + p_2 \sin^2 \theta \qquad \qquad ...(4.7)$$

$$= 70 \cos^2 35° + 50 \sin^2 35° = \textbf{63.42 N/mm}^2$$

$$p_t = -\frac{p_1 - p_2}{2} \sin 2\theta \qquad \qquad ...(4.8)$$

$$= -\frac{70 - 50}{2} \sin 70° = \textbf{9.4 N/mm}^2 \ \text{(numerically)}$$

$$p_r = \sqrt{p_n^2 + p_t^2} = \sqrt{(63.42)^2 + (9.4)^2} = \textbf{64.11 N/mm}^2$$

$$\tan \alpha = \frac{p_2}{p_1} \tan \theta = \frac{50}{70} \tan 35° = 0.5$$

From which $\qquad \alpha = \textbf{26.57}°$ with the direction of p_1.

Example 4.5. *A piece of material is subjected to tensile stress of 70 N/mm^2 in one direction and a compressive stress of 50 N/mm^2 in a direction at right angles to the previous one.*

Find fully the stresses on a plane the normal of which makes an angle of 40° with the 70 N/mm^2 stress.

Solution

In this case, p_1 is tensile while p_2 is compressive.

Hence $\qquad p_n = p_1 \cos^2 \theta - p_2 \sin^2 \theta = 70 \cos^2 40° - 50 \sin^2 40° = \textbf{20.42 N/mm}^2$

$$p_t = -\frac{p_1 + p_2}{2} \sin 2\theta = -\frac{70 + 50}{2} \sin 80° = \textbf{59.09 N/mm}^2 \ \text{(numerically)}$$

$$p_r = \sqrt{p_n^2 + p_t^2} = \sqrt{(20.42)^2 + (59.09)^2} = \textbf{62.52 N/mm}^2$$

$$\tan \alpha = \frac{p_2}{p_1} \tan \theta = \frac{50}{70} \tan 40° = 0.5994$$

From which $\qquad \alpha = \textbf{30.94}°$

Example 4.6. *The stresses on two perpendicular planes through a point are 60 N/mm^2 tension, 40 N/mm^2 compression and 30 N/mm^2 shear (Fig 4.14 a). Find the stress components and the resultant stress on a plane at 60° to that of the tensile stress.*

Solution :

Given $\qquad p_1 = 60 \ \text{N/mm}^2$ (tension)

$\qquad \qquad p_2 = 40 \ \text{N/mm}^2$ (comp.) $\quad q = 30 \ \text{N/mm}^2$

and $\qquad \quad \theta = 60°$

$$p_n = p_1 \cos^2 \theta + p_2 \sin^2 \theta + q \sin 2\theta \quad \text{(Eq. 4.14)}$$

$$= 60 \cos^2 60° - 40 \sin^2 60° + 30 \sin (2 \times 60°) = \textbf{10.98 N/mm}^2$$

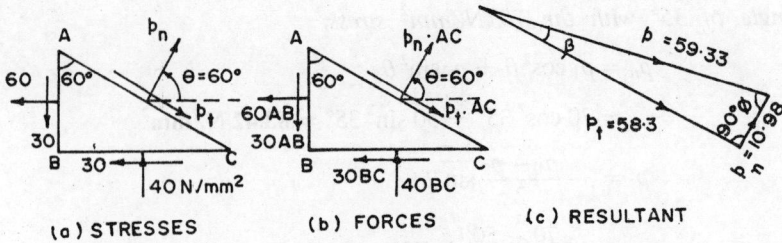

FIG. 4.14

$$p_t = -\frac{p_1 - p_2}{2} \sin 2\theta + q \cos 2\theta \qquad \qquad ...(4.16)$$

$$= -\frac{60 + 40}{2} \sin 120° + 30 \cos 120° = -58.3 \text{ N/mm}^2$$

(*i.e.* in the direction as marked in Fig. 4.14)

$$\therefore \qquad p_r = \sqrt{(10.98)^2 + (58.3)^2} = 59.33 \text{ N/mm}^2 \text{ (tensile)}$$

$$\varphi = \tan^{-1}\frac{p_t}{p_n} = \tan^{-1}\left(\frac{58.3}{10.98}\right) = 79.33°$$

(or $\qquad \qquad \beta = \tan^{-1}\frac{p_n}{p_t} = \tan^{-1}\frac{10.98}{58.3} = 10.67°$)

Example 4.7. *A piece of material is subjected to tensile stresses of p_1 and p_2 at right angles to each other ($p_1 > p_2$).*

Find the plane across which the resultant stress is most inclined to the normal. Find the value of this inclination and the resultant stress when $p_1 = 60 \text{ N/mm}^2$ and $p_2 = 40 \text{ N/mm}^2$ (both tensile).

Solution :

Let φ be the inclination of the resultant with the normal (Fig. 4.9).

We have $\qquad \tan \varphi = \dfrac{p_t}{p_n} = \dfrac{(p_1 - p_2) \sin \theta \cos \theta}{p_1 \cos^2 \theta + p_2 \sin^2 \theta} \qquad \qquad ...(i)$

For φ to be maximum, $\tan \varphi$ is also maximum, and $\dfrac{d (\tan \varphi)}{d \theta} = 0$

Hence, differentiating and dividing out common factors,

$$\left(p_1 \cos^2 \theta + p_2 \sin^2 \theta\right) \cos 2\theta + \left(p_1 - p_2\right) \sin \theta \cos \theta \times \sin 2\theta = 0$$

or $\qquad p_n \cos 2\theta + p_t \sin 2\theta = 0$

Hence $\qquad \qquad \tan 2\theta = -\dfrac{p_n}{p_t} = -\cot \varphi = \tan\left(\dfrac{\pi}{2} + \varphi\right)$

or
$$2\theta = \frac{\pi}{2} + \varphi \qquad ...(ii)$$

Substituting the value of θ in (i), we get

$$\tan \varphi = \frac{(p_1 - p_2)\cos\varphi}{p_1(1 - \sin\varphi) + p_2\left(1 + \sin\varphi\right)}$$

or
$$\frac{p_2}{p_1} = \frac{1 - \sin\varphi}{1 + \cos\varphi}$$

or
$$\sin\varphi = \frac{p_1 - p_2}{p_1 + p_2} \qquad ...(iii)$$

Hence from (ii)
$$\theta = \frac{1}{2}\left(\frac{\pi}{2} + \sin^{-1}\frac{p_1 - p_2}{p_1 + p_2}\right)$$

which gives the position of the required plane.

Substituting the values of p_1 and p_2, we get

$$\theta = \frac{1}{2}\left(90° + \sin^{-1}\frac{60° - 40°}{60° + 40°}\right) = \frac{1}{2}\left(90° + 11°32'\right)$$

$$= \mathbf{50° \ 46'}$$

$$\varphi = \sin^{-1}\frac{p_1 - p_2}{p_1 + p_2} = \sin^{-1}\frac{60° - 40°}{60° + 40°} = \mathbf{11° \ 32'}$$

$$p_r = \sqrt{(60\cos 50°\ 46')^2 + (40\sin 50°\ 46')^2} = \mathbf{48.9 \ N/mm^2}$$

Example 4.8. *An element in plane stress is subjected to stresses $p_1 = 120 \ N/mm^2$ and $p_2 = 45 \ N/mm^2$ (both tensile) and shearing stress of $30 \ N/mm^2$, as shown in Fig. 4.15(a). Determine the stresses acting as an element rotated through an angle $\theta = 45°$.*

Solution :

The required stresses p_n and p_t can be found by Eqs. 4.15 and 4.16

Here
$$\frac{p_1 + p_2}{2} = \frac{120 + 45}{2} = 82.5 \ N/mm^2$$

and
$$\frac{p_1 - p_2}{2} = \frac{120 - 45}{2} = 37.5 \ N/mm^2$$

$$q = 30 \ N/mm^2$$

$$\sin 2\theta = \sin (2 \times 45°) = 1$$

and
$$\cos 2\theta = \cos (2 \times 45°) = 0$$

Hence
$$p_n = p_1' = \frac{1}{2}(p_1 + p_2) + \frac{1}{2}(p_1 - p_2)\cos 2\theta + q \sin 2\theta$$

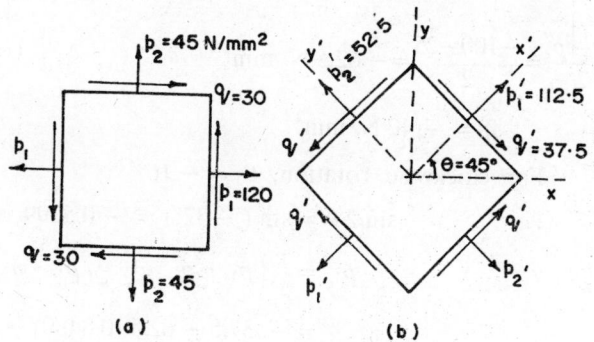

FIG. 4.15

$$= 82.5 + 37.5 \times 0 + 30 \times 1 = \mathbf{112.5\ N/mm^2}$$

and
$$p_t = q' = -\frac{p_1 - p_2}{2} \sin 2\theta + q \cos 2\theta$$

$$= -37.5 \times 1 + 30 \times 0 = -37.5\ N/mm^2$$

The normal stress on the other plane, at right angles to the previous one can be found by substituting $\theta = 90° + 45° = 135°$, so that $\sin 2\theta = \sin(2 \times 135°) = -1$ and $\cos 2\theta = \cos(2 \times 135°) = 0$

$\therefore$
$$p_2' = \frac{1}{2}(p_1 + p_2) + \frac{1}{2}(p_1 - p_2) \cos 2\theta + q \sin 2\theta$$

$$= 82.5 + 37.5 \times 0 + 30(-1) = \mathbf{52.5\ N/mm^2}$$

The stresses on the original stress element are shown in Fig. 4.15 (a) while the stresses on the stress element rotated through 45° are shown in Fig. 4.15 (b). It is to be noted that $p_1 + p_2 = p_1' + p_2'$.

Example 4.9. *A plane stress condition exists at a point in a loaded structure. The stresses have the magnitude and directions shown on the stress element of Fig. 4.16 (a). Calculate the stresses acting on the planes obtained by rotating the element clockwise through an angle of 16°.*

Solution :

Here we have

$$p_1 = -100\ N/mm^2$$

$$p_2 = 25\ N/mm^2$$

and
$$q = -40\ N/mm^2$$

$$\frac{p_1 + p_2}{2} = \frac{-100 + 25}{2} = -37.5\ N/mm^2$$

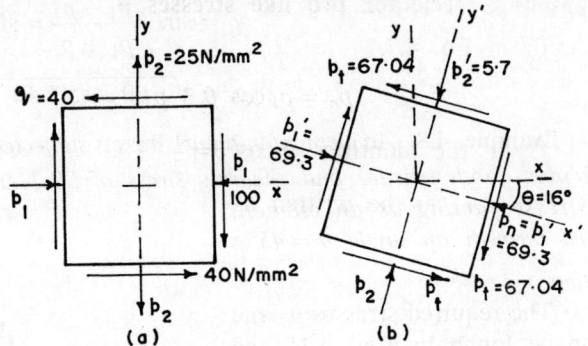

$$\frac{p_1 - p_2}{2} = \frac{-100 - 25}{2} = -62.5\ N/mm^2$$

(a)   (b)

$$q = -40\ N/mm^2$$

FIG. 4.16

For clockwise rotation, $\theta = -16°$

$\therefore \qquad \sin 2\theta = \sin(-32°) = -0.5299$ and $\cos 2\theta = \cos(-32°) = 0.8480$

$\therefore \qquad p_1' = \frac{1}{2}(p_1 + p_2) + \frac{1}{2}(p_1 - p_2) \cos 2\theta + q \sin 2\theta$

$$= -37.5 - 62.5(0.8480) - 40(-0.5299) = \mathbf{-69.3\ N/mm^2}$$

(i.e. compressive)

$$p_t = -\frac{p_1 - p_2}{2} \sin 2\theta + q \cos 2\theta$$

$$= +62.5(-0.5299) + (-40)(0.8480) = -67.04\ N/mm^2$$

For finding stresses on the y' face, substitute $\theta = \theta + 90° = -16° + 90° = 74°$

Hence $\quad \sin 2\theta = \sin(2 \times 74°) = 0.5299$ and $\cos 2\theta = \cos(2 \times 74°) = -0.8480$

$$\therefore \qquad p_2' = \frac{1}{2}\left(p_1 + p_2\right) + \frac{1}{2}\left(p_1 - p_2\right)\cos 2\theta + q\sin 2\theta$$

$$= -37.5 - 62.5(-0.8480) - 40(0.5299) = -5.7 \text{ N/mm}^2$$

(i.e. compression)

Here $\quad p_1' + p_2' = -69.3 - 5.7 = -75$, and $p_1 + p_2 = -100 + 25 = -75$

Hence $\quad p_1' + p_2' = p_1 + p_2$

The stresses acting on the stress element rotated through 16° in the clockwise direction are shown in Fig 4.16 (b) :

4.7. CIRCULAR DIAGRAM FOR STRESSES : MOHR CIRCLE

In the previous articles, we have discussed the analytical methods of computing the normal, shear and resultant stresses on any inclined plane. The so called *transformation equations*, used for such computations can be easily represented in a *graphical form* known as Mohr's circle. Such a graphical representation, commonly known as *circular diagram for stress*, is extremely useful in visualising the relationships between normal and shear stresses acting on various inclined planes at a point is a stressed body. We shall consider here different cases.

(a) Mohr's Circle for two like stresses p_1 and p_2

From Eq. 4.7,

$$p_n = p_1 \cos^2\theta + p_2 \sin^2\theta \qquad \qquad ...(4.7)$$

Using the identities : $\cos^2\theta = \frac{1}{2}\left(1 + \cos 2\theta\right)$ and $\sin^2\theta = \frac{1}{2}(1 - \cos 2\theta)$

Eq. 4.7 can be written as :

$$p_n = \frac{1}{2}\left(p_1 + p_2\right) + \frac{1}{2}\left(p_1 - p_2\right)\cos 2\theta \qquad \qquad ...(4.17)$$

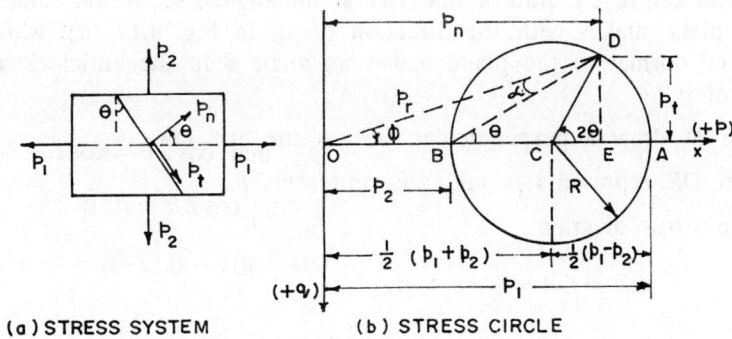

(a) STRESS SYSTEM   (b) STRESS CIRCLE

FIG. 4.17

Also, from Eq. 4.8,

$$p_t = -\frac{p_1 - p_2}{2}\sin 2\theta \qquad \qquad ...(4.18)$$

These two equations are the equations of a circle in parametric form, with the angle 2θ as the parameter. This parameter can be eliminated by squaring both sides of each equations and then adding. Thus :

$$\left(p_n - \frac{p_1 + p_2}{2}\right)^2 + p_t^2 = \left(\frac{p_1 - p_2}{2}\right)^2 \qquad ...(4.19\ a)$$

Introducing $p_{av} = \frac{p_1 + p_2}{2}$ and $R = \sqrt{\left(\frac{p_1 - p_2}{2}\right)^2}$ ...(4.19 b)

Equation 4.19 (a) takes the following form :

$$(p_n - p_{av})^2 + p_t^2 = R^2 \qquad \qquad ...(4.19)$$

This is the equation of a circle with p_n and p_t as the coordinates. The radius of the circle is $\frac{1}{2}(p_1 - p_2)$ and its centre has coordinates $p_n = p_{av}$ and $p_t = 0$

Procedure for construction of Mohr's circle

To construct Mohr's circle, we take p_n as the abscissa and p_t as the ordinate. We take p_n *positive to the right* and p_t *positive downwards* ; then angle 2θ is positive when taken counter clockwise.

(i) Locate centre C of the circle at the point having coordinates $p_{av} = \frac{1}{2}(p_1 + p_2)$ and $p_t = 0$.

(ii) Measure OA and OB equal to p_1 and p_2 respectively to some scale to the same side of O.

(iii) With C (which is midway between B and A) as centre, and CA or CB as radius $= \frac{1}{2}(p_1 - p_2)$, draw a circle.

(iv) At the centre C, draw a line CD at an angle 2θ, in the same direction as the normal to the plane makes with the direction of p_1. In Fig. 4.17 (a), which represents the stress system, the normal to the plane makes an angle θ in the anticlockwise direction with the directions of p_1.

(v) From D, draw a perpendicular DE on the axis OX.

(vi) Then DE represents p_t and OE represents p_n.

From the stress diagram :

$$CD = CA = \frac{1}{2}(p_1 - p_2)$$

$\therefore$
$$DE = CD\sin 2\theta = \frac{1}{2}(p_1 - p_2)\sin 2\theta = p_t$$

Similarly, $\qquad OE = OC + CE = \frac{1}{2}\left(p_1 + p_2\right) + \frac{1}{2}\left(p_1 - p_2\right)\cos 2\theta = p_n.$

Hence it is proved that the two rectangular projections of the radius vector give p_t and p_n.

From the stress circle, p_t is maximum when $2\theta = 90°$ (or $\theta = 45°$) and $p_{t,max} = \frac{1}{2}\left(p_1 - p_2\right)$.

In Fig 4.17 (b) p_t is above the axis and hence it is *negative*. Hence, in the stress system shown in Fig. 4.17 (a), p_t has been shown in the clockwise direction (*i.e.* negative). Hence we follow the following sign conventions for Mohr's stress circle.

Sign Conventions

(*i*) Tensile stresses are reckoned positive and are plotted to the right of origin O. Similarly, compressive stress is reckoned negative and is plotted to the left of origin O.

(*ii*) p_t is taken positive when it gives anticlockwise rotation of the element and is plotted below the axis. Similarly, p_t that gives clockwise rotation is reckoned *negative* and is plotted above the axis.

(*iii*) θ is reckoned positive when it is in the anticlockwise direction,

Thus, as per the above sign conventions, both p_1 and p_2 marked in the stress system of Fig 4.17 (a) are positive and have been plotted to the R.H. side of the origin in Fig. 4.17 (b). The angle θ is positive since it is measured in the anticlockwise direction. The resulting normal stress p_n is thus positive (i.e. tensile) while the shear stress p_t ($= DE$), is *negative* (since it falls above the x-axis of the stress circle) and has been adequately marked in Fig 4.17 (a).

Mohr's circle construction for two unlike stresses p_1 and p_2

Let p_1 be tensile (*i.e.* +ve) and p_2 be compressive (*i.e.* –ve). It is required to find the stresses on a plane normal to which makes an angle θ in the anticlockwise direction, with the direction of p_1, as marked in the stress system shown in Fig ·4.18 (a).

Steps.

(*i*) Mark $OA = p_1$ to the right of O and $OB = p_2$ to the left.

(*ii*) Find point C, midway between A and B. Thus, $OC = \left(\dfrac{p_1 - p_2}{2}\right)$.

If $p_1 > p_2$, C will be to the right O; otherwise it will be to the left.

(*iii*) At C, draw radius vector CD, at angle 2θ in the anticlockwise

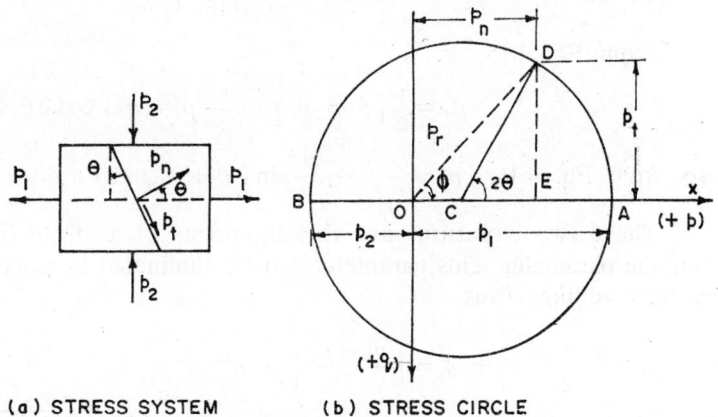

(a) STRESS SYSTEM (b) STRESS CIRCLE

FIG. 4.18

direction. We have radius $CD = \dfrac{p_1 + p_2}{2} = CA$.

(*iv*) Draw DE perpendicular to the x-axis.

Then $CE = p_n$ and $DE = p_t$

It is clear that the direction of p_n will depend upon the position of point E. If it is to the right of O, the direction of p_n will be the same as that of p_1. For the stress system marked and shown in Fig. 4.18, p_n is positive (*i.e.* tensile), while p_t ($= DE$) is negative.

The *resultant stress* $p_r = OD$ and it makes an angle φ ($= DOC$) with the direction of p_n or an angle α ($= ODC$) with the direction of p_1.

(c)   Mohr's circle for the general case of plane stress

Let is now take the general case of plane stress in which the material is subjected to direct stresses p_1 and p_2 accompanied with the state of simple shear as marked in Fig 4.19 (*a*). All the stresses (*i.e.* p_1, p_2 and q) marked in the stress system are positive according to our sign convention discussed earlier.

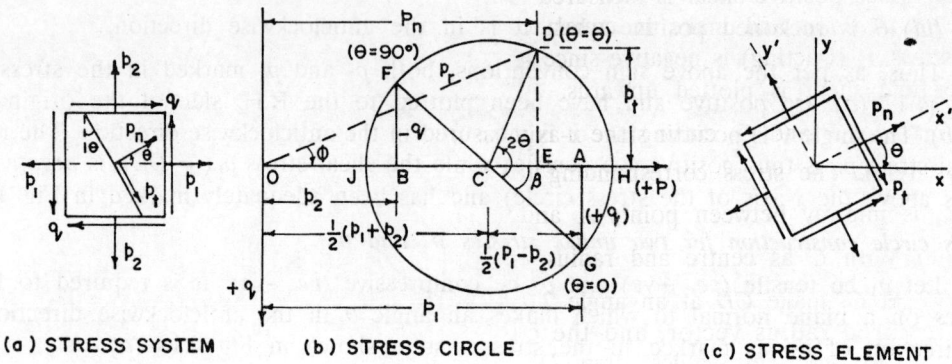

(a) STRESS SYSTEM   (b) STRESS CIRCLE   (c) STRESS ELEMENT

FIG. 4.19

From Eq. 4.15

$$p_n = \tfrac{1}{2}\left(p_1 + p_2\right) + \tfrac{1}{2}\left(p_1 - p_2\right)\cos 2\theta + q \sin 2\theta \qquad \dots(4.15)$$

Also, from Eq. 4.16, $p_t = -\dfrac{p_1 - p_2}{2}\sin 2\theta + q \cos 2\theta \qquad \dots(4.16)$

These two equations are the equations of a circle in parametric form, with angle 2θ as the parameter. This parameter can be eliminated by squaring both sides of each equation and then adding. Thus.

$$\left(p_n - \dfrac{p_1 + p_2}{2}\right)^2 + p_t^2 = \left(\dfrac{p_1 - p_2}{2}\right)^2 + q^2 \qquad \dots(4.20\ a)$$

Introducing $p_{av} = \tfrac{1}{2}\left(p_1 + p_2\right)$ and $R = \sqrt{\left(\dfrac{p_1 - p_2}{2}\right)^2 + q^2} \qquad \dots(4.20\ b)$

Eq. 4.20 (a) takes the following form.

$$\left(p_n - p_{av}\right)^2 + p_t^2 = R^2 \qquad \ldots(4.20)$$

This is the equation of a circle with p_n and p_t as coordinates. The radius R of the circle is $\sqrt{\left[\frac{1}{2}(p_1 - p_2)\right]^2 + q^2}$ and its centre has the co-ordinates $p_n = p_{av}$ and $p_t = 0$. The corresponding Mohr's circle is shown in Fig. 4.19 (b), with the procedure for its construction described below.

Procedure for construction of Mohr's circle

To construct Mohr's circle, we take p_n as the abscissa and p_t as ordinate. We take p_n *positive to the right* and p_t *positive downwards ; then angle 2θ is positive when taken counter clockwise.*

(i) Make $OA = p_1$ and $OB = p_2$ to the same side of O, since both p_1 and p_2 are alike, and are positive.

(ii) The shear stress q marked on x-face (i.e. face ab) in Fig 4.19 (a) is positive as per our sign conventions. Hence draw AG perpendicular to OX, and equal to q, in the downward direction, since positive shear is measured downwards. Similarly make BF perpendicular to OX in *upward direction* and make in equal to q; it is to be noted that shear on face da (on which stress p_2 is acting) is negative since it tends to rotate the element in clockwise direction, and negative shear is plotted upwards.

(iii) Join F and G, cutting the x-axis in C, which is the centre of the stress circle (i.e. Mohr's circle). The stress corresponding to point C is evidently equal to $\frac{1}{2}\left(p_1 + p_2\right)$ since point C is midway between points A and B.

(iv) With C as centre and radius equal to CG (or CF) draw a circle.

(v) At C, make CD at an angle 2θ with CG in the anticlockwise direction. Line CD is the required radius vector, and the coordinates of point D give the required stresses p_n and p_t. To find their values, draw DE perpendicular to x-axis.

Then $DE = p_t$, $OE = p_n$ and $OD = p_r$.

Here p_n is positive and p_t negative as per over sign conventions. It is interesting to note that point G represents the stress conditions on x-face (i.e. face ab) for which $\theta = 0$ where $p_n = OA = p_1$ and $p_t = AG = +q$. Similarly, point F represents the stress conditions on y-face (i.e. face da) for which $2\theta = 180°$ (or $\theta = 90°$), where stress $p_n = OB = p_2$ and $p_t = BF = -q$

Proof :   Let R = radius of the stress circle

$$= \sqrt{CA^2 + AG^2} = \sqrt{\left(\frac{p_1 - p_2}{2}\right)^2 + q^2}$$

$$R \cos \beta = CA = \frac{p_1 - p_2}{2}$$

$$R \sin \beta = AG = q$$

Now $\qquad OE = OC + CE = OC + R \cos(2\theta - \beta)$

$$= OC + R \cos \beta \cos 2\theta + R \sin \beta \sin 2\theta$$

$$= \frac{1}{2} \left(p_1 + p_2 \right) + \frac{1}{2} \left(p_1 - p_2 \right) \cos 2\theta + q \sin 2\theta$$

$$= p_n \text{ (as per Eq. 4.15)}$$

Similarly, $DE = R \sin(2\theta - \beta) = R \cos \beta \sin 2\theta - R \sin \beta \cos 2\theta$

$$= \frac{1}{2} \left(p_1 - p_2 \right) \sin 2\theta - q \cos 2\theta$$

$$= - p_t \text{ (as per Eq. 4.16)}$$

The stress conditions are marked on the stress element shown in Fig 4.19 (c).

Conclusions

From the stress circle, we draw the following conclusions :

(i) When D coincides with H (i.e. $2\theta = \beta$),

p_n attains its *maximum* value :

$$p_{n,max} = OC + CH$$

$$= \frac{1}{2} \left(p_1 + p_2 \right) + \sqrt{\left(\frac{p_1 - p_2}{2} \right)^2 + q^2}$$

where $p_{n,max}$ is known as the *major principal stress* σ_1 (see § 4.9).

Also, $p_t = 0$ and $p_{r,max} = p_{t,max}$

$$\tan 2\theta = \tan \beta = \frac{q}{\frac{1}{2}(p_1 - p_2)} = \frac{2q}{p_1 - p_2}$$

(see § 4.9)

(ii) When D coincides with J, p_n attains the minimum value :

$$p_{n,min} = OJ = OC - CJ$$

$$= \frac{1}{2} \left(p_1 + p_2 \right) - \sqrt{\left(\frac{p_1 - p_2}{2} \right)^2 + q^2}$$

$p_{n,min}$ is known as the minor principal stress σ_2 (see § 4.9)

$p_t = 0$; $p_{r,min} = p_{n,min}$; $2\theta = 180° + \beta$ or $\theta = 90° + \dfrac{\beta}{2}$

(iii) When $2\theta = \beta + 90°$, p_t attains its maximum value

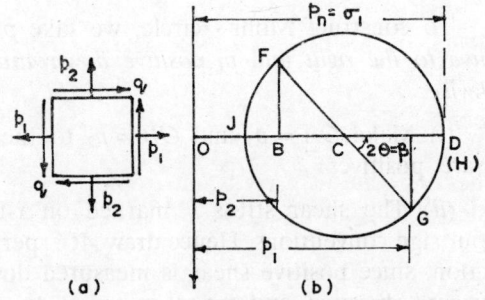

FIG. 4.20

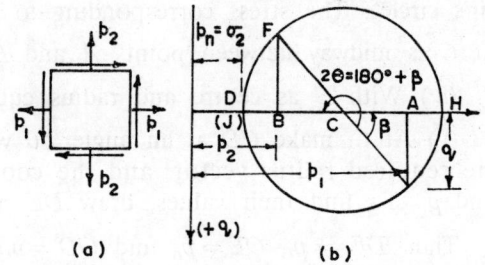

FIG. 4.21

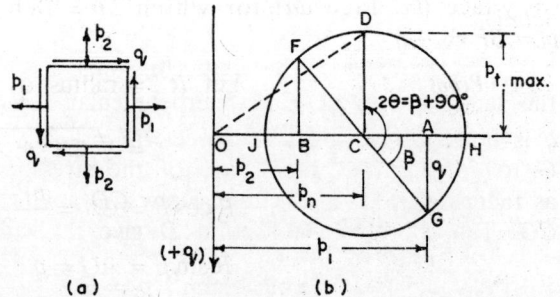

FIG. 4.22

$$p_{t,max} = R = -\sqrt{\tfrac{1}{4}(p_1 - p_2)^2 + q^2} = -\frac{\sigma_1 - \sigma_2}{2}$$

(*iv*) Similarly, when $2\theta = \beta + 270°$

$$p_{t,max} = R = \sqrt{\tfrac{1}{4}(p_1 - p_2)^2 + q^2} = \tfrac{1}{2}(\sigma_1 - \sigma_2)$$

Example 4.10. *A piece of material is subjected to tensile stresses of 70 N/mm² and 30 N/mm² at right angles to each other. Find fully the stresses on a plane the normal of which makes an angle of 35° with the 70 N/mm² stress.*

Solution :

To construct Mohr circle, mark $OA = p_1 = 70$ N/mm² and $OB = p_2 = 30$ N/mm² to the same side of O, since both of them are positive. There are no shearing stresses present in the stress system. Bisect AB to get C, the centre of the circle. Draw the stress circle with C as centre and CA (or CB) as radius. Draw CD at $2\theta = 70°$ to x-axis, in the counter clockwise direction, Drop perpendicular DE. The stress circle is shown in Fig. 4.23 (*b*) from which we obtain

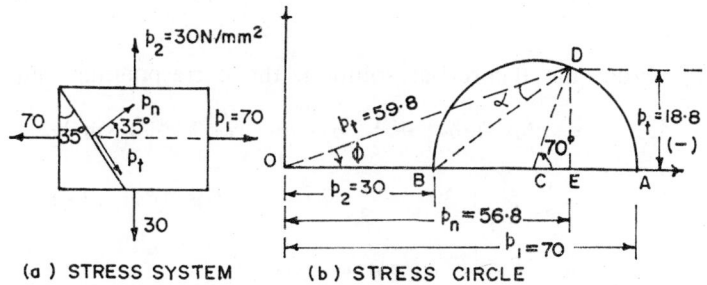

(a) STRESS SYSTEM (b) STRESS CIRCLE

FIG. 4.23

$$p_n = OE \approx \mathbf{56.8\ N/mm^2};$$

$p_t = DE \approx -\mathbf{18.8\ N/mm^2}$ (*i.e.* anticlockwise rotation) $p_r = OD \approx \mathbf{59.8\ N/mm^2}$

Also $\qquad \varphi \approx -\mathbf{18.5°}$ and $\alpha \approx \mathbf{16.5°}$.

Example 4.11. *At a point in a material, the stresses on two mutually perpendicular planes are 50 N/mm² (tensile) and 30 N/mm² (tensile). The shear stress across these planes is 12 N/mm². Using Mohr circle, find magnitude and direction of the resultar.: stress on a plane making an angle of 35° with the plane of the first stress. Find also, the normal and tangential stresses on this plane.*

Solution :

To draw Mohr's circle (Fig 4.24 *b*), make $OA = 50$ N/mm² and $OB = 30$ N/mm², to the same side of O. Erect perpendicular $AG = 12$ N/mm² in the downward direction (since q is positive on x-face) and erect $BF = 12$ N/mm² (since q is negative on y-face). Join F and G to get point C, the centre of the stress circle. With C as the centre and CG (or CF) as radius, draw Mohr's circle. Draw CD at angle $2\theta = 70°$ in the anti-clockwise direction with CG. The coordinates of point D give the values of p_n and p_t. Thus, we obtain :

$$p_n = OE = \mathbf{54.5\ N/mm^2};\ p_t = ED = -\mathbf{5.5\ N/mm^2};\ p_r = OD = \mathbf{54.5\ N/mm^2}$$

$$\varphi = -\mathbf{5.5°}$$

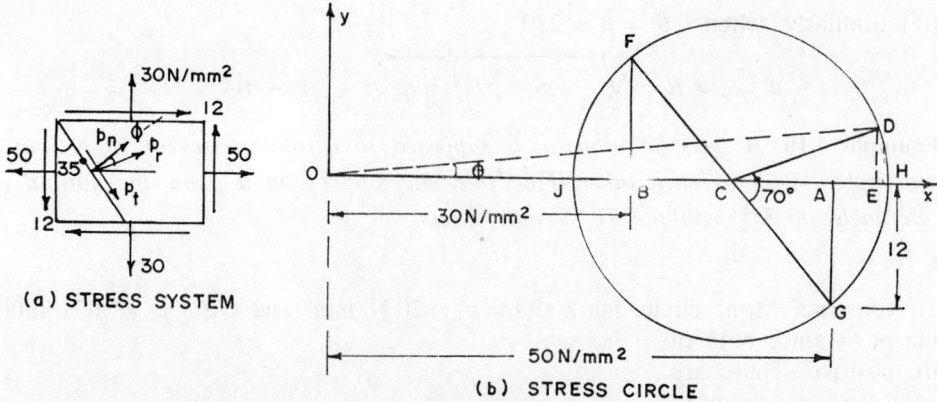

(a) STRESS SYSTEM

(b) STRESS CIRCLE

FIG. 4.24

From the theoretical solution, the corresponding values will be as under :

$$p_n = \frac{1}{2}\left(p_1 + p_2\right) + \frac{1}{2}\left(p_1 - p_2\right)\cos 2\theta + q\sin 2\theta$$

$$= \frac{1}{2}\left(50 + 30\right) + \frac{1}{2}(50 - 30)\cos 70° + 12\sin 70° = \mathbf{54.7\ N/mm^2}$$

$$p_t = -\frac{p_1 - p_2}{2}\sin 2\theta + q\cos 2\theta$$

$$= -\frac{50 - 30}{2}\sin 70° + 12\cos 70° = \mathbf{-5.29\ N/mm^2}$$

$$p_r = \sqrt{(54.7)^2 + (-5.29)^2} = \mathbf{54.96\ N/mm^2}$$

$$\varphi = \tan^{-1}\left(\frac{p_t}{p_n}\right) = \tan^{-1}\left(\frac{-5.29}{54.7}\right) = \mathbf{-5.52°}$$

(*i.e.* in the clockwise direction as marked in Fig 4.24 *a*)

Example 4.12. *For the data of Example 4.11, find the stresses on a plane making an angle of 15° with the plane of the first stress.*

Solution :

The stress circle is shown in Fig 4.25 (*b*). Here the point *D* falls below the *x*-axis. Hence the shear stress $p_t\,(=DE)$ comes out to be positive, as marked in Fig. 4.25 (*a*). From the stress circle we get

$$p_n = OE = \mathbf{54.5\ N/mm^2};\ \ p_t = ED = \mathbf{5.5\ N/mm^2};\ \ p_r = OD = \mathbf{54.5\ N/mm^2}$$

$$\varphi \approx \mathbf{+5.5°}$$

Analytical check :

$$p_n = \frac{1}{2}(50 + 30) + \frac{1}{2}(50 - 30)\cos 30° + 12\sin 30° = \mathbf{54.67\ N/mm^2}$$

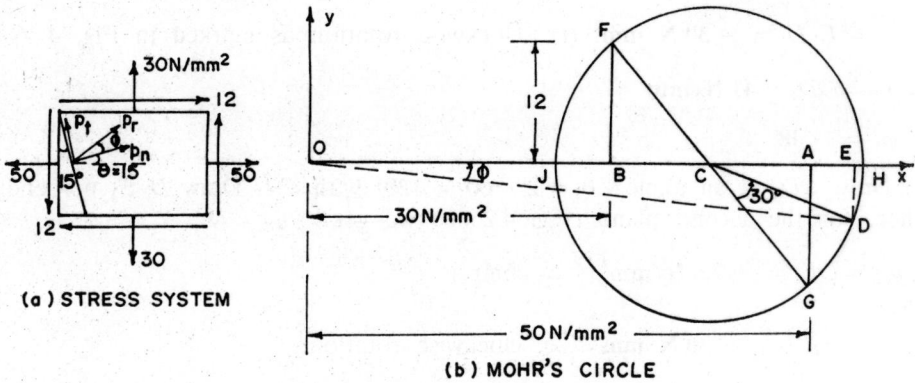

(a) STRESS SYSTEM

(b) MOHR'S CIRCLE

FIG. 4.25

$$p_t = -\frac{50-30}{2}\sin 30° + 12\cos 30° = +5.39 \text{ N/mm}^2$$

$$p_r = \sqrt{(54.67)^2 + (5.39)^2} = 54.94 \text{ N/mm}^2 \; ; \; \varphi = \tan^{-1}\left(\frac{p_t}{p_n}\right) = \tan^{-1}\left(\frac{5.39}{54.67}\right) = +5.63°$$

Example 4.13. *Draw Mohr's stress circle for direct stresses of 45 N/mm² (tensile) and 25 N/mm² (comp.) and find the magnitude and direction of resultant stresses on planes making angles of 30° and 60° with the plane of first principal stress. Also, find the normal and tangential stresses on these planes.*

Solution : To draw Mohr's circle, plot $OA = 45$ N/mm² to the right and $OB = 25$ N/mm² to the left of origin O. Bisect AB to get C. With C as centre and CA (or CB) as radius, draw the stress circle.

(*a*) Draw CD_1, at an angle $2\theta_1 = 2 \times 30° = 60°$ with CA. Draw D_1E_1 perpendicular to *x*-axis. Then for the first plane (Fig 4.26 *a*), we get

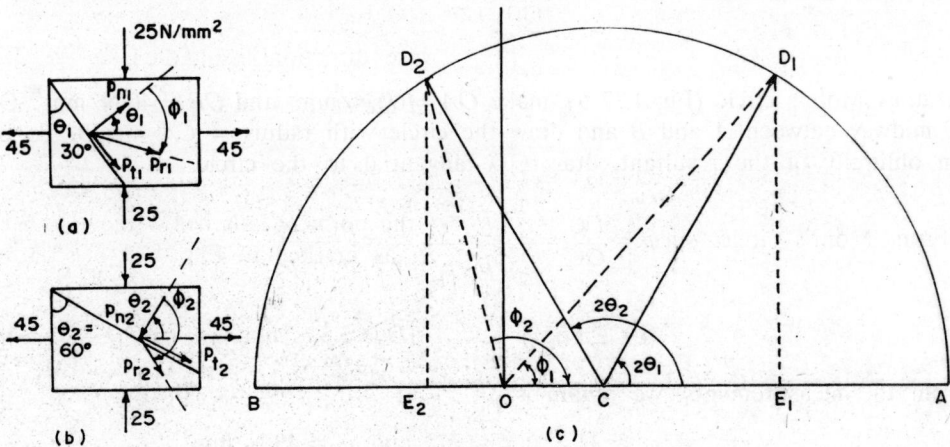

FIG. 4.26

$$p_{n1} = OE_1 = \mathbf{27.5\,N/mm^2} \text{ (tensile)}$$

$$p_{t1} = E_1 D_1 = \mathbf{-30\,N/mm^2} \text{ (i.e. clockwise rotation as marked in Fig. 4.26 }a\text{)}$$

$$p_{r1} = OD_1 = \mathbf{41\,N/mm^2}$$

and $\qquad \varphi_1 = \mathbf{-48°}$

(b) Draw CD_2 at an angle $2\,\theta_2 = 2 \times 60° = 120°$ with CA. Draw $D_2 E_2$ perpendicular to x-axis. Then, for the second plane (Fig. 4.26 b) we get

$$p_{n2} = OE_2 = \mathbf{-7.5\,N/mm^2} \text{ (i.e. comp.)}$$

$$p_{t2} = E_2 D_2 = \mathbf{-30\,N/mm^2} \text{ (i.e. clockwise rotation)}$$

$$p_{r2} = OD_2 = \mathbf{31\,N/mm^2}$$

and $\qquad \varphi_2 = \mathbf{-104°}$

Example 4.14. *Solve example 4.7, using Mohr's stress circle solution.*

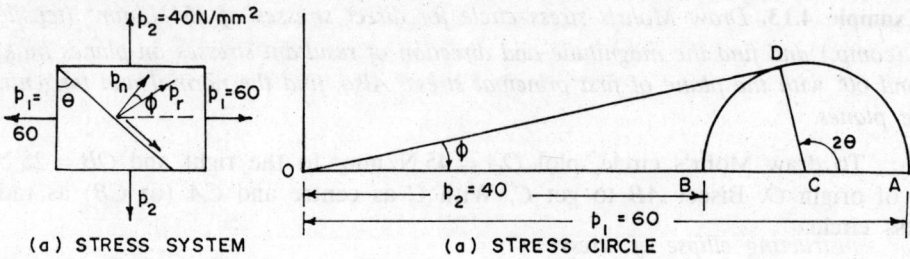

(a) STRESS SYSTEM   (a) STRESS CIRCLE

FIG. 4.27

Solution :

To draw Mohr's circle (Fig 4.27 b), make $OA = 60\,N/mm^2$ and $OB = 40\,N/mm^2$. Obtain centre C midway between A and B and draw the circle with radius $= CA = CB$. To obtain maximum obliquity of the resultant, draw OD tangential to the circle.

From Mohr's circle, $\sin \varphi = \dfrac{DC}{OC} = \dfrac{\frac{1}{2}(p_1 - p_2)}{\frac{1}{2}(p_1 + p_2)} = \dfrac{p_1 - p_2}{p_1 + p_2}$

and $\qquad\qquad\qquad \theta = \dfrac{1}{2}\left(90 + \varphi\right)$

From the measurements, we obtain

$$\varphi \approx 11.5° \ ; \ \theta \approx 51° \text{ and } p_r = 49\,N/mm^2$$

4.8. ELLIPSE OF STRESS

There are two graphical methods available for finding stresses on an inclined plane in a material : (i) method of *stress circle* (Mohr's circle) and (ii) method of *ellipse of stress*. Though the first method (*i.e.* stress circle method) is applicable for a two dimensional generalised stress system, the method of ellipse of stress is suitable when the material is subjected to direct stresses p_1 and p_2 only (Fig 4.28 a).

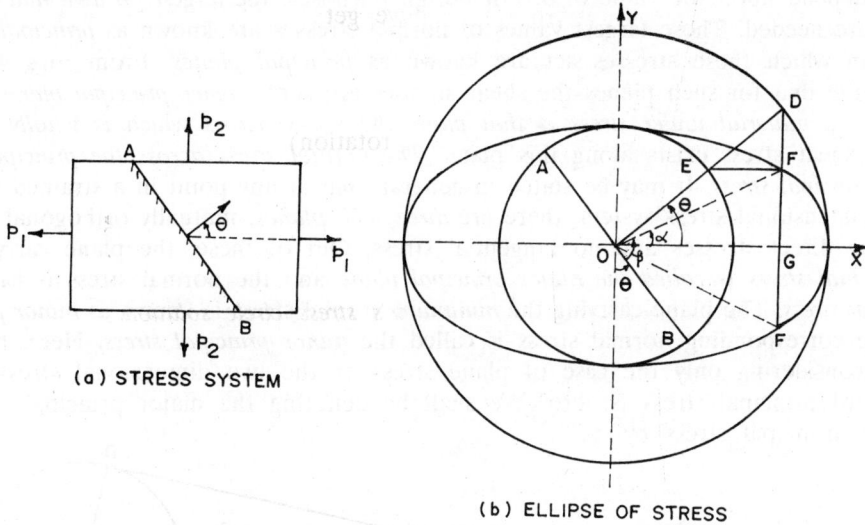

(a) STRESS SYSTEM

(b) ELLIPSE OF STRESS

FIG. 4.28

Steps for constructing ellipse of stress

1. Let O be the origin through which x and y axes pass. Through O, draw two concentric circles with radius $R_1 = p_1$ and $R_2 = p_2$, to some suitable scale.

2. Draw the plane AB at an angle θ with the y-axis. Draw its normal OD cutting the inner and outer circles at E and D respectively. Obviously, the normal OD makes an angle θ with the x-axis which represents the direction of p_1. It is to be noted that the y-axis represents the direction of p_2.

3. Through E, draw a line EF parallel to x-axis and through D, draw a line DG parallel to the y-axis, so that both the lines meet at point F. Join OF.

4. Point F is one of the points on the ellipse. For different values of angle θ, the point F may be established. *The locus of F will evidently be an ellipse.* The diagram is, therefore, known as ellipse of stress (Fig. 4.28 b). From the diagram,

$$OG = OD \cos \theta = p_1 \cos \theta; \quad FG = p_2 \sin \theta.$$

$$\therefore \qquad OF = \sqrt{p_1^2 \cos^2 \theta + p_2^2 \sin^2 \theta} = p_r$$

Hence OF gives the resultant stress p_r of this plane.

Also, $\tan \alpha = \dfrac{p_2 \sin \theta}{p_1 \cos \theta} = \dfrac{p_2}{p_1} \tan \theta$, as earlier.

4.9. PRINCIPAL STRESSES AND PRINCIPAL PLANES

We have seen that when a material is subjected to a plane stress system (consisting of p_1, p_2 and q) the resulting normal and shear stress on a plane through the point varies with the angle θ. This variation is continuous as the stress element is rotated. The magnitudes of p_n and p_t depend upon the value of θ. For design purposes, the *largest positive and negative* values of p_n are needed. These largest values of normal stresses are known as *principal stresses* and planes on which these stresses act are known as *principal planes*. From Figs 4.20 and 4.21, we observe that for such planes the shear stresses are zero. *Hence principal plane through a point within a material under stress is that plane the stress across which is wholly normal*; evidently, no shear stress exists along this plane. *The normal stress across the principal plane is known as principal stress*. It may be stated in general, that at any point in a strained material under three dimensional stress system, there are *three such planes*, mutually orthogonal to each other, carrying direct stresses and no tangential stress. Out of these, the plane carrying the *maximum normal stress is called the major principal plane* and the normal stress is called the *major principal stress*. The plane carrying the *minimum* normal stress is known as *minor principal plane* and the corresponding normal stress is called the *minor principal stress*. Here, however, we shall be considering only the case of plane stress or the two dimensional stress system where the third principal stress is zero. We shall be denoting the major principal stress by σ_1 and minor principal stress by σ_2.

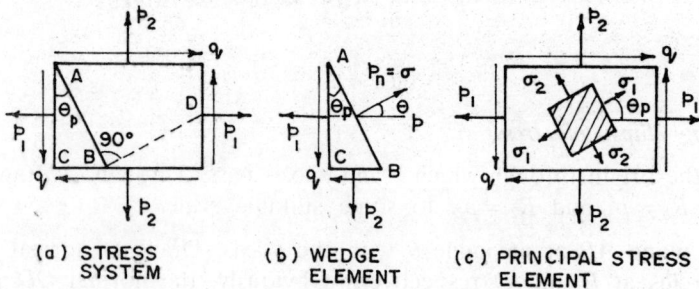

(a) STRESS SYSTEM (b) WEDGE ELEMENT (c) PRINCIPAL STRESS ELEMENT

FIG. 4.29

Fig 4.29 (*a*) shows the plane stress case where the element is subjected to p_1, p_2 and q. Fig. 4.29 (*b*) shows wedge shaped element in equilibrium, where the resultant stress $p_n = \sigma$ is wholly normal to the inclined plane AB called the *principal plane*.

Resolving the *forces* parallel to BC, we have

$$(\sigma . AB) \cos \theta_p = p_1 . AC + q . BC$$

or $\sigma \cos \theta_p = p_1 \dfrac{AC}{AB} + q . \dfrac{BC}{AB} = p_1 \cos \theta_p + q \sin \theta_p.$

$\therefore$ $(\sigma - p_1) \cos \theta_p = q \sin \theta_p$

or $(\sigma - p_1) = q \tan \theta_p$ ...(1)

Similarly, resolving the forces along AC, we have

$$(\sigma . AB) \sin \theta_p = p_2 . BC + q . AC$$

or

$$\sigma \sin \theta_p = p_2 . \frac{BC}{AB} + q . \frac{AC}{AB} = p_2 \sin \theta_p + q \cos \theta_p$$

or

$$(\sigma - p_2) = q \cot \theta_p \qquad \qquad ...(2)$$

Subtracting (1) from (2), we get

$$(p_1 - p_2) = q \left(\cot \theta_p - \tan \theta_p \right) = \frac{2q}{\tan 2\theta_p}$$

$\therefore$

$$\tan 2\theta_p = \frac{2q}{p_1 - p_2} \qquad \qquad ...(4.21)$$

where θ_p defines the position of the principal planes,

Again, multiplying (1) and (2), we get

$$(\sigma - p_1)(\sigma - p_2) = q^2$$

or

$$\sigma^2 - p_1 \sigma - p_2 \sigma + p_1 p_2 - q^2 = 0$$

or

$$\sigma^2 - \sigma \left(p_1 + p_2 \right) + \left(p_1 p_2 - q^2 \right) = 0$$

which is the quadratic equation for the principal stress σ, from which

$$\sigma = \frac{1}{2}\left(p_1 + p_2 \right) \pm \sqrt{\frac{1}{4}\left(p_1 + p_2 \right)^2 + \left(q^2 - p_1 p_2 \right)}$$

or

$$\sigma = \frac{1}{2}\left(p_1 + p_2 \right) \pm \sqrt{\left(\frac{p_1 - p_2}{2} \right)^2 + q^2}$$

Hence

$$\sigma_1 = \frac{p_1 + p_2}{2} + \sqrt{\left(\frac{p_1 - p_2}{2} \right)^2 + q^2} \qquad \qquad ...(4.22 \ a)$$

and

$$\sigma_2 = \frac{p_1 + p_2}{2} - \sqrt{\left(\frac{p_1 - p_2}{2} \right)^2 + q^2} \qquad \qquad ...(4.22 \ a)$$

where σ_1 is the *major principal stress* and σ_2 is the *minor principal stress*.

The orientation of principal planes are shown in Fig. 4.29 (c)

Alternative method for finding θ_p , σ_1 and σ_2

We have

$$p_n = \frac{p_1 + p_2}{2} + \frac{p_1 - p_2}{2} \cos 2\theta + q \sin 2\theta \qquad \qquad ...(Eq. \ 4.15)$$

For getting maximum (or minimum) value of p_n, differentiate the above expression with θ and equate it to zero.

$\therefore$

$$\frac{d p_n}{d \theta} = -(p_1 - p_2) \sin 2\theta + 2q \cos 2\theta$$

From which, we get $\tan 2\theta_p = \dfrac{2q}{p_1 - p_2} \qquad \qquad ...(4.21)$

Eq. 4.21 can be represented *diagrammatically* by Fig. 4.30, in which

$$\tan 2\theta_p = \frac{q}{\dfrac{p_1 - p_2}{2}} \left(= \frac{2q}{p_1 - p_2} \right)$$

Hence diagonal $R = \sqrt{\left(\dfrac{p_1 - p_2}{2}\right)^2 + q^2}$

(Taking only the positive root)

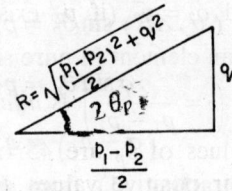

FIG. 4.30. DIAGRAMMATIC REPRESENTATION OF EQ. 4.21

Thus, $\cos 2\theta_p = \dfrac{p_1 - p_2}{2R}$ and $\sin 2\theta_p = \dfrac{q}{R}$ ...(4.21 a, b)

Substituting the values of $\cos 2\theta_p$ and $\sin 2\theta_p$ in Eq. 4.15 and setting $p_n = \sigma_1$, we get

$$\sigma_1 = \frac{p_1 + p_2}{2} + \sqrt{\left(\frac{p_1 - p_2}{2}\right) + q^2}   ...(4.22\ a)$$

The minor principal stress σ_2 is obtained from the relation :

$$\sigma_1 + \sigma_2 = p_1 + p_2$$

$\therefore$ $$\sigma_2 = \left(p_1 + p_2\right) - \left[\frac{p_1 + p_2}{2} + \sqrt{\left(\frac{p_1 - p_2}{2}\right)^2 + q^2}\right]$$

From which $$\sigma_2 = \frac{p_1 + p_2}{2} - \sqrt{\left(\frac{p_1 - p_2}{2}\right)^2 + q^2}   ...(4.22\ b)$$

Hence $$\sigma_{1,2} = \frac{1}{2}\left(p_1 + p_2\right) \pm \sqrt{\left(\frac{p_1 - p_2}{2}\right)^2 + q^2}   ...(4.22)$$

Note : An important characteristic concerning the principal planes can be observed from Eq. 4.16 for shear stress :

$$p_t = -\frac{p_1 - p_2}{2}\sin 2\theta + q\cos 2\theta$$

Setting the above to zero and solving for θ, we get

$$\tan 2\theta = \frac{2q}{p_1 - p_2}$$

Comparing this with Eq 4.21, we observe that *shear stresses are zero on the principal planes.*

Orientation of principal planes

The orientation of principal planes for the cases of uniaxial, and biaxial stress systems are shown in Fig. 4.31. The principal planes for such stresses are the x and y planes them selves because than $2\theta_p = 0$ and hence the

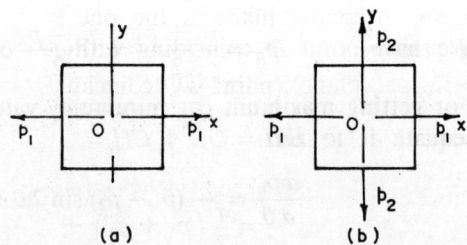

FIG. 4.31. ELEMENTS IN UNIAXIAL AND BIAXIAL STRESS

two values of θ_p are $0°$ and $90°$, Here, $\sigma_1 = p_1$ and $\sigma_2 = p_2$ (if p_2 exists).

For an element in pure shear (Fig. 4.32 a), $\tan 2\theta_p \left(= \dfrac{2q}{p_1 - p_2} \right)$ is *infinite* and hence the two values of θ_p are $45°$ and $135°$ (Fig 4.32 b). For positive values of q (Fig 4.32 a), we get (from Eq 4.22), $\sigma_1 = q$ and $\sigma_2 = -q$.

For a general case of two dimensional stress system (Fig 4.33 a,c) or the plane stress case, the orientation of principal plane are shown in Fig 4.33 (b) and 4.33 (c).

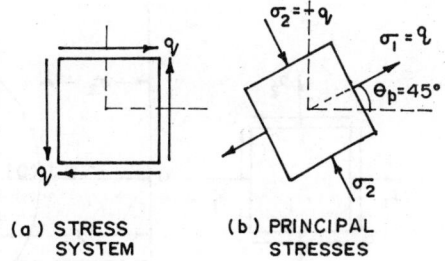

(a) STRESS SYSTEM   (b) PRINCIPAL STRESSES

FIG. 4.32. ELEMENT IN PURE SHEAR

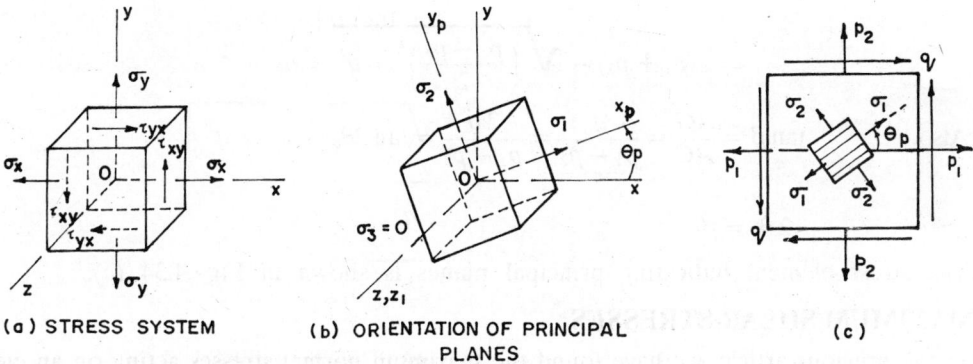

(a) STRESS SYSTEM   (b) ORIENTATION OF PRINCIPAL PLANES   (c)

FIG. 4.33. PRINCIPAL PLANES FOR AN ELEMENT IN PLANE STRESS

Mohr's stress circle method

Principal stresses and principal planes can also be found by Mohr's circle method, illustrated in Fig. 4.34(b). To locate the principal plane, mark OA and OB equal to p_1 and p_2 respectively to some scale. At A, perpendicular $AG = q$ in downward direction (since q is positive). Similarly, erect perpendicular $BF = q$ in upward direction. Joint F and G intersecting the axis in C. Since, by definition, principal plane is the one at which shear stress is zero, CH represents major principal plane (point D coinciding with H) and angle $2\theta_p = \beta$. Similarly, CJ represents the minor principal plane (point D' coinciding with J), and angle $2\theta_p = 180° + \beta$.

Now $\qquad OH = OC + CH = \dfrac{1}{2}\left(p_1 + p_2 \right) + R$, where R=radius of circle

$$= \dfrac{1}{2}\left(p_1 + p_2 \right) + \sqrt{ \left(\dfrac{p_1 - p_2}{2} \right)^2 + q^2 } = \sigma_1$$

Similarly, $\qquad OJ = OC - CJ = \dfrac{1}{2}(p_1 + p_2) - R$, where R= radius of circle

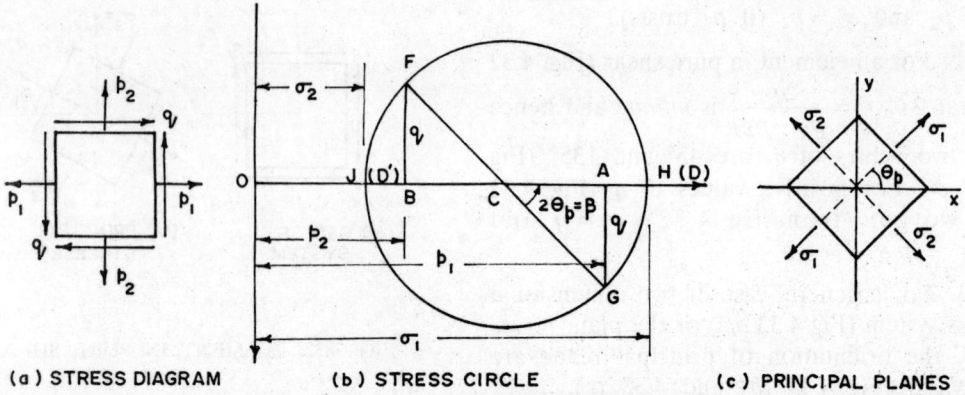

(a) STRESS DIAGRAM   (b) STRESS CIRCLE   (c) PRINCIPAL PLANES

FIG. 4.34. MOHR'S CIRCLE METHOD

$$= \tfrac{1}{2}(p_1 + p_2) - \sqrt{\left(\frac{p_1 - p_2}{2}\right)^2 + q^2} = \sigma_2$$

Also, $\tan \beta = \dfrac{AG}{AC} = \dfrac{q}{\dfrac{p_1 - p_2}{2}} = \dfrac{2q}{p_1 - p_2} = \tan 2\theta_p$

where $2\theta_p = \beta$

The stress element indicating principal planes is shown in Fig. 4.34 (c).

4.10. MAXIMUM SHEAR STRESSES

In the previous article, we have found the maximum normal stresses acting on an element in plane stress and have seen that the shearing stresses are zero on the planes (called principal planes) on which these maximum normal stresses (called principal stresses) act. Let us now determine the maximum shear stresses and the planes on which they act.

In general, the shear stress varies with angle θ, and its magnitude is given by :

$$p_t = -\left(\frac{p_1 - p_2}{2}\right) \sin 2\theta + q \cos 2\theta \qquad \qquad ...(4.16)$$

For maximum value of p_t, differentiate it with respect to θ and equate it to zero.

$\therefore$ $\dfrac{dp_t}{d\theta} = -(p_1 - p_2) \cos 2\theta - 2q \sin 2\theta = 0$

from which $\tan 2\theta = \tan 2\theta_s = -\dfrac{p_1 - p_2}{2q}$ $...(4.23)$

Eq. 4.23 gives one value of θ_s between $0°$ and $90°$ and another value of θ_s between $90°$ and $180°$, both values differing by $90°$. This means that the maximum and minimum values of p_t occur on perpendicular planes. However, since shear stresses on perpendicular planes are equal in absolute value, the *maximum and minimum shear stress differ only in sign*.

Also, by comparing Eqs. 4.23 with Eq. 4.21, we observe that

$$\tan 2\theta_s = -\frac{1}{\tan 2\theta_p} = -\cot 2\theta_p \qquad \qquad ...(4.24)$$

Since $\tan(\alpha \pm 90°) = -\cot\alpha$, we have :

$$2\theta_s = 2\theta_p \pm 90° \text{ or } \theta_s = \theta_p \pm 45° \qquad \qquad ...(4.25)$$

Hence *planes of maximum shear stress occur at 45° to the principal planes.*

Eq. 4.23 is diagrammatically represented by Fig. 4.35, where

$$\tan 2\theta_s = \frac{-\dfrac{p_1 - p_2}{2}}{q} = -\frac{p_1 - p_2}{2q}$$

$$\therefore \qquad \cos 2\theta_{s1} = \frac{q}{R} \text{ and } \sin 2\theta_{s1} = -\frac{p_1 - p_2}{2R} \qquad ...(4.26)$$

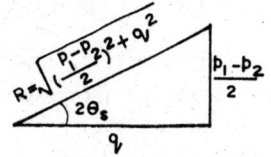

where
$$R = \sqrt{\left(\frac{p_1 - p_2}{2}\right)^2 + q^2}$$

Also, θ_{s1} is related to θ_{p1} by the relation

$$\theta_{s1} = \theta_{p1} - 45°$$

FIG. 4.35   ...(4.27)

Substituting the values of $\cos 2\theta_{s1}$ and $\sin 2\theta_{s1}$ in Eq. 4.16, we get

$$p_{t,\,max} = -\left(\frac{p_1 - p_2}{2}\right) \times \left(-\frac{p_1 - p_2}{2R}\right) + q \cdot \frac{q}{R}$$

or
$$p_{t,\,max} = \sqrt{\left(\frac{p_1 - p_2}{2}\right)^2 + q^2} \qquad \qquad ...(4.28)$$

Note that, algebraically, minimum shear stress $p_{t,\,min}$ has the same magnitude but has opposite sign. Again, subtracting σ_2 from σ_1 (Eq. 4.22 b and 4.22 a), we get

$$\sigma_1 - \sigma_2 = 2\sqrt{\left(\frac{p_1 - p_2}{2}\right)^2 + q^2} \qquad \qquad ...(4.22\ c)$$

Comparing this with Eq. 4.28, we get

$$p_{t,\,max} = \frac{\sigma_1 - \sigma_2}{2} \qquad \qquad ...(4.29)$$

Hence the maximum shear stress is equal to one-half the difference of principal stresses.
It should be very clearly noted that *normal stresses also act on the planes of maximum shear stress.* The values of these normal stresses (p_{ns}, say) can be found by substituting the value of θ_{s1} in Eq. 4.15. Thus, we have

$$p_{ns} = \frac{p_1 + p_2}{2} + \frac{p_1 - p_2}{2} \times \frac{q}{R} + q\left(-\frac{p_1 - p_2}{2R}\right)$$

or
$$p_{ns} = \frac{p_1 + p_2}{2} = p_{av} \qquad \qquad ...(4.30)$$

Thus stress p_{av} acts on the plane of maximum shear stress and the plane of minimum shear stress.

Mohr's circle method : Mohr's stress circle method can also be used for locating the planes of maximum shear stress. Fig. 4.36 (b), shows Mohr's stress circle, for the stress system of Fig. 4.36 (a). Maximum shear stress corresponds to point D, when $2\theta_s = \beta + 90°$.

Evidently,

$$p_{t,\,max} = R = \sqrt{\left(\frac{p_1 - p_2}{2}\right)^2 + q^2}$$

$$= \frac{\sigma_1 - \sigma_2}{2} \text{ (numerically)}.$$

The corresponding normal stress is evidently equal to OC.

$$\therefore \quad p_{ns} = OC = \frac{1}{2}\left(p_1 + p_2\right)$$

Similarly, when $2\,\theta_s = \beta + 270°$ (corresponding to point D'),

$$p_{t,\,max} = R$$

$$= \sqrt{\left(\frac{p_1 - p_2}{2}\right)^2 + q^2}$$

$$= \frac{\sigma_1 - \sigma_2}{2}$$

...(4.28, 4.29)

Also, $2\,\theta_s = \beta + 90°$

$$\therefore \quad \tan 2\,\theta_s = \tan\left(\beta + 90°\right)$$

$$= -\cot\beta = -\frac{p_1 - p_2}{2\,q}$$

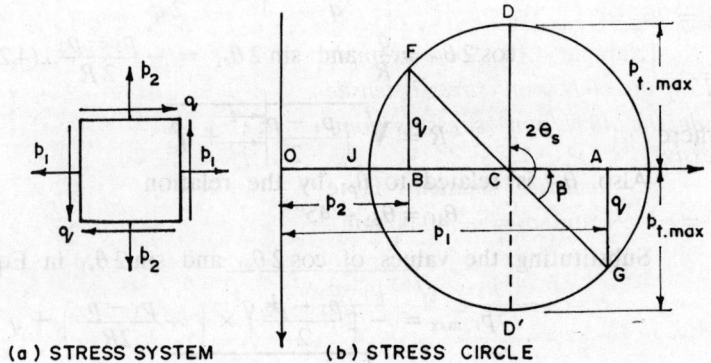

(a) STRESS SYSTEM   (b) STRESS CIRCLE

FIG. 4.36

Example 4.15. *At a point in an elastic material under strain, there are normal stresses of 60 N/mm² and 40 N/mm²(both tensile) respectively at right angles to each other, with positive shearing stress of 20 N/mm². Find (i) principal stresses and the position of principal planes, and (ii) maximum shear stress and its plane.*

(a) Analytical Solution

$$\sigma = \frac{p_1 + p_2}{2} \pm \sqrt{\left(\frac{p_1 - p_2}{2}\right)^2 + q^2} = \frac{60 + 40}{2} \pm \sqrt{\left(\frac{60 - 40}{2}\right)^2 + (20)^2}$$

$$= 50 \pm 22.36$$

$$\therefore \qquad \sigma_1 = \textbf{72.36 N/mm}^2 \text{ (tensile) and } \sigma_2 = \textbf{27.64 N/mm}^2 \text{ (tensile)}$$

$$\tan 2\,\theta_p = \frac{2\,q}{p_1 - p_2} = \frac{2 \times 20}{60 - 40} = 2 \text{ or } 2\,\theta_p = 63.43 = 63°26'$$

$$\therefore \qquad \theta_{p1} = \textbf{31°43}' \text{ and } \theta_{p2} = \textbf{121°43}'$$

$$p_{t.\,max} = \frac{\sigma_1 - \sigma_2}{2} = \frac{72.36 - 27.64}{2} = \textbf{22.36 N/mm}^2$$

$$\theta_{s1} = 45° + \theta_{p1} = 45° + 31°31' = \textbf{76°43}'$$

(b) Graphical Solution

Fig. 4.37 shows the graphical solution in the form of Mohr's circle. The method is self-explanatory. From the Mohr's stress circle, we obtain the following results :

$\sigma_1 = OH \approx 72.5 \text{ N/mm}^2$ (tension)

$\sigma_2 = OJ \approx 28 \text{ N/mm}^2$ (tension)

$\theta_{p1} \approx 31° 30'$; $\theta_{p2} \approx 121°30'$

$p_{t.\,max} = CD' = 22.3 \text{ N/mm}^2$;

$\theta_{s1} = 76° 30'$

Example 4.16. *Solve example 4.15 if the 60 N/mm² stress is tensile while the 40 N/mm² stress is compressive.*

(a) Analytical solution : Here $p_1 = +60$ and $p_2 = -40 \text{ N/mm}^2$.

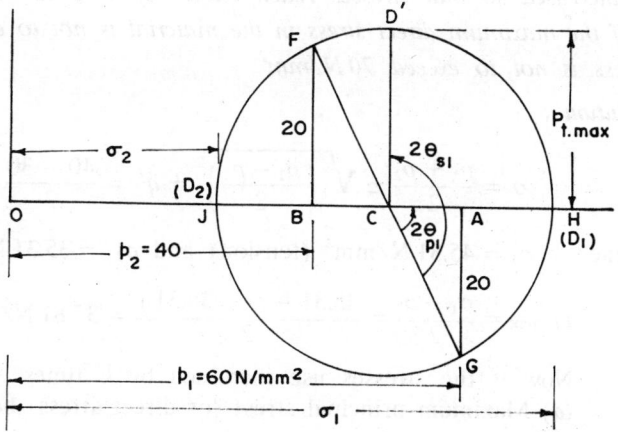

FIG. 4.37

$$\sigma = \frac{p_1 + p_2}{2} \pm \sqrt{\left(\frac{p_1 - p_2}{2}\right)^2 + q^2} = \frac{60 - 40}{2} \pm \sqrt{\left(\frac{60 + 40}{2}\right)^2 + (20)^2} = 10 \pm 53.85$$

$\therefore \qquad \sigma_1 = \textbf{63.85 N/mm}^2$

(tensile)

and $\sigma_2 = -\textbf{43.85 N/mm}^2$

(i.e. comp.)

$\tan 2\theta_p = \dfrac{2q}{p_1 - p_2} = \dfrac{2 \times 20}{60 + 40} = 0.4$

$\therefore 2\theta_p = 21.8°$ or $\theta_{p1} = \textbf{10° 34'}$

and $\theta_{p2} = \textbf{100° 34'}$

$p_{t,\,max} = \dfrac{\sigma_1 - \sigma_2}{2} = \dfrac{63.85 - (-43.85)}{2}$

$= \textbf{53.85 N/mm}^2$

$\theta_{s1} = 45° + \theta_{p1} = 45° + 10°34' = \textbf{55°34'}$

Graphical Solution : Graphical solution is shown in Fig 4.38. From Mohr's circle, we obtain the following results;

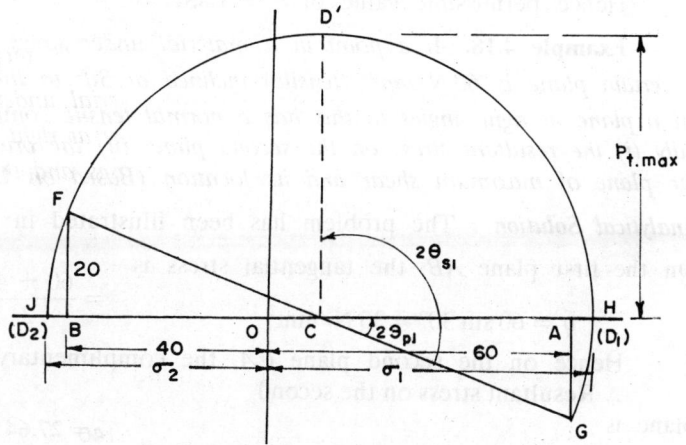

FIG. 4.38

$\sigma_1 \approx 64 \text{ N/mm}^2$ (tension) ; $\sigma_2 \approx 44 \text{ N/mm}^2$ (comp.)

$\theta_{p1} = 10°30'$; $\theta_{p2} = 100°30'$; $p_{t,\,max} \approx 54 \text{ N/mm}^2$; $\theta_{s1} = 55°30'$

Example 4.17. *At a certain point in a piece of elastic material, there are normal stresses of 40 N/mm² (tension) and 30 N/mm² (compression) on two planes at right angles to one another,* *together with shearing stress of 20 N/mm² on the same planes. If the loading on the material is increased so that stresses reach values of k times those given, find the maximum value of k if the maximum direct stress in the material is not to exceed 100 N/mm², and maximum shear stress is not to exceed 70 N/mm².*

Solution :

$$\sigma = \frac{p_1 + p_2}{2} \pm \sqrt{\left(\frac{p_1 - p_2}{2}\right)^2 + q^2} = \frac{40 - 30}{2} \pm \sqrt{\left(\frac{40 + 30}{2}\right)^2 + (20)^2} = 5 \pm 40.31$$

Hence $\sigma_1 = 45.31 \, \text{N/mm}^2$ (tension) and $\sigma_2 = 35.31 \, \text{N/mm}^2$ (comp.)

$$p_{t,\,max} = \frac{\sigma_1 - \sigma_2}{2} = \frac{45.31 - (-35.31)}{2} = 37.81 \, \text{N/mm}^2$$

Now if the stresses use increased by k times, we have

(a) Maximum principal stress (or direct stress) becomes 45.31 k, which is not to exceed 100 N/mm².

∴ $45.31 \, k = 100$

From which $k = 100/45.31 = 2.207$

(b) Maximum shear stress becomes 37.81 k, which is not to exceed 70 N/mm².

∴ $37.81 \, k = 70$

From which $k = 70/37.81 = 1.851$

Hence permissible value of k = **1.851**

Example 4.18. *At a point in a material under stress, the intensity of resultant stress on a certain plane is 60 N/mm² (tensile) inclined at 30° to the normal of that plane. The stress on a plane at right angles to this has a normal tensile component of intensity 40 N/mm². Find fully (i) the resultant stress on the second plane (ii) the principal planes and stresses, and (iii) the plane of maximum shear and its location (Based on U.L.).*

Analytical Solution : The problem has been illustrated in Fig. 4.39 (a).

On the first plane AB, the tangential stress is

$$q = 60 \sin 30° = 30 \, \text{N/mm}^2$$

Hence on the second plane CA, the complimentary shear stress is 30 N/mm².

∴ Resultant stress on the second plane is

$$p_r = \sqrt{(40)^2 + (30)^2}$$
$$= \textbf{50 N/mm}^2$$

The intensity of stress normal to the first plane (AB) is

$$p_n = 60 \cos 30° \approx 52 \, \text{N/mm}^2$$

The final stress system has been represented in Fig. 4.39 (b) from which the principal stresses are

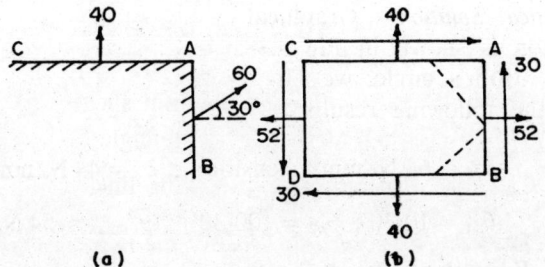

(a)   (b)

FIG. 4.39

$$\sigma = \frac{p_1 + p_2}{2} \pm \sqrt{\left(\frac{p_1 - p_2}{2}\right)^2 + q^2}$$

$$= \frac{52 + 40}{2} \pm \sqrt{\left(\frac{52 - 40}{2}\right)^2 + (30)^2} = 46 \pm 30.6$$

$\therefore$ $\sigma_1 = \mathbf{76.6\ N/mm^2}$ (tension) and $\sigma_2 = \mathbf{15.4\ N/mm^2}$ (tension)

$$\tan 2\theta_p = \frac{2q}{p_1 - p_2} = \frac{2 \times 30}{52 - 40} = \frac{60}{12} = 5,\ \text{from which}\ 2\theta_p = 78°42'$$

$\therefore$ $\theta_{p1} = \mathbf{39°21'}$ and $\theta_{p2} = \mathbf{129°21'}$

$$p_{t,\,max} = \frac{\sigma_1 - \sigma_2}{2} = \frac{76.6 - 15.4}{2} = \mathbf{30.6\ N/mm^2}$$

$$\theta_{s1} = 45° + \theta_{p1} = 45° + 39°21' = \mathbf{84°\,21'}$$

Graphical Solution (Refer Fig. 4.40)

On the plane AB, p_n is positive (being tensile) and p_t is positive being in the anticlockwise direction; the resultant stress is $60\ N/mm^2$. Hence draw OD at an inclination of $30°$ to OX, in the clockwise direction and make $OD = 60\ N/m\ m^2$. Draw DE perpendicular to OX. Since stress of CA is tensile (or is positive), set off $OE' = 40\ N/mm^2$ to the right of O. Bisect EE' to get the centre C. With C as centre and CD as radius, draw the Mohr's circle. The circle will cut the x-axis in H and J. From

FIG. 4.40

the circle, we have $OH = \sigma_1 = 76.5\ N/mm^2$; $OJ = \sigma_2 = 15.4\ N/mm^2$; $\angle HCD = 2\theta_p = 78°42'$ or $\theta_p = 39°21'$. Thus, normal to the principal plane is inclined at $39°21'$, in the anticlockwise direction, to the normal to AB. In other words, the principal plane is inclined at $39°21'$ to AB, in the anticlockwise direction.

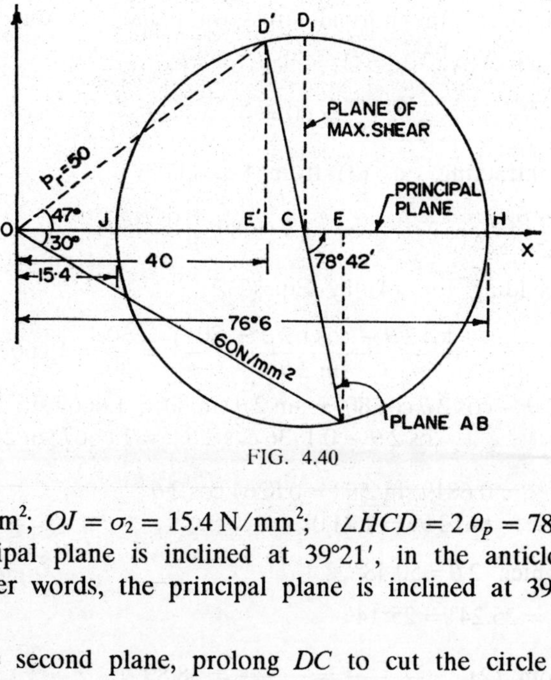

To find the resultant stress on the second plane, prolong DC to cut the circle in D'. Join O and D'. Thus $OD' = 50\ N/mm^2$ is the resultant on the second plane inclined at $47°$.

To locate the plane of maximum shear stress, draw CD_1 perpendicular to the axis OC. Thus $p_{t,\,max} = CD_1 = 30.6\ N/mm^2$. The angle of inclination of the plane of maximum shear stress $= \frac{1}{2}DCD_1 \approx 84°15'$, anticlockwise with line CD (i.e. with plane AB).

Example 4.19. *Fig. 4.41 shows the normal and tangential stresses on two planes. Determine the principal stresses. Also determine shear stress along CB.*

Solution :

Let the plane AB make an angle θ, in the anticlockwise direction, with the principal plane. Hence the angle made by plane BC with the principal plane will be $\theta + 40°$.

Let σ_1 and σ_2 be the principal stresses.

The normal and tangential stresses on plane AB, due to stresses σ_1 and σ_2 on the principal planes are given by

$$\left(p_n \right)_{AB} = 110 = \frac{\sigma_1 + \sigma_2}{2} + \frac{\sigma_1 - \sigma_2}{2} \cos 2\theta \qquad ...(4.15)$$

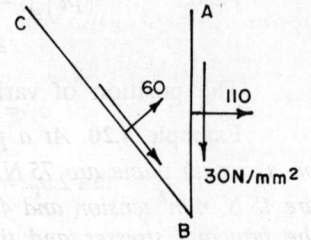

FIG. 4.41

and $\left(p_t \right)_{AB} = -30 = -\frac{\sigma_1 - \sigma_2}{2} \sin 2\theta \qquad ...(4.16)..(1)$

or $\qquad 30 = \frac{\sigma_1 - \sigma_2}{2} \sin 2\theta \qquad\qquad ...(2)$

Similarly, the normal stress on plane BC, due to stresses σ_1 and σ_2 on the principal planes is given by

$$\left(p_n \right)_{BC} = 60 = \frac{\sigma_1 + \sigma_2}{2} + \frac{\sigma_1 - \sigma_2}{2} \cos \left(2\theta + 80° \right) \qquad ...(4.15)...(3)$$

Subtracting Eq. (3) from Eq. (1),

$$\frac{\sigma_1 - \sigma_2}{2} \left[\cos 2\theta - \cos \left(2\theta + 80° \right) \right] = 50 \qquad ...(4)$$

Dividing Eq. (4) by Eq. (2),

$$\frac{\cos 2\theta - \cos \left(2\theta + 80° \right)}{\sin 2\theta} = \frac{50}{30} = 1.6667$$

or $\cos 2\theta - \cos 2\theta \cos 80° + \sin 2\theta \sin 80° = 1.6667 \sin 2\theta$

or $\qquad \cos 2\theta - 0.1736 \cos 2\theta = 1.6667 \sin 2\theta - 0.9848 \sin 2\theta$

or $\qquad 0.6819 \sin 2\theta = 0.8264 \cos 2\theta$

or $\qquad \tan 2\theta = 1.2119$

From which $2\theta = 50.48°$

or $\qquad \theta = 25.24° = 25°14'$

Now from (2) $\dfrac{\sigma_1 - \sigma_2}{2} = \dfrac{30}{\sin 2\theta} = 38.89$

or $\qquad \sigma_1 - \sigma_2 = 77.79 \qquad ...(i)$

From (i), $\dfrac{\sigma_1 + \sigma_2}{2} + \dfrac{\sigma_1 - \sigma_2}{2} \cos 2\theta = 110$

or $\qquad \dfrac{\sigma_1 + \sigma_2}{2} + \dfrac{77.79}{2} \cos 50.48° = 110$

From which $\qquad\qquad \sigma_1 + \sigma_2 \approx 170.5 \qquad\qquad ...(ii)$

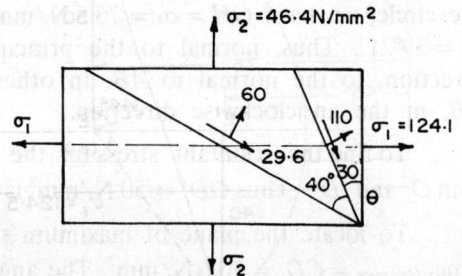

FIG 4.42

From (i) and (ii) we get $\sigma_1 = 124.1$ N/mm^2 and $\sigma_2 = 46.4$ N/mm^2

Also, $(p_t)_{BC} = -\dfrac{\sigma_1 - \sigma_2}{2} \sin\left(2\theta + 80\right)° = -\dfrac{77.79}{2}\sin\left(50.48° + 80°\right)$

≈ -29.6 N/mm^2 (*i.e* 29.6 in the direction marked in Fig 4.41)

The position of various planes are marked in Fig. 4.42.

Example 4.20. *At a point in a material subjected to two dimensional stresses, the stresses on a certain plane are 75 N/mm^2 tension and 50 N/mm^2 shear and on another plane the stresses are 45 N/mm^2 tension and 40 N/mm^2 shear as shown in Fig. 4.43. Find the principal stresses and their directions relative to the given planes.*

Solution :

For Plane AB

$p_n = +75$ (being tensile) and $p_t = -50$ (being clockwise)

Hence make $OE = +75$ N/mm^2 and $ED = -50$ N/mm^2 (*i.e.* upwards)

For plane AC : $p_n = +45$ (being tensile) and $p_t = +40$ (being anticlockwise)

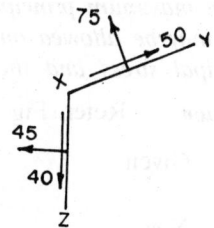

FIG. 4.43

Hence make $OE' = +45$ N/mm^2 and $E'D' = +40$ N/mm^2 (i.e downwards), as shown in Fig. 4.44 (*a*).

The Mohr's circle should pass through D and D'. Hence join D and D' and draw its perpendicular bisector to cut the x-axis is C, giving the centre of the circle. In this special case, C coincides with E. Join E and D'. Angle $DCH = 90°$. The plane AB is therefore inclined

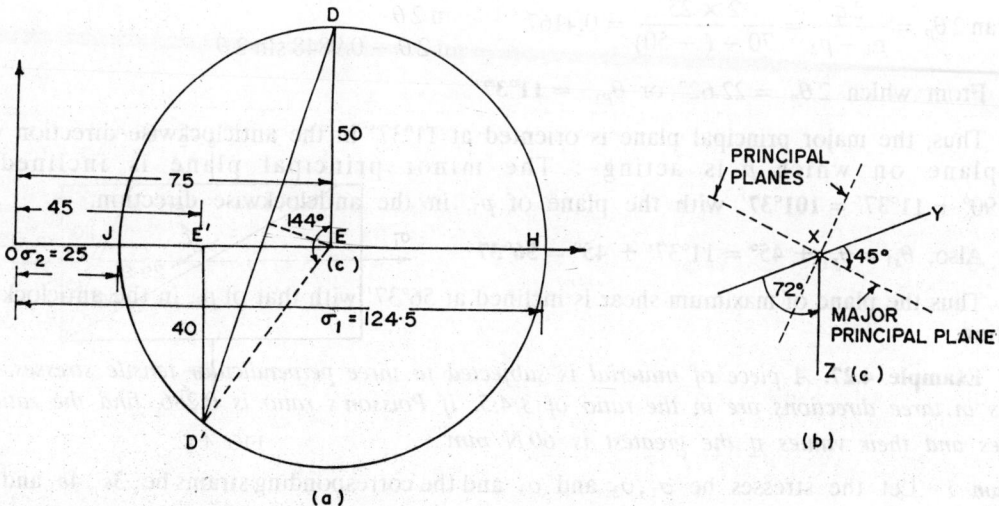

FIG. 4.44

at 45° to the principal planes in anticlockwise direction. Thus the principal planes are inclined at 45° to the AB plane in clockwise direction. The position of principal planes have been marked in Fig 4.44 (b). From Mohr's circle, we get

$$\sigma_1 = OH = + 124.5 \text{ N/mm}^2 \text{ and } \sigma_2 = OJ = + 25 \text{ N/mm}^2.$$

Also, $\angle DED' = 144°$. Hence angle between AB and $AC = 72°$ in the anticlockwise direction, as marked in Fig. 4.44 (b).

Example 4.21. *At a point in an elastic material a direct tensile stress of 70 N/mm² and a direct compressive stress of 50 N/mm² are applied on planes at right angles to each other. If the maximum principal stress in the material is limited to 75 N/mm², find out the shear stress that may be allowed on the planes. Also, determine the magnitude and direction of the minimum principal stress and the maximum shear stress.*

Solution :   Refer Fig 4.29.

Given $p_1 = + 70 \text{ N/mm}^2; \ p_2 = - 50 \text{ N/mm}^2 \text{ and } \sigma_1 = 75 \text{ N/mm}^2$

Now $\sigma_1 = \dfrac{p_1 + p_2}{2} + \sqrt{\left(\dfrac{p_1 - p_2}{2}\right)^2 + q^2}$

or $75 = \dfrac{70 - 50}{2} + \sqrt{\left(\dfrac{70 + 50}{2}\right)^2 + q^2}$

From which $q = 25 \text{ N/mm}^2$

Also, $\sigma_2 = \dfrac{p_1 + p_2}{2} - \sqrt{\left(\dfrac{p_1 - p_2}{2}\right)^2 + q^2} = \dfrac{70 - 50}{2} - \sqrt{\left(\dfrac{70 + 50}{2}\right)^2 + (25)^2}$

$$= 10 - 65 = - 55 \text{ N/mm}^2 \ (i.e. \text{ compressive}).$$

$$p_{t,\,max} = \dfrac{\sigma_1 - \sigma_2}{2} = \dfrac{75 - (-55)}{2} = 65 \text{ N/mm}^2$$

$$\tan 2\,\theta_p = \dfrac{2q}{p_1 - p_2} = \dfrac{2 \times 25}{70 - (-50)} = 0.4167$$

From which $2\,\theta_p = 22.62°$ or $\theta_{p1} \approx \mathbf{11°37'}$

Thus, the major principal plane is oriented at 11°37' in the anticlockwise direction with the plane on which p is acting : The minor principal plane is inclined at $\theta_{p2} = 90° + 11°37' = \mathbf{101°37'}$ with the plane of p_1, in the anticlockwise direction.

Also, $\theta_{s1} = \theta_{p1} + 45° = 11°37' + 45° = \mathbf{56°37'}$

Thus the plane of maximum shear is inclined at 56°37' with that of p_1, in the anticlockwise direction.

Example 4.27. *A piece of material is subjected to three perpendicular tensile stresses. The strains in three directions are in the ratio of 3:4:5. If Poisson's ratio is 0.286, find the ratio of stresses and their values if the greatest is 60 N/mm².*

Solution :   Let the stresses be σ_1, σ_2 and σ_3 and the corresponding strains be $3\varepsilon, 4\varepsilon$ and 5ε.

$$\therefore \qquad\qquad 3\,\varepsilon\,E = \sigma_1 - 0.286\left(\sigma_2 + \sigma_3\right) \qquad\qquad\qquad ...(i)$$

$$4 \varepsilon E = \sigma_2 - 0.286 \left(\sigma_3 + \sigma_1 \right) \qquad \qquad ...(ii)$$
$$5 \varepsilon E = \sigma_3 - 0.286 \left(\sigma_1 + \sigma_2 \right) \qquad \qquad ...(iii)$$

Subtracting (i) from (iii), we get $2 \varepsilon E = \left(\sigma_3 - \sigma_1 \right) - 0.286 \left(\sigma_1 - \sigma_3 \right)$

from which $\qquad \sigma_3 - \sigma_1 = \dfrac{2 \varepsilon E}{1.286} \qquad \qquad ...(iv)$

or $\qquad 1.286 \, \sigma_3 - 1.286 \, \sigma_1 = 2 \varepsilon E \qquad \qquad ...(a)$

Again, from (iii), $\dfrac{\sigma_3}{0.286} - \sigma_1 - \sigma_2 = \dfrac{5 \varepsilon E}{0.286} \qquad \qquad ...(v)$

and from (ii), $\sigma_2 - 0.286 \, \sigma_3 - 0.286 \, \sigma_1 = 4 \varepsilon E \qquad \qquad ...(vi)$

Adding (v) and (vi), $3.21 \, \sigma_3 - 1.286 \, \sigma_1 = 21.5 \, \varepsilon E$

Subtracting (a) and (b), we get $1.924 \, \sigma_3 = 19.5 \, \varepsilon E$

$\therefore \qquad \qquad \sigma_3 = 10.14 \, \varepsilon E$

Hence $\sigma_1 = 8.58 \, \varepsilon E$ (from iv) and $\sigma_2 = 9.35 \, \varepsilon E$ (from ii)

$\therefore \qquad \sigma_1 : \sigma_2 : \sigma_3 = 8.58 : 9.35 : 10.14$

$\therefore \qquad \sigma_1 : \sigma_2 : \sigma_3 = 0.847 : 0.923 : 1$

Taking $\qquad \sigma_3 = 60 \, \text{N/mm}^2$, we get

$\qquad \sigma_1 = 0.847 \times 60 = \mathbf{50.8 \, N/mm^2}$ and $\sigma_2 = 0.923 \times 60 = \mathbf{55.4 \, N/mm^2}$

4.11. ADDITIONAL ILLUSTRATIVE EXAMPLES

Example 4.22 *At a point in a piece of elastic material, there are three mutually perpendicular planes on which the stresses are as follows: tensile stress $50 \, N/mm^2$ and shear stress $40 \, N/mm^2$ on one plane, compressive stress $35 \, N/mm^2$ and complimentary shear stress $40 \, N/mm^2$ on the second plane, and no stress on the third plane. Find (a) the principal stresses and the positions of the planes on which they act (b) the position of planes on which there is no normal stress.*

Solution :

(a) **Graphical solution** (Fig 4.45 *a*)

(i) Mark off $OA = 50 \, \text{N/mm}^2$

$AG = -40 \, \text{N/mm}^2$ *(i.e.* upwards) $OB = -35 \, \text{N/mm}^2$ and $BF = +40 \, \text{N/mm}^2$ *(i.e.* downwards)

(ii) Join F and G, cutting AB in C. Draw the circle with C as the centre and CG (or CF) as radius, cutting the x-axis in H and J.

From Mohr circle, we get

$$\sigma_1 = OH = \mathbf{65.9 \, N/mm^2} \text{ (tensile)}$$

$$\sigma_2 = OJ = \mathbf{50.9 \, N/mm^2} \text{ (comp.)}$$

$$2 \theta_p = 43° \text{ or } \theta_{p1} = \mathbf{21° \, 30'}$$

The relative positions of the planes are shown in Fig. 4.45 (*a*).

If there is no normal stress on a plane, then for that plane O and A will coincide. The radius vector for that plane will be CG' in Fig. 4.45 (*a*) for which $2 \theta' = 97°$ or $\theta' = \mathbf{48° \, 30'}$

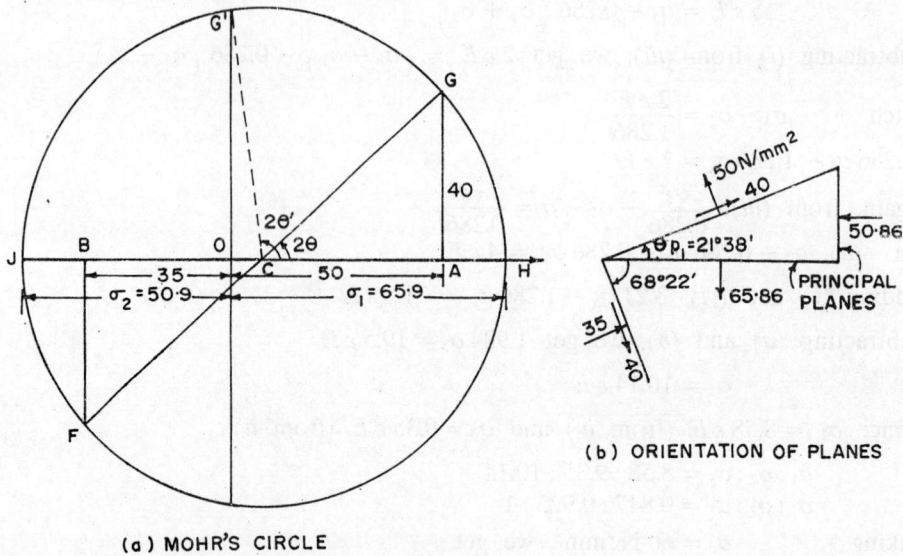

(a) MOHR'S CIRCLE

(b) ORIENTATION OF PLANES

FIG. 4.45

(b) Analytical Solution

$$\sigma = \frac{50 - 35}{2} \pm \sqrt{\left(\frac{50 + 35}{2}\right)^2 + (40)^2} = 7.5 \pm 58.36$$

∴ $\sigma_1 = 65.86 \text{ N/mm}^2$ (tensile)   and $\sigma_2 = -50.86 \text{ N/mm}^2$ (i.e. compressive)

$$2\,\theta_p = \tan^{-1}\frac{2 \times 40}{50 + 35} = 43° \, 16'$$

∴ $\theta_{p1} = 21° \, 38'$

If there is no normal stress on a plane, then for that plane θ and A will coincide and therefore the radius vector for that plane will be CG' (Fig. 4.45 a).

Then $2\,\theta' = 180° - \cos^{-1}\dfrac{OC}{CG'}$ where $OC = OA - CA = 50 - \dfrac{1}{2}\left(50 + 35\right) = 7.5$

and $CG' = R = CG = \sqrt{(40)^2 + (42.5)^2} = 58.36$

∴ $2\,\theta' = 180° - \cos^{-1}\dfrac{7.5}{58.36} = 180° - 82° \, 37' = 97°23'$

∴ $\theta' = 48° \, 41.5'$ to the principal plane.

Example 4.24. *An element in plane stress is subjected to stresses $p_1 = 120 \text{ N/m m}^2$, $p_2 = -40 \text{ N/mm}^2$ and $q = -45 \text{ N/mm}^2$, as shown in Fig 4.46 (a). Determine (a) the principal stresses and show them on a sketch of a properly oriented element. (b) the maximum shear stresses and show them on a properly oriented element. Consider only the in-plane stresses.*

Solution : Here $p_1 = +120 \text{ N/mm}^2$; $p_2 = -40 \text{ N/mm}^2$ and $q = -45 \text{ N/mm}^2$

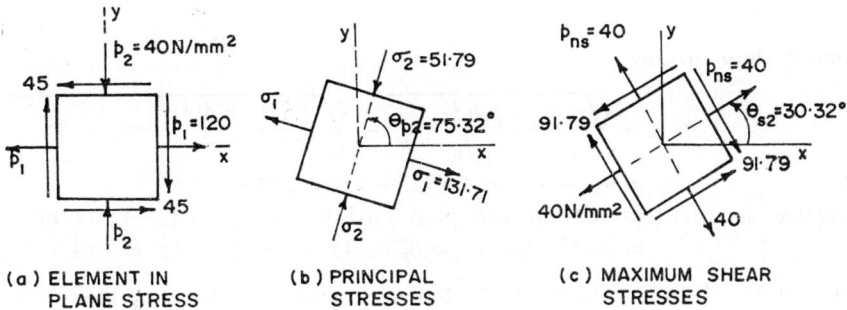

(a) ELEMENT IN PLANE STRESS   (b) PRINCIPAL STRESSES   (c) MAXIMUM SHEAR STRESSES

FIG. 4.46

(a) **Principal Stresses**

$$\sigma = \frac{p_1 + p_2}{2} \pm \sqrt{\left(\frac{p_1 - p_2}{2}\right)^2 + q^2} = \frac{120 + (-40)}{2} \pm \sqrt{\left(\frac{120 + 40}{2}\right)^2 + (-45)^2}$$

$$= 40 \pm 91.79$$

From which $\sigma_1 = 131.79 \, \text{N/mm}^2$ (tensile) and $\sigma_2 = -51.79 \, \text{N/mm}^2$ (i.e. compressive)

$$\tan 2\theta_p = \frac{2q}{p_1 - p_2} = \frac{2 \times (-45)}{120 + 40} = -0.5625, \text{ from which } 2\theta_p = -29.36°$$

Since $2\theta_p$ varies in the range from $0°$ to $360°$, we have

$$2\theta_p = 360° - 29.36° = 330.64° \text{ and } \theta_p = 165.32°$$

or
$$2\theta_p = 180° - 29.36° = 150.64° \text{ and } \theta_p = 75.32°$$

One of this angle is associated with the major principal stress while the other is associated with minor principal stress. Both these angles differ by $90°$. However, in order to remove confusion, we study Eqs. 4.21 (a,b) and Fig 4.30, correlating principal angles and stresses. The only angle that satisfies both the equations is θ_{p1}. Hence we can rewrite these equations as follows :

$$\cos 2\theta_{p1} = \frac{p_1 - p_2}{2R} \text{ and } \sin 2\theta_{p1} = \frac{q}{R}$$

where $R = \sqrt{\left(\frac{p_1 - p_2}{2}\right)^2 + q^2} = 91.79$ (found earlier)

$\therefore \quad \cos 2\theta_{p1} = \dfrac{120 + 40}{2 \times 91.79} = 0.8716$ from which $2\theta_{p1} = 29.36°$ (or $360° - 29.36° = 330.64°$)

and $\sin 2\theta_{p1} = -\dfrac{45}{91.79} = -0.4905$, from which $2\theta_{p1} = -29.30°$ (or $360° - 29.36°) = 330.64°$

The only angle between $0°$ and $360°$, satisfying both of these conditions is $2\theta_{p1} = 330.64°$. Hence $\theta_{p1} = \mathbf{165.32°}$

The other angle θ_{p2} is $90°$ larger or smaller than θ_{p1}

Hence $\theta_{p2} = 165.32° - 90° = \mathbf{75°32'}$

Fig. 4.46 (*b*) shows the rotated stress element showing the principal planes and principal stresses.

(*b*) Maximum shear stresses

$$q_{max} = \sqrt{\left(\frac{p_1 - p_2}{2}\right)^2 + q^2} = \sqrt{\left(\frac{120 + 40}{2}\right)^2 + (-45)^2} = 91.79$$

Also $\theta_{s1} = \theta_{p1} - 45° = 165.32° - 45° = 120.32°$

Negative shear stress acts as the plane for which $\theta_{s2} = 120.32° - 90°$
                    $= 30.32°$ (or $\theta_{s2} = \theta_{p2} - 45° = 75.32° - 45° = 30.32°$)

The normal stresses acting on the plane of maximum shear stresses are given by Eqs.

4.30 : $$p_{ns} = p_{av} = \frac{p_1 + p_2}{2} = \frac{120 - 40}{2} = 40 \text{ N/mm}^2$$

Fig. 4.46(*c*) shows the rotated stress element showing the maximum shear stresses and the planes on which they act, along with the corresponding normal stresses.

Example 4.25. *An element in plane stress is subjected to stresses $p_1 = 150 \text{ N/mm}^2$, $p_2 = 50 \text{ N/mm}^2$ and $q = 40 \text{ N/mm}^2$, as shown in Fig. 4.47 (a). Using Mohr's circle, determine (a) the stresses acting on an element rotated through an angle $\theta = 41°$ (b) the principal stresses, and (c) the maximum shear stresses. Show all results on sketches of properly oriented elements.*

Solution :

The Mohr's circle is shown in Fig. 4.47 (*b*), the construction of which is self explanatory.

From the stress circle of Fig. 4.47 (*b*), we get the following values :

$(p_n)_D = OE = + 147 \text{ N/mm}^2$; $(p_t)_D = ED = -44 \text{ N/mm}^2$; $(p_n)_{D'} = OE' = 54 \text{ N/mm}^2$
$\sigma_1 = OH = + 164 \text{ N/mm}^2$; $\sigma_2 = OJ = 36 \text{ N/mm}^2$

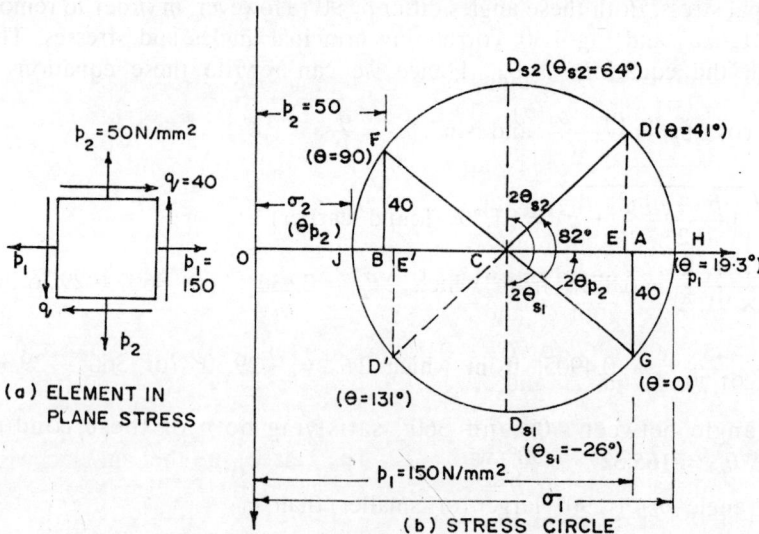

(*a*) ELEMENT IN PLANE STRESS

(*b*) STRESS CIRCLE

FIG. 4.47

$$2\,\theta_{p1} = +\,38.6° \; ; \; \theta_{p1} = 19.3°$$

$$\left(p_t\right)_{max} = CD_1 = +\,64\,\text{N/mm}^2; \; \left(p_t\right)_{min} = CD_2 = -\,64\,\text{N/mm}^2$$

$$2\,\theta_{s1} = -\,52°; \; \theta_{s1} = -\,26° \; ; \; 2\,\theta_{s2} = +\,128°; \; \theta_{s2} = +\,64°$$

$$\left(p_n\right)_{D1} = p_{av} = 100\,\text{N/mm}^2 = \left(p_n\right)_{D2}$$

Fig 4.48(a) shows the stresses on stress element at $\theta = +\,41°$

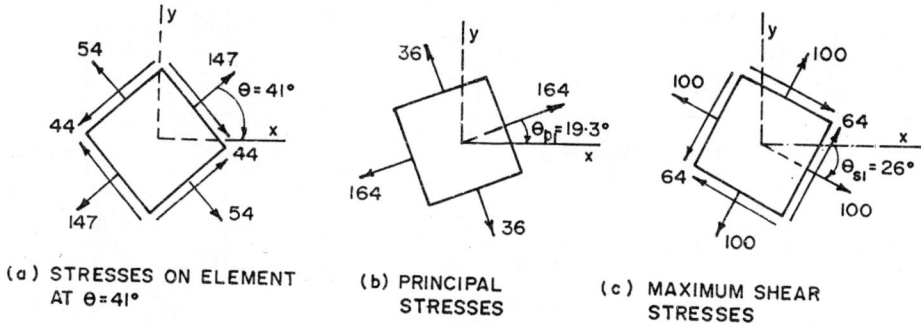

(a) STRESSES ON ELEMENT AT θ=41° (b) PRINCIPAL STRESSES (c) MAXIMUM SHEAR STRESSES

FIG. 4.48

Fig 4.48(b) shows the stress element containing principal planes on which only the principal stresses act and there are no shearing stresses. Fig. 4.48(c) shows the orientation of stress element containing the planes on which maximum shear stresses act. The corresponding normal stresses on these planes are evidently equal to the average stress.

Example 4.26. *An element in plane stress is subjected to stresses* $p_1 = -\,75\,N/mm^2$, $p_2 = 15\,N/mm^2$ *and* $q = -\,60\,N/mm^2$, *as shown in Fig. 4.49 (a). Using Mohr's circle, determine (a) the stresses acting on an element rotated through an angle = 45° in the anticlockwise direction, (b) the principal stresses and (c) the maximum shear stresses. Show all results on sketches of properly oriented elements.*

Solution : Given : $p_1 = -\,75\,\text{N/mm}^2$; $p_2 = 15\,\text{N/mm}^2$ and $q = -\,60\,\text{N/mm}^2$. The Mohr's circle is shown in Fig 4.49 (b). The centre C of the circle has x-coordinate $= p_{av} = \dfrac{p_1 + p_2}{2} = \dfrac{-\,75 + 15}{2} = -\,30\,\text{N/mm}^2$. The coordinates of point G ($\theta = 0$) are given by the stresses on the x-face of the element (Fig. 4.49 a). Hence mark $OA = -\,75$ and $AG = -\,60$ (i.e. upwards). Similarly, the co-ordinates of point F ($\theta = 90°$) are given by the stresses on the y-face of the element of Fig. 4.49 (a). Hence make $OB = +\,15$ and $BF = +\,60$ (i.e. downwards). Join G and F, to intersect x-axis on C, giving the centre of the circle. With C as centre, and CG (or CF) as radius $R \left(= \sqrt{(45)^2 + (60)^2} = 75\,\text{N/mm}^2 \right)$, The circle cuts the x-axis in points H and J.

(a) Stresses on element rotated through $\theta = 45°$

Draw CD at $2\theta = 2 \times 45° = 90°$ with CG (i.e. x face) in the anticlockwise direction. Then, stresses acting on a plane at $\theta = 45°$ is represented by D. Similarly, the coordinates of point D' represent the stresses on the other face, (i.e. at $\theta = 90° + 45° = 135°$ with x-face). From Mohr's circle, we get the following values :

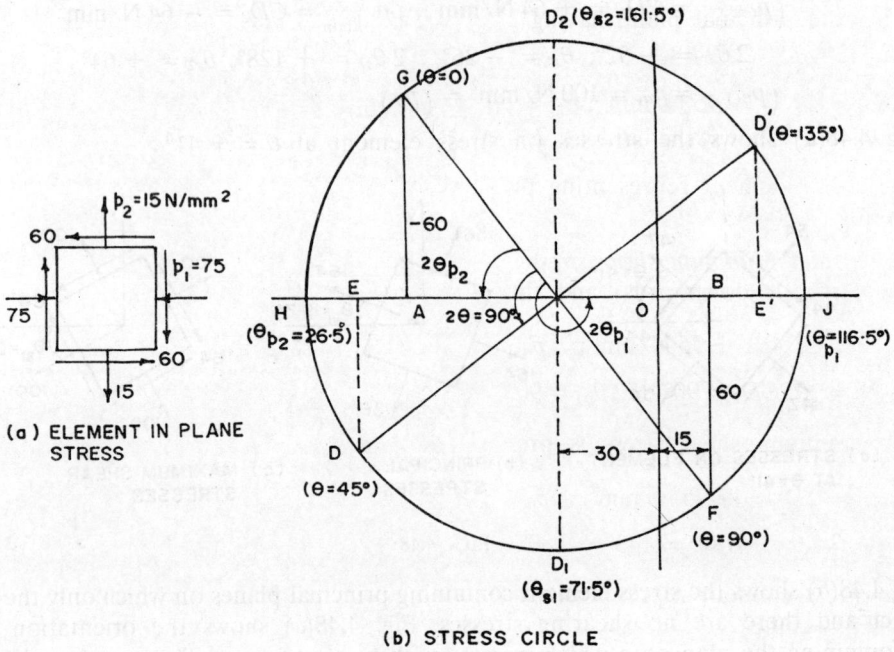

(a) ELEMENT IN PLANE STRESS

(b) STRESS CIRCLE

FIG. 4.49

$$(p_n)_D = -90 \text{ N/mm}^2; \quad (p_t)_D = +45 \text{ N/mm}^2$$

$$(p_n)_{D'} = +30 \text{ N/mm}^2; \quad (p_t)_{D'} = -45 \text{ N/mm}^2.$$

The corresponding stress element is shown in Fig. 4.50 (a)

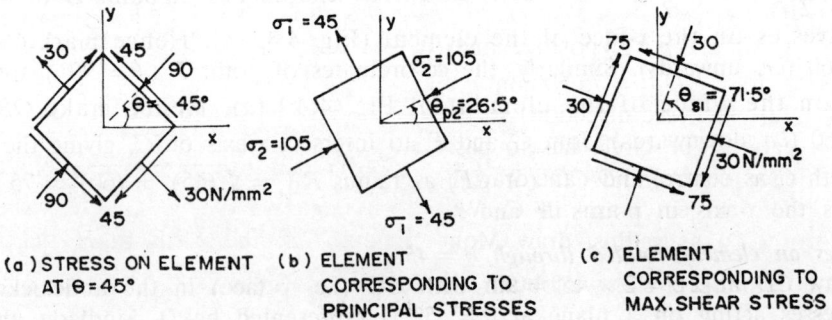

(a) STRESS ON ELEMENT AT θ = 45°

(b) ELEMENT CORRESPONDING TO PRINCIPAL STRESSES

(c) ELEMENT CORRESPONDING TO MAX. SHEAR STRESS

FIG. 4.50

(b) **Principal planes and principal stresses** : The principal stresses are represented by point H and J on stress circle. The angle GCH is the angle $2\theta_{p2}$, from point G ($\theta = 0$) to point H, representing the principal plane having the algebraically smaller principal stress. Hence from the stress circle, we obtain.

$$\sigma_1 = OJ = +45 \text{ N/mm}^2; \quad \sigma_2 = OH = -105 \text{ N/mm}^2$$
$$2\theta_{p1} = 233° \; ; \quad \theta_{p1} = 116.5° \; ; \quad 2\theta_{p2} = 53°; \quad \theta_{p2} = 26.5°$$

The stress element representing principal planes and corresponding principal stresses is shown in Fig. 4.50(b).

(c) **Maximum and Minimum shear stresses** : Maximum shear stress is represented by point D, (measured vertically downwards) and the corresponding values are

$$\left(p_t\right)_{max} = CD_1 = +75 \text{ N/mm}^2; \quad \left(p_n\right)_{D1} = -30 \text{ N/mm}^2 \; (=p_{av})$$
$$2\theta_{s1} = \angle GCD_1 = 90° + 2\theta_{p2} = 90° + 53° = 143°; \theta_{s1} = 71.5°$$

The minimum shear stress is presented by point D_2.

$$\left(p_t\right)_{min} = CD_2 = -75 \text{ N/mm}^2; \quad \left(p_n\right)_{D2} = -30 \text{ N/mm}^2 \; (=p_{av})$$
$$2\theta_{s2} = 2\theta_{s1} + 180° = 143° + 180° = 323° \; ; \quad \theta_{s2} = 161.5$$

The stress element representing maximum shear stresses (and corresponding planes) is shown in Fig. 4.50(c).

Example 4.27. *At a point in a material under stress, the resultant intensity of stress across a certain plane is 100 N/mm² (compressive) inclined at 30° to its normal. On another plane, the intensity of resultant stress is 75 N/mm² (tensile) inclined at 45° to its normal, as shown in Fig. 4.51. Find the principal stresses and their directions to the given plane. Find also the angle between the two planes.*

Solution :

For the Plane AB : $p_r = 100$ N/mm², p_n is negative and p_t is positive. Hence draw $OD' = 100$ N/mm² at $\varphi = 30°$ in the anticlockwise direction, as shown in Fig. 4.52, so that p_n is negative and p_t is positive.

For Plane AC

$p_r = 75$ N/mm². p_n is positive and p_t is negative.

Hence draw $OD \left(= 75 \text{ N/mm}^2 \right)$ at 45° with OX (in the counter clockwise direction) so that p_n is positive but p_t is negative. The circle has to pass through point D and D'. Hence join D and D', and draw the perpendicular bisector of DD' to cut x-axis in C. With C as centre and CD' (or CD) as radius, draw Mohr circle to cut the x-axis in H and J.

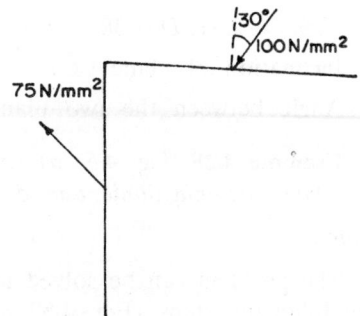

FIG. 4.51

From Mohr's circle, we obtain the following values :

$$\sigma_1 = OJ = -82 \text{ N/mm}^2 \; (i.e. \text{ compressive})$$
$$\sigma_2 = OH = +58 \text{ N/mm}^2 \; (i.e. \text{ tensile})$$

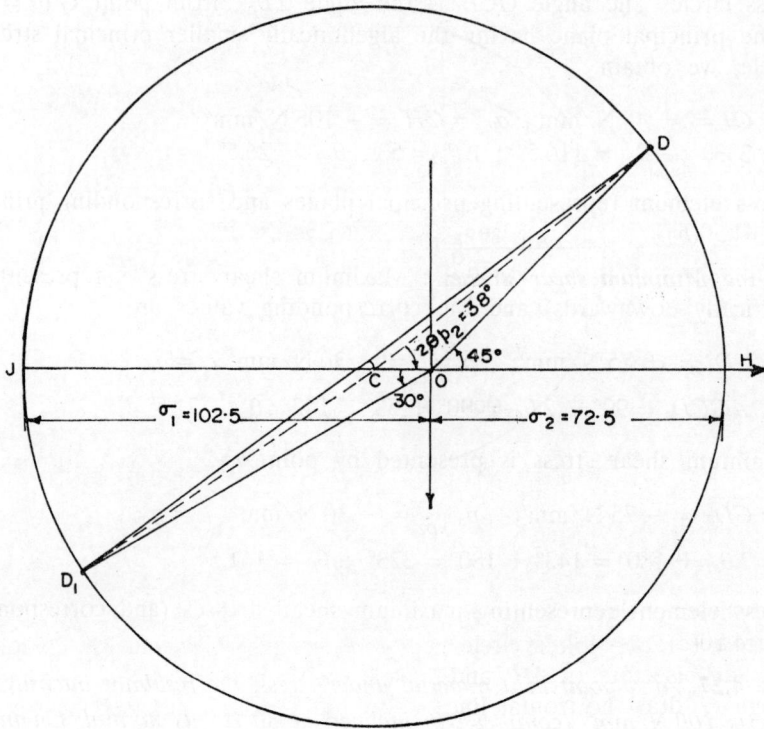

FIG. 4.52

$2\theta_{p2} = \angle HCD = 38°$; $\theta_{p2} = 19°$ (clockwise with plane AC)

Inclination of plane of $\sigma_1 = \theta_{p1} = 90 + 19° = 109°$, (clockwise with plane AC)

Angle between the two planes $= \frac{1}{2} \angle D'CD = \frac{1}{2} \times 178° = 89°$.

Example 4.28. *Fig. 4.53(a) shows the direct stresses in three co-planer directions differing by 60°. Find the magnitude and directions of principal stresses.*

Solution :

The problem can be solved more conveniently, using Mohr's circle which can be drawn in the following steps (Fig. 4.53 b) :

1. Draw vertical line representing y-axis. Set off three vertical lines representing $+80 \text{ N/mm}^2$, $+30 \text{ N/mm}^2$ and -50 N/mm^2 normal stresses.

2. On the intermediate vertical line corresponding to a normal stress of $+30 \text{ N/mm}^2$, select any arbitrary point P.

3. Through point P, draw a line PN at $+60°$ (*i.e.* in anticlockwise direction) with vertical, intersecting vertical line of 80 N/mm^2 in point N. Similarly draw another line at $+120°$ with vertical, intersecting the vertical line of -50 N/mm^2 in point M, when produced back.

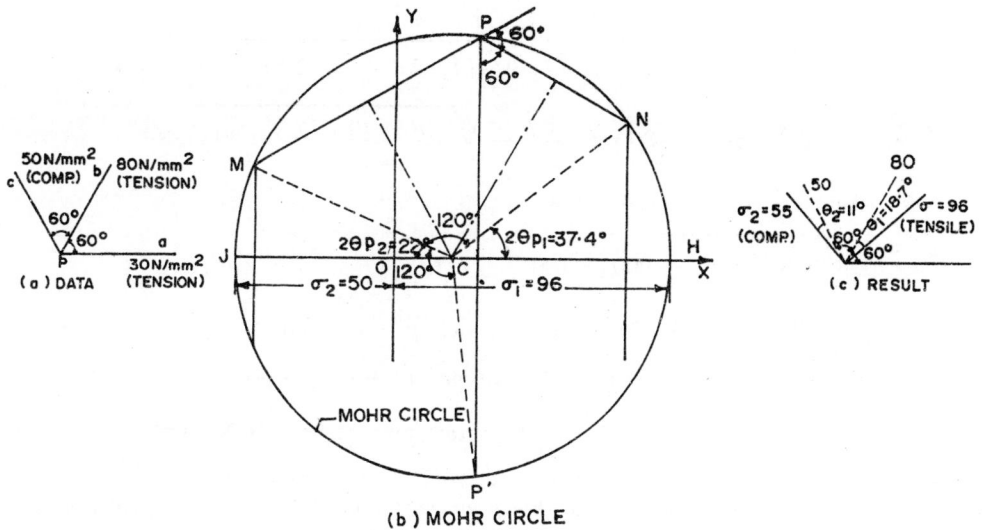

FIG. 4.53

4. Thus, we have three points P, N and M on three vertical lines corresponding to three normal stresses. The Mohr's circle will pass through P, N and M. To locate its centre, draw perpendicular bisectors of MP and PN, intersecting at C.

5. Through C, draw horizontal lines, representing x-axis, intersecting y-axis in O. Thus, we get the origin O and centre C. Draw the Mohr's circle with radius CM ($= CN$). The circle will pass through point M, P and N.

6. The stress conditions on the three given planes are represented by points M, N and P, where P' is the point on the circle, vertically below P. The justification of the construction lies from the fact that the angles between the three radius vectors CM, CN and CP' are $120°$, which is twice the angle between each pair of given direct stresses.

Result : From Fig. 4.53(b), we obtain the following results :

$\sigma_1 = OH = + 96$ N/mm^2 (*i.e.* tension); $\sigma_2 = OJ = - 55$ N/mm^2 (*i.e.* compressive)

$\theta_{p1} = \frac{1}{2} \angle NCH = 18.7°$ to the 80 N/mm^2 stress.

$\theta_{p2} = \frac{1}{2} \angle CJM = 11°$ to the $- 55$ N/mm^2 stress.

The directions of σ_1 and σ_2 relative to the given normal stresses are shown in Fig 4.53 (c).

Example 4.29. *For the element shown in Fig. 4.54 determine the values of p_1 and p_2 if the principal stresses are known to be 20 N/mm^2 and $- 80$ N/mm^2.*

Solution :

Given : $\sigma_1 = 20$ N/mm^2, $\sigma_2 = - 80$ N/mm^2

and $q = - 30$ N/mm^2.

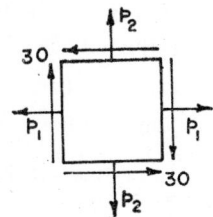

FIG. 4.54

$$\sigma = \frac{p_1 + p_2}{2} \pm \sqrt{\left(\frac{p_1 - p_2}{2}\right)^2 + q^2}$$

$$\sigma_1 = 20 = \frac{p_1 + p_2}{2} \pm \sqrt{\left(\frac{p_1 - p_2}{2}\right)^2 + (-30)^2} \qquad \text{...(1)}$$

and
$$\sigma_2 = -80 = \frac{p_1 + p_2}{2} - \sqrt{\left(\frac{p_1 - p_2}{2}\right)^2 + (-30)^2} \qquad \text{...(2)}$$

Subtracting (2) from (1), we get

$$2\sqrt{\left(\frac{p_1 - p_2}{2}\right)^2 + 900} = 100$$

or
$$\left(\frac{p_1 - p_2}{2}\right)^2 + 900 = 2500, \text{ from which } p_1 - p_2 = 80 \qquad \text{...(a)}$$

Also, adding (1) and (2), we get $p_1 + p_2 = -60$ ...(b)

From (a) and (b), we get $p_1 = \mathbf{10 \, N/mm^2}$ and $p_2 = \mathbf{-70 \, N/mm^2}$.

Example 4.30. *The state of stress at a point is the result of the three separate actions that produce the three states of stresses shown in Fig. 4.55. Determine the principal stresses and principal planes caused by the superposition of these three stress states.*

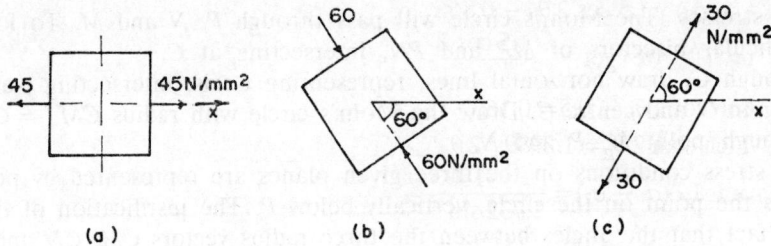

FIG 4.55

Solution : Let the principal stresses be σ and its inclination be θ_p with x-axis as shown in Fig. 4.56.

Hence stress on the element shown in Fig. 4.55 (a) is given by

$$p_{na} = \frac{1}{2}\left(\sigma_1 + \sigma_2\right) + \frac{1}{2}(\sigma_1 - \sigma_2)\cos 2\theta \qquad \text{...(4.15)}$$

Here, $p_{na} = +45$, and $\theta = -\theta_p$ (since x axis is rotated by θ_p in the clockwise direction with respect to x_p axis.

$$\therefore \qquad 45 = \frac{1}{2}\left(\sigma_1 + \sigma_2\right) + \frac{1}{2}(\sigma_1 - \sigma_2)\cos(-2\theta_p)$$

or
$$(\sigma_1 + \sigma_2) + (\sigma_1 - \sigma_2)\cos 2\theta_p = 90 \quad \text{...(1)}$$

Also, stress on the element shown in Fig. 4.55 (b) is given by Eq. 4.15 where

$$p_{na} = -60 \text{ and } \theta = -\left(60° + \theta_p\right)$$

$$\therefore \qquad -60 = \frac{1}{2}\left(\sigma_1 + \sigma_2\right) + \frac{1}{2}(\sigma_1 - \sigma_2)\cos\left\{-2\left(60 + \theta_p\right)\right\}$$

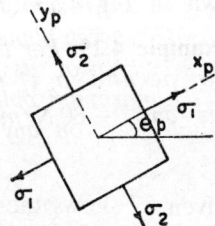

FIG 4.56

or $\qquad \left(\sigma_1 + \sigma_2\right) + \left(\sigma_1 - \sigma_2\right) \cos\left(120° + 2\,\theta_p\right) = -120$

or $\qquad \left(\sigma_1 + \sigma_2\right) + \left(\sigma_1 - \sigma_2\right)\left\{\cos 120° \cos 2\,\theta_p - \sin 120° \sin 2\,\theta_p\right\} = -120$

or $\qquad \left(\sigma_1 + \sigma_2\right) + \left(\sigma_1 - \sigma_2\right)\left\{0.5\cos 2\,\theta_p + 0.866 \sin 2\,\theta_p\right\} = -120$

Lastly, the stress on element shown in Fig. 4.55 (c) is given by Eq. 4.15,

where $p_{na} = +30$ and $\theta = \left(60° - \theta_p\right)$

$\therefore \qquad 30 = \frac{1}{2}\left(\sigma_1 + \sigma_2\right) + \frac{1}{2}\left(\sigma_1 - \sigma_2\right)\cos 2\left(60° - \theta_p\right)$

or $\qquad \left(\sigma_1 + \sigma_2\right) + \left(\sigma_1 - \sigma_2\right)\cos\left(120° - 2\theta_p\right) = 60$

or $\qquad \left(\sigma_1 + \sigma_2\right) + \left(\sigma_1 - \sigma_2\right)\left\{\cos 120° \cos 2\,\theta_p + \sin 120° \sin 2\,\theta_p\right\} = 60$

or $\qquad \left(\sigma_1 + \sigma_2\right) + \left(\sigma_1 - \sigma_2\right)\left\{-0.5\cos 2\,\theta_p + 0.866 \sin 2\,\theta_p\right\} = 60$ $\qquad$ ...(3)

Thus we have three equations (i.e. Eqs 1, 2 and 3) corresponding to the three unknowns σ_1, σ_2 and θ_p. Adding Eqs (2) and (3) we get

$$\left(\sigma_1 - \sigma_2\right)\left\{1.732 \sin 2\,\theta_p\right\} = 180 \qquad \text{...(I)}$$

Also, subtracting (3) from (1), we get

$$\left(\sigma_1 - \sigma_2\right)\left(1.5\cos 2\,\theta_p - 0.866 \sin 2\,\theta_p\right) = 30 \qquad \text{...(II)}$$

Dividing (II) by (I), we get $\qquad \dfrac{1.5\cos 2\,\theta_p - 0.866 \sin 2\,\theta_p}{1.732 \sin 2\,\theta_p} = \dfrac{30}{180} = \dfrac{1}{6}$

or $\qquad 0.866 \cot 2\,\theta_p - 0.5 = 0.1667$

From which $\tan 2\,\theta_p = 1.2989$; $2\,\theta_p = 52.4°$; $\theta_p = \mathbf{26.2°}$

Also, from I, $(\sigma_1 - \sigma_2) = \dfrac{180}{1.732 \sin 52.4°} = 131.16 \qquad \text{...(a)}$

and from (1), $(\sigma_1 + \sigma_2) = 90 - 131.16 \cos 52.4° \approx 10 \qquad \text{...(b)}$

From (a) and (b), we get $\sigma_1 = \mathbf{70.58\ N/mm^2}$ (tensile) and $\sigma_2 = -\mathbf{60.58}$ (i.e. comp.)

Example 4.31. At a point in a piece of material, the principal stress on a plane P is 35 N/mm² tensile and the component stresses on a second plane Q at the same point are a normal stress of 126 N/m m̃ tensile and a shear stress of 70 N/mm². The principal stress on a third plane perpendicular to plane P and Q is zero. Determine by Mohr circle method (a) the angle between planes P and Q (b) the other principal stress and location of its plane (c) maximum shear stress, and (d) the maximum obliquity of the resultant stress with the normal stress on any plane.

Solution :

Fig 4.57 shows the position of planes and the corresponding stresses. Fig. 4.58 shows the Mohr's circle of stress which is drawn in the following steps.

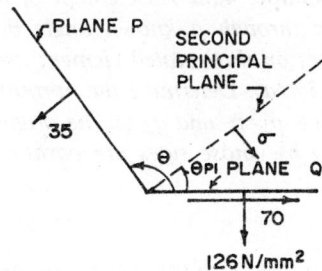

FIG 4.57

1. Mark $OA = 126 \text{ N/mm}^2$ in the positive direction.

2. Draw perpendicular AG in the downward direction (since q is positive on plane Q) and make it equal to 70 N/mm^2.

3. Mark $OB = 35 \text{ N/mm}^2$ in the positive direction.

4. Since plane P is the principal plane (q being zero on it), the circle must pass through point B. Circle must also pass through point G. Hence join points B and G and draw its perpendicular bisector to cut the x-axis in point C, the centre of the circle.

5. With C as the centre and CB or CG as radius, draw the circle cutting the x-axis in point $B(J)$ and H.

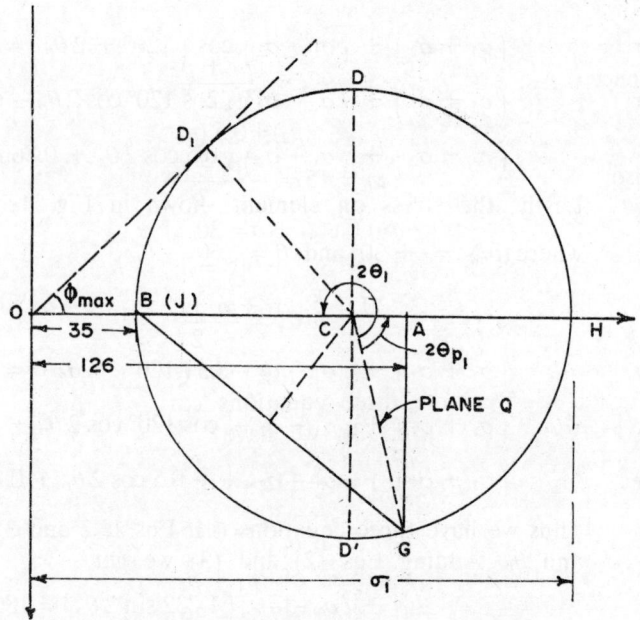

FIG 4.58

6. Through C, draw CD perpendicular to x-axis. Point D corresponds to maximum shear stress.

7. To find the maximum obliquity of the resultant stress, draw line OD_1 tangential to the circle.

From the above construction, we obtain the following :

(i) Angle between planes P and $Q = \theta$ (or θ_{P2}) $= \frac{1}{2} \angle GCO = \frac{1}{2} (256°)$ $= \mathbf{128°}$

(ii) Other principal stress $= \sigma_1 = OH = \mathbf{180 \text{ N/mm}^2}$. Inclination of other principal plane with plane $Q = \theta_{p1} = \frac{1}{2} \angle GCH = \frac{1}{2} \times 76° = \mathbf{38°}$

(iii) Maximum shear stress $= CD$ (or CD') $= \mathbf{71.7 \text{ N/mm}^2}$

(iv) Maximum obliquity of the resultant stress $\varphi_{max} = \angle D_1OC = \mathbf{41.5°}$

Example 4.32. *An element of plane stress is rotated through a known angle $\theta = 30°$ and the stresses on this rotated element are as shown in Fig. 4.59 (a). Determine the normal and shear stresses (i.e. p_1, p_2 and q) on the original element (Fig. 4.59 b) whose sides are parallel to the x-y axes.*

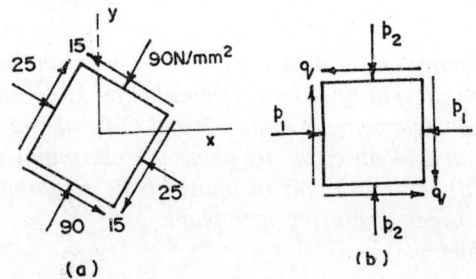

FIG 4.59

Solution :

Let the stresses be p_1, p_2 and q.

Here $\theta = + 30°$.

Hence
$$p_{n1} = -90 = \frac{p_1 + p_2}{2} + \frac{p_1 - p_2}{2} \cos 60° + q \sin 60°$$

or
$$(p_1+p_2)+0.5\,(p_1-p_2)+1.732\,q = -180 \qquad \text{...(1)}$$

Also
$$p_t = 15 = -\frac{p_1 - p_2}{2} \sin 60° + q \cos 60°$$

or
$$-(p_1 - p_2)\,0.866 + q = 30 \qquad \text{...(2)}$$

At $\theta = 30° + 90° = 120°$, we have

$$p_{n2} = -25 = \frac{p_1 + p_2}{2} + \frac{p_1 - p_2}{2} \cos 240° + q \sin 240°$$

or
$$(p_1 + p_2) - 0.5\,(p_1 - p_2) - 1.732\,q = -50 \qquad \text{...(3)}$$

Thus, we have three equations corresponding to the three unknowns. Adding (1) from (3), we have

$$(p_1 + p_2) = -115 \qquad \text{...(a)}$$

From (2), $p_1 - p_2 = \dfrac{q - 30}{0.866} = 1.1547\,(q - 30)$ ...(b)

Substituting the values of $(p_1 + p_2)$ and $(p_1 - p_2)$ in (1), we get
$$-115 + 0.5 \times 1.1547\,(q - 30) + 1.732\,q = -180$$

From which $q = -20.65\ \text{N/mm}^2$. Substituting the values of q in (b), we get

or
$$p_1 - p_2 = -58.48 \qquad \text{...(c)}$$

From (a) and (c), we get $p_1 = -86.74\ \text{N/mm}^2$ and $p_2 = -28.26\ \text{N/mm}^2$.

Example 4.33. *An element in a structure subjected to the plane stress; the stresses have the magnitudes and directions shown acting on a element A (Fig 4.60 a). Element B located at the same point in the structure, is rotated through an angle θ_b of such magnitude that the stresses have the values shown in Fig 4.60 (b). Calculate the normal stress p_b and the angle θ_b.*

Solution :

Here $p_1 = +144\ \text{N/mm}^2$,

$p_2 = -48\ \text{N/mm}^2$ and $q = -40$

$$p_{n1} = 48 = \frac{144 - 48}{2} + \frac{144 + 48}{2} \cos 2\theta_b - 40 \sin 2\theta_b$$

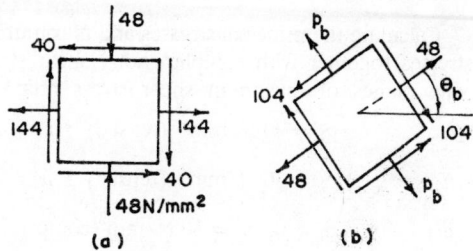

FIG. 4.60

or
$$96 \cos 2\theta_b - 40 \sin 2\theta_b = 0$$

From which $\tan 2\theta_b = 2.4$
or $2\theta_b = 67.38°$ or $\theta_b = 33.69°$.

Also, at $\theta = 90° + \theta_b = 90° + 33.69° = 123.69°$, we have

$$p_{n2} = p_b = \frac{144 - 48}{2} + \frac{144 + 48}{2} \cos (2 \times 123.69°) - 40 \sin (2 \times 123.69)$$

or
$$p_b = 48 + (-36.92) - 40\,(-0.923) = 48\ \text{N/mm}^2$$

PROBLEMS

1. At a point in a bracket, the stresses on two mutually perpendicular planes are 100 N/mm^2 (tensile) and 50 N/mm^2 (tensile). The shear stress across these planes is 25 N/mm^2. Find, using Mohr's circle, the magnitude and direction of the resultant stress on a plane making an angle of $30°$ with the plane of the first stress. Find also, the normal and tangential stresses on this plane.

2. At a point in a loaded specimen, the principal stresses acting on two mutually perpendicular planes are 90 N/mm^2 and 60 N/mm^2, both being compressive. Determine the resultant stress acting on a plane inclined at $60°$ measured clockwise to the plane on which the larger normal stress is acting.

3. In a piece of material, a tensile stress p_1 and shearing stress q act on a given plane. Show that principal stresses are always of opposite sign.

If an additional tensile stress p_2 acts on a plane perpendicular to that on which p_1 acts and all the stresses are coplanar, find the condition that both principal stresses may be of the same sign.

4. The principal stresses at a point subjected to two dimensional stresses are 56 N/mm^2 and 40 N/mm^2 tensile. Find the plane on which the resultant stress has maximum obliquity and the magnitude of the obliquity. Find also the resultant stress.

5. In each of the following cases, p_1 and p_2 are perpendicular direct stresses. Calculate the normal, tangential and resultant stress on planes making angle of (i) $20°$, (ii) $40°$ and (iii) $80°$ with the plane of p_1 and also for the plane having maximum shear stress. Find also the obliquity of the resultant (i.e. its inclination to the normal).

(a) $p_1 = + 64 \text{ N/mm}^2$; $p_2 = + 24 \text{ N/mm}^2$

(b) $p_1 = + 64 \text{ N/mm}^2$; $p_2 = - 24 \text{ N/mm}^2$

(c) $p_1 = + 32 \text{ N/mm}^2$; $p_2 = - 64 \text{ N/mm}^2$

Use Mohr's circle method.

6. At a certain point in stressed body, the principal stress are $\sigma_x = 120 \text{ N/mm}^2$ and $\sigma_y = - 60 \text{ N/mm}^2$. Determine p_n and p_t on planes whose normals are at $+ 30°$ and $+ 120°$ with the x-axis. Show your results on a sketch of a differential element.

7. Calculate the principal stresses and maximum shear stress for the following cases of two perpendicular direct stresses together with complimentary shear stresses. Draw diagram showing the positions of principal planes and planes of maximum shear stress relative to the planes the applied stresses.

(i) $p_1 = 90 \text{ N/mm}^2$ (tensile) ; $p_2 = 30 \text{ N/mm}^2$ (tensile) and $q = + 15 \text{ N/mm}^2$

(ii) $p_1 = 30 \text{ N/mm}^2$ (tensile) ; $p_2 = + 75 \text{ N/mm}^2$ (comp.) and $q = + 15 \text{ N/mm}^2$

(iii) $p_1 = 0$; $p_2 = 30 \text{ N/mm}^2$(comp.) and $q = + 60 \text{ N/mm}^2$

8. The stresses at a particular point in a piece of material act upon three planes whose relative angular positions are given by triangle ABC, in which B is a right angle and C is $30°$. The normal stresses on these planes are 105 N/mm^2 (tension) on AB, 45 N/mm^2 (compression) on BC and 60 N/mm^2 (tension) on AC. Determine the magnitude and direction of the shearing stresses on the given planes and the magnitude of the greatest direct stress and the greatest shearing stress at the point.

9. A right angled triangle ABC with the right angle at C represents planes in an elastic material. There are shearing stresses of 50 N/mm^2 acting along planes AC and CB towards C, and normal tensile stresses on AC and CB of 80 N/mm^2 and 60 N/mm^2 respectively. There is no stress on the plane perpendicular to planes AC and CB.

Determine the positions of the plane AB when the resultant stress on AB is

(a) the greatest magnitude

(b) the least magnitude

(c) the greatest component normal to AB

(d) the greatest tangential component along AB

(e) the least inclination to AB.

Analytical or graphical methods may be used. State for each plane found, its angular position relative to AC and the magnitude of the stress referred to.

10. At a point in two dimensional stress system, the normal stress on two mutually perpendicular planes are p and p' (both alike) and the shear stress q. Show that one of the principal stresses is zero if $q^2 = pp'$.

11. An element in plane stress is rotated through a known angle $\theta = 60°$ (Fig. 4.61). On the rotated element, the normal and shear stresses have the magnitude and direction as shown. Determine the normal and shear stresses on an element whose sides are parallel to x-y axes.

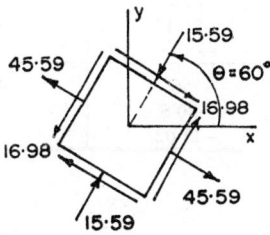

FIG. 4.61

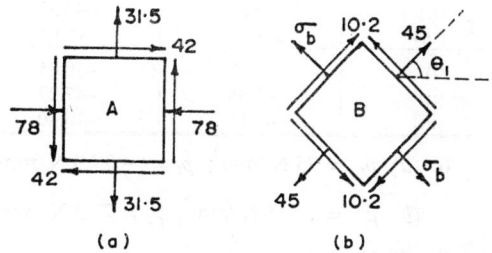

(a)

(b)

FIG. 4.62

12. At a point in a structure subjected to plane stress, the stresses have the magnitudes and directions shown acting an element A in Fig. 4.62. Element B, located at the same point in the structure is rotated through an angle θ_1 of such magnitude that the stresses have the values shown in Fig. 4.62 (b). Determine σ_b and θ_1.

13. Construct Mohr's circle for an element in uniaxial stress p_1.

(a) From the circle, derive the following stress transformation equations

$$p_n = \frac{p_1}{2}(1 + \cos 2\theta); p_t = -\frac{p_1}{2}\sin 2\theta.$$

(b) Show from the circle that the principal stresses are $\sigma_1 = p_1$ and $\sigma_2 = 0$

(c) Obtain from the circle the maximum shear stresses and show them on a sketch of a properly oriented element.

14. Construct Mohr's circle for an element in pure shear q.

(a) From the circle, derive the following stress transformation equations :

$$p_n = q \sin 2\theta \; ; \; p_t = q \cos 2\theta.$$

(b) Obtain from the circle the principal stresses and show them on a sketch of properly oriented element.

(c) Show from the circle that the maximum and minimum shear stresses are $\pm q$.

ANSWERS

1. $p_n = 109.15$ N/mm^2; $p_t = -9.15$ N/mm^2; $p_r = 109.53$ N/mm^2; $\theta = -4.8°$

2. $p_n = -67.5$ N/mm^2; $p_t = 12.99$ N/mm^2; $p_r = 68.74$ N/

3. $p_1 p_2 > q^2$

4. $\theta = 49.8°$; $\varphi = 9.59°$; $p_r = 47.33$ N/mm^2

5. Table below :

		p_n (N/mm^2)	p_t (N/mm^2)	p_r (N/mm^2)	φ	$p_{t,\,max}$ (N/mm^2)
(a)	(i)	59.32	−12.86	60.7	−12.23°	20
	(ii)	47.47	−19.70	51.4	−22.54°	20
	(iii)	25.21	−6.84	26.12	−15.18°	20
(b)	(i)	53.70	−28.28	60.69	−27.77°	44
	(ii)	27.64	−43.33	51.40	−57.47°	44
	(iii)	−21.35	−15.05	26.12	+35.18°	44
(c)	(i)	20.77	−30.85	37.19	− 56°	48
	(ii)	−7.66	−47.27	47.89	−80.8°	48
	(iii)	−61.11	−16.40	63.27	−15.02°	48

6. (a) $p_n = 75$ N/mm^2; $p_t = -77.9$ N/mm^2

   (b) $p_n = -15$ N/mm^2; $p_t = 77.9$ N/mm^2

7. Table below :

	σ_1 (N/mm^2)	σ_2 (N/mm^2)	θ_{p1}	θ_{p2}	$p_{t\,max}$ (N/mm^2)
(i)	+ 93.54	+26.46	13.3°	103.3°	33.54
(ii)	+ 32.1	− 77.1	8°	98°	54.6
(iii)	+ 46.84	− 76.84	38°	128°	61.84

8. Shear on $AB = +77.94$ N/mm^2; shear on $AC = -105$ N/mm^2

   $\sigma_1 = 138.16$ N/mm^2 (tension); $p_{t,\,max} = +108.16$ N/mm^2.

9. (a) 121 N/mm^2 (tensile) at $39°\,21'$ to AC

   (b) 19 N/mm^2 (tensile) at $129°\,21'$ to AC

   (c) Same as (a)

   (d) 51 N/mm^2 at $84°\,21'$ to AC

   (e) $107°\,45'$

11. $p_1 = 45$ N/mm^2; $p_2 = -15$ N/mm^2; $q = -18$ N/mm^2

12. $\sigma_b = -91.5$ N/mm^2; $\theta_1 = 67°$

5

Analysis of Strain : Principal Strains

5.1. LONGITUDINAL AND LATERAL STRAINS

We have seen in chapter 3 that within the elastic limit, strain is proportional to stress. A direct stress produces a change in length in the direction of stress. *Strain* is a measure of the *deformation* produced in the member by the load. If a rod of length L is in tension and the stretch or elongation is ΔL, then the *direct strain* (ε) or the longitudinal strain is defined as the ratio.

$$\varepsilon = \frac{\Delta L}{L} = \frac{\text{Change in length}}{\text{Original length}} \qquad \qquad ...(5.1)$$

It is to be noted that strain is a *ratio*, and hence is dimensionless. As per Hooke's law, *strain is proportional to stress producing it.*

In addition to the *longitudinal deformation* of the bar subjected to a direct load along its longitudinal axis, there also occurs deformations in its lateral dimensions. If an axial load is applied to a bar, its length will increase, and at the same time its lateral dimensions (*i.e.* either the diameter or the width and breadth) will decrease. *Thus, any direct stress produces a strain in its own direction and an opposite kind of strain in every direction at right angles to it.* The ratio of the lateral strain to the longitudinal strain is constant for a given material and is known as Poisson's ratio :

$$\text{Thus} \quad \frac{\text{Lateral Strain}}{\text{Longitudinal Strain}} = \text{Constant} = \frac{1}{m} = \mu$$

or

$$\text{Lateral Strain} = \frac{1}{m} \times \text{longitudinal strain} \qquad \qquad ...(5.2)$$

where $\frac{1}{m}$ (or μ) is known as the Poisson's ratio, the value of which lies between 0.25 to 0.42 for most of the metals.

5.2. PRINCIPAL STRAINS IN THREE DIMENSIONS

Let us take a case of small element subjected to three dimensional principal stresses σ_1, σ_2 and σ_3 (Fig. 5.1), acting on three mutually perpendicular planes at a point in an isotropic material. Taking all the three stresses alike, the principal strains $\varepsilon_1, \varepsilon_2$ and ε_3 can be obtained from the generalised Hooke's law:

$$\varepsilon_1 = \frac{\sigma_1}{E} - \frac{\sigma_2 + \sigma_3}{m\,E}$$

$$\varepsilon_2 = \frac{\sigma_2}{E} - \frac{\sigma_3 + \sigma_1}{m\,E}$$

and
$$\varepsilon_3 = \frac{\sigma_3}{E} - \frac{\sigma_1 + \sigma_2}{m\,E}$$

Let σ_1 be the greatest (or major) principal stress, σ_2 be the least (or minor) principal stress and σ_3 be the *intermediate* principal stress. Then the greatest difference of principal strains is

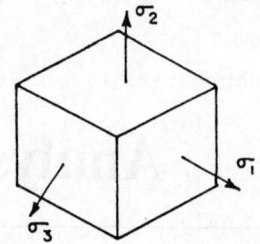

FIG. 5.1

$$\varepsilon_1 - \varepsilon_2 = \frac{\sigma_1 - \sigma_2}{E} + \frac{\sigma_1 - \sigma_2}{m\,E} = \frac{\sigma_1 - \sigma_2}{E}\left(1 + \frac{1}{m}\right) = \left(\frac{m+1}{m}\right)\left(\frac{\sigma_1 - \sigma_2}{E}\right) \quad ...(4)$$

As found earlier, $q_{max} = \dfrac{\sigma_1 - \sigma_2}{2}$ and $\dfrac{m\,E}{m+1} = 2\,N$

We have $\quad \varepsilon_1 - \varepsilon_2 = \dfrac{1}{2\,N}(\sigma_1 - \sigma_2) = \dfrac{q_{max}}{N}$ \hfill ...(5.2 a)

$\therefore \qquad\qquad \varphi_{max} = \dfrac{q_{max}}{N} = \varepsilon_1 - \varepsilon_2$ \hfill ...(5.2)

Thus, the greatest shear strain (φ_{max}) *is equal to greatest difference* $(\varepsilon_1 - \varepsilon_2)$ *of principal strains.*

It should be carefully noted that *stress and strain in any given direction are not proportional where stress exists in more than one direction.* In fact, strain can exist without a stress in the same direction (*i.e.* even if $\sigma_3 = 0$, the $\varepsilon_3 = -\dfrac{\sigma_1 + \sigma_2}{m\,E}$).

Example 5.1. *A piece of material is subjected to three perpendicular tensile stresses and the strains in the three directions are in the ratio of 2 : 3 : 4. If the Poisson's ratio is 0.286, find the ratio of the stresses and their values if the greatest is 100 N/mm².*

Solution :

Let the stresses be σ_1, σ_2 and σ_3 and the corresponding strains $2\,k, 3\,k$ and $4\,k$.

Then $\qquad 2\,kE = \sigma_1 - 0.286\,(\sigma_2 + \sigma_3)$ \hfill ...(1)

$\qquad\qquad\quad 3\,kE = \sigma_2 - 0.286\,(\sigma_3 + \sigma_1)$ \hfill ...(2)

$\qquad\qquad\quad 4\,kE = \sigma_3 - 0.286\,(\sigma_1 + \sigma_2)$ \hfill ...(3)

Subtracting (1) from (3), we get $(\sigma_3 - \sigma_1) - 0.286\,(\sigma_1 - \sigma_3) = 2\,k\,E$

or $\qquad\qquad\qquad (\sigma_3 - \sigma_1) = \dfrac{2\,k\,E}{1.286}$ \hfill ...(4)

Also, from (3) $\quad \dfrac{\sigma_3}{0.286} - \sigma_1 - \sigma_2 = \dfrac{4\,k\,E}{0.286}$ \hfill ...(5)

and from (2), $\sigma_2 - 0.286\,\sigma_3 - 0.286\,\sigma_1 = 3\,k\,E$ ...(6)

Adding (5) and (6), $3.2105\,\sigma_3 - 1.286\,\sigma_1 = 16.986\,kE$ ...(7)

Again from (4) $1.286\,\sigma_3 - 1.286\,\sigma_1 = 2\,k\,E$ ...(8)

Subtracting (8) from (7), $1.9245\,\sigma_3 = 14.486\,k\,E$

From which $\sigma_3 = 7.527\,k\,E$

Hence from (4) $\sigma_1 = \sigma_3 - \dfrac{2\,k\,E}{1.286} = 7.527\,k\,E - 1.555\,k\,E = 5.972\,k\,E$

and from (2), $\sigma_2 = 3\,k\,E + 0.286\,(5.972\,k\,E + 7.527\,k\,E) = 6.861\,k\,E$

$\therefore$ $\sigma_1 : \sigma_2 : \sigma_3 = 5.972 : 6.861 : 7.527 = 0.7934 : 0.9115 : 1$

If the greatest $\sigma_3 = 100\,\text{N/mm}^2$,

we have $\sigma_1 = \mathbf{79.34\ N/mm^2}$ and $\sigma_2 = \mathbf{91.15\ N/mm^2}$

Example 5.2. *A circle of 400 mm diameter is scribed on a mild steel plate before it is subjected to stresses as shown in Fig. 5.2. In stressing, the circle deforms to an ellipse. Calculate the lengths of the major and minor axes of the ellipse and also find their directions. Take* $\dfrac{1}{m} = 0.286$ *and* $E = 205\ kN/mm^2.$

Solution :

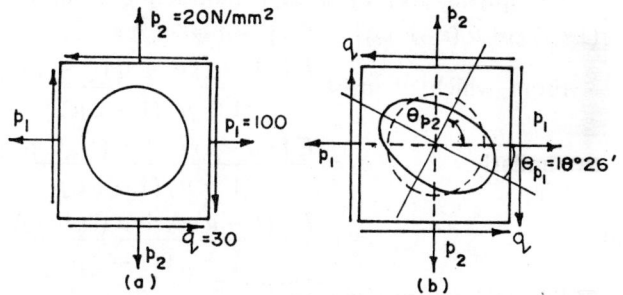

FIG. 5.2

$\sigma = \dfrac{p_1 + p_2}{2} \pm \sqrt{\left(\dfrac{p_1 - p_2}{2}\right)^2 + q^2}$

$\qquad = \dfrac{100 + 20}{2} \pm \sqrt{\left(\dfrac{100 - 20}{2}\right)^2 + (30)^2} = 60 \pm 50$

$\therefore \qquad \sigma_1 = +110\,\text{N/mm}^2$ and $\sigma_2 = +10\,\text{N/mm}^2$

$\tan 2\theta = \dfrac{2q}{p_1 - p_2} = -\dfrac{2 \times 30}{100 - 20} = -0.75\,;\ 2\,\theta_p = -36.87° = -36°52'$

$\theta_{p1} = -18°26'$ (*i.e.* in the clockwise direction) and $\theta_{p2} = -18°26' + 90° = 71°34'$

Major principal strain, $\varepsilon_1 = \dfrac{\sigma_1}{E} - \dfrac{\sigma_2}{m\,E} = (110 - 0.286 \times 10)\dfrac{1}{205 \times 1000}$

$\qquad = +5.226 \times 10^{-4}$ (increase)

Minor principal strain, $\varepsilon_2 = \dfrac{\sigma_2}{E} - \dfrac{\sigma_1}{m\,E} = (10 - 110 \times 0.286)\dfrac{1}{205 \times 1000}$

$\qquad = -1.047 \times 10^{-4}$ (increase) $= 1.047 \times 10^{-4}$ (decrease)

$\therefore$ Length of diameter along $\sigma_1 = d + \varepsilon_1 d = d\,(1 + \varepsilon_1)$

$\qquad = 400\,(1 + 5.226 \times 10^{-4}) = \mathbf{400.209}$ mm

Length of the diameter along σ_2

$= d - \varepsilon_2 d = d\,(1 - \varepsilon_2) = 400\,(1 - 1.047 \times 10^{-4}) = \mathbf{399.958\ mm}$

Hence the circle will be converted into ellipse having major axis = 400.209 mm at 18°26′ with the x-axis (measured in clock wise direction) and minor axis = 399.958 mm at 71°34′ with x-axis (measured in anticlockwise direction).

5.3. COMPUTATION OF PRINCIPAL STRESSES FROM PRINCIPAL STRAINS

In most of the experimental investigations, strains are measured with the help of strain gauges or 'Strain Rosettes'. Hence principal strains are known from these measurements. Knowing the principal strains, principal stresses can be computed as follows.

Let ε_1, ε_2 and ε_3 be the principal strains and σ_1, σ_2 and σ_3 be the corresponding principal stresses. If $\mu\,(= 1/m)$ is the Poisson's ratio, we have :

$$E\,\varepsilon_1 = \sigma_1 - \mu\,\sigma_2 - \mu\,\sigma_3 \qquad \qquad ...(i)$$
$$E\,\varepsilon_2 = \sigma_2 - \mu\,\sigma_3 - \mu\,\sigma_1 \qquad \qquad ...(ii)$$
and $\qquad \qquad E\,\varepsilon_3 = \sigma_3 - \mu\,\sigma_1 - \mu\,\sigma_2 \qquad \qquad ...(iii)$

Subtracting (ii) from (i), $E\,(\varepsilon_1 - \varepsilon_2) = (\sigma_1 - \sigma_2)\,(1 + \mu) \qquad ...(iv)$

Eliminating σ_3 from (i) and (iii), $E\,(\varepsilon_1 + \mu\,\varepsilon_3) = \sigma_1\,(1 - \mu^2) - \sigma_2\,(1 + \mu)\,\mu \qquad ...(v)$

Multiplying (iv) by μ and subtracting from (v) we get

$$E\left[(1-\mu)\,\varepsilon_1 + \mu\,(\varepsilon_2 + \varepsilon_3)\right] = \sigma_1\,(1 - \mu - 2\,\mu^2) = \sigma_1\,(1 + \mu)\,(1 - 2\,\mu)$$

From which, $\qquad \sigma_1 = \dfrac{E\,[\,(1 - \mu)\,\varepsilon_1 + \mu\,(\varepsilon_2 + \varepsilon_3)\,]}{(1 + \mu)\,(1 - 2\,\mu)} \qquad \qquad ...(5.3\ a)$

Similarly, $\qquad \sigma_2 = \dfrac{E\,[\,(1 - \mu)\,\varepsilon_2 + \mu\,(\varepsilon_3 + \varepsilon_1)\,]}{(1 + \mu)\,(1 - 2\,\mu)} \qquad \qquad ...(5.3\ b)$

and $\qquad \sigma_3 = \dfrac{E\,[\,(1 - \mu)\,\varepsilon_3 + \mu\,(\varepsilon_1 + \varepsilon_2)\,]}{(1 + \mu)\,(1 - 2\,\mu)} \qquad \qquad ...(5.3\ c)$

For *two dimensional stress system*, $\sigma_3 = 0$

$\therefore \qquad \qquad E\,\varepsilon_1 = \sigma_1 - \mu\,\sigma_2 \text{ and } E\,\varepsilon_2 = \sigma_2 - \mu\,\sigma_1$

Solving these we get : $\sigma_1 = \dfrac{E\,(\varepsilon_1 + \mu\,\varepsilon_2)}{1 - \mu^2} \qquad \qquad ...(5.4\ a)$

and $\qquad \sigma_3 = \dfrac{E\,(\mu\,\varepsilon_1 + \varepsilon_2)}{1 - \mu^2} \qquad \qquad ...(5.4\ b)$

5.4. PLANE STRAIN

The strain caused by a normal stress is called the *normal strain or direct strain* denoted by e, while the strain caused by shear stress is called *shear strain* and is denoted by φ or γ. *The normal and shear strains at a point in a body vary with the direction*, in a manner *analogous to that for stresses*. If we consider any plane, say xy plane, three strain components may exist (Fig. 5.3) :

(i) Normal strain $e_x = e_1$, in x direction (ii) Normal strain $e_y = e_2$, in y direction

and (iii) Shear strain $\gamma_{xy} = \varphi_{xy} = \varphi$ (say)

An element of material subjected to only these strains is said to be in the *state of plane strain*. When an element is in the state of plane strain, the element does not have normal strain e_z (or e_3) in z-direction, and also does not have shear strains γ_{yz} and γ_{zx} in y-z and z-x planes respectively. Hence the *conditions of plane strain* are :

(a) STRAIN e_x (OR e_1)   (b) STRAIN e_y (OR e_2)   (c) STRAIN γ_{xy} (OR ϕ)

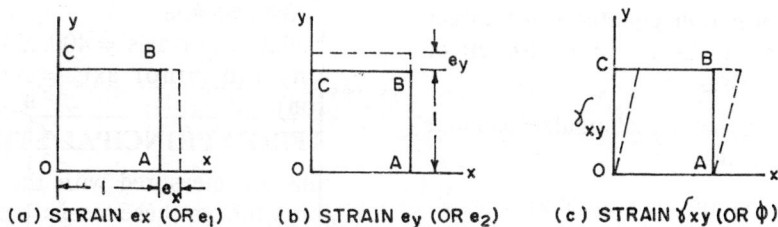

FIG. 5.3. STRAIN COMPONENTS IN X–Y PLANE

$$e_z \text{ (or } e_3) = 0 \ , \ \gamma_{yz} = 0 \, ; \gamma_{zx} = 0 \qquad \qquad ...(5.5)$$

It should be remembered that the conditions of plane strain are analogous to the *conditions of plane stress* where

$$\sigma_3 \text{ (or } p_3) = 0 \ , \ \tau_{yz} \text{ (or } q_{yz}) = 0 \ \text{ and } \ \tau_{zx} = 0 \qquad \qquad ...(5.6)$$

This does not mean that the conditions of plane stress and plane strain occur simultaneously. In fact, an element in plane stress undergoes e_z is z-direction. The conditions of plane stress and those of plane strain are depicted in Table 5.1

TABLE 5.1
CONDITIONS OF PLANE STRESS AND PLANE STRAIN CASES

	Plane stress condition	*Plane strain condition*
Element	 FIG. 5.4(a)	 FIG. 5.4(b)
Stresses	σ_z (or p_3) $= 0$; $\tau_{yz} = 0$; $\tau_{zx} = 0$ σ_x (or p_1) $= 0$; σ_y (or p_2) and τ_{xy} (or q) may have non-zero values	$\tau_{yz} = 0$ $\tau_{zx} = 0$ σ_x (or p_1) ; σ_y (or p_2), σ_z ($= p_3$) and τ_{xy} ($= q$) may have non-zero values
Strains	$\gamma_{yz} = 0$; $\gamma_{zx} = 0$ e_x (or e_1), e_y (or e_2), e_z (or e_3) and γ_{xy} (or q) may have non-zero values	e_z ($= e_3$) $= 0$; $\gamma_{yz} = 0$; $\gamma_{zx} = 0$ and e_x ($= e_1$) , e_y ($= e_2$) and γ_{xy} ($= \varphi$) may have non-zero values

5.5. STRAIN COMPONENTS IN AN INCLINED DIRECTION

In the previous chapter, we have found stress components p_n and p_t on an inclined plane through a point when it is subjected to normal stresses p_1 and p_2 in two mutually perpendicular directions, along with shear stress q. In a similar manner, if direct and shearing strains are given in two mutually perpendicular directions, we can find direct and shearing strains in any other direction. In other words, we can also find the transformation equations for direct and shearing strains, as was done for direct and shearing stresses.

Fig. 5.5 shows a rectangular element $OABC$ in X-Y plane.

Let $e_1 =$ Strain in x-direction
            $e_2 =$ Strain in y-direction
and $\varphi =$ Shearing strain relative to OX and OY

Let OB be any direction, inclined at θ with x-direction along which it is required to find *direct strain* (or normal strain) e_θ and *shearing strain* φ_θ.

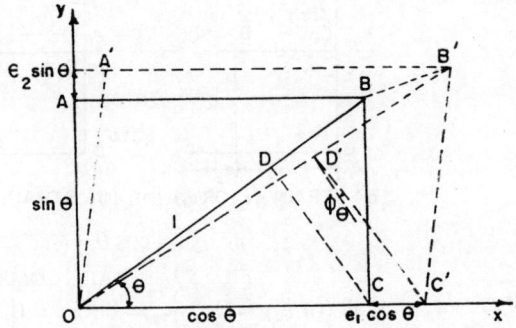

FIG. 5.5

Let us consider all the strains to be very small. Taking the length of diagonal OB as unity, side OA will be of length $\sin\theta$ while side OC will be of length $\cos\theta$. When the material is strained, OA extends by small amount $e_2\sin\theta$ while OC extends by small amount $e_1\cos\theta$. Also, due to shearing strain, OA rotates to OA' by small shearing angle φ. The distorted shape of the rectangle $OABC$ is represented by $OA'B'C'$, in which point A moves to A', B moves to B', and C moves to C', relative to point O.

Movement of B parallel to x-axis $= e_1\cos\theta + \varphi\sin\theta$ ...(i)

Movement of B parallel to y-axis $= e_2\sin\theta$ ...(ii)

$\therefore$ Movement of B parallel to $OB = (e_1\cos\theta + \varphi\sin\theta)\cos\theta + (e_2\sin\theta)\sin\theta$ ...(iii)

This movement of B will be approximately equal to the extension of OB in the strained condition. However, since OB has been taken to be of unit length, the extension of OB is equal to the direct strain e_θ in the direction OB.

$\therefore$ $e_\theta = (e_1\cos\theta + \varphi\sin\theta)\cos\theta + (e_2\sin\theta)\sin\theta$

or $e_\theta = e_1\cos^2\theta + e_2\sin^2\theta + \varphi\sin\theta\cos\theta$ ...(5.7 a)

or $e_\theta = e_1\cos^2\theta + e_2\sin^2\theta + \dfrac{\varphi}{2}\sin 2\theta$ ...(5.7)

Note that this expression is *analogous* to Eq. 4.14 for p_n, where p_1 and p_2 have been replaced by e_1 and e_2 respectively and q has been replaced by $\dfrac{\varphi}{2}$.

Eq. 5.7 can also be re-written in the form

$$e_\theta = \frac{1}{2}(e_1 + e_2) + \frac{1}{2}(e_1 - e_2)\cos 2\theta + \frac{1}{2}\varphi\sin 2\theta \qquad ...(5.8)$$

which is analogous to Eq. 4.15 for p_n

Again, in order to find shearing strain φ_θ in the required direction, draw CD perpendicular to OB (Fig. 5.5). Point D' is the strained position of D. When OB extends to e_θ, OD extends by amount $= e_\theta \cdot OD = e_\theta \cdot \cos^2\theta$ (since $OD = OC\cos\theta = \cos\theta \cdot \cos\theta = \cos^2\theta$).

During straining, the perpendicular CD rotates in the anti clockwise direction through a small angle

$$= \frac{e_1 \cos^2 \theta - e_\theta \cos^2 \theta}{\cos \theta \sin \theta} = (e_1 - e_\theta) \cot \theta$$

At the same time, OB rotates (in the clockwise direction) through a small angle $= -(e_1 \cos \theta + \varphi \sin \theta) \sin \theta + (e_2 \sin \theta) \cos \theta$. Now, the *shearing strain* φ_θ *in the direction OB is the amount by which angle ODC diminishes during straining*. Hence

$$\varphi_\theta = \text{Rotation of } OB - \text{Rotation of } CD$$

$$= [-(e_1 \cos \theta + \varphi \sin \theta) \sin \theta + e_2 \sin \theta \cos \theta] - [(e_1 - e_\theta) \cot \theta]$$

or $\qquad \varphi_\theta = -(e_1 - e_\theta) \cot \theta - (e_1 \cos \theta + \varphi \sin \theta) \sin \theta + (e_2 \sin \theta) \cos \theta$

Substituting the value of e_θ from Eq. 5.7 (a), we have

$$\varphi_\theta = -2 (e_1 - e_2) \cos \theta \sin \theta + \varphi (\cos^2 \theta - \sin^2 \theta) \qquad ...(5.9)$$

This can also be written as

$$\frac{1}{2} \varphi_\theta = -2 (e_1 - e_2) \sin 2\theta + \frac{1}{2} \varphi \cos 2\theta \qquad ...(5.10)$$

The negative sign with φ_θ indicates that the angle at the origin will *increase* while positive sign shows that the angle will decrease.

It is interesting to note that Eq. 5.10 is analogous to Eq. 4.16, where p_1 and p_2 have been replaced by e_1 and e_2 respectively, q has been replaced by $\frac{1}{2} \varphi$ and p_t has been replaced by $\frac{1}{2} \varphi_\theta$.

Eqs. 5.8 and 5.10 are also known as *transformation equations* for strains. The direct strain ($e_{\theta 2}$) in the other direction, perpendicular to the previous one, can be found by replacing θ by $(90° + \theta)$ in Eq. 5.8 :

Thus $\qquad e_{\theta 2} = \frac{1}{2} (e_1 + e_2) + \frac{1}{2}(e_1 - e_2) \cos 2 (90° + \theta) + \frac{1}{2} \varphi \sin 2 (90° + \theta)$

or $\qquad e_{\theta 2} = \frac{1}{2} (e_1 + e_2) - \frac{1}{2} (e_1 - e_2) \cos 2\theta - \frac{\theta}{2} \sin 2\theta \qquad ..(5.8 \; a)$

Taking $e_\theta = e_{\theta 1}$, we observe that

$$e_{\theta 1} + e_{\theta 2} = e_1 + e_2 \qquad ...(5.11)$$

Thus, the sum of normal strains in perpendicular directions is a constant.

5.6. PRINCIPAL STRAINS

We have seen in the above article that the direct strain (e_θ) changes with the angle θ. *The maximum and minimum direct strains in a material, subjected to complex stresses, are called the principal strains.* These strains act in the direction of principal stresses. The maximum and minimum values of direct strain occur when the position of plane OB is such that shearing strain φ_θ is zero. This occurs at values of θ obtained by equating $\frac{d \varphi_\theta}{d \theta}$ to zero.

Thus, differentiating Eq. 5.10 with respect to θ and equating it to zero, we get

$$\tan 2 \theta_{p\varepsilon} = \frac{\varphi}{e_1 - e_2} \qquad ...(5.12)$$

This equation is analogous to Eq. 4.21.

From Eq. 5.12, $\tan 2\theta_{p\varepsilon} = \dfrac{\dfrac{q}{N}}{\left(\dfrac{p_1}{E} - \dfrac{p_2}{mE}\right) - \left(\dfrac{p_2}{E} - \dfrac{p_1}{mE}\right)} = \dfrac{q}{p_1 - p_2} \cdot \dfrac{E}{N\left(1 + \dfrac{1}{m}\right)}$

or $\qquad \tan 2\theta_{p\varepsilon} = \dfrac{2q}{p_1 - p_2}$ ...(5.12 a)

which is same as Eq. 4.21.

Study of Eqs. 5.12 and 4.21 reveal that *principal strains and principal stresses act in the same direction.*

Hence, $\qquad \theta_{p\varepsilon} = \theta_p$

Eq. 5.12 can be represented diagrammatically by Fig. 5.6, in which

$$\tan 2\theta_{p\varepsilon} = \dfrac{\varphi/2}{\dfrac{(e_1 - e_2)}{2}}$$

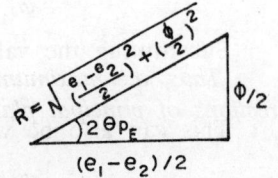

FIG. 5.6

Hence diagonal $R = \sqrt{\left(\dfrac{e_1 - e_2}{2}\right)^2 + \left(\dfrac{\varphi}{2}\right)^2}$ (Taking the positive root)

Thus $\qquad \cos 2\theta_{p\varepsilon} = \dfrac{e_1 - e_2}{2R}$ and $\sin 2\theta_{p\varepsilon} = \dfrac{\varphi/2}{R} = \dfrac{\varphi}{2R}$ ...(5.13)

Substituting the values of $\cos 2\theta_{p\varepsilon}$ and $\sin 2\theta_{p\varepsilon}$ in Eq. 5.8 and setting

$e_\theta = \varepsilon_1$ we get

$$\varepsilon_1 = \dfrac{1}{2}(e_1 + e_2) + \sqrt{\left(\dfrac{e_1 - e_2}{2}\right)^2 + \left(\dfrac{\varphi}{2}\right)^2}$$ ...(5.14 a)

The minor principal strain ε_2 is obtained from the relation

$\varepsilon_1 + \varepsilon_2 = e_1 + e_2$

or $\qquad \varepsilon_2 = (e_1 + e_2) - \left[\dfrac{e_1 + e_2}{2} + \sqrt{\left(\dfrac{e_1 - e_2}{2}\right)^2 + \left(\dfrac{\varphi}{2}\right)^2}\right]$

or $\qquad \varepsilon_2 = \dfrac{e_1 + e_2}{2} - \sqrt{\left(\dfrac{e_1 - e_2}{2}\right)^2 + \left(\dfrac{\varphi}{2}\right)^2}$ ...(5.14 b)

Hence $\qquad \varepsilon_{1,2} = \dfrac{e_1 + e_2}{2} \pm \sqrt{\left(\dfrac{e_1 - e_2}{2}\right)^2 + \left(\dfrac{\varphi}{2}\right)^2}$ ...(5.14)

5.7. MAXIMUM SHEAR STRAINS

In general, the shear strain varies with angle θ and its value is given by Eq. 5.10

$$\dfrac{1}{2}\varphi_\theta = -\dfrac{1}{2}(e_1 - e_2)\sin 2\theta + \dfrac{1}{2}\varphi\cos 2\theta$$ ...(5.10)

For maximum value of φ_θ, differentiate it with respect to θ and equate it to zero.

$$\therefore \qquad \frac{d\left(\frac{\varphi_\theta}{2}\right)}{d\theta} = -(e_1 - e_2)\cos 2\theta - \varphi \sin 2\theta = 0$$

From which
$$\tan 2\theta_{se} = -\frac{e_1 - e_2}{\varphi} \qquad \qquad ...(5.15)$$

Comparing this with Eq. 5.12, we observe that

$$\tan 2\theta_{se} = -\frac{1}{\tan 2\theta_{pe}} = -\cot 2\theta_{pe} \qquad \qquad ...(5.16)$$

Since
$$\tan(\alpha \pm 90°) = -\cot \alpha, \text{ we have}$$
$$2\theta_{se} = 2\varphi_{pe} \pm 90° \text{ or } \theta_{se} = \theta_{pe} \pm 45°$$

Thus, the maximum shear strains in the xy plane are associated with axes at 45° to the directions of principal planes. The algebraically maximum shear strain in the xy plane is given by

$$\frac{\varphi_{max}}{2} = \sqrt{\left(\frac{e_1 - e_2}{2}\right)^2 + \left(\frac{\varphi}{2}\right)^2} \qquad \qquad ...(5.17)$$

The minimum shear strain has the same magnitude but is negative. In the directions of maximum shear strain, the normal strains are equal to $\frac{(e_1 + e_2)}{2}$.

5.8. MOHR'S CIRCLE FOR PLANE STRAIN

Since the expressions for linear strain (or direct strain) e_θ and shearing strain φ_θ on any plane are analogous to the corresponding expression for p_n and p_t, Mohr's circle method can be used for the graphical solution in a way similar to the one used for plane stress case.

Eq. 5.8 for e_θ can be rewritten as :

$$e_\theta - \frac{1}{2}(e_1 + e_2) = \frac{1}{2}(e_1 - e_2)\cos 2\theta + \frac{1}{2}\varphi \sin 2\theta \qquad \qquad ...(i)$$

Similarly Eq. 5.10 for φ_θ can be rewritten as

$$\frac{1}{2}\varphi_\theta = -\frac{1}{2}(e_1 - e_2)\sin 2\theta + \frac{1}{2}\varphi \cos 2\theta \qquad \qquad ...(ii)$$

Squaring (i) and (ii) and adding, we get

$$\left[e_\theta - \frac{1}{2}(e_1 + e_2)\right]^2 + \left[\frac{1}{2}\varphi_\theta\right]^2 = \left[\frac{1}{2}(e_1 - e_2)\right]^2 + \left[\frac{1}{2}\varphi\right]^2$$

Thus, all values of e_θ and $\frac{1}{2}\varphi_\theta$ lie on a circle whose radius is $\sqrt{\left[\frac{1}{2}(e_1 - e_2)^2\right] + \left[\frac{1}{2}\varphi\right]^2}$ and whose centre is at point $\left[\frac{1}{2}(e_1 + e_2), 0\right]$.

To draw the Mohr circle of strains, mark $OA = e_1$ and $OB = e_2$. Also, mark $AG = \frac{1}{2}\varphi = BF$. Join F and G, to get point C, the centre of the circle. Mohr circle is now drawn with C as the centre and FG or CF as radius, cutting the x-axis in points H and J. Draw the line CD, making an angle 2θ, in appropriate direction with CG. Here, the line CD corresponds to a positive angle while AG corresponds to a positive shear strain

$\left(\frac{1}{2}\varphi\right)$. Similarly, e_1 and e_2 are positive (being tensile). The coordinates of point D represents direct strain e_θ and shear strain $\frac{1}{2}\varphi_\theta$ (as marked) on a plane making an angle θ (in anti clockwise direction) with the direction of e_1. It should be noted that points H and J correspond to principal strains ε_1 and ε_2 respectively, since the shearing stain $\left(\frac{1}{2}\varphi_\theta\right)$ at these points are each zero.

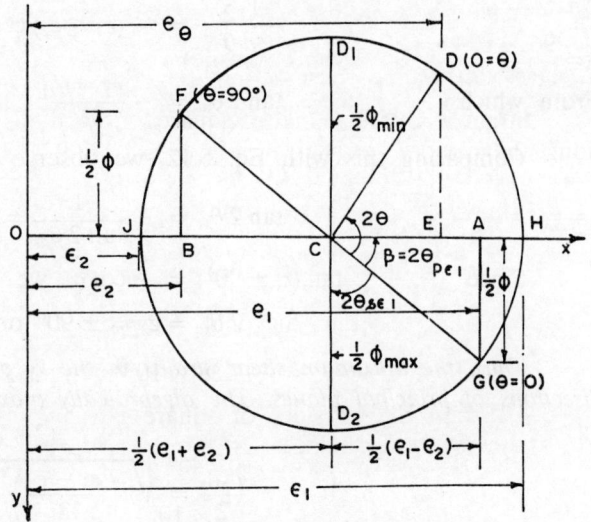

FIG. 5.7. MOHR CIRCLE OF STRAINS

Conclusions : From the strain circle, we draw the following conclusions :

(*i*) When D coincides with H (i.e. $2\theta = \beta$), e_θ attains its maximum value :

$$(e_\theta)_{max} = \varepsilon_1 = OC + CH$$

$$= \frac{1}{2}(e_1 + e_2) + \sqrt{\left(\frac{e_1 - e_2}{2}\right)^2 + \left(\frac{1}{2}\varphi\right)^2}$$

where $(e_\theta)_{max}$ is known as *major principal strain* (See Eq. 5.14 *a*)

$$\tan 2\theta_{p\varepsilon} = \tan \beta = \frac{\frac{1}{2}\varphi}{\frac{1}{2}(e_1 - e_2)} = \frac{\varphi}{e_1 - e_2}$$

(*ii*) when point D coincides with J, e_θ attains its minimum value :

$$(e_\theta)_{min} = \varepsilon_2 = OC - CJ = \frac{1}{2}(e_1 + e_2) - \sqrt{\left(\frac{e_1 - e_2}{2}\right)^2 + \left(\frac{1}{2}\varphi\right)^2}$$

where $(e_\theta)_{min} = \varepsilon_2$, is known as the *minor principal strain* (See Eq. 5.14 *b*)

(*iii*) When point D_1 occupies the highest position of the circle, $2\theta = \beta + 90°$ and $\frac{1}{2}\varphi_\theta$ attains its maximum value :

$$\frac{1}{2}\varphi_{max} = \sqrt{\left(\frac{e_1 - e_2}{2}\right)^2 + \left(\frac{1}{2}\varphi\right)^2}$$

Direct strain (e_θ) corresponding to the point D_1, is obviously equal to $\frac{1}{2}(e_1 + e_2) = e_{av}$.

Example 5.3. *A flat bar 10 mm thick and 100 mm wide is subjected to a pull of 96 kN. One side of the bar is polished and lines are ruled on it to form a square of 50 mm side, one diagonal of the square being along the middle line of the polished side. Taking $E = 210 \, kN/mm^2$ and $\mu = 0.28$, calculate the change in the sides and angles of the square.*

Solution :

Axial stress in bar,

$$p_1 = \frac{96 \times 1000}{100 \times 10} = 96 \text{ N/mm}^2 \text{ (tensile)}$$

Strain in one diagonal of square along the axis of the bar is

$$e_1 = \frac{p_1}{E} = \frac{96}{210 \times 10^3} = 4.571 \times 10^{-4}$$

(tensile)

FIG. 5.8

∴ Strain in other diagonal $= e_2 = -\mu e_1 = -0.28 \times 4.571 \times 10^{-4}$

$$= -1.28 \times 10^{-4} \text{ (compressive)}$$

∴ Strain in the sides of square is given by

$$e_\theta = e_1 \cos^2 45° + e_2 \sin^2 45° \qquad \qquad ...(5.7)$$

$$= 4.571 \times 10^{-4} \times 0.5 - 1.28 \times 10^{-4} \times 0.5 = 1.645 \times 10^{-4} \text{ (tensile)}$$

Hence change in length of each side of square $= \left(1.645 \times 10^{-4} \right) \times 50$

$$= \mathbf{0.008225 \text{ mm}} \text{ (increase)}$$

Total shear strain or change in the angles of the square $= \varphi_\theta$

$$= -(e_1 - e_2) \sin 2\theta \qquad \qquad ...(5.10)$$

$$= -(4.571 + 1.280) \times 10^{-4} \sin 90° = -\mathbf{5.851 \times 10^{-4}} \text{ radian}$$

Thus the two angles of the square which are along the line of pull will be decreased and the other two will be increased by the above amount.

Example 5.4. *A brass plate 3 mm thick, is stretched in the plane of the plate in two directions at right angles. An extensometer, arranged in the X-direction gave an extension of 0.0413 mm on a gauge length of 50 mm, while another, arranged in Y-direction gave an extension of 0.0187 mm on a 100 mm gauge length. If the normal stress on a plane making angle θ with the Y-axis is 66 N/mm², find angle θ. Find also the decrease in the thickness of the plate. Take E for brass = 80 N/mm² and μ = 0.3.*

Solution :

Let σ_x and σ_y be the principal stresses in two directions (say x and y directions respectively) and ε_1 and ε_2 be the corresponding principal strains.

Then $\qquad \varepsilon_x = \dfrac{0.0413}{50} = 8.26 \times 10^{-4} \text{ and } \varepsilon_y = \dfrac{0.0187}{100} = 1.87 \times 10^{-4}$

Also, $\qquad \varepsilon_x = \dfrac{\sigma_x}{E} - \dfrac{\mu \, \sigma_y}{E} \text{ and } \varepsilon_y = \dfrac{\sigma_y}{E} - \dfrac{\mu \, \sigma_x}{E}$

∴ $\qquad 8.26 \times 10^{-4} = \dfrac{1}{80 \times 10^3} \left[\sigma_x - 0.3 \, \sigma_y \right] \text{ or } \sigma_x - 0.3 \, \sigma_y = 66.08 \qquad ...(i)$

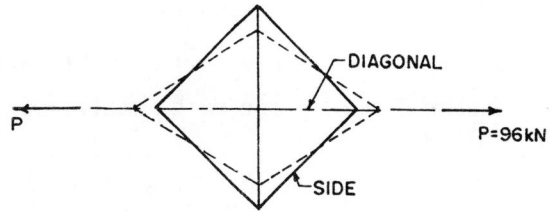

and $\qquad 1.87 \times 10^4 = \dfrac{1}{80 \times 10^3} \left[\sigma_y - 0.3\,\sigma_x \right]$ or $\sigma_y - 0.3\,\sigma_x = 14.96 \qquad\qquad$ ...(ii)

Solving (i) and (ii), we get $\sigma_x = 75.66 \text{ N/mm}^2$ and $\sigma_y = 31.91 \text{ N/mm}^2$

Inclination of plane with y axis $= \theta$. Hence inclination of plane with x axis $= 90° - \theta = \theta_1$ (say).

The direct stress at θ_1 with x-axis is given by Eq. 4.15

or $\qquad\qquad p_n = \dfrac{1}{2}\,(\sigma_x + \sigma_y) + \dfrac{1}{2}\,(\sigma_x - \sigma_y)\cos 2\theta_1$

or $\qquad\qquad 66 = \dfrac{1}{2}\,(75.65 + 31.91) + \dfrac{1}{2}\,(75.65 - 31.91)\cos 2\theta_1$

from which $\cos 2\theta_1 = 0.5587$ or $2\theta_1 = 56°$ or $\theta_1 = 28°$

$\therefore \qquad\qquad \theta = 90° - \theta_1 = \mathbf{62°}$

Strain in the direction of thickness

$$= -\frac{\mu\,\sigma_x}{E} - \mu\,\frac{\sigma_y}{E} = -\frac{0.3}{80000}\,(75.65 - 31.91)$$

or $\qquad\qquad \dfrac{\Delta t}{t} = -1.64 \times 10^{-4}$

$\therefore \qquad\qquad \Delta t = -1.64 \times 10^{-4} \times 3 = \mathbf{-4.92 \times 10^{-4}\,mm}$ (i.e. decrease)

Example 5.5. *A flat brass plate was stretched by tensile forces acting in direction x and y at right angle. Strain gauges show that strains in x-direction was 0.00108 and in the y- direction 0.00024. Find (a) stresses acting in x and y directions, and (b) direct and shearing strains on a plane inclined at 40° to the x-direction (c) normal and shearing stresses on that plane. Take $E = 80\,kN/mm^2$ and $\mu = 0.3$.*

Solution :

(a) Stresses in x and y directions

For two dimensional stress system, we have, from Eqs. 5.4(a), (b)

$$p_1 = \frac{E\,(e_1 + \mu\,e_2)}{1 - \mu^2} = \frac{80 \times 10^3\,(0.00108 + 0.3 \times 0.00024)}{1 - (0.3)^2} = 101.27 \text{ N/mm}^2$$

$$p_2 = \frac{E\,(e_2 + \mu\,e_1)}{1 - \mu^2} = \frac{80 \times 10^3\,(0.00024 + 0.3 \times 0.00108)}{1 - (0.3)^2} = 49.58 \text{ N/mm}^2$$

(b) Direct and shearing strains at 40° plane

From Eq. 5.8, noting that $\varphi = 0$,

$$e_\theta = \frac{1}{2}\,(e_1 + e_2) + \frac{1}{2}\,(e_1 - e_2)\cos 2\theta$$

$$= \frac{1}{2}\,(0.00108 + 0.00024) + \frac{1}{2}\,(0.00108 - 0.00024)\cos 80°$$

$$= \mathbf{7.33 \times 10^{-4}}$$

Also, from Eq. 5.10, $\dfrac{1}{2}\,\varphi_\theta = \dfrac{1}{2}\,(e_1 - e_2)\sin 2\theta$ (numerically) or $\frac{1}{2}\varphi_\theta = \frac{1}{2}(0.00108 - 0.00024)\sin 80°$

$$= 4.14 \times 10^{-4} \text{radian}$$

or $\varphi_\theta = 8.28 \times 10^{-4}$ radian

The values of e_θ and φ_θ can also be obtained from Mohr's circle for strain shown in Fig. 5.9. The construction is self explanatory.

From graphical construction, we get

$$e_\theta = 7.3 \times 10^{-4}$$

and $\varphi_\theta = 8.2 \times 10^{-4}$

FIG. 5.9

(c) The normal and shearing stresses at 40° plane

The normal stress is given by Eq. 4.14 noting that in that equation, θ is the angle made with y direction. Hence $\theta = 90° - 40° = 50°$.

∴ $p_n = p_1 \cos^2\theta + p_2 \sin^2\theta = 101.27 \cos^2 50° + 49.58 \sin^2 50° = \mathbf{70.94 \ N/mm^2}$

Also, $p_t = \dfrac{p_1 - p_2}{2}\sin 2\theta$ (numerically) $= \dfrac{101.27 - 49.58}{2}\sin 100° = \mathbf{25.45 \ N/mm^2}$

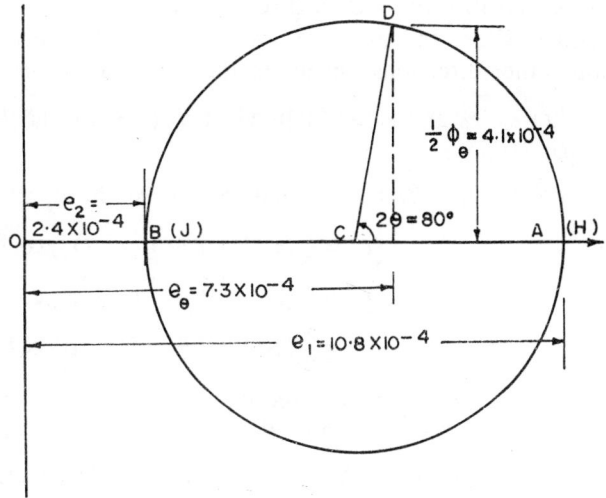

5.9. STRAIN ROSETTES

The stress in a bar subjected to uniaxial stress can be determined experimentally by attaching a strain gauge oriented in the direction of stress. The stress is then calculated from the measured strain (e), using the relation $p = E.e$. Since the strain is very small (usually 1 part in 1000), sensitive gauges are required for measuring it. Originally these gauges were mechanical or optical, but these have now been completely replaced by electrical *strain gauges*. Electrical strain gauge consists of a small length of fine wire which is connected (or glued) to the surface of the material. When the material is strained, the length of the strain gauge wire also changes, resulting in the change of its resistance which can be measured on a Wheat Stone- Bridge. The change in the resistance is converted into strain measurement. Such gauges are sensitive and can measure strain as small as 1×10^{-6}. Since each gauge measures the normal strain (or the direct strain) in only one direction, it is often necessary to use three strain gauges in combination, with each gauge measuring the strain in a different direction. From three such measurements, it is possible to compute the strains in any direction on the surface. *The group of three gauges arranged in a particular pattern is called a strain rosette.*

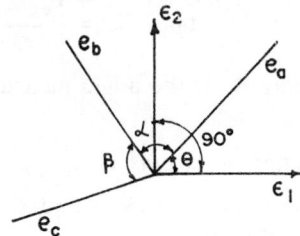

In plane strain case there are direct strains e_1 and e_2 and a shearing strain φ. However, the shear strain cannot

FIG. 5.10

be measured directly. Hence direct strains e_a, e_b and e_c are measured in any three convenient directions. From the measured values of these direct strains, we can calculate the strains in various other directions, including the principal strains $(\varepsilon_1, \varepsilon_2)$, using transformation equations.

Let e_a, e_b and e_c be inclined at θ, $(\theta + \alpha)$ and $(\theta + \alpha + \beta)$ with the direction of major principal strain ε_1.

From Eq. 5.8, noting that $\varphi = 0$, we have

$$e_a = \frac{1}{2}(\varepsilon_1 + \varepsilon_2) + \frac{1}{2}(\varepsilon_1 - \varepsilon_2)\cos 2\theta \qquad \ldots(i)$$

$$e_b = \frac{1}{2}(\varepsilon_1 + \varepsilon_2) + \frac{1}{2}(\varepsilon_1 - \varepsilon_2)\cos 2(\theta + \alpha) \qquad \ldots(ii)$$

and $$e_c = \frac{1}{2}(\varepsilon_1 + \varepsilon_2) + \frac{1}{2}(\varepsilon_1 - \varepsilon_2)\cos 2(\theta + \alpha + \beta) \qquad \ldots(iii)$$

Thus we have above three equations corresponding to three unknowns ε_1, ε_2 and θ.

(a) 45° strain rosette or rectangular strain rosette

If the strain gauges are so arranged that $\alpha = \beta = 45°$, forming a 45° *strain rosette* (or a *rectangular rosette*), as shown in Fig. 5.11, the above pair of equations reduce as under :

$$e_a = \frac{1}{2}(\varepsilon_1 + \varepsilon_2) + \frac{1}{2}(\varepsilon_1 - \varepsilon_2)\cos 2\theta \qquad \ldots(a)$$

$$e_b = \frac{1}{2}(\varepsilon_1 + \varepsilon_2) - \frac{1}{2}(\varepsilon_1 - \varepsilon_2)\sin 2\theta \qquad \ldots(b)$$

$$e_c = \frac{1}{2}(\varepsilon_1 + \varepsilon_2) - \frac{1}{2}(\varepsilon_1 - \varepsilon_2)\cos 2\theta \qquad \ldots(c)$$

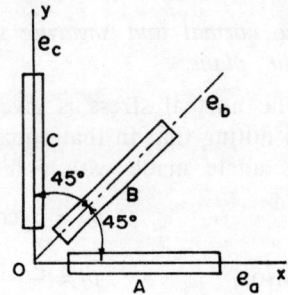

FIG. 5.11. THE 45° STRAIN ROSETTE

Eliminating θ, we get

$$\varepsilon^2 + (e_a + e_c)\varepsilon + \left[e_a e_c - \frac{1}{4}(2e_b - e_a - e_c)^2\right] = 0 \qquad \ldots(5.19\ a)$$

The roots of the above quadratic equation gives the values of principal strains ε_1 and ε_2. Thus

$$\varepsilon_{1,2} = \frac{e_a + e_b}{2} \pm \frac{1}{\sqrt{2}}\sqrt{(e_a - e_b)^2 + (e_b - e_c)^2} \qquad \ldots(5.19)$$

The directions of ε_1 and ε_2, relative to e_a, e_b and e_c are given by the roots of the equation

$$\tan 2\theta_{p\varepsilon} = \frac{2e_b - e_a - e_c}{e_c - e_a} \qquad \ldots(5.20)$$

where $\theta_{p\varepsilon}$ is the angle measured between ε_1 and e_a, measured *clockwise*, from the direction of ε_1.

Determination of strains e_x, e_y and φ_{xy} with a 45° strain rosette

The strain gauges A and C are aligned in x-y directions and hence they give the strains e_x and e_y directly.

Thus, $$e_x = e_a \qquad \text{and} \qquad e_y = e_c$$

In order to determine shear strain φ_{xy}, we use the transformation equation for e_θ :

$$e_\theta = \frac{e_x + e_y}{2} + \frac{e_x - e_y}{2} \cos 2\theta + \frac{\varphi_{xy}}{2} \sin 2\theta$$

For $\qquad \theta = 45°$, we have $e_\theta = e_{45°} = e_b$

Hence $\qquad e_b = \frac{e_a + e_c}{2} + \frac{e_a - e_c}{2} (\cos 90°) + \frac{\varphi_{xy}}{2} (\sin 90°)$

Solving this for φ_{xy}, we get $\quad \varphi_{xy} = 2 e_b - e_a - e_c$ $\qquad$ ...(5.21)

Thus, strains e_x, e_y and φ_{xy} are easily determined from the strain gauge readings, and consequently, stresses can be computed.

2. Equiangular Rosette : The 60° Rosette

The transformation equations are :

$$e_a = \frac{e_x + e_y}{2} + \frac{e_x - e_y}{2} \cos 2\theta_a - \frac{\varphi_{xy}}{2} \sin 2\theta_a$$

$$e_b = \frac{e_x + e_y}{2} + \frac{e_x - e_y}{2} \cos 2\theta_b - \frac{\varphi_{xy}}{2} \sin 2\theta_b$$

$$e_c = \frac{e_x + e_y}{2} + \frac{e_x - e_y}{2} \cos 2\theta_c - \frac{\varphi_{xy}}{2} \sin 2\theta_c$$

$$...(5.22)$$

Here, e_a, e_b and e_c are the measured strain components. The solution of these equations determines the required strain components e_x, e_y and φ_{xy}.

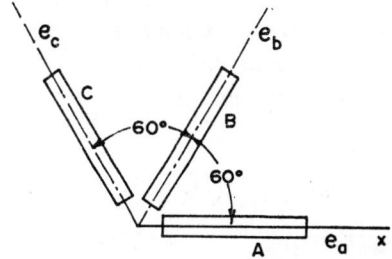

FIG. 5.12. THE 60° ROSETTE

Here the reference angles are : $\theta_a = \theta = 0°$; $\theta_b = \theta + \alpha = 60°$ and $\theta_c = \theta + \alpha + \beta = 120°$. Hence substituting these values in Eq. 5.22 and solving, we get

$$e_x = e_a$$

$$e_y = \frac{1}{3} (2 e_b + 2 e_c - e_a)$$ $\qquad$ ...(5.23)

and $$\varphi_{xy} = \frac{2}{\sqrt{3}} (e_c - e_b)$$

Again, substituting $\alpha = \beta = 120°$ in Eqs. 5.18 we have

$$e_a = \frac{1}{2} (\varepsilon_1 + \varepsilon_2) + \frac{1}{2} (\varepsilon_1 - \varepsilon_2) \cos 2\theta$$

$$e_b = \frac{1}{2} (\varepsilon_1 + \varepsilon_2) - \frac{1}{2} (\varepsilon_1 - \varepsilon_2) \left(\frac{1}{2} \cos 2\theta - \frac{\sqrt{3}}{2} \sin 2\theta \right)$$

and $$e_c = \frac{1}{2} (\varepsilon_1 + \varepsilon_2) - \frac{1}{2} (\varepsilon_1 - \varepsilon_2) \left(\frac{1}{2} \cos 2\theta + \frac{\sqrt{3}}{2} \sin 2\theta \right)$$

Eliminating θ, we get the following quadratic equation for ε

$$3 \varepsilon^2 - 2 (\varepsilon_a + \varepsilon_b + \varepsilon_c) \varepsilon - (\varepsilon_a^2 + \varepsilon_b^2 + \varepsilon_c^2 - 2 \varepsilon_a \varepsilon_b - 2 \varepsilon_b \varepsilon_c - 2 \varepsilon_c \varepsilon_a) = 0$$

The roots of the above quadratic equation give the principal strains. Thus

$$\varepsilon_{1,2} = \frac{e_a + e_b + e_c}{3} \pm \frac{2}{3} \sqrt{e_a(e_a - e_b) + e_b(e_b - e_c) + e_c(e_c - e_a)} \quad ...(5.24)$$

and the direction of maximum principal strain in defined by

$$\tan 2\theta_{p\varepsilon} = \frac{\sqrt{3}\,(e_b - e_c)}{2\,e_a - e_b - e_c} \qquad\qquad ...(5.25)$$

in which the positive value of θ is measured in the counter clockwise direction from the direction of e_a.

Another forms of *equiangular rosettes* are the 120° rosettes shown in Fig. 5.15 and 5.16.

Example 5.6. *A rectangular rosette strain gauge records the following values for linear strain at a point in two dimensional stress system : $e_x = 500 \times 10^{-6}$, $e_y = -125 \times 10^{-6}$ and $e_{45} = 250 \times 10^{-6}$, the latter being at 45° to the X and Y axes. Determine the principal strains and stresses. Take $E = 2.1 \times 10^5 \, N/mm^2$ and $\mu = 0.3$.*

Solution :

Refer Fig. 5.11.

Here $\qquad e_a = e_x = 500 \times 10^{-6}; e_c = e_y = -125 \times 10^{-6}$ and $e_b = e_{45} = 250 \times 10^{-6}$

The principal strains are given by Eq. 5.19

$$\varepsilon_{1,2} = \frac{e_a + e_b}{2} \pm \frac{1}{\sqrt{2}} \sqrt{(e_a - e_b)^2 + (e_b - e_c)^2}$$

$$= \frac{500 \times 10^{-6} + (-125 \times 10^{-6})}{2} \pm \frac{10^{-6}}{\sqrt{2}} \sqrt{(500 - 250)^2 + (250 + 125)^2}$$

$$= 187.5 \times 10^{-6} \pm 318.7 \times 10^{-6}$$

∴ $\qquad\qquad \varepsilon_1 = \mathbf{506.2 \times 10^{-6}}$ and $\varepsilon_2 = \mathbf{-131.2 \times 10^{-6}}$

$$\tan 2\theta_{p\varepsilon} = \frac{2\,e_b - e_a - e_c}{e_c - e_a} = \frac{2 \times 250 - 500 + 125}{-125 - 500} = -0.2$$

which gives $\quad 2\theta_{p\varepsilon} = -11.31°$ (*i.e.* anticlockwise)

∴ $\qquad\qquad \theta_{p\varepsilon} \approx \mathbf{5°39'}$

Knowing the principal strains, the principal stresses are given by Eq. 5.4 (*a*)

$$\sigma_1 = \frac{E\,(\varepsilon_1 + \mu\,\varepsilon_2)}{1 - \mu^2} = \frac{2.1 \times 10^5\,(506.2 - 0.3 \times 131.2)\,10^{-6}}{1 - (0.3)^2} = \mathbf{107.73\ N/mm^2}$$

$$\sigma_2 = \frac{E\,(\varepsilon_2 + \mu\,\varepsilon_1)}{1 - \mu^2} = \frac{2.1 \times 10^5\,(0.3 \times 506.2 - 131.2)\,10^{-6}}{1 - (0.3)^2} = \mathbf{4.77\ N/mm^2}$$

Example 5.7. *The strains measured on a 60° strain rosette are $e_a = 300 \times 10^{-6}$, $e_b = -400 \times 10^{-6}$ and $e_c = 100 \times 10^{-6}$. If $E = 200 \, kN/mm^2$ and $\mu = 0.3$, compute the principal stresses and their directions.*

Solution : (Fig. 5.12). The principal stresses are given by Eq. 5.24 :

$$\varepsilon_{1,2} = \frac{e_a + e_b + e_c}{3} \pm \frac{2}{3}\sqrt{e_a(e_a - e_b) + e_b(e_b - e_c) + e_c(e_c - e_a)}$$

$$= \left[\frac{300 - 400 + 100}{3} \pm \frac{2}{3}\sqrt{300(300+400)-400(-400-100)+100(100-300)}\right]10^{-6}$$

$$= (0 \pm 416.33) \times 10^{-6}$$

$\therefore \qquad \varepsilon_1 = 416.33 \times 10^{-6}$ and $\varepsilon_2 = -416.33 \times 10^{-6}$

$$\tan 2\theta_{p\varepsilon} = \frac{\sqrt{3}(e_b - e_c)}{2e_a - e_b - e_c} = \frac{\sqrt{3}(-400-100)}{2\times300+400-100} = -0.9623$$

$\therefore \qquad 2\theta_{p\varepsilon} \approx -44°$ or $\theta_{p\varepsilon} = -22°$ (i.e. clockwise e_a)

Now $\qquad \sigma_1 = \dfrac{E(\varepsilon_1 + \mu\varepsilon_2)}{1-\mu^2} = \dfrac{2\times10^5(416.33 - 0.3\times416.33)10^{-6}}{1-(0.3)^2} = \mathbf{64.1 \ N/mm^2}$

and $\qquad \sigma_2 = \dfrac{E(\varepsilon_2 + \mu\varepsilon_1)}{1-\mu^2} = \dfrac{2\times10^5(-416.33 + 0.3\times416.33)\times10^{-6}}{1-(0.3)^2} = \mathbf{-64.1 \ N/mm^2}$

5.10. ADDITIONAL ILLUSTRATIVE EXAMPLES

Example 5.8. *At a point in a strained material subjected to plane strain,* $e_x = 510 \times 10^{-6}$, $e_y = 165 \times 10^{-6}$ *and* $\varphi_{xy} = 270 \times 10^{-6}$. *Determine the following :*

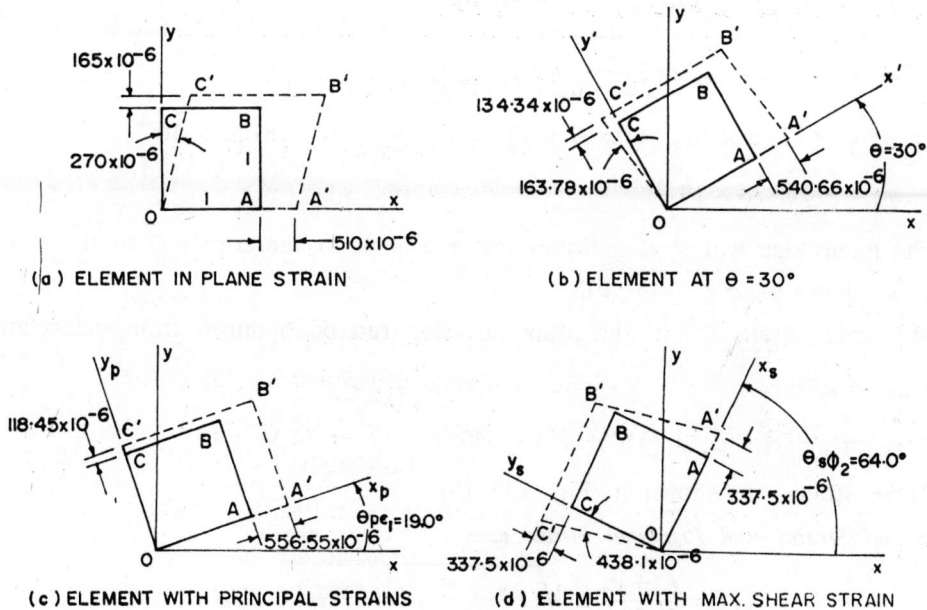

(a) ELEMENT IN PLANE STRAIN

(b) ELEMENT AT θ = 30°

(c) ELEMENT WITH PRINCIPAL STRAINS

(d) ELEMENT WITH MAX. SHEAR STRAIN

FIG. 5.13. DIFFERENT POSITIONS OF ELEMENT

(a) *Strains for an element rotated through an angle* $\theta = 30°$

(b) *Principal strains, and principal strains axes*

(c) *Maximum shearing strain.*

Solve the problem both analytically as well as graphically. Also, show the corresponding strains of the elements in various positions.

Solution :

Fig. 5.13 (a) shows the element *OABC* in plane strain, wherein, the sides of the element has been taken as unity. Hence the deformation will be equal to the corresponding strains. *O A' B' C'* shows the deformed shape of the element, keeping the position of the corner *O* fixed at the origin. Obviously, deformation $AA' = e_x = 510 \times 10^{-6}$, $\angle COC' = \varphi_{xy} = 270 \times 10^{-6}$ and deformation of *C* along *y* axis $= e_y = 165 \times 10^{-6}$.

(a) *Strain in element rotated through* $\theta = 30°$

Fig. 5.13 (b) shows the element, with its distorted position indicated by the dotted lines. The strains can be found by the transformation equations 5.8 and 5.10.

Here $\dfrac{e_x + e_y}{2} = \dfrac{(510 + 165)\,10^{-6}}{2} = 337.5 \times 10^{-6}$; $\dfrac{e_x - e_y}{2} = \dfrac{(510 - 165)\,10^{-6}}{2} = 172.5 \times 10^{-6}$

$\dfrac{\varphi_{xy}}{2} = \dfrac{270 \times 10^{-6}}{2} = 135 \times 10^{-6}$; $\cos 2\theta = \cos 60° = 0.5$; $\sin 2\theta = \sin 60° = 0.866$

Now $\quad e_{\theta x'} = \dfrac{1}{2}(e_x + e_y) + \dfrac{1}{2}(e_x - e_y)\cos 2\theta + \dfrac{1}{2}\varphi_{xy}\sin 2\theta$ ...(5.8)

$= 337.5 \times 10^{-6} + 172.5 \times 10^{-6} \times 0.5 + 135 \times 10^{-6} \times 0.866 = \textbf{540.66} \times \textbf{10}^{-6}$

and $\quad \dfrac{1}{2}\varphi_\theta = -\dfrac{1}{2}(e_x - e_y)\sin 2\theta + \dfrac{1}{2}\varphi\cos 2\theta$ ...(5.10)

$= -172.5 \times 10^{-6} \times 0.866 + 135 \times 10^{-6} \times 0.5 = -81.89 \times 10^{-6}$

or $\quad\quad \varphi_\theta = -\textbf{163.78} \times \textbf{10}^{-6}$

The minus sign with $\dfrac{1}{2}\varphi_\theta$ indicates that the angle at the corner *O* of the element will increase, as shown in Fig. 5.13 (b).

The direct strain $e_{\theta y'}$ in the other direction can be obtained from the relation

$e_{\theta x'} + e_{\theta y'} = e_x + e_y$

or $\quad\quad e_{\theta y'} = e_x + e_y - e_{\theta x'} = (510 + 165 - 540.66)\,10^{-6} = \textbf{134.34} \times \textbf{10}^{-6}$

These strains are shown in Fig. 5.13 (b).

(b) *Principal Strains and Principal Strain axes*

$$\varepsilon_{1,2} = \frac{e_x + e_y}{2} \pm \sqrt{\left(\frac{e_x - e_y}{2}\right)^2 + \left(\frac{\varphi_{xy}}{2}\right)^2} \quad\quad ...(5.14)$$

$$= \left[\, 337.5 \pm \sqrt{(172.5)^2 + (135)^2}\,\right] 10^{-6}$$

$$= 337.5 \times 10^{-6} \pm 219.05 \times 10^{-6}$$

Hence $\qquad \varepsilon_1 = \textbf{556.55} \times \textbf{10}^{-6}$ and $\varepsilon_2 = \textbf{118.45} \times \textbf{10}^{-6}$

$$\tan 2\,\theta_{p\varepsilon} = \frac{\dfrac{\varphi_{xy}}{2}}{\dfrac{(e_x - e_y)}{2}} = \frac{135}{172.5} = 0.7826 \; ; 2\,\theta_{p\varepsilon} \approx 38°$$

Hence $\qquad \theta_{p\varepsilon} = \textbf{19}°$ and $\textbf{109}°$

Substituting $\theta_{p\varepsilon} = 19°$ in Eq. 5.8, we get

$$e_\theta = 337.5 \times 10^{-6} + 172.5 \times 10^{-6} \cos (2 \times 19) + 135 \times 10^{-6} \sin (2 \times 19) = 556.55 \times 10^6$$

This shows that the larger principal stress is associated with $\theta_{p\varepsilon 1} = 19°$ and the smaller principal stress of 118.45×10^{-6} is associated with $= \theta_{p\varepsilon 2} = 109°$. The principal stresses and principal planes are shown marked in Fig. 5.13 (c).

(c) Maximum shear strains and the corresponding planes

$$\frac{\varphi_{max}}{2} = \sqrt{\left(\frac{e_x - e_y}{2} \right)^2 + \left(\frac{\varphi_{xy}}{2} \right)^2} = 10^{-6} \sqrt{(172.5)^2 + (135)^2}$$

$$= 219.05 \times 10^{-6}$$

$\therefore \qquad \varphi_{max} = 2 \times 219.05 \times 10^{-6} = 438.1 \times 10^{-6}$

The orientation of the element for maximum shear strains is at $45°$ to the principal directions.

$\therefore \qquad \theta_{s\varepsilon} = 19° + 45° = 64°$ and $2\,\theta_{s\varepsilon} = 128°$

Substituting this value of $2\,\theta_{s\varepsilon}$ in Eq. 5.10, we get

$$\left(\frac{1}{2}\varphi_\theta \right) = -\frac{1}{2}(e_x - e_y) \sin 2\,\theta_{s\varepsilon} + \frac{1}{2}\varphi_{xy} \cos 2\,\theta_{s\varepsilon}$$

$$= -172.5 \times 10^{-6} \sin 128° + 135 \times 10^{-6} \cos 128° = -219 \times 10^{-6}$$

or $\qquad \varphi_{max} = -438.1 \times 10^{-6}$

This result shows that the element rotated through an angle $\varphi_{s\,\varepsilon 2} = 64°$ has the maximum negative shear strain.

Since the maximum negative and maximum positive shear strains have the same numerical values,

$$(\varphi)_{max} = \pm 438.1 \times 10^{-6}$$

having $\qquad \varphi_{s\,\varepsilon 2} = 64°$ and $\varphi_{s\varepsilon 1} = \theta_{p\varepsilon 1} - 45° = 19° - 45° = -26°$

The normal strains on the element having maximum and minimum shear strains are

$$e_{av} = \frac{\varepsilon_x + \varepsilon_y}{2} = 337.5 \times 10^{-6}$$

Graphical Solution

Fig. 5.14 shows the Mohr's circle of strains, the construction of which is self-explanatory. From the circle, we obtain the following results:

(i) $\varepsilon_{\theta x'} = 540 \times 10^{-6}$

(ii) $\frac{1}{2}\varphi_{\theta} = 82 \times 10^{-6}$

(iii) $\varepsilon_1 = 557 \times 10^{-6}$

(iv) $\varepsilon_2 = 119 \times 10^{-6}$

(v) $2\theta_{pe1} = 38° ; \theta_{pe1} = 19°$

(vi) $2\theta_{se1} = -52° ; \theta_{se1} = -26°$

(vii) $2\theta_{se2} = 128° ; \theta_{se2} = 64°$

(viii) $\frac{1}{2}\varphi_{max} = +219 \times 10^{-6};$

        $\varphi_{max} = +438 \times 10^{-6}$

(ix) $\frac{1}{2}\varphi_{min} = -219 \times 10^{-6};$

        $\varphi_{min} = -438 \times 10^{-6}$

(x) $e_{av} = 337.5 \times 10^{-6}$

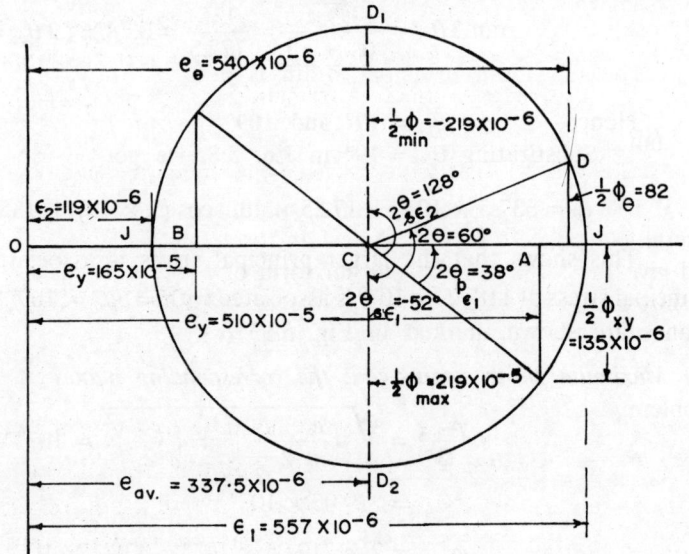

FIG. 5.14

Example 5.9. *A strain gauge rosette has the axes of the three gauges OA, OB and OC at 120° to each other. The observed stains are $720 \times 10^{-6}, -593 \times 10^{-6}$ and 84×10^{-6} along OA, OB and OC respectively.*

Determine the inclination of the principal planes at O relative to OA and the magnitudes of the principal stresses. Determine also the strain at right angles to OA. Take $E = 200 \, kN/mm^2$ and $\mu = 0.3$.

Solution :

Fig. 5.15 shows the 120° rosette. Here $\alpha = \beta = 120°$. Hence putting these values in Eqs. 5.18, we get

$$e_a = \frac{1}{2}(\varepsilon_1 + \varepsilon_2) + \frac{1}{2}(\varepsilon_1 - \varepsilon_2)\cos 2\theta. \qquad ...(1)$$

$$e_b = \frac{1}{2}(\varepsilon_1 + \varepsilon_2) - \frac{1}{2}(\varepsilon_1 - \varepsilon_2)\left[\frac{1}{2}\cos 2\theta - \frac{\sqrt{3}}{2}\sin 2\theta\right] \qquad ...(2)$$

$$e_c = \frac{1}{2}(\varepsilon_1 + \varepsilon_2) - \frac{1}{2}(\varepsilon_1 - \varepsilon_2)\left[\frac{1}{2}\cos 2\theta + \frac{\sqrt{3}}{2}\sin 2\theta\right] \qquad ...(3)$$

The principal strains ε_1 and ε_2 are given by the roots of the equation:

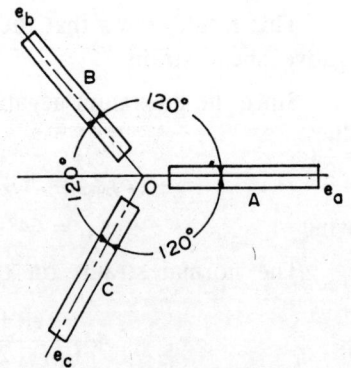

FIG. 5.15. 120° ROSETTE

$$3 \varepsilon^2 - 2 (e_a + e_b + e_c) \varepsilon - (e_a^2 + e_b^2 + e_c^2 - 2e_a e_b - 2e_b e_c - 2e_c e_a) = 0$$

From which, $\varepsilon_{1,2} = \dfrac{e_a + e_b + e_c}{3} \pm \dfrac{2}{3} \sqrt{e_a (e_a - e_b) + e_b (e_b - e_c) + e_c (e_c - e_a)}$ ...(5.26)

This is the same as Eq. 5.24 obtained for a 60° rosette.

The maximum principal strain is defined by

$$\tan 2\theta_{p\varepsilon} = \dfrac{\sqrt{3} \ (e_b - e_c)}{2e_a - e_b - e_c} \qquad ...(5.27)$$

This is also same as Eq. 5.25 obtained for the 60° rosette. Hence a 60° rosette and a 120° rosette are identical and give the same result. Another form of a 120° rosette is shown in Fig. 5.16. *All the forms of 60° rosettes and 120° rosettes are known as equiangular rosettes.*

Substituting the values of e_a, e_b and e_c for the present problem, we get.

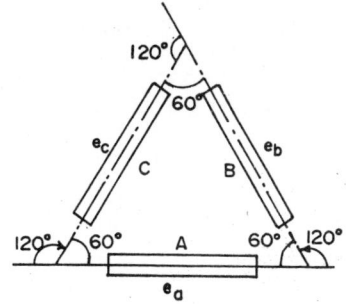

FIG. 5.16. 120° ROSETTE

$$\varepsilon_{1,2} = \left[\dfrac{720 - 593 + 84}{3} \pm \dfrac{2}{3} \sqrt{720(720 + 593) - 593(-593 - 84) + 84(84 - 720)} \right] \times 10^{-6}$$

or $\qquad \varepsilon_{1,2} = 70.3 \pm 758.2$

From which $\qquad \varepsilon_1 = \textbf{828.5}$ and $\varepsilon_2 = -\textbf{687.9}$

$$\tan 2\theta_{p\varepsilon} = \dfrac{\sqrt{3} \ (-593 - 84)}{2 \times 720 + 593 - 84} = -0.60164$$

$\therefore \ 2\theta_{p\varepsilon} = -31°$ or $\theta_{p\varepsilon} = -\textbf{15.5}°$ (*i.e.* in clockwise direction with OA) and $+\textbf{74.5}°$

Knowing the principal strain, principal stresses are given by

$$\sigma_1 = \dfrac{E (\varepsilon_1 + \mu \varepsilon_2)}{1 - \mu^2} = \dfrac{2 \times 10^5 (828.5 - 0.3 \times 687.9) \ 10^{-6}}{1 - (0.3)^2} = \textbf{136.73 kN/mm}^2$$

and $\qquad \sigma_2 = \dfrac{E (\varepsilon_2 + \mu \varepsilon_1)}{1 - \mu^2} = \dfrac{2 \times 10^5 (-687.9 + 0.3 \times 828.5) \ 10^{-6}}{1 - (0.3)^2} = -\textbf{96.56 kN/mm}^2$

For a plane at 90° to OA, θ with the principal plane = 90° + 15.5° = 105.5°.

Hence linear strain at θ = 105.5° is computed by

$$e_\theta = \dfrac{1}{2} (\varepsilon_1 + \varepsilon_2) + \dfrac{1}{2} (\varepsilon_1 - \varepsilon_2) \cos 2\theta = \left[\dfrac{1}{2} (828.5 - 687.9) + \dfrac{1}{2} (828.5 + 687.9) \cos (2 \times 105.5°) \right] 10^{-6}$$
$$= -579.6 \times 10^{-6}$$

Example 5.10. *The measured strains in three directions inclined at 60° to one another are 500 × 10^{-6}, -120 × 10^{-6} and 200 × 10^{-6}, as shown in Fig. 5.17 (a). Compute the magnitude and direction of principal strains in this plane.*

If there is no shear stress perpendicular to the given plane, determine the principal stresses at the point. Take $E = 2 \times 10^5 \ N/mm^2$ and $\mu = 0.3$.

Solution :

Fig. 5.17 (*a*) shows the magnitudes and directions of the three strains measured.

Taking   strain $e_a = 500 \times 10^{-6}$ in the *x*-direction, we get

$e_a = e_0 = +500 \times 10^{-6}$

$e_b = e_{60} = -120 \times 10^{-6}$

$e_c = e_{120} = +200 \times 10^{-6}$

The Mohr circle of strains is shown in Fig. 5.17 (*b*), which is constructed in the following steps :

1. Draw a vertical line representing *y*-axis and set of three vertical lines at $+500 \times 10^{-6}$, $+200 \times 10^{-6}$ and -120×10^{-6} distance (to some scale) from the *y*-axis.

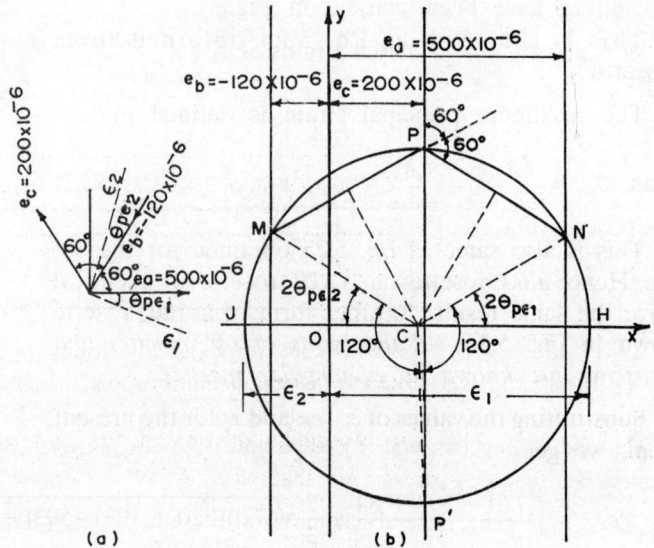

FIG. 5.17

2. On the intermediate strain (e_c) line, select any point *P*.

3. Through *P*, draw a line *PM* at 60° angle, intersecting the vertical line e_b ($= e_{60}$) at *M*. Similarly, draw another line *PN* at 120° angle, intersecting the vertical line representing e_a ($= e_0$) at *N*.

4. Thus, we have three points *P, M* and *N*, on the three vertical lines, corresponding to three strains. The Mohr circle has to pass through these three points *M, P* and *N*. To locate the centre of Mohr's circle, draw perpendicular bisectors of *MP* and *PN*, intersecting at *C*.

5. Through *C*, draw a horizontal line, representing *x*-axis, intersecting *y*-axis in *O*. Thus, we get origin *O* and the centre *C* of the Mohr's circle. Draw the Mohr's circle, with radius *CM* (or *CN*). The circle will pass through *M, P* and *N*.

6. The strain conditions on three given planes are represented by point *M, N* and *P'*, where *P'* is the point on the circle vertically below point *P*. The justification of the construction lies from the fact that the angles between the three radius vectors *CM, CN* and *CP'* are 120°, which is twice the angle between each pair of given direct strains.

7. The principals strains are given by

$$\varepsilon_1 = OH = +555 \times 10^{-6} \text{ and } \varepsilon_2 = OJ = -165 \times 10^{-6}$$

8. Strain ε_1 is inclined at $\theta_{p\varepsilon 1} = \frac{1}{2} \angle NCH = 16°30'$ to strain e_a ($= e_0$). Similarly, strain ε_2 is inclined at $\theta_{p\varepsilon 2} = \frac{1}{2} \angle MCJ = 130°$ with strain e_b ($= e_{60}$). The directions of ε_1 and ε_2, relative to e_a and e_b have been marked in Fig. 5.17 (a).

9. Knowing the principal strains ε_1 and ε_2 the principal stresses are determined as follows:

$$\sigma_1 = \frac{E(\varepsilon_1 + \mu \, \varepsilon_2)}{1 - \mu^2} = \frac{2 \times 10^5 (555 - 0.3 \times 165) \, 10^{-6}}{1 - (0.3)^2} = + 111.1 \text{ N/mm}^2$$

$$\sigma_2 = \frac{E(\mu \, \varepsilon_1 + \varepsilon_2)}{1 - \mu^2} = \frac{2 \times 10^5 (0.3 \times 555 - 165) \, 10^{-6}}{1 - (0.3)^2} = + 0.33 \text{ N/mm}^2$$

PROBLEMS

1. A flat brass plate was stretched by tensile forces acting in direction x and y at right angles. Strain gauges show that strains in x direction was 0.00072 and in the y-direction 0.00016. Find (a) stresses acting in x and y directions, and (b) direct and shearing strains on a plane inclined at 30° to the x-direction (c) normal and shearing stresses on that plane. Take $E = 0.8 \times 10^5$ N/mm^2 and $\mu = 0.3$.

2. A strain gauge rosette has the axes of the three gauges OA, OB and OC at 120° to each other. The observed strains are $+ 554 \times 10^{-6}$, $- 456 \times 10^{-6}$ and $+ 64 \times 10^{-6}$ along OA, OB and OC respectively.

Determine the inclinations of the principal planes at O relative to OA and the magnitudes of the principal stresses. Determine also the strain at right angles to OA.

Take $E = 2 \times 10^5$ N/mm^2 and $\mu = 0.3$.

3. Measured strains in three directions inclined at 60° to one another (Fig. 5.18) are 550×10^{-6}, $- 100 \times 10^{-6}$ and 150×10^{-6}. Calculate the magnitude and direction of principal strains in this plane.

If there is no stress perpendicular to the given plane, determine the principal stresses at the point. Take $E = 2 \times 10^5$ N/mm^2 and $\mu = 0.3$.

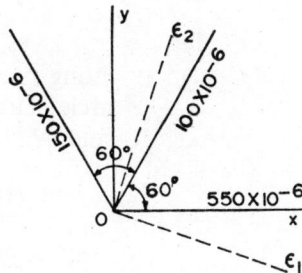

FIG. 5.18

4. In a body subjected to plane strain, there act at a certain point $e_x = 800 \times 10^{-6}$, $e_y = 200 \times 10^{-6}$ and $\varphi_{xy} = 600 \times 10^{-6}$.

Compute (a) the principal strains and the principal strains axes also (b) the strain e_a in a direction of 60° with the x-axis, the strain e_b perpendicular to e_a and the shearing strain φ_{ab}. Further, if $E = 200 \text{ kN/mm}^2$ and $\mu = 0.3$, determine the principal stresses and the normal and shearing stresses on the element rotated 60° from the x-axis.

5. The three readings on 45° strain rosette are :

$e_a = 400 \times 10^{-6}$, $e_b = -200 \times 10^{-6}$ and $e_c = -100 \times 10^{-6}$. If $E = 200 \text{ kN/mm}^2$ and $\mu = 0.3$, determine the principal stresses and their directions.

6. A element of material subjected to plane strain has :

$e_x = 230 \times 10^{-6}$, $e_y = 510 \times 10^{-6}$ and $\varphi_{xy} = 180 \times 10^{-6}$. Calculate the strains for an element rotated through an angle $\theta = 40°$.

ANSWERS

1. (a) $p_1 = 67.52 \text{ N/mm}^2$; $p_2 = 33.05 \text{ N/mm}^2$

   (b) $e_\theta = 0.00058$; $\varphi_\theta = 0.000484$

   (c) $p_n = 41.67 \text{ N/mm}^2$; $p_t = 14.93 \text{ N/mm}^2$

2. $\theta_{p\varepsilon 1} = -15°29'$; $\theta_{p\varepsilon 2} = +74°31'$
         $\sigma_1 = 105.2 \text{ N/mm}^2$; $\sigma_2 = -74.3 \text{ N/mm}^2$; $e_\theta = -446 \times 10^{-6}$

3. $\theta_{p\varepsilon 1} = -11.2°$; $\theta_{p\varepsilon 2} = 78.8°$; $\varepsilon_1 = 579 \times 10^{-6}$; $\varepsilon_2 = -179 \times 10^{-6}$
         $\sigma_1 = 115.5 \text{ N/mm}^2$; $\sigma_2 = -1.16 \text{ N/mm}^2$.

4. (a) $\varepsilon_1 = 924 \times 10^{-6}$; $\varepsilon_2 = 76 \times 10^{-6}$; $\theta_{p\varepsilon 1} = -22.5°$

   (b) $e_a = 90 \times 10^{-6}$; $\varphi_{ab} = 220 \times 10^{-6} \text{ rad}$; $e_b = 910 \times 10^{-6}$

   (c) $\sigma_1 = 208 \text{ N/mm}^2$; $\sigma_2 = 77.8 \text{ N/mm}^2$; $p_{na} = 79.8 \text{ N/mm}^2$; $q_a = 16.92 \text{ N/mm}^2$

5. $\sigma_1 = 64.2 \text{ N/mm}^2$ at $\theta_{p1} = -22°$

6. $e_1 = 434 \times 10^{-6}$; $e_2 = 306 \times 10^{-6}$; $\varphi_{1,2} = 307 \times 10^{-6}$

6

Strain Energy, Resilience and Impact Loading

6.1. INTRODUCTION

When an elastic material is *deformed* under load, work is done by the applied load against the *internal resisting forces* induced in the material. The work done by the load in straining the body is stored within the strained material in the form of *strain energy*. The strain energy is a form of energy and is recoverable without loss on removal of the load. As soon as the load is removed, the strain energy is given up, the material behaving like a perfect spring. This is true only when the material is strained only upto the elastic limit. However, if the elastic limit is exceeded, the work done during non-elastic strain is spent in overcoming the cohesion of the particles of the material, causing them to slide one over another and the energy expended appears as heat in the material strained.

Since strain energy (U) of the body is defined as the work done by the load in straining it, it is always a positive quantity and is expressed in work units, *i.e.* in N-m (or Joules). The deformation of the body, when subjected to axial load (tension or compression) depends upon the *manner* in which the load is applied. The applied load may be gradual, sudden or by impact. If the applied load is not gradual, the maximum instantaneous stress and elongation (or deformation) will be much greater and can be easily calculated by considerations of principle of work. The concept of strain energy is of fundamental importance in applied mechanics, and strain energy principles are widely used when determining the response of machines or structures to both static and dynamic loads. In this chapter, we shall discuss the strain energy of only the axially loaded members. Other cases of strain energy stored in the body due to other actions (such as bending, deflection, torsion etc.) will be discussed later in individual chapters.

6.2. LOAD-DEFLECTION DIAGRAM : STRAIN ENERGY

We shall first consider *gradually applied load or statically applied load*, applied axially to a prismatic bar (Fig. 6.1 a). Let L be the length and A be the area of cross-section of the bar. Let Δ_L be the total deformation (Fig. 6.1 a) of the bar under axial load. When the load (P) is applied, resistance (R) is set up in the bar, and this is stored up in the form of strain energy. As the load P is increased gradually, the resistance $R(=P)$ is increased gradually. In order to evaluate strain energy, we plot load deformation (or resistance deformation) diagram, as shown in Fig. 6.1 (b). The vertical axis represents the load (say P_1 at any stage) and the

(201)

horizontal axis represents deformation (say corresponding Δ_1 at any stage). An increment δP_1 in load results in corresponding incremental deformation $\delta \Delta_1$. Hence work done during this incremental deformation is $P_1 . \delta \Delta_1$, represented by hatched strip in Fig. 6.1 (*b*).

The total work (W) done by the load, as its value P_1 varies from zero to maximum value P and as Δ_1 varies from zero to the maximum deformation Δ is given by

$$W = \int_0^\Delta P_1 . \delta \Delta_1 \qquad ...(6.1 \ a)$$

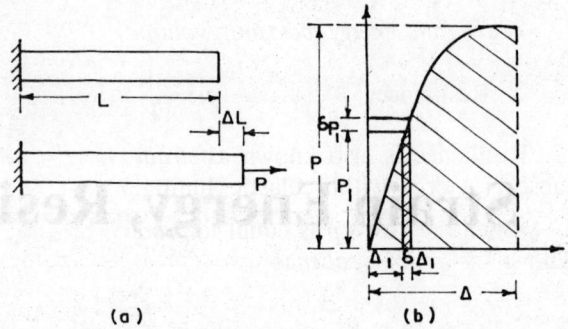

(a)   (b)

FIG. 6.1 LOAD DEFLECTION DIAGRAM

In order words, the work done is equal to the shaded area of load deformation diagram.

The increase in load P results in increase in strain in the bar. The effect of these strains is to increase the energy level of the bar it self in the form of *strain energy* which is defined as the energy absorbed by the bar during the loading process. This strain energy (U) is evidently equal to workdone (W) by the load, provided that no energy is added or substracted in the form of heat.

$$\therefore \qquad U = W = \int_0^\Delta P_1 \delta \Delta_1 \qquad\qquad ...(6.1)$$

When load-deformation is within elastic limit, the diagram will be linear (Fig. 6.2)

$$\therefore \qquad U = W = \frac{1}{2} P . \Delta = \frac{1}{2} p . A . \frac{\Delta}{L} . L \qquad ...(6.2)$$

or

$$U = \frac{1}{2} p . e . V \qquad ...(6.3)$$

i.e.

$$U = \frac{1}{2} \times \text{stress} \times \text{strain} \times \text{volume}$$

Also, strain

$$e = \frac{p}{E}$$

Hence

$$U = \frac{1}{2} p . \frac{p}{E} . V = \frac{1}{2} \frac{p^2}{E} \times V \qquad ...(6.4)$$

Also, from Eq. 6.2,

$$U = \frac{1}{2} P . \frac{PL}{AE} = \frac{P^2 L}{2 AE} \qquad ...(6.5)$$

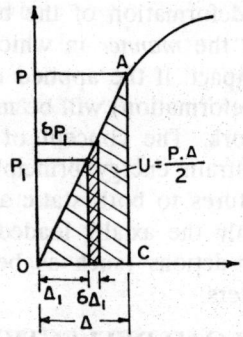

FIG. 6.2

Also, noting that $P = \dfrac{AE\Delta}{L}$, we get from Eq. 6.2

$$U = \frac{1}{2} . \frac{AE\Delta}{L} . \Delta = \frac{EA\Delta^2}{2 L} \qquad ...(6.6)$$

The unit of work done in SI units is the Joule (J), which is equal to one Newton meter (1 J = 1 N–m)

6.3. PROOF RESILIENCE

The strain energy per unit volume of the material is known as resilience.

$\therefore$ Resilience, $\qquad\qquad u = \dfrac{1}{V} \times U = \dfrac{p^2}{2E} = \dfrac{1}{2} p \cdot e = \dfrac{1}{2} E e^2$ ...(6.7)

Resilience is also known as *strain energy density*. It represents the ability of the material to absorb energy within elastic limit.

When the stress p is equal to *proof stress f* at the elastic limit, the corresponding resilience is known as *proof resilience*

$$\therefore \qquad\qquad u_p = \dfrac{f^2}{2E} \qquad\qquad\qquad ...(6.7\ a$$

The proof resilience, also known as *modulus of resilience,* may be looked upon as the property of the material. The units of resilience are in Joules/m^3 (N-m/m^3 = N/m^2).

The term resilience is sometimes employed to denote total quantity of strain energ stored but in specific problems the implication is obvious.

6.4. INELASTIC STRAIN ENERGY

When the bar is stretched only upto the elastic limit, the deformation will disappear completely on the removal of the load and there will be no residual deformation. The strain energy stored in the bar is then known as *elastic strain energy* shown shaded in Fig. 6.2. If, however, the bar is loaded upto point B, beyond the elastic limit (A), the deformation will not disappear completely on the removal of the load. (Fig. 6.3). During loading, the work done is equal to the area under the curve, i.e. the area $OABCDO$. However when the load is removed, the load deflection follows the line BD, and a permanent elongation OD remains, OD being known as the *permanent set.* Hence the *recovered strain energy* is only the one represented by the triangle BCD. This recoverable energy is known as *elastic strain energy* while the area $OABDO$ represents the *inelastic strain energy* which is lost in the process of permanently deforming the bar.

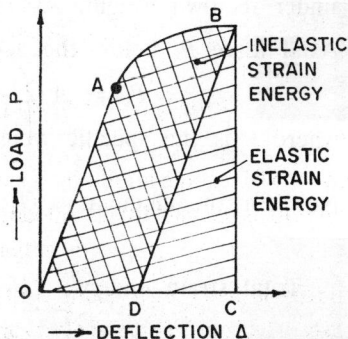

FIG. 6.3

6.5. STRAIN ENERGY OF PRISMATIC BARS WITH VARYING SECTIONS

Fig. 6.4 shows a prismatic bar with varying section along its length. In general, from Eq. 6.5

$$U = \dfrac{P^2 L}{2AE}$$

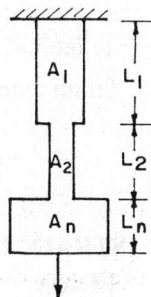

FIG. 6.4

$\therefore$ Total $\qquad U = \Sigma \dfrac{P^2 L}{2 A E} = \dfrac{P^2}{2 E} \left[\dfrac{L_1}{A_1} + \dfrac{L_2}{A_2} + \dfrac{L_n}{A_n} \right]$ $\qquad$ ...(6.8)

6.6. STRAIN ENERGY OF NON-PRISMATIC BAR WITH VARYING AXIAL FORCE

In general strain energy of a bar is given by Eq. 6.5

$$U = \frac{P^2 L}{2 A E}$$

Applying this to a differential section of length dx, where the axial force is P_x, we have

$$U = \int_0^L \frac{P_x^2 \, dx}{2 E A_x} \qquad \text{...(6.9)}$$

where A_x is the area of cross-section of the differential section.

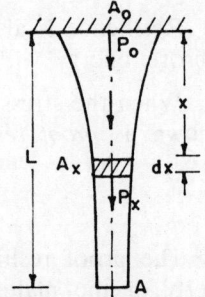

6.7. STRAIN ENERGY OF PRISMATIC BAR HANGING UNDER ITS OWN WEIGHT

FIG. 6.5

Consider an element of length dx, at distance x from the support A, for a bar hanging freely under its own weight. Assume that elastic conditions prevail.

Axial force P_x below the section is

$$P_x = \gamma A (L - x)$$

where γ is the specific weight of the material.

Now for the element, $\qquad U_x = \dfrac{P_x^2 \, dx}{2 A E}$

$\therefore$ Total strain energy, $\qquad U = \int_0^L \dfrac{P_x^2 \, dx}{2 A E} = \int_0^L \dfrac{[\gamma A (L - x)]^2 \, dx}{2 A E}$

$$= \frac{\gamma^2 A L^3}{6 E} \qquad \text{...(6.10)}$$

Alternatively, stress $\qquad p_x = \dfrac{P_x}{A} = \gamma (L - x)$

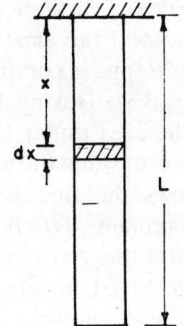

FIG. 6.6

Strain energy density of the element, $u_x = \dfrac{p_x^2}{2 E} = \dfrac{\gamma^2 (L - x)^2}{2 E}$

$\therefore \qquad U = \int u_x \, dV = \int_0^L \dfrac{\gamma^2 (L - x)^2}{2 E} (A \cdot dx) = \dfrac{\gamma^2 A L^3}{6 E}$

6.8. STRAIN ENERGY OF FREELY HANGING PRISMATIC BAR WITH AN AXIAL LOAD

As found earlier, axial force below the sections, due to self weight $= \gamma A (L - x)$

$\therefore$ Total $\qquad P_x = \gamma A (L - x) + P$

$$\therefore \quad U = \int_0^L \frac{[\gamma A (L - x) + P]^2 dx}{2 A E} = \frac{\gamma^2 A L^3}{6 E} + \frac{P^2 L}{2 A E} + \frac{\gamma P L^2}{2 E} \quad ...(6.11)$$

$$= U_1 + U_2 + U_3$$

The above result shows that the total strain energy stored in the bar consists of *three* components :

(*i*) U_1 = strain energy due to a freely hanging bar (Eq. 6.10)

(*ii*) U_2 = Strain energy due to an axial load (Eq. 6.5), and

(*iii*) U_3 = Strain energy component which is a function of both P as well as γ.

This shows that the strain energy of an elastic body due to more than one load cannot be found merely by adding the strain energies obtained from individual loads. This is because of the fact that strain is *not* a linear function but is a quadratic function of the loads, as is evident from Eq. 6.9.

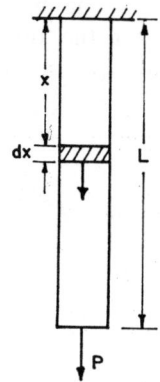

FIG. 6.7

Example 6.1. *A bar 2 m long and 25 mm in diameter is subjected to a tensile load of 60 kN. Taking $E = 2 \times 10^5 N/mm^2$, calculate the strain energy and modulus of resilience.*

Solution :

$$A = \frac{\pi}{4} (25)^2 = 490.87$$

$$U = \frac{P^2 L}{2 A E} = \frac{(60000)^2 \times 2000}{2 (490.87) \times 2 \times 10^5}$$

$$= 36670 \text{ mm-N} = 36.67 \text{ m-N} = 36.67 \text{ J}$$

Modulus of resilience $\quad u = \frac{U}{V} = \frac{36670}{490.87 \times 2000} = 3.7 \times 10^{-2} \text{ mm-N/mm}^3$

Example 6.2. *Two bars are subjected to gradually applied tensile loads. One bar has diameter d throughout and the other, which has the same length is turned down to a diameter d/2 over the middle third of the length, the remainder having the same diameter d. Compare the strain energies of the two bars, if they are of the same material.*

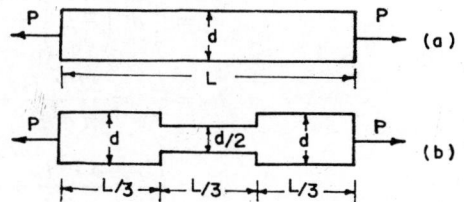

FIG. 6.8

(*b*) *Compare also the amount of energy which the two bars can absorb in simple tension without exceeding a given stress within the limits of proportionality.*

(*c*) *Also, compare the amount of energy per unit volume if the maximum stress is the same in both the cases.*

Solution :

(a) The two bars are shown in Fig. 6.8 (a), (b). Let us use suffix 1 for uniform bar and 2 for the other bar.

$$U_1 = \frac{P^2 L}{2 A E} = \frac{P^2 L}{2 \left(\frac{\pi}{4} d^2\right) E} = \frac{2 P^2 L}{\pi d^2 E} \qquad \qquad \text{...(i)}$$

$$U_2 = \frac{P^2 \left(\frac{2}{3} L\right)}{2 \left(\frac{\pi}{4} d^2\right) E} + \frac{P^2 \left(\frac{1}{3} L\right)}{2 \times \frac{\pi}{4} \left(\frac{d}{2}\right)^2 E} = \frac{4}{3} \frac{P^2 L}{\pi d^2 E} + \frac{8}{3} \frac{P^2 L}{\pi d^2 E}$$

$$= \frac{4 P^2 L}{\pi d^2 E} \qquad \qquad \text{...(ii)}$$

$$\therefore \qquad \frac{U_1}{U_2} = \frac{2 P^2 L}{\pi d^2 E} \div \frac{4 P^2 L}{\pi d^2 E} = \frac{1}{2}$$

(b) Let P = load applied to the non-uniform bar, for a given stress. For the non-uniform bar, max given stress occurs in the $d/2$ diameter portion. If the same stress is to occur in the uniform bar, the required load $= \left(\frac{d}{d/2}\right)^2 P = 4 P$. Hence replacing P by $4P$ in (i), we get

$$U_1 = \frac{2 (4 P)^2 L}{\pi d^2 E} = \frac{32 P^2 L}{\pi d^2 E}$$

Also, $$U_2 = \frac{4 P^2 L}{\pi d^2 E}, \text{ as before}$$

$$\therefore \qquad \frac{U_1}{U_2} = \frac{32 P^2 L}{\pi d^2 E} \div \frac{4 P^2 L}{\pi d^2 L} = 8$$

(c) Again $$V_1 = \frac{\pi}{4} d^2 . L = \frac{\pi d^2 L}{4}$$

$$V_2 = \frac{\pi}{4} d^2 \left(\frac{2}{3} L\right) + \frac{\pi}{4} \left(\frac{d}{2}\right)^2 \left(\frac{L}{3}\right) = \frac{\pi d^2 L}{6} + \frac{\pi d^2 L}{48} = \frac{3}{16} \pi d^2 L$$

$$\therefore \qquad u_1 = \frac{U_1}{V_1} = \frac{32 P^2 L}{\pi d^2 E} \div \frac{\pi d^2 L}{4} = \frac{128 P^2}{\pi^2 d^4 E}$$

and $$u_2 = \frac{U_2}{V_2} = \frac{4 P^2 L}{\pi d^2 L} \div \frac{3}{16} \pi d^2 L = \frac{64}{3} \frac{P^2}{\pi^2 d^4 E}$$

$$\therefore \qquad \frac{u_1}{u_2} = \frac{128 P^2}{\pi^2 d^4 E} \div \frac{64}{3} \frac{P^2}{\pi^2 d^4 E} = \frac{128 \times 3}{64} = 6$$

Example 6.3. *Calculate the strain energy of the bolt shown in Fig. 6.9 under a tensile load of 16 kN. Show that the strain energy is increased for the same maximum stress, by turning down the shank of the bolt to the root diameter of the thread. Take* $E = 2 \times 10^5 \, N/mm^2$.

Solution :

It is the normal practice to assume that the load is distributed evenly over the core of the screwed portion (*i.e.* the root diameter 16.6 mm). Area of core $= \frac{\pi}{4} (16.6)^2 = 216.4$ mm^2.

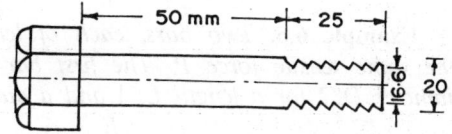

FIG. 6.9

$\therefore$ Stress in screw portion $= \frac{16000}{216.4} = 73.93$ N/mm^2

Stress in shank (at 20 mm dia, area $= 314.2$ mm^2) $= \frac{16000}{314.2} = 50.93$ N/mm^2

$\therefore$ Total strain energy $= \Sigma \frac{p^2}{2E} \cdot V$

$$= \frac{1}{2 \times 2 \times 10^5} \left[(50.93)^2 \times 314.2 \times 50 + (73.93)^2 \times 216.4 \times 25 \right] = 175.8 \text{ N-mm}$$

Alternatively $\quad U = \Sigma \frac{P^2 L}{2AE} = \frac{(16000)^2}{2 \times 2 \times 10^5} \left[\frac{50}{314.2} + \frac{25}{216.4} \right] = \textbf{175.8 N-mm}$

If now the shank is turned down to 16.6 mm dia, the stress in the bolt will be 73.93 N/mm^2 throughout.

$\therefore \qquad\qquad U = \frac{p^2}{2E} V = \frac{(73.93)^2}{2 \times 2 \times 10^5} \times 216.4 \times 75 = \textbf{221.8 N-mm}$

Alternatively, $\quad U = \frac{P^2 L}{2AE} = \frac{(16000)^2 \times 75}{2 \times 216.4 \times 2 \times 10^5} = 221.8$ N-mm.

Thus, the strain energy is increased by $\frac{221.8 - 175.8}{175.8} \times 100 = \textbf{26.2 \%}$ by turning down the shank of the bolt to the root dia. of the thread.

Example 6.4. *Two elastic bars of the same material and length, one of circular section of diameter d and the other of square section of side d, absorb the same amount of energy delivered by axial forces. Compare the stresses in the two bars.*

Solution :

Let us use suffix 1 for circular section and 2 for square section.

For circular section, area $A_1 = \frac{\pi}{4} d^2$

For square section, area $A_2 = d^2$.

Let p_1 and p_2 be the stresses in the circular section and square section respectively. If the strain energies absorbed by the two bars is to be the same, we have

$$\frac{p_1^2 A_1 L}{2E} = \frac{p_2^2 A_2 L}{2E}$$

or
$$\frac{p_1}{p_2} = \sqrt{\frac{A_2}{A_1}} = \sqrt{d_2 / (\frac{\pi}{4} d^2)} = \sqrt{\frac{4}{\pi}} = 1.128$$

Example 6.5. *Two bars, each of length L and of different materials are each subjected to the same tensile force P. The first bar has a uniform diameter D and the second bar has a diameter D/2 for a length L/4 and a diameter D for the remaining length. Compare the strain energies of the two bars if (a)* $\frac{E_1}{E_2} = \frac{4}{7}$ *and (b)* $E_1 = E_2$.

Solution :

Let us use suffix 1 for uniform bar and suffix 2 for non-uniform bar.

$$U_1 = \frac{P^2 L}{2 A E_1} = \frac{P^2 L}{2 \left(\frac{\pi}{4} D^2\right) E_1}$$

$$= \frac{2 P^2 L}{\pi D^2 E_1}$$

Also,
$$U_2 = \frac{P^2}{2 E_2} \left[\frac{\frac{3}{4} L}{\frac{\pi}{4} D^2} + \frac{\frac{1}{4} L}{\frac{\pi}{4} \left(\frac{D}{2}\right)^2} \right] = \frac{P^2}{2 E_2} \left[\frac{3 L}{\pi D^2} + \frac{4 L}{\pi D^2} \right]$$

$$= \frac{7 P^2 L}{2 \pi D^2 E_2}$$

∴
$$\frac{U_1}{U_2} = \frac{2 P^2 L}{\pi D^2 E_1} \div \frac{7 P^2 L}{2 \pi D^2 E_2} = \frac{4}{7} \frac{E_2}{E_1}$$

(*a*) If
$$\frac{E_1}{E_2} = \frac{4}{7} \text{ (or } \frac{E_2}{E_1} = \frac{7}{4} \text{)}, \; \frac{U_1}{U_2} = \frac{4}{7} \times \frac{7}{4} = 1$$

(*b*) If
$$E_1 = E_2, \; \frac{U_1}{U_2} = \frac{4}{7}$$

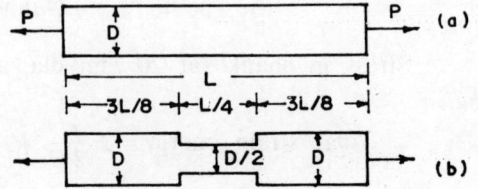

FIG. 6.10

6.9. STRESSES DUE TO GRADUAL, SUDDEN AND IMPACT LOADINGS

(*a*) Gradual Loading

Let a bar of cross-sectional area A be subjected to a gradually applied axial load P due to which the deformation is Δ.

Then work done by external load

$$= \frac{1}{2} P . \Delta$$

Work stored in the body $= \frac{1}{2} R \Delta = \frac{1}{2} p A \Delta$

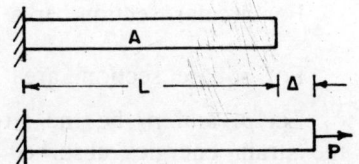

FIG. 6.11

Now buckling load $P_E = \dfrac{\pi^2 E I}{L^2}$, for strut with both ends pinned

$$= \frac{\pi^2 \times 0.8 \times 10^5 \times 267035}{(6000)^2} = 5865 \text{ N.}$$

$\therefore$ Safe load $= \dfrac{P_E}{F.S.} = \dfrac{5865}{3} = 1955 \text{ N} = \textbf{1.955 kN}$

Example 20.3. *An I-section joist ISWB 400 and 8 m long is used as a strut with both ends fixed. Taking $E = 2 \times 10^5 \, N/mm^2$, determine Euler's crippling load.*

Given for the section $I_{xx} = 23426.7 \, cm^4$, $I_{yy} = 1388.0 \, cm^4$

Solution :

$$I_{min} = I_{yy} = 1388 \times 10^4 \, \text{mm}^4$$

For a strut fixed at both ends, $L_E = \dfrac{L}{2} = \dfrac{8}{2} = 4 \text{ m}$

$$P_E = \frac{\pi^2 E I}{L_c^2} = \frac{\pi^2 \times 2 \times 10^5 \times 1388 \times 10^4}{(4000)^2}$$

$$= 1712 \times 10^3 \, \text{N} = \textbf{1712 kN}$$

Example 20.4. *A straight bar of mild steel, 1 m long and 12 mm×6 mm in section is mounted in strut testing machine and loaded axially till it buckles. Assuming Euler's formula for pinned ends to apply, estimate the maximum central deflection before the material attains its yield point of $300 \, N/mm^2$. Take $E = 2 \times 10^5 \, N/mm^2$.*

Solution :

$$I_{min} = \frac{1}{12} (12) (6)^3 = 216 \, \text{mm}^4$$

$\therefore$
$$P_E = \frac{\pi^2 E I}{L^2} = \frac{9.8696 \, (2 \times 10^5) \, (216)}{(1000)^2} = 426.4 \text{ N}$$

Maximum deflection (δ) occurs at half the height, where

$$M_{max} = P.\delta = p_b.Z = p_b \left(\frac{216}{3} \right) = 72 \, p_b$$

$\therefore$
$$p_b = \frac{P.\delta}{72} = \frac{426.4 \, \delta}{72} = 5.922 \, \delta$$

Also,
$$p_0 = \frac{P}{A} = \frac{426.4}{12 \times 6} = 5.922 \, \text{N/mm}^2$$

Now
$$p_{max} = p_b + p_0 = 300 \quad \text{(given)}$$

$\therefore$
$$5.922 \, \delta + 5.922 = 300$$

From which
$$\delta = \frac{300 - 5.922}{5.922} = \textbf{49.66 mm}$$

20.8. LONG COLUMN UNDER ECCENTRIC LOADING : SECANT FORMULA

(a) Empirical approach : Modified Rankine's formula

When a short column is subjected to a compressive load P applied at an eccentricity e, we have

$$p = p_0 + p_b = \frac{P}{A} + \frac{P \cdot e}{Z} = \frac{P}{A} + \frac{P \cdot e \cdot y_c}{A r^2} = \frac{P}{A}\left(1 + \frac{e\, y_c}{r^2}\right)$$

where r = radius of gyration

and y_c = distance of extreme compressive fibre from the N.A.

Taking f_c as the permissible stress in the material, the corresponding load is given by

$$P = \frac{f_c A}{\left(1 + \dfrac{e\, y_c}{r^2}\right)} \qquad\qquad ...(20.24)$$

In the above expression, $\left(1 + \dfrac{e\, y}{r^2}\right)$ is the *reduction factor* which takes into account the *eccentricity of loading.*

Rankine's formula for a long column with axial loading is

$$P = \frac{f_c A}{1 + a\left(\dfrac{L}{r}\right)^2} \qquad\qquad ...(20.15)$$

In the above expression, $\left[1 + a\left(\dfrac{L}{r}\right)^2\right]$ is a *reduction factor* which takes into account the *buckling of the column.*

Combining Eqs. 20.24 and 20.15, the *modified Rankine's formula* for a long column loaded with eccentric loading can be stated as follows :

$$P = \frac{f_c A}{\left(1 + e\dfrac{y_c}{r^2}\right)\left(1 + a\dfrac{L^2}{r^2}\right)} \qquad\qquad ...(20.25)$$

The above formula is applicable for the standard case. For other cases, the factor a can be changed accordingly.

(b) Theoretical approach : Secant formula

Fig. 20.13 shows the column of length L, hinged at both the ends, subjected to a load P applied at an eccentricity e. At any section distant x from A, y is the deflection of the column with reference to the line of action of P; the B.M. at that section is $P \cdot y$

$$\therefore \qquad\qquad E I \frac{d^2 y}{d x^2} = -M - -P \cdot y$$

or

$$\frac{d^2 y}{d x^2} + \frac{P}{E I} y = 0$$

Solving the above differential equation, we obtain

$$y = C_1 \sin x \sqrt{\frac{P}{E I}} + c_2 \cos x \sqrt{\frac{P}{E I}} \qquad ...(1)$$

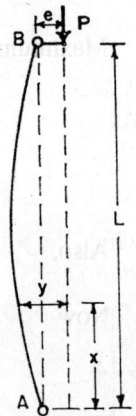

FIG. 20.13

ranging between 30 and 120. Similarly, American Bridge Co. adopted this formula with a maximum value of permissible stress as 915 kg/cm^2, taking $C_1 = 1335$ kg/cm^2 and $C_2 = 7.03$ kg/cm^2.

Eq. 7.11 is known as *parabolic formula*, sometimes written in the form

$$\frac{P}{A} = C_3 - C_4 \left(\frac{l}{r}\right)^2 \qquad ...(20.19 \ a)$$

AISC adopted this formula for members having $l/r < 120$, taking $C_3 = 1190$ kg/cm^2 and $C_4 = 0.0334$ kg/cm^2. A.R.E.A. and A.A.S.H.O. adopted this formula for members having $l/r < 140$, taking the following values :

$C_3 = 1090$ kg/cm^2 and $C_4 = 0.0175$ kg/cm^2, for riveted structures.

and $C_3 = 1050$ kg/cm^2 and $C_4 = 0.0233$ kg/cm^2, for welded structures.

5. AISC formula : The American Institute of Steel Construction (AISC) defines the limit between the intermediate and long columns to be the value of slenderness ratio λ_c given by

$$\lambda_c = \sqrt{\frac{2 \pi^2 E}{\sigma_{YP}}} \qquad ...(20.20)$$

where σ_{YP} is the yield point stress for the particular steel under consideration. Taking $\sigma_{YP} = 280$ N/m m^2 and $E = 2 \times 10^5$ N/mm^2, we get

$$\lambda_c = \sqrt{\frac{2 \pi^2 (2 \times 10^5)}{280}} \approx 119$$

The working stress σ_w, for $\dfrac{L_E}{r}$ (or $\dfrac{l}{r}$) greater than λ_c is given by

$$\sigma_w = \frac{12 \pi^2 E}{23 \left(\dfrac{L_E}{r}\right)^2} \qquad ...(20.21)$$

It is interesting to note that this is Euler's formula with factor of safety (FS) equal to 23/12 (= 1.92).

For $\dfrac{L_E}{r} < \lambda_c$, AISC specifies the following *parabolic formula*

$$\sigma_w = \left[1 - \frac{\left(\dfrac{L_E}{r}\right)^2}{2 \lambda_c^2}\right] \frac{\sigma_{yp}}{FS} \qquad ...(20.22)$$

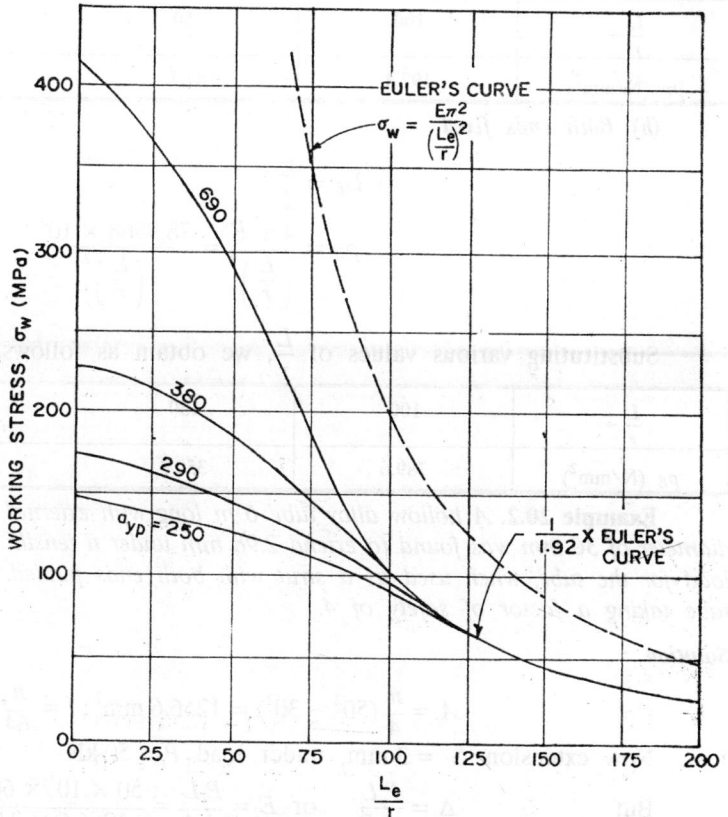

FIG. 20.12. AISC SPECIFICATION FOR σ_w

where the factor of safety (FS) is given by

$$FS = \frac{5}{3} + \frac{3\left(\frac{L_E}{r}\right)}{8\lambda_c} - \frac{\left(\frac{L_E}{r}\right)^3}{8\lambda_c^3} \qquad ...(20.23)$$

FS comes out to be 1.92 at $\frac{L_E}{r} = \lambda_c$, and it becomes smaller for larger values of slenderness ratio. Fig. 20.12 shows the variation of σ_w with $\frac{L_E}{r}$ for several grades of steel, based on the AISC formula.

Example 20.1. *Calculate Euler's critical stresses for a series of columns having slenderness ratio of 50, 100, 150, 200 and 250 under the following conditions : (a) both ends hinged, and (b) both ends fixed. Take $E = 2 \times 10^5 N/mm^2$.*

Solution :

(a) Both ends hinged : $\quad p_E = \frac{\pi^2 E r^2}{L^2} = \frac{\pi^2 E}{\left(\frac{L}{r}\right)^2} = \frac{19.739 \times 10^5}{\left(\frac{L}{r}\right)^2}$

Substituting the values of $\frac{L}{r}$ in the above formula, we obtain following values.

$\frac{L}{r} \rightarrow$	100	150	200	250
p_E (N/mm²)	197.4	87.7	49.3	31.6

(b) Both ends fixed

$$L_E = \frac{L}{2}$$

∴
$$p_E = \frac{4\pi^2 E}{\left(\frac{L}{r}\right)^2} = \frac{78.9568 \times 10^5}{\left(\frac{L}{r}\right)^2}$$

Substituting various values of $\frac{L}{r}$, we obtain as follows.

$\frac{L}{r} \rightarrow$	100	150	200	250
p_E (N/mm²)	789.6	350.9	197.4	126.3

Example 20.2. *A hollow alloy tube 6 m long with external diameter of 50 mm and internal diameter of 30 mm was found to extend 2.98 mm under a tensile load of 50 kN. Find the buckling load for the tube, when used as a strut with both ends pinned. Also, find the safe load on the tube taking a factor of safety of 4.*

Solution :

$$A = \frac{\pi}{4}(50^2 - 30^2) = 1256.6 \text{ mm}^2 \text{ ; } I = \frac{\pi}{64}(50^4 - 30^4) = 267035 \text{ mm}^4$$

Now extension $\Delta = 3$ mm, under load $P = 50$ kN

But $\quad\quad \Delta = \frac{PL}{AE} \quad$ or $\quad E = \frac{PL}{A\Delta} = \frac{50 \times 10^3 \times 6000}{1256.6 \times 2.98} = 0.8 \times 10^5 \text{ N/mm}^2$

Taking $\quad m =$ factor of safety, we get $p_c = m \cdot \sigma_{ac}$

where $\quad \sigma_{ac} =$ allowable stress. Similarly, taking $p_{max} = f_y =$ yield stress,

$$\text{we get} \qquad \sigma_{ac} = \frac{\dfrac{f_y}{m}}{1 + \dfrac{e\,y_c}{r^2} \sec \dfrac{l}{2r} \sqrt{\dfrac{m\,\sigma_{ac}}{E}}} \qquad \qquad ...(20.30\ a)$$

Indian Standard Code (IS : 800-1962) adopted the above formula for determining the permissible stress in the material by taking factor of safety $m = 1.68$ and $\dfrac{e\,y_c}{r^2} = 0.2$

$$\text{Thus} \qquad \sigma_{ac} = \frac{\dfrac{f_y}{m}}{1 + 0.2 \sec \dfrac{l}{2r} \sqrt{\dfrac{m\,\sigma_{ac}}{E}}} \qquad \qquad ...(20.30)$$

The above formula is valid for $\dfrac{l}{r} \le 160$. However, for $\dfrac{l}{r} > 160$, the allowable stress can be found from the expression

$$\sigma_{ac}' = \sigma_{ac} \left(1.2 - \frac{l}{800\,r} \right) \qquad \qquad ...(20.31)$$

where σ_{ac} is the value found from Eq. 20.30 for the value of $\dfrac{l}{r}$.

The above formula, suggested by IS : 800-1962 was later dropped in its 1984 version.

(b) **IS Code formula as per IS : 800 - 1984 : Merchant Rankine Formula**
IS : 800-1984 has recommended the following *Merchant Rankine formula* for determining the permissible stress :

$$\sigma_{ac} = \frac{f_{cc} \cdot f_y}{m \left[\left(f_{cc} \right)^n + \left(f_y \right)^n \right]^{1/n}} \qquad \qquad ...(20.32\ a)$$

where $\quad \sigma_{ac} =$ permissible stress in axial compression, N/mm^2 or MPa

$f_{cc} =$ elastic critical stress in compression $= \dfrac{\pi^2 E}{\lambda^2} \qquad \qquad ...(20.33)$

$f_y =$ yield stress in steel, $=$ N/mm^2 or MPa

$E =$ modulus of elasticity of steel $= 2 \times 10^5$ N/mm^2

$\lambda = \dfrac{l}{r} =$ slenderness ratio

$m =$ factor of safety $= \dfrac{10}{6}$

$n =$ a factor, assumed as 0.4

$$\text{Hence} \qquad \sigma_{ac} = 0.6 \frac{f_{cc} \cdot f_y}{\left[\left(f_{cc} \right)^n + \left(f_y \right)^n \right]^{1/n}} \qquad \qquad ...(20.32)$$

According to IS:800-1984, the direct stress in compression on the gross cross-sectional area of axially loaded compression member shall not exceed $0.6 f_y$, nor the permissible value

σ_{ac} calculated using the above formula. The value of σ_{ac} for some of the Indian Standard structural steels are given its Table 20.5.

TABLE 20.5. PERMISSIBLE STRESS σ_{ac} (N/mm^2) IN AXIAL COMPRESSION.

$f_y \rightarrow$ / $\lambda \downarrow$	220	230	240	250	260	280	300	320	340	360	380	400	420	450	480	510	540
10	132	138	144	150	156	168	180	192	204	215	227	239	251	269	287	305	323
20	131	137	142	148	154	166	177	189	201	212	224	235	246	263	280	297	314
30	128	134	140	145	151	162	172	183	194	204	215	225	236	251	266	280	295
40	124	129	134	139	145	154	164	174	183	192	201	210	218	231	243	255	267
50	118	123	127	132	136	145	153	161	168	176	183	190	197	207	216	225	233
60	111	115	118	122	126	133	139	146	152	158	163	168	173	180	187	193	199
70	102	106	109	112	115	120	125	130	135	139	142	147	150	155	160	164	168
80	93	96	98	101	103	107	111	115	118	121	124	127	129	133	136	139	141
90	85	87	88	90	92	95	98	101	103	105	108	109	111	114	116	118	119
100	76	78	79	80	82	84	86	88	90	92	93	94	96	97	99	100	101
110	68	69	71	72	73	74	76	77	79	80	81	82	83	84	85	86	87
120	61	62	63	64	64	66	67	67	69	70	71	71	72	73	73	74	75
130	55	55	56	57	57	58	59	60	61	61	62	62	63	63	64	64	65
140	49	50	50	51	51	52	53	53	54	54	54	55	55	56	56	56	57
150	44	45	45	45	46	46	47	47	48	48	48	49	49	49	49	50	50
160	40	40	41	41	41	42	42	42	43	43	43	43	43	44	44	44	44
170	36	36	37	37	37	37	38	38	38	38	39	39	39	39	39	39	39
180	33	33	33	33	33	34	34	34	34	35	35	35	35	35	35	35	35
190	30	30	30	30	30	30	31	31	31	31	31	31	32	32	32	32	32
200	27	27	28	28	28	28	28	28	28	28	28	28	28	28	28	28	28
210	25	25	25	25	25	25	26	26	26	26	26	26	26	26	26	26	26
220	23	23	23	23	23	23	23	24	24	24	24	24	24	24	24	24	24
230	21	21	21	21	21	21	21	21	22	22	22	22	22	22	22	22	22
240	20	20	20	20	20	20	20	20	20	20	20	20	20	20	20	20	20
250	18	18	18	18	18	18	18	18	18	19	19	19	19	19	19	19	19

20.11. COMPARISON OF VARIOUS FORMULAE

The graphical comparison of various column formulae is shown in Fig. 20.14.

At A, $\qquad$ $x = 0$ and $y = e$. Hence we get $C_2 = e$

Also, $\qquad \dfrac{dy}{dx} = C_1 \sqrt{\dfrac{P}{EI}} \cos x \sqrt{\dfrac{P}{EI}} - e \sqrt{\dfrac{P}{EI}} \sin x \sqrt{\dfrac{P}{EI}}$

At the mid height, where $\qquad x = \dfrac{L}{2}$, we have $\dfrac{dy}{dx} = 0$

$\therefore \qquad 0 = C_1 \sqrt{\dfrac{P}{EI}} \cos \dfrac{L}{2} \sqrt{\dfrac{P}{EI}} - e \sqrt{\dfrac{P}{EI}} \sin \dfrac{L}{2} \sqrt{\dfrac{P}{EI}}$

From which we get $\qquad C_1 = e \, \dfrac{\sin \dfrac{L}{2} \sqrt{\dfrac{P}{EI}}}{\cos \dfrac{L}{2} \sqrt{\dfrac{P}{EI}}}$

Substituting the value of C_1 and C_2 in (1), we get

$$y = e \left[\dfrac{\sin \dfrac{L}{2} \sqrt{\dfrac{P}{EI}}}{\cos \dfrac{L}{2} \sqrt{\dfrac{P}{EI}}} \sin x \sqrt{\dfrac{P}{EI}} + \cos x \sqrt{\dfrac{P}{EI}} \right] \qquad ...(2)$$

At $\qquad x = \dfrac{L}{2}, y = y_{max}$

$\therefore \qquad y_{max} = e \left[\dfrac{\sin^2 \dfrac{L}{2} \sqrt{\dfrac{P}{EI}}}{\cos \dfrac{L}{2} \sqrt{\dfrac{P}{EI}}} + \cos \dfrac{L}{2} \sqrt{\dfrac{P}{EI}} \right] = e \sec \dfrac{L}{2} \sqrt{\dfrac{P}{EI}} \qquad ...(3)$

The largest B.M. $\left(M_{max} \right)$ occurs at $x = \dfrac{L}{2}$, where y is maximum.

$\therefore \qquad M_{max} = P \cdot y_{max} = P \cdot e \sec \dfrac{L}{2} \sqrt{\dfrac{P}{EI}} \qquad ...(20.26)$

Now, the maximum compressive stress in the column is given by

$$p = \dfrac{P}{A} + \dfrac{M}{Z} = \dfrac{P}{A} + \dfrac{P \cdot e \sec \dfrac{L}{2} \sqrt{\dfrac{P}{EI}}}{Z} \qquad ...(20.27\ a)$$

or $\qquad p = \dfrac{P}{A} \left(1 + \dfrac{e\, y_c}{r^2} \sec \dfrac{L}{2} \sqrt{\dfrac{P}{EI}} \right) \qquad ...(20.27)$

This is the well known *secant formula*

For secant formula for all end conditions may be written as

$$p = \dfrac{P}{A} + \dfrac{P \cdot e \sec \dfrac{L_E}{2} \sqrt{\dfrac{P}{EI}}}{Z} = \dfrac{P}{A} \left(1 + \dfrac{e\, y_c}{r^2} \sec \dfrac{L_E}{2} \sqrt{\dfrac{P}{EI}} \right) \qquad ...(20.28)$$

It is pertinent to note that the value of r in Eqs. 20.27 and 20.28 need not be minimum, since it is obtained from the value of I associated with the axis around which bending occurs. It should also be noted that while in the case of short column, the B.M. *at all the sections* is *P.e*, in the case of long columns, the max. B.M. is increased by a factor

$$\sec \frac{L_E}{2} \sqrt{\frac{P}{EI}}$$

20.9. LONG COLUMN UNDER ECCENTRIC LOADING : PERRY'S FORMULA

For a long column with eccentric loading, the maximum stress can be *conveniently* computed Eq. 20.27, if P and e are given. If however, it is required to find the value of P for a given value of e, Eq. 20.27 is not convenient since the secant term contains P itself. Hence it is required to find a more workable expression from which P can be directly computed.

Now
$$\sec \frac{L}{2} \sqrt{\frac{P}{EI}} = \sec \sqrt{\frac{PL^2}{4EI}} = \sec \frac{\pi}{2} \sqrt{\frac{P}{P_E}}$$

where
$$P_E = \text{Eulerian load} = \frac{\pi^2 EI}{L^2}$$

Prof. Perry observed that $\sec \dfrac{\pi}{2} \sqrt{\dfrac{P}{P_E}} \approx \dfrac{1.2\, P_E}{P_E - P}$.

$\therefore$
$$\sec \frac{L}{2} \sqrt{\frac{P}{EI}} \approx \frac{1.2\, P_E}{P_E - P} \qquad\qquad ...(20.29a)$$

Substituting this in Eq. 20.27, we have

$$p = \frac{P}{A} \left(1 + \frac{e\, y_c}{r^2} \frac{1.2\, P_E}{P_E - P} \right)$$

But
$$\frac{P}{A} = p_0 \text{ and } \frac{P_E}{A} = p_E$$

Hence
$$p = p_0 \left(1 + \frac{e\, y_c}{r^2} \frac{1.2\, p_E}{p_E - p_0} \right)$$

or
$$\left(\frac{p}{p_0} - 1 \right) \left(1 - \frac{p_0}{p_E} \right) = \frac{1.2\, e\, y_c}{r^2} \qquad\qquad ...(20.29)$$

The above equation is known as Perry's approximate formula from which p_0 and hence $P\,(= p_0 . A)$ can be easily computed

20.10. DESIGN FORMULA : IS CODE FORMULA

(a) IS Code formula as per IS : 800-1962

Putting $p = p_{max}$ in secant formula (Eq. 20.27), we get

$$p_{max} = \frac{P}{A} \left(1 + \frac{e\, y_c}{r^2} \sec \frac{l}{2} \sqrt{\frac{P}{EI}} \right)$$

or
$$\frac{P}{A} = p_c = \frac{p_{max}}{1 + \dfrac{e\, y_c}{r^2} \sec \dfrac{l}{2r} \sqrt{\dfrac{p_c}{E}}}$$

Example 20.8. *A hollow cast iron column with fixed ends supports an axial load of 800 kN. If the column is 3 m long and has an external diameter of 200 mm, find the thickness of metal required. Use Rankine's formula, taking a constant of $\dfrac{1}{6400}$ and assume a working stress of 90 N/mm².*

Solution :

The value of Rankine's constant a for cast iron is $\dfrac{1}{1600}$, for the standard case. Since the given value of a is $\dfrac{1}{4}$ of this value, it includes the effect of end conditions.

$$\therefore \qquad P = \frac{f_c \cdot A}{1 + \dfrac{1}{6400}\left(\dfrac{L}{r}\right)^2}$$

Here, $\qquad A = \dfrac{\pi}{4}(D^2 - d^2)$ and $r^2 = \dfrac{D^2 + d^2}{16}$

where $\qquad D$ = external diameter = 200 mm and d = internal diameter, is mm.

$$\therefore \qquad P = 800 \times 10^3 = \frac{90 \times \dfrac{\pi}{4}(D^2 - d^2)}{1 + \dfrac{1}{6400} \times \dfrac{16\,(3000)^2}{D^2 + d^2}} = \frac{70.686\,(D^2 - d^2)}{1 + \dfrac{22500}{D^2 + d^2}}$$

or $\qquad 800 \times 10^3 (D^2 + d^2) + 800 \times 10^3 (22500) = 70.686\,(D^4 - d^4)$

or $\; 800 \times 10^3 (200^2 + d^2) + 800 \times 10^3 (22500) = 70.686\,(200^4 - d^4)$

On simplification, we get $d^4 + 11318\,d^2 - 8.927 \times 10^8 = 0$

From which $\qquad\qquad d^2 = 24750$ mm² or $d = 157.32$ mm

$$\therefore \qquad \text{Metal thickness} = \frac{D - d}{2} = \frac{200 - 157.32}{2} = \mathbf{21.34\ mm}$$

Example 20.9. *A mild steel column is of hollow circular section with 100 mm as external diameter and 80 mm as internal diameter. The column is 2.4 m long, hinged at both the ends and has to carry a load of 60 kN at an eccentricity of 16 mm from the geometrical axis. Calculate the maximum and minimum intensities of stresses. Also, calculate the maximum possible eccentricity so that no tension is induced any where in the section. Take $E = 2 \times 10^5\ N/mm^2$.*

Solution :

$$A = \frac{\pi}{4}(100^2 - 80^2) = 2827.4\ \text{mm}^2\, ; I = \frac{\pi}{64}(100^4 - 80^4) = 2898119\ \text{mm}^4$$

$$\therefore \qquad r^2 = \frac{I}{A} = \frac{2898119}{2827.4} = 1025\ \text{mm}^4$$

$$Z = \frac{2898119}{50} = 57962\ \text{mm}^3$$

Now, $M_{max} = P \cdot e \sec \dfrac{L}{2} \sqrt{\dfrac{P}{EI}}$ $= 60 \times 10^3 \times 16 \left[\sec \dfrac{2400}{2} \sqrt{\dfrac{60 \times 10^3}{2 \times 10^5 \times 2898119}} \right]$

$$= 60 \times 10^3 \times 16 \,(1.0795)$$

$$= 1.036 \times 10^6 \text{ N-mm}$$

Now $\hat{f}_b = \dfrac{M_{max}}{Z} = \dfrac{1.036 \times 10^6}{57962} = 17.88 \text{ N/mm}^2$

Also, $f_0 = \dfrac{P}{A} = \dfrac{60000}{2827.4} = 21.22 \text{ N/mm}^2$

$\therefore$ $f_{max} = f_0 + f_b = 21.22 + 17.88 = \mathbf{39.1 \text{ N/m}^2}$ (comp.)

$f_{min} = f_0 - f_b = 21.22 - 17.88 = \mathbf{3.34 \text{ N/mm}^2}$ (comp.)

For no tension to develop, we get $f_b = f_0$

$$17.88 \times \dfrac{e}{16} = 21.22$$

or $e = \dfrac{21.22 \times 16}{17.88} = \mathbf{18.99 \text{ mm}}$

Example 20.10. *A mild steel column is of hollow circular section 100 mm as external diameter and 80 mm as internal diameter. The column is 2.4 m long and is hinged at both the ends. Calculate the maximum permissible load with an eccentricity of 16 mm if the maximum compressive stress is limited to 80 N/mm². Take $E = 2 \times 10^5$ N/mm².*

Solution :

From the previous example, we have

$$A = 2827.4 \text{ mm}^4 \,;\, I = 2898119 \text{ mm}^4$$

$$r^2 = 1025 \text{ mm}^2 \,;\, Z = 57962 \text{ mm}^3$$

$$P_E = \dfrac{\pi^2 EI}{L^2} = \dfrac{\pi^2 (2 \times 10^5)(2898119)}{(2400)^2} = 993170 \text{ N}$$

$\therefore$ $p_E = \dfrac{P_E}{A} = \dfrac{993170}{2827.4} = 351.3 \text{ N/mm}^2$

$$f = 90 \text{ N/mm}^2 \text{ (given)}$$

Substituting in Perry's approximate formula, we have

$$\left(\dfrac{f}{f_0} - 1 \right) \left(1 - \dfrac{f_0}{p_E} \right) = \dfrac{1.2 \, e \, y_c}{r^2}$$

or $\left(\dfrac{80}{f_0} - 1 \right) \left(1 - \dfrac{f_0}{351.3} \right) = \dfrac{1.2 \times 16 \times 40}{1025} = 0.7493$

or $(80 - f_0)(351.3 - f_0) = 0.7493 \times 351.3 \, f_0 = 263.2 \, f_0$

or $208104 - 351.3 \, f_0 - 80 f_o + f_0^2 = 263.2 \, f_0$

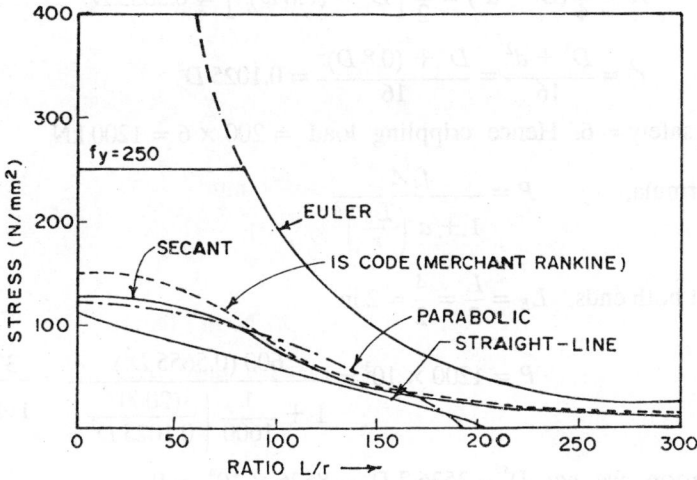

FIG. 20.14. COMPARISON OF VARIOUS COLUMN FORMULAE

Example 20.5. *A cast iron hollow column, having 100 mm external diameter and 80 mm internal diameter, is used as a column of 2.4 m length. Using Rankine's formula, determine the cripling load, when both the ends are fixed. Take $f_c = 600 \, N/mm^2$ and $a = \dfrac{1}{1600}$.*

Solution :

$$A = \frac{\pi}{4}(100^2 - 80^2) = 2827.4 \text{ mm}^2$$

$$I = \frac{\pi}{64}(100^4 - 80^4) = 289.8 \times 10^4 \text{ mm}^4 \, ; r^2 = \frac{I}{A} = \frac{289.8 \times 10^4}{2827.4} = 1025 \text{ mm}$$

For a column with fixed ends, $L_E = \dfrac{L}{2} = \dfrac{2.4}{2} = 1.2 \text{ m} = 1200 \text{ mm}$

Now Rankine's $P = \dfrac{f_c \cdot A}{1 + a\left(\dfrac{L_E}{r}\right)^2}$

$$= \frac{600 \times 2827.4}{1 + \dfrac{1}{1600}\dfrac{(1200)^2}{1025}} = 903300 \text{ N} = \textbf{903.3 kN}$$

Example 20.6. *A hollow cast iron cylindrical column, 4 m long with both ends firmly fixed carries an axial load of 200 kN. The internal diameter of the column is equal to 0.8 times the external diameter. Determine the section of the column, taking $f_c = 600 \, N/mm^2$, Rankine's constant $a = \dfrac{1}{1600}$, and a factor of safety of 6.*

Solution :

Let D = external diameter and d = internal dia. = $0.8 D$

$$\therefore \qquad A = \frac{\pi}{4}(D^2 - d^2) = \frac{\pi}{2}\left[D^2 - (0.8\,D)^2\right] = 0.5655\,D^2$$

$$r^2 = \frac{D^2 + d^2}{16} = \frac{D^2 + (0.8\,D)^2}{16} = 0.1025\,D^2$$

Factor of safety = 6. Hence crippling load = $200 \times 6 = 1200$ kN

From Rankine's formula, $\qquad P = \dfrac{f_c A}{1 + a\left(\dfrac{L_E}{r}\right)^2}$

For column fixed at both ends, $\quad L_E = \dfrac{L}{2} = \dfrac{4}{2} = 2$ m

$$\therefore \qquad P = 1200 \times 10^3 = \frac{600\,(0.5655\,D^2)}{1 + \dfrac{1}{1600}\left(\dfrac{(2000)^2}{0.1025\,D^2}\right)} = \frac{339.3\,D^2}{1 + \dfrac{24390}{D^2}}$$

On simplification, we get $D^4 - 3536.7\,D^2 - 8626 \times 10^4 = 0$

From which, $\qquad\qquad\qquad D^2 = 11222.8$ and hence $D = \mathbf{106\ mm}$

$\therefore \qquad\qquad\qquad\qquad d = 0.8\,D = \mathbf{84.8\ mm}$

Example 20.7. *Compare the crippling loads given by Euler's and Rankine's formulae, for a tubular steel strut 2.5 m long, having outer and inner diameters as 40 mm and 30 mm respectively, loaded through pin joints at the ends. Take yield stress as 320 N/mm², the Rankine's constant* $= \dfrac{1}{7500}$ *and* $E = 2 \times 10^5$ *N/mm². for what length of the strut of this cross-section does the Euler's formula cease to apply ?*

Solution :

$$I = \frac{\pi}{64}(40^4 - 30^4) = 85903 \text{ mm}^4 \,; A = \frac{\pi}{4}(40^2 - 30^2) = 549.8 \text{ mm}^2$$

$$r = \sqrt{\frac{I}{A}} = \sqrt{\frac{85903}{549.8}} = 12.5 \text{ mm} \,; L = 2.5 \text{ m} = 2500 \text{ mm}$$

$$P_E = \frac{\pi^2 E I}{L^2} = \frac{\pi^2 \times 2 \times 10^5 \times 85903}{(2500)^2} = 27131 \text{ N} = \mathbf{27.131\ kN}$$

$$P_R = \frac{f_c \cdot A}{1 + a\left(\dfrac{L}{r}\right)^2} = \frac{320 \times 549.8}{1 + \dfrac{1}{7500}\left(\dfrac{2500}{12.5}\right)^2} = 27779 \text{ N} = \mathbf{27.779\ kN}$$

$$\therefore \qquad \frac{P_E}{P_R} = \frac{27.131}{27.779} = \mathbf{0.977}$$

Now $\qquad\qquad p_E = \dfrac{P_E}{A} = 320 = \dfrac{\pi^2 E}{\left(\dfrac{L}{r}\right)^2}$

$\therefore$ Validity limit of $\quad \dfrac{L}{r} = \sqrt{\dfrac{\pi^2 E}{320}} = \sqrt{\dfrac{\pi^2 (2 \times 10^5)}{320}} = \mathbf{78.54}$

20.12. COMMON SHAPES OF COMPRESSION MEMBERS

We have seen in the IS Code column formula as well as in other formulae that the *permissible stress* in a compression member decreases with increase in slenderness ratio. Hence the section must be so proportioned that it has largest possible moment of inertia for the same cross-sectional area. Also, the section should have approximately the same radius of gyration about both the principal axes. Fig. 20.16 show various type of compression members. *Solid circular section* is used as compression member in machines and special structures such as legs of tall, guyed transmission towers. The cylindrical tube or *hollow circular section* (Fig. 20.16 *a*) is the optimum section for a column with equal unbraced lengths in each direction. Such sections are extensively used in *tubular trusses*. However, there are connection problems in such a section. In *square* or *rectangular tube* (Fig. 20.16 *c*), the efficiency of circular tube may be approached and at the same

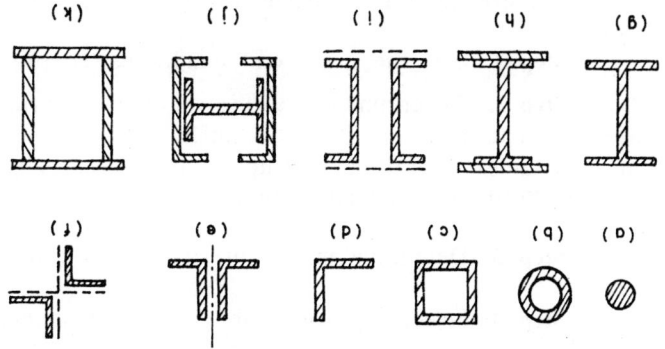

FIG. 20.16. TYPICAL COMPRESSION MEMBERS

time the connection problem can be made simple. The *single angle section* shown in Fig. 20.16 *d* are useful only for truss members and compression legs of towers. *Tee sections* are often used in welded trusses. The *double angle sections* (Fig. 20.16 *e*) are commonly used in trusses, while the *cruciform arrangement* of double angles (Fig. 20.16 *f*) gives approximately equal radii of gyration in two directions. The wide flange section shown in Fig 20.16 (*g*) is commonly used in buildings because of its easy availability in different sizes and ease with which it can be spliced and connected. If the requirement of area is in excess of available section, additional plates can be attached to the flanges as shown in Fig. 20.16 *(h)*.

The choice of arrangement of multiple rolled sections or *built-up sections* depends upon (*i*) functional aspect of the structure (*ii*) functional aspect of the member, (*iii*) inter-connection requirements, and (*iv*) high radius of gyration. Fig. 20.16 shows a large variety of built-up sections. The elements of built-up sections are placed at the farthest possible distance from the centroid of the section. A section consisting of two channel sections, suitably spaced (Fig. 20.16 *i*) is used as web compression member in lattice-girder bridges. If suitable channel sections are not available, built-up sections using four angles and plates can be conveniently used. A combination of two channels and an I-section (Fig 20.16 *j*) can be used as web member in a truss bridge. Fig 20.16 (*i*), (*j*), (*k*) show built-up column sections, to carry heavy loads.

20.13. STRENGTH OF COMPRESSION MEMBERS

The *strength* of a compression member is the load carrying capacity of a member at a safe (allowable) compressive stress corresponding to the slenderness ratio of the column. It depends upon several factors, most important amongst these being radius of gyration, effective length and area of cross-section. Thus :

$$P = \sigma_{ac} . A \qquad \qquad ...(20.34)$$

In compression members, full gross-sectional area is effective in resisting compression, and no deduction is made for rivet holes since the rivets are assumed to fill the holes. The axial compression has a tendency to further tighten the rivets in the holes and the rivets tend to bear against the adjoining material.

It is seen in the design formula that the allowable stress σ_{ac} varies parabolically with slenderness ratio. Hence it can be easily shown that *efficiency of a shape*, which is defined as the ratio of allowable load for a given slenderness ratio to that for slenderness ratio equal to zero, is related to A/r^2.

The strength or load carrying capacity of compression member is determined in the following steps.

Step 1. For the given end conditions, compute   ctive length l of the member.

Step 2. Determine the values of radius of gyration of the member about the principal axes and determine r_{min}. If it is a single rolled steel section, these values are already available in steel tables. If it is a built-up section these values are determined either with the help of Fig. 20.10 or by actual computations.

Step 3. Determine maximum slenderness ratio $\lambda = \dfrac{l}{r_{min}}$

Step 4. Select σ_{ac} from Table 20.5 corresponding to this maximum value of λ.

Step 5. Find gross cross-sectional area of the section, from steel tables.

Step 6. Finally, compute the strength of the compression member, using Eq. 20.34.

Example 20.14. *An I-joist ISMB 250 @ 37.3 kg/m has an effective length of 5 m. It is used as a stanchion with two plates 250 mm × 10 mm welded to its sides, as shown in Fig. 20.17. Compute the load carrying capacity. What will be its load capacity if one plate is attached to each flange?*

Solution : From steel tables, for ISMB 250@ 37.3 kg/m, we have :
$a = 47.55$ cm^2; $I_{xx} = 5131.6 \times 10^4$ mm^4; $I_{yy} = 334.5 \times 10^4$ mm^4.

(*a*) *Plates attached to sides* (Fig 20.17)

$$I_{xx} = 5131.6 \times 10^4 + 2 \left[\frac{1}{12} \times 10 \times 250^3 \right] = 77.35 \times 10^6 \text{ mm}^4$$

$$I_{yy} = 334.5 \times 10^4 + 2 \left[\frac{1}{12} \times 250 \, (10)^3 + 2500 \, (62.5 + 5)^2 \right]$$

$$= 26.17 \times 10^6 \text{ mm}^4$$

$$A = 4755 + 2 \, (250 \times 10) = 9755 \text{ mm}^2$$

$$r_{min} = r_{yy} = \sqrt{\frac{26.17 \times 10^6}{9755}} \approx 51.8 \text{ mm}$$

$$\lambda_{max} = \frac{l}{r_{min}} = \frac{5000}{51.8} = 96.53.$$

$$\therefore \quad \sigma_{ac} = 90 - 6.53 \left(\frac{10}{10} \right) = 83.47 \text{ N/mm}^2$$

$$\therefore \quad P = A \, \sigma_{ac} = 9755 \times 83.47 \times 10^{-3} = \mathbf{814.25 \text{ kN}}$$

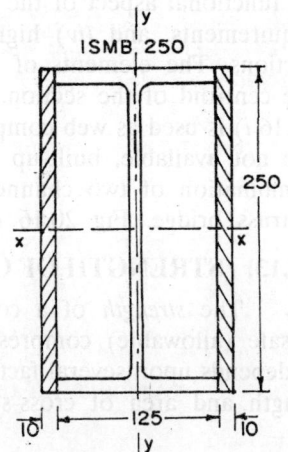

FIG. 20.17.

or $f_0^2 - 694.5 f_0 + 28104 = 0$

From which we get $f_0 = 43.147 \text{ N/mm}^2$

$\therefore$ Safe load $P = f_0 A = 43.147 \times 2827.4 = 121994 \text{ N} \approx \mathbf{122 \ kN}$

Example 20.11. *A rolled steel beam section ISWB 200 @ 28.8 kg/m is used as a stanchion and has an unsupported length of 5 m. It is hinged at both the ends. Determine the axial load this stanchion can carry, if the yield stress for steel is 250 N/mm² and E = 2 × 10⁵ N/mm². Use IS Code formula. For ISWB 200@28.8 kg/m, $r_{xx} = 8.46$ cm, $r_{yy} = 2.99$ cm and A = 36.71 cm².*
Solution :

Given $f_y = 250 \text{ N/mm}^2 ; L = 5 \text{ m}$

For a column with hinged ends, $L_E = L = 5 \text{ m}$

$$r_{min} = r_{yy} = 29.9 \text{ mm}$$

$$\lambda_{max.} = \frac{L_E}{r_{min}} = \frac{5000}{29.9} = 167.2$$

$\therefore$

$$f_{cc} = \frac{\pi^2 E}{\lambda^2} = \frac{\pi^2 (2 \times 10^5)}{(167.2)^2} = 70.61 \text{ N/mm}^2$$

Hence

$$\sigma_{ac} = 0.6 \frac{f_{cc} \cdot f_y}{\left[(f_{cc})^n + (f_y)^n \right]^{1/n}} = \frac{0.6 \times 70.61 \times 250}{\left[(70.61)^{1.4} + (250)^{1.4} \right]^{1/1.4}}$$

$$= 37.86 \text{ N/mm}^2$$

Alternatively, from Table 20.5, for $f_y = 250 \text{ N/mm}^2$ and $\lambda = 167.2$

we get $\sigma_{ac} = 41 - (41 - 37) \times \dfrac{7.2}{10} = 38.12 \text{ N/mm}^2$

$\therefore$ $P = A \cdot \sigma_{ac} = 3671 \times 37.86 = 138984 \text{ N} = \mathbf{138.984 \ kN}$

Example 20.12. *A hollow steel shaft, outside diameter 150 mm and inside diameter 100 mm is to be used as a column. Determine the maximum allowable length of this column for a maximum allowable load of 800 kN. Take $f_y = 250 N/mm^2$. Use I.S. Code formula.*
Solution :

$$I_{xx} = \frac{\pi}{64} (D^4 - d^4) = \frac{\pi}{64} (150^4 - 100^4) = 19.9418 \times 10^6 \text{ mm}^4$$

$$A = \frac{\pi}{4} (D^2 - d^2) = \frac{\pi}{4} (150^2 - 100^2) = 9817.477 \text{ mm}^2$$

$$r = \sqrt{\frac{I}{A}} = \sqrt{\frac{9.9418 \times 10^6}{9817.477}} = 45.069 \text{ mm}$$

$$\sigma_{ac} = \frac{P}{A} = \frac{800 \times 100}{9817.477} = 81.49 \text{ N/mm}^2$$

Corresponding to this value of $\sigma_{ac} = 81.49$ and $f_y = 250 \text{ N/mm}^2$, we get from Table 20.5,

$\lambda = 100 - (100 - 90) \dfrac{81.49 - 80}{90 - 80} = 98.51$

$\therefore$ $L = \lambda r = 98.51 \times 45.069 \approx 4440 \text{ mm} = \mathbf{4.44 \ m}$

Example 20.13. *A solid member has the cross-section as shown in Fig. 20.15. It is to be used as a column having 3.5 m effective length. Determine the value of d if the maximum allowable load is to be 400 kN. Take $f_y = 250 \, N/mm^2$ and $E = 2 \times 10^5 \, N/mm^2$.*

Solution

$$A = 2 \times \frac{1}{2} (2d) \left(\frac{d}{2} \right) = d^2$$

$$I_X = 2 \times \frac{1}{12} (2d) \left(\frac{d}{2} \right)^3 = \frac{d^4}{24}$$

$$I_Y = 2 \times \frac{1}{12} (d) (d)^3 = \frac{d^4}{6}$$

$$\therefore \quad I_{min} = I_X = \frac{d^4}{24}.$$

$$r_{min} = \sqrt{\frac{I_{min}}{A}} = \sqrt{\frac{d^4/24}{d^2}} = \frac{d}{\sqrt{24}}$$

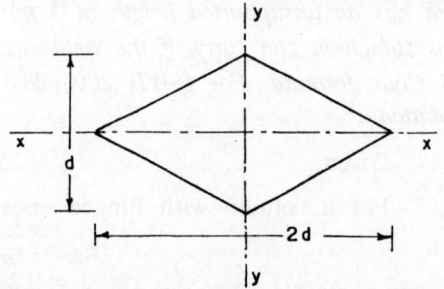

FIG. 20.15.

$$\lambda_{max} = \frac{l}{r_{min}} = \frac{3500}{d/\sqrt{24}} = \frac{17146.4}{d};$$

$$f_{cc} = \frac{\pi^2 E}{\lambda^2} = \frac{\pi^2 \times 2.0 \times 10^5}{(17146.4/d)^2} = 6.714 \times 10^{-3} d^2$$

Now

$$P = 400 \times 10^3 = \sigma_{ac} \times A$$

$$\therefore \quad \sigma_{ac} = \frac{P}{A} = \frac{400 \times 10^3}{d^2}$$

But

$$\sigma_{ac} = \frac{0.6 f_{cc} \cdot f_y}{\left[(f_{cc})^n + (f_y)^n \right]^{\frac{1}{n}}}$$

or

$$\sigma_{ac}^n \left[(f_{cc})^n + (f_y)^n \right] = \left(0.6 \cdot f_y \cdot f_{cc} \right)^n$$

or

$$\left(\frac{400 \times 10^3}{d^2} \right)^{1.4} \left[(6.714 \times 10^{-3} d^2)^{1.4} + (250)^{1.4} \right] = \left[0.6 \times 250 \times 6.714 \times 10^{-3} d^2 \right]^{1.4}$$

or

$$9.0736 \times 10^{-4} d^{2.8} + 2275.7 = 1.45 \times 10^{-8} d^{5.6}$$

or

$$d^{5.6} - 62569.4 \, d^{2.8} - 1.5693 \times 10^{11} = 0.$$

or

$$x^2 - 62569.4 \, x - 1.5693 \times 10^{11} = 0 \quad \text{(where } x = d^{2.8})$$

From which

$$x = 428658$$

$$\therefore \quad d = x^{1/2.8} = (428658)^{1/2.8} = 102.7$$

Keep

$$d = \mathbf{103 \, mm}.$$

$$\therefore \quad r_{min} = \frac{103}{\sqrt{24}} = 21.02 \; ; \; \lambda = \frac{17146.4}{103} = 166.5$$

$$\therefore \quad \sigma_{ac} = 41 - (41 - 37) \frac{6.5}{10} = 38.4 \, N/mm^2$$

$$A = (103)^2$$

$$\therefore \quad P = (103)^2 \times 38.4 \times 10^{-3} = 407.4 \, kN. \quad \text{Hence O.K.}$$

of the force P that will cause the total length of the member to decrease by 0.20 m. Take
$E_s = 2 \times 10^5 \, N/mm^2$ *and* $E_a = 0.7 \times 10^5 \, N/mm^2$. *Also, compute the work done by force P.*

Solution :

Area of steel bar, $\qquad A_s = \dfrac{\pi}{4}(20)^2 = 314.16 \, \text{mm}^2$

Area of aluminium bar, $A_a = \dfrac{\pi}{4}(50)^2 = 1963.5 \, \text{mm}^2 = 6 \, A_s$

Now $\qquad \dfrac{P L_s}{A_s E_s} + \dfrac{P L_a}{A_a E_a} = \Delta$

or $\qquad P\left[\dfrac{500}{314.16 \times 2 \times 10^5} + \dfrac{500}{1963.5 \times 0.7 \times 10^5}\right] = 0.2$

or $\qquad P\left[1.15955 \times 10^{-5}\right] = 0.2$ from which $P = \mathbf{17248 \, N}$

Total work done by $\qquad P = \dfrac{1}{2}\text{Load} \times \text{deflection}$

$\qquad\qquad = \dfrac{1}{2} \times 17248 \times 0.2 = \mathbf{1724.8 \; mm\text{-}N}$

$\qquad\qquad = 1725 \; \text{m-N} = \mathbf{1.725 \; J}$

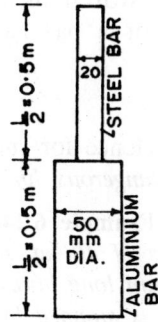

FIG. 6.18

Example 6.23. *Compare the amount of strain energy in three circular bars shown in Fig 6.19, assuming a uniform distribution of stresses over the cross-section of the bars. Comment on the result, taking a large value of n.*

Solution :

For the prismatic bar of Fig. 6.19 (a)

$$U = \dfrac{P^2 L}{2 A E} \qquad\qquad ...(1)$$

For the grooved bar of Fig. 6.19 (b),

$$U_1 = \dfrac{P^2 (L/4)}{2 A E} + \dfrac{P^2 (3L/4)}{2(4A)E} = \dfrac{7}{16}\dfrac{P^2 L}{2 A E} \quad ...(2)$$

For the grooved bar of Fig. 6.19 (c),
Area of grooved portion = A and area of other portions $= \dfrac{\pi}{4}(nd)^2 = n^2 A$.

$\therefore \qquad U_2 = \dfrac{P^2 (L/4)}{2 A E} + \dfrac{P^2 (3L/4)}{2(n^2 A)E}$

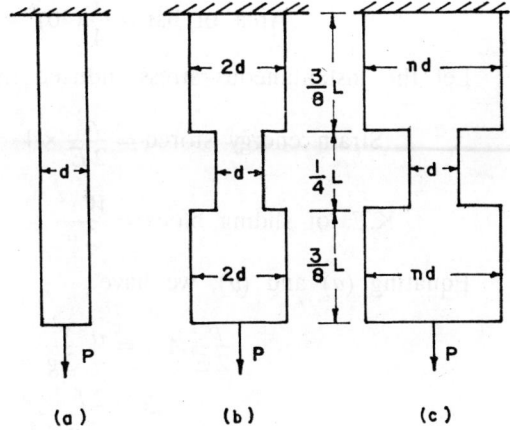

(a) (b) (c)

FIG. 6.19

$\qquad\qquad = \dfrac{P^2 L}{2 A E}\left(\dfrac{1}{4} + \dfrac{3}{4 n^2}\right)$

or $\qquad U_2 = \dfrac{1}{4}\dfrac{P^2 L}{2 A E}\left(1 + \dfrac{3}{n^2}\right) \qquad\qquad ...(3)$

Hence $\dfrac{U_1}{U} = \dfrac{7}{16}$ ...(a)

and $\dfrac{U_2}{U} = \dfrac{1}{4}\left(1 + \dfrac{3}{n^2}\right)$ ...(b)

From (a) and (b), it is seen that for a given maximum stress, the quantity of strain energy stored in a grooved bar is less than that of a bar of uniform thickness. Taking $n = 4$, or a bar having large outer diameter and a very narrow groove, we have

$$\dfrac{U_2}{U} = \dfrac{1}{4}\left(1 + \dfrac{3}{16}\right) = \dfrac{19}{64} = \dfrac{1}{3.368}$$

Hence for such a case, it takes a very small amount of work to bring the tensile stress to a *dangerous limit*.

Example 6.24. *A sliding block, having a mass of 40 kg, slides over a 40 mm dia 1200 mm long horizontal rod at a velocity of 2 m/s, is stopped by its impact, with a rigid collar provided at the end of the rod as shown in Fig. 6.20. Ignoring friction and bending of the bar, find the instantaneous stress induced in the bar. Take $E = 2 \times 10^5 \, N/mm^2$.*

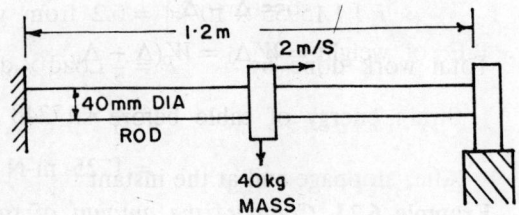

FIG. 6.20

Solution :

Mass of sliding weight $= M = 40$ kg

∴ Weight $W = Mg = 40 \times 9.81 = 392.4 \, \text{N}$

Area of bar $= \dfrac{\pi}{4}(40)^2 = 1256.6 \, \text{mm}^2$

Let the instantaneous stress induced in the bar $= p$

∴   Strain energy stored $= \dfrac{p^2}{2E} \times V = \dfrac{p^2}{2E} \times A L$ ...(a)

K.E. of sliding block $= \dfrac{W v^2}{2g}$ ...(b)

Equating (a) and (b), we have

$$\dfrac{p^2}{2E} A L = W \dfrac{v^2}{2g}$$

or $p^2 = \dfrac{2 E W v^2}{2 g A L} = \dfrac{2 \times 2 \times 10^5 \times 392.4 \,(2000)^2}{2 \times 9810 \times 1256.6 \times 1200} = 21221$

From which $p = 145.68 \, \text{N/mm}^2$

Example 6.25. *An elevator car of weight W is supported by a cable that is moving with constant velocity v (Fig. 6.21). Determine the maximum stress produced when the drum is suddenly locked.*

Hence find the value of the stress if $L = 10$ m, $W = 15$ kN, $v = 1$ m/sec. and diameter of rope is 30 mm. Take $E = 2.05 \times 10^5 \, N/mm^2$ and $g = 9.81 \, m/sec^2$.

Solution :

The cable in this example supports the weight W and hence strain energy (in the form of K.E.) is stored in the cable even before the drum is locked. Hence total energy of the system is K.E. plus potential energy (P.E.).

K.E. of moving elevator $= \dfrac{W v^2}{2g}$

Let $\quad \Delta_{st} =$ static elongation of cable under load W

$\quad\quad \Delta =$ total elongation of the cable.

$\quad\quad \Delta_1 =$ the distance that the weight moves downward after the drum locks

$\quad\quad\quad = \Delta - \Delta_{st}$

$\therefore$ P.E. of weight $= W \Delta_1 = W(\Delta - \Delta_{st})$

Strain energy of cable before stoppage $= \dfrac{E A \Delta_{st}^2}{2L}$ (Eq. 6.6)

After stoppage and at the instant the cable has its maximum elongation Δ,

FIG. 6.21

Strain energy $= E A \dfrac{\Delta^2}{2L}$ (Eq. 6.6). No K.E. exists at this instant because the velocity is zero.

Hence using the principle of conservation of energy

$$\underset{(i)}{\dfrac{W v^2}{2g}} + \underset{(ii)}{W(\Delta - \Delta_{st})} + \underset{(iii)}{\dfrac{E A \Delta_{st}^2}{2L}} = \dfrac{E A \Delta^2}{2L} \qquad \ldots (6.26)$$

This equation can be solved for max, elongation Δ as follows

(i) $\quad \Delta_{st} = \dfrac{WL}{EA}$, from which $W = \dfrac{E A \Delta_{st}}{L}$

(ii) Substitute this value of W into term (ii) of Eq. 6.26.

Thus $\dfrac{W v^2}{2g} + \dfrac{E A \Delta_{st}}{L}(\Delta - \Delta_{st}) = \dfrac{E A}{2L}(\Delta^2 - \Delta_{st}^2)$

After rearrangement of terms

$$\dfrac{W v^2}{2g} = \dfrac{E A}{2L}(\Delta - \Delta_{st})^2$$

From which $\quad \Delta = \Delta_{st} + \sqrt{\dfrac{W v^2 L}{g E A}} \qquad \ldots (6.27)$

Hence maximum stress in the cable is given by

$$p = \dfrac{E \Delta}{L} = \dfrac{W}{A}\left(1 + \sqrt{\dfrac{v^2 E A}{g W L}}\right) \qquad \ldots (6.28)$$

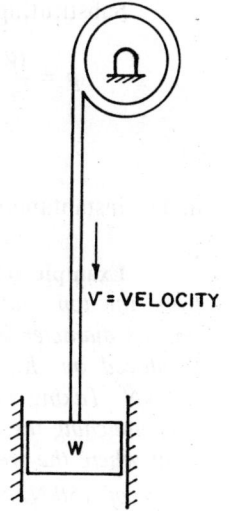

Substituting the numerical values, noting that $A = \dfrac{\pi}{4}(30)^2 = 706.9$ mm^2

$$p = \frac{W}{A}\left(1 + \sqrt{\frac{v^2 E A}{g W L}}\right) = \frac{15000}{706.9}\left(1 + \sqrt{\frac{(1000)^2 \times 2.05 \times 10^5 \times 706.9}{9810 \times 15000 \times 10000}}\right)$$

or $\qquad\qquad p = \textbf{231.8 N/mm}^2$

and Instantaneous elongation $= \Delta = \dfrac{pL}{E} = \dfrac{2.31.8 \times 10000}{2.05 \times 10^5} = \textbf{11.31 mm}$

Example 6.26. *A sliding mass of 500 kg is dropped down a vertical rod which is suspended from the top and is provided with a collar at the bottom end. The length of the rod is 2 m and its diameter is 12 mm. In order to reduce the shock, a buffer spring is placed on the collar which compresses 10 mm by a dead load of 2.5 kN. Taking into account the work done in compressing the spring and stretching the rod, find the height measured from the top of the spring from where the weight must be dropped in order to provide a momentary stress of 150 N/mm^2 in the rod. Take $E = 2 \times 10^5$ N/mm^2.*

Solution :

$A = \dfrac{\pi}{4}(12)^2 = 113.1$ mm^2 ; Sliding mass $M = 500$ kg

$\therefore$ Sliding weight $W = 500 \times 9.81 = 4905$ N

Equivalent dead load, required to produce a stress of 150 N/mm^2 is

$$P_e = 150 \times 113.1 = 16965 \text{ N}$$

FIG. 6.22

Compression of spring due to this dead load $= x = \dfrac{10}{2.5 \times 1000} \times 16965 = 67.86$ mm

Momentary extension of bar at a stress of 150 N/mm^2 is

$$\Delta = \frac{P}{E}L = \frac{150}{2 \times 10^5} \times 2000 = 1.5 \text{ mm}$$

Let $\qquad\qquad h = $ height of fall, measured for the top of spring.

$\therefore \qquad P(h + x + \Delta) = \dfrac{1}{2}P_e x + \dfrac{p^2}{2E}.AL$

or $4905\,(h + 67.86 + 1.5) = \dfrac{1}{2} \times 16965 \times 67.86 + \dfrac{(150)^2}{2 \times 2 \times 10^5} \times 113.1 \times 2000$

or $\qquad\qquad h + 69.36 = 119.95$

From which $\qquad h = \textbf{50.6 mm}$

Example 6.27. *Determine the vertical deflection Δ_b of joint B for the truss of Fig. 6.23, when the truss is subjected to a vertical load P at joint B. Assume that both the members have the same axial rigidity EA.*

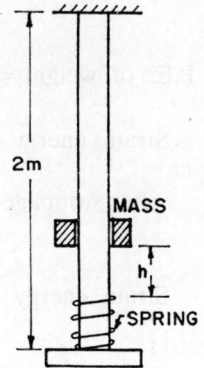

Solution : From statics, force in either member is, $F = \dfrac{P}{2\cos\beta}$

Also, length of each bar, $L = \dfrac{H}{\cos\beta}$

Hence strain energy of the two bars is

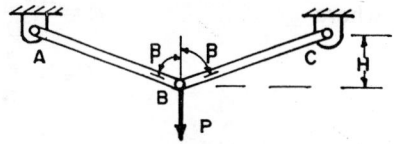

$$U = 2\left[\frac{F^2 L}{2EA}\right] = \frac{P^2 H}{4EA\cos^3\beta} \qquad ...(a)$$

The work done by the load is $W = \dfrac{1}{2}P.\Delta$ ...(b)

FIG. 6.23

Equating the, we get $\qquad \dfrac{1}{2}P\Delta = \dfrac{P^2 H}{4EA\cos^3\beta}$

or $\qquad\qquad\qquad\qquad \Delta = \dfrac{PH}{2EA\cos^3\beta} \qquad\qquad ...(6.29)$

Example 6.28. *Find an expression for strain energy U stored in the bar shown in Fig. 6.24 if the cross-sectional area of the bar is A and modulus of elasticity is E.*

Solution :

Reaction at $B = (4 + 1 - 2)P = 3P$ $(\leftarrow)$

∴ Force in $AB = 3P$ (tension)

Force in $BC = P$ (comp.)

Force in $CD = P$ (tension)

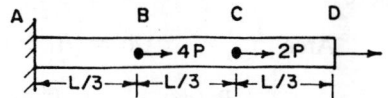

FIG. 6.24

Now strain energy in the bar $= \Sigma \dfrac{P^2 L}{2AE}$

∴ $\qquad U = \dfrac{(3P)^2 (L/3)}{2AE} + \dfrac{(-P)^2 (L/3)}{2AE} + \dfrac{(P)^2 (L/3)}{2AE}$

or $\qquad U = \dfrac{11}{6}\dfrac{P^2 L}{AE}$

Example 6.29. *A uniformly tapered bar AB of circular cross-section is subjected to a tensile load P at the free end B, as shown in Fig. 6.25. Derive expressions for (a) strain energy U of the bar and (b) elongation of the bar due to load P.*

Solution : Consider an elementary strip of length dx at distance x from end B.

Diameter at $\quad X = d_x = d_1 + \dfrac{d_2 - d_1}{L}x$

Area of cross-section $= \dfrac{\pi}{4}\left(d_1 + \dfrac{d_2 - d_1}{L}x\right)^2$

Force $= P$; length of section $= dx$

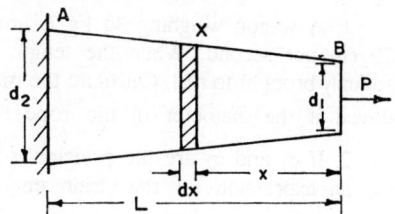

∴ $\qquad U = \int_0^L \dfrac{P^2\, dx}{2A_x E}$

FIG. 6.25

or
$$U = \int_0^L \frac{P^2 \, dx}{2 \times \frac{\pi}{4} \left\{ d_1 + \frac{d_2 - d_1}{L} x \right\}^2 E} = \int_0^L \frac{2 P^2 \, dx}{\pi (d_1 + kx)^2 E}$$

where
$$k = \frac{d_2 - d_1}{L}$$

$$\therefore \qquad U = -\frac{2 P^2}{\pi E} \cdot \frac{1}{k} \left[\frac{1}{d_1 + kx} \right]_0^L = -\frac{2 P^2 L}{\pi E (d_2 - d_1)} \left[\frac{1}{d_1 + d_2 - d_1} - \frac{1}{d_1} \right]$$

or
$$U = \frac{2 P^2 L}{\pi E (d_2 - d_1)} \left[\frac{1}{d_1} - \frac{1}{d_2} \right] = \frac{2 P^2 L}{\pi E d_1 d_2} \qquad \qquad ...(6.30)$$

Example 6.30. *A uniformly tapered bar AB of length L and constant thickness t, is acted upon by force P as shown in Fig .6.26. Determine (a) the strain energy in the bar, and (b) the elongation of the bar.*

Solution : Consider an elementary section dx at a distance x from B_1.

Width
$$B_x = B_1 + \frac{B_2 - B_1}{L} x = B_1 + kx$$

where
$$k = \frac{B_2 - B_1}{L}$$

Area
$$A_x = (B_1 + kx) t$$

$$\therefore \qquad U_x = \frac{P^2 (dx)}{2 A_x E} = \frac{P^2 \, dx}{2 (B_1 + kx)^2 t E}$$

Total
$$U = \int_0^L U_x = \int \frac{P^2 \, dx}{2 (B_1 + kx) t E}$$

$$= \frac{P^2}{2 t E} \int \frac{dx}{B_1 + kx}$$

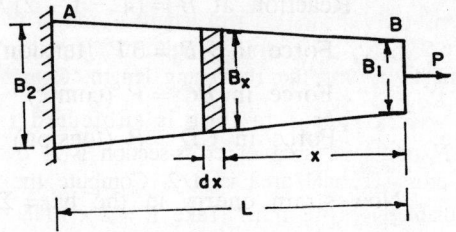

FIG. 6.26

$$= \frac{P^2}{2 t E k} \left[\log_e (B_1 + kx) \right]_0^L = \frac{P^2}{2 k t E} \log_e \frac{B_1 + k L}{B_1}$$

or
$$U = \frac{P^2}{2 k t E} \log_e \frac{B_2}{B_1} = \frac{P^2 L}{2 t E (B_2 - B_1)} \log_e \frac{B_2}{B_1} \qquad \qquad ...(6.31)$$

PROBLEMS

1. A wagon weighing 30 kg is attached to a wire rope and is moving down an incline at a speed of 70 cm per second. When the length of the rope unwound is 30 m, it gets jammed and the wagon is suddenly brought to rest. Calculate the maximum instantaneous stress and maximum instantaneous elongation produced if the diameter of the rope is 4 cm. Take $E = 2.05 \times 10^5$ N/mm^2 and $g = 981$ cm/sec^2.

2. If σ_1 and σ_2 are the principal stresses at a point in a material in a two dimensional stress system, derive an expression for the strain energy per unit volume in terms of σ_1, σ_2, μ and E.

Find the strain energy stored in a steel bar 50 cm long and of cross-section 5 cm × 1 cm when it is subjected to an axial pull of 50 kN and to a compressive stress of 120 N/mm^2 and on its narrow edges. Take $E = 2.05 \times 10^5$ N/mm^2 and $1/m = 0.29$.

3. Two bars are subjected to equal gradually applied tensile loads. One bar is of diameter D throughout and the other, which has the same length, is turned down to diameter $D/3$ over the middle third of its length, and the remainder having a diameter of D. Compare the strain energies of the two bars assuming that they are of the same material.

Compare also the amount of energy which the two bars can absorb in simple tension without exceeding a given stress within the limits of proportionality. Also, compare the amount of energy per unit volume if the maximum stress is to be the same in both the cases.

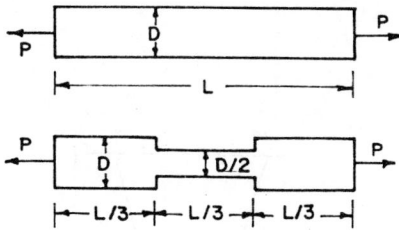

FIG. 6.27

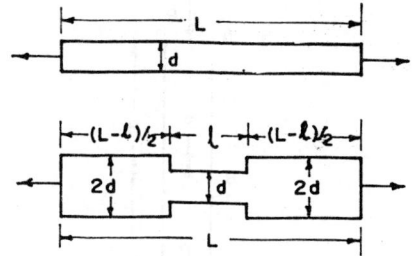

FIG. 6.28

4. Two bars each of length L and of the same material are each subjected to the same axial tensile force P. The first bar has uniform diameter $2d$. The second bar has a diameter d for length l and a diameter $2d$ for the remaining length. Compare the strain energies of the two bars.

5. A bar 1 m long is subjected to a pull such that the maximum stress is equal to 150 N/mm^2. Its area of cross-section is A over a length of $0.95 L$ and for the middle $0.05 L$ length, the cross-sectional area is $A/2$. Compute the strain energy stored in the bar. What will be its value if its diameter is 16 mm? Take $E = 2 \times 10^5 \text{ N/mm}^2$.

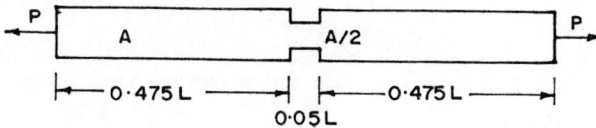

FIG. 6.29

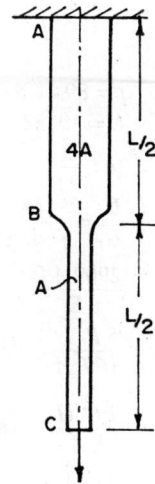

FIG. 6.30

6. A tensile force P acts on a bar ABC having two different cross-sections A and $4A$, as shown in Fig. 6.30. Find an expression for strain energy stored in the bar, and what will be its value if the dia. of lower portion is 20 mm and total length of the bar is 2 m ? What will be the increase in the value of strain energy if the load P is doubled to a value of $2P$?

7. A three storey column in a building is subjected to floor loads as shown in Fig. 6.31. The column has adequate lateral support so that it will not buckle. Calculate the amount of strain energy stored in the column, assuming $P = 100$ kN ; $H = 3$ m, Dia $= 60$ mm and $E = 200$ GPa.

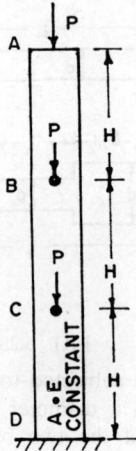

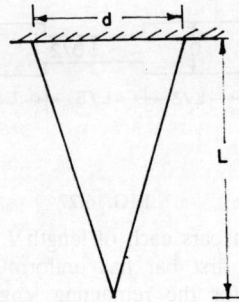

FIG. 6.31   FIG. 6.32

8. A conical bar of diameter d at the support and length E hangs vertically under its own weight. Find an expression for the strain energy of the bar. Take the modulus of elasticity as E and specific weight as γ.

ANSWER

1. $p = 89.41$ N/mm^2 ; $\Delta = 13.4$ mm

2. $U = 19122$ mm-N

3. (a) $\dfrac{3}{11}$ (b) 22.1   (c) 15.55

4. $\dfrac{U_1}{U_2} = \dfrac{4L}{L + 3l}$; 2

5. $\dfrac{2969\,AL}{E}$; 2.969 J

6. $\dfrac{5\,P^2 L}{16\,EA}$; 9.95 mm-N ; $\dfrac{15\,P^2 L}{16\,EA}$

7. $\dfrac{7\,P^2 H}{EA}$; 185.683 J

8. $\dfrac{\pi\,d^2 \lambda^2 L^3}{360\,E}$

Theories of Elastic Failure

7.1. INTRODUCTION

In all the previous chapters, we have assumed that the material is loaded within *elastic limit* so that it obeys Hooke's law. The formulae derived so far cease to exist the moment the stress at any point in the material exceeds the elastic limit. *A material is said to have failed if it is stressed beyond the elastic limit and if permanent deformations have taken place.*

When tensile test is performed on a metal specimen, the specimen fails at a certain stage of loading. The failure may be either (i) by direct separation of particles (such failure being known as brittle failure) without appreciable elongation (as in the case of cast iron bars), or (ii) by slipping of particles (such failure being known as ductile failure) when there will be appreciable *inelastic elongation* before ultimate failure occurs, (as in the case of mild steel rods). Since excessive deformation in structural or machine parts are not tolerated, *the body may be taken to have failed when the elastic limit is reached and when material starts yielding.*

Hence the word 'failure' used in this context may mean either fracture or permanent deformation beyond the operational range, due to the yielding of the material. The factor that causes a ductile material to yield might be quite different from the factor that causes fracture in a brittle material under the same loading conditions. Consequently there will be many criteria or theories of failure. All along, *it is necessary to remember that failure may mean fracture or yielding, whichever occurs first.* Failure resulting from local buckling or elastic instability is not considered here.

Various theories of failure have been proposed, their purpose being to establish from the behaviour of a material subjected to simple tension or compression tests, the point at which failure (as defined above) will occur under any type of *combined loading*. The beginning of plastic flow, *i.e.* yielding is indicated in a uniaxial tensile test by the deviation from proportionality of stress to strain. When several components of stress occur, yielding depends on some combination of these components. The mode of failure of a member and the factor that is responsible for failure depend on a large number of factors such as the nature and properties of material, types of loading, shape and temperature of the member etc.

7.2. THEORIES OF FAILURE (OR STRENGTH THEORIES)

Several hypothesis have been advanced as to the conditions which determine the *elastic failure* of metals subjected to steady constant stresses. No great-uniformity of opinion has been reached so far. This is due to complex nature of failure. According to the chief theories, perfect elasticity ceases when a certain limiting value is reached by one of the following stresses (*i*) the maximum principal stress, (*ii*) the maximum principal strain, (*iii*) the maximum shear stress, (*iv*) the maximum strain energy and (*v*) the maximum shear strain energy.

Accordingly, we have the following common five theories of failure :

(1) Maximum principal stress theory, or Rankine's theory

(2) Maximum principal strain theory, or Saint Venant's theory

(3) Maximum shear stress theory or Guest's theory

(4) Maximum strain energy theory or Haigh's theory

(5) Maximum shear strain energy theory or Mises Henky theory

Apart from the above, several other more and more complex theories of failure have been evolved, such as octahedral shear stress theory and Mohr's theory etc.

7.3. MAXIMUM PRINCIPAL STRESS THEORY : RANKINE'S THEORY

This is the simplest and the oldest theory of failure often called Rankine's theory after W.J.M. Rankine (1820-1872) an eminent engineering educator at the university level in England.

According to this theory, permanent set takes place under a state of complex stress when the value of maximum principal stress is equal to that of yield point stress as found in a simple tensile test, or the minimum principal stress (*i.e.* the compressive stress) is equal to that of yield point stress in simple compression. Thus the condition of yielding are :

$$\sigma_1 = f_y \quad \text{or} \quad |\sigma_3| = f_y' \qquad \qquad ...(7.1)$$

where f_y is the yield point stress in simple tension and f_y' is the yield point stress in simple compression.

If the maximum principal stress is the design criterion, the maximum principal stress must not exceed the working stress f for the material. Hence

$$\sigma_1 \leq f \qquad \qquad ...(7.2)$$

Limitations of the theory

1. This theory disregards the effect of other principal stresses, and effect of shearing stresses on other planes through the element.

2. When the element is in pure shear, *i.e.* $\sigma_1 = |\sigma_3| = |\tau_{max}|$ and $\sigma_2 = 0$, this theory predicts that failure will occur when the magnitude of $|\tau_{max}|$ (*i.e.* σ_1) reaches a value f_y but experiments show that failure occurs much earlier, when $|\tau_{max}|$ reaches $0.55 f_y$ to $0.6 f_y$ with an average value of $0.57 f_y$, where f_y is the yield stress in ductile material.

3. Material in tension test piece slips along 45° to the axis of the test piece, where normal stress is neither maximum nor minimum, but shear stress is maximum.

4. It has been experimentally shown that even a material weak in compression sustains very high hydrostatic pressure without failure *i.e.* a stress state $\sigma_1 = \sigma_2 = \sigma_3 \geq f_y$ can be applied without failure.

For brittle materials which do not fail by yielding but fail by brittle fracture, the maximum principal stress theory is considered to be reasonably satisfactory.

7.4 MAXIMUM PRINCIPAL STRAIN THEORY : ST. VENANT'S THEORY

This theory is often called Saint Venant's theory because of the work of Barre de Saint Venant (1767-1886), a great French mathematician and elastician. According to this theory, a ductile material begins to yield when the maximum principal strain reaches the strain at which yielding occurs in simple tension, or when the minimum principal strain (*i.e.* the compressive strain) equals the yields point strain in simple compression.

(a) Three dimensional stress system

In a three dimensional stress system, we have

$$e_1 = \frac{\sigma_1}{E} - \frac{1}{mE}(\sigma_2 + \sigma_3)$$

$$e_2 = \frac{\sigma_2}{E} - \frac{1}{mE}(\sigma_3 + \sigma_1)$$

and $$e_3 = \frac{\sigma_3}{E} - \frac{1}{mE}(\sigma_1 + \sigma_2)$$

If $$e_y = \text{yield point strain (tensile)} = \frac{f_y}{E}$$

and $$e_y' = \text{yield point strain (compressive)} = \frac{f_y'}{E}$$

Then, according to this theory, $e_1 = e_y$

or $$\sigma_1 - \frac{1}{m}(\sigma_2 + \sigma_3) = f_y \qquad \qquad ...(7.3\ a)$$

and $$e_3 = e_y'$$

or $$\left| \sigma_3 - \frac{1}{m}(\sigma_1 + \sigma_2) \right| = f_y' \qquad \qquad ...(7.3\ b)$$

(b) Two dimensional stress system

In two dimensional stress system, let σ_1 and σ_2 be the major and minor principal stresses. Then Eqs. 7.3(*a*) and 7.3(*b*) reduces to :

$$\sigma_1 - \frac{1}{m}\sigma_2 = f_y \qquad \qquad ...(7.3\ c)$$

and $$\sigma_3 - \frac{1}{m}\sigma_1 = f_y' \qquad \qquad ...(7.3\ d)$$

Thus the stress which, acting alone, will produce same maximum strain e_1 is equal to $\left(\sigma_1 - \frac{\sigma_2}{m} \right)$. Hence the *design criterion* according to this theory will be

$$\left(\sigma_1 - \frac{\sigma_2}{m} \right) \le f \qquad \qquad ...(7.4)$$

where f is the working stress for the material.

Limitations of the theory

Though this theory considers the intermediate principal stress σ_2, and is also satisfactory for brittle materials, it has following draw backs for ductile materials :

1. When $\sigma_1 = \sigma_2$ and $\sigma_3 = 0$, the failure value of σ_1 by this theory is given by $\sigma_1 = \dfrac{f_y}{1 - \mu}$, i.e. $\sigma_1 > f_y$. In other words, the theory predicts that tensile stress in biaxial tension will be the higher than the yield stress in uniaxial tension which is contradicted by experimental results.

2. If the material is subjected to hydrostatic pressure p, this theory predicts the failure value of p to be $\dfrac{f_y}{1 - 2\mu}$. Though in this case, it gives better value for the failure stress than given by Rankine's theory, still the value predicted is much lower than the experimental value.

3. If for mild steel, μ is taken to be 0.3, then in pure shear where $\sigma_1 = -\sigma_3 = |\tau_{max}|$, this theory predicts that at failure, $\tau_{max} = \dfrac{f_y}{1.3} = 0.77 f_y$. This still maintains a good gap with the experimental value.

4. The theory over estimates the elastic strength of ductile materials.

7.5. MAXIMUM SHEAR STRESS THEORY : GUEST'S THEORY

This theory is sometimes called Coulombs theory because it was originally stated by him in 1773. More frequently, the theory is called *Guest's theory*, or *Guest's law*, because of the work of J.J. Guest in England in 1900. Observations made in the course of extrusion test on the flow of soft metals through orifices lend support to the assumption that plastic state (or yielding) in such metals is created when the maximum shear stress just reaches the value of resistance of the metal against shear. The maximum shearing stress theory predicts failure of a specimen subjected to any combination of loads when the maximum shearing stress at any point reaches the failure value (τ_f) equal to that developed at the yielding in an axial tensile or compressive test of the same material.

Since the maximum shear is equal to half the difference between the maximum and minimum principal stress, and since the maximum shear in simple tension is equal to half the tensile stress, we have

$$\tau_{max} = \frac{1}{2}(\sigma_1 - \sigma_3) = \frac{f_y}{2} \qquad \qquad ...(7.5\ a)$$

Hence the condition of yielding is $(\sigma_1 - \sigma_3) = f_y$ $\qquad \qquad$ ...(7.5 b)

In the case of two dimensional stress system, where σ_3 is zero, the design criterion corresponding to an allowable stress f is

$$(\sigma_1 - \sigma_2) = f \qquad \qquad ...(7.5)$$

(Limited to negative value of σ_2 when $\sigma_2 < 0$)

Limitations of the theory

Ductile materials yield along 45° slip planes which are the planes of maximum shear stress. Hence this theory is fairly well justified for ductile materials and for states of stress encountered in most load resisting members and machine parts. However, it has following limitations:

1. The theory does not give accurate results for the state of stress of pure shear in which the maximum amount of shear is developed (*i.e.* in torsion test). In pure shear, it gives

$|\tau_{max}| = 0.5 f_y$ whereas the experimental results give a value of $0.57 f_y$, giving an error upto about 15 percent.

2. This theory is not applicable to materials subjected to hydrostatic pressure subjected to state of stress consisting of triaxial tensile stresses of nearly equal magnitude, since it will predict the shear stress to be almost zero, meaning thereby that the material will never fail, however large the applied stresses be. This is physically impossible.

3. The results of this theory differ from the experimental results for materials for which elastic limit stresses in tension and compression differ by large amount. This is so for brittle material like cast iron.

7.6. MAXIMUM STRAIN ENERGY THEORY OR HAIGH'S THEORY

This theory, originally put forward by Beltrami, is generally known as Haigh's theory or Beltrami-Haigh's theory. According to this theory, a body under complex stresses fails when the total strain energy on the body is equal to the strain energy at elastic limit in simple tension. According to this theory, if a body is brought to a particular state by various methods, then the work done by passing from the initial to final state will be *independent* of the method applied. Hence when a material is caused to take permanent set by stress which increase gradually from zero, then the initial strain energy is independent of the nature of stresses and is almost constant in value.

The theory states that inelastic action at any point in a body due to any state of stress begins only when the energy per unit volume absorbed at the point is equal to the energy absorbed per unit volume of the material when subjected to the elastic limit under a uniaxial state of stress, as occurs in a simple tensile test.

(a) Three dimensional stress system

The strain energy per unit volume is given by

$$U = \frac{1}{2E} \left\{ \sigma_1^2 + \sigma_2^2 + \sigma_3^2 - \frac{2\sigma_1\sigma_2 + 2\sigma_2\sigma_3 + 2\sigma_3\sigma_1}{m} \right\}$$

where σ_1, σ_2 and σ_3 are of the same sign.

Hence the yield criterion can be represented as

$$\sigma_1^2 + \sigma_2^2 + \sigma_3^2 - \frac{2\sigma_1\sigma_2 + 2\sigma_2\sigma_3 + 2\sigma_3\sigma_1}{m} = f_y^2 \qquad \text{...(7.6 } a)$$

(b) Two dimensional case

For two dimensional case ($\sigma_3 = 0$), the above criterion reduces to :

$$\sigma_1^2 + \sigma_2^2 - \frac{2\sigma_1\sigma_2}{m} = f_y^2 \qquad \text{...(7.6)}$$

If f is the working stress in the material, the design criterion may be stated as :

$$\left(\sigma_1^2 + \sigma_2^2 - \frac{2\sigma_1\sigma_2}{m} \right) < f^2 \qquad \text{...(7.7)}$$

Limitation of the theory

The theory has considerable experimental support from tests on ductile materials, specially, the thick cylinders. However, it has the following limitations.

1. The theory does not apply to brittle materials for which elastic limit stress in tension and in compression are quite different.

2. The greatest objection to this theory comes from the *fact* that high hydrostatic pressure ($p = \sigma_1 = \sigma_2 = \sigma_3$) can be applied to body of homogeneous isotropic material without producing inelastic deformation, while according to this theory, the value of pressure p at failure is given by

$$p = \frac{f_y}{\sqrt{3(1-2\mu)}} \qquad \qquad ...(7.8)$$

The maximum strain energy theory has been largely replaced by the maximum-distortion-energy theory described below.

7.7. MAXIMUM SHEAR STRAIN ENERGY (OR DISTORTION ENERGY) THEORY : MISES - HENKY THEORY

This theory is frequently called the Huber-Henky-Von-Mises theory, as it was proposed by M.T.Huber of Poland in 1904 and independently by R. Von Mises of Germany in 1913. This theory differs from the maximum strain energy theory in that the portion of the strain energy, producing volume change, is considered *ineffective* in causing failure by yielding. Supporting evidence comes from the capacity of materials to withstand very high hydrostatic pressures. *The portion of strain energy producing change in shape of the element is assumed to be completely responsible for the failure of the material by yielding.*

The maximum shear strain energy theory, also known as *energy of distortion theory* states that inelastic action at any point in a body under any combination of stresses begins when the strain energy of distortion per unit volume absorbed at the point is equal to the strain energy of distortion absorbed per unit volume at any point in a bar stressed to the elastic limit under the state of uniaxial stress as occurs in a simple tension (or compression) test.

The energy of distortion can be obtained by subtracting the energy of volumetric change from the total energy. Under a system of stresses acting externally on a body, the total external work done causes (*a*) change in volume due to operation of direct stresses, and (*b*) distortion due to the shearing stresses which does not affect the volumetric change.

Thus, total $\qquad U = U_v + U_s$

Now $\qquad U_v = \frac{1}{2}(\text{average } \sigma)\,\Delta V = \frac{1}{2}\left(\frac{\sigma_1 + \sigma_2 + \sigma_3}{3}\right)\Delta V = \frac{\sigma_1 + \sigma_2 + \sigma_3}{6}\Delta V$

But $\qquad \Delta V = \frac{1}{E}\left\{\sigma_1 + \sigma_2 + \sigma_3 - \frac{2}{m}(\sigma_1 + \sigma_2 + \sigma_3)\right\} = \frac{1}{E}(\sigma_1 + \sigma_2 + \sigma_3)\left(\frac{m-2}{m}\right)$

$\therefore \qquad U_v = \frac{(\sigma_1 + \sigma_2 + \sigma_3)^2}{6E}\left(\frac{m-2}{m}\right) = \frac{m-2}{6mE}\left[\sigma_1^2 + \sigma_2^2 + \sigma_3^2 + 2(\sigma_1\sigma_2 + \sigma_2\sigma_3 + \sigma_3\sigma_1)\right]$

or $\qquad U_v = \frac{m-2}{6mE}(X + 2Y) \qquad \qquad ...(1)$

Where $\qquad X = \sigma_1^2 + \sigma_2^2 + \sigma_3^2$ and $Y = \sigma_1\sigma_2 + \sigma_2\sigma_3 + \sigma_3\sigma_1$

Also, $\qquad U = \dfrac{1}{2E}\left[\sigma_1^2 + \sigma_2^2 + \sigma_3^2 - \dfrac{2}{m}(\sigma_1\sigma_2 + \sigma_2\sigma_3 + \sigma_3\sigma_1)\right]$

or $\qquad U = \dfrac{1}{2E}\left[X - \dfrac{2}{m}Y\right]$ $\qquad$ ...(2)

Hence $\qquad U_s = U - U_v = \dfrac{1}{2E}\left[X - \dfrac{2}{m}Y\right] - \dfrac{m-2}{6mE}\left[X + 2Y\right]$

$$= \dfrac{1}{6E}\left[3X - \dfrac{6Y}{m} - X - 2Y + \dfrac{2X}{m} + \dfrac{4Y}{m}\right]$$

$$= \dfrac{1}{3E}\left[X\left(1 + \dfrac{1}{m}\right) - Y\left(1 + \dfrac{1}{m}\right)\right] = \dfrac{m+1}{3mE}(X - Y)$$

$$= \dfrac{m+1}{3mE}\left[\sigma_1^2 + \sigma_2^2 + \sigma_3^2 - (\sigma_1\sigma_2 + \sigma_2\sigma_3 + \sigma_3\sigma_1)\right]$$

or $\qquad U_s = \dfrac{m+1}{6mE}\left[(\sigma_1 - \sigma_2)^2 + (\sigma_2 - \sigma_3)^2 + (\sigma_3 - \sigma_1)^2\right]$ $\qquad$ ...(7.9)

This is thus the expression for *strain energy of distortion*.

Under the action of uniaxial stress f_y, the strain energy of distortion will evidently be equal to $\dfrac{m+1}{3mE}f_y^2$. Hence the failure criterion may be stated as follows :

$$\dfrac{m+1}{6mE}\left[(\sigma_1 - \sigma_2)^2 + (\sigma_2 - \sigma_3)^2 + (\sigma_3 - \sigma_1)^2\right] = \dfrac{m+1}{3mE}f_y^2$$

or $\qquad \dfrac{1}{2}(\sigma_1 - \sigma_2)^2 + \dfrac{1}{2}(\sigma_2 - \sigma_3)^2 + \dfrac{1}{2}(\sigma_3 - \sigma_1)^2 = f_y^2$ $\qquad$ ...(7.10)

In a two dimensional case ($\sigma_3 = 0$), this reduces to

$$\sigma_1^2 + \sigma_2^2 - \sigma_1\sigma_2 = f_y^2 \qquad ...(7.11)$$

If f is the working stress in the material, the design criterion may be stated as follows:

$$\sigma_1^2 + \sigma_2^2 - \sigma_1\sigma_2 \ge f^2 \qquad ...(7.12)$$

Limitations of the theory

This theory is in good agreement with experimental results with various combination of principal stresses for ductile materials. For example, in pure shear, the value of maximum shear stress at yielding given by this theory is $0.577\,f_y$ which coincides with the average experimental value. Hence this theory is accepted to be valid for ductile materials. However, this theory has the following limitations :

1. The theory does not apply to brittle materials for which the elastic limit stress in tension and compression is quite different.

2. It cannot be applied for materials under hydrostatic pressure.

7.8. GRAPHICAL REPRESENTATION OF VARIOUS FAILURE THEORIES FOR TWO DIMENSIONAL STRESS SYSTEM

1. Maximum principal stress theory

The failure is given by Eq. 7.1:

$$\sigma_1 = f_y \text{ and } |\sigma_3| = f_y'$$

Let us take $f_y > f_y'$.

Fig. 7.1 (a) shows the graphical representation of the theory. The diagram is divided into four quadrants with the following signs of σ_1 and σ_2.

(i) I quadrant : both σ_1 and σ_2 positive (i.e. tensile)

(ii) II quadrant : σ_1 negative (i.e. compressive) and σ_2 positive (i.e. tensile)

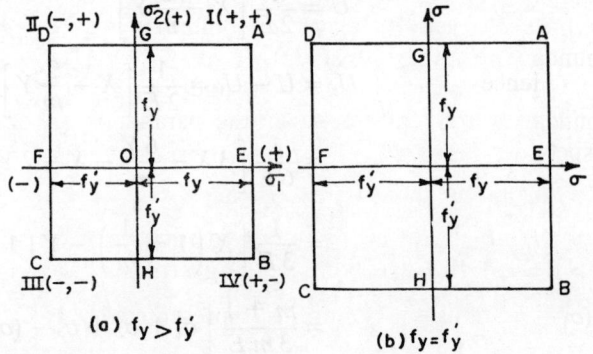

FIG. 7.1. MAXIMUM PRINCIPAL STRESS THEORY

(iii) III quadrant : Both σ_1 and σ_2 negative (i.e. compressive)

(iv) IV quadrant : σ_1 positive and σ_2 negative (compressive)

The square ABCD represents the graphical representation of the maximum stress theory. The maximum principal stress equal numerically to the elastic limit (f_y). The material will reach its elastic limit when the stress point (σ_1, σ_2) passes outside the square ABCD. If $f_y = f_y'$, then the centre of the square will be at the origin, as shown in Fig. 7.1 (b).

2. Maximum principal strain theory

The yield criterion is expressed as

$$\sigma_1 - \frac{1}{m} \sigma_2 = f_y \qquad \text{...(Ia)}$$

and

$$\sigma_2 - \frac{\sigma_1}{m} = f_y' \qquad \text{...(Ib)}$$

In the above set of equations, both σ_1 and σ_2 are positive (i.e. tensile). The boundary representing the elastic limit are shown by lines AE and GA representing Eq. I (a) and I (b).

If σ_1 is positive and σ_2 is negative (quadrant IV) and if f_y' and E' are the values in compression, the yield criterion is expressed by the following equations:

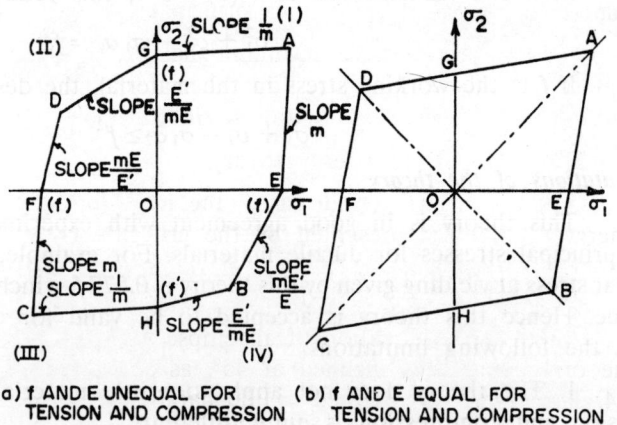

(a) f AND E UNEQUAL FOR TENSION AND COMPRESSION

(b) f AND E EQUAL FOR TENSION AND COMPRESSION

FIG 7.2. MAXIMUM PRINCIPAL STRAIN THEORY

$$\frac{\sigma_1}{E} - \frac{\sigma_2}{m\,E'} = \frac{f_y}{E} \qquad \text{or} \qquad \sigma_1 - \frac{E}{E'}\frac{\sigma_2}{m} = f_y \qquad \text{...(IIa)}$$

$$\frac{\sigma_2}{E'} - \frac{\sigma_1}{m\,E} = \frac{f_y'}{E} \qquad \text{or} \qquad \sigma_2 - \frac{E'}{E} \cdot \frac{\sigma_1}{m} = f_y' \qquad \text{...(IIb)}$$

The boundaries given by Eq. II(a) and II(b) are represented by lines EB and HB. Similarly by lines HC and FC give the boundaries in III quadrant while FD and GD represent the boundary in the II quadrant.

For the case when $f_y = f_y'$ and $E = E'$, as is common for most metals, the corresponding boundaries are represented by the parallelogram $ABCD$ (Fig. 7.2 b) symmetrically placed with respect to the axes.

3. Maximum shear stress theory

If σ_1 and σ_2 are of opposite sign (*i.e.* $\sigma_1 > 0 > \sigma_2$) the greater shearing stress is given by $\frac{1}{2}(\sigma_1 - \sigma_2)$ and the failure is represented by

$$\sigma_1 - \sigma_2 = f_y$$

or

$$\sigma_2 - \sigma_1 = f_y$$

The boundaries of these equations are represented by parallel lines FG and HE.

If σ_1 and σ_2 are like (*i.e.* I or III quadrant), the maximum shear is equal to $\frac{\sigma_1}{2}$ or $\frac{\sigma_2}{2}$, whichever is more. Hence the failure criterion is represented by $\sigma_1 = f_y$ or $\sigma_2 = f_y$.

The conditions are represented by lines GA and AE in the first quadrant and FC and CH in the third quadrant. Hence for like stresses, the theory gives the same boundary as the maximum principal stress theory.

Hence according to maximum shear stress theory, material will reach its elastic limit when the stress point (σ_1, σ_2) falls outside the figure $AEHCFGA$.

4. Maximum strain energy theory

For two dimensional case, the maximum strain energy theory is represented by the criterion

$$\sigma_1^2 + \sigma_2^2 - \frac{2}{m}\sigma_1\sigma_2 = f_y^2$$

This is the equation of an ellipse with centre at the origin and axes inclined at 45°, as shown in Fig. 7.4. The ellipse is inscribed by the parallelogram given by the maximum strain theory. The material will reach its elastic limit when the stress point (σ_1, σ_2) falls outside the ellipse.

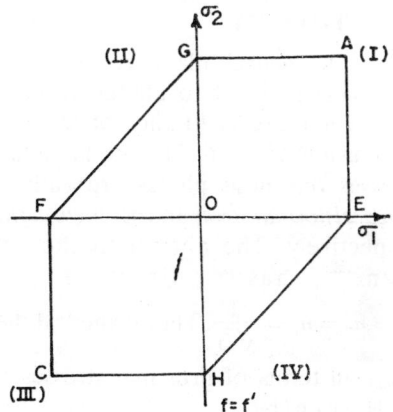

FIG. 7.3. MAXIMUM SHEAR STRESS THEORY

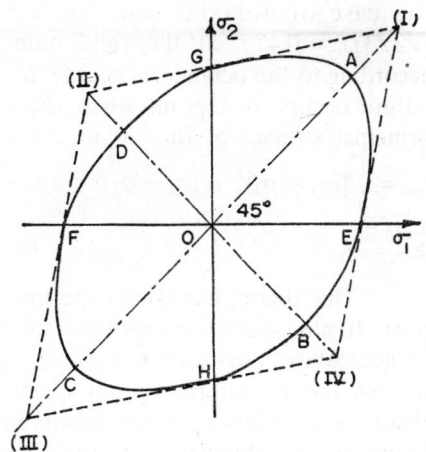

FIG 7.4 MAXIMUM STRAIN ENERGY THEORY

5. Maximum shear strain energy theory

The yield criterion is given by

$$\sigma_1^2 + \sigma_2^2 - \sigma_1 \sigma_2 = f_y^2$$

This criterion is also represented by an ellipse, similar to Haigh's ellipse. Both the ellipses become identical when m has its smallest possible value of 2.

Fig. 7.5 shows the graphical representation of various theories on the same diagram, when $f = f'$ and $E = E'$.

7.9.   OCTAHEDRAL SHEAR STRESS THEORY

Octahedral plane is the plane which is equally inclined to all the three principal axes. There are eight such octahedral planes, as shown in Fig. 7.6. The normal and shearing stresses on these planes are called the *octahedral normal stress* and *octahedral shear stress* respectively. The normal to the octahedral plane   has   direction   cosines $n_x = n_y = n_z = \dfrac{1}{\sqrt{3}}$. The octahedral shear stress

(τ_{oct}), in terms of principal stresses σ_1, σ_2 and σ_3 is given by

$$\tau_{oct} = \frac{1}{3} \left[(\sigma_1 - \sigma_2)^2 + (\sigma_2 - \sigma_3)^2 + (\sigma_3 - \sigma_1)^2 \right]^{\frac{1}{2}}$$

$$..(7.13a)$$

The value of octahedral shear stress, in the case of uniaxial test, has a value of $(\sqrt{2}/3) f_y = 0.47 f_y$ at the yield point. Hence according to the octahedral shear stress theory, failure occurs at a point when the values of principal stresses at that point are such that

$$\tau_{oct} = \frac{1}{3} [(\sigma_1 - \sigma_2)^2 + (\sigma_2 - \sigma_3)^2 + (\sigma_3 - \sigma_1)^2]^{1/2}$$

$$\geq \frac{\sqrt{2}}{3} f_y \qquad \qquad ...(7.13)$$

This theory has good experimental support. It has special significance for the case

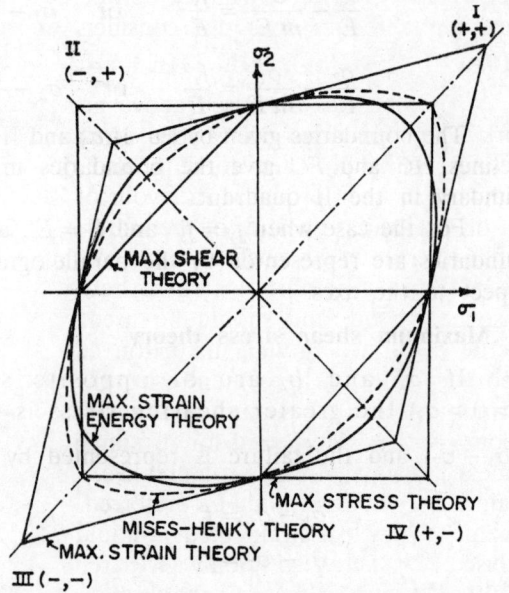

FIG. 7.5. GRAPHICAL REPRESENTATION OF VARIOUS THEORIES

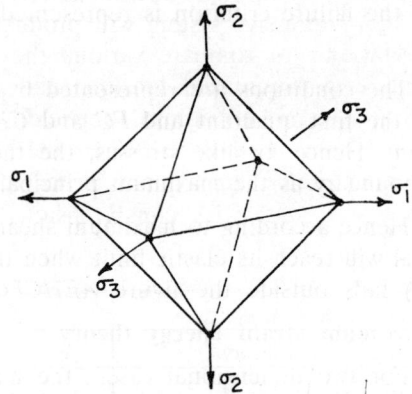

FIG. 7.6. OCTAHEDRAL PLANES

of hydrostatic pressure, $\sigma_1 = \sigma_2 = \sigma_3 = -p$ where τ_{oct} is equal to zero. Consequently, according to this theory, failure cannot occur and this fact is supported by experimental results. This theory is *equivalent* to the maximum distortion energy theory, as is evident from Table 7.1. However, the distortion energy theory is based on *energy conception* while octahedral shear stress theory is based on *stress conception* and hence it is preferred by engineers. Actually these two theories are two different interpretations of the same phenomenon. Also, in distortional energy theory, perfect linearity between stress and strains upto failure is assumed while the shear stress theory does not consider the stress-strain relationship.

7.10. COMPARISON OF THE FAILURE THEORIES

The theories discussed above are all for static loading only. Considerable experimental work has been done on various stress systems, such as tubes under the action of internal pressure, end loads and torsion; also on different materials. So far, however, no conclusive evidence has been produced in favour of any one theory. This is because cause of failure depends not only on the properties of the materials but also on the stress system to which it is subjected.

For brittle materials, such as cast iron etc., the maximum principal stress theory is reasonably good, and should be used. For ductile materials, though distortion energy theory is quite in agreement with the experimental results, maximum shear stress theory is most widely used for its simplicity. If mean principal stress is compressive, shear strain energy theory should be preferred. The maximum principal strain theory should not be used in general, as it only gives reliable results in particular cases. It should be noted that, since the shear stress and shear strain

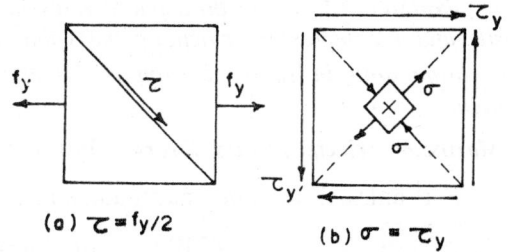

FIG. 7.7

energy theories depend only on the stress difference, they are independent of the value of the mean stress and imply that a material will not fail under a hydrostatic stress system (*i.e.* $\sigma_1 = \sigma_2 = \sigma_3$). In practice the effect of such a stress system, if tensile, is to produce a brittle type fracture in a normally ductile material, no plastic deformation having taken place. Conversely, a triaxial compressive system will produce a ductile type failure in a normally brittle material.

In order to compare various theories, let us conduct two tests on bar (*i*) test under uniform tension (uniaxial tension) and (*ii*) shear test (torsion test). Let f_y be the stress in the tension test when failure (or yielding) occurs, and let τ_y be the shear stress in a torsion test at the time of failure. When the bar is subjected to uniaxial tension f_y, the maximum shear stress induced on a plane at 45° to the tensile stress axis is $f_y/2$. Similarly, a pure shear τ_y is a biaxial state with equal tension ($\sigma = \tau_y$) and compression ($\sigma = \tau_y$), as shown in Fig.

TABLE 7.1

Failure Theory	Tension	Shear	Relationship
1. Max. normal stress theory	f_y	$\sigma = \tau_y$	$\tau_y = f_y$
2. Max. strain theory $\left(\mu = \frac{1}{4}\right)$	$\varepsilon = \dfrac{f_y}{E}$	$\varepsilon = \dfrac{5}{4}\dfrac{\tau_y}{E}$	$\tau_y = 0.8 f_y$
3. Max. shear stress theory	$\tau = \dfrac{1}{2} f_y$	τ_y	$\tau_y = 0.5 f_y$
4. Max. strain energy theory $\left(\mu = \frac{1}{4}\right)$	$U = \dfrac{1}{2E} f_y^2$	$U = \dfrac{5}{4}\dfrac{1}{E}\tau_y^2$	$\tau_y = 0.817 f_y$
5. Max. distortion energy theory	$U_s = \dfrac{1+\mu}{3}\dfrac{f_y^2}{E}$	$U_s = (1+\mu)\dfrac{\tau_y^2}{E}$	$\tau_y = 0.577 f_y$
6. Octahedral shear theory	$\tau_{oct} = \dfrac{\sqrt{2}}{3} f_y$	$\tau_{oct} = \dfrac{\sqrt{2}}{3}\tau_y$	$\tau_y = 0.577 f_y$

7.7. Hence based on this, the critical values for failure according to the five theories of failure can be calculated and tabulated, as shown in Table 7.1. Last column of table 7.1 shows how both τ_y and f_y are related at failure. The results on many tests on ductile materials show that τ_y determined from torsion tests varies from about 0.55 to 0.60 of the tensile yield strength f_y, the average value being 0.57. This result agrees well with the distortion energy theory and octahedral shear theory. On the other hand, the maximum shear stress theory predicts that shear yield value τ_y is 0.5 times the tensile yield value. This is about 15 % less than the value predicted by the distortion energy theory or the octahedral shear theory. Thus, the maximum shear stress theory gives value for design on the safer side. However, because of simplicity, the maximum shear stress theory is widely used in machine design with ductile materials.

Example 7.1. *If the principal stresses at a point in an elastic material are 2f tensile, 1.5f tensile and f compressive, calculate the value of f at failure according to five different theories. The elastic limit in simple tension is 210 N/mm² and μ = 0.3.*
Solution :

1. Maximum principal stress theory : For complex stress system, maximum stress $= 2f$

For uniaxial tension, maximum stress $= 210 \, \text{N/mm}^2$

$$\therefore \qquad 2f = 210, \qquad \text{or } f = \textbf{105 N/mm}^2$$

2. Maximum strain theory : The failure criterion is given by

$$\sigma_1 - \mu \, (\sigma_2 + \sigma_3) = f_y$$

or $\qquad 2f - 0.3 \, (1.5f - f) = f_y = 210$

or $\qquad\qquad 1.85 f = 210$ from which $f = \textbf{113.51 N/mm}^2$

3. Maximum shear stress theory

$$\tau_{\max} = \frac{1}{2} \, (\sigma_1 - \sigma_2) = \frac{1}{2} \{ 2f - (-f) \} = 1.5f$$

In simple (or uniaxial) tension, the principal stresses are 210, 0 and 0. Hence maximum shear stress $= \dfrac{1}{2} \, (210 - 0) = 105 \, \text{N/mm}^2$.

$$\therefore \qquad 1.5f = 105, \text{ from which } f = \textbf{70 N/mm}^2$$

4. Maximum strain energy theory : The yield criterion is given by

$$\sigma_1^2 + \sigma_2^2 + \sigma_3^2 - 2\mu \, (\sigma_1 \sigma_2 + \sigma_2 \sigma_3 + \sigma_3 \sigma_1) = f_y^2$$

$\therefore \quad (2f)^2 + (1.5f)^2 + (-f)^2 - 2 \times 0.3 \left[(2f)(1.5f) + (1.5f)(-f) + (-f)(2f) \right] = (210)^2$

or $\qquad 4f^2 + 2.25f^2 + f^2 - 0.6 \left[3f^2 - 1.5f^2 - 2f^2 \right] = (210)^2$

or $\qquad 7.55 f^2 = (210)^2$ from which $f = \dfrac{210}{\sqrt{7.55}} = \textbf{76.43 N/mm}^2$

5. Maximum shear strain energy theory : The failure criterion is

$$\frac{1}{2} \left[(\sigma_1 - \sigma_2)^2 + (\sigma_2 - \sigma_3)^2 + (\sigma_3 - \sigma_1)^2 \right] = f_y^2$$

or $\qquad (2f - 1.5f)^2 + (1.5f + f)^2 + (-f - 2f)^2 = 2 \, (210)^2$

or $\qquad 0.25f^2 + 6.25f^2 + 9f^2 = 2\,(210)^2$

or $\qquad 15.5f^2 = 2\,(210)^2$ from which $f = \dfrac{210\sqrt{2}}{\sqrt{15.5}} = \mathbf{75.43\ N/mm^2}$

Example 7.2. *The load on a bolt consists of an axial pull of 15 kN together with a transverse shear of 7.5 kN. Determine the diameter of the bolt according to (i) maximum principal stress theory (ii) maximum shear stress theory (iii) maximum strain theory (iv) strain energy theory and (v) shear strain energy theory. Elastic limit in tension is 285 N/mm², and a factor of safety of 3 is be applied. Take $\mu = 0.3$.*

Solution :

Permissible tensile stress $= f = \dfrac{285}{3} = 95\ \text{N/mm}^2$

Let d be the diameter of the bolt, in mm.

Hence applied $\quad p = \dfrac{15000}{\pi\,d^2/4} = \dfrac{19098.6}{d^2}\ \text{N/mm}^2$

Applied $\qquad q = \dfrac{7500}{\pi\,d^2/4} = \dfrac{9549.3}{d^2}\ \text{N/mm}^2$

1. Maximum principal stress theory

In bolt, $\qquad \sigma_1 = \dfrac{p}{2} + \sqrt{\left(\dfrac{p}{2}\right)^2 + q^2}$

$$= \dfrac{1}{2}\left(\dfrac{19098.6}{d^2}\right) + \sqrt{\left(\dfrac{19098.6}{2\,d^2}\right)^2 + \left(\dfrac{9549.3}{d^2}\right)^2}$$

$$= \dfrac{9549.3}{d^2} + \dfrac{13504.7}{d^2} = \dfrac{23054}{d^2}$$

Hence $\qquad \dfrac{23054}{d^2} = 95$, from which $d = \mathbf{15.58\ mm}$

2. Maximum principal strain theory

$$\sigma_1 = \dfrac{p}{2} + \sqrt{\left(\dfrac{p}{2}\right)^2 + q^2} = \dfrac{23054}{d^2}\ \text{(as above)}$$

$$\sigma_2 = \dfrac{p}{2} - \sqrt{\left(\dfrac{p}{2}\right)^2 + q^2} = \dfrac{9549.3}{d^2} - \dfrac{13504.7}{d^2} = -\dfrac{3955.4}{d^2}$$

$\therefore \qquad$ Max. strain $= \dfrac{\sigma_1}{E} - \dfrac{\sigma_2}{mE} = \dfrac{1}{E}\left[\dfrac{23054}{d^2} - \left(-\dfrac{3955.4}{d^2}\right) \times 0.3\right]$

$$= \dfrac{24240.7}{d^2\,E}$$

In simple tension, max. strain $= \dfrac{f}{E} = \dfrac{95}{E}$

$$\therefore \qquad \frac{24240.7}{d^2 E} = \frac{95}{E}$$

From which $\qquad d = \sqrt{24240.7/95} = \mathbf{15.97\ mm}$

3. Maximum shear stress theory

Max. shear stress $= \sqrt{\left(\dfrac{p}{2}\right)^2 + q^2} = \dfrac{13504.7}{d^2}$

In simple tension, max. shear stress $= \dfrac{f}{2} = \dfrac{95}{2} = 47.5\ \mathrm{N/mm^2}$

$$\therefore \qquad \frac{13504.7}{d^2} = 47.5, \text{ from which } d = \sqrt{\frac{13504.7}{47.5}} = \mathbf{16.86\ mm}$$

4. Maximum strain energy theory

The principal stresses are :

$$\sigma_1 = \frac{23054}{d^2} \qquad \text{and} \qquad \sigma_2 = -\frac{3955.4}{d^2}$$

$$\therefore \qquad U = \frac{1}{2E}\left[\left(\frac{23054}{d^2}\right)^2 + \left(-\frac{3955.4}{d^2}\right)^2 + 2 \times 0.3 \left(\frac{23054}{d^2}\right)\left(-\frac{3955.4}{d^2}\right)\right]$$

$$= \frac{1}{2E}\frac{49242 \times 10^4}{d^4}$$

Strain energy in simple tension $= \dfrac{f^2}{2E} = \dfrac{(95)^2}{2E} = \dfrac{9025}{2E}$

$$\therefore \quad \frac{1}{2E}\frac{49242 \times 10^4}{d^4} = \frac{9025}{2E}$$

or $\qquad d = \left(\dfrac{49242 \times 10^4}{9025}\right)^{1/4} = \mathbf{15.28\ mm}$

5. Maximum shear strain energy theory

$$U_s = \frac{m+1}{6mE}\left[(\sigma_1 - \sigma_2)^2 + (\sigma_2 - \sigma_3)^2 + (\sigma_3 - \sigma_1)^2\right], \text{ where } \sigma_3 = 0$$

$$\therefore \quad U_s = \frac{m+1}{3mE} \times \frac{1}{2}\left[\left(\frac{23054}{d^2} + \frac{3955.4}{d^2}\right)^2 + \left(-\frac{3955.4}{d^2} - 0\right)^2 + \left(0 - \frac{23054}{d^2}\right)^2\right]$$

or $\qquad U_s = \dfrac{m+1}{3mE} \times \dfrac{1}{2}\left[\dfrac{7.295 \times 10^8}{d^4} + \dfrac{0.156 \times 10^8}{d^4} + \dfrac{5.315 \times 10^8}{d^4}\right]$

or $\qquad U_s = \dfrac{m+1}{3mE} \times \dfrac{6.383 \times 10^8}{d^4}$

Shear strain energy under uniaxial stress $= \dfrac{m+1}{3mE}f^2 = \dfrac{m+1}{3mE}(95)^2$

$$\therefore \qquad \frac{6.383 \times 10^8}{d^4} = (95)^2 \qquad \qquad ..$$

From which $\qquad\qquad d = 16.31 \text{ mm}$

7.11. ADDITIONAL ILLUSTRATIVE EXAMPLES

Example 7.3. *Two of the principal stresses at a point are 130 N/mm² and 90 N/mm². Determine the safe range of the third principal stress at the point by five different theories. Take $E = 2 \times 10^5 N/mm^2$, failure stress in tension test to Le 210 N/mm², and $\mu = 0.25$. Failure stress in tension and compression is the same.*

Solution :

The third principal stress (σ) may be the highest, the lowest or the intermediate one. Hence the range is $\sigma_3 \leq \sigma \leq \sigma_1$.

(i) Maximum principal stress theory

$$\sigma_1 = f_y = 210 \text{ N/mm}^2 \ ; \ \sigma_3 = f_y' = -210 \text{ N/mm}^2$$

Hence the range is $\quad -210 \leq \sigma \leq 210$

(ii) Maximum strain theory

$$\sigma_1 - 0.25 \,(130 + 90) = f_y = 210$$

or $\qquad\qquad \sigma_1 = 210 + 55 = 265 \text{ N/mm}^2$

Also, $\qquad \sigma_3 - 0.25\,(130 + 90) = f_y' = -210$

or $\qquad\qquad \sigma_3 = -210 + 55 = -155 \text{ N/mm}^2$

Hence the range is $\quad -155 \leq \sigma \leq 210 \text{ N/mm}^2$

(iii) Maximum shear stress theory

$$\sigma_1 - 90 = f_y = 210$$

Hence $\qquad\qquad \sigma_1 = 210 + 90 = 300 \text{ N/mm}^2$

Also, $\qquad 130 - \sigma_3 = f_y = 210$

Hence $\qquad\qquad \sigma_3 = 130 - 210 = -80 \text{ N/mm}^2$

Hence the range is $\quad -80 \leq \sigma \leq 300 \text{ N/mm}^2$

(iv) Maximum strain energy theory

$$\sigma^2 + (90)^2 + (130)^2 - 2 \times 0.25\,(130\,\sigma + 90\,\sigma + 90 \times 130) = (210)^2$$

or $\qquad\qquad \sigma^2 - 110\,\sigma - 24950 = 0$

From which $\qquad \sigma_1 = 222.3 \text{ N/mm}^2 \quad$ and $\sigma_3 = -112.3 \text{ N/mm}^2$

Hence the range is $\quad -112.3 \leq \sigma \leq 222.3 \text{ N/mm}^2$

(v) Max. Distortion energy theory

$$(\sigma - 90)^2 + (\sigma - 130)^2 + (130 - 90)^2 = 2\,(210)^2$$

or $\qquad\qquad \sigma_2 - 220\,\sigma - 30800 = 0$

From which $\qquad \sigma_1 = 317.1 \text{ N/mm}^2 \text{ and } \sigma_3 = -97.1 \text{ N/mm}^2$

Hence the range is $-97.1 \leq \sigma \leq 317.1 \text{ N/mm}^2$

Example 7.4. *A body is under the action of two principal stresses of 40 N/mm² and −70 N/mm², the third principal stress being zero. If the elastic limit in simple tension as well as compression is 200 N/mm², find the factor of safety, based on the elastic limit according to the five theories of failure. Take $\mu = 0.3$.*

Solution :

Here $\qquad \sigma_1 = 40 \text{ N/mm}^2, \quad \sigma_2 = 0 \text{ and } \sigma_3 = -70 \text{ N/mm}^2$

1. Maximum principal stress theory

Since σ_3 is numerically the largest stress, it will be the basis of failure.

$\therefore \qquad\qquad\qquad \sigma_3 = \dfrac{f_y}{N} \qquad \text{or} \quad N = \dfrac{f_y}{\sigma_3} = \dfrac{200}{70} = \mathbf{2.86}$

2. Maximum principal strain theory

Here, either $\sigma_1 - \mu (\sigma_2 + \sigma_3) = \dfrac{f_y}{N} \qquad$ or $\sigma_3 - \mu (\sigma_1 + \sigma_2) = \dfrac{f_y}{N}$

Hence either $40 - 0.3 (0 - 70) = \dfrac{200}{N} \quad$ or $\quad -70 - 0.3 (40 + 0) = \dfrac{200}{N}$

Hence either $\qquad\qquad N = \dfrac{200}{61} = 3.28 \text{ or } N = \dfrac{200}{82} = 2.44$

Hence actual $\qquad\qquad N = \mathbf{2.44}$

3. Maximum shear stress theory

$$\sigma_1 - \sigma_3 = \dfrac{f_y}{N} \qquad \text{or} \quad 40 - (-70) = \dfrac{200}{N}$$

From which $\qquad\qquad N = \dfrac{200}{110} = \mathbf{1.818}$

4. Maximum strain energy theory

$$\sigma_1^2 + \sigma_2^2 + \sigma_3^2 - 2\mu (\sigma_1 \sigma_2 + \sigma_2 \sigma_3 + \sigma_3 \sigma_1) = \left(\dfrac{f_y}{N}\right)^2$$

or $\quad (40)^2 + (0)^2 + (-70)^2 - 2 \times 0.3 \left[40 \times 0 + 0 \times (-70) + (-70)(40) \right] = \left(\dfrac{200}{N}\right)^2$

or $\quad \left(\dfrac{200}{N}\right)^2 = 8180$, from which $N = \mathbf{2.21}$

5. Maximum shear strain energy theory

$$\sigma_1^2 + \sigma_2^2 + \sigma_3^2 - (\sigma_1 \sigma_2 + \sigma_2 \sigma_3 + \sigma_3 \sigma_1) = \left(\dfrac{f_y}{N}\right)^2$$

or $\quad (40)^2 + (0)^2 + (-70)^2 - \left[40 \times 0 + 0 \times (-70) + (-70)(40) \right] = \left(\dfrac{200}{N}\right)^2$

or $\quad \left(\dfrac{200}{N}\right)^2 = 9300$, from which $N = \mathbf{2.07}$

Example 7.5. *The B.M. M applied to a solid shaft carries a maximum direct stress f_y at elastic failure. Determine the numerical relationships between M and twisting moment T which, acting alone on the shaft, will produce elastic failure according to each of the following theories of failure. (a) Maximum principal stress (b) Maximum principal strain (c) Maximum shear stress, (d) Maximum strain energy and (e) shear strain energy. Take $\mu = 0.3$.*

Solution :

The elastic limit stress f_y caused by bending moment M is given by

$$f_y = \frac{32\,M}{\pi\,d^3}$$

Similarly, the shear stress τ produced by the torque T acting alone is

$$\tau = \frac{16\,T}{\pi\,d^3}$$

This shear stress is accompanied by complimentary shear stress, giving a state of shear stress, due to which the induced principal stress are

$$\sigma_1 = -\sigma_2 = \frac{16\,T}{\pi\,d^3}$$

Hence the principal stresses acting on the shaft are

$$\frac{16\,T}{\pi\,d^3},\, 0,\, -\frac{16\,T}{\pi\,d^3}$$

(a) Maximum principal stress theory

$$\frac{16\,T}{\pi\,d^3} = f_y = \frac{32\,M}{\pi\,d^3} \text{ at elastic failure}$$

$$\therefore \qquad \frac{M}{T} = \mathbf{0.5}$$

(b) Maximum principal strain theory

$$\sigma_1 - \mu\,\sigma_2 = f_y$$

or
$$\frac{16\,T}{\pi\,d^3} + \frac{0.3 \times 16\,T}{\pi\,d^3} = \frac{32\,M}{\pi\,d^3}$$

From which
$$\frac{M}{T} = \frac{16 + 4.8}{32} = \mathbf{0.65}$$

(c) Maximum shear stress theory

$$\sigma_1 - \sigma_2 = f_y$$

or
$$\frac{16\,T}{\pi\,d^3} + \frac{16\,T}{\pi\,d^3} = \frac{32\,M}{\pi\,d^3}$$

From which
$$\frac{M}{T} = \mathbf{1}$$

(d) Maximum strain energy theory

$$\sigma_1^2 + \sigma_2^2 - 2\,\mu\,\sigma_1\,\sigma_2 = f_y^2$$

or
$$\left(\frac{16\,T}{\pi\,d^3}\right)^2 + \left(\frac{16\,T}{\pi\,d^3}\right)^2 + 2 \times 0.3 \left(\frac{16\,T}{\pi\,d^3}\right)^2 = \left(\frac{32\,M}{\pi\,d^3}\right)^2$$

or
$$2.6 \left(\frac{16\,T}{\pi\,d^3} \right)^2 = \left(\frac{32\,M}{\pi\,d^3} \right)^2$$

or
$$1.612 \left(\frac{16\,T}{\pi\,d^3} \right) = \frac{32\,M}{\pi\,d^3}$$

From which
$$\frac{M}{T} = \frac{1.612}{2} = 0.806$$

(e) Maximum shear strain energy theory

$$\sigma_1^2 + \sigma_2^2 - \sigma_1 \sigma_2 = f_y^2$$

or
$$\left(\frac{16\,T}{\pi\,d^3} \right)^2 + \left(\frac{16\,T}{\pi\,d^3} \right)^2 + \left(\frac{16\,T}{\pi\,d^3} \right)^2 = \left(\frac{32\,M}{\pi\,d^3} \right)^2$$

or
$$3 \left(\frac{16\,T}{\pi\,d^3} \right)^2 = \left(\frac{32\,M}{\pi\,d^3} \right)^2$$

$\therefore$
$$\frac{M}{T} = \frac{\sqrt{3}}{2} = 0.866$$

PROBLEMS

1. Discuss in brief various prominent theories of failure.

2. Write a note on significance of theories of failure.

3. The principal stresses at a point in an elastic material are $1.5\,f$ (tensile), f (tensile) and $\frac{1}{2}f$ (compressive). If the elastic limit in simple tension is $200\ \text{N/mm}^2$, determine the value of f at failure, according to the five different theories. Take $\mu = 0.3$.

4. A bolt is subjected to an axial pull of $12\,\text{kN}$ together with a transverse shear of $6\,\text{kN}$. Determine the diameter of the bolt according to (i) Maximum principal stress theory, (ii) Maximum shear stress theory, (iii) Maximum strain theory, (iv) Strain energy theory, and (v) shear strain energy theory. Take elastic limit in tension $= 300\ \text{N/mm}^2$, factor of safety $= 3$ and $\mu = 0.3$.

5. A circular shaft 100 mm diameter is subjected to combined bending and twisting of moments the B.M. being 3 times the twisting moment. If the direct tensile yield point of the material is $350\ \text{N/mm}^2$, and the factor of safety is 4, calculate the allowable twisting moment according to the following theories of elastic failure.

   (a) Maximum principal stress theory
   (b) Maximum shear stress theory
   (c) Shear strain energy theory if the simple shear is not to exceed $60\ \text{N/mm}^2$

(Based on U.L.)

ANSWERS

3. (i) $133.3\ \text{N/mm}^2$ (ii) $148.1\ \text{N/mm}^2$ (iii) $100\ \text{N/mm}^2$ (iv) $109.3\ \text{N/mm}^2$ (v) $110.9\ \text{N/mm}^2$

4. (i) $13.58\ \text{mm}$ (ii) $13.93\ \text{mm}$ (iii) $14.7\ \text{mm}$ (iv) $14.01\ \text{mm}$ (v) $14.22\ \text{mm}$

5. (a) 2.789 kN-m (b) 2.718 kN-m (c) 3.268 kN-m

Centroids and Moments of Inertia of Plane Areas

8.1. INTRODUCTION : CENTRE OF GRAVITY AND CENTROID

The *centre of gravity* of a body is that point through which the resultant of system of parallel forces formed by the weights of all the particles of the body passes, for all positions of the body.

The *plane areas*, like triangle, rectangle, quadrilateral, circle etc., have only *areas* and no mass. The *centre of area* of such figures is known as *centroid*. In common terminology, we use the term *area* to mean *plane surface*. Strictly speaking area is a measure of size of the surface. The method of finding out the centroid of a figure is the same as finding out the centre of gravity of a body. Hence many Authors write *c.g.* for *centroid* and *vice- versa*. The location of centroid of a plane area is an important geometrical property of the area.

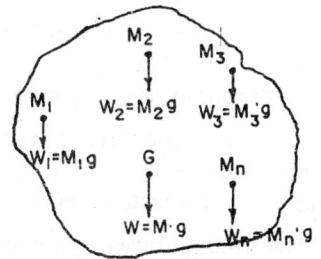

FIG. 8.1

8.2. CENTROID OF PLANE AREAS

Fig. 8.2 shows a plane area A, with its centroid G having its coordinates $\bar{x}$, $\bar{y}$, the values of which are required to be determined. Consider a small area dA, having co-ordinates x and y.

The total area $A = \int dA$ (by definition) ...(8.1)

The *first moments* of the area about x and y axes respectively are

$$Q_x = \int y \cdot dA \quad \text{and} \quad Q_y = \int x \cdot dA \qquad ...(8.2)$$

The coordinates $\bar{x}$ and $\bar{y}$ of the centroid G are evidently equal to the first moments divided by the area itself.

Hence
$$\bar{x} = \frac{\int x \, dA}{\int dA} = \frac{Q_y}{A} \quad \text{and} \quad \bar{y} = \frac{\int y \, dA}{\int dA} = \frac{Q_x}{A} \qquad ...(8.3)$$

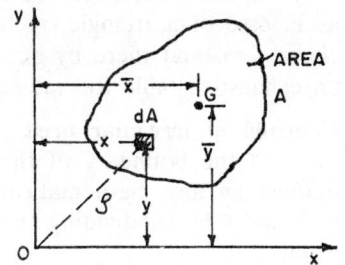

FIG. 8.2. CENTROID OF PLANE AREA

(251)

1. Centroid of area symmetric about an axis

If a plane area has an axis of symmetry, the centroid will lie on that axis of symmetry. This is so because the first moment about an axis of symmetry is zero. Fig. 8.3 shows a section having x-axis as the axis of symmetry; hence the centroid G will lie on that axis. In such a case, only one distance need be calculated.

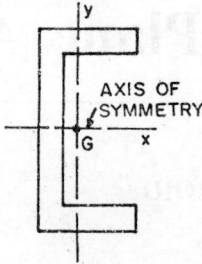

FIG. 8.3 AREA WITH ONE AXIS
OF SYMMETRY

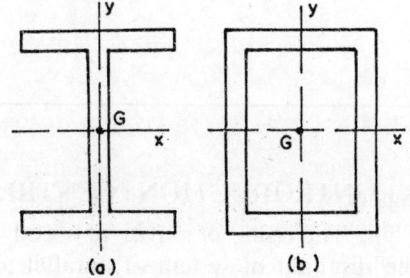

FIG. 8.4. AREA WITH TWO AXES
OF SYMMETRY

2. Centroid of area symmetric about two axes

If a plane area has two axes of symmetry, the centroid of such an area will be lie at the intersection of the two axes of symmetry. Thus, the centroid of such an area can be located by inspection. Here first moment of area about both the axes will be zero (Fig. 8.4).

3. Centroid of area symmetric about a point

Fig. 8.5 shows the special case of an area which is *symmetric about a point*. Such a point is called the *centre of symmetry* and is so located that every line in the area drawn through that point is symmetric about that point. The centroid of such an area will lie at that point, which can be located by inspection.

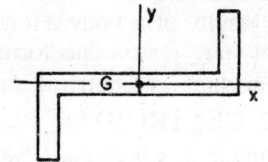

FIG. 8.5 AREA SYM-
METRIC ABOUT A POINT

Centroid of regular areas

If the boundaries of the areas are defined by simple mathematical expressions (such as in case of a triangle, rectangle, circle etc.), we can evaluate the integral of Eq. 8.3 in the *closed form* and there by get formulae for $\bar{x}$ and $\bar{y}$. Table 8.1 gives an exhaustive table for values of $\bar{x}$ and $\bar{y}$ for common plane areas.

Centroid of irregular areas

If the boundary of the area is *irregular curve*, which is not defined by any mathematical expression, we can find the values of $\bar{x}$ and $\bar{y}$ by subdividing the area into small element of area dA. Then

$$A = \sum_{i=1}^{n} \Delta A_i$$

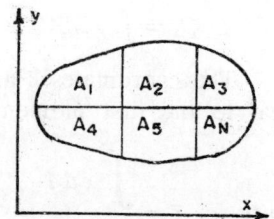

FIG. 8.6. CENTROID OF
IRREGULAR AREA

$$Q_x = \sum_{i=1}^{n} y_i \, \Delta A_i \qquad \qquad \text{...(8.4)}$$

$$Q_y = \sum_{i=1}^{n} x_i \, \Delta A_i$$

Hence
$$\bar{x} = \frac{Q_y}{A} = \frac{\sum\limits_{i=1}^{n} x_i \, \Delta A_i}{\sum\limits_{i=1}^{n} \Delta A_i} \quad \text{and} \quad \bar{y} = \frac{Q_x}{A} = \frac{\sum\limits_{i=1}^{n} y_i \, \Delta A_i}{\sum\limits_{i=1}^{n} A_i} \qquad \text{...(8.5)}$$

Here n=total number of elements in the area and x_i and y_i are x and y coordinates of the centroid of area ΔA_i.

8.3. CENTROID OF COMPOSITE AREAS

Most of the sections used in engineering works consist of areas composed of two, three or more parts. Each part generally consist of a rectangular area, such as that shown in Fig. 8.7 (a) and 8.7 (b). Alternatively, a composite section, such as the one shown in Fig. 8.7 (c), may be made up of regular section such as (i) a rectangular plate, (ii) an I-section and (iii) a channel section, and the properties (i.e. area and location of the centroid) of each of these regular sections are known from available *section tables*.

The area and first moment of a composite area may be calculated by summing the corresponding properties of its parts using Eqs. 8.4. Thus :

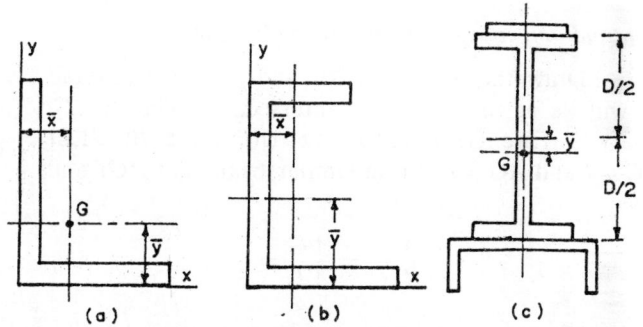

FIG. 8.7. CENTROID OF COMPOSITE AREA

$$A = \sum_{i=1}^{n} \Delta \Delta_i = A_1 + A_2 + \ldots\ldots A_n$$

$$Q_x = \sum_{i=1}^{n} y_i \, \Delta A_i = y_1 A_1 + y_2 A_2 + \ldots\ldots y_n A_n$$

$$Q_y = \sum_{i=1}^{n} x_i \, \Delta A_i = x_1 A_1 + x_2 A_2 + \ldots\ldots x_n A_n$$

Hence
$$\bar{x} = \frac{Q_y}{A} = \frac{x_1 A_1 + x_2 A_2 + \ldots\ldots x_n A_n}{A_1 + A_2 + \ldots\ldots A_n}$$

and
$$\bar{y} = \frac{Q_x}{A} = \frac{y_1 A_1 + y_2 A_2 + \ldots\ldots y_n A_n}{A_1 + A_2 + \ldots\ldots A_n} \qquad \text{...(8.7)}$$

8.4. SOME CASES OF CENTROID OF COMMON AREAS

1. Centroid of a triangular lamina

Fig. 8.8 shows a triangular lamina *ABC*, and we are required to locate its centroid *G*. Draw a narrow strip *bc*, parallel to the side *BC*. The centroid of the narrow strip *bc* will lie at the middle point *m* of the strip. Similarly, the centroid of a narrow strip at *BC* will lie at the middle point *D*. Hence the centroid of any narrow strip drawn parallel to *BC* will lie on the meridian *AD*. Similarly, the centroid of any narrow strip, drawn parallel to *AC*, will lie of the meridian *BE*, where *E* is the midpoint of *AC*. Lastly, the centroid of any narrow strip, drawn parallel to the side *AB*, will lie on the meridian *CF*. Hence the centroid *G* of the whole triangular lamina will lie at the point of intersection of the three meridians.

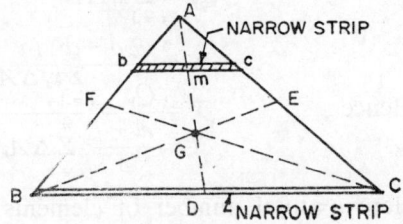

FIG. 8.8. CENTROID OF TRIANGULAR LAMINA

It can be shown that $DG = \frac{1}{3}DA$; $EG = \frac{1}{3}EB$ and $FG = \frac{1}{3}FC$

Centroid for a right angled triangle (Fig. 8.9)

Draw the meridians *BE* and *AD*; the centroid *G* will lie at their point of intersection. Through *G*, draw a line *GI* parallel to the base *BC*. Let *BC* = *l* and *AC* = *h*. From similar triangular *AGI* and *ADC*,

$$\frac{GI}{DC} = \frac{AG}{AD} = \frac{2}{3}$$

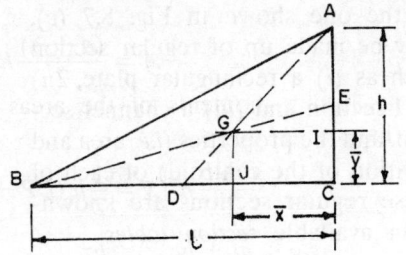

FIG. 8.9. CENTROID OF RIGHT ANGLED TRIANGLE

Hence $GI = \bar{x} = \frac{2}{3}DC = \frac{2}{3} \times \frac{l}{2} = \frac{l}{3}$

Similarly, it can be shown that $GJ = \bar{y} = \frac{h}{3}$

Centroid of any triangle (**Fig. 8.10**)

Let   *l* = length of the base *BC*

           h = height of the triangle = *AP*

where *AP* is perpendicular to *BC*.

Let   *BP* = *a*

and   *PC* = *b*, such that *a* + *b* = *l*

Let the centroid *G* be at a distance $\bar{x}$ from *B*.

Now sum of moments of areas *ABP* and *APC* about *B* = moment of area about *B*.

$$\therefore \quad \frac{1}{2}ah\left(\frac{2}{3}a\right) + \frac{1}{2}bh\left(a + \frac{b}{3}\right) = \frac{1}{2}lh\bar{x}$$

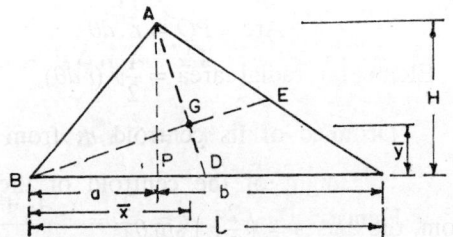

FIG. 8.10

or
$$\frac{2}{3}a^2 + ab + \frac{b^2}{3} = l\bar{x}$$

or
$$\frac{2a^2 + 3ab + b^2}{3} = \frac{(2a + b)(a + b)}{3} = l\bar{x}$$

$\therefore$
$$\bar{x} = \frac{(2a + b)(a + b)}{3l} = \frac{(2a + b)l}{3l} = \frac{2a + b}{3} = \frac{a + (a + b)}{3}$$

or
$$\bar{x} = \frac{a + l}{3} \qquad \qquad ...(8.8\ a)$$

If, however, $\bar{x}$ is measured from right hand end C, then
$$\bar{x} = \frac{b + l}{3} \qquad \qquad ...(8.8\ b)$$

Also, $\bar{y} = \dfrac{h}{3}$, where h is the height of the triangle.

2. Centroid of a trapezium

Fig. 8.11 shows a trapezoid $ABCD$, having side AB ($= a$) and CD ($= b$) parallel to each other, and h is its height. Draw AP and BQ perpendicular to DC.

Let the distance of centroid G be $\bar{y}$ from the base BC.

Total area $\qquad A = \dfrac{(a + b)}{2}h$

Taking moments of the areas about base DC, we have

$$\left(\frac{a + b}{2}h\right)\bar{y} = \frac{1}{2}h(DP + QC)\frac{h}{3} + ah.\frac{h}{2}$$

or
$$\frac{a + b}{2}h\bar{y} = \frac{h^2}{6}(b - a) + \frac{ah^2}{2} = \frac{h^2}{6}(b - a + 3a)$$

or
$$\bar{y} = \frac{h}{3}\frac{b + 2a}{b + a} \qquad \qquad ...(8.9)$$

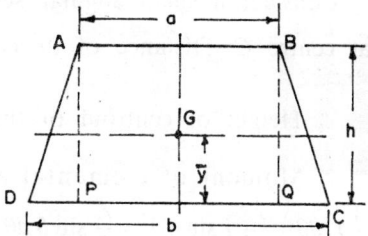

FIG. 8.11

3. Centroid of a Semicircular lamina :

Fig. 8.12 shows a semi-circular lamina of radius r. Consider an element radial area CPQ, subtending an angle $d\theta$ at the centre C.

$\qquad$ Arc $\quad PQ = r.d\theta$

Elemental radial area $= \dfrac{1}{2}r(r\,d\theta)$

Distance of its centroid m from $C = \dfrac{2}{3}r$

$\therefore$ Height of the centroid of the elemental area

from the base $= \left(\dfrac{2}{3}r\right)\sin\theta$

$\therefore$ Moment of elemental area about the base

$$= \left(\frac{1}{2}r^2\,d\theta\right)\left(\frac{2}{3}r\sin\theta\right) = \frac{r^3}{3}\sin\theta\,d\theta$$

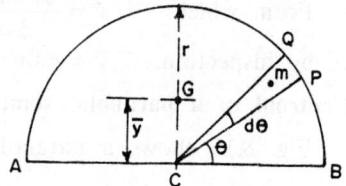

FIG. 8.12

$\therefore$ Moment of the whole area about the base $= \displaystyle\int_0^{\pi} \dfrac{r^3}{3} \sin\theta\, d\theta = \dfrac{2r^3}{3} \displaystyle\int_0^{\frac{\pi}{2}} \sin\theta\, d\theta = \dfrac{2}{3} r^3$

$$\text{Area of semicircle} = \dfrac{\pi r^2}{2}$$

Hence $\qquad\qquad \dfrac{\pi r^2}{2} \bar{y} = \dfrac{2}{3} r^3$

From which $\qquad\qquad \bar{y} = \dfrac{4r}{3\pi}$ \qquad\qquad ...(8.10)

4. Centroid of a Quarter-Circular lamina

From the previous discussions we get

$$\bar{x} = \bar{y} = \dfrac{4r}{3\pi} \qquad\qquad ...(8.11)$$

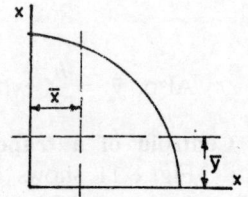

5. Centroid of a circular sector :

Consider a small angular sector CPQ, subtending an angle $d\theta$ at centre C. Distance of its centroid m from $C = \dfrac{2}{3} r$

FIG. 8.13

$\therefore$ Height of centroid of the elemental area from the base $= \dfrac{2}{3} r \sin\theta$

$\therefore$ Moment of elemental area about the base

$$= \left(\dfrac{1}{2} r^2\, d\theta \right) \left(\dfrac{2}{3} r \sin\theta \right) = \dfrac{r^3}{3} \sin\theta\, d\theta$$

$\therefore$ Moment of the whole area about the base

$$= \int_{\frac{\pi}{2}-\alpha}^{\frac{\pi}{2}+\alpha} \dfrac{r^3}{3} \sin\theta\, d\theta = \dfrac{2r^3}{3} \int_{\frac{\pi}{2}-\alpha}^{\frac{\pi}{2}} \sin\theta\, d\theta$$

$$= \dfrac{2r^3}{3} \left[-\cos\theta \right]_{\frac{\pi}{2}-\alpha}^{\pi/2} = \dfrac{2r^3}{3} \sin\alpha$$

Area of the sector $= \alpha r^2$

Hence $\qquad \alpha r^2 . \bar{y} = \dfrac{2r^3}{3} \sin\alpha$

From which $\qquad \bar{y} = \dfrac{2r \sin\alpha}{3\alpha}$ \qquad ...(8.12)

Also, by inspection, $\qquad \bar{x} = r \sin\alpha$ \qquad ...(8.13)

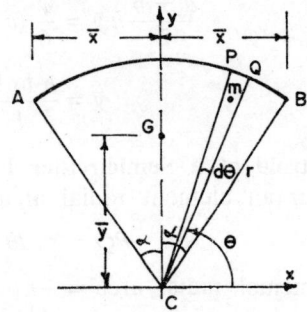

FIG. 8.14

6. Centroid of a parabolic semi-segment

Fig. 8.15 shows a parabolic semi-segment CAB, the equation of the curve being

$$y = f(x) = h \left(1 - \dfrac{x^2}{b^2} \right)$$

Let us take a strip of thickness dx and height y, located at a distance x from the origin C.

$$\therefore \quad dA = y\,dx = h\left(1 - \frac{x^2}{b^2}\right)dx$$

$$\therefore \quad A = \int dA = \int_0^b h\left(1 - \frac{x^2}{b^2}\right)dx$$

$$= h\left[x - \frac{x^3}{3b^2}\right]_0^b = \frac{2bh}{3} \qquad ...(8.14)$$

$$Q_x = \int \frac{y}{2}\,dA = \int_0^b \frac{h^2}{2}\left(1 - \frac{x^2}{b^2}\right)^2 dx = \frac{4bh^2}{15}$$

and

$$Q_y = \int x\,dA = \int_0^b h\,x\left(1 - \frac{x^2}{b^2}\right)dx = \frac{b^2 h}{4}$$

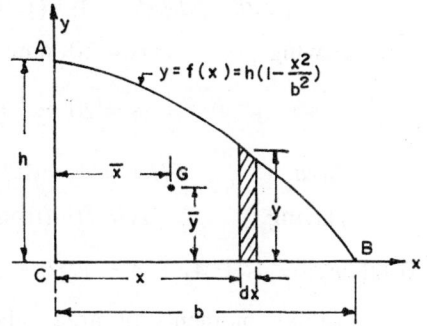

FIG. 8.15

$$\therefore \qquad \bar{x} = \frac{Q_y}{A} = \frac{b^2 h}{4} \times \frac{3}{2bh} = \frac{3}{8}b \quad \text{and} \quad \bar{y} = \frac{Q_x}{A} = \frac{4bh^2}{15} \times \frac{3}{2bh} = \frac{2h}{5} \quad ...(8.15)$$

Example 8.1. *Find the centroid of a* $120\,mm \times 150\,mm \times 20\,mm$ *T section.*

Solution :

Let the centroid be G at $\bar{y}$ above GH. Area $ABDC$ $= A_1 = 120 \times 20 = 2400$ mm².

Distance of its centroid $G_1 = y_1 = 150 - 10 = 140$ mm

Area $EFHG = A_2 = (150 - 20) \times 20 = 2600$ mm²

Distance of its centroid $G_2 = y_2 = \frac{1}{2}(150-20) = 65$ mm

Total area $\qquad A = A_1 + A_2 = 2400 + 2600 = 5000$ mm²

Taking moments of the area along GH, we get

$$A\bar{y} = A_1 y_1 + A_2 y_2$$

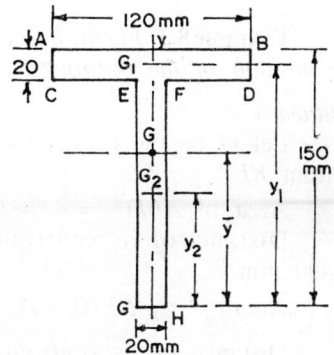

FIG. 8.16

$$\therefore \qquad \bar{y} = \frac{A_1 y_1 + A_2 y_2}{A_1 + A_2} = \frac{2400 \times 140 + 2600 \times 65}{5000} = \mathbf{101} \text{ mm}$$

(measured from the bottom)

or $\qquad \bar{y} = 150 - 101 = 49$ mm, measured from the top.

Example 8.2. *Find the centroid of an unsymmetrical channel section showing Fig. 8.17.*

Solution :

Let G be the centroid, distant $\bar{x}$ rom face AI and $\bar{y}$ from face IJ.

Area $\qquad ABCE = A_1 = 80 \times 16 = 1280$ mm^2

Having $\qquad x_1 = 40$ mm (From AI)

and $\qquad\qquad y_1 = 150 - 8 = 142$ mm (from IJ)

$\qquad$ Area $CDGF = A_2 = (150 - 16 - 20) \times 20 = 2280$ mm^2

Having $\qquad x_2 = 10$ mm (from AI) and

$$y_2 = 20 + \frac{1}{2}(150 - 16 - 20) = 77 \text{ mm}$$

Area $\qquad FHJI = A_3 = 100 \times 20 = 2000$ mm^2

Having $\qquad x_3 = 50$ (from AI) and $y_3 = 10$ (from IJ)

Total area $= A_1 + A_2 + A_3 = 1280 + 2280 + 2000 = 5560$ mm^2

Taking moments of areas about AI, we get

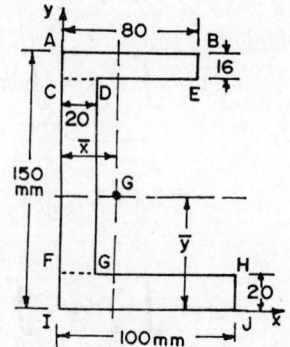

FIG. 8.17

$$\bar{x} = \frac{A_1 x_1 + A_2 x_2 + A_3 x_3}{A_1 + A_2 + A_3} = \frac{1280 \times 40 + 2280 \times 10 + 2000 \times 50}{5560} = \mathbf{31.29 \text{ mm}}$$

Similarly, taking moments of areas about $I\ J$, we get

$$\bar{y} = \frac{A_1 y_1 + A_2 y_2 + A_3 y_3}{A} = \frac{1280 \times 142 + 2280 \times 77 + 2000 \times 10}{5560}$$
$$= \mathbf{67.86 \text{ mm}}$$

Example 8.3. *For the I-section shown in Fig. 8.18, determine the position of the centroid.*

Solution :

$\qquad$ Let G be the centroid of the section, distant $\bar{y}$ from bottom KL.

$\qquad$ Area of $ABFC = A_1 = 150 \times 20 = 3000$ mm^2

$\qquad$ Distance of its centroid G_1 from $KL = y_1 = 500 - 10 = 490$ mm

$\qquad$ Area $\qquad DEIH = A_2 = 456 \times 16 = 7296$ mm^2

$\qquad$ Distance of its centroid G_2 from KL

$$= y_2 = 24 + \frac{1}{2} \times 456$$
$$= 252 \text{ mm}$$

$\qquad$ Area $\qquad GJLK = A_3 = 250 \times 24 = 6000$ mm^2

$\qquad$ Distance of its centroid G_3 from KL

$$= y_3 = \frac{1}{2} \times 24 = 12 \text{ mm}$$

Total area $A = A_1 + A_2 + A_3 = 3000 + 7296 + 6000 = 16296$ mm^2

$\qquad$ Taking moment of the areas about KL, we get

$\therefore \qquad 16296\,\bar{y} = 3000 \times 490 + 7296 \times 252 + 6000 \times 12$

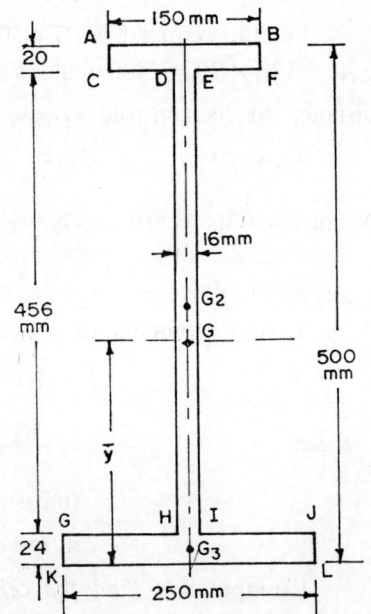

FIG. 8.18

From which $\bar{y} = 207.4$ mm

Example 8.4. *Determine the position of the centroid of an unsymmetrical Z-section shown in Fig. 8.19.*

Solution :

Let G be the centroid, distant $\bar{x}$ from ACK and $\bar{y}$ from KIJ.

Area $ABEC = A_1 = 150 \times 20 = 3000$ mm^2

Having $\qquad x_1 = \dfrac{1}{2} \times 150 = 75$ mm from ACK

and $\qquad y_1 = 500 - 10 = 490$ mm from KIJ

Area $\quad DEFG = A_2 = 460 \times 20 = 9200$ mm^2

Having $\qquad x_2 = 130 + 10 = 140$ mm from ACK

and $\qquad y_2 = 20 + \dfrac{1}{2} \times 460 = 250$ mm from KIJ

Area $\quad FHJI = A_3 = 300 \times 20 = 6000$ mm^2

Having $\qquad x_3 = 130 + \dfrac{1}{2} \times 300 = 280$ mm from ACK

and $\qquad y_3 = 10$ mm from $KIJ.$

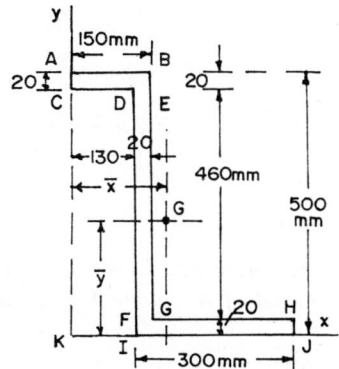

FIG. 8.19

Total $\qquad A = 3000 + 9200 + 6000 = 18200$ mm^2

Taking moments of areas about ACK, we get

$\therefore \qquad 18200\,\bar{x} = 3000 \times 75 + 9200 \times 140 + 6000 \times 280$

From which $\qquad \bar{x} = 175.44$ mm

Similarly, taking moments of areas about KIJ, we get

$\qquad 18200\,\bar{y} = 3000 \times 490 + 9200 \times 250 + 6000 \times 10$

From which $\qquad \bar{y} = 210.44$ mm

Example 8.5. *Find the position of centroid of a uniform plate which is in the form of uniform trapezium whose parallel sides are 2 m and 4 m and height is 3 m.*

If it has a rectangular extension of the same weight per square meter attached to the 2 m edge and 2 m long so as to just fit that edge, find what should be the height of the rectangular piece if the centroid of the whole assembly is to be at a height of 4 m above the base.

Solution :

For the trapezoidal plate, $A_1 = \dfrac{a+b}{2} \times H = \dfrac{4+2}{2} \times 3 = 9$ m^2

and $\qquad \bar{y}_1 = \dfrac{a+2b}{a+b} \times \dfrac{H}{3} = \dfrac{4+2\times 2}{4+2} \times \dfrac{3}{3} = 1.333$ m

For the composite section, let A_2 be the area of the rectangular extension.

$\therefore \quad A_2 = 2 \times h = 2h \ \text{m}^2$, and

$y_2 \ (\text{from} \ AB) = 3 + \dfrac{h}{2} = (3 + 0.5\,h) \ \text{m}$

Total area $A = A_1 + A_2 = 9 + 2h \ \text{m}^2$

Taking moments of areas about AB, we get

$(9 + 2h)\,\bar{y} = 9 \times 1.333 + 2h\,(3 + 0.5\,h)$

But $\qquad \bar{y} = 4 \ \text{m}$ (given)

$\therefore \ (9 + 2h)\,4 = 12 + 2h(3 + 0.5\,h)$

or $\qquad\qquad h^2 - 2h - 24 = 0$

From which $\qquad h = \textbf{6 m}$

Example 8.6. *Determine the position of the centroid of the plane Figure shown in Fig. 8.21*

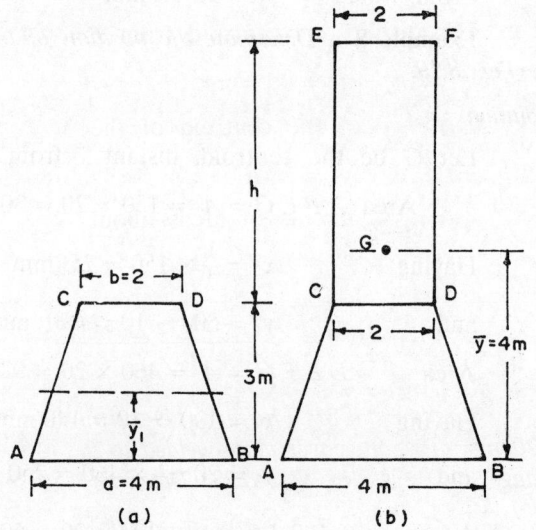

Solution :

Let the distance of the centroid G be $\bar{y}$ from the base.

Area of the trapezium $= A_1 = \dfrac{120 + 240}{2} \times 110$

$\qquad\qquad\qquad\qquad = 19800 \ \text{mm}^2$

The distance of its centroid from the bar

$= y_1 = \dfrac{a + 2b}{a + b} \times \dfrac{h}{3} = \dfrac{240 + 2 \times 120}{240 + 120} \times \dfrac{120}{3} = 53.33 \ \text{mm}$

Area of semi-circle $= A_2 = \dfrac{\pi r^2}{2} = \dfrac{\pi\,(90)^2}{2} = 12723.5 \ \text{mm}^2$

The distance of its centroid from the base

$= y_2 = \dfrac{4r}{3\pi} = \dfrac{4 \times 90}{3\pi} \approx 38.2 \ \text{mm}$

FIG. 8.20

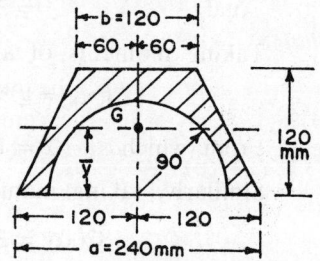

FIG. 8.21

Total area $= A = A_1 - A_2 = 19800 - 12723.5 = 7076.5 \ \text{mm}^2$

Now taking moments of the areas about the base,

$A\,\bar{y} = A_1 y_1 - A_2 y_2$

or $\qquad\qquad \bar{y} = \dfrac{19800 \times 53.33 - 12723.5 \times 38.2}{7076.5} = \textbf{80.53 mm}$

Example 8.7. *A circular sheet of metal has a radius R. If a hole of radius r is made as shown in Fig. 8.22, determine the position of the centroid of the remaining part.*

Solution :

Let G be the position of the centroid, distance $\bar{x}$ from P.

Area of circular sheet $= A_1 = \pi R^2$

Distance of its centroid from $P = x_1 = R$

Area of hole $= A_2 = \pi r^2$

Distance of the centroid of the hole $= x_2 = r$

Total area $A = \pi (R^2 - r^2)$

Taking moments of areas about point P, we get

$$A \bar{x} = A_1 x_1 - A_2 x_2$$

$\therefore$
$$\bar{x} = \frac{A_1 x_1 - A_2 x_2}{A_1 + A_2} = \frac{\pi R^2 . R - \pi r^2 . r}{\pi R^2 - \pi r^2} = \frac{R^3 - r^3}{R^2 - r^2}$$

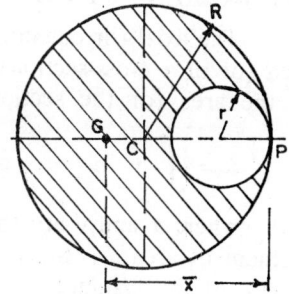

FIG. 8.22

Example 8.8. *The cross-section of a beam is constructed of an I-section with a 120 mm × 20 mm cover plate welded to the top flange and a channel section welded to the bottom flange as shown in Fig. 8.23. Determine the position of the centroid, given the following :*

(i) I-section : b = 100, h = 200, A = 3233 mm²

(ii) Channel section: h=200; b=75, C_y=21.7 mm, A = 2821 mm².

What is the distance between the centroid of the I-section and the centroid of the composite section ?

Solution :

Let G_1, G_2 and G_3 be the centroids of the three individual parts, and let G be the centroid of the composite section, located at $\bar{y}$ above the base line AB.

For I section, $\qquad A_1 = 3233$ mm²

and $\qquad\qquad y_1 = 75 + 100 = 175$ mm (above AB)

For the plate, $\qquad A_2 = 120 \times 20 = 2400$ mm²

and $\qquad\qquad y_2 = 75 + 200 + 10 = 285$ mm

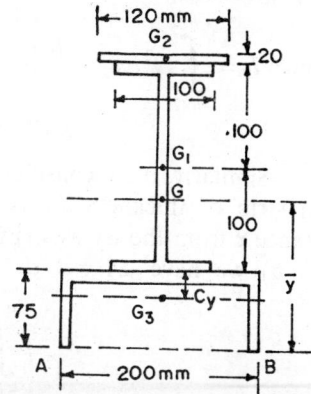

FIG. 8.23

For the channel, $\qquad A_3 = 2821$ mm² and $y_3 = 75 - 21.7 = 53.3$ mm

Total $\qquad\qquad A = A_1 + A_2 + A_3 = 3233 + 2400 + 2821 = 8454$ mm²

Taking moments about AB, we get $\bar{y} = \dfrac{A_1 y_1 + A_2 y_2 + A_3 y_3}{A_1 + A_2 + A_3}$

$$= \frac{(3233 \times 175) + (2400 \times 285) + (2821 \times 53.3)}{8454} = \mathbf{165.6 \ mm}$$

Hence distance between G_1 and $G = y_1 - \bar{y} = 175 - 165.6 = \mathbf{9.4 \ mm}$

8.5. MOMENT OF INERTIA

The axial (or equatorial) moment of inertia of a plane area (or of a cross-section) is the geometrical characteristic of the area (or the section) defined by the integrals :

$$I_{xx} = \int y^2 \, . \, dA \qquad \text{and} \quad I_{yy} = \int x^2 \, dA \qquad ...(8.16)$$

where x and y are the co-ordinates of the differential element of area dA. Since this area dA is multiplied by the square of the distance, the *moment of inertia* is also called the *second moment of area*.

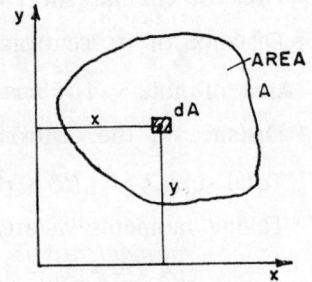

FIG. 8.24

To illustrate the method of finding the moment of inertia, let us find the moments in Fig. 8.25 (*a*). Consider is thin strip of thickness dy, at a distance y from x-axis.

Then $dA = b \, dy$

Hence $I_{xx} = \displaystyle\int_{-h/2}^{+h/2} y^2 b \, dy = \dfrac{b \, d^3}{12}$

$...(8.17 \ a)$

Similarly, if we consider a thin strip of thickness dx, at a distance x from the y-y axis (Fig. 8.25 *b*) we have $dA = d \, . \, dx$

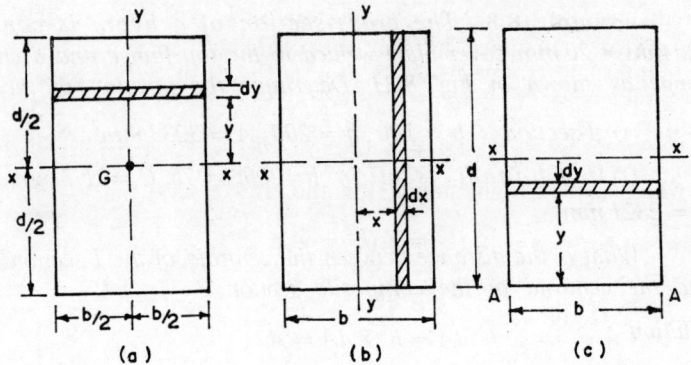

FIG. 8.25

$$\therefore \qquad I_{yy} = \int_{-b/2}^{b/2} x^2 d \, . \, dx = \frac{d \, b^3}{12} \qquad\qquad ...(8.17 \ b)$$

Lastly, let us find the moment of inertia about the base AA. Consider a strip of width b, and the thickness dy, at a distance y from AB (Fig. 8.25 *c*). Evidently,

$$dA = b \, . \, dy$$

$$\therefore \qquad I_{AA} = \int_{0}^{d} y^2 b \, dy = \frac{b \, d^3}{3} \qquad\qquad ...(8.17 \ c)$$

Thus we observe that the value of moment of inertia of a plane area will vary with the position of the axis about which we wish to find the moment of inertia. Also, we observe that the moment of inertia is larger with respect to axis AA than with respect to the centroidal x-axis. Hence the moment of inertia increases as the reference axis is moved parallel to itself farther from the centroid. Also, the moments of inertia are always positive quantities, regardless of the positions of axes selected since coordinates x and y are squared in Eq. 8.16.

Before finding the expressions for moments of inertia for different sections we shall consider the following three propositions in the next three articles.

Proposition 1 : *Parallel axis theorem.*

Proposition 2 : *Polar moment of inertia.*

Proposition 3 : *Moment of inertia of composite section*

8.6. PROPOSITION 1 : PARALLEL AXIS THEOREM

Statement : *The moment of inertia with respect to any axis parallel to the centroidal axis is equal to the moment of inertia with respect to the centroidal axis plus the product of area of the figure and the square of the distance between the axes.*

Fig. 8.26 shows a plane area with G-G as its centroidal axis. Let AA be any other axis, parallel to the centroidal axis at a distance h from GG axis. Let us consider an elementary area dA at a distance y from the centroidal axis.

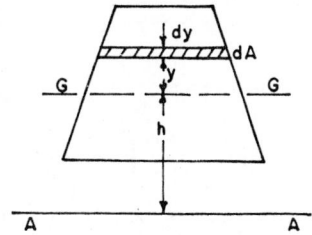

FIG. 8.26

The $\qquad I_{GG} = \Sigma\, y^2\, dA$

Also, $\qquad I_{AA} = \Sigma\, (h \pm y)^2 . dA$

(in which minus sign stands for the area dA below GG axis)

$\therefore \qquad I_{AA} = \Sigma\, (h^2 + y^2 \pm 2\,hy)\, dA = \Sigma\, h^2\, dA + \Sigma\, y^2\, dA \pm 2\,h\, \Sigma\, y\, dA$

where $\qquad \Sigma\, y^2\, dA = I_{GG} \qquad \Sigma\, y\, dA = 0$

and $\qquad \Sigma\, h^2\, dA = h^2\, \Sigma\, dA = A\, h^2$, where A is the area of cross-section

Hence $\qquad I_{AA} = I_{GG} + A\, h^2$ ...(8.18)

which proves the proposition.

From the parallel axis theorem, we conclude that the moment of inertia increases as the axis is moved parallel to it self farther from the centroid. Hence for a given direction of axes, *the moment of inertia about a centroidal axis is the least moment of inertia of the area.*

In order to test this theorem, let us find the moment of inertia of a rectangle about its base AA (Fig. 8.25 c)

This $\qquad I_{AA} = I_{GG} + A\, h^2 = \dfrac{b\, d^3}{12} + (bd) \left(\dfrac{d}{2}\right)^2 = \dfrac{b\, d^3}{3}$

This agrees with equation 8.17 (c).

8.7. PROPOSITION 2 : POLAR MOMENT OF INERTIA

Statement: *The moment of inertia about an axis perpendicular to the plane and passing through the intersection of the other two axes x-x and y-y contained by the plane is equal to the sum of moments of inertia about x-x and y-y.*

Fig. 8.27 shows an area A, which contains axes x-x and y-y in its plane. Let z-z axis be perpendicular to this plane, passing through the point O, the point of intersection of the x and y axes.

Let the elementary area dA have co-ordinates x, y and ρ with respect to x, y and z axes respectively, where ρ is the *polar distance*, given by the relation $\rho = x^2 + y^2$.

By definition, the *polar moment of inertia* (I_p or I_{zz}) is given by

$$I_p \ (\text{or } I_{zz}) = \int \rho^2 \, dA \qquad ...(8.19)$$

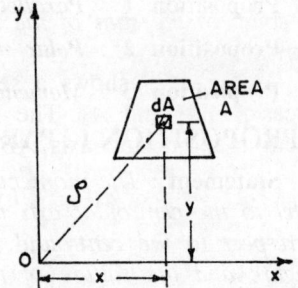

Hence

$$I_p = \int \rho^2 \, dA = \int (x^2 + y^2) \, dA$$

$$= \int x^2 \, dA + \int y^2 \, dA$$

But $\quad \displaystyle\int y^2 \, dA = I_{xx} \ \text{and} \ \int x^2 \, dA = I_{yy}$

FIG. 8.27

Hence I_p (or I_{zz}) $= I_{xx} + I_{yy}$ $\hspace{4cm}$ ...(8.20)

which proves the proposition.

Parallel axis theorem for polar moments of inertia

Let $\quad I_{po}$ = polar moment of inertia about the origin O.

$\qquad\quad I_{pg}$ = Polar moment of inertia about the centroid G.

Let x_g, y_g be the centroidal axes passing through the centroid G and let x_0 and y_0 be the two axes, parallel to the corresponding centroidal axes, passing through O.

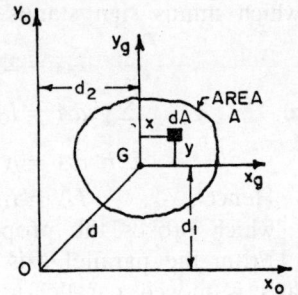

Now $I_{pg} = I_{xg} + I_{yg}$ $\quad$ and $I_{po} = I_{xo} + I_{yo}$ (Eq. 8.20)
$$...(a)$$

Also, from the parallel axis theorem,

$$I_{xo} = I_{xg} + A \, d_1^2 \quad \text{and} \quad I_{yo} = I_{yg} + A \, d_2^2 \qquad ...(b)$$

FIG. 8.28

Adding these two, $I_{xo} + I_{yo} = I_{xg} + I_{yg} = A \, (d_1^2 + d_2^2)$ $\hspace{3cm}$ ...(c)

But $\qquad d_1^2 + d_2^2 = d^2$ (From Fig. 8.28)

$$I_{xo} + I_{yo} = I_{po} \qquad \text{and} \qquad I_{xg} + I_{yg} = I_{pg}$$

Hence from (c), we get $I_{po} = I_{pg} + A \, d^2$ $\hspace{5cm}$ ...(8.21)

This is the parallel axis theorem for polar moments of inertia, which can be stated as follows :

"The polar moment of inertia of an area with respect to any point O in its plane is equal to the polar moment of inertia with respect to the centroid G plus the product of the area and the square of the distance between the points O and G."

8.8. PROPOSITION 3 : MOMENT OF INERTIA OF COMPOSITE SECTION

Statement : *The moment of inertia of a composite section is equal to the sum of the moments of inertia of its separate parts..*

Fig. 8.29 shows a section consisting of three regular areas A_1, A_2 and A_3. The moment of inertia of the whole section about any axis AB is given by

$$I_{AA} = \int y^2 \, dA = \int y_1^2 \, dA_1 + \int y_2^2 \, dA_2 + \int y_3^2 \, dA_3$$

where dA_1, dA_2 and dA_3 refer to the individual parts 1, 2, 3.

$$\therefore \qquad I_{AA} = I_{AA1} + I_{AA2} + I_{AA3} \qquad ...(8.22)$$

which proves the proposition.

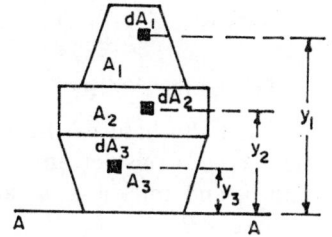

FIG. 8.29

8.9. MOMENT OF INERTIA OF SIMPLE COMMON SECTIONS

1. Rectangle (Fig. 8.25)

As found in Eq 8.5,

$$I_{xx} = \frac{b \, d^3}{12}; \quad I_{yy} = \frac{d \, b^3}{12} \quad \text{and} \quad I_{AA} = \frac{b \, d^3}{3} \qquad ...(8.17)$$

2. Hollow rectangular section : I-section : Channel section

(a) Hollow rectangular section

Fig. 8.30 (*a*) shows a hollow rectangular section, having external dimensions $B \times D$, and internal dimensions $b \times d$. The moment of inertia of external rectangle, about x-axis, is $\frac{1}{12} B.D^3$ and that for internal rectangle is $\frac{1}{12} bd^3$. Hence for the whole section

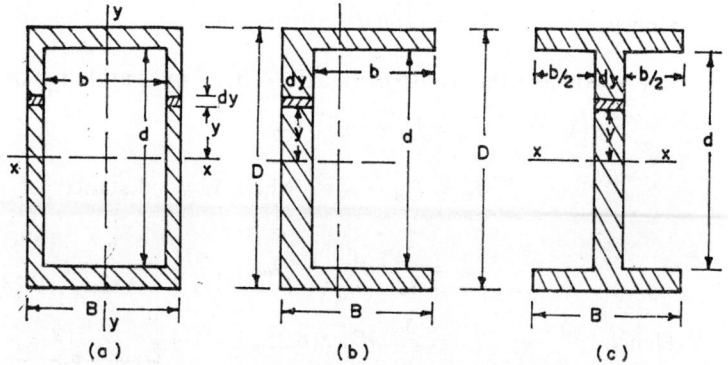

FIG. 8.30

$$I_{xx} = \frac{1}{12} BD^3 - \frac{1}{12} bd^3 \doteq \frac{1}{12} (BD^3 - bd^3) \qquad ...(8.23 \ a)$$

(b) Channel Section (Fig. 8.30 *b*) : A channel section can be formed by shifting one side-web of the hollow rectangular section to the other end. By doing so, the quantity $y^2 \, dA$ is not changed. Hence for the channel section also,

$$I_{xx} = \frac{1}{12} (BD^3 - bd^3) \qquad ...(8.23 \ b)$$

(b) I-section (Fig. 8.30 *c*) : An I-section can also be formed by shifting both the side webs of the hollow rectangular section to the centre. Here also, the quantity $y^2 dA$ is not changed by such shifting.

Hence $$I_{xx} = \frac{1}{12}(BD^3 - bd^3)$$ ...(8.23 *c*)

3. Triangular Section

Let the base of the triangle be *b* and height be *d*. Consider an elementary strip of width b_y and thickness dy, at height y above the base *AB*.

Then $$b_y = b\left(\frac{d-y}{d}\right)$$

∴ $$dA = b_y . dy = \frac{b}{d}(d-y)\,dy$$

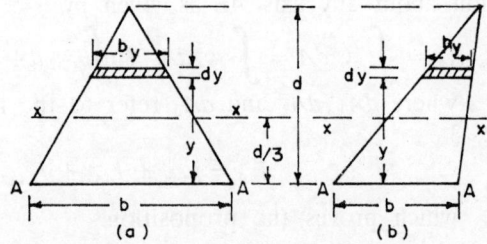

FIG. 8.31

Hence $$I_{AA} = \Sigma\, y^2\, dA = \int_0^d y^2\left(\frac{b}{d}\right)(d-y)\,dy = \frac{b}{d}\int_0^d (y^2 d - y^3)\,dy$$

or $$I_{AA} = \frac{b}{d}\left[\frac{y^3 d}{3} - \frac{y^4}{4}\right]_0^d = \frac{b}{d}\left[\frac{d^4}{3} - \frac{d^4}{4}\right] = \frac{b}{d}.\frac{1}{12}d^4.$$

Hence $$I_{AA} = \frac{1}{12}b\,d^3$$ ...(8.24)

Let *x*-axis be the centroidal axis. Then, by parallel axis theorem,

$$I_{AA} = I_{xx} + A\,\bar{x}^2$$

or $$I_{xx} = I_{AA} - A\,\bar{x}^2, \text{ when } \bar{x} = \text{ distance of centroidal axis from } AA = \frac{d}{3}$$

∴ $$I_{xx} = \frac{1}{12}bd^3 - \left(\frac{1}{2}bd\right)\left(\frac{d}{3}\right)^2 = \frac{1}{12}bd^3 - \frac{b\,d^3}{18}$$

Hence $$I_{xx} = \frac{1}{36}bd^3$$ ...(8.25)

4. Circular Section

First Method (Fig. 8.32 *a*)

Consider an elementary strip of width b_y and thickness dy, at a distance y from the *x*-axis. If r is the radius of the circle, then we have

$$y = r \sin\theta$$

∴ $$dy = r\cos\theta\, d\theta$$

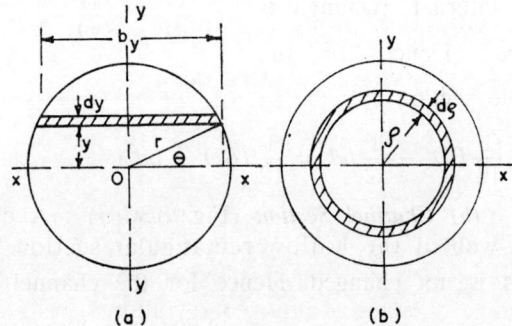

FIG. 8.32

Also, width of strip, $b_y = 2r \cos \theta$

$\therefore$ $\qquad dA = b_y . dy = 2r \cos \theta . r \cos \theta . d\theta = 2r^2 \cos^2 \theta \, d\theta$

Hence $\qquad I_{xx} = \int y^2 \, dA = \int\limits_{-\pi/2}^{\pi/2} \left(r^2 \sin^2 \theta \right) \left(2r^2 \cos^2 \theta \right) d\theta$

or $\qquad I_{xx} = 4r^4 \int\limits_0^{\pi/2} \sin^2 \theta \, (1 - \sin^2 \theta) d\theta = 4r^4 \left[\int\limits_0^{\pi/2} \sin^2 \theta \, d\theta - \int\limits_0^{\pi/2} \sin^4 \theta \, d\theta \right]$

or $\qquad I_{xx} = 4r^4 \left[\dfrac{\pi}{4} - \dfrac{3\pi}{16} \right] = \dfrac{\pi r^4}{4} = \dfrac{\pi}{64} d^4$ ...(8.26)

where d is the diameter of the circle.

Second method (8.32 b)

The moment of inertia about x-axis can be easily obtained by first finding the moment of inertia about z-axis and then applying proposition 2 for the polar moment of inertia.

Consider an elementary concentric ring of thickness $d\rho$, at a distance ρ from the centre.

dA of the elementary ring $= 2\pi \rho \, d\rho$

$\therefore$ $\qquad I_p = I_{zz} = \Sigma \rho^2 \, dA = \int\limits_0^r \delta^2 . 2\pi \rho . d\rho = \dfrac{2\pi r^4}{4} = \dfrac{\pi}{32} d^4$ ...(8.27)

But $\qquad I_{zz} = I_{xx} + I_{yy} = 2 I_{xx}$, due to symmetry.

$\therefore$ $\qquad I_{xx} = \dfrac{I_{zz}}{2} = \dfrac{\pi}{64} d^4$ ...(8.28)

5. Hollow circular section

Consider a hollow circular section of external diameter D and internal diameter d.

Then, $\qquad I_{xx} = \dfrac{\pi}{64} (D^4 - d^4)$ ...(8.29)

The moment of inertia for other sections are given in Table 8.1.

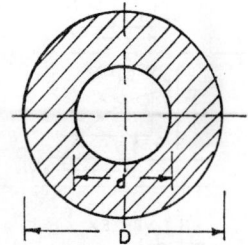

FIG. 8.33

8.10. RADIUS OF GYRATION

Radius of gyration is defined as the square root of moment of inertia divided by the area itself. Thus,

$$r_x = \sqrt{\dfrac{I_{xx}}{A}} \; ; \; r_y = \sqrt{\dfrac{I_{yy}}{A}}$$ ...(8.30)

where r_x and r_y are the radius of gyration with respect to x and y axes respectively. It has the unit of length. Radius of gyration of an area can be considered to be a distance from the axis at which the entire area could be concentrated and still have the same moment of inertia as the original area.

TABLE 8.1. PROPERTIES OF PLANE AREAS

PLANE AREAS	PROPERTIES
	Rectangle : $A = b \cdot d$; $\bar{x} = b/2$; $\bar{y} = d/2$ $I_x = \dfrac{1}{12} bd^3$; $I_y = \dfrac{1}{12} db^3$; $I_{xy} = 0$ $I_{x'} = \dfrac{1}{3} bd^3$; $I_{y'} = \dfrac{1}{3} db^3$; $I_{x'y'} = \dfrac{b^2 d^2}{4}$
	Triangle : $A = \dfrac{1}{2} bd$; $\bar{x} = \dfrac{(b + c)}{3}$; $\bar{y} = \dfrac{d}{3}$ $I_x = \dfrac{1}{36} bd^3$; $I_y = \dfrac{bd}{36}(b^2 - bc + c^2)$; $I_{xy} = \dfrac{bd^2}{72}(b - 2c)$ $I_{x'} = \dfrac{1}{12} bd^3$; $I_{y'} = \dfrac{bd}{12}(3b^2 - 3bc + c^2)$; $I_{x'y'} = \dfrac{bd^2}{24}(3b - 2c)$
	Trapezoid : $A = d \dfrac{(a + b)}{2}$; $\bar{y} = \dfrac{d}{3}\left(\dfrac{2a + b}{a + b}\right)$ $I_x = \dfrac{d^3(a^2 + 4ab + b^2)}{36(a + b)}$; $I_{x'} = \dfrac{d^3(3a + b)}{12}$
	Circle : $A = \dfrac{\pi}{4} d^2$; $\bar{y} = \dfrac{d}{2}$; $\bar{x} = 0$ $I_x = \dfrac{\pi}{64} d^4 = I_y$; $I_{xy} = 0$; $I_{x'} = \dfrac{5\pi}{64} d^4$
	Half Circle : $A = \dfrac{\pi r^2}{2}$; $\bar{y} = \dfrac{4r}{3\pi}$ $I_x = \dfrac{(9\pi^2 - 64) r^4}{72\pi} = 0.1098\, r^4$; $I_y = \dfrac{\pi r^4}{8}$; $I_{xy} = 0$; $I_{x'} = \dfrac{\pi r^4}{8}$
	Quarter Circle : $A = \dfrac{\pi r^2}{4}$; $\bar{x} = \bar{y} = \dfrac{4r}{3\pi}$ $I_x = I_y = \dfrac{(9\pi^2 - 64) r^4}{144\pi} = 0.05488\, r^4$; $I_{x'} = I_{y'} = \dfrac{\pi r^4}{16}$
	Parabolic Semi-Segment : $y = f(x) = h(1 - x^2/b^2)$; $A = \dfrac{2}{3} bd$; $\bar{x} = \dfrac{3}{8} b$; $\bar{y} = \dfrac{2}{5} d$ $I_x = \dfrac{16}{105} bd^3$; $I_y = \dfrac{2}{15} db^3$; $I_{xy} = \dfrac{1}{12} b^2 d^2$
	Semi-Segment of nth degree : $y = f(x) = h(1 - x^n/b^n)$, $n > 0$ $A = bd \left(\dfrac{n}{n + 1}\right)$; $\bar{x} = \dfrac{b(n + 1)}{2(n + 2)}$; $\bar{y} = \dfrac{dn}{2n + 1}$ $I_x = \dfrac{2\, bd^3 n^3}{(n + 1)(2n + 1)(3n + 1)}$; $I_y = \dfrac{db^3 n}{3(n + 3)}$
	Parabolic Spandrel : $y = f(x) = d(x^2/b^2)$ $A = (b \cdot d)/3$; $\bar{x} = 3b/4$; $\bar{y} = 3d/10$ $I_x = \dfrac{bd^3}{21}$; $I_y = \dfrac{db^3}{5}$; $I_{xy} = \dfrac{b^2 d^2}{12}$
	Spandrel of nth degree : $y = f(x) = d(x^n/b^n)$, $n > 0$ $A = \dfrac{bd}{n + 1}$; $\bar{x} = \dfrac{b(n + 1)}{(n + 2)}$; $\bar{y} = \dfrac{d(n + 1)}{2(2n + 1)}$ $I_x = \dfrac{bd^3}{3(3n + 1)}$; $I_y = \dfrac{db^3}{(n + 3)}$; $I_{xy} = \dfrac{b^2 d^2}{4(n + 1)}$

For a rectangular section, $I_{xx} = \dfrac{1}{12} bd^3$ and $I_{yy} = \dfrac{1}{12} db^3$

$$\therefore \qquad k_x = \sqrt{\dfrac{I_{xx}}{A}} = \sqrt{\dfrac{1}{12} \dfrac{bd^3}{b\,d}} = \dfrac{d}{\sqrt{12}} = \dfrac{d}{2\sqrt{3}}$$

and $\qquad k_y = \sqrt{\dfrac{I_{yy}}{A}} = \sqrt{\dfrac{1}{12} \dfrac{db^3}{bd}} = \dfrac{b}{\sqrt{12}} = \dfrac{b}{2\sqrt{3}} \qquad \qquad ...(8.31)$

For hollow rectangular section, C-section and I-section,

$$I_{xx} = \dfrac{1}{12}\,(BD^3 - bd^3)\,;\, A = BD - bd$$

$$\therefore \qquad k_x = \sqrt{\dfrac{BD^3 - bd^3}{12\,(Bd - bd)}} \qquad \qquad ...(8.27)$$

For a circular section, $I_{xx} = \dfrac{\pi}{64} d^4$ and $A = \dfrac{\pi}{4} d^2$

$$\therefore \qquad k_x = \sqrt{\dfrac{I_{xx}}{A}} = \sqrt{\dfrac{\pi}{64} d^4 \times \dfrac{4}{\pi d^2}} = \dfrac{d}{4} \qquad \qquad ...(8.32)$$

For a hollow circular section, $I_{xx} = \dfrac{\pi}{64}\,(D^4 - d^4)$ and $A = \dfrac{\pi}{4}\,(D^2 - d^2)$

$$\therefore \qquad k_x = \sqrt{\dfrac{I_{xx}}{A}} = \sqrt{\dfrac{\pi}{64}\,(D^4 - d^4) \times \dfrac{4}{\pi\,(D^2 - d^2)}} = \sqrt{\dfrac{D^2 + d^2}{16}} \qquad ...(8.33)$$

8.11. PRODUCTS OF INERTIA

The product of inertia of a plane area is defined by the following integral :

$$I_{xy} = \int xy\,dA \qquad \qquad ...(8.34)$$

In the above expression, each elementary area dA is multiplied by the product of the coordinates of the area; hence product of inertia may be positive, negative or zero. If the whole area lies in the first quadrant, the product of inertia will be positive since both x and y are positive for each element of area. Similarly, if the entire area lies in the third quadrant, both x and y will be negative and hence I_{xy} will be positive. However, if the entire area lies either in the second quadrant or in the fourth quadrant, I_{xy} will be negative.

If one axis is the axis of symmetry, the product of inertia of the area with respect to the pair of axes is zero. This is clear from Figs 8.34 (a) and 8.34 (b). Thus, the products of inertia with respect to the centroidal axes of a rectangle, hollow rectangle channel section, I-section and circular section are each zero.

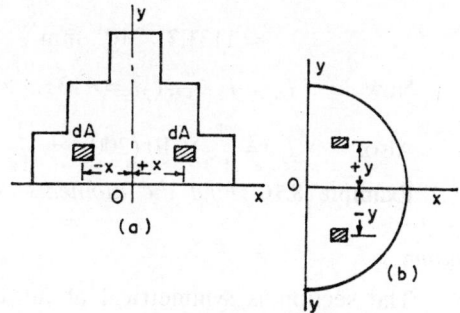

FIG. 8.34

Parallel axis theorem for product of inertia

Let us derive the parallel axis theorem of product of inertia, while referring to Fig. 8.28.

We get $\qquad I_{x_0 y_0} = \int (x + d_2)(y + d_1)\, dA$

or $\qquad\qquad I_{x_0 y_0} = \int xy\, dA + d_1 \int x\, dA + d_2 \int y\, dA + d_1 d_2 \int dA$

(where d_1 and d_2 are the coordinates of the centroid G)

In the above expression, $\int xy\, dA = I_{x_g y_g}$

$$\int x\, dA = 0 \ ; \ \int y\, dA = 0 \text{ and } \int dA = A$$

Hence $\qquad I_{x_0 y_0} = I_{x_g y_g} + A . d_1 d_2$ $\qquad\qquad\qquad$ ...(8.35)

Hence the product of inertia with respect to any pair of axes in its plane is equal to the product of inertia with respect to the parallel centroidal axes plus the product of the area and the coordinates of the centroid with respect to the pair of axes.

Example 8.9. *Find the moments of inertia I_{xx} and I_{yy} for a T-section shown in Fig. 8.35.*

Solution :

$$A = (150 \times 10) + (190 \times 10) = 3400 \text{ mm}^2$$

To find the value of $\bar{y}$, take moments of the individual areas about base AB.

Thus $\qquad A\bar{y} = A_1 y_1 + A_2 y_2$

or $\qquad 3400\,\bar{y} = (150 \times 10 \times 75) + (190 \times 10 \times 5)$

From which $\qquad \bar{y} = 35.88$ mm

Now $\qquad I_{AA} = \dfrac{1}{3} \times 10 \times 150^3 + \dfrac{1}{3} \times 190 \times 10^3$

$\qquad\qquad = 1131.3 \times 10^4 \text{ mm}^4$

FIG. 8.35

Now $\qquad I_{xx} = I_{AA} - A\bar{y}^2 = 1131.3 \times 10^4 - 3400\,(35.88)^2 = \mathbf{693.6 \times 10^4} \quad \mathbf{mm}^4$

Also, $\qquad I_{yy} = \dfrac{1}{12} \times 10\,(200)^3 + \dfrac{1}{12} \times 140\,(10^3) = \mathbf{667.8 \times 10^4\,mm^4}$

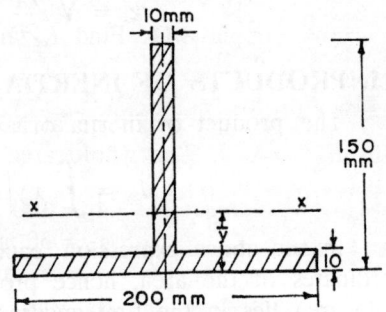

Example 8.10. *Find the moments of inertia I_{xx} and I_{yy} for a channel section shown in Fig. 8.36.*

Solution :

The section is symmetrical about the axis xx. Let the axis yy be at a distance $\bar{x}$ from the face AB. The whole area can be splitted into three parts.

(i) *Top flange* : $A_1 = 100 \times 12 = 1200 \text{ mm}^2$

$$x_1 = 100/2 = 50 \text{ mm, from face } AA.$$

(*ii*) **Bottom flange** : $\quad A_2 = 100 \times 12 = 1200 \text{ mm}^2$

$$x_2 = 100/2 = 50 \text{ mm, from face } AA.$$

(*iii*) **Web** : $\quad A_3 = (200 - 2 \times 12) \times 8 = 1408 \text{ mm}^2$

$$x_3 = 4 \text{ mm, from face } AA.$$

∴ Total area, $\quad A = A_1 + A_2 + A_3 = 1200 + 1200 + 1408$

$$= 3808 \text{ mm}^2$$

Taking moments about AB, we get

$$\bar{x} = \frac{A_1 x_1 + A_2 x_2 + A_3 x_3}{A_1 + A_2 + A_3}$$

or

$$\bar{x} = \frac{1200 \times 50 + 1200 \times 50 + 1408 \times 4}{3808}$$

$$= 32.99 \text{ mm}$$

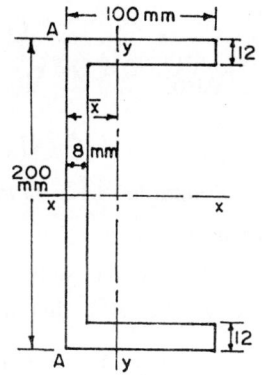

FIG. 8.36

Now $\quad I_{xx} = \dfrac{1}{12}(BD^3 - bd^3) = \dfrac{1}{12}(100 \times 200^3 - 92 \times 176^3) = \mathbf{2487 \times 10^4 \ mm^4}$

Also $\quad I_{AA} = 2\left(\dfrac{1}{3} \times 12 \times 100^3\right) + \dfrac{1}{3} \times 92 \times 8^3 = 801.6 \times 10^4 \text{ mm}^4$

∴ $\quad I_{yy} = I_{AA} - A\bar{x}^2 = 801.6 \times 10^4 - 3808(32.99)^2 = \mathbf{387 \times 10^4 \ mm^4}$

Example 8.11. Find I_{xx} and I_{yy} for an unequal angle section shown in Fig. 8.37.

Solution :

Let the x-x axis be at a distance $\bar{y}$ from face AC and the yy axis be at a distance $\bar{x}$ from face AB. The whole area can be splitted into two parts :

(*i*) **Flange** : $\quad A_1 = 100 \times 10 = 1000 \text{ mm}^2$

$\quad x_1 = 50 \text{ mm (from face } AB)$

$\quad y_1 = 5 \text{ mm (from face } AC)$

(*ii*) **Web** : $\quad A_2 = 140 \times 10 = 1400 \text{ mm}^2$

$\quad x_2 = 5 \text{ mm (from } AB)$

and $\quad y_2 = 80 \text{ mm (from } AC)$

Total area, $\quad A = A_1 + A_2 = 1000 + 1400$

$$= 2400 \text{ mm}^2$$

Taking moments about AB,

$$\bar{x} = \frac{(1000 \times 50) + (1400 \times 5)}{2400}$$

$$= 23.75 \text{ mm}$$

Taking moments about AC,

$$\bar{y} = \frac{(1000 \times 5) + (1400 \times 80)}{2400}$$

$$= 48.75 \text{ mm}$$

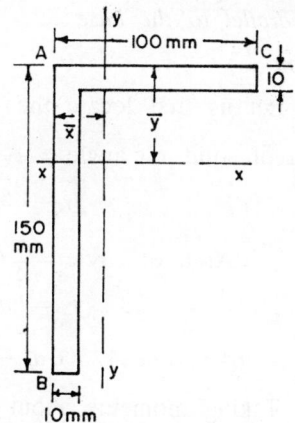

FIG. 8.37

Now $I_{AC} = \dfrac{1}{3} \times 10 \times 150^3 + \dfrac{1}{3} \times 90 \times 10^3 = 1128 \times 10^4 \, mm^4$

$\therefore$ $I_{xx} = I_{AC} - A\,\bar{y}^2 = 1128 \times 10^4 - 2400 \,(48.75)^2 = \mathbf{557.6 \times 10^4 \, mm^4}$

Also, $I_{AB} = \dfrac{1}{3} \times 10 \,(100)^3 + \dfrac{1}{3} \times 140 \,(10)^3 = 338 \times 10^4 \, mm^4$

$\therefore$ $I_{yy} = I_{AB} - A\,\bar{x}^2 = 338 \times 10^4 - 2400 \,(23.75)^2 = \mathbf{202.6 \times 10^6 \, mm^4}$

Example 8.12. *Find the moment of inertia for I-section shown in Fig. 8.38.*

Solution :

Here, y-axis will be symmetrical, as shown. Let x-axis be at a distance $\bar{y}$ above the base AA.

Total $A = (100 \times 30) + (250 \times 30) + (300 \times 50)$

$\qquad\qquad = 3000 + 7500 + 15000 = 25500 \, mm^2$

$$\bar{y} = \frac{3000 \times 315 + 7500 \times 175 + 15000 \times 25}{25500}$$

$\qquad\qquad = 103.24 \, mm$

$I_{AA} = \left(\dfrac{1}{3} \times 30 \times 300^3 \right) + \left(\dfrac{1}{3} \times 270 \times 50^3 \right)$

$\qquad\qquad + \left[\left(\dfrac{1}{12} \times 100 \times 30^3 \right) + \left(3000 \times 315^2 \right) \right]$

$\qquad\qquad = 57915 \times 10^4 \, mm^4$

Now $I_{xx} = I_{AB} - A\,\bar{y}^2 = 57915 \times 10^4 - 25500 \,(103.24)^2$

$\qquad\qquad = \mathbf{30736 \times 10^4 \, mm^4}$

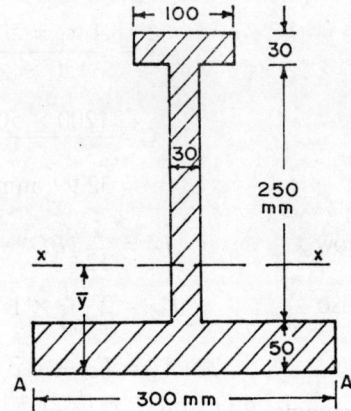

FIG. 8.38

Example 8.13. *Find the moment of inertia of a section shown in Fig. 8.39, about the centroidal axis parallel to the base.*

Solution :

Let us first locate the centroidal axis.

Area of solid rectangle $= A_1 = 2\,a \times 3\,a = 6\,a^2$

$\qquad\qquad y_1 = 1.5\,a$ (from AA)

$\qquad$ Area of circle $= \dfrac{\pi}{4} \,(1.5\,a)^2 = 1.767\,a^2$

$\qquad\qquad y_2 = 2\,a$ (from AA)

Total $A = A_1 - A_2 = 6\,a^2 - 1.767\,a^2 = 4.233\,a^2$

Taking moments about AA,

$$\bar{y} = \frac{6\,a^2 \,(1.5\,a) - 1.767\,a^2 \,(2\,a)}{(4.233\,a^2)} = 1.2913\,a$$

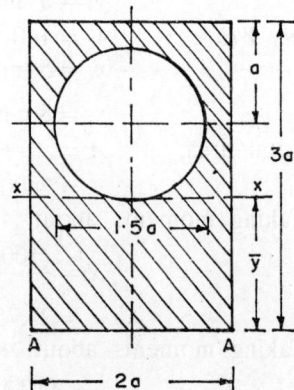

FIG. 8.39

$$I_{AA} = \frac{1}{3}(2a)(3a)^3 - \left[\frac{\pi}{64}(1.5a)^4 + \frac{\pi}{4}(1.5a)^2(2a)^2\right] = 10.683 a^4$$

$$\therefore \quad I_{xx} = I_{AA} - A\bar{y}^2 = 10.683 a^4 - 4.233 a^2 (1.2913 a)^2 = \mathbf{3.6279 a^4}$$

Example 8.14. *Find the moment of inertia of the shaded area shown in Fig. 8.40, about the axis AB.*

Solution :

Moment of inertia of the triangle, about its base AA

$$= I_1 = \frac{1}{12}(2b)(2b)^3 = 1.3333 b^4$$

Moment of inertia of outer half circle about its diameter

$$I_2 = \frac{1}{2}\frac{\pi}{64}(2b)^4 = 0.3927 b^4$$

Moment of inertia of the inner full circle, about AA

$$I_3 = \frac{\pi}{64}(b)^4 = 0.0491 b^4$$

$\therefore$ Moment of inertia of whole section,

$$I = I_1 + I_2 - I_3$$

$$= 1.3333 b^4 + 0.3927 b^4 - 0.0491 b^4$$

$$= \mathbf{1.6769 b^4}$$

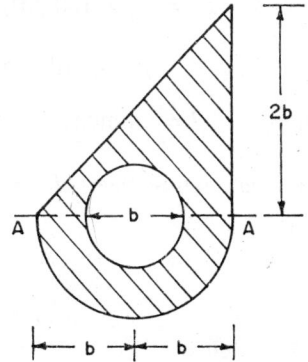

FIG. 8.40

Example 8.15. *Find the moment of inertia of the shaded area shown in Fig. 8.41, about the base BC and also about the centroidal axis parallel to the base.*

Solution :

Let the centroidal axis be at a distance $\bar{y}$ above BC

$$\text{Area of triangle} = A_1 = \frac{1}{2}(5a)(4.5a) = 11.25 a^2$$

and

$$y_1 = \frac{1}{3}(4.5a) = 1.5 a \text{ from } BC$$

Area of rectangular hole $= A_2 = a \times 1.5 a = 1.5 a^2$

and

$$y_2 = 1.5 a + 0.75 a = 2.25 a \text{ from } BC$$

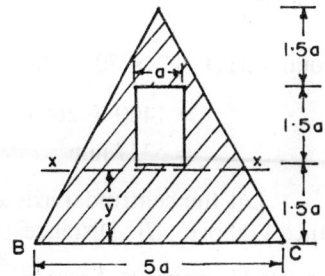

FIG. 8.41

$\therefore$ Total

$$A = A_1 - A_2 = 11.25 a^2 - 1.5 a = 9.75 a^2$$

$\therefore$

$$\bar{y} = \frac{11.25 a^2 \times 1.5 a - 1.5 a^2 \times 2.25 a}{9.75 a^2} = 1.3846 a$$

Now

$$I_{BC} = \frac{1}{12}(5a)(4.5a)^3 - \left[\frac{1}{12}(a)(1.5a)^3 + 1.5 a^2 (2.25 a)^2\right] = \mathbf{30.094 a^4}$$

Hence

$$I_{xx} = I_{BC} - A\bar{y}^2 = 30.094 a^4 - 9.75 a^2 (1.3846 a)^2 = \mathbf{11.402 a^4}$$

Example 8.16. *Fig. 8.42 shows the section of a beam. Find I_{xx} and I_{yy}.*

Solution :

$$I_{xx} = \frac{1}{12} \, 90 \, (120)^3 - \frac{\pi}{64} \, (80)^4$$

$$= 1296 \times 10^4 - 201 \times 10^4 = \mathbf{1095 \times 10^4 \, mm^4}$$

$$I_{yy} = \frac{1}{12} \times 120 \, (90)^3 - 2 \, I$$

$$= 729 \times 10^4 - 2 \, I$$

where $\quad I$ = moment of inertia of each semicircle about yy-axis

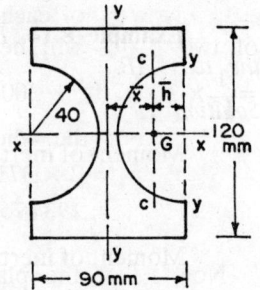

FIG. 8.42

For each semi-circle: $\quad I_{vv} = \frac{1}{2} \frac{\pi}{64} \, (80)^4 = 100.5 \times 10^4 \, mm^4$

$$A = \frac{\pi}{2} \, (40)^2 = 2513 \, mm^2 \, ; \, \overline{h} = \frac{4 \, r}{3 \, \pi} = \frac{4 \times 40}{3 \, \pi} = 17 \, mm$$

$\therefore \qquad I_{cc} = I_{vv} - A \, h^2 = 100.5 \times 10^4 - 2513 \, (17)^2 \approx 28 \times 10^4 \, mm^4$

Hence $\qquad I = I_{cc} + A \, \overline{x} = 28 \times 10^4 + 2513 \, (45 - 17)^2 = 225 \times 10^4 \, mm^4$

$\therefore \qquad I_{yy} = 729 \times 10^4 - 2 \, I = 729 \times 10^4 - 2 \times 225 \times 10^4 = \mathbf{279 \times 10^4 \, mm^4}$

Example 8.17. *Fig. 8.43 shows the section of a steel beam in the shape of an inverted semi-circular channel with flanges. Determine the position of the centroid and the second moment of the area of the section about the centroidal axis parallel to the base.*

Solution :

Total area $A = 2 \times 70 \times 10 + \dfrac{\pi}{2} \, (130^2 - 120^2)$

$$= 1400 + 26546 - 22619$$

$$= 5327 \, mm^2$$

Let the centroidal axis x-x be at a distance $\overline{y}$ above AB. Distance of centroid of a semicircle from its base $= \dfrac{4 \, r}{3 \, \pi} = 0.4244 \, r$

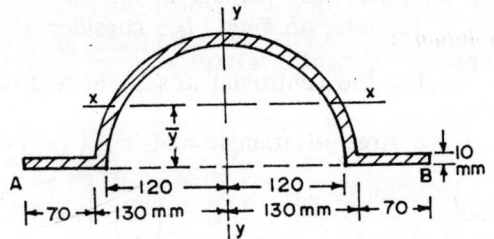

FIG. 8.43

$\therefore \qquad 5327 \, \overline{y} = 1400 \times 5 + 26546 \, (0.4244 \times 130) - 22619 \, (0.4244 \times 120)$

From which $\qquad \overline{y} = 60 \, mm$

$$I_{AB} = \frac{1}{3} \times 140 \times 10^3 + \frac{1}{2} \frac{\pi}{4} \, (130^4 - 120^4) = 3077 \times 10^4 \, mm^4$$

Now $\qquad I_{xx} = I_{AB} - A \, \overline{y}^2 = 3077 \times 10^4 - 5327 \, (60)^2 = \mathbf{1160 \times 10^4 \, mm^4}$

Example 8.18. *A compound section is built up of two $250 \times 125 \, mm \times 27.9 \, kg$ R.S.J. beams placed side by side with two 10 mm thick plates 300 mm wide welded to each top and bottom flange. Calculate the I_{xx} and I_{yy} of the section. For each $250 \times 125 \, mm \times 27.9 \, kg$ joist, area of section $A = 35.53 \, cm^2 \, I_{xx} = 3718 \, cm^4$ and $I_{yy} = 193.4 \, cm^4$.*

Solution : The I_{xx} of the built up section will be equal to I_{xx} for the two joists, plus the I_{xx} of the rectangular plates.

Now I_{xx} of each 300 mm × 20 mm rectangular area of two plates will be

$$= \frac{1}{12} \times 300 \,(20)^3 + 300 \times 20 \,(125 + 10)^2 = 10955 \times 10^4 \,\text{mm}^4$$

∴ For the whole built up section,

$$I_{xx} = 2 \times 3718 \times 10^4 + 2 \times 10955 \times 10^4$$
$$= \textbf{29346} \times \textbf{10}^4 \, \textbf{mm}^4$$

Now I_{yy} of the plates $= \frac{1}{12} \times 40 \,(300)^3 = 9000 \times 10^4 \,\text{mm}^4$

I_{yy} of the two joists $= 2 \,[193.4 \times 10^4 + 3553 \,(87.5)^2]$
$$= 5827 \times 10^4 \,\text{mm}^4$$

FIG. 8.44

∴ For the whole built up section, $I_{yy} = 9000 \times 10^4 + 5827 \times 10^4 = \textbf{14827} \times \textbf{10}^4 \, \textbf{mm}^4$

Example 8.19. *For a parabolic semi-segment shown in Fig. 8.45, determine (a) moments of inertia about x_0, y_0 axes, and (b) moments of inertia about the centroidal axes x_g, y_g.*
Solution :

As found in § 8.4 $A = \dfrac{2 \, b \, h}{3}$, $\bar{x} = \dfrac{3}{8} b$ and $\bar{y} = \dfrac{2 h}{5}$

$$I_{y0} = \int_0^b x^2 \cdot y \, dx = \int_0^b x^2 h \left(1 - \frac{x^2}{b^2}\right) dx = \frac{2}{15} h \, b^3 \quad \text{(Ans.)}$$

In order to find I_{x0}, consider a strip of thickness dy at distance y from the x-axis. The width of the strip

$$= x = b \left(1 - \frac{y}{h}\right)^{1/2}$$

∴ $I_{x0} = \displaystyle\int_0^h y^2 \cdot x \, dy$

$$= \int_0^h y^2 \cdot b \left(1 - \frac{y}{h}\right)^{1/2} dy$$

$$= \frac{16 \, b \, h^3}{105} \quad \text{(Ans)}$$

Now, from the parallel axis theorem,

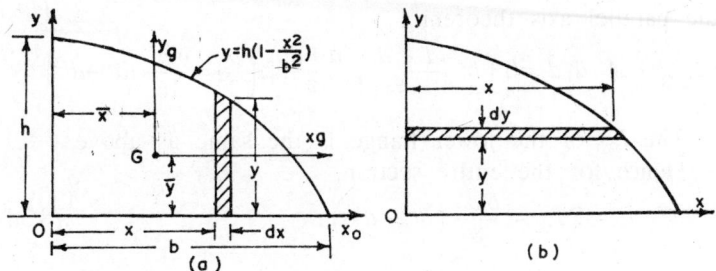

FIG. 8.45

$$I_{xg} = I_{xo} - A \, \bar{y}^2 = \frac{16 \, bh^3}{105} - \frac{2 \, b \, h}{3} \left(\frac{2h}{5}\right)^2 = \frac{8}{175} b \, h^3 \quad \text{(Ans.)}$$

and

$$I_{yg} = I_{yo} - A \, \bar{x}^2 = \frac{2}{15} b \, h^3 - \frac{2 \, b \, h}{3} \left(\frac{3}{8} b\right)^2 = \frac{19}{480} h \, b^3 \quad \text{(Ans.)}$$

Example 8.20. *Determine the product of inertia of a right angled triangle shown in Fig. 8.46, with respect to x and y axes, and (b) centroidal axes.*

Solution : Let us consider an elementary strip of thickness dy, at height y, parallel to the base. Width of strip, b_y
$= \dfrac{d-y}{d} b$.

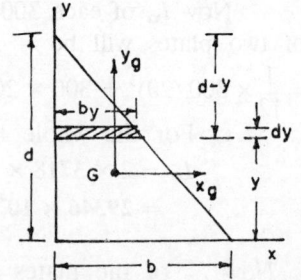

This elementary strip is a rectangle, and hence product of inertia of this strip with respect to its own centroidal axes, parallel to x-y axes is zero because of symmetry. Hence from the parallel axis theorem

$$dI_{xy} = (dA)\, d_1 d_2 = \left[\frac{(d-y)}{d} b \, dy \right] (y) \left[\frac{(d-y)}{2d} b \right]$$

$$= \frac{b^2}{2d^2} (d-y)^2 \, y \, dy$$

Hence for the whole triangle,

FIG. 8.46

$$I_{xy} = \int dI_{xy} = \frac{b^2}{2d^2} \int_0^d (d-y)^2 \, y \, dy = \frac{b^2 d^2}{24} \qquad \ldots(8.36)$$

In order to find the product of inertia with respect to the centroidal axes, let us again apply the parallel axis theorem.

$$I_{x_g y_g} = I_{xy} - A \cdot d_1 d_2 = \frac{b^2 d^2}{24} - \frac{bd}{2} \left(\frac{d}{3} \right) \left(\frac{b}{3} \right) = -\frac{b^2 d^2}{72} \qquad \ldots(8.37)$$

Example 8.21. *Determine the product of inertia of the Z- section about its centroidal axes.*

Solution : The Z-section consists of (*i*) one web rectangle of width $(b - b')$ and height d, and (*ii*) two flange rectangles, each of width b and height $(d - d')/2$.

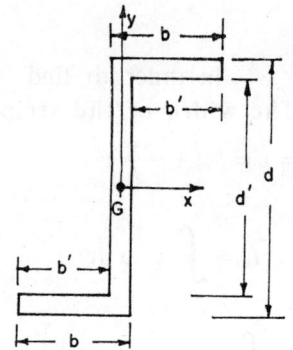

The web rectangle is symmetrical, and hence its product of inertia is zero. The product of inertia (I_{xyf}) of each flange is determined by the parallel axis theorem :

$$I_{xyf} = I_{x_g y_g} + A \cdot d_1 d_2 = 0 + b' \left(\frac{d-d'}{4} \right) \left(\frac{d+d'}{4} \right) \left(\frac{b}{2} \right) = \frac{b b'}{16} \left(d^2 - d'^2 \right)$$

The I_{xyf} of the lower flange is the same as above.
Hence for the entire section,

$$I_{xy} = 2 I_{xyf} = \frac{b b'}{8} \left(d^2 - d'^2 \right) \qquad \ldots(8.38)$$

FIG. 8.47

8.12. GRAPHICAL METHOD FOR FIRST AND SECOND MOMENTS OF AREA

Let A be the area, the moment of which is to be found about axis PQ.

Draw a line $P'Q'$ parallel to PQ at a distance h, and to the other side of the area. Take any strip BC of thickness dy, distant y from the axis PQ. Project B and C on line $P'Q'$, getting B' and C' correspondingly. Select any suitable pole O in PQ and join $B'O$ and $C'O$, cutting BC in B_1 and C_1 respectively. This procedure can be repeated for other strips of the area. After joining the points B_1, C_1 etc., a figure, such as the one shown hatched with single lines will be obtained. Let the area of the figure so obtained by A_1. The first moment of the area will be $A_1 \times h$. To prove this proposition, consider two similar triangles in Fig. 8.48. Thus, for strip BC, we have

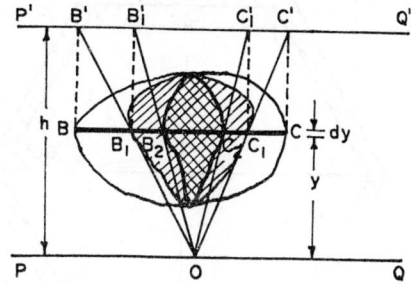

$$\frac{B_1C_1}{y} = \frac{B'C'}{h} \quad \text{or} \quad h.B_1C_1 = y.B'C' = y.BC$$

or $\quad h.B_1C_1.dy = y.BC.dy \quad \quad \text{...(1)}$

Now for the whole area,

$$A\bar{y} = \Sigma ydA = \Sigma h.dA_1 = h\Sigma dA_1 = hA_1 \text{...(2)}$$

This proves the proposition

The figure so obtained is also known as the *modulus figure*.

To find the second moment of area (*i.e.* moment of inertia), find the *first moment of area* of the modulus figure obtained above. The same procedure will be followed and an area such as shown by the double-hatched lines will be obtained. The second moment of the original area will be equal to $h^2.A_2$, where A_2 is the area of the figure so obtained.

FIG. 8.48

We have already proved that

$$A\bar{y} = A_1.h$$

Now $\quad\quad A\bar{y}^2 = A\bar{y}.\bar{y} = (A_1h)\bar{y} \quad\quad\quad \text{...(3)}$

But $\quad\quad A_1\bar{y} = hA_2 \quad \text{or} \quad A_1h\bar{y} = h^2A_2$

Hence from (3), we get $A\bar{y}^2 = h^2A_2$, which proves the proposition.

PROBLEMS

1. A square hole is punched out of a circular lamina, the diagonal of the square being the radius of the circle, as shown in Fig. 8.49. Find the position of the centroid of the remainder, if the radius of the circle is r.

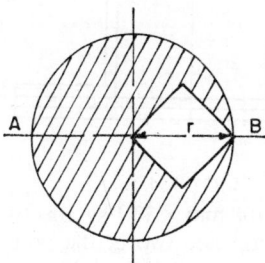

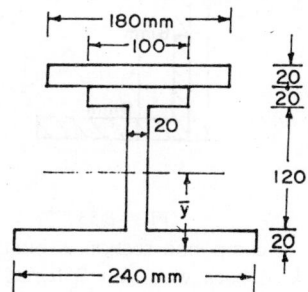

FIG. 8.49

FIG. 8.50

2. Find the position of centroid of the section shown in Fig. 8.50.

3. A tube of uniform thickness 2.5 mm has section in the shape of a regular hexagon as shown in Fig. 8.51, the outside hexagon having a side of 4 cm. Find the value of I_{xx} of the hollow hexagon.

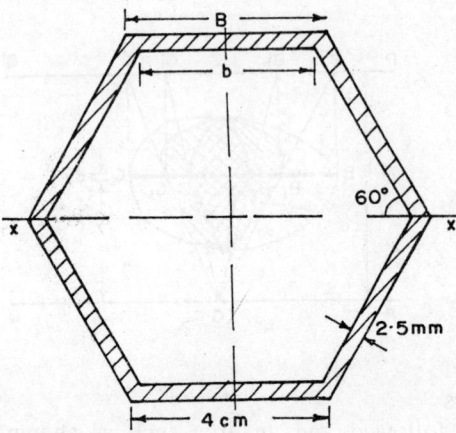

FIG. 8.51

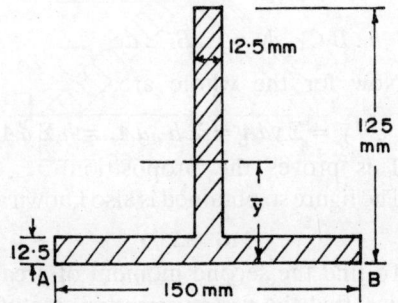

FIG. 8.52

4. Find the position of the centroid and calculate the I_{xx} and I_{yy} for a 150 mm × 12.5 mm × 125 mm section shown in Fig. 8.52.

5. The thickness of flanges and web of a 150 mm × 75 mm I.S. channel section are 9 mm and 6 mm respectively (Fig. 8.53). Find the position of the centroid and its I_{xx} and I_{yy}.

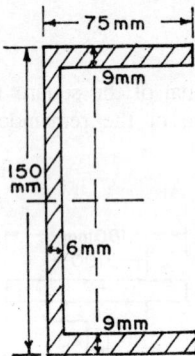

FIG. 8.53

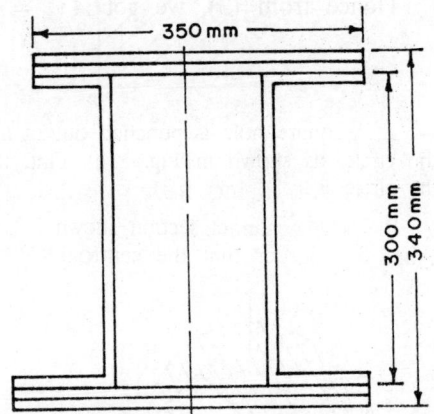

FIG. 8.54

6. A compound section is built up of two I.S.L. channels 300 × 100 mm × 33.1 kg spaced 150 mm apart back to back with four 350 mm × 1 cm plates welded two at the top and two at the bottom flange (Fig. 8.54). Find the I_{xx} and I_{yy} for the built-up section. For each channel 300 × 100 mm × 32.1 kg, $A = 42.11$ cm^2, $\bar{y} = 2.55$ cm, $I_{xx} = 6048$ cm^4 and $I_{yy} = 346.0$ cm^4.

7. A beam section is symmetrical about y-axis, as shown in Fig. 8.55. Determine I_{xx} and I_{AB}.

8. Fig. 8.56 shows a cast iron beam section. Determine I_{xx}.

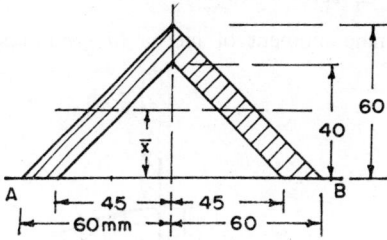

FIG. 8.55

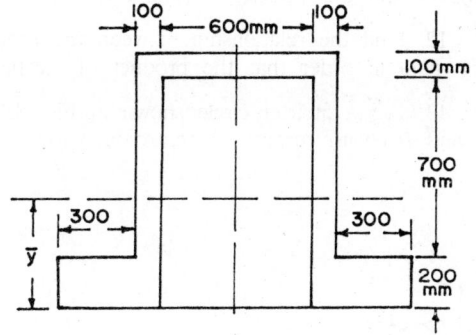

FIG. 8.56

9. One quarter of a square of side is removed, as shown in Fig. 8.57. What are the coordinates of the centroid of the remaining part ?

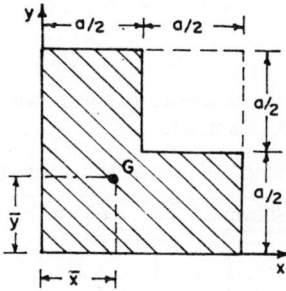

FIG. 8.57

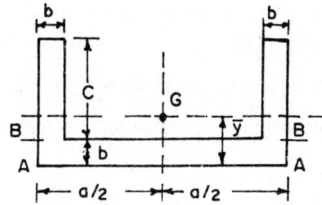

FIG. 8.58

10. For a channel section shown in Fig. 8.58, determine the relationship between the dimensions a, b, and c in order that the centroid G will be on BB.

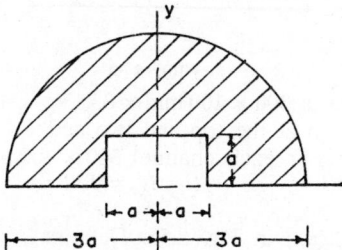

FIG. 8.59

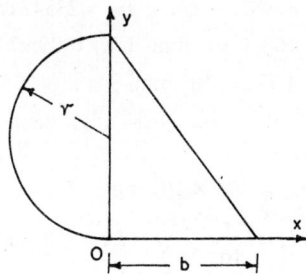

FIG. 8.60

11. A semicircular area of radius $3a$ has a rectangular cutout of dimension $2a \times a$ as shown in Fig. 8.59. Find the values of I_{xx} and I_{yy}.

12. Find the relationship between the radius r and the distance b for the composite area shown in Fig. 8.60 in order that the product of inertia I_{xy} will be zero.

13. For a quarter circle shown in Fig. 8.61, determine moment of inertia (a) with respect of xy axes, and (b) with respect to centroidal x-axis.

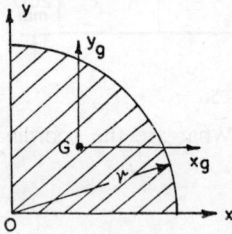

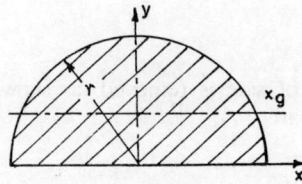

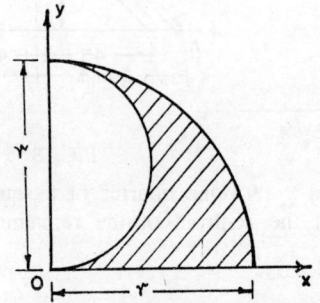

FIG. 8.61   FIG. 8.62   FIG. 8.63

14. For a semi circle shown in Fig. 8.62, determine moment of inertia (a) with with respect to xy axes, and (b) with respect to the centroidal axis parallel to the diameter.

15. For the semi-circle shown in Fig. 8.61, determine the product of inertia with respect of xy axes.

16. Determine the product of inertia of the shaded area shown in Fig. 8.63, with respect to x and y axes.

ANSWERS

1. $\bar{x} = \dfrac{r(\pi - 0.75)}{(\pi - 0.5)} = 0.9054\, r$ from A ;   2. 90 mm

3. $I_{xx} = 35.5 \times 10^4$ mm^4

4. $\bar{x} = 33.1$ mm ; $I_{xx} = 462 \times 10^4$ mm^4 ; $I_{yy} = 350.8 \times 10^4$ mm^4

5. $\bar{y} = 24.7$ mm ; $I_{xx} = 783 \times 10^4$ mm^4 ; $I_{yy} = 124 \times 10^4$ mm^4

6. $I_{xx} = 47982.66$ cm^4 ; $I_{yy} = 23542$ cm^4

7. $I_{AB} = 168 \times 10^4$ mm^4 ; $I_{xx} = 39.97 \times 10^4$ mm^4

8. $I_{xx} = 4.731 \times 10^4$ mm^4

9. $\bar{x} = \bar{y} = 5a/12$

10. $2c^2 = ab$

11. $I_x = I_y = 195 \times 10^4$ mm^4 ;   12. $b = 2r$

13.   (a) $I_x = I_y = \dfrac{\pi r^4}{16}$;   (b) $I_{xg} = 0.055\, r^4$;   14.   (a) $I_x = I_y = \dfrac{\pi r^4}{8}$;   (b) $I_{xg} = 0.11\, r^4$

15. $I_{xy} = \dfrac{r^4}{8}$;   16. $I_{xy} = \dfrac{r^4}{12}$

9

Shear Force and Bending Moment

9.1. INTRODUCTION : DEFINITIONS

1. Beam : Beam is a structural member that is acted upon by a system of external loads that act transverse to its axis. Thus, a beam differs from a bar in tension or a bar in compression, primarily because of the direction of loads acting on them. In addition to the point loads or uniformly distributed loads acting transverse to its axis, a beam may also loaded with force-couples acting in a plane passing through the axis of the bar.

2. Bending : Bending implies the deformation of a bar produced by loads perpendicular to its axis as well as force couples acting in a plane passing through the axis of the bar.

3. Plane Bending : Beams are planar structures because all of the loads act in the plane of the figure and all deflections occur in that same plane, which is called the *plane of bending*. If the plane of loading passes through one of the principal centroidal axes of inertia of the cross-section of the beam, the bending is said to be *plane* or *direct*.

4. Oblique bending : If, however, the plane of loading does not pass through one of the principal centroidal axes of inertia of the cross-section of the beam, the bending is called *oblique bending*.

9.2. TYPES OF LOADS (Fig 9.1)

1. Point Load : A point load, also called *concentrated load*, is the one which is considered to act at a point, as shown in Fig 9.1 (*a*). However, in actual practice, the load has to be distributed over some definite area, howsoever small it may be, because such knife-edge contacts are generally neither possible, nor desirable.

2. Distributed load : Distributed loads are those loads which act over some area, as shown in Fig. 9.1 (*b*). Such loads are measured by their *intensity* which is expressed by the force per unit distance along the axis of the beam.

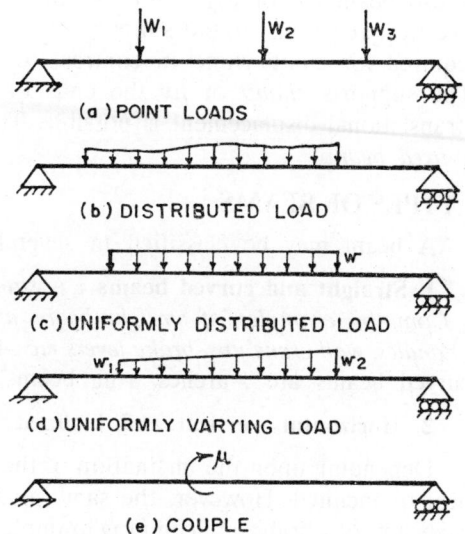

FIG. 9.1. VARIOUS TYPES OF LOADS

(281)

3. Uniformly distributed load : A uniformly distributed load, commonly abbreviated as U.D.L. is the one which has *uniform intensity*, say w kN/m, such as the one shown in Fig. 9.1 (*c*).

4. Uniformly varying load : A uniformly varying load is the one in which the load intensity varies from one end to the other, such as w_1 at A to w_2 at B, as shown in Fig. 9.1 (*d*). Such load is also known as *linearly varying load*. If $w_1 = 0$ and $w_2 = w$, the load loading is known as *triangularly distributed load*.

5. Couple : A beam may also be subjected to a couple μ, as shown in Fig. 9.1 (*e*).

9.3. TYPES OF SUPPORTS

A beam may have following types of supports.

1. Hinged support 2. Roller support and 3. Fixed support

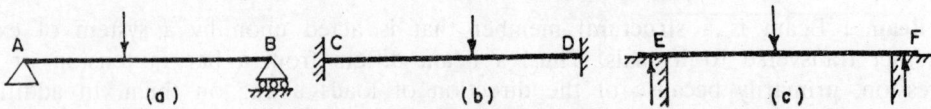

FIG. 9.2. TYPES OF SUPPORTS.

A *hinged support* is the one at which the beam is free to *rotate* but *translational displacement* is not possible. Such a support is shown at end A of Fig. 9.2 (*a*). If, however, the end of the beam is free to rotate about the hinge and also translational displacement along the plane of rolling, the support is known as the *roller support* or *movable hinged support*. Such a support is shown at the end B of the beam shown in Fig. 9.2 (*a*). The beam AB of Fig. 9.2 (*a*) (and also beam EF of Fig. 9.2 *c*) is known as the *simply supported beam* or a *simple beam*. The vertical reactions at the supports of a simple beam may act either upward or downward, as required for equilibrium. In contrast to these, Fig. 9.2 (*b*) shows fixed supports at C and D. The supports *clamp* or *fix* the ends of the beam, such that neither rotation is possible nor translational displacement is possible. The beam, such as beam CD of Fig 9.2 (*b*) is known as a *fixed beam*.

9.4. TYPES OF BEAMS

A beam may be classified in several ways, as shown below :

1. Straight and curved beams : A *straight beam* is the one whose axis is along a straight line. *Common examples of straight beam are : beams of building frames, electric poles, screw jack handles, wall crane jibs, brake levers etc. A curved beam* has its axis curved. Common examples of curved beams are : arches, ring beams, chain hooks, crane hooks etc.

2. Horizontal, vertical and inclined beams :

Depending upon the inclination of the axis of a straight beam, the beam may be horizontal vertical or inclined. However, the same analysis applies to all. The beams of a building frame or the beams of a bridge are common examples of horizontal beams, while a ladder is most-common example of an inclined beam. Electric poles, subjected to horizontal thrust of transmission lines, are the common examples of vertical beams.

3. Statically determinate and statically indeterminate beams :

A beam is said to be statically determinate if all its reaction components can be calculated by applying the three conditions of statical equilibrium, *i.e.* $\Sigma V = 0, \Sigma H = 0$ and $\Sigma M = 0$, where ΣV is the algebraic sum of all vertical forces, ΣH is the algebraic sum of all horizontal forces and ΣM is the algebraic sum of moments of all the forces about a point. However, when the number of unknown reaction components exceeds the static conditions of equilibrium the beam is said to be *statically indeterminate*.

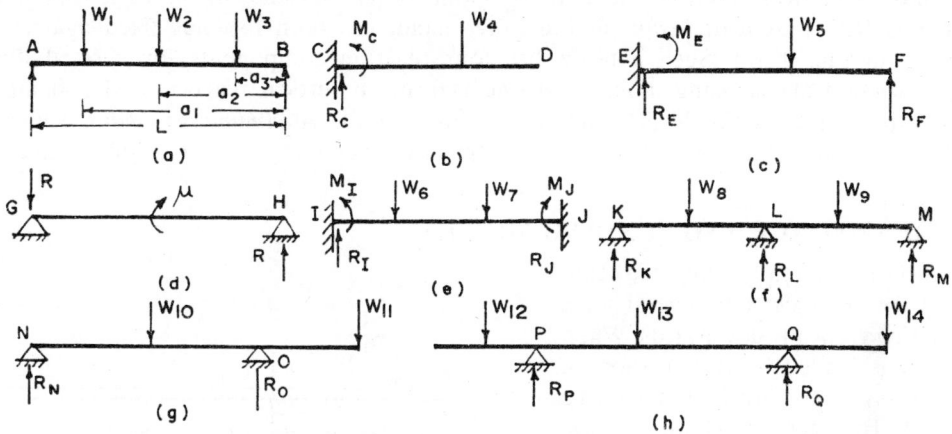

FIG. 9.3.

For vertical loading, there are only two conditions of statical equilibrium available (*i.e.* $\Sigma V = 0$ and $\Sigma M = 0$). Fig.9.3(a), 9.3(b), 9.3(d), 9.3(g), 9.3(h) are the examples of statically determinate beams, while Fig. 9.3(c), 9.3(e) and 9.3(f) are the examples of statically indeterminate beams. For such beams, we will have the *equations of displacements or deformations*, additional to the equations of statics, to determine the reactions at the supports.

In the beam of Fig. 9.3(a), there are two reaction components : R_A and R_B. Applying the condition $\Sigma V = 0$, we get

$$R_A + R_B = W_1 + W_2 + W_3 \qquad \qquad ...(i)$$

Also, taking moments of all the forces about B, we get

$$\Sigma M_B = 0 = R_A \times L - (W_1 a_1 + W_2 a_2 + W_3 a_3) \qquad \qquad ...(ii)$$

From these two equations, R_A and R_B can be found. Thus, the beam is *statically determinate*. In contrast to this, let us take the case of a beam of Fig. 9.3(c), where there are three reaction components : R_E, R_F and M_E. Only two conditions of statical equilibrium (*i.e.* $\Sigma V = 0$ and $\Sigma M = 0$) are available for vertical system of loading. Hence the beam is *statically indeterminate* to *first degree*. Similarly, the beam of Fig. 9.3(e) has four reaction components: R_I, R_J, M_I and M_J while only two conditions of statical equilibrium are available; hence the beam is statically indeterminate to *second degree* for vertical system of loading.

4. Simply supported beams, cantilever beams, fixed beams and continuous beams :

Based on *support conditions*, the beams can be (*i*) simply supported beams (*ii*) over hanging beams (*iii*) cantilever beams (*iv*) propped beams (*v*) Fixed beams and (*vi*) Continuous beams.

A *simply supported beam* or *freely supported beam*, shown in Fig. 9.2(*a*) and 9.3(*a*), is the one in which the reaction at the two ends are vertical. Such a beam is free to rotate at the ends, when it bends. Such a beam may have *overhang* either at one end (Fig. 9.3(*g*)) or at both the ends (Fig. 9.3 *h*). Such beams are known as *overhanging beams*. A *cantilever beam* or simply a *cantilever*, shown in Fig. 9.3 (*b*) has one end fixed while the other end is *free* having no support. However, if there is a support at the other end, it is known as a *propped cantilever* as shown in Fig. 9.3(*c*). Such a propped cantilever is a statically indeterminate beam. Both a cantilever as well as a propped cantilever has two reaction components at the fixed end : a vertical reaction and a fixing moment (*i.e.* R_C and M_C in Fig. 9.3*b* and R_E and M_E in Fig. 9.3 *c*). A *fixed beam* on the other hand, has both its ends fixed against rotation, as shown in Fig. 9.3(*e*). Such a beam has four reaction components for vertical loading : a vertical reaction and a fixing moment at one end and a vertical reaction and a fixing moment at the other end (*i.e.* R_I, M_I, R_J and M_J in Fig. 9.3 *e*). A *continuous beam*, shown in Fig. 9.3 (*f*) is the one which extends over more than two supports. It is a statically indeterminate beam.

9.5. SHEAR FORCE AND BENDING MOMENT

Consider a simply supported beam *AB* (Fig. 9.4 *a*) subjected to several point loads acting vertically downwards. When the beam is loaded by external forces, internal stresses and strains are produced. To determine these stresses, we must first find the *internal forces* and *internal couples* that act on the cross-sections of the beam. Let it be desired to study the internal stresses across the section at *X*, located at a distance *x* from the left hand support *A*. The free body diagram of the left hand portion is shown in Fig. 9.4(*b*). The net vertical force acting on the left hand portion is $R_A - W_1$. To keep the left hand portion in equilibrium, a *downward internal force* *F* of equal magnitude must act on the

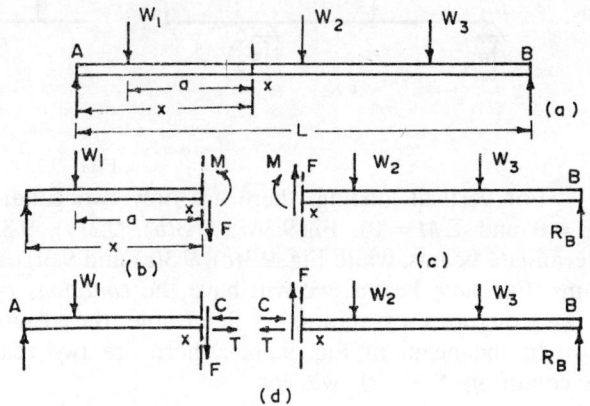

FIG. 9.4

face cut, as shown on Fig. 9.4(*b*). Similarly, the considering the equilibrium of the right hand portion *XB*, an *upward internal force* equal to $W_2 + W_3 - R_B$ must act at *X*, as shown in Fig. 9.4(*c*). Since the whole beam is in equilibrium, the two internal forces at *X*, shown in Fig. 9.4 (*b*) and (*c*) must be equal in magnitude but opposite in direction. Hence the section *X* is in the state of shear, and the force *F* is known as the *shear force*.

Hence a *shear force* (*F*) is defined as the algebraic sum of all the vertical forces, either to the left or to the right hand side of the section. Mathematically, it is defined by the equation:

$$F = (\Sigma V)_L \qquad \text{or} \qquad (\Sigma V)_R \qquad \qquad ...(9.1)$$

Again consider the equilibrium of the left hand portion *AX*, under the action of vertical forces R_A and W_1. These forces give rise to a moment $\left(R_A . x - W_1 a\right)$ in the clockwise direction at the section X. Since the portion is in equilibrium, an *internal moment* M must act as X, in the anticlockwise direction so that $\Sigma M = 0$. This *internal moment* is known as the *bending moment* which is generated by the resultant couple due to *internal stresses* that are distributed over the vertical section at X, as marked in Fig. 9.4(d). These internal stresses act in the horizontal direction and are compressive over certain depth and tensile over the remaining depth of the section. The nature of these stresses (known as bending stresses) will be discussed in the next chapter.

Hence a *bending moment* is defined as the algebraic sum of the moments of all the forces either to the left or to the right of a section. It is expressed mathematically as follows:

$$M = (\Sigma M)_L = (\Sigma M)_R \qquad ...(9.2)$$

SIGN CONVENTIONS

(a) For shear force : Shear force having an upward direction to the left hand side of a section or downward direction to the right hand side of the section will be taken as *positive* (Fig. 9.5 *ai*). Similarly, a negative S.F. will be one that has a downward direction to the left of the section or upward direction to the right of the section (Fig. 9.5 *aii*). In other words, a *clockwise shear will be taken as positive and an anticlockwise shear will be taken as negative.*

(b) For bending moment : A bending moment causing concavity upward will be taken as positive and will be called as sagging B.M. (Fig. 9.5 *bi*). Similarly, a B.M. causing convexity upwards will be taken as *negative* and will be called a hogging B.M.

The above sign conventions are known as *deformation sign convention*. It should be clearly noted that a different sign convention, called *static sign convention* is used in the equations of static equilibrium.

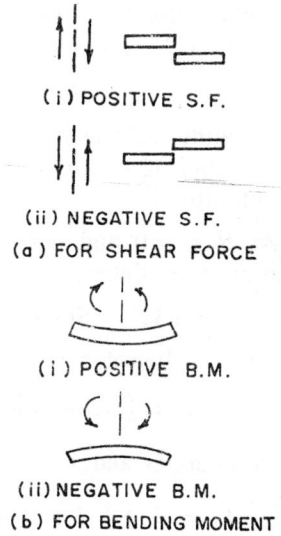

(i) POSITIVE S.F.

(ii) NEGATIVE S.F.
(a) FOR SHEAR FORCE

(i) POSITIVE B.M.

(ii) NEGATIVE B.M.
(b) FOR BENDING MOMENT

FIG. 9.5. SIGN CONVENTIONS

9.6. SHEAR FORCE AND BENDING MOMENT DIAGRAMS

A *shear force diagram* (S.F.D.) is a graphical representation of the variation of shear force (S.F.) along the length of the beam. The *ordinate* of the S.F.D. *at any section* gives the value of the S.F. *at that section*, due to the fixed load positions on the beam.

Similarly, bending moment diagram (B.M.D.) is a graphical representation of the variation of bending moment (B.M.) along the length of the beam. The *ordinate* of the B.M.D. *at any section* gives the value of the B.M. *at that section*, due to the fixed load positions on the beam.

We shall now take different cases of beams and loadings for plotting S.F.D. and B.M.D.

1. Cantilever : Point load at the end

S.F.D. : Consider a section at X, distance x from the cantilever end B. By definition, the S.F. at a section is the algebraic sum of all the forces to one side (say R.H. side) of the section.

Hence $\qquad F_x = +W$ ...(9.3)

The S.F. is positive since it is downward to the R.H. side of the section. In other words, clockwise shearing force is positive. Also, the above equation for S.F. indicates that S.F. does not depend on x and hence is constant along the length. The S.F.D. will therefore be rectangle of height W (Fig. 9.6 b). At the end A, the vertical reaction R_A will evidently be equal to W, acting upwards.

B.M.D. : Similarly, the bending moment at the section X is given by

$$M_x = -W.x \quad ...(9.4)$$

the minus sign being used because the B.M. is of hogging nature, bending the beam convex upwards.

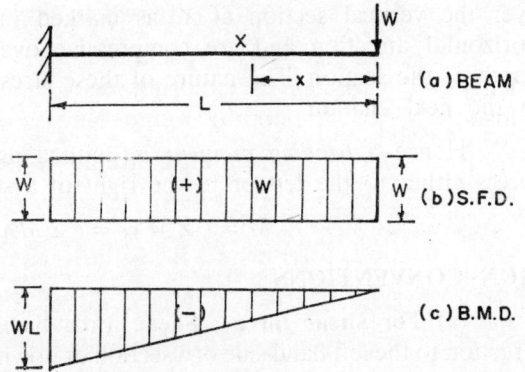

FIG. 9.6

At $B, x = 0$ and hence $M_B = 0$. Similarly, at end $A, x = L$ and hence $M_A = -W.L$. The variation is linear; hence the B.M.D. will be a triangle as shown in Fig. 9.6 (c).

2. Cantilever : Several point loads

S.F.D. : Between B and D,

$\qquad F_x = +2$ (constant)

Between D and C

$\qquad F_x = +2+2 = +4$ (constant)

Between C and A,

$\qquad F_x = +2+2+1 = +5$ (constant)

The S.F.D. will therefore consist of several rectangles, as shown in Fig. 9.7(b). At end A, reaction R_A will evidently be equal to $1 + 2 + 2 = 5$ kN ($\uparrow$).

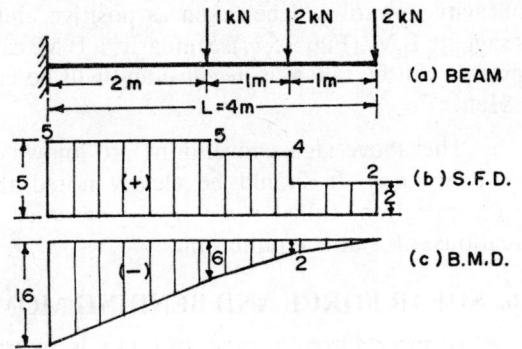

FIG. 9.7

Hence $\qquad F_A = R_A = +5$ kN.

B.M.D. : Between B and D, $M_x = -2x$ (linear variation)

At $B, x = 0$ and hence $M_B = 0$. At D, $x = 1$ m and hence $M_D = -2 \times 1 = -2$ kN-m

Between D and C, $M_x = -2x - 2(x-1)$, the variation being linear.

At D, $\qquad x = 1$ m, and hence $M_D = -2$.

At C, $\qquad x = 2$ m, and hence $M_C = -2 \times 2 - 2(2-1) = -6$ kN-m

Between C and A, $M_x = -2x - 2(x-1) - 1(x-2)$, variation being linear.

At C, $x = 2$ m. Hence $M_C = -6$ kN-m. At A, $x = 4$ m. Hence $M_A = -16$ kN-m. The B.M.D. is shown in Fig. 9.7(c).

3. Cantilever : U.D.L. over whole length

Fig. 9.8 (a) shows a cantilever AB of length L, subjected to uniformly distributed load (U.D.L.) of intensity w/unit length.

S.F.D. : At any section X, distant x from the free end B,

$$F_x = +wx \text{ (Linear)} \qquad ...(9.5)$$

At $x = 0$, $F_B = 0$; At $x = L$, $F_B = +wL$.

The *S.F.D.* will therefore consist of a triangle as shown in Fig. 9.8 (b). At A, $R_A = wL(\uparrow)$, which is equal to F_A.

FIG. 9.8

B.M.D. : $M_x = -wx\left(\dfrac{x}{2}\right) = -\dfrac{wx^2}{2}$ (parabolic variation) $\qquad ...(9.6)$

At $\qquad x = 0$, $M_B = 0$; At $x = L$, $M_A = -\dfrac{wL^2}{2}$.

The B.M.D. will be a parabola, as shown in Fig. 9.8(c).

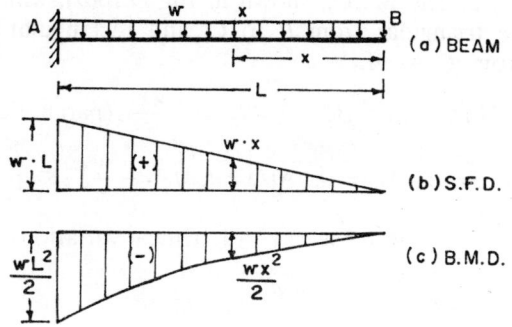

4. Cantilever : U.D.L. on part span from the support

S.F.D. : From B to C, there is no load. Hence

$$F_x = 0$$

$\therefore \quad F_B = 0$ and $F_C = 0$

From C to A, *measuring x from C,*

$$F_x = +w.x. \text{ (linear variation)}$$

At $x = 0$, $F_C = 0$; At A, $x = a$, $F_C = +wa$.

The S.F.D. is shown in Fig. 9.9 (b).

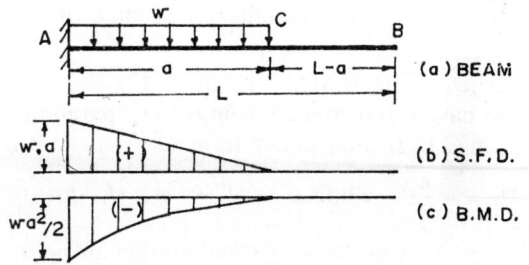

FIG. 9.9

B.M.D. : From B to C, B.M. will be zero. From C to A, measuring x from C $M_x = -\dfrac{wx^2}{2}$, giving $M_C = 0$ and $M_A = -\dfrac{wa^2}{2}$. The B.M.D. will therefore be a parabola from C to A, as shown in Fig. 9.9 (c).

5. Cantilever : U.D.L. on part span from the free end

S.F.D. : For BC, $\qquad F_x = +w.x$ (linear)

At $\quad x = 0$, $\qquad\qquad F_B = 0$; At $x = a$, $F_C = +w.a$

For CA, $F_x = +wa$ (constant)

Hence $F_C = +wa = F_A$

The S.F.D., shown in Fig. 9.10(b), will be triangular from B to C, and rectangular from C to A.

B.M.D. : For BC, $M_x = -\dfrac{wx^2}{2}$ (parabolic)

At $x=0$, $M_B = 0$; At $x=a$, $M_C = -\dfrac{wa^2}{2}$

For CA, $M_x = -wa\left(x-\dfrac{a}{2}\right)$ ...(linear variation)

At $x=a$, $M_C = -\dfrac{wa^2}{2}$ as before.

At $x=L$, $M_A = -wa\left(L-\dfrac{a}{2}\right)$

The B.M.D., shown in Fig. 9.10(c), will be parabolic from B to C and linear from C to A.

6. Cantilever : U.D.L. Somewhere on the beam

S.F.D. The S.F.D., shown in Fig. 9.11(b) will have zero ordinate from B to C, triangular from C to D and rectangular from D to A. Evidently $F_D = +wa = F_A$.

B.M.D. : The B.M.D. shown in Fig. 9.11(c), will have zero ordinate from B to C, parabolic from C to D, and linear from C to A. At D,

$M_D = -\dfrac{wa^2}{2}$, while at A, $M_A = -wa\left(L-b-\dfrac{a}{2}\right)$

7. Cantilever : Combination of point loads and U.D.L.

S.F.D. While plotting S.F.D, the same principle will be followed : S.F.D. will be rectangular between point load to point load and triangular for U.D.L. Thus, we find that $F_B = +3$ kN; $F_C = +4$ kN; $F_D(right)$ $= +6$ kN ; $F_D(left) = +8$ kN ; $F_E = +10$ kN; $F_F = +12$ kN$=F_A$.

B.M.D. : Similarly, B.M.D. will be triangular between point load and parabolic for U.D.L. portion. Thus, we find that $M_B = 0$; $M_C = -3$ kN-m ; $M_D = -8$ kN-m; $M_E = -17$ kN-m ; $M_F = -27$ kN-m and

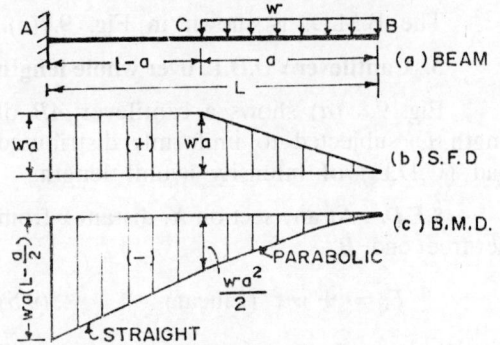

FIG. 9.10

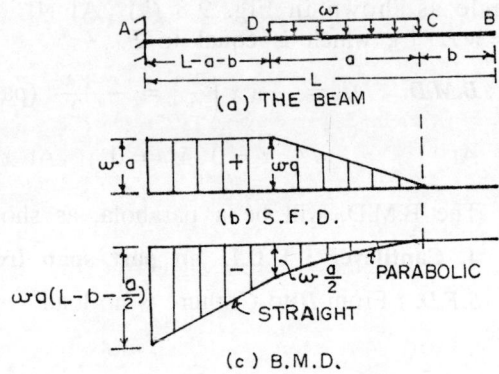

FIG. 9.11

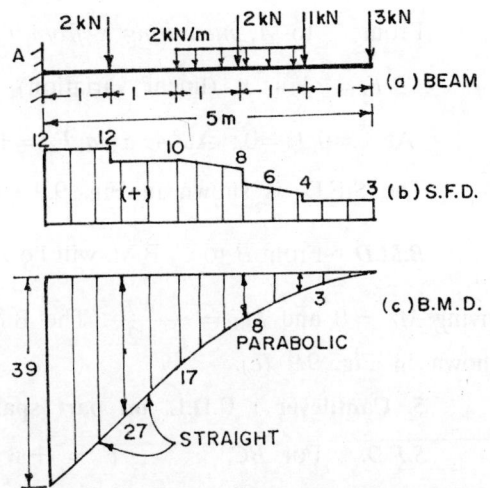

FIG. 9.12

$M_A = -39$ kN-m. The B.M.D. is shown in Fig. 9.12 (c).

8. Simply supported beam : Point load at the centre (Fig. 9.13 a)

S.F.D. : Due to symmetry,

$$R_A = R_B = \frac{W}{2} \ (\uparrow)$$

At section x, distant x from A,

$$F_x = +R_A = +\frac{W}{2} \text{ (constant)}$$

$$\therefore \quad F_A = +\frac{W}{2} \text{ and}$$

$$F_C \text{ (left)} = +\frac{W}{2}$$

For portion CB $\left(x > \dfrac{L}{2} \right)$,

$$F_x = +R_A - W$$
$$= +\frac{W}{2} - W = -\frac{W}{2} \text{ (constant)}$$

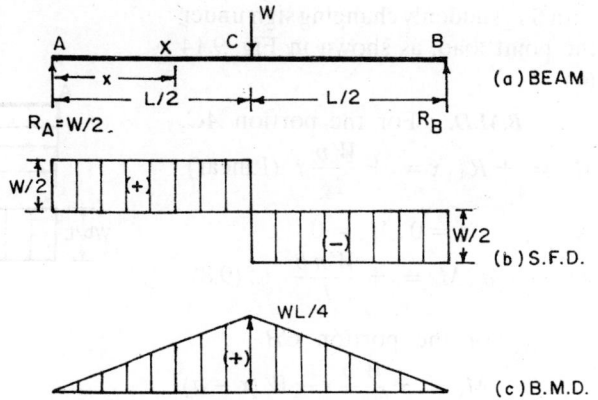

FIG. 9.13

Hence F_C (right) $= -\dfrac{W}{2}$ and $F_B = -\dfrac{W}{2}$. The S.F.D. will therefore consist of two rectangles, with S.F. suddenly changing sign at C (position of point load), as shown in Fig. 9.13 (b).

B.M.D. For portion AC, $M_x = R_A \cdot x = \dfrac{W}{2} \cdot x$ (Linear)

At $x = 0$, $\qquad M_A = 0$.   At $x = \dfrac{L}{2}, M_C = \dfrac{W}{2} \cdot \dfrac{L}{2} = \dfrac{WL}{4}$ \qquad ...(9.7)

For portion CB, $\qquad M_x = R_A \cdot x - W\left(x - \dfrac{L}{2} \right) = \dfrac{W}{2}x - W\left(x - \dfrac{L}{2} \right)$ ... (Linear)

At $x = L/2$, $\qquad M_C = +\dfrac{WL}{4}$, as before; At $x = L, M_B = \dfrac{WL}{2} - W\left(L - \dfrac{L}{2} \right) = 0$

The B.M.D. will therefore be a triangle, having maximum ordinate of $+\dfrac{WL}{4}$ under the point load, as shown in Fig. 9.13 (c).

9. Simply supported beam : Eccentric point load (Fig. 9.14 a)

Reactions : Taking moments about B, $R_A = \dfrac{Wb}{L} \ (\uparrow)$

Similarly, taking moments about A, $R_B = \dfrac{Wa}{L} \ (\uparrow)$

S.F.D. For portion AC,

$$F_x = +R_A = +\frac{Wb}{l} \text{ (constant from } A \text{ to } C)$$

For portion CB,

$$F_x = \frac{Wb}{L} - W = \frac{W(b-L)}{L} = -\frac{Wa}{L}$$

which is constant between C to B. The S.F.D., will therefore consist of two rectangles, with S.F. suddenly changing sign under the point load, as shown in Fig. 9.14 (b).

B.M.D. : For the portion AC,

$$M_x = + R_A \cdot x = + \frac{Wb}{L} x \quad \text{(Linear)}$$

At $\qquad x = 0 , M_A = 0.$

At $\quad x = a , M_C = + \dfrac{Wab}{L}$ ...(9.8)

For the portion CB,

$$M_x = + \frac{Wb}{L} x - W(x-a)$$

At $\qquad x = a , M_C = + \dfrac{Wab}{L}$

(as before).

At $x = L, M_B = Wb - W(L-a) = 0.$

The B.M.D., shown in Fig. 9.14

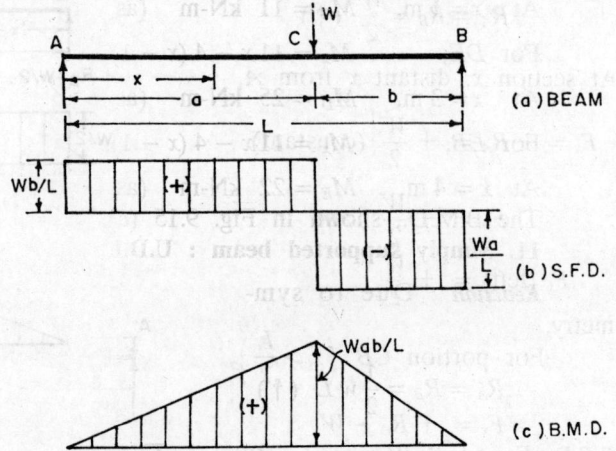

FIG. 9.14

(c), will be a triangle, having a maximum ordinate of $+\dfrac{Wab}{L}$ under the point load.

10. Simply supported beam : Several point loads (Fig. 9.15 a)

Reactions :

Taking moments about B,

$$R_A = \frac{1}{6}(8 \times 2 + 10 \times 3 + 4 \times 5)$$

$$= 11 \text{ kN } (\uparrow)$$

Hence

$R_B = (4 + 10 + 8) - 11 = 11 \text{ kN } (\uparrow)$

S.F.D. :

$F_A = + R_A = + 11 \text{ kN};$

$F_C = + 11 - 4 = + 7 \text{ kN}$

$F_D \text{ (left)} = + 11 - 4 = + 7 \text{ kN}$

$F_D(\text{right}) = + 11 - 4 - 10 = - 3 \text{ kN}$

$F_E = + 11 - 4 - 10 - 8 = - 11 \text{ kN}$

$\qquad = F_B$

The S.F.D. is shown in Fig. (b).

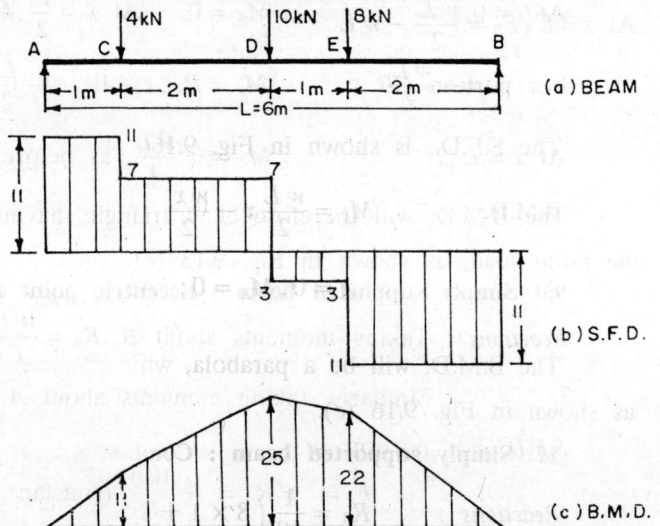

FIG. 9.15

B.M.D. For AC, $M_x = + R_A . x = + 11x$ (linear)

At $x = 0$, $M_A = 0$. At $x = 1$ m, $M_C = +11$ kN-m.

For CD, $M_x = 11x - 4(x - 1)$ ... linear variation

At $x = 1$ m, $M_C = 11$ kN-m (as before). At $x = 3$ m, $M_D = 25$ kN-m

For DE, $M_x = 11x - 4(x - 1) - 10(x - 3)$ ... linear variation.

At $x = 3$ m, $M_D = 25$ kN-m (as before). At $x = 4$ m, $M_E = 22$ kN-m

For EB, $M_x = 11x - 4(x - 1) - 10(x - 3) - 8(x - 4)$ ...linear variation

At $x = 4$ m, $M_E = 22$ kN-m (as before). At $x = 6$ m, $M_B = 0$

The B.M.D., shown in Fig. 9.15 (c), consists of a series of triangles and trapeziums.

11. Simply supported beam : U.D.L. over the whole span

Reaction : Due to symmetry,

$$R_A = R_B = \frac{1}{2}wL \ (\uparrow)$$

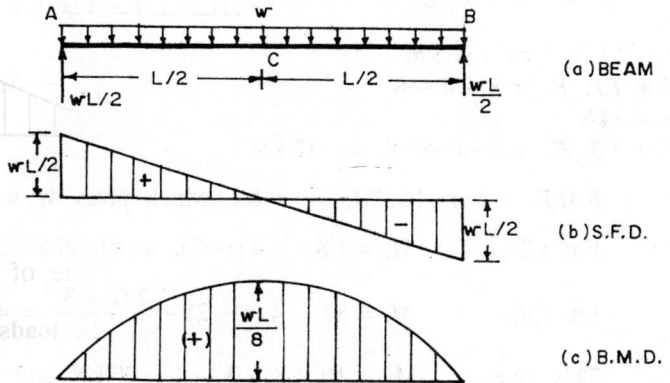

(a) BEAM

(b) S.F.D.

(c) B.M.D.

FIG. 9.16

S.F.D. $F_x = + R_A - w.x$

$= \dfrac{wL}{2} - w.x$ (linear variation)

At $x = 0$, $F_A = +\dfrac{wL}{2}$

At $x = \dfrac{L}{2}$, $F_C = \dfrac{wL}{2} - \dfrac{wL}{2} = 0$

At $x = L$, $F_B = \dfrac{wL}{2} - wL$

$= -\dfrac{wL}{2}$

The S.F.D., is shown in Fig. 9.16(b), with S.F. changing sign gradually, at mid-span.

B.M.D. $M_x = \dfrac{wL}{2}x - \dfrac{wx^2}{2}$ (parabolic variation)

At $x = 0$, $M_A = 0$; At $x = \dfrac{L}{2}$, $M_C = \dfrac{wL}{2} . \dfrac{L}{2} - \dfrac{w}{2}\left(\dfrac{L}{2}\right)^2 = +\dfrac{wL^2}{8}$ ...(9.9)

The B.M.D. will be a parabola, with a maximum ordinate of $+\dfrac{wL^2}{8}$ at the midspan, as shown in Fig. 9.16 (c).

12. Simply supported beam : Combination of loads

Reactions : $R_A = \dfrac{1}{10}\left(8 \times 1 + 2 \times 4 \times 5 + 4 \times 8\right) = 8$ kN

$\therefore$ $R_B = (8 + 8 + 4) - 8 = 12$ kN

S.F.D. For AC,

$$F = R_A + 8 \text{ kN}$$

For CD,

$$F = 8 - 4 = +4 \text{ kN}$$

For DE,

$$F_x = 8 - 4 - 2(x-3) = 10 - 2x$$

At $x = 3$ m,

$$F_D = 10 - 6 = 4 \text{ kN}$$

(as before)

At $x = 7$ m,

$$F_E = 10 - 2 \times 7 = -4 \text{ kN}.$$

The position of section having zero S.F. is given by

$$10 - 2x = 0 \text{ or } x = 5 \text{ m}$$

For EF, $F_x = 8 - 4 - 8$

$$= -4 \text{ kN}$$

For FB, $F_x = 8 - 4 - 8 - 8 = -12 \text{ kN}$

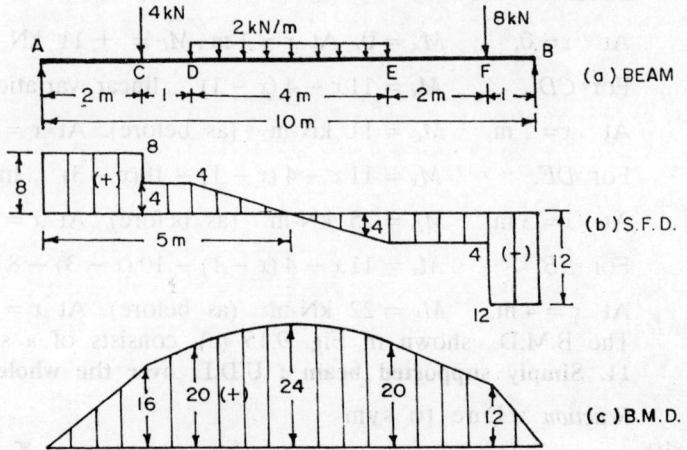

FIG. 9.17

B.M.D. : For AC, $M_x = +8x$, which gives $M_A = 0$ and $M_C = 8 \times 2 = +16$ kN-m

For CD, $\qquad M_x = +8x - 4(x-2)$, which gives $M_C = +16$ kN-m and $M_D = +20$ kN-m

For DE, $\qquad M_x = 8x - 4(x-2) - \dfrac{2(x-3)^2}{2} = 4x + 8 - (x^2 - 6x + 9) = 10x - x^2 - 1$

This gives $\qquad M_D = 10 \times 3 - 3^2 - 1 = 20$ kN and $M_E = 10 \times 7 - (7)^2 - 1 = 20$ kN-m

For max. B.M. in DE, $\dfrac{dM_x}{dx} = 0 = 10 - 2x$, which gives $x = 5$ m.

Hence B.M. is maximum which S.F. is zero.

$$M_{max} = 10 \times 5 - 5^2 - 1 = 24 \text{ kN-m}$$

The B.M.D. is parabolic between D and E.

For EF, $\qquad M_x = 8x - 4(x-2) - 2 \times 4(x-5) = 48 - 4x$

This gives $\qquad M_E = 48 - 4 \times 7 = 20$ kN-m (as before) and $M_F = 48 - 4 \times 9 = 12$ kN-m

For FB, $\qquad M_x = 8x - 4(x-2) - 2 \times 4(x-5) - 8(x-9) = 120 - 12x$

This gives $\qquad M_F = 120 - 12 \times 9 = 12$ kN-m (as before) and $M_B = 120 - 2 \times 10 = 0$

13. Simply supported beam with one side overhang : Point load

Reactions Taking moments about B,

$$R_A \times L = W \times a, \text{ Hence } R_A = \frac{Wa}{L} \ (\downarrow)$$

$$\therefore \qquad R_B = R_A + W = \frac{Wa}{L} + W = \frac{W(a+L)}{L} \ (\uparrow)$$

S.F.D. For AB,

$$F = -R_A = -\frac{Wa}{L}$$

For BC,

$$F = -\frac{Wa}{L} + \frac{W(a+L)}{L}$$

$$= +W$$

The S.F.D. is shown in Fig. 9.18 (b).

B.M.D. : For AB,

$$M_x = -\frac{Wa}{L}x$$

This gives

$$M_A = 0 \text{ and } M_B = -Wa$$

FIG. 9.18

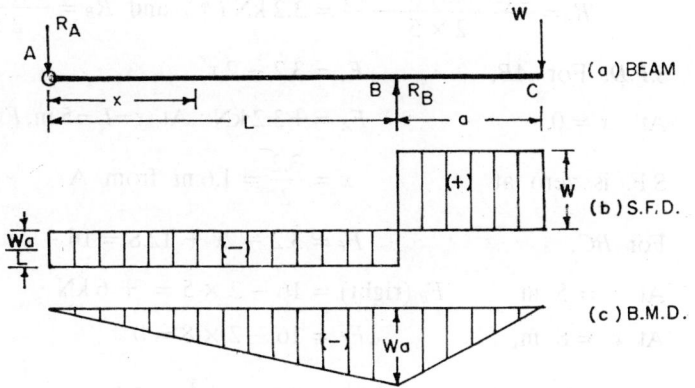

For BC, $\qquad M_x = -\frac{Wa}{L}x + \frac{W(a+L)}{L}(x-L)$

This gives $\qquad M_B = -Wa$ (as before)

and $\qquad M_C = -\frac{Wa}{L}(L+a) + \frac{W(a+L)}{L}(L+a-L) = 0$

The B.M.D. is shown in Fig. 9.18 (c).

14. Simply supported beam with one side overhang : U.D.L.

Reactions : Taking moments about A,

we get $\qquad R_B = \frac{w(L+a)^2}{2L}(\uparrow)$

Hence $\qquad R_A = w(L+a)$

$$-\frac{w(L+a)^2}{2L}$$

$$= \frac{w(L+a)(L-a)}{2L}(\uparrow)$$

If $L > a$, R_A will act upwards

If $L < a$, R_A will act downwards.

If $\qquad L = a$, $R_A = 0$

FIG. 9.19

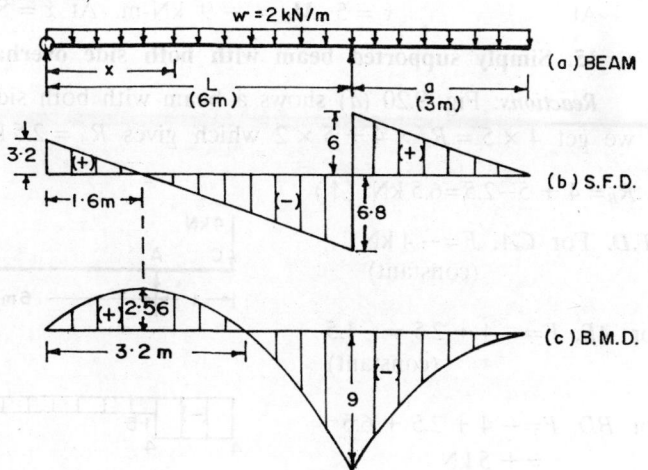

Hence for plotting S.F.D. and B.M.D., let us take a numerical example, taking

$$L = 5 \text{ m}, a = 3 \text{ m and } w = 2 \text{ kN/m}$$

$$\therefore \qquad R_A = \frac{2\,(5+3)\,(5-3)}{2\times 5} = 3.2 \text{ kN } (\uparrow) \text{ and } R_B = \frac{2\,(5+3)^2}{2\times 5} = 12.8 \text{ kN } (\uparrow)$$

S.F.D. For *AB*, $\qquad\qquad F_x = 3.2 - 2x$

At $\quad x = 0$, $\qquad\qquad F_A = +3.2$ kN; At $x = L = 5$ m, F_B (left) $= 3.2 - 2\times 5 = -6.8$ kN

S.F. is zero at $\qquad\qquad x = \dfrac{3.2}{2} = 1.6$ m from A

For *BC*, $\qquad\qquad\qquad F_x = 3.2 - 2x + 12.8 = 16 - 2x$

At $x = 5$ m $\qquad F_B$ (right) $= 16 - 2\times 5 = +6$ kN

At $x = 8$ m, $\qquad\qquad F_C = 16 - 2\times 8 = 0$

B.M.D. For *AB*, $\qquad\qquad M_x = 3.2x - \dfrac{2x^2}{2} = 3.2x - x^2$

At $\quad x = 0$, $\qquad\qquad M_A = 0$; At $x = 5$ m , $M_B = 3.2\times 5 - 5^2 = -9$ kN-m

For max. B.M., $\qquad\qquad \dfrac{dM_x}{dx} = 0 = 3.2 - 2x$, which gives $x = 1.6$ m

Hence the B.M. is maximum where S.F. is zero.

$$M_{\max} = 3.2 \times 1.6 - (1.6)^2 = +2.56 \text{ kN-m}$$

For B.M. to be zero in *AB*, we have $3.2x - x^2 = 0$ which gives $x = 3.2$ m

For *BC*, $\qquad M_x = 3.2x - \dfrac{2x^2}{2} + 12.8\,(x - 5) = 16x - x^2 - 64$

At $\qquad\qquad x = 5 , M_B = -9$ kN-m. At $x = 8$ m , $M_C = 128 - 64 - 64 = 0$

15. Simply supported beam with both side overhangs : Point loads

Reactions: Fig. 9.20 (*a*) shows a beam with both side overhangs. Taking moments about *B*, we get $4 \times 5 = R_A \times 4 + 5 \times 2$ which gives $R_A = 2.5$ kN $(\uparrow)$

$\therefore \ R_B = 4 + 5 - 2.5 = 6.5$ kN $(\uparrow)$

S.F.D. For *CA*, $F = -4$ kN
(constant)

For *AB*, $F = -4 + 2.5 = -1.5$
(constant)

For *BD*, $F = -4 + 2.5 + 6.5$
$= +5$ kN

Hence F_B (left) $= -1.5$ kN

and F_B (right) $= +5$ kN.

Thus S.F. changes sign at *B*.

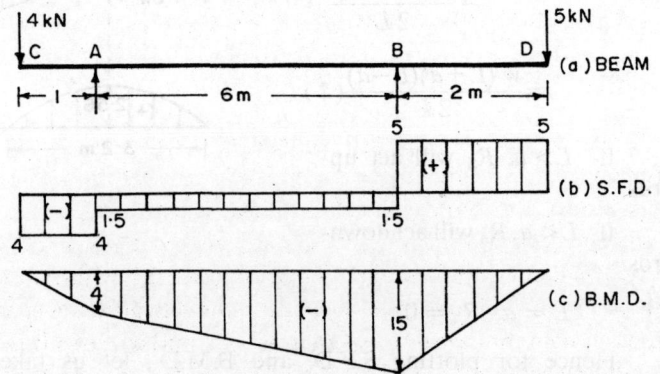

FIG. 9.20

B.M.D. For CA, $M_x = -4x$ which gives $M_C = 0$ and $M_A = -4$ kN-m

For AB, $M_x = -4x + 2.5(x-1) = -1.5x - 2.5$ (linear variation)

This gives $M_A = -4$ kN-m (as before) and $M_B = -1.5 \times 5 - 2.5 = -10$ kN-m

For BD, $M_x = -4x + 2.5(x-1) + 6.5(x-5) = 5x - 35$ (linear)

This gives $M_B = -10$ kN-m (as before) and $M_D = 5 \times 7 - 35 = 0$

The B.M.D. is shown in Fig. 9.20(a), from which we find that M_{max} is at B, *where S.F. changes sign.*

16. Simply supported beam with both side overhangs : U.D.L.

Reactions Let both overhangs be equal.

Then $R_A = R_B = \dfrac{wL}{2}$ ($\uparrow$)

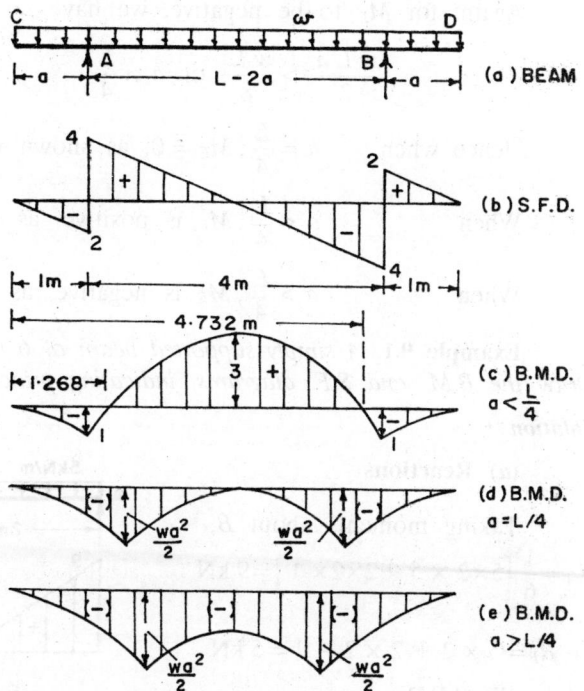

Let us take a numerical example, taking $a = 1$ m, $L = 6$ m and $w = 2$ kN/m.

Then $R_A = R_B = \dfrac{2 \times 6}{2} = 6$ kN

S.F.D. : For CA, $F_x = -2x$ which gives :
$F_C = 0$ and F_A (left) $= -2 \times 1 = -2$ kN.

For AB, $F_x = -2x + 6$ which gives F_A (right) $= +4$ and F_B (left) $= -4$ kN

S.F. is zero at $x = 3$ m from C.

For BD $F_x = -2x + 6 + 6$ which gives R_B (right) $= +2$ kN and $F_D = 0$.

B.M.D. : For CA,

$M_x = -\dfrac{2x^2}{2} = -x^2$

which gives $M_C = 0$ and $M_A = -1$ kN-m

FIG. 9.21

For AB, $M_x = \dfrac{-2x^2}{2} + 6(x-1) = -x^2 + 6x - 6$

B.M. will be maximum at $x = 3$ m where S.F. is zero

$\therefore$ $M_{max} = -3^2 + 6 \times 3 - 6 = +3$ kN-m.

This shows that B.M. changes sign from -1 kN-m at A to $+3$ kN-m at $x = 3$ m (*i.e.* at midspan). B.M. is zero at $-x^2 + 6x - 6 = 0$ which gives $x = 1.268$ m and 4.732 m

Also, M_B (at $x = 5$ m) $= -(5)^2 + 6 \times 5 - 6 = -1$ kN-m

The complete B.M.D. is shown in Fig. 9.21 (c). Here, we had taken $a = 1$ m and $L = 6$ m , and hence a was less than $L/4$. However, the general shape of B.M.D. will depend upon the ratio of L and a. Taking a general case, we have

$$M_E = -\frac{wL}{2} \cdot \frac{L}{4} + \frac{wL}{2}\left(\frac{L}{2} - a\right) = -\frac{wL^2}{8} + \frac{wL^2}{4} - \frac{wLa}{2} = \frac{wL^2}{8} - \frac{wLa}{2}$$

For M_E to be zero, we have $\dfrac{wLa}{2} = \dfrac{wL^2}{8}$ which gives $a = \dfrac{L}{4}$

Hence if $a = L/4$, M_E will be zero as shown in Fig. 9.21 (d).

Again, for M_E to be negative, we have

$$\frac{wLa}{2} > \frac{wL^2}{8} \text{ or } a > \frac{L}{4}$$

Hence when $a = \dfrac{L}{4}, M_E = 0$, as shown in Fig. 9.21 (d).

When $a < \dfrac{L}{4}, M_E$ is positive, as shown in Fig. 9.21 (c).

When $a > \dfrac{L}{4}, M_E$ is negative, as shown in Fig. 9.21 (e).

Example 9.1. *A simply supported beam of 6 m span is loaded as shown in Fig. 9.22 (a). Draw the B.M. and S.F. diagrams, indicating principal values.*

Solution :

(a) Reactions

Taking moments about B,

$R_A = \dfrac{1}{6}\left[5 \times 2 \times 5 + 2 \times 2 \times 1\right] = 9$ kN

$\therefore\ R_B = 5 \times 2 + 2 \times 2 - 9 = 5$ kN

(ii) S.F.D.

For **AC** $F_x = 9 - 5x$

At A, $x = 0$; $F_A = 9$ kN
At C, $x = 2$ m;
        $F_c = 9 - 5 \times 2 = -1$ kN

Hence S.F. change sign in AC,
its value being zero at $x = 9/5 = 1.8$ m from A.

For **CD**, $F_x = 9 - 5 \times 2 = -1$ (constant)

$\therefore$ $F_C = -1$ and $F_D = -1$ kN

For **DB**, $F_x = 9 - 2 \times 5 - 2(x - 4)$

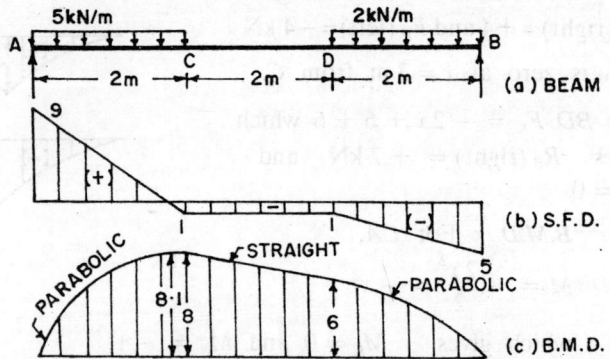

FIG. 9.22

At $x = 4$, $F_D = 9 - 10 - 2(4 - 4) = -1$ kN (as before)

At $x = 6$ m, $F_B = 9 - 10 - 2(6 - 4) = -5$ kN $= R_B$

The S.F.D. is shown in Fig 9.22 (b).

(c) B.M.D. : For AC, $M_x = 9x - 5\dfrac{x^2}{2} = 9x - 2.5x^2$ (parabolic)

At $x = 0$, $M_A = 0$;   At $x = 2, M_C = 9 \times 2 - 2.5(2)^2 = +8$ kN-m

For maxima, $\dfrac{dM_x}{dx} = 0 = 9 - 5x$, which gives $x = 1.8$ m. Hence here again we find that B.M. is maximum where S.F. is zero.

$$M_{max} = 9 \times 1.8 - 2.5(1.8)^2 = 8.1 \text{ kN-m}$$

For CD $M_x = 9x - 5 \times 2(x - 1) = 10 - x$ (linear)

At $x = 2$, $M_C = 10 - 2 = 8$ kN-m (as before). At $x = 4$ m, $M_D = 10 - 4 = 6$ kN-m

For DB $M_x = 9x - 5 \times 2(x - 1) - \dfrac{2(x - 4)^2}{2} = 10 - x - (x - 4)^2$...(Parabolic)

At $x = 4$, $M_D = 6$ kN-m (as before). At $x = 6$ m, $M_B = 10 - 6 = (6 - 4)^2 = 0$

The complete B.M.D is shown in Fig 9.22 (c)

Example 9.2. *A simply supported beam of 9 m span is loaded as shown in Fig. 9.23 (a). Draw the B.M. and S.F. diagrams indicating principal values.*

Solution :

  (a) Reactions :

$R_A = \dfrac{1}{9}(30 \times 7 + 12 \times 4 \times 2) = 34$ kN($\uparrow$)

$\therefore\ R_B = 30 + 12 \times 4 - 34 = 44$ kN($\uparrow$)

  (b) S.F.D.

For AC $F_x = 34$ kN (constant)

  $\therefore\ F_A = 34$ kN ; $F_C = 34$ kN

For CD : $F_x = 34 - 30 = 4$ kN

For DB $F_x = 34 - 30 - 12(x - 5)$

    $= 64 - 12x$ ... linear

At $x = 5$ m , $F_D = 64 - 60 = 4$ kN

       (as before)

At $x = 9$ m , $F_B = 64 - 12 \times 9$

    $= -44$ kN

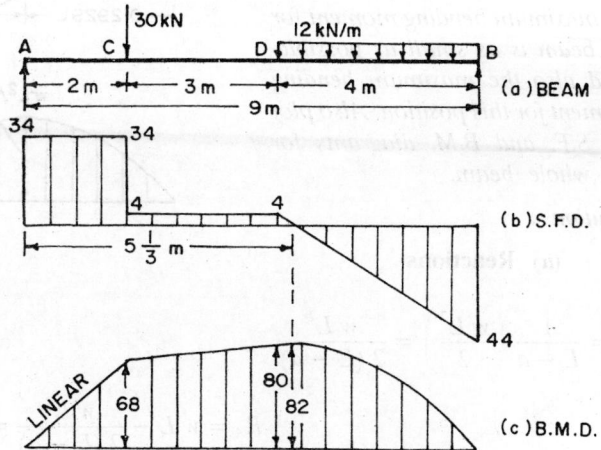

FIG. 9.23

Hence S.F. changes sign in DB, and is zero at $x = 64/12 = 5\frac{1}{3}$ from A.

The S.F.D. is shown in Fig. 9.23 (b).

(c) B.M.D. For AC, $M_x = 34x$ ... (linear variation)

At $\qquad$ $x = 0\,,\, M_A = 0\,;$ At $x = 2\ \text{m}\,,\, M_C = 34 \times 2 = 68$ kN-m

For CD : $\qquad$ $M_x = 34\,x - 30\,(x - 2) = 4\,x + 60$ (linear)

At $x = 2,$ $\qquad$ $M_C = 4 \times 2 + 60 = 68$ kN-m;

At $x = 5\ \text{m}\,,$ $\qquad$ $M_D = 4 \times 5 + 60 = 80$ kN-m

For DB : $\qquad$ $M_x = 34\,x - 30\,(x - 2) + \dfrac{12\,(x - 5)^2}{2} = 4\,x + 60 + 6\,(x - 5)^2\ ...\text{Parabolic}$

At $\qquad$ $x = 5\ \text{m}\,,\, M_D = 4 \times 5 + 60 = 80$ kN-m as before.

At $\qquad$ $x = 9\ \text{m}\,,\, M_B = 4 \times 9 + 60 + 6\,(9 - 5)^2 = 0$

B.M. is maximum at $x = 5\dfrac{1}{3}$ m where S.F. is zero.

$\therefore$ $\qquad\qquad$ $M_{\max} = 4 \times 5\dfrac{1}{3} + 60 + 6\left(5\dfrac{1}{3} - 5\right)^2 = 82$ kN-m

The complete B.M.D. is shown in Fig. 9.23 (c).

Example 9.3. *A beam of length L carries a uniformly distributed load w per unit run on its whole length. It has one support at its left end and the other support is at a distance a from the other end. Find the value of a so that the maximum bending moment for the beam is as small as possible. Find also the maximum bending moment for this position. Also plot the S.F. and B.M. diagrams for the whole beam.*

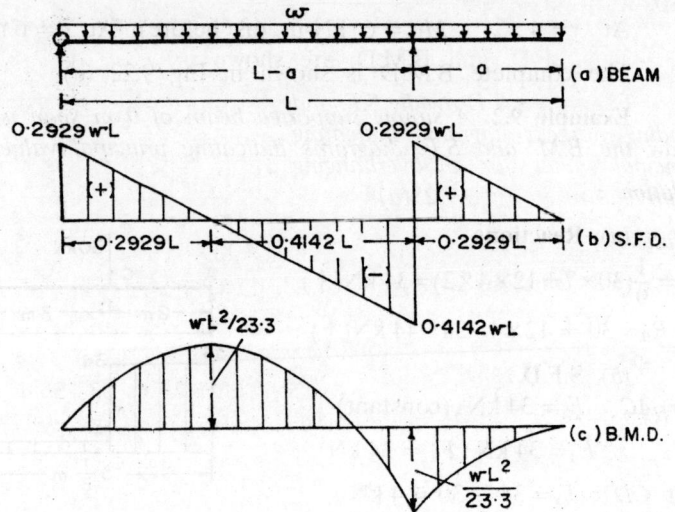

FIG. 9.24

Solution :

(a) **Reactions**

$$R_B = \frac{1}{L - a}\left(\frac{w L^2}{2}\right) = \frac{w L^2}{2\,(L - a)}$$

$\therefore$ $\qquad\qquad$ $R_A = w L - \dfrac{w L^2}{2\,(L - a)} = \dfrac{w L\,(L - 2\,a)}{2\,(L - a)}$

Maximum +ve B.M. (or sagging B.M.) occurs in AB, at a section where S.F. is zero. Hence at a section distant x from A, we have

$$F_x = \frac{w L\,(L - 2\,a)}{2\,(L - a)} - w x$$

Putting this to zero, we get

$$x = \frac{L\,(L - 2\,a)}{2\,(L - a)}$$

$$\therefore \qquad M_{max} = \frac{w\,L\,(L - 2\,a)}{2\,(L - a)} \times \frac{L\,(L - 2\,a)}{2\,(L - a)} - \frac{w}{2}\left[\frac{L\,(L - 2\,a)}{2\,(L - a)}\right]^2$$

$$= \frac{wL^2}{8}\left(\frac{L - 2a}{L - a}\right)^2$$

Also, maximum hogging B.M. (at B) $= \dfrac{w\,a^2}{2}$

For the conditions that maximum bending moment shall be as small as possible, the hogging B.M. at B should be numerically equal to the maximum sagging B.M. in AB.

$$\therefore \qquad \frac{w\,L^2}{8}\left(\frac{L - 2\,a}{L - a}\right)^2 = \frac{w\,a^2}{2} \qquad \text{or} \qquad L\left(\frac{L - 2\,a}{L - a}\right) = 2\,a$$

or $\qquad 2\,a^2 - 4\,a\,L + L^2 = 0$. From which $a = 0.2929\,L$

For this value of a, we get $R_A = 0.2929\,wL \qquad$ and $\qquad R_B = 0.7071\,w\,L$, $x = 0.2929\,L$

Also, $M_{max} = \dfrac{w\,a^2}{2} = \dfrac{w\,(0.2929\,L)^2}{2} = \dfrac{w\,L^2}{23.3}$

The S.F.D. and B.M.D. are shown in Fig. 9.24(*b*) and (*c*) respectively.

Example 9.4. *Draw the S.F. and bending moment diagrams, indicating principal values, for an overhanging beam shown in Fig. 9.25(a).*

Solution :

(a) Reactions

$$R_A = \frac{1}{4}\,(20 \times 2 \times 3 - 6 \times 2) = 27 \text{ kN } (\uparrow)$$

$$\therefore \quad R_B = 20 \times 2 + 6 - 27 = 19 \text{ kN}(\uparrow)$$

(b) S.F.D.

For AC : $F_x = 27 - 20\,x$ (linear)

At $\;x = 0 , F_A = 27$;

At $x = 2 , F_C = \; - 13$ kN

Hence S.F. changes sign in AC, and its value is zero at $x = 27/20 = 1.35$ m from A.

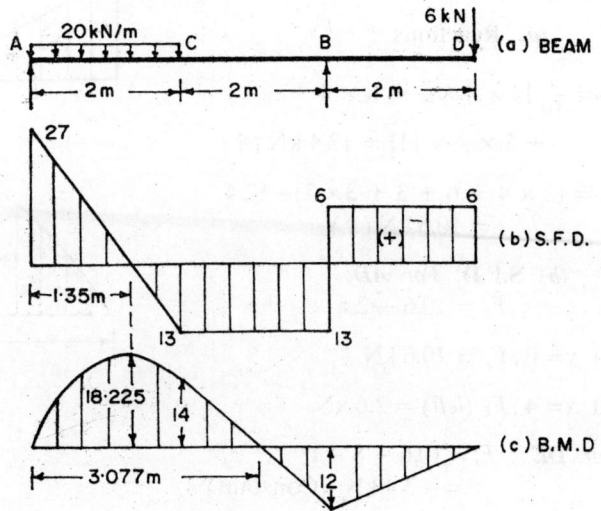

FIG. 9.25

For CB : $\qquad F_x = 27 - 40 = \; - 13$ kN (constant)

$\therefore \qquad F_C = \; - 13$ kN and F_B *(left)* $= \; - 13$ kN

For BD : $\qquad F_x = 27 - 40 + 19 = + 6$ kN (constant)

$$\therefore \qquad\qquad F_B \ (right) = \ + \ 6 \ kN \ \text{and} \ F_D = \ + \ 6 \ kN$$

The S.F.D. is shown in Fig. 9.25 (b).

(c) B.M.D.: For AC, $\qquad M_x = 27x - \dfrac{20x^2}{2} = 27x - 10x^2$ (Parabolic)

At $\quad x = 0$, $\qquad\qquad M_A = 0$; at $x = 2 \ m$, $M_C = 27 \times 2 - 10 \ (2)^2 = 14 \ kN\text{-}m$

B.M. is maximum at $\qquad x = 1.35 \ m$, where S.F. is zero.

$$\therefore \qquad\qquad M_{max} = 27 \ (1.35) - 10 \ (1.35)^2 = 18.225 \ kN\text{-}m$$

For CB : $\qquad\qquad\qquad M_x = 27x - 40 \ (x - 1) = 40 - 13x$ (linear)

At $\qquad\qquad x = 2$, $M_C = 40 - 13 \times 2 = 14 \ kN\text{-}m$ (as before)

At $\qquad\qquad x = 4$, $M_C = 40 - 13 \times 4 = \ - \ 12 \ kN\text{-}m$

Hence B.M. changes sign in *CB*, and its value is zero at $x = \dfrac{40}{13} = 3.077 \ m$ from *A*.
The B.M.D. is shown in Fig. 9.25(c).

Example 9.5. *Draw the S.F.
and B.M. diagrams for the beam
shown in Fig. 9.26, indicating principal values.*

Solution :

(a) Reactions :

$$R_B = \frac{1}{10} \ [2 \times 4 \times 2 + 6 \times 4 + 3 \times 6$$
$$+ \ 3 \times 2 \times 11] = 12.4 \ kN \ (\uparrow)$$

$$R_A = (2 \times 4 + 6 + 3 + 3 \times 2) - 12.4$$
$$= 10.6 \ kN \ (\uparrow)$$

(b) S.F.D. For AD,
$$F_x = 10.6 - 2x$$

At $x = 0$, $F_A = 10.6 \ kN$;

At $x = 4$, $F_D \ (left) = 2.6 \ kN$

For DE : $F_x = 10.6 - 8 - 6$
$$= - \ 3.4 \ kN \ (\text{Constant})$$

FIG. 9.26

$$\therefore \qquad\qquad F_D \ (right) = \ - \ 3.4 \ ; F_E \ (left) = \ - \ 3.4 \ kN$$

For EB : $\qquad F_x = 10.6 - 8 - 6 - 3 = - 64 \ kN$ (constant)

$$\therefore \qquad\qquad F_E \ (right) = - \ 6.4 \ kN \ ; \ F_B \ (left) = - \ 6.4 \ kN$$

For BC : $\qquad F_x = 10.6 - 8 - 6 - 3 + 12.4 - 3 \ (x - 10) = 36 - 3x$ (linear)

$$\therefore \qquad\qquad F_B \ (right) = 36 - 3 \times 10 = \ + \ 6 \ kN \ ; F_C = 36 - 36 = 0$$

The complete S.F.D. is shown in Fig. 9.26(b).

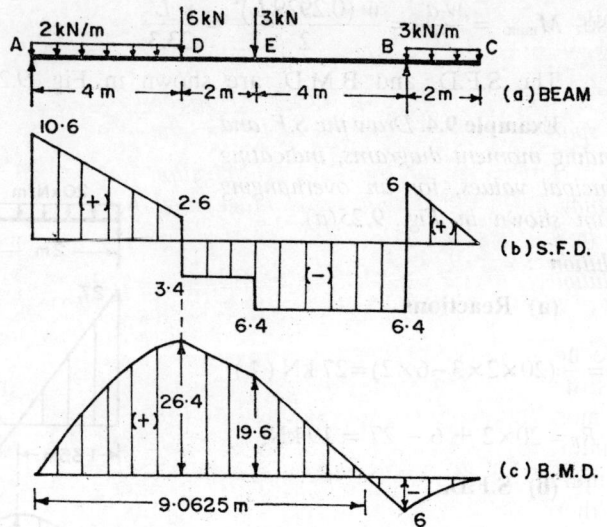

(c) **B.M.D.:** *For AD*, $M_x = 10.6x - \dfrac{2x^2}{2} = 10.6x - x^2$ (Parabolic)

At $\qquad x = 0$, $M_A = 0$; at $x = 4$ m, $M_D = 10.6 \times 4 - (4)^2 = 26.4$ kN-m

For DE, $\qquad M_x = 10.6x - 8(x-2) - 6(x-4) = 40 - 3.4x$ (linear)

At $\qquad x = 4$, $M_D = 26.4$ kN-m (as before); at $x = 6$ m, $M_E = 19.6$ kN-m

For EB $\qquad M_x = 10.6x - 8(x-2) - 6(x-4) - 3(x-6) = 58 - 6.4x$ (linear)

At $x = 6$ m $\quad M_E = 19.6$ kN-m (as before); at $x = 10$ m, $M_B = -6$ kN-m

Hence B.M. changes sign in *EB*, its value being zero at $x = \dfrac{58}{6.4} = 9.0625$ m from *A*.

Hence maximum sagging B.M. is at D where S.F. changes sign.

For BC : $M_x = 10.6x - 8(x-2) - 6(x-4) - 3(x-6) + 12.4(x-10) - \dfrac{3}{2}(x-10)^2$

$\qquad = 6x - 66 - 1.5(x-10)^2$, variation being parabolic. At $x = 10$ m, $M_B = -6$ (as before), while at $x = 12$ m $M_C = 6 \times 12 - 66 - 1.5(12-10)^2 = 0$. The complete B.M.D. is shown in Fig. 9.26(c).

Example 9.6. *Two slings are to be used in raising a newly cast reinforced concrete pile of span L and uniform cross-section, the pile remaining horizontal during the lift.*

Determine the most suitable position for the slings and sketch the S.F. and B.M. diagrams. It may be assumed that the damage to the pile due to S.F. is negligible and that failure would be by bending the pile under its own weight.

Solution :

Let the self weight of the pile be w per unit length. The positions of the slings (C,D) will be most suitable if the maximum bending moment at any point is as minimum as possible. This can be there when the max. hogging B.M. is equal to the max. sagging B.M. Let the position of each sling be at a from the corresponding ends.

Then $\qquad R = \dfrac{wL}{2}$

$\therefore$ Max. hogging B.M. $= \dfrac{wa^2}{2}$

Max. sagging B.M. at the mid-span

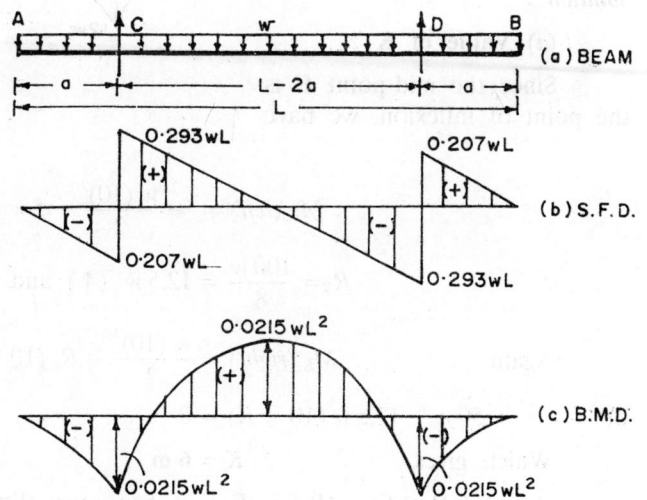

FIG. 9.27

$$= R \left(\frac{L}{2} - a \right) - \frac{w}{2} \left(\frac{L}{2} \right)^2$$

Equating the two, $\dfrac{w \, a^2}{2} = \dfrac{w L}{2} \left(\dfrac{L}{2} - a \right) - \dfrac{w}{2} \times \dfrac{L^2}{4}$

From which $a^2 + a L - \dfrac{L^2}{4} = 0$. This gives $a = \mathbf{0.207\,L}$

$\therefore$ $$M_C = \frac{w \, (0.207 \, L)^2}{2} = 0.0215 \, w \, L^2$$

Also, $$M_E = \frac{w L}{2} \left(\frac{L}{2} - 0.207 \, L \right) - \frac{w L^2}{8} = 0.0215 \, w \, L^2 = M_C$$

The S.F. and B.M. diagrams are shown in Fig. 9.27(b) and (c) respectively.

Example 9.7. *A beam ABCD, 20 m long, is loaded as shown in Fig. 9.28 (a). The beam is supported at B and C and has an overhang of 2 m of the left of the support B and an overhang of K metres to the right of support C which is in the right hand half of the beam. Determine the value of K if the mid-point of the beam is the point of inflexion and for this arrangement, plot S.F. and B.M. diagrams indicating the principal numerical values.*

Solution :

  (a) **Value of K :**

Since the mid-point E is the point of inflexion, we have

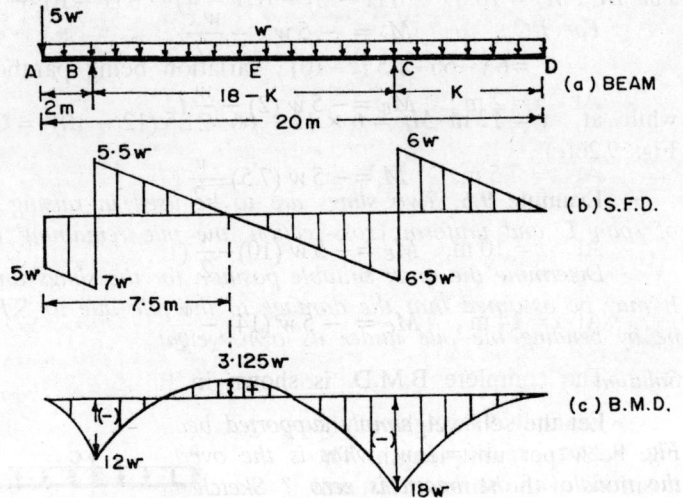

FIG. 9.28

$$M_E \, (left) = - \frac{w \, (10)^2}{2} - 5 \, w \, (10) + 8 \, R_B = 0$$

$\therefore$ $R_B = \dfrac{100 \, w}{8} = 12.5 \, w \ (\uparrow)$ and $R_C = (20 \, w + 5 \, w) - 12.5 \, w = 12.5 \, w \ (\uparrow)$

Again $$M_E \, (right) = \frac{w \, (10)^2}{2} - R_c \, (10 - K) = 0$$

or $50 \, w - 12.5 \, w \, (10 - K) = 0$

Which gives $K = \mathbf{6\,m}$

  (b) **S.F.D. :** **For AB** $F_x = - 5 \, w - w \, x$ (linear)

$\therefore$ $F_A = - 5 \, w$ and $F_B = - 7 \, w$

For BC : $\qquad F_x = -5w - wx + 12.5w = 7.5w - wx$

At $\qquad x = 2$ m, F_B (right) $= 7.5w - 2w = +5.5w$;

At $x = 14$ m, $\qquad F_C$ (left) $= 7.5w - 14w = -6.5w$

The S.F. is zero at $\qquad x = \dfrac{7.5w}{w} = 7.5$ m

For CD $\qquad F_x = -5w - wx + 12.5w + 12.5w = 20w - wx$

At $x = 14$, $\qquad F_C$ (right) $= 20w - 14w = 6w$. At $x = 20$ m, $F_D = 20w - 20w = 0$

(c) **B.M.D. : For AB :** $\quad M_x = -5wx - \dfrac{wx^2}{2}$ (Parabolic)·

At $\qquad x = 0, M_A = 0$; At $x = 2$ m , $M_B = -5w(2) - \dfrac{w}{2}(2)^2 = -12w$

For BC $\qquad M_x = -5wx - \dfrac{wx^2}{2} + 12.5w(x-2)$

At $x = 2$ m , $\quad M_B = -5w(2) - \dfrac{w}{2}(2)^2 = -12w$ (as before)

At $x = 7.5$ m, $\quad M = -5w(7.5) - \dfrac{w}{2}(7.5)^2 + 12.5w(7.5-2) = +3.125w$

At $x = 10$ m, $\quad M_E = -5w(10) - \dfrac{w}{2}(10)^2 + 12.5w(10-2) = 0$ (as expected)

At $x = 14$ m , $\quad M_C = -5w(14) - \dfrac{w}{2}(14)^2 + 12.5w(14-2) = -18w$

The complete B.M.D. is shown in Fig. 9.28(c).

Example 9.8. *A simply supported beam with overhanging ends carries loads as shown in Fig. 9.29(a). If $W = Lw$, what is the overhanging length on each side such that the B.M. at the middle of the beam is zero ? Sketch the S.F. and B.M. diagrams.*

Solution :

(a) **Value of a :**

Given : $\qquad W = Lw$

∴ $\qquad R = \dfrac{wL + wL + wL}{2} = 1.5wL$

∴ $\qquad M_E = -wL\left(a + \dfrac{L}{2}\right) + 1.5wL \cdot \dfrac{L}{2} - \dfrac{w}{2}\left(\dfrac{L}{2}\right)^2 = -wLa + \dfrac{wL^2}{8}$

Since M_E has to be zero, we get $\quad -wLa + \dfrac{wL^2}{8} = 0$

From which $\qquad a = \dfrac{L}{8}$

(b) **S.F.D. For AB,** $\qquad F_x = -W = -wL$ (constant)

$\therefore \quad F_A = -wL \; ; F_B \, (left) = -WL$

For BC,

$F_x = -wL + 1.5\,wL - w\,(x-a)$

$\quad = 0.5\,wL - w\,(x-a)$

At $\quad x = a \, , F_B \, (right) = 0.5\,wL \; ;$

At $\quad x = a + L \, , F_C \, (left) = -0.5\,wL$

Hence S.F. changes sign in *BC*, and has zero value at $x = 0.5\,L + a$ (*i.e.* mid-span)

For CD $\quad F_x = -wL + 1.5\,wL - wL$

$\qquad\qquad + 1.5\,w = wL$ (constant)

The S.F.D. is shown in Fig. 9.29(*b*).

$\therefore \qquad\qquad F_C \,(\text{right}) = +wL$

and $\qquad\qquad\qquad F_D = +wL$

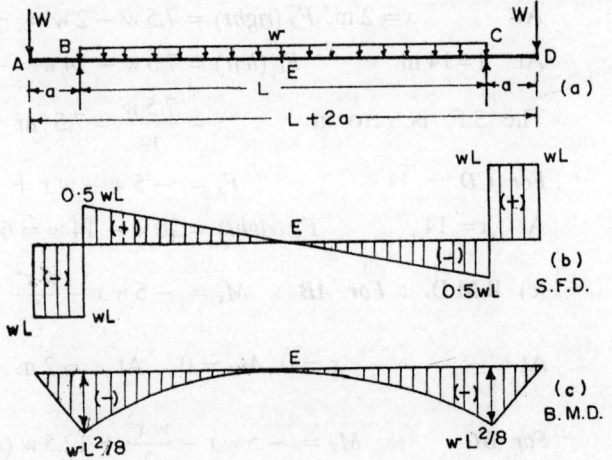

FIG. 9.29

(c) B.M.D.:

For AB : $\qquad M_x = -wLx$ which gives $M_A = 0$ and $M_B = -wLa = -\dfrac{wL^2}{8}$

For BC $\qquad M_x = -wLx + 1.5\,wL\,(x-a) - \dfrac{w\,(x-a)^2}{2}$ (Parabolic)

At $\qquad x = a \, , M_B = -wLa = -wL\left(\dfrac{L}{8}\right) = \dfrac{-wL^2}{8}$ (as before)

At $\qquad x = a + \dfrac{L}{2} = \dfrac{L}{8} + \dfrac{L}{2} = \dfrac{5}{8}L \, , M_E = -wL\left(\dfrac{5}{8}L\right) + 1.5\,wL\left(\dfrac{L}{2}\right) - \dfrac{w}{2}\left(\dfrac{L}{2}\right)^2 = 0$

At $\qquad x = a + L = \dfrac{L}{8} + L = \dfrac{9}{8}L \, , M_C = -wL\left(\dfrac{9}{8}L\right) + 1.5\,wL\,(L) - \dfrac{w}{2}\,(L)^2 = -\dfrac{wL^2}{8}$

The B.M.D. is shown in Fig. 9.29(*c*).

9.7. RELATIONSHIPS BETWEEN BENDING MOMENT, SHEAR FORCE AND LOAD

Let us now obtain relationships between load, shear force and bending moment. Fig. 9.30 shows an element *ABCD* of beam, cut out between two cross-sections that are at a distance dx apart. Let the shear force and bending moment on face *AD* be F and M respectively, both acting in their positive directions. The corresponding stress resultants on the right hand section *BC* will be $F + dF$ and $M + dM$ respectively where dF and dM are the increments in shear and B.M. in the length dx of the beam. Let us first consider uniformly distributed load w per unit length, taken positive when acting downwards.

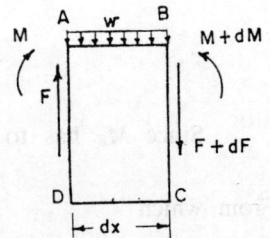

From equilibrium of forces in vertical direction, we get

$$F - \left(F + dF\right) - w\,dx = 0$$

FIG. 9.30. ELEMENT OF BEAM

or
$$\frac{dF}{dx} = -w \qquad \qquad ...(9.10)$$

Thus, the rate of change of shear force (and hence the slope of the S.F.D.) is equal to $-w$.

Again, let us consider the equilibrium of the element by taking the algebraic sum of moments about the left hand face AD of the element, considering *counterclockwise* moment as *positive*.

Thus $\quad -M - (F + dF)\, dx - w\, dx \cdot \dfrac{dx}{2} + (M + dM) = 0$

Neglecting the products and squares of small quantities, we get
$$F\, dx - dM = 0$$

or
$$\frac{dM}{dx} = F \qquad \qquad ...(9.11)$$

Thus, the rate of change of bending moment M along the length of the beam is equal to the shear force.

Now, integrating Eq. 9.10, between two section A and B on the beam,

we get
$$\int_A^B dF = -\int_A^B w\, dx \qquad \qquad ...(9.10\ a)$$

The left hand side of the above equation is the difference $F_B - F_A$ of the shear forces at sections B and A, while the integral on the R.H.S. represents the area of the *load intensity diagram* between B and A

∴
$$F_B - F_A = -\int_A^B w \cdot dx = -\left(A_w\right)_A^B \qquad \qquad ...(9.10\ b)$$

where $\left(A_w\right)_A^B$ is the area of the load intensity diagram between A and B.

Hence
$$F_x = -\int_0^x w\, dx \qquad \qquad ...(9.10\ c)$$

where $\quad F_x =$ S.F. at any section X, distant x from the supports.

Similarly, integrating equation 9.11 between two sections A and B,

we get
$$\int_A^B dM = \int_A^B F\, dx \qquad \qquad ...(9.12\ a)$$

or
$$M_B - M_A = \int_A^B F\, dx = \left(A_F\right)_A^B \qquad \qquad ...(9.12\ b)$$

where $\left(A_F\right)_A^B$ is the area of the S.F.D. between A and B.

Hence
$$M_x = \int_0^x F\, dx = -\int_0^x \int_0^x w\, dx \qquad \qquad ...(9.12)$$

from B.M. to be maximum, $\dfrac{dM}{dx} = 0$. But $\dfrac{dM}{dx} = F$ from Eq. 9.11.

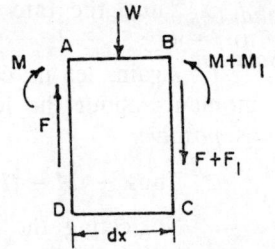

Hence *B.M. is maximum where S.F. is zero or changes sign.*

Let us now consider a concentrated load W acting on the beam element (Fig. 9.31) considered positive when acting downward. Let the stress elements on the left hand face AD be F and M, and the stress elements on the right hand face BC be $(F + F_1)$ and $(M + M_1)$, where F_1 and M_1 are the increments in S.F. and B.M. in the length dx, due to the application of point load W.

From the equilibrium of forces in vertical direction, we obtain

$$F - W - (F + F_1) = 0$$

FIG. 9.31

or $$F_1 = -W$$ ...(9.13)

Thus there is an abrupt change F_1 (equal to W) due to the application of point load, as we pass from left to the right through the point of application of the load.

Again, from summing up of the moments, about face AD, we get

$$-M - W\left(\frac{dx}{2}\right) - (F + F_1)\,dx + (M + M_1) = 0$$

or $$M_1 = W\left(\frac{dx}{2}\right) + F \cdot dx + F_1\,dx$$

Here we observe that since the length dx is infinitesimally small, the increment M_1 is also infinitesimally small. Hence *the B.M. does not change as we pass through the point of application of the concentrated load.* However, its derivative (dM/dx) under goes abrupt change at the location of the concentrated load. At the left hand section AD, dM/dx is equal to F while at the right hand section BC, $dM/dx = F + F_1 = F - W$. Hence dM/dx decreasse abruptly by an amount equal to W at the point of application of the concentrated load.

Lastly, let us consider a couple μ, considered positive when acting in the counter clockwise direction.

Considering the equilibrium of the element in the vertical direction we get

$$F - (F + F_1) = 0$$

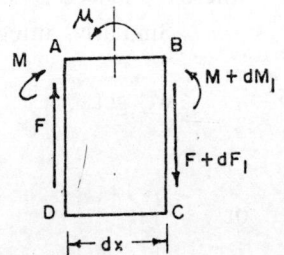

or $$F_1 = 0$$

This shows that the *S.F. does not change at the point of application of a couple.*

Again, equilibrium of moments for the element yields :

$$-M + \mu - (F + F_1)\,dx + (M + M_1) = 0$$

Neglecting the terms that contain differential dx, we get

FIG. 9.32

$$M_1 = -\mu$$ ...(9.14)

Thus, there is abrupt change in the B.M. at the point of application of a couple.

Example 9.9 *A beam of span L, simply supported at the ends, is loaded with a triangular load with intensity zero at one end to w per unit length at the other end. Plot the shear force and bending moment diagrams, indicating the principal values.*

Solution :

$$R_A = \frac{\left(\frac{1}{2}wL\right)\left(\frac{1}{3}L\right)}{L} = \frac{wL}{6}; \quad R_B = \frac{\left(\frac{1}{2}wL\right)\left(\frac{2}{3}L\right)}{L} = \frac{wL}{3}$$

At any section distant x from A,

Rate of loading, $\qquad w_x = \frac{w \cdot x}{L}$

But $\qquad \dfrac{dF_x}{dx} = -w_x$

$$\therefore \qquad F_x = -\int w_x\,dx = -\int \frac{w\,x}{L}\,dx$$

$$= -\frac{w}{L}\frac{x^2}{2} + C_1$$

At $x = 0$, $F_x = +R_A$; $\quad \therefore\ C_1 = +R_A$

$$\therefore \qquad F_x = -\frac{wx^2}{2L} + R_A = -\frac{w\,x^2}{2L} + \frac{wL}{6} \qquad \dots(i)$$

The variation is parabolic.

At $\qquad x = 0, F_A = +\dfrac{wL}{6}$; At $x = L, F_B = -\dfrac{wL^2}{2L} + \dfrac{wL}{6} = -\dfrac{wL}{3}$

S.F. is zero at x is given by $-\dfrac{w\,x^2}{2L} + \dfrac{wL}{6} = 0 \quad$ or $\quad x = \dfrac{L}{\sqrt{3}}$

Again, integrating Eq(ii), $M_x = \displaystyle\int F_x\,dx = -\frac{w}{2L}\frac{x^3}{3} + \frac{wL}{6}x + C_1$

At $\qquad x = 0, M_x = M_A = 0\ \therefore\ C_2 = 0$

$$\therefore \qquad M_x = -\frac{w\,x^3}{6L} + \frac{wL\,x}{6}$$

At $\qquad x = L, M_x = M_B = -\dfrac{wL^3}{6L} + \dfrac{wL^2}{6} = 0$, as expected.

$$x = \frac{L}{\sqrt{3}}, M_{\max} = -\frac{w}{6L}\left(\frac{L}{\sqrt{3}}\right)^3 + \frac{wL}{6}\left(\frac{L}{\sqrt{3}}\right) = -\frac{wL^2}{6\times 3\sqrt{3}} + \frac{wL^2}{6\sqrt{3}}$$

$$= \frac{wL^2}{9\sqrt{3}}$$

The S.F.D. and B.M.D. are shown in Fig. 9.33 (b) and (c) respectively.

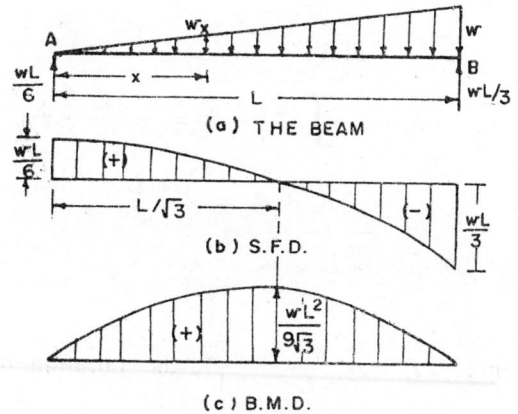

(a) THE BEAM

(b) S.F.D.

(c) B.M.D.

FIG. 9.33

Example 9.10. *A beam of span L, simply supported at the ends, is loaded with distributed load of intensity zero at the ends and w per unit length at the centre. Plot the S.F. and B.M. diagrams, indicating principal values.*

Solution :

$$R_A = R_B = \frac{1}{2}\left(\frac{1}{2}wL\right) = \frac{wL}{4}$$

At any section distant x from A, rate of loading is given by

$$w_x = \frac{w}{L/2}x = \frac{2wx}{L}$$

$\therefore \quad F_x = -\int \frac{2wx}{L}dx = -\frac{2w}{L}\frac{x^2}{2} + C_1$

At $\qquad x = 0, F_A + R_A = +\dfrac{wL}{4}$

$\therefore \qquad C_1 = \dfrac{wL}{4}$

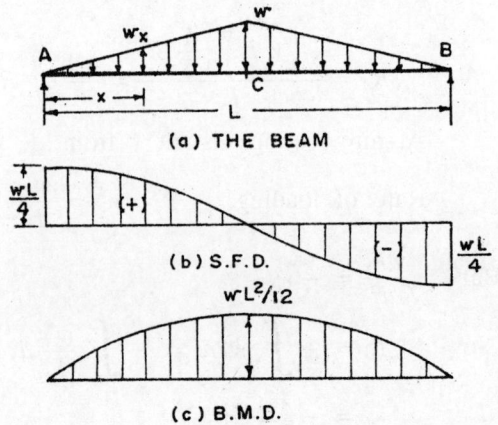

(a) THE BEAM

(b) S.F.D.

$wL^2/12$

(c) B.M.D.

FIG 9.34

Hence $\quad F_x = -\dfrac{wx^2}{L} + \dfrac{wL}{4}$, the variation being parabolic.

S.F. is zero at $x = L/2$

Again, $\quad M_x = \int F_x\,dx = \int\left(-\frac{wx^2}{L} + \frac{wL}{4}\right) = -\frac{wx^3}{3L} + \frac{wLx}{4} + C_2$

At $\qquad\qquad x = 0, M_x = 0 \quad \therefore \; C_2 = 0$

Hence $\qquad\qquad M_x = -\dfrac{wx^3}{3L} + \dfrac{wLx}{4}$

B.M. is maximum at $x = L/2$, where S.F. is zero.

$\therefore \qquad M_{max} = -\dfrac{w}{3L}\left(\dfrac{L}{2}\right)^3 + \dfrac{wL}{4}\left(\dfrac{L}{2}\right) = \dfrac{wL^2}{12}$

The S.F.D. and B.M.D. are shown in Fig. 9.34 (b) and (c) respectively.

Example 9.11. *A beam of span L, simply supported at the ends, is loaded with distributed load which varies parabolically from zero at each end to a maximum at the midspan. Taking the span equal to 4 m, and the value of total load equal to 6000 N, plot the S.F. and B.M. diagrams, indicating principal values.*

Solution : Let w be the rate of loading at mid-span and w_x be the rate of loading at a distance x from the support.

$$\text{Total load} = \frac{2}{3} \times w \times 4 = \frac{8}{3}w$$

$$\frac{8}{3}w = 6000$$

From which $\quad w = \dfrac{6000 \times 3}{8} = 2250$ kN/m

With C as the origin, the equation of the parabola is $a = k x'^2$

When $x' = 2$ m, $\quad a = w = 2250$

$\therefore \qquad\qquad k = \dfrac{2250}{4}$

Hence the equation of the parabola is

$$a = \dfrac{2250}{4} x'^2 = \dfrac{2250}{4}(2-x)^2 \quad ...(1)$$

Again, $\quad w_x = w - a = 2250 - \dfrac{2250}{4}(2-x)^2 ...(2)$

Now $\quad F_x = -\displaystyle\int w_x\, dx$

$$= -\int \left\{ 2250 - \dfrac{2250}{4}(2-x)^2 \right\} dx$$

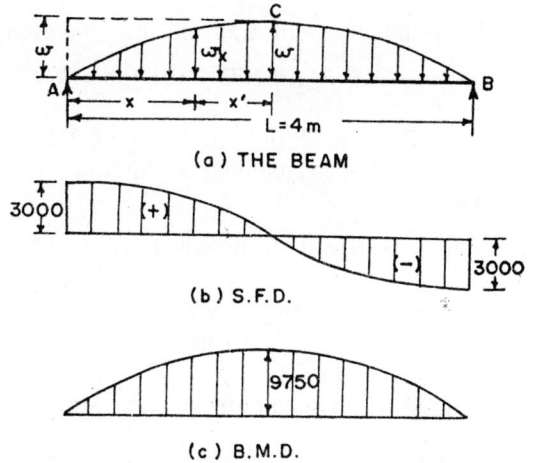

(a) THE BEAM

(b) S.F.D.

(c) B.M.D.

FIG. 9.35

or $\quad F_x = -2250\,x + \dfrac{2250}{4}\left(4x + \dfrac{x^3}{3} - \dfrac{4x^2}{2}\right) + C_1 = \dfrac{2250}{12}x^3 - 1125\,x^2 + C_1$

At $x = 0$, $\qquad\qquad F_x = +R_A = +3000 \quad \therefore \quad C_1 = +3000$

Hence $\qquad\qquad F_x = \dfrac{2250}{12}x^3 - 1125\,x^2 + 3000 \qquad\qquad ...(3)$

S.F. is evidently zero at mid-span

Again, $\qquad M_x = \displaystyle\int F_x\, dx = \int \left(\dfrac{2250}{12}x^3 - 1125\,x^2 + 3000 \right) dx$

$$= \dfrac{2250}{12} \cdot \dfrac{x^4}{4} - 1125 \dfrac{x^3}{3} + 3000\,x + C_2 \qquad\qquad ...(4)$$

Since at $x = 0$, $\qquad M_x = 0$, we get $C_2 = 0 \quad \therefore \quad M_x = \dfrac{2250}{48}x^4 - \dfrac{1125\,x^3}{3} + 3000\,x$

Eqs. (3) and (4) give variation of S.F. and B.M. respectively. The values of S.F. and B.M. are calculated at every 0.5 m in the table below.

x (m)	0	0.5	1	1.5	2	2.5	3	3.5	4
F (N)	+3000	+2742.2	+2062.5	+1101.6	0	−1101.6	−2062.5	−2742.2	−3000
M (N–m)	0	+1456.1	+2671.7	+3471.7	+9750	+3471.7	+267.9	+1456.1	0

Example 9.12 *A lintel of 2 metre span carries a stone wall of 30 cm thick. Assuming that the effective load on the lintel is an equilateral triangle on the span as the base, calculate the maximum B.M. Take the unit weight of masonry as 20 kN/m³. Sketch the S.F. and B.M. diagrams.*

Solution :

The central height h of the triangle $= \dfrac{L}{2} \tan 60° = \dfrac{2}{2} \tan 60° = 1.73$ m

Volume of wall transmitting the effective load on the lintel

$$= \frac{1}{2} \times 2 \times 1.73 \times 0.3 = 0.519 \text{ m}^3$$

Total load on the lintel $= 0.519 \times 20 = 10.38$ kN

If w is the maximum load intensity at the mid-span, we have

$$\frac{1}{2} w \times 2 = 10.38, \text{ from which } w = 10.38 \text{ kN/m}$$

Now, from example 9.10,

$$F_x = -\frac{w x^2}{L} + \frac{w L}{4} = -\frac{10.38}{2}\left(x^2 + \frac{4}{4}\right) = -5.19\,(x^2 + 1)$$

This is the equation of S.F. at any point.

Also, $M_x = \dfrac{-w x^3}{3 L} + \dfrac{w L x}{4} = \dfrac{w x}{12 L}\left(-4 x^2 + 3 L^2\right)$

or $M_x = -\dfrac{10.38 x}{12 \times 2}\left(-4 x^2 + 3 \times 4\right) = 0.4325\,x\,(-4 x^2 + 12)$

This is the equation for B.M. at any point

At $x = 1$ m , $M_{max} = 0.4325 \times 1\,(-4 \times 1 + 12) = +3.46$ kN-m

Alternatively, $M_{max} = \dfrac{w L^2}{12} = \dfrac{10.38\,(2)^2}{12} = 3.46$ kN-m

The ordinate of S.F. and B.M. diagrams can now be calculated by assigning different values to x.

Example 9.13. *A lintel of 3 m span supports a brick wall of 20 cm thickness. The height of wall is 1 m at one end, and increases to 3 m at the other end. Compute the max. B.M. on the lintel if the brick masonry weights 20 kN/m³. Also, sketch the S.F. and B.M. diagrams.*

Solution :

Intensity of load of A
$\qquad = 1 \times 1 \times 0.2 \times 20 = 4$ kN/m

Intensity of load at B
$\qquad = 1 \times 3 \times 0.2 \times 20 = 12$ kN/m

The above loading condition can be·divided into (*i*) a uniformly distributed load of 4 kN/m and (*ii*) a triangular load varying from zero intensity at A to 8 kN/m intensity at B.

Due to U.D.L., $R_A = R_B = \dfrac{1}{2} \times 4 \times 3 = 6$ kN

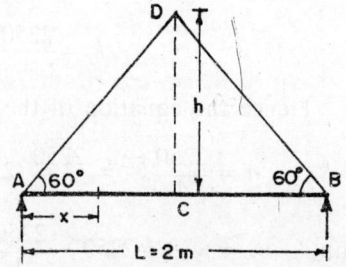

FIG. 9.36

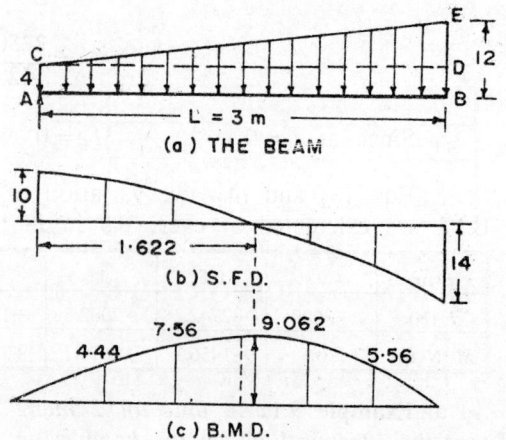

(a) THE BEAM

(b) S.F.D.

(c) B.M.D.

FIG. 9.37

Due to triangular load,

$$R_A = \frac{1}{3} \times \frac{1}{2} \times 3 \times 8 = 4 \text{ kN};$$

$$R_B = \frac{2}{3} \times \frac{1}{2} \times 3 \times 8 = 8 \text{ kN}$$

∴ Total $R_A = 6 + 4 = 10$ kN Total $R_B = 6 + 8 = 14$ kN

At a distance x from A, $w_x = 4 + \frac{8}{3}x$

∴ $F_x = -\int w_x\, dx = -\int \left(4 + \frac{8}{3}x\right) dx = -4x - \frac{8}{6}x^2 + C_1$

At $x = 0$, $F_x = R_A = 10$ kN. Hence $C_1 = 10$ kN

∴ $F_x = -4x - \frac{4}{3}x^2 + 10$ ...(i)

This is the equation of S.F. at any section. The S.F. is zero at x given by

$$-4x - \frac{4}{3}x^2 + 10 = 0 \qquad \text{or} \quad x^2 + 3x - 7.5 = 0$$

This gives $x = 1.622$ m

Again, $M_x = \int F_x \cdot dx = \int \left(-4x - \frac{4}{3}x^2 + 10\right) dx = -\frac{4x^2}{2} - \frac{4}{3}\frac{x^3}{3} + 10x + C_2$

At $x = 0$, $M_A = 0$.   Hence $C_2 = 0$

∴ $M_x = -2x^2 - \frac{4}{9}x^3 + 10x$ ...(ii)

This is the equation of B.M. at any section. The B.M. is maximum at $x = 1.622$ m

∴ $M_{\max} = -2\,(1.622)^2 - \frac{4}{9}(1.622)^3 + 10\,(1.622) = 9.062$ kN-m

The values of S.F. and B.M. at every 0.5 m are tabulated below

x (m)	0	0.5	1	1.5	1.622	2	2.5	3
S.F. (kN)	+10	+ 7.67	+4.67	+1.0	0	−3.33	−8.33	−14
B.M. (kN–m)	0	+4.44	+7.56	+9.0	+9.062	+8.44	+5.56	0

The S.F. and B.M. diagrams are shown in Fig 9.37 (b) and (c) respectively.

9.8. FREELY SUPPORTED BEAM SUBJECTED TO COUPLE

(a) Couples at both ends

Fig. 9.37(a) shows a simply supported beam subjected to couples μ_A and μ_B at ends A and B respectively $(\mu_B > \mu_A)$. Since $\Sigma V = 0$, we have $R_A = -R_B = R$ (say). Net unbalanced external moment is $(\mu_B - \mu_A)$, anticlockwise. Hence from statics, we have

$$R \times L = \mu_B - \mu_A$$

$$\therefore \qquad R = \frac{\mu_B - \mu_A}{L}$$

Thus, the reaction R at A will be acting upwards while the reaction R at B will be acting downwards, so as to give a reactive couple in the clockwise direction to counter balance the external anticlockwise moment.

S.F.D. : At any distance x from A,

$$F_x = R = \frac{\mu_B - \mu_A}{L},$$

which is constant from A to B. Hence the S.F. diagram will be a rectangle, as shown in Fig. 9.38(b).

B.M.D. At any distance x from A,

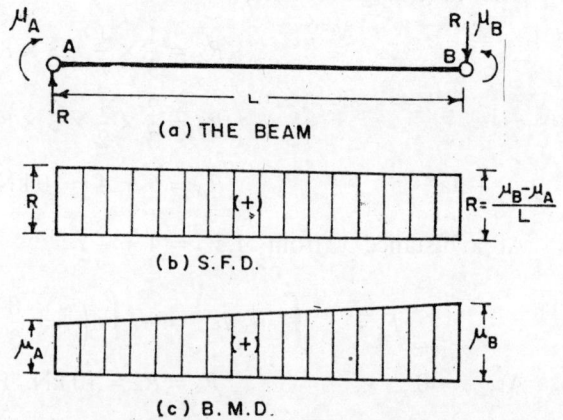

(a) THE BEAM

(b) S.F.D.

(c) B.M.D.

FIG. 9.38

$$M_x = + \mu_A + R x = + \mu_A + \frac{\mu_B - \mu_A}{L} x$$

This gives linear variation along the length of the beam.

At $\qquad x = 0, M_x = M_A = + \mu_A$; At $x = L, M_x = M_B = \mu_A + \mu_B - \mu_A = \mu_B$.

The B.M. diagram will be a trapezium, as shown in Fig. 9.38(c).

(b) Couple at intermediate point

Fig. 9.39(a) shows a beam AB, hinged at both the ends, subjected to a couple μ at some intermediate point C, where $AC = a$ and $CB = b$. Since there is no vertical force,

$$R_A = - R_B = R \text{ (say)}.$$

Hence from the moment equilibrium of the beam. we have

$$R \times L = \mu$$

From which $\qquad R = \frac{\mu}{L}$

Thus, the reaction R at A will be acting vertically *downwards* while the reaction R at B will be acting vertically *upwards*, so as to give a reactive couple in the anticlockwise direction to counter balance the external clockwise couple μ.

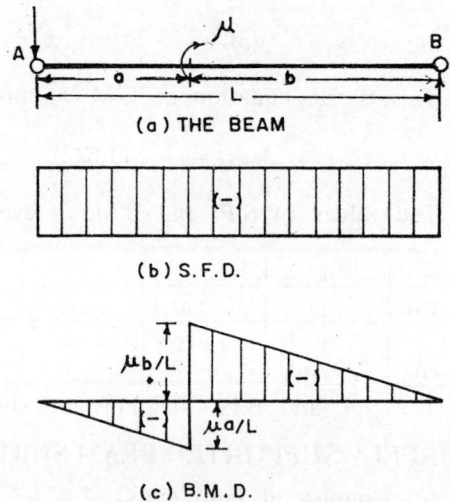

(a) THE BEAM

(b) S.F.D.

(c) B.M.D.

FIG. 9.39

S.F.D. : At any distance x from A ,

$$F_x = - R = - \frac{\mu}{L}, \text{ which is constant along the length.}$$

Hence the S.F. diagram will be a rectangle, as shown in Fig. 9.39(b).

B.M.D. At any distance x from A, but upto point C,

$$M_x = -R \cdot x = -\frac{\mu}{L}x, \text{ the variation being linear.}$$

At $x = 0$, $\qquad M_x = M_A = 0$. At $x = a$, M_C (left) $= -\dfrac{\mu a}{L}$

At any distant x from A, for a portion CB,

$$M_x = -\frac{\mu}{L}x + \mu$$

At $x = a$, $\qquad M_C$ (right) $= -\dfrac{\mu a}{L} + \mu = \dfrac{\mu(L-a)}{L} = +\dfrac{\mu b}{L}$

Thus, at a point C, there is sudden change in the B.M. from a value $-\mu a/L$ to a value $+\mu b/L$.

At $\qquad x = L$, $M_B = -\dfrac{\mu}{L} \cdot L + \mu = 0$

The B.M. diagram is shown in Fig. 9.39(c). Here, we observe that there is a sudden kink in the B.M. diagram, at the point of application of the external couple, due to which the curvature of the beam changes from convexity in AC to concavity in CB. *This results in the hogging B.M. in AC and sagging B.M. in CB.*

Example 9.14. *A beam AB, simply supported at the ends is loaded as shown in Fig. 9.40(a). Draw the S.F. and B.M. diagrams.*

Solution :

Since $\quad \Sigma V = 0$, we have

$R_A + R_B = 80 \qquad \qquad \dots(i)$

Taking moments about A, we get

$R_B = \dfrac{1}{8}\left[80 \times 2 + 40 + 40\right]$

$\quad = 30 \text{ kN} (\uparrow)$

$\therefore \qquad R_A = 80 - 30 = 50 \text{ kN} (\uparrow)$

S.F.D. For AC, $F_x = +R_A = +50 \text{ kN}$ which is constant from A to C.

For CB, $F_x = +R_A - 80$

$\qquad = 50 - 80 = -30$.

This is constant from C to B, since there is no vertical load in CB. The S.F. diagram is shown in Fig. 9.40(b).

B.M.D. : For AC, $\quad M_x = +50x$, the variation being linear.

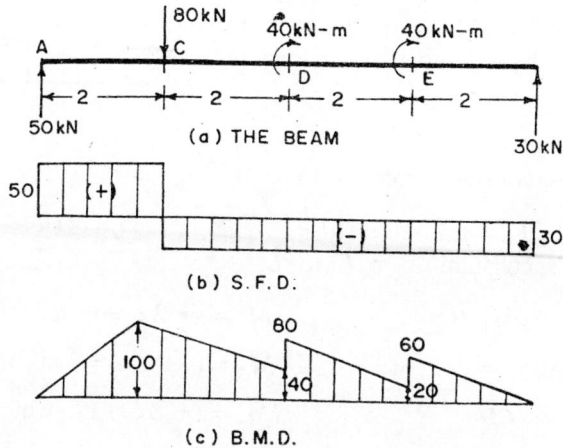

(a) THE BEAM

(b) S.F.D.

(c) B.M.D.

FIG. 9.40

At $x = 0$, $\qquad M_x = M_A \overset{\Omega}{=} 0$;

At $x = 2$ m, $\qquad M_x = M_C = +50 \times 2 = +100$ kN-m

For CD $\qquad M_x = +50x - 80(x-2)$, the variation being linear.

At $x = 2$ m, $\qquad M_C = +50 \times 2 - 80(2-2) = +100$;

At $x = 4$ m, $\qquad M_D$ (left) $= +50 \times 4 - 80(4-2) = +40$

For DE, $\qquad M_x = +50x - 80(x-2) + 40$, the variation being linear.

At $x = 4\,\text{m}$, $\quad M_D\,(right) = 50 \times 4 - 80(4-2) + 40 = +80$ kN-m

At $x = 6\,\text{m}$, $\quad M_E\,(left) = 50 \times 6 - 80(6-2) + 40 = +20$ kN-m

For EB, $\qquad M_x = +50x - 80(x-2) + 40 + 40$, the variation being linear.

At $x = 6\,\text{m}$, $\quad M_E\,(right) = 50 \times 6 - 80(6-2) + 40 + 40 = +60$ kN-m

At $x = 8\,\text{m}$, $\quad M_B = 50 \times 8 - 80(8-2) + 40 + 40 = 0$, as expected.

The complete B.M. diagram is shown in Fig. 9.40(c). Here, we observe kinks in the B.M.D. at point D and E of the application of external couples.

Example 9.15. *For the beam shown in Fig 9.41(a), draw the B.M. and S.F. diagrams, indicating the principal values.*

Solution :

Taking moments about A,

$$R_B = \frac{1}{9}\left[6 \times 11 + 6 \times 6 - 12\right]$$

$$= 10 \text{ kN} (\uparrow)$$

$\therefore \qquad R_A = 6 + 6 - 10 = 2 \text{ kN} (\uparrow)$

S.F.D. : *For AD,*

$\qquad F_x = +R_A = +2\,\text{kN},$

which is constant from A to D since there is no vertical load in AD.

For DB $\quad F_x = +2 - 6 = -4\,\text{kN}$ which is constant from D to B.

For BE $\quad F_x = +2 - 6 + 10 = +6\,\text{kN}$ which is constant from B to E.

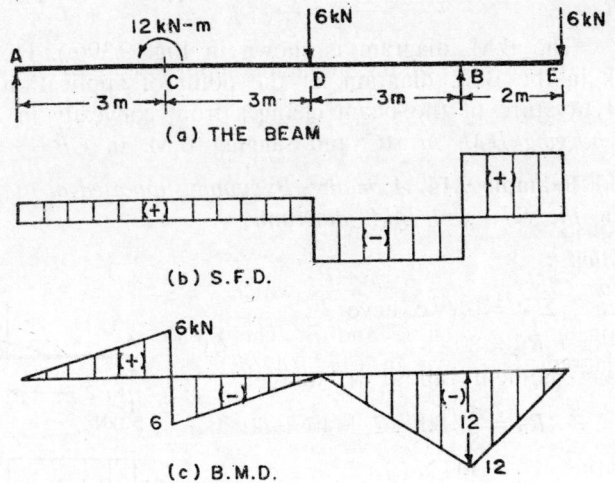

(a) THE BEAM

(b) S.F.D.

(c) B.M.D.

FIG. 9.41

B.M.D. : *For AC,* $\qquad M_x = +2x$, which gives linear variation.

At $x = 0$, $\qquad M_A = 0$. At $x = 3\,\text{m}$, $M_C\,(left) = +2 \times 3 = +6$ kN-m

For CD $\qquad M_x = +2x - 12$, which gives linear variation.

At $x = 3\,\text{m}$, $\qquad M_C\,(right) = 2 \times 3 - 12 = -6$ kN-m.

At $x = 6\,\text{m}$, $\qquad M_D = 2 \times 6 - 12 = 0$

For DB : $\qquad M_x = +2x - 12 - 6(x-6)$, the variation being linear.

At $x = 6\,\text{m}$, $\qquad M_D = 2 \times 6 - 12 - 6(6-6) = 0$, as before.

At $x = 9\,\text{m}$, $\qquad M_B = 2 \times 9 - 12 - 6(9-6) = -12$ kN-m

For BE : $\qquad M_x = +2x - 12 - 6(x-6) + 10(x-9)$, the variation being linear.

At $x = 9\,\text{m}$, $\qquad M_B = +2 \times 9 - 12 - 6(9-6) + 10(9-9) = -12$ kN-m as before.

At $x=11$ m, $M_E = +2\times11-12-6\,(11-6)+10\,(11-9)=0$, as expected.

The complete B.M.D. is shown in Fig. 9.41(c).

Example 9.16. *A simply supported beam ACB supports a vertical load P by means of a bracket CDE, as shown in Fig. 9.42(a). Draw the S.F. and B.M. diagrams for the beam.*

Solution : Apply equal and opposite forces P at point C (Fig. 9.42 b). Then the given system of forces is equivalent to (i) a downward force P at C and (ii) a moment $\mu = PL/4$ at C, as shown in Fig. 9.42(c).

Reactions : Taking moments about B,

$$R_A = \frac{1}{L}\left[P \times \frac{3L}{4} - \frac{PL}{4} \right] = \frac{P}{2}\,(\uparrow)$$

Similarly, taking moments about A, $R_B = \frac{1}{L}\left[\frac{PL}{4} + \frac{PL}{4} \right] = \frac{P}{2}\,(\uparrow)$

S.F.D. : *For AC,* $F_x = +\dfrac{P}{2}$, which is constant between A and C.

For CB $F_x = \dfrac{P}{2} - P = -\dfrac{P}{2}$, which is constant between C and B. The S.F. diagram is shown in Fig. 9.42(d).

B.M.D. : *For AC,* $M_x = \dfrac{P}{2}x$, which varies linearly.

At $x = 0$, $M_A = 0$

At $x = \dfrac{L}{4}$, $M_C\,(left) = \dfrac{P}{2} \times \dfrac{L}{4} = \dfrac{PL}{8}$

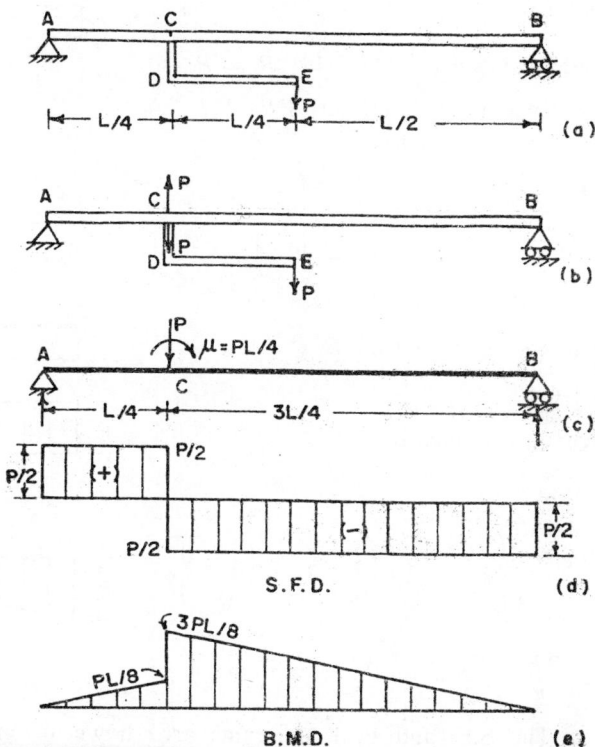

FIG. 9.42

For CB $\quad M_x = \dfrac{P}{2}x + \dfrac{PL}{4} - P\left(x - \dfrac{L}{4} \right)$, which varies linearly.

At $x = \dfrac{L}{4}$, $\quad M_C\,(right) = \dfrac{P}{2} \times \dfrac{L}{4} + \dfrac{PL}{4} - P\left(\dfrac{L}{4} - \dfrac{L}{4} \right) = \dfrac{3PL}{8}$

At $x = L$, $\quad M_B = \dfrac{PL}{2} + \dfrac{PL}{4} - P\left(L - \dfrac{L}{4} \right) = 0$, as expected.

The B.M.D. is shown in Fig. 9.42 (e).

Example 9.17. *Draw the S.F. and B.M. diagrams for the cantilever ACB shown in Fig. 9.43(a).*

Solution :

Due to a load P applied to the rope, (i) a vertical force P and a horizontal force P are transmitted at D, and (ii) a horizontal force P is transmitted at E. These are shown in

Fig 9.43(b). Due to these, the following forces are transmitted to the cantilever, as shown in Fig 9.43(c) :

(i) At B, an anticlockwise Couple = $PL/2$ and a horizontal force P.

(ii) At C, a vertical load P, a horizontal force P and a clockwise couple = $PL/2$.

Reactions : Since $\Sigma V = 0$, $R_A = P(\uparrow)$

Reacting moment at $A = P.L$, in anticlockwise direction.

S.F.D. : For BC, $F_x = 0$

For CA, $F_x = +P$, which is constant from C to A.

B.M.D. : For BC, $M_x = +\dfrac{PL}{2}$, which is constant from BC,

For CA, $M_x = \dfrac{PL}{2} - \dfrac{PL}{2} - P\left(x - \dfrac{L}{2}\right)$, which varies linearly.

At $x = \dfrac{L}{2}$,

$M_C\,(left) = \dfrac{PL}{2} - \dfrac{PL}{2} - P\left(\dfrac{L}{2} - \dfrac{L}{2}\right) = 0$

At $x = \dfrac{3L}{2}$,

$M_A = \dfrac{PL}{2} - \dfrac{PL}{2} - P\left(\dfrac{3L}{2} - \dfrac{L}{2}\right) = -PL$

FIG. 9.43

The S.F. and B.M. diagrams are shown in Fig 9.43(d) and (e) respectively.

Example 9.18. *For the simply supported beam AB, shown in Fig. 9.44(a) draw the S.F. and B.M. diagrams.*

Solution :

Reactions :

$$R_A = \frac{1}{5}(4 \times 2 \times 4 + 6 \times 2 - 9) = 7\ kN(\uparrow)$$

$$R_B = 4 \times 2 + 6 - 7 = 7\ kN(\uparrow)$$

S.F.D. : **For AC,** $F_x = +7 - 4x$

At $x = 0$, $F_A = +7\ kN$

At $x = 2$ m, $F_C = 7 - 4 \times 2 = -1\ kN$

S.F. is zero at $x = \dfrac{7}{4} = 1.75$ m

For CD, $F_x = +7 - 8 = -1\ kN$, which is constant between C and E.

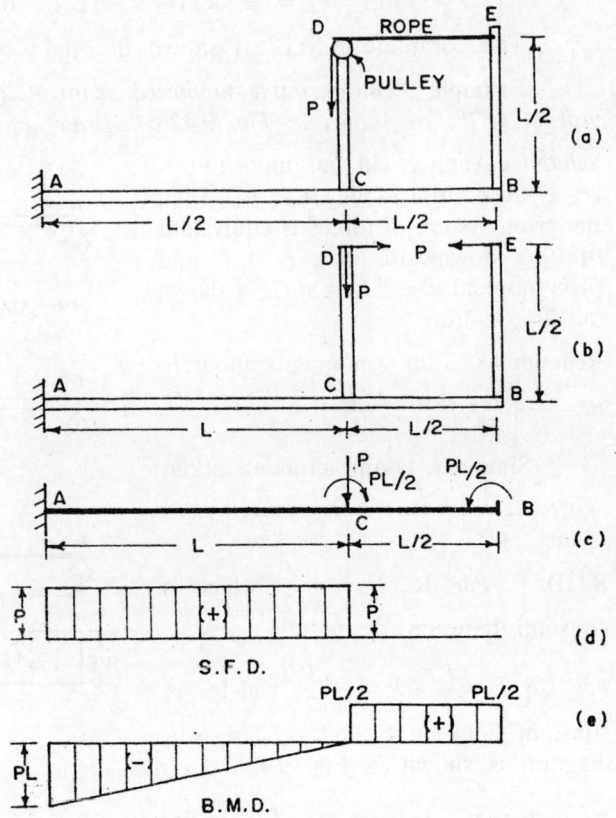

For EB $F_x = +7 - 8 - 6 = -7$ kN
which is constant between E and A.

The S.F. diagram is shown in Fig. 9.44(b).

B.M.D. : **For AC** $\qquad M_x = 7x - \dfrac{4x^2}{2}$ (Parabolic)

At $x = 0$, $\qquad M_A = 0$.

B.M. is maximum at $x = 1.75$ m where S.F. is zero.

$\therefore \qquad M_{max} = 7\,(1.75) - 2\,(1.75)^2 = 6.125$ kN-m.

For CD, $M_x = 7x - 4 \times 2\,(x - 1) = -x + 8$
which gives linear variation.

At $\qquad x = 2.5$ m,

$\qquad M_D\,(left) = -2.5 + 8 = +5.5$ kN-m

For DE, $M_x = 7x - 4 \times 2\,(x-1) + 9 = -x + 17$
which give linear variation.

At $\qquad x = 2.5$ m,

$\qquad M_D\,(right) = -2.5 + 17 = +14.5$ kN-m.

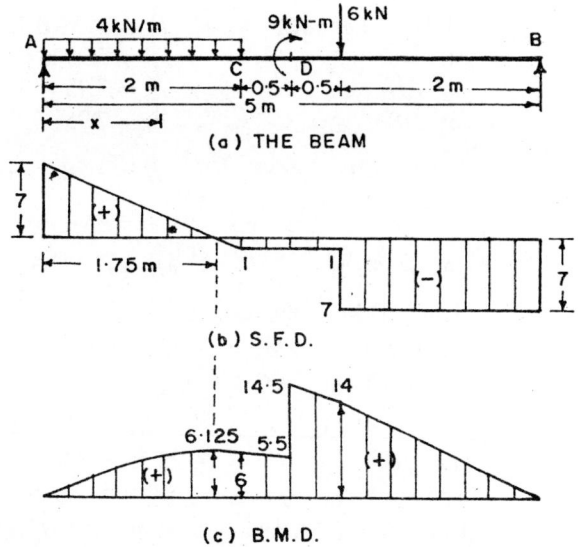

(a) THE BEAM

(b) S.F.D.

(c) B.M.D.

FIG. 9.44

At $x = 3$ m, $\qquad\qquad M_E = -3 + 17 = 14$ kN-m.

For EB, $\qquad\qquad M_x = 7x - 4 \times 2\,(x - 1) + 9 - 6\,(x - 3) = 35 - 7x$ (linear)

At $x = 3$ m, $\qquad\qquad M_D = 35 - 7 \times 3 = 14$ kN-m as before

At $x = 5$ m, $\qquad\qquad M_B = 35 - 7 \times 5 = 0$.

The B.M. diagram is shown in Fig. 9.44(c).

Example 9.19. *A beam of 20 m span is hinged at each end. It carries a U.D.L of 3/4 kN/m on the left hand half of the beam together with a 12 kN point load at 15 m from the left hand end. In addition to this, it is subjected to couples of 28.25 kN-m is anticlockwise direction on left hand support and 41.75 kN-m in the clockwise direction at the right hand support. Find the reactions at the ends and draw the B.M. and S.F. diagrams inserting principal values.*

Solution :

Reactions : Taking moments about B, we get

$\Sigma M_B = 0 = 28.25 + \left(10 \times \dfrac{3}{4} \times 15\right)$
$+ 12 \times 5 - R_A \cdot 20 - 41.75$, which gives $R_A = 7.95$ kN ($\uparrow$)

$\therefore R_B = 7.5 + 12 - 7.95 = 11.55$ kN ($\uparrow$)

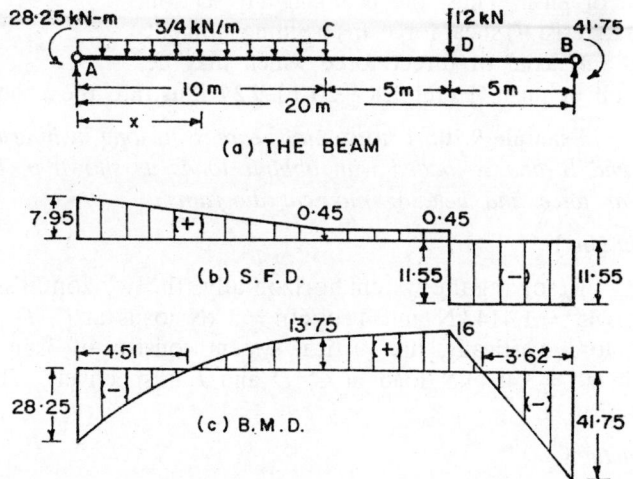

(a) THE BEAM

(b) S.F.D.

(c) B.M.D.

FIG. 9.45

S.F.D. : *For AC*, $F_x = 7.95 - 0.75x$, which is a linear variation.

At $x = 0$, $F_A = 7.95$ kN. At $x = 10$ m, $F_C = 7.95 - 7.5 = 0.45$ kN

For CD $F_x = 7.95 - 7.5 = 0.45$ kN, which is constant from C to D.

For DB $F_x = 7.95 - 7.5 - 12 = -11.55$ kN, which is constant from D to E

B.M.D. : *For AC*, $M_x = -28.25 + 7.95x - \dfrac{0.75 x^2}{2}$, which is a parabolic variation.

At $x = 0$, $M_A = -28.25$ kN-m.

At $x = 10$ m, $M_C = -28.25 + 79.5 - \dfrac{0.75\,(10)^2}{2} = +13.75$ kN-m

Hence B.M. changes sign and is zero at $x = 4.51$ m.

For CD : $M_x = -28.25 + 7.95x - 7.5\,(x - 5)$, which is linear.

At $x = 10$ m, $M_C = -28.25 + 79.5 - 7.5 \times 5 = 13.75$ kN-m, as before

At $x = 15$ m, $M_D = -28.25 + 7.95 \times 15 - 7.5\,(15 - 5) = 16$ kN-m

For DB : $M_x = -28.25 + 7.95x - 7.5\,(x - 5) - 12\,(x - 15)$, which is linear.

At $x = 20$ m, $M_B = -28.25 + 7.95 \times 20 - 7.5\,(20 - 5) - 12\,(20 - 15) = -41.75$ kN-m

Thus, the B.M. changes sign in DB, and is zero at $x = 16.38$ m from A, or at 3.62 m from B.

The S.F. and B.M. diagrams are shown in Fig. 9.45(*b*) and (*c*) respectively.

9.9. BEAMS WITH INCLINED LOADING

When a beam is subjected to a load P which is inclined at an angle θ with the axis of the beam, the load P can be resolved into two components (*i*) a transverse (or vertical) component $P_v\,(= P \sin \theta)$ and (*ii*) axial (or horizontal) component $P_h\,(= P \cos \theta)$. The transverse component will produce S.F. and B.M. while the axial component will produce pull or push. Thus, the beam at any section has to resist (*i*) shear force, (*ii*) bending moment and (*iii*) axial or direct force which may be

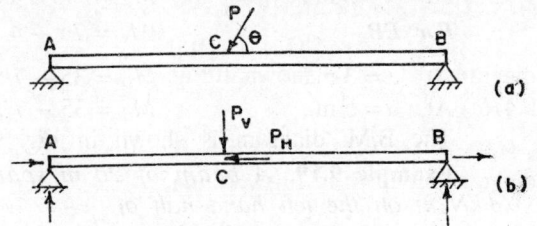

FIG. 9.46

a pull or push. Examples 9.20 to 9.24 illustrate the procedure for the analysis of such beams.

Example 9.20. *A horizontal beam, 8 m long in hinged at support A and has a roller support at end B, and is loaded with oblique loads as shown in Fig. 9.47(a). Construct the axial thrust, shear force and bending moment diagrams.*

Solution :

Resolving the system horizontally, the horizontal system consists of $3 \cos 30° = 2.598$ kN, $2 \cos 45° = 1.414$ kN and $4 \cos 60° = 2$ kN loads at C, D and E respectively. Similarly resolving the force vertically, the vertical system consists of $3 \sin 30° = 1.5$ kN, $2 \sin 45° = 1.414$ kN and $4 \sin 60° = 3.464$ kN load at C, D and E respectively. These forces have been marked in Fig. 9.47(*b*).

Reactions

Let H_A be the horizontal reaction at A. Then $H_A = 2 + 1.414 - 2.598 = 0.816$ kN ($\rightarrow$). The horizontal reaction at B will be zero since it is a roller support.

Similarly, let V_A and V_B be the vertical reactions at A and B. Taking moments about B, we get

$$V_A = \frac{1}{8}[1.5 \times 6 + 1.414 \times 4$$
$$+ 3.464 \times 2] = 2.698 \text{ kN } (\uparrow)$$

Hence $V_B = [1.5 + 1.414 + 3.464]$
$$- 2.698 = 3.68 \text{ kN } (\uparrow)$$

(i) Horizontal thrust diagram

For AC, horizontal thrust $H_T = 0.816$ kN

For CD, horizontal thrust $H_T = 0.816 + 2.598 = 3.414$ kN

For DE, horizontal thrust $H_T = 0.816 + 2.598 - 1.414 = 2$ kN

For EB, horizontal thrust $H_T = 0.816 + 2.598 - 1.414 - 2 = 0$

The horizontal thrust diagram (H.T.D.) is shown in Fig. 9.47(c)

(ii) S.F.D. : The S.F. diagram is shown in Fig 9.47 (d).

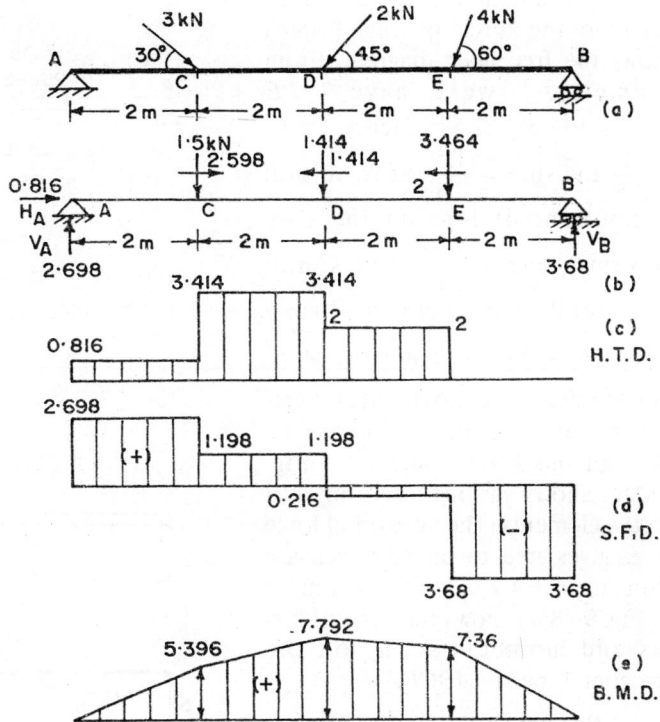

FIG. 9.47

(iii) B.M.D. : For AC $M_x = 2.698 x$, which varies linearly

At $x = 0$, $M_A = 0$. At $x = 2$, $M_C = 2.698 \times 2 = 5.396$ kN-m

For CD : $M_x = 2.698 x - 1.5(x - 2)$, which varies linearly.

At $x = 2$ m, $M_C = 2.698 \times 2 = 5.396$ kN-m

At $x = 4$ m, $M_D = 2.698 \times 4 - 1.5(4 - 2) = 7.792$ kN-m

For DE : $M_x = 2.698 x - 1.5(x - 2) - 1.414(x - 4)$, which is a linear variation.

At $x = 4$ m, $M_D = 7.792$, as before. At $x = 6$ m, $M_E = 7.36$ kN-m

For EB : $M_x = 2.698 x - 1.5(x - 2) - 1.414(x - 4) - 3.464(x - 6)$

At $x = 6$ m, $M_E = 7.36$ as before. At $x = 8$, we get $M_B = 0$.

The B.M.D. is shown in Fig. 9.47(e).

Example 9.21. *A beam ABCD is loaded by a force $W = 8$ kN by the arrangement shown in Fig. 9.48. The cable passes over a small frictionless pulley at B and is attached at E to the vertical arm. Compute the shear force and bending moment at the section, which is just to the left of the vertical arm. Also, sketch the S.F. and B.M. diagrams for the beam.*

Solution :

Tension in the cable will be equal to the force W. Fig. 9.48(b) shows the free body diagram. From geometry, we have $BE = \sqrt{(2)^2 + (1.5)^2} = 2.5$ m. Hence $\cos \theta = \dfrac{2}{2.5}$ and $\sin \theta = \dfrac{1.5}{2.5}$. At B, vertical component of tension in cable $= W \sin \theta = 8 \times \dfrac{1.5}{2.5} = 4.8$ kN and horizontal component $= W \cos \theta = 8 \times \dfrac{2}{2.5} = 6.4$ kN. Similarly, at E, the vertical and horizontal components of the cable tension are 4.8 kN and 6.4 kN respectively. Fig. 9.48(c) shows various forces marked on the elements. The horizontal force at E gives rise to an anticlockwise moment $= 6.4 \times 1.5 = 9.6$ kN-m at C. Fig. 9.48(d) shows the vertical forces and moments acting on the horizontal beam $ABCD$.

Reactions :

Taking moments at D,

$$R_A = \frac{1}{8}(3.2 \times 5 + 4.8 \times 3 + 9.6) = 5 \text{ kN}(\uparrow)$$

$$\therefore \qquad R_B = 3.2 + 4.8 - 5 = 3 \text{ kN } (\uparrow)$$

S.F.D. : Fig. 9.48(e) shows the S.F. diagram, which is self explanatory.

Hence S.F. just to the left of $C = $ **1.8 kN**

B.M.D. :

For AB, $M_x = 5x$, which gives $M_B = 5 \times 3 = 15$ kN-m

For BC, $M_x = 5x - 3.2(x - 3)$, which gives M_C *(left)* $= 5 \times 5 - 3.2(5 - 2) = $ **18.6 kN-m**

For CD, $M_x = 5x - 3.2(x - 3) - 9.6 - 4.8(x - 5)$, which gives M_C *(right)* $= 9$ kN-m
and $\qquad M_D = 5 \times 8 - 3.2(8 - 3) - 9.6 - 4.8(8 - 5) = 0$, as expected.

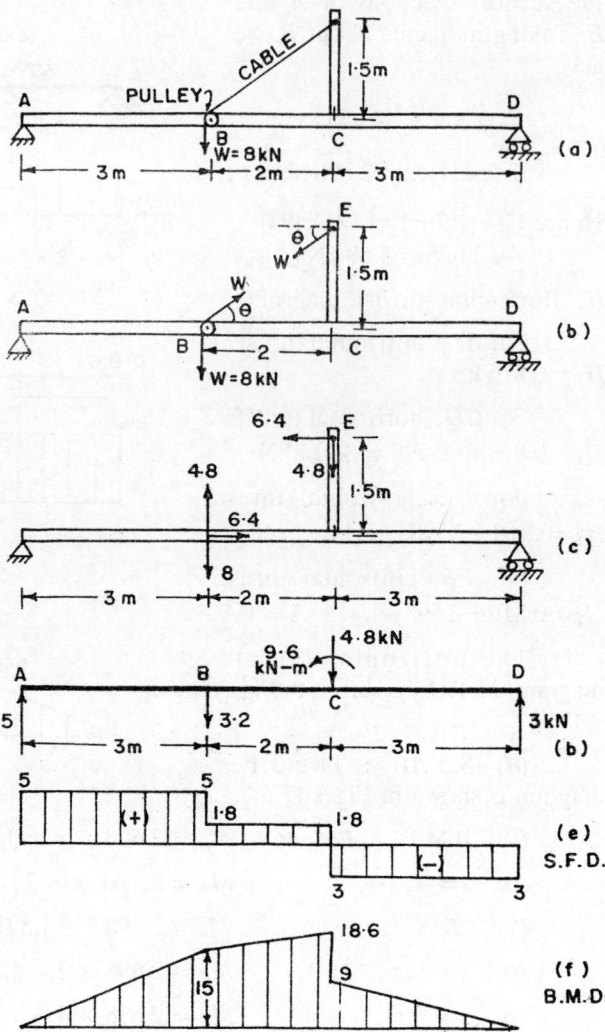

FIG. 9.48

Example 9.22. *A ladder 6 m long weighing 250 N/metre run, rests against a smooth vertical wall with bottom resting on rough ground, the vertical distance between the ends of the ladder being 4 m. A man weighting 650 N is standing on the ladder at 1.5 m from the bottom end and another man weighting 700 N on the ladder at 3 m from the bottom. Construct the axial* *thrust, shear force and B.M. diagrams for the ladder and calculate the reactions at the ground and at the wall.*

Solution :

Let the ladder be inclined at an angle θ to horizontal.

$\sin\theta=\dfrac{4}{6}=\dfrac{2}{3}$; $\cos\theta=\dfrac{4.47}{6}=\dfrac{1.49}{2}$

Let R_1 = Normal reaction

on rough ground

R_2 = Normal reaction

on wall

R_f = Frictional resistance

of ground.

Resolving   vertically

$R_1= 700 + 650 + 250 \times 6$

$= 2850\,\text{N}$

Resolving horizontally,

$R_2 = R_f$

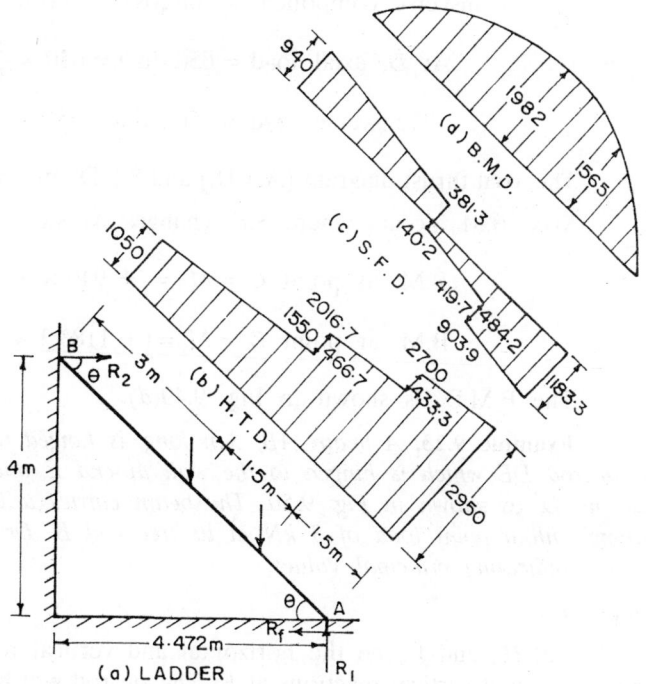

(a) LADDER

FIG. 9.49

Taking moments about A,

$$R_2 \times 4 = 700 \times 3 \cos\theta + 650\times 1.5 \cos\theta + 250 \times 6 \times \frac{4.472}{2}$$

$$= \left(2100 \times \frac{1.49}{2}\right) + \left(975 \times \frac{1.49}{2}\right) + \left(\frac{1500 \times 4.472}{2}\right)$$

or $R_2 = 1410\,\text{N} = R_f$

Resolving the system axially and transversely to AB

At B, axial component $P_B = R_2 \cos\theta = 1410 \times \dfrac{1.49}{2} = 1050\,\text{N}$

Transverse component $F_B = R_2 \sin\theta = 1410 \times \dfrac{2}{3} = 940\,\text{N}$

At A, axial component $P_A = R_1 \sin\theta + R_f \cos\theta = \left(2850 \times \dfrac{2}{3}\right) + \left(1410 \times \dfrac{1.49}{2}\right) = 2950\,\text{N}$

Transverse component $F_A = R_1 \cos\theta - R_f \sin\theta = \left(2850 \times \dfrac{1.49}{2}\right) - \left(1410 \times \dfrac{2}{3}\right) = 1183.3\,\text{N}$

For ladder, axial load $= 250 \sin\theta = 250 \times \dfrac{2}{3} = 166.7\,\text{N/m}$

Transverse load $= 250 \cos\theta = 250 \times \dfrac{1.49}{2} = 186.25\,\text{N/m}$

$$\text{At } C, \text{ axial load} = 700 \sin \theta = 700 \times \frac{2}{3} = 466.7 \text{ N}$$

$$\text{Transverse component} = 700 \cos \theta = 700 \times \frac{1.49}{2} = 521.5 \text{ N}$$

$$\text{At } D, \text{ axial load} = 650 \sin \theta = 650 \times \frac{2}{3} = 433.3 \text{ N}$$

$$\text{Transverse load} = 650 \cos \theta = 650 \times \frac{1.49}{2} = 484.2 \text{ N}$$

The axial thrust diagram (A.T.D.) and S.F.D. are shown in Fig. 9.49(b) and (c) respectively. Max. B.M. occurs where S.F. changes its sign.

$$\text{B.M. at point } C = M_C = +940 \times 3 - \left(186.25 \times 3 \times \frac{3}{2}\right) = +1982 \text{ N-m}$$

$$\text{B.M. at point } D = M_D = \left(+1183.3 \times 1.5\right) - \left(186.25 \times 1.5 \times \frac{1.5}{2}\right) = +1565 \text{ N-m}$$

The B.M.D. is shown in Fig. 9.49(d).

Example 9.23. *A beam AB, 3 m long, is hinged to a wall at end A and is supported by a tie rod DE which is hinged to the wall at end E and also hinged to a vertical bracket CD at end D, as shown in Fig. 9.50. The beam carries a U.D.L. of 5 kN/m throughout its length along with a point load of 3 kN at its free end B. Draw the S.F. and B.M. diagrams for the beam, indicating principal values.*

Solution :

Let H_A and V_A be the horizontal and vertical reactions at A, while H_E and V_E be the horizontal and vertical reactions at E. The tie rod will be in tension, as marked in Fig. 9.50(a).

Taking moments about hinge E, we get

$$H_A \times 2.5 = \frac{5 \, (3)^2}{2} + 3 \times 3$$

From which $H_A = 12.6 \text{ kN } (\rightarrow)$

Since $\Sigma H = 0$ for the whole structure, we have $H_E = 12.6 \text{ kN } (\leftarrow)$

Again, if T is the tension in the tie rod, we have, by resolving the forces horizontally at E,

$$T \cos \theta = H_E$$

Also, $T \sin \theta = V_E$

$\therefore$ $\tan \theta = \dfrac{V_E}{H_E} = \dfrac{2}{2} = 1$

$\therefore$ $V_E = 1 \times H_E = 12.6 \text{ kN } (\uparrow)$

Again, for the whole structure,

$$\Sigma V = 0. \quad \text{Hence}$$

$$V_A = (5 \times 3 + 3) - 12.6 = 5.4 \text{ kN } (\uparrow)$$

Thus, the reactions at A and E are completely known.

Again, resolving the tension in tie rod at end D, we have

$H_D = $ Horizontal component of tension in tie rod $= T \cos \theta = H_E = 12.6 \text{ kN } (\leftarrow)$

$V_D =$ Vertical component of tension in tie rod
$= T \sin\theta = V_E = 12.6$ kN $(\uparrow)$

Hence the beam ACB is subjected to the following loads and reactions :

(i) External loading

(ii) Reactions H_A and V_A at end A

(iii) Horizontal force H_D and vertical force V_D at D.

These forces are shown marked in Fig. 9.50 (b). However, the horizontal load H_D (= 12.6 kN) acting at a lever arm of 0.5 m, gives rise to an anticlockwise moment = 12.6 × 0.5 = 6.3 kN-m, and a horizontal force of 12.6 kN ($\leftarrow$), both acting at C. These final forces/reactions on beam AB have been marked in Fig. 9.50 (c).

S.F. Diagram : *For AC*, $F_x = 5.4 - 5x$, which gives a linear variation.

At $x = 0$, $F_A = 5.4$ kN.
At $x = 2$ m,
F_C (*left*) $= 5.4 - 5 \times 2 = -4.6$ kN.
The S.F. is zero at $x = 5.4/5 = 1.08$ m from A.

For CB
$F_x = 5.4 - 5x + 12.6$, which again gives linear variation.
At $x = 2$ m, we get F_C (*right*)
$= 5.4 - 5 \times 2 + 12.6 = +8$ kN.

FIG. 9.50

At $x = 3$ m, we get $F_B = 5.4 - 5 \times 3 + 12.6 = +3$ kN. The complete S.F. diagram has been shown in Fig. 9.50(d).

B.M. Diagram : *For AC*, $M_x = 5.4x - \dfrac{5x^2}{2}$, which is a parabolic variation.

At $x = 2$ m, M_C (*left*) $= 5.4 \times 2 - \dfrac{5(2)^2}{2} = 0.8$ kN-m. B.M. is maximum at $x = 1.08$ m.

$$M_{max} = 5.4 (1.08) - \frac{5}{2}(1.08)^2 = 2.916 \text{ kN-m}$$

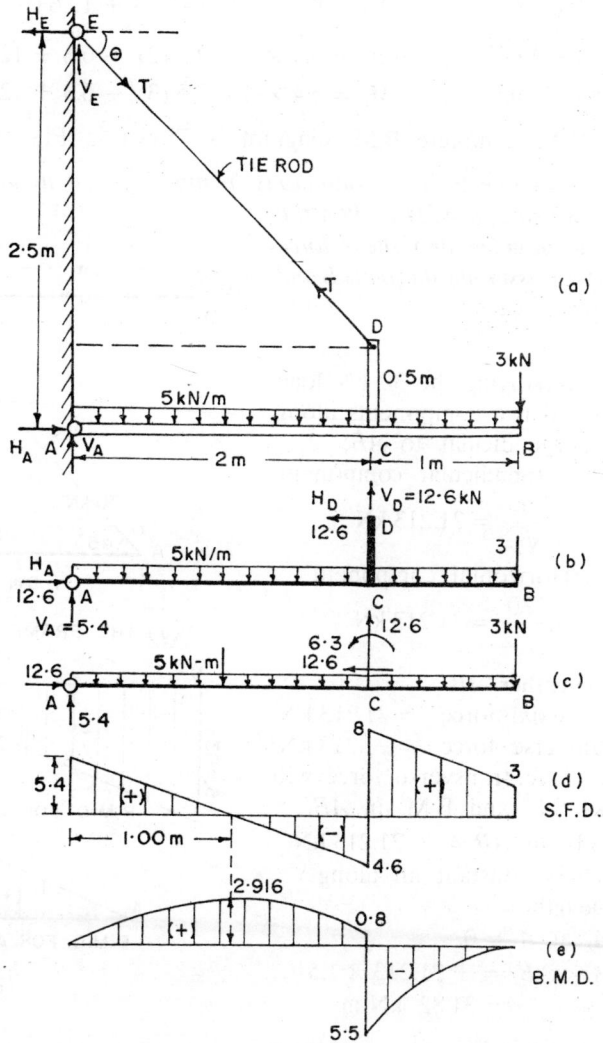

For CB :
$$M_x = 5.4\,x - \frac{5\,x^2}{2} - 6.3 + 12.6\,(x - 2)$$

At $x = 2$ m, $\quad M_C\,(right) = 5.4 \times 2 - 2.5\,(2)^2 - 6.3 + 12.6\,(2 - 2) = -5.5$ kN-m

At $x = 3$ m, $\qquad M_B = 5.4 \times 3 - 2.5\,(3)^2 - 6.3 + 12.6\,(3 - 2) = 0$, as expected.

The complete B.M. diagram is shown in Fig. 9.50(e).

Example 9.24. *A continuous member is bent in one plane and loaded in the same plane, as shown in Fig. 9.51(a). Plot the bending moment and shear force diagrams, assuming the joints B and C to be rigid.*

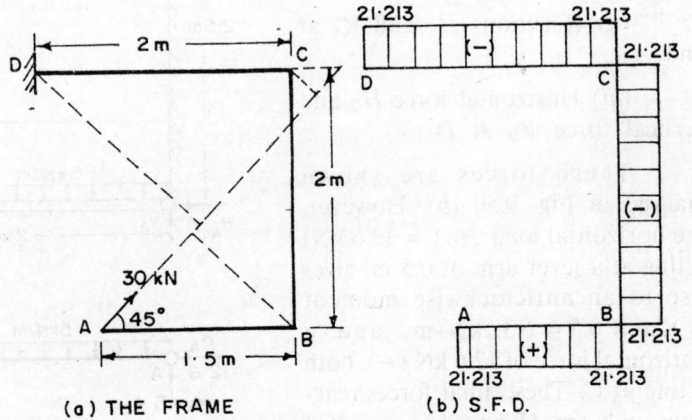

Solution :

Resolving the 30 kN load at A into two components along and perpendicular to AB,

Perpendicular component
$$= \frac{30}{\sqrt{2}} = 21.213 \text{ kN}$$

Horizontal component
$$= \frac{30}{\sqrt{2}} = 21.213 \text{ kN}$$

(a) THE FRAME

(b) S.F.D.

For member AB

Axial force $= 21.213$ kN

Transverse force $= 21.213$ kN

The transverse force will cause S.F. and B.M. in AB.

$\therefore$ S.F. in $AB = +21.213$ kN, which is constant all along its length

B.M. at $A = 0$.

B.M. at $B = +21.213 \times 1.5$
$= 31.82$ kN-m.

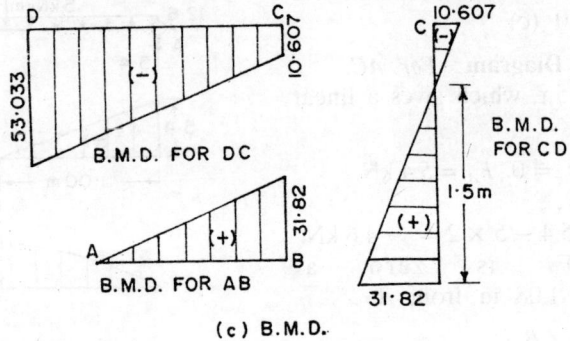

(c) B.M.D.

For member BC : The axial force

FIG. 9.51

of 21.213 kN in AB will form transverse force in BC. Thus S.F. in $BC = -21.213$ kN which is constant all along its length. In addition to this, member BC will also have an axial force of 21.213 kN. The B.M. at any section in BC is the product of the force of 30 kN and the perpendicular distance of that section from the line of action of this force.

Thus $\qquad M_B = +31.82$ kN-m. B.M. at 1.5 m from $B = 0$.

$$\text{B.M. at } C = M_C = -30 \times \frac{0.5}{\sqrt{2}} = -10.607 \text{ kN-m}$$

For member CD

S.F. in $CD = -21.213$ kN

$$M_C = -30 \times \frac{0.5}{\sqrt{2}} = -10.607 \text{ kN-m} \;; \quad M_D = -30 \times \frac{2.5}{\sqrt{2}} = -53.033 \text{ kN-m.}$$

9.10. LOADING AND B.M. (or S.F.) DIAGRAMS FROM S.F. (or B.M.) DIAGRAMS

Many times, shear force diagram (or B.M. diagram) for the beam is given. In that case, the loading diagram for the beam can be very easily drawn keeping in mind the following important properties :

(a) Properties of S.F. diagrams

(1) The S.F. diagram consists of a rectangle (or a series of rectangles) if the beam is loaded with point load(s).

(2) The S.F. diagram consists of inclined line for the portion on which U.D.L. is acting.

(3) The S.F. diagram consists of parabolic curve for the portion over which triangular or trapezoidal load distribution is acting.

(4) The S.F. diagram consists of 'cubic curve' for the portion over which parabolic load distribution is acting.

(b) Properties of B.M. Diagrams

1. The B.M. diagram consists of inclined lines for the beam loaded with point loads.

2. The B.M. diagram consists of parabolic curve for the portion over which U.D.L. is acting.

3. The B.M. diagram consists of 'cubic' or 'third degree' curve for the portion on which load distribution is triangular or trapezoidal.

4. The B.M. diagram consists of fourth degree curve if the load distribution is parabolic.

Example 9.25 to 9.28 illustrate the procedure.

Example 9.25. *The S.F. diagram for a simply supported beam is shown in Fig. 9.52(a). Determine the loading on the beam and draw the bending moment diagram, assuming that no couple acts on the beam.*

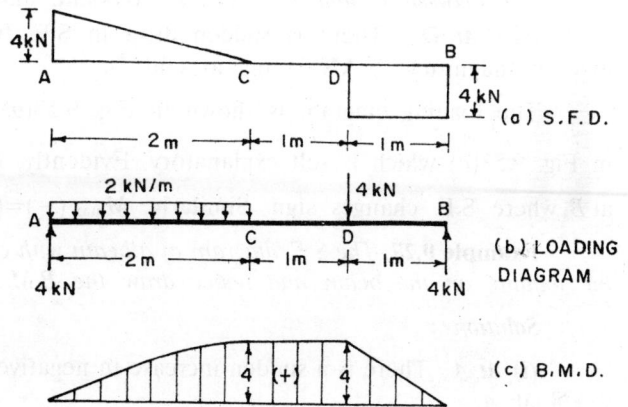

FIG. 9.52

Solution : By inspection, since F_A = 4 kN, R_A = 4 kN. Similarly, $R_B = 4$ kN. Since S.F. diagram consists of inclined line from A to C, U.D.L. acts on this portion, its value being equal to $\dfrac{4-0}{2} = 2$ kN/m. Also, since $F_D = -4$ kN, a point load of 4 kN acts at D. The loading diagram is now shown in Fig. 9.52(b). The consequent B.M. diagram is shown in Fig. 9.52(c), where $M_{max} = 4$ kN-m.

Example 9.26. *Fig. 9.53(a) shows the shearing force diagram for a beam which rests on two supports, one being at the left hand end. Deduce from the S.F. diagram, the loading on the beam, indicating the position of the second support. Also draw the B.M. diagram for the beam.*

Solution :

(i) *At A* : $F_A = 20$ kN. Hence $R_A = 20$ kN, there being a support at left hand end *A*.

(ii) *Between A to B* : S.F. varies linearly from 20 to 11. Hence U.D.L. of intensity $\dfrac{20 - 11}{6} = 1.5$ kN/m acts between *A* and *B*.

(iii) *At C* : There is sudden change in S.F. from $+ 11$ kN to $- 3$ kN. Hence there acts a point load at *B*, of magnitude $11 + 3 = 14$ kN.

(iv) *Between B and C* : S.F. varies linearly, and hence U.D.L. of magnitude $\dfrac{(18 - 3)}{10} = 1.5$ kN/m acts between *B* and *C*.

FIG. 9.53

(v) *At C* : There is sudden increase in S.F. from $- 18$ kN to $+ 6$ kN, suggesting a support, the value of reaction there being equal to $18 + 6 = 24$ kN.

(vi) *Between C and D* : S.F. is constant, and hence there is no loading.

(vii) *At D* : There is sudden drop in S.F. from $+ 6$ kN to zero, suggesting a point load of magnitude 6 kN acting at end *D*.

The loading diagram is shown in Fig. 9.53(*b*). The consequent B.M. diagram is shown in Fig. 9.53(*c*) which is self explanatory. Evidently, $M_{max} (+) = 20 \times 6 - \dfrac{1.5 \, (6)^2}{2} = +93$ kN-m at *B*, where S.F. changes sign. Similarly, $M_{max} (-) = 6 \times 2 = 12$ kN-m at *C*.

Example 9.27. *The S.F. diagram of a beam with overhangs is shown in Fig. 9.54(a). Determine the loading on the beam and hence draw the B.M. diagram.*

Solution :

(i) *At A* : There is a sudden increase in negative S.F., suggesting a point load of magnitude 2 kN at *A*.

(ii) *Between A to B* : S.F. is constant, and hence there is no load.

(iii) *At B* : There is sudden increase in S.F. from $- 2$ kN to $+ 4$ kN, suggesting a support, the value of reaction being equal to $2 + 4 = 6$ kN.

(iv) *Between B and C* : The S.F. decreases linearly from $+ 4$ kN to $- 5$ kN, suggesting the existence of U.D.L. of value $\dfrac{4 - (- 5)}{6} = 1.5$ kN/m.

(v) *At C* : There is sudden change in S.F. from $- 5$ kN to $+ 3$ kN. Hence the other support is at *C*, the value of reaction being equal to $5 + 3 = 8$ kN.

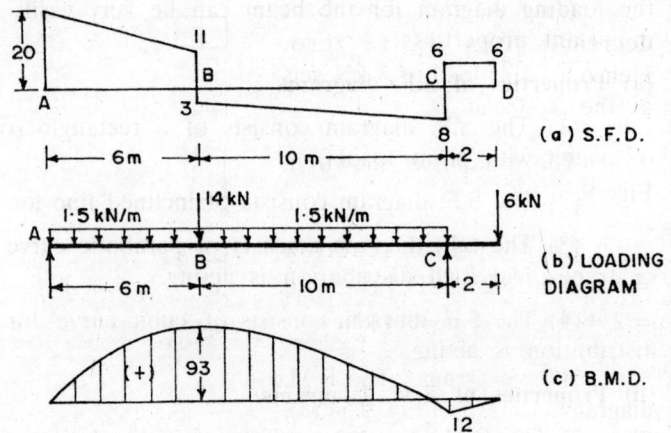

(vi) Between C and D : S.F. is constant, and there is no load.

(vii) At D : The S.F. decreases from + 3 to zero. Hence a point load of 3 kN acts at the free end *D*.

The loading is shown in Fig. 9.54(*b*).

Check : Total reaction = 6 + 8 = 14 kN. Total load = 2 + 1.5 × 6 + 3 = 14 kN.

B.M. diagram : The B.M. diagram is shown in Fig. 9.54 (*c*). Shear force is zero at distance $x = 4/1.5 = 2.667$ m from *B*.

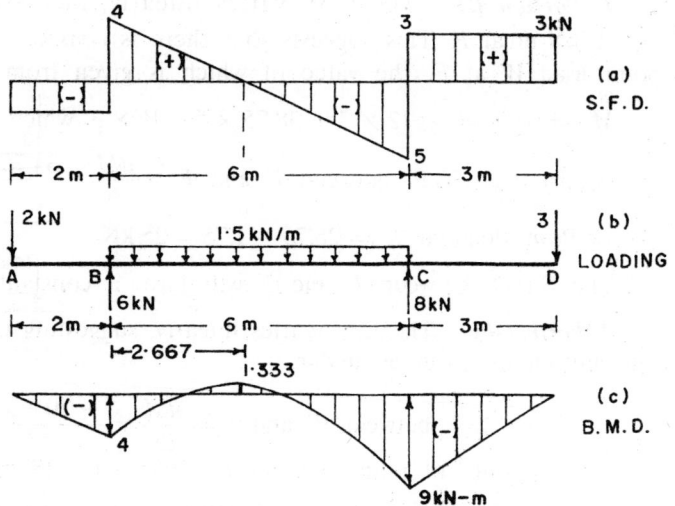

FIG. 9.54

Hence $M_{max}(+) = 6 \times 2.667 - 2(2 + 2.667) - \dfrac{1.5(2.667)^2}{2} = +1.333$ kN-m.

Also, $M_B = -2 \times 2 = 4$ kN-m and $M_C = -3 \times 3 = -9$ kN-m.

Example 9.28. *The B.M. diagram for a beam ABCD, supported at B and C is shown in Fig. 9.55(a). Draw the loading diagram and shear force diagram for the beam.*

Solution :

1. Portion AB : The B.M. varies linearly, suggesting that there is a point load of magnitude 24/2=12 kN acting at *D*. The S.F.D. will have constant ordinate of 12 kN in this portion.

2. Portion BE : The B.M. varies linearly changing from − 24 kN-m at *B* to + 29.50 kN-m at *E*. Hence there is no external loading for this portion. For finding reaction at *B*, write down the equation for B.M. at *E* and equate this to + 29.50 kN-m.

∴ $M_E = +29.50 = -12 \times 4 + R_B \times 2$, from which $R_B = 38.75$ kN (↑).

The S.F.D. between *B* and *E* will have a constant ordinate = − 12 + 38.75 = + 26.75 kN.

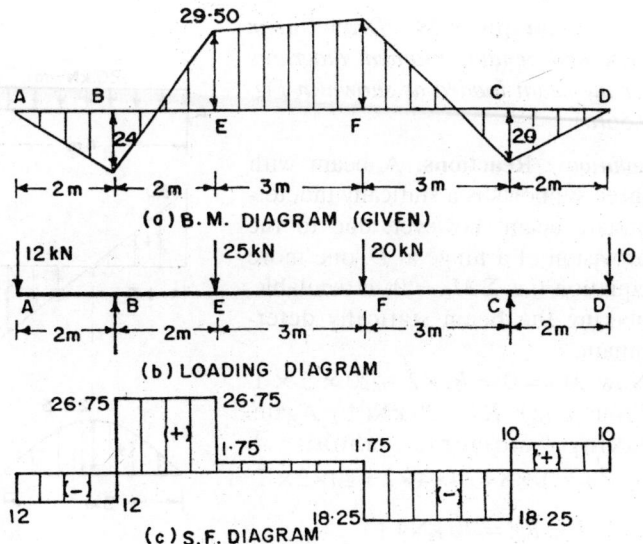

FIG. 9.55

3. Portion EF : The B.M. varies linearly, increasing from $+29.50$ kN-m at E to $+34.75$ kN-m at F. This suggests that there is *constant* S.F. between E and F, resulting in a point load W at E, the value of which is given from the equation

$$M_F = 34.75 = -12 \times 7 + 38.75 \times 5 - W \times 3 \text{ which gives, } W = 25 \text{ kN } (\downarrow)$$

Alternatively, S.F. between E and $F = \dfrac{dM}{dx} = \dfrac{34.75 - 29.50}{3} = 1.75$ kN

$\therefore$ Point load at $E = 26.75 - 1.75 = 25$ kN

The S.F.D. between E and F will have a constant ordinate of $+1.75$ kN

4. Portion FC : The B.M. varies linearly, suggesting that S.F. in this portion is *constant*. It's magnitude is given as under :

$$\text{S.F. between } F \text{ and } C = \frac{dM}{dx} = \frac{-20 - (+34.75)}{3} = -18.25 \text{ kN}$$

$\therefore$ Magnitude of point load at $F = 1.75 - (-18.25) = 20$ kN $(\downarrow)$.

The S.F.D. between F and C will have a constant ordinate of -18.25 kN.

5. Portion DC : The B.M. varies linearly, suggesting that there is a point load of magnitude $20/2 = 10$ kN $(\downarrow)$ at D. Hence S.F.D. between C and D will have constant ordinate of magnitude $+10$ kN.

Reactions : $R_B = 26.75 - (-12) = 38.75$ kN($\uparrow$). Reaction at $C = 10 - (-18.25) = 28.25$ kN($\uparrow$)

Check :   Total downward load $= 12 + 25 + 20 + 10 = 67$ kN

Total upward reaction $= 38.75 + 28.25 = 67$ kN

9.11. ADDITIONAL ILLUSTRATIVE EXAMPLES

Example 9.29. *Draw shear force and bending moment diagrams for the beam loaded as shown in Fig. 9.56(a).*

Solution : Reactions: A beam with three supports is a statically indeterminate beam; however, due to the provision of a hinge at D, one more equation (*i.e.* $\Sigma M_D = 0$) is available, making the beam statically determinate.

Now $M_D = 0 = R_B \times 2 - 20 \times 2 \times 1$.

From which $R_B = 20$ kN($\uparrow$) Again, taking moments about A,

$R_C \times 4 + 20 \times 8 = 20 \times 4 \times 2 + 20 \times 2 \times 7$

$\therefore$ $R_C = 70$ kN $(\uparrow)$

$\therefore$ $R_A = (20 \times 4) + (20 \times 2) - (20 + 70)$

$= 30$ kN $(\uparrow)$

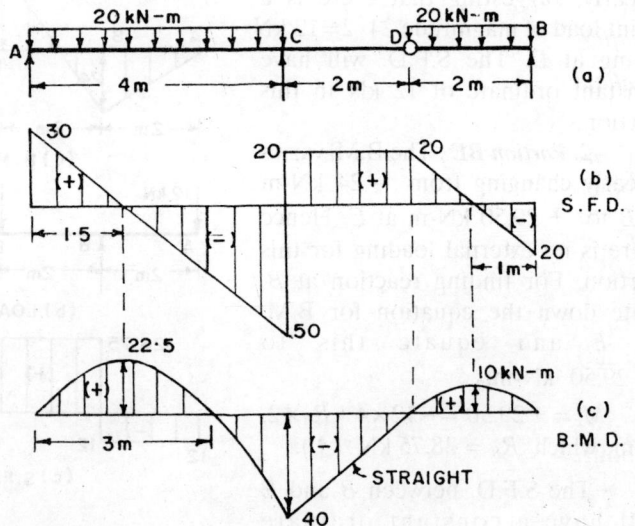

FIG. 9.56

S.F. diagram : *For AC*

$$F_x = 30 - 20x$$

At A, $F_A = 30$ kN.

At C, F_C (*left*) $= 30 - 20 \times 4 = -50$ kN. Shear force is zero at $x = 30/20 = 1.5$ m

For CD : $F_x = 30 - 20 \times 4 + 70$, $= 20$ kN which is constant between C and D.

For DB : $F_x = 30 - 20 \times 4 + 70 - 20(x - 6)$, where is a linear variation.

At $x = 6$ m, $F_D = 30 - 80 + 70 = 20$ kN. At $x = 8$ m, $F_B = 20 - 20(8-6) = -20$ kN.

S.F. is zero at $x = 20/20 = 1$ m from B. The S.F.D. is shown in Fig. 9.56(b).

B.M. diagram : *For AC*, $M_x = 30x - (20x^2)/2$ (Parabolic variation)

M_{max} (at $x = 1.5$ m) $= 30 \times 1.5 - 10(1.5)^2 = 22.5$ kN/m.

$M_C = 30(4) - 10(4)^2 = -40$ kN-m

B.M. is zero at $x = 30/10 = 3$ m.

For CD : $M_x = 30x - 20 \times 4(x - 2) + 70(x - 4)$

At $x = 6$ m, $M_D = 30 \times 6 - 80(6 - 2) + 70(6 - 4) = 0$, as expected.

For DB : Measuring x from B, $M_x = 20x - \dfrac{20x^2}{2}$ (parabolic variation)

This is maximum at $x = 1$ m. $M_{max} = 20 \times 1 - 10(1)^2 = 10$ kN-m.

At $x = 2$, $M_D = 20 \times 2 - 10(2)^2 = 40 - 40 = 0$, as expected.

The B.M.D is shown in Fig. 9.56(c).

Example 9.30. *A simply supported beam ABC is loaded as shown in Fig. 9.57(a). Determine the location at which a concentrated load of 2.5 kN must act from A to make the reactions at A and B equal. For this location, draw the S.F. and B.M. diagrams. Also locate the point of contraflexure.*

Solution :

Let the 2.5 kN load act at a from A. Taking moments about B,

$$R_A = \frac{1}{4}\left[2.5(4 - a) + \frac{1}{2} \times 2 \times 2 \times \left(2 + \frac{2}{3} \times 2\right) - 2 \times 1\right]$$

$$= \frac{1}{4}[14.666 - 2.5a]$$

Similarly, taking moments about A,

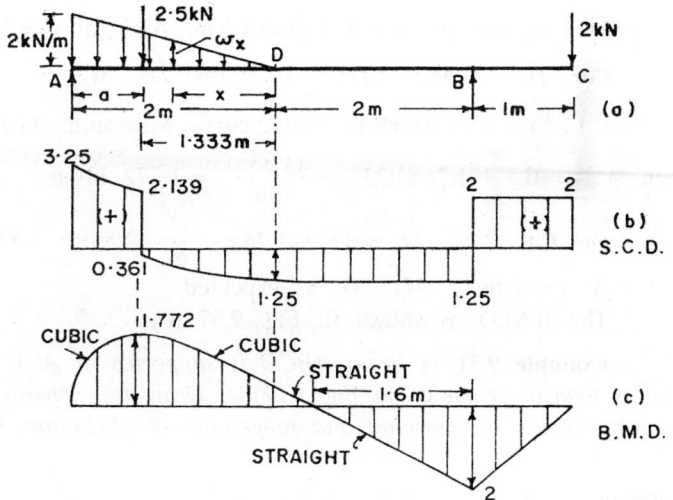

FIG. 9.57

$$R_B = \frac{1}{4}\left[2 \times 5 + 2.5a + \frac{1}{2} \times 2 \times 2 \times \frac{1}{3} \times 2\right] = \frac{1}{4}(11.333 + 2.5a)$$

For the two reactions to be equal, we have

$$\frac{1}{4}[14.666 - 2.5\,a] = \frac{1}{4}\left(11.333 + 2.5\,a\right)$$

From which we get $a = 0.667$ m. Substituting this value of a, we get

$$R_A = \frac{1}{4}[14.667 - 2.5 \times 0.667] = 3.25 \text{ kN } (\uparrow)$$

Also, $R_B = \frac{1}{4}\left(11.333 + 2.5 \times 0.667\right) = 3.25$ kN $(\uparrow)$.

S.F. Diagram : Rate of loading at $E = \frac{2}{2}(2 - 0.667) = 1.333$ kN/m.

Rate of loading at x from $D = \frac{2}{2}x = x$ kN/m

For CB, $F_x = +2$ kN, which is constant between C and B.

For BD $F_x = 2 - 3.5 = -1.25$ kN, which is constant from B to D.

For BE, Measuring x from D, $F_x = 2 - 3.25 + \frac{1}{2}x \cdot x = 0.5\,x^2 - 1.25$, which is a parabolic variation. At $x = 2 - 0.667 = 1.333$ m , F_E (*right*) $= 0.5\,(1.333)^2 - 1.25 = -0.361$ kN

For EA, Measuring x from D, $F_x = 2 - 3.25 + \frac{1}{2}x^2 + 2.5 = 0.5\,x^2 + 1.25$, which is a parabolic variation. At $x = 1.333$, F_E (*left*) $= 0.5\,(1.333)^2 + 1.25 = +2.139$ kN

At $x = 2$ m , $F_A = 0.5\,(2)^2 + 1.25 = +3.25$ kN

The S.F. diagram is shown in Fig. 9.57 (*b*).

B.M. diagrams : **For CB**, $M_x = -2x$, giving $M_C = 0$ and $M_B = -2$ kN-m.

For BD : Measuring x from B, $M_x = -2(1 + x) + 3.25\,x = 1.25\,x - 2$

This is zero at $x = 2/1.25 = 1.6$ m. Also, at $x = 2$ m , $M_D = 1.25 \times 2 - 2 = 0.5$ kN-m

For DE : Measuring x from D, $M_x = -2(3 + x) + 3.25(2 + x) - \frac{1}{2}x \cdot x \cdot \frac{x}{3}$

$= 0.5 + 1.25\,x - x^3/6$ which is a cubic curve. Maximum occurs at $x = 1.333$ m where S.F. changes

sign. $M_{max} = 0.5 + 1.25\,(1.333) - \dfrac{(1.333)^3}{6} = 1.772$ kN-m.

For EA : $M_x = 0.5 + 1.25\,x - \dfrac{x^3}{6} - 2.5\,(x - 1.333)$.

At $x = 2$ m, $M_A = 0$, as expected

The B.M.D. is shown in Fig. 9.57 (*c*).

Example 9.31. *A beam ABCD is supported at A, C and D, has an internal hinge at B and is loaded as shown in Fig. 9.58(a). Draw the bending moment and shear force diagrams, showing clearly the position and magnitude of maximum B.M. in the beam.*

(Based on U.L.)

Solution :

1. **Reactions** : Due to hinge at B, the B.M. M_B is zero.

Hence $M_B = 0 = 6\,R_A - \frac{1}{2} \times 6 \times 6 \left(\frac{2}{3}6\right)$ which gives $R_A = 12$ kN $(\uparrow)$. Similarly, considering all the forces to the right of B, $M_B = 0 = R_D \cdot 6 + R_C \cdot 2 - 8 \times 4 \times 4$.

$$\therefore \qquad\qquad 3R_D + R_C = 64 \qquad\qquad\qquad ...(i)$$

Also, for the whole beam,

$$R_A + R_C + R_D = \left(\frac{1}{2} \times 6 \times 6\right) + 6 + \left(8 + 4\right)$$

or $\qquad\qquad\qquad R_C + R_D = 56 - R_A = 56 - 12 = 44 \qquad\qquad ...(ii)$

From (i) and (ii) we get $R_D = 10$ kN and $R_C = 34$ kN.

2. S.F. Diagram: For DC. Measuring x from D, $F_x = -10 + 8x$, which gives $F_D = -10$ kN and F_C (right) $= -10 + 8 \times 4 = +22$ kN. S.F. is zero at $x = 10/8 = 1.25$ m.

For CB: $F_x = -10 + 32 - 34 = -12$ kN, which is constant for CB.

For BA : Measuring x from B. $w_x = \dfrac{6}{6}x = x$ kN/m

$$\therefore F_x = -10 + 32 - 34 + 6 + \frac{1}{2}x \cdot x$$
$$= -6 + 0.5x^2, \text{ which is a}$$
parabolic variation.

S.F. is zero at $x = \left(\dfrac{6}{0.5}\right)^{1/2} = 3.464$ m. At $= 6$ m, $F_A = -6 + 0.5\,(6)^2 = +12$ kN

The S.F. diagram is shown in Fig. 9.58(b).

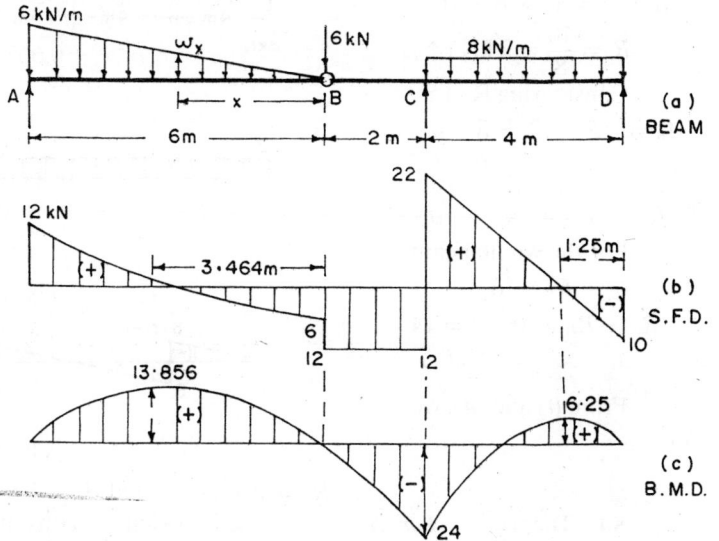

FIG. 9.58

3. B.M. Diagram : For DC, $M_x = 10x - \dfrac{8x^2}{2} = 10x - 4x^2$ (Parabolic)

M_{max} (at $x = 1.25$ m) $= 10 \times 1.25 - 4\,(1.25)^2 = +6.25$ kN-m.
B.M. is zero at $x = 10/4 = 2.5$ m.
Also, at $x = 4$, $M_C = 10 \times 4 - 4\,(4)^2 = -24$ kN-m

For CB : Measuring x from C, $M_x = 10\,(4 + x) - 32\,(2 + x) + 34x = 12x - 24$ which is a linear variation. At $x = 2$ m, $M_B = 12 \times 2 - 24 = 0$, as expected.

For BA : Measuring x from B, $M_x = 10\,(6 + x) - 32\,(4 + x) + 32\,(2 + x) - 6x - \dfrac{1}{2}x \cdot x \cdot \dfrac{x}{3} = 6x - \dfrac{x^3}{6}$, which is a cubic curve. Maximum occurs at $x = 3.464$ m, where

S.F. is zero. Hence $M_{max} = 6 \times 3.464 - \dfrac{(3.464)^3}{6} = 13.856$ kN-m. At $x = 6$ m, $M_A = 6 \times 6 - \dfrac{(6)^3}{6} = 0$ as expected. The B.M.D. is shown in Fig. 9.58(c).

Example 9.32. *A beam ABCD has an internal hinge at B and is loaded as shown in Fig. 9.59(a). Determine the reactions at A, C and D and plot the S.F. and B.M. diagrams, indicating principal values.*

Solution :

Reactions :
Considering L.H.S.,
$$M_B = 0 = R_A \times 8 - 16$$
$$\therefore \quad R_A = \frac{16}{8} = 2 \text{ kN } (\uparrow)$$
Considering R.H.S.,
$$M_B = 0 = R_D \cdot 12 + R_C \cdot 4$$
$$- 16 \times 6$$
or $R_C + 3 R_D = 24$ ...(i)

For the whole beam
$R_A + R_C + R_D = 16$.
$$\therefore \quad R_C + R_D = 16 - 2 = 14$$
...(ii)

From (i) and (ii), we get

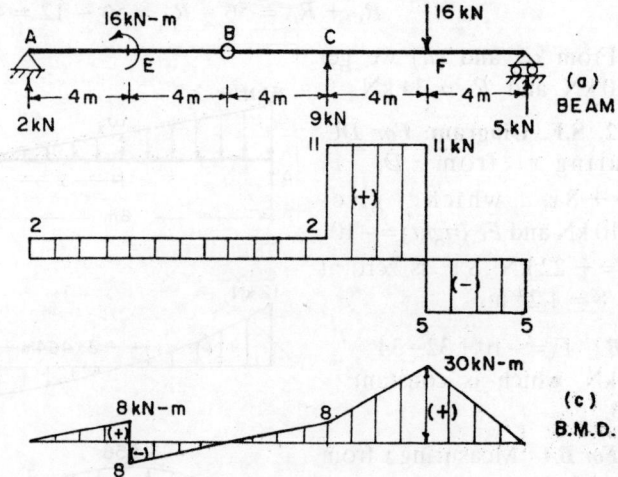

FIG. 9.59

$$R_D = 5 \text{ kN } (\uparrow) \text{ and } R_C = 9 \text{ kN}(\uparrow)$$

S.F. Diagram : For AC : $F_x = 2$ kN, which is constant from A to C.

For CF : $F_x = 2 + 9 = 11$ kN, which is a constant from C to F.

For FD : $F_x = 2 + 9 - 16 = -5$, which is constant from F to D.
The S.F. diagram is shown in Fig 9.59(b).

B.M. Diagram: For AE : $M_x = 2x$, which is a linear variation

At $x = 0$, $M_A = 0$. At $x = 4$ m, M_E *(left)* $= 2 \times 4 = 8$ kN-m

For EC : $M_x = 2x - 16$, which is a linear variation

At $x = 4$ m, $M_x = 2 \times 4 - 16 = -8$ kN. At $x = 8$, $M_B = 2 \times 8 - 16 = 0$, as expected.
At $x = 12$, $M_x = 2 \times 12 - 16 = 8$ kN-m

For CF : $M_x = 2x - 16 + 9 (x - 12)$, which is a linear variation.

At $x = 14$ m, $M_{max} = 2 \times 14 - 16 + 9 (14 - 12) = +30$ kN-m

For FD : $M_x = 2x - 16 + 9 (x - 12) - 16 (x - 14)$, which is a linear variation.

At $x = 20$ m, $M = 2 \times 20 - 16 + 9 (20 - 12) - 16 (20 - 14) = 0$, as expected.
The B.M.D. is shown in Fig. 9.59(c).

Example 9.33. *A beam AB, 8 m long and supported at A, has a simple support of 1 m length between C and D. Assuming uniformly distributed reaction between C and D, draw the S.F. and B.M. diagrams for the loading shown in Fig. 9.60(a).*

Solution :

Reactions : Since the reaction at CD is uniformly distributed over a length of 1 m, it can be replaced by its resultant R_2 acting at the middle of CD. Taking moments about A, we get

$$R_2 \cdot (6.5) = \frac{1}{2} \times 1 \times 4.5 \left(\frac{2}{3} \times 4.5 \right) + 1 \times 8$$

From which
$R_2 = 2.2692$ kN
Taking moments
about R_2,
$R_1 \times 6.5 + 1 \times 1.5$
$= \frac{1}{2} \times 4.5 \times 1 \left(2 + \frac{1}{3} \times 4.5 \right)$

$\therefore R_1 = 0.9808$ kN (↑)

Check : $R_1 + R_2$
$= 2.2692 + 0.9808 = 3.25$ kN
Total load
$= 1 + \frac{1}{2} \times 1 \times 4.5 = 3.25$ kN

At any distance x
from A, rate of loading in
$AE = \frac{1}{4.5} x = \frac{x}{4.5}$

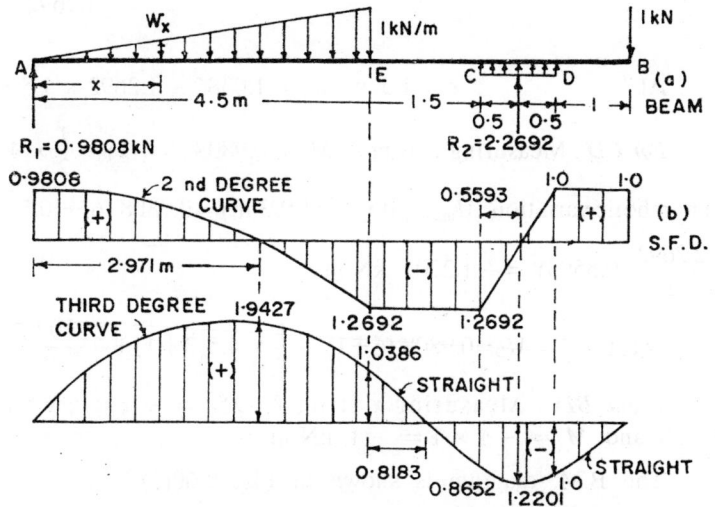

FIG. 9.60

S.F. diagram : *For AE* : $F_x = 0.9808 - \frac{1}{2} \times x \times \frac{x}{4.5} = 0.9808 - \frac{x^2}{9}$ which is a second degree curve. At $x = 0$, $F_A = 0.9808$ kN. At $x = 4.5$ m, $F_E = -1.2692$ kN. S.F. is zero at $x = (0.9808 \times 9)^{1/2} = 2.971$ m.

For EC, $F_x = 0.9808 - \frac{1}{2} \times 1 \times 45 = -1.2692$ kN, which is constant between E and C.

For CD : Rate of reaction $= \frac{R_2}{1} = 2.2692$ kN/m

Hence $F_x = 0.9808 - \frac{1}{2} \times 1 \times 4.5 + 2.2692 (x - 6) = -1.2692 + 2.2692 (x - 6) = 2.2692 x - 14.8844$, which is a linear variation. S.F. is zero at $x = 14.8844 / 2.2692 = 6.5593$ m from A or at $6.5593 - 6 = 0.5593$ m from C. At $x = 7$ m, $F_D = 2.2692 \times 7 - 14.8844 = +1$ kN.

For DB : $F_x = 0.9808 - \frac{1}{2} \times 1 \times 4.5 + 2.2692 = 1$ kN, which is constant between D to B.

B.M. Diagram : *For AE*, $M_x = 0.9808 x - \frac{1}{2} \times x \times \frac{x}{4.5} \times \frac{1}{3} x = 0.9808 x - \frac{x^3}{27}$ which is a third degree curve. B.M. is maximum at $x = 2.971$ m, where S.F. is zero.

$$M_{\max} = 0.9808 \times 2.971 - \frac{(2.971)^3}{27} = 1.9427 \text{ kN-m.}$$

At $\qquad x = 4.5$ m , $M_E = 0.9808 \times 4.5 - \frac{(4.5)^3}{27} = +1.0386$ kN-m

For EC : Measuring x from E, $M_x = 0.9808\ (x + 4.5) - \frac{1}{2} \times 1 \times 4.5\ (x + 4.5) = 1.0386 - 1.2692\ x$.

This is a linear variation. The B.M. is zero at $x = \dfrac{1.0386}{1.2692} = 0.8183$ m from E.

At $x = 1.5$ m, $M_C = 1.0386 - 1.2692 \times 1.5 = -0.8652$ kN-m

For CD : Measuring x from C, $M_x = 0.9808\ (6 + x) - \dfrac{1}{2} \times 4.5 \times 1\ (3 + x) + \dfrac{2.2692\ x^2}{2}$, which

is a parabolic variation. M_{max} (at $x = 0.5593$ m) $= 0.9808\ (6 + 0.5593) - \dfrac{1}{2} \times 4.5 \times 1 \times (3 + 0.5593)$

$+ \dfrac{2.2692}{2}\ (0.5593)^2 = -1.2201$ kN-m.

At $x = 1$, $M_D = 0.9808\ (6+1) - \dfrac{1}{2} \times 4.5(3+1) + \dfrac{2.2692\ (1)^2}{2} = -1.0$ kN-m.

From BD : Measuring x from B, $M_x = -1 \times x$, which is a linear variation, giving $M_B = 0$ and $M_x = -1 \times 1 = -1$ kN-m.

The B.M. diagram is shown in Fig. 9.60(c).

Example 9.34. *The S.F. diagram for a beam AB, hinged at both the ends is shown in Fig. 9.61(a). Determine the loading on the beam and draw the B.M. diagram, indicating principal values.*

Solution :

Reactions

Since the beam is hinged at both the ends, reaction at end $A = R_A$ $= F_A = -4.4$ kN. Hence $R_A = 4.4$ kN($\downarrow$). Similarly, reaction at $B = $ S.F. at B.

Hence $R_B = F_B = 2$ kN($\uparrow$)

Loading Diagram

For AC : S.F. is constant between A to C. Hence there is no loading between A to B.

For CD : At C, there is sudden decrease of 2.4 kN in the negative S.F. This suggests that there is an upward point load of 2.4 kN at C. Between C and D, there is linear variation in the S.F., suggesting that there is U.D.L. of magnitude $\dfrac{2 + 1.2}{4} = 0.8$ kN/m, *acting upwards*.

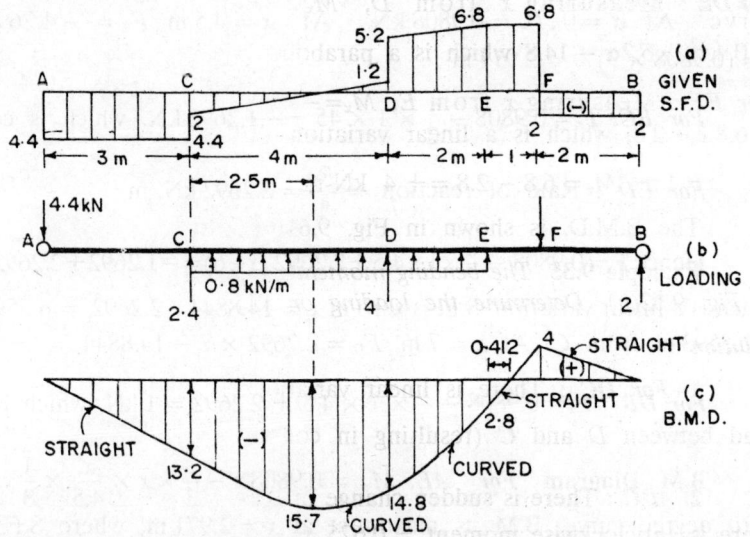

FIG. 9.61

For DE : There is sudden increase in S.F. by 4 kN, suggesting that there is a point load of 4 kN acting *upwards* at D. Also, there is linear variation in S.F. Hence an upward U.D.L. of magnitude $\dfrac{6.8 - 5.2}{2} = 0.8$ kN/m acts in this portion.

For EF : Since the S.F. is constant in this length, there is no external load on this portion.

For FB : At F, there is sudden decrease in S.F., from $+ 6.8$ kN to $- 2$ kN. Hence a point load of magnitude $6.8 + 2 = 8.8$ kN acts downwards at F. Again, since S.F. is constant between F and B, no other load is acting in this portion.

The loading diagram is shown in Fig. 9.61(b).

Check   Total load $= 8.8 - 2.4 - 4 - 0.8 \times 6 = -2.4$ kN, i.e. 2.4 kN ($\uparrow$)

Total reaction $= 2 - 4.4 = -2.4$, i.e. 2.4 kN ($\downarrow$)

B.M. Diagram   For AC : $M_x = -4.4x$, which is a linear variation. At $x = 3$ m, $M_C = -4.4 \times 3 = -13.2$ kN-m.

For CD: S.F. is zero at $x = \dfrac{2}{0.8} = 2.5$ m from C. Measuring x from C, $M_x = -4.4(3+x)$ $+2.4x + \dfrac{0.8x^2}{2} = 0.4x^2 - 2x - 13.2$ which is a parabolic variation. At $x=0, M_C = -13.2$ kN-m. At $x = 4$ m, $M_D = -14.8$ kN-m. M_{max} (at $x = 2.5$ m)$= 0.4(2.5)^2 - 2 \times 2.5 - 13.2 = -15.7$ kN-m.

For DE : Measuring x from D, $M_x = -4.4(x+7)+2.4(x+4) + 0.8 \times 4(2+x)+0.8\dfrac{x^2}{2}+4x$ $= 0.4x^2 + 5.2x - 14.8$ which is a parabolic variation. At $x = 2$ m, we get $M_E = -2.8$ kN-m.

For EF : Measuring x from E, $M_x = -4.4(9+x)+2.4(6+x)+4(2+x)+0.8 \times 6(x+3)$ $= 6.8x - 2.8$, which is a linear variation.

At $x = 1$ m, $M_F = 6.8 - 2.8 = +4$ kN-m. B.M. is zero at $x = 2.8/6.8 = 0.412$ m from F.

The B.M.D. is shown in Fig. 9.61(c).

Example 9.35. *The bending moment diagram of a beam AD, hinged at A and D, is shown in Fig. 9.62(a). Determine the loading on the beam and draw the S.F. diagram.*

Solution :

1. For DC : There is linear variation of B.M. between D and C. Hence there is no load between D and C (resulting in constant S.F) and hence $R_D = \dfrac{0.625}{2.5} = 0.25$ kN ($\downarrow$).

2. At C : There is sudden change in B.M. from -0.625 kN-m to $+11.875$ kN-m. Hence there is anticlockwise moment $= 0.625 + 11.875 = 12.5$ kN-m at C, causing concavity upwards, for the remaining portion.

3. For CB : From C to B, there is linear variation of B.M. resulting in a constant S.F. $= \dfrac{dM}{dx} = \dfrac{\text{Initial B.M.} - \text{Final B.M}}{2.5} = \dfrac{11.875 - 10.625}{2.5} = 0.5$ kN.

Since $R_D = 0.25$ kN only, there exists a point load $= 0.5 - 0.25 = 0.25$ kN ($\downarrow$) at C.

4. For BA : From B to A, there is parabolic variation of B.M. Hence there will be linear variation in S.F., indicating U.D.L. between A and B.

Taking moments about A, we have

$$M_A = 0 = -0.25 \times 10 - 0.25 \times 7.5$$
$$+ 12.5 - \frac{w\,(5)^2}{2}$$

This gives $w = 0.65$ kN/m

Hence $R_A = 0.65 \times 5 + 0.25$
    $+ 0.25 = 3.75$ kN ($\uparrow$)

The loading diagram is shown in Fig. 9.62(b). Knowing the loading diagram, the S.F.

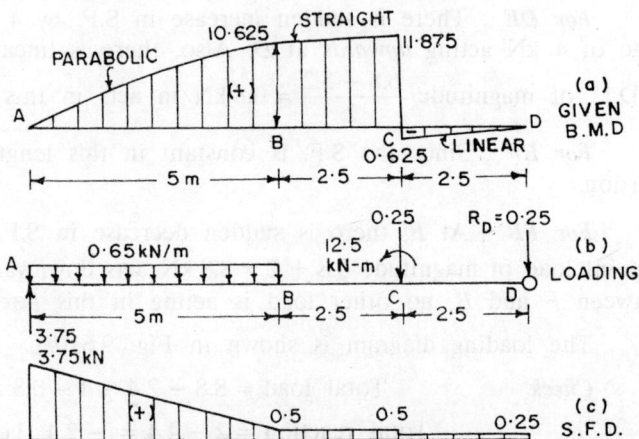

FIG. 9.62

diagram can now be drawn, as shown in Fig. 9.62(c). It is to be noted that the S.F. is positive throughout.

Example 9.36. *A beam ABCD is supported at B and C and has overhangs AB and CD. The B.M. diagram for the beam is shown in Fig. 9.63(a). Draw the loading on the beam and the S.F. diagram.*   *(Based on U.L.)*

Solution :

(i) For Portion AB

The B.M. diagram is a second degree curve. Hence U.D.L. acts on AB having

$$w = \frac{24 \times 2}{x^2} = \frac{24 \times 2}{(4)^2} = 3 \text{ kN/m}$$

The S.F. will vary linearly having
$F_B = -3 \times 4 = -12\,kN$

(ii) For Portion BE

The B.M.D. is linear, suggesting that there is no load on portion BE. The B.M. at E is zero. This gives
$M_E = 0 = -3 \times 4\,(2 + 2) + R_B \times 2$,
yielding $R_B = 24$ kN ($\uparrow$).

Hence F_B (*right*) $= -3 \times 4 + 24$
$= +12$ kN. Also, $F_E = 12$ kN.

(iii) For Portion EF : The B.M.D is a second degree curve, increasing from

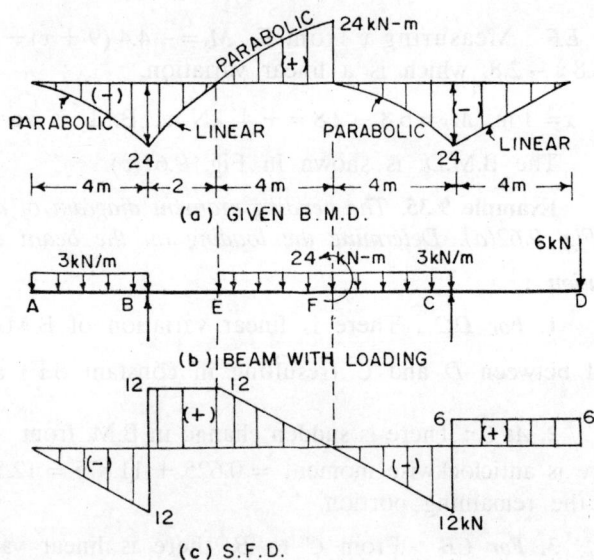

FIG. 9.63

zero value at E to $+24$ kN-m at F. Hence U.D.L. acts between E and F, and its magnitude is given by writing expression for M_F and equating it to $+24$ kN-m.

$$\therefore \qquad M_F = +24 = -3 \times 4\,(2+6) + 24 \times 6 - \frac{w\,(4)^2}{2}, \text{ which gives } w = 3 \text{ kN/m}$$

Alternatively, considering portion EF alone, $\dfrac{w\,(4)^2}{2} = 24$, giving $w = 3$ kN/m. The S.F. for EF will vary linearly. At F, $F_F = 12 - 4 \times 3 = 0$.

Again, at F, B.M. suddenly drops from $+24$ kN-m to zero, suggesting that there is a localised moment of 24 kN-m is the anticlockwise direction.

(iv) **For Portion FC** : The B.M. diagram is a second degree curve, suggesting that U.D.L. is acting on this portion. To find the value of w, write expression for M_C for the left portion of the beam.

Thus $\qquad M_C = -24 = -3 \times 4\,(2+10) + 24 \times 10 - 3 \times 4 \times 6 - 24 - \dfrac{w\,(4)^2}{2}$

This gives $\qquad w = 3$ kN/m

Alternatively, considering FC alone (Since $M_F = 0$), we have

$$\frac{w\,(4)^2}{2} = 24, \text{ giving } w = 3 \text{ kN/m}$$

The S.F. will increase linearly from zero at F to -12 kN at C.

(v) **For Portion CD** : The B.M. varies linearly, suggesting that a point load of magnitude $24/4 = 6$ kN $(\downarrow)$ acts at D. The S.F. will, therefore, be constant from D to C, of magnitude $+6$ kN.

Hence $\qquad\qquad R_C = 6 + 12 = 18$ kN $(\uparrow)$

Check : Total downward load $= (3 \times 4) + (3 \times 8) + 6 = 42$ kN

Total upward reaction $= R_B + R_C = 24 + 18 = 42$ kN

Example 9.37. *AB is a vertical post of a crane (Fig 9.64 a). The sockets at A and B offer no constraint against flexure. The horizontal arm CD is hinged to AB at C and supported by strut FE which is freely hinged at its two extremities to AB and CD. Construct the bending moment diagrams for AB and CD.*

Solution :

$$FE = \sqrt{3^2 + 2^2} = 3.606 \qquad \therefore \ \sin\theta = \frac{2}{3.606} = 0.5547 \qquad \cos\theta = \frac{3}{3.606} = 0.8321$$

1. Reactions

Considering the equilibrium of the whole frame, the horizontal reactions at A and B will be equal and opposite, and its couple must balance the moment of the external loads about AB. Thus,

$$H \times 6 = 20 \times 6 + 2 \times 6 \times 3$$

$\therefore \qquad H = 26 \text{ kN}$

Let T be the thrust in EF. For the arm CD,

$M_C = 0 = T \sin \theta \, (3) - 2 \times 6 \times 3 - 20 \times 6$

From which

$T \quad = \dfrac{36 + 120}{3 \times 0.5547} = 93.74 \text{ kN}$

The vertical reaction at E
$= T \sin \theta = 93.74 \times 0.5547 = 52 \text{ kN}$

Horizontal pull in $CE = P = T \cos \theta$
$= 93.74 \times 0.8321 = 78 \text{ kN} \ (\rightarrow)$

Also, horizontal load at F
$= T \cos \theta = 78 \text{ kN} \ (\leftarrow)$

2. Post AB : The various forces acting on the vertical post AB are shown in Fig. 9.64(b). Evidently, $M_A = M_B = 0$

$M_C = + 26 \times 2 = + 52 \text{ kN-m}$

$M_F = + 26 \times 4 - 78 \times 2 = -52 \text{ kN-m}$

For CF, $\qquad M_x = 26 x - 78 \, (x - 2) = 156 - 52 x,$

which is zero at $\qquad x = \dfrac{156}{52} = 3$ m from A. The B.M.D. is shown in Fig. 9.64 $b(ii)$.

3. Beam CD : The loading on CD is shown in Fig. 9.64 $(c \ ii)$.

For DE : At any distance x from D, $M_x = -20 x - \dfrac{2 x^2}{2} = -20 x - x^2$, which is a parabolic variation. At $x = 3$, $M_E = -20 \times 3 - (3)^2 = -69$ kN-m.

For EC : $\qquad M_x = -20 x - \dfrac{2 x^2}{2} + 52 \, (x - 3)$, which is a parabolic variation.

At $\qquad x = 6 \text{ m}, M_C = -20 \times 6 - (6)^2 + 52 \, (6 - 3) = 0$, as expected.

The B.M. diagram for beam CD is shown in Fig. 9.64 $(c \ ii)$.

Example 9.38. *Draw the B.M. and S.F. diagrams for the beam shown in Fig. 9.65(a), indicating the principal values.*

Solution :

1. Reactions

Taking moments about A,

$$R_B = \frac{1}{9} \left[18 + 4.5 \times 6 + 3 \times 3 + \frac{1}{2} \times 2 \times 9 \times 3 \right] = 9 \text{ kN}(\uparrow)$$

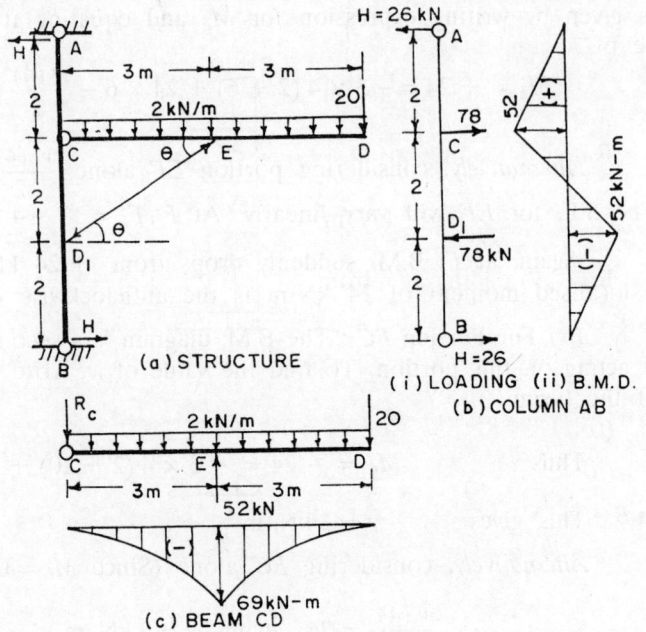

FIG. 9.64

(a) STRUCTURE

(b) COLUMN AB
(i) LOADING (ii) B.M.D.

(c) BEAM CD

$$\therefore \qquad R_A = \left(3 + 4.5 + \frac{1}{2} \times 2 \times 9\right) - 9 = 7.5 \text{ kN } (\uparrow)$$

Rate of loading at E

$$= \frac{2}{9} \times 3 = \frac{2}{3} \text{ kN/m}$$

Rate of loading at D

$$= \frac{2}{9} \times 6 = \frac{4}{3} \text{ kN/m}$$

Rate of loading at x from

$$B = \frac{2}{9} x$$

2. S.F. Diagram

(i) For CB : $\quad F = 0$

(ii) For BE : Measuring x

from B, $F_x = -9 + \frac{1}{2} \times x \times \frac{2}{9} x$

$$= -9 + \frac{x^2}{9}$$

At $x = 0$, $F_B = -9$ kN. At $x = 3$

$$F_E \text{ (right)} = -9 + \frac{(3)^2}{9} = -8$$

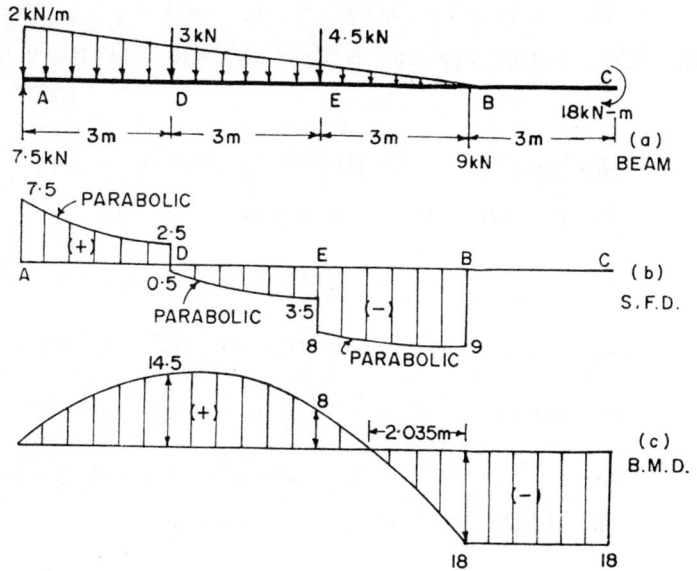

FIG. 9.65

(iii) For ED : Measuring x from B, $F_x = -9 + 4.5 + \frac{1}{2} x \times \frac{2}{9} x = -4.5 + \frac{x^2}{9}$

At $x = 3$ m, $\qquad F_E \text{ (left)} = -4.5 + \frac{(3)^2}{9} = -3.5$ kN.

At $x = 6$ m, $\qquad F_D \text{ (right)} = -4.5 + \frac{(6)^2}{9} = -0.5$ kN.

(iv) For DA : $F_x = -9 + 4.5 + 3 + \frac{1}{2} x \times \frac{2}{9} x = -1.5 + \frac{x^2}{9}$

At $x = 6$ m, $\qquad F_D \text{ (left)} = -1.5 + \frac{(6)^2}{9} = +2.5$ kN . Thus S.F. Changes sign at D.

At $x = 9$ m, $\qquad F_A = -1.5 + \frac{(9)^2}{9} = +7.5$ kN.

The S.F. diagram is shown in Fig. 9.65(b)

3. B.M. Diagram

(i) For CB : $\qquad M_x = -18$ kN-m, which is constant from C to B.

(ii) For EB : Measuring x from B,

$M_x = -18 + 9x - \dfrac{1}{2} \times \dfrac{2}{9} x \times x \times \dfrac{x}{3} = -18 + 9x - \dfrac{x^3}{27}$, which is a third degree curve. At

$x = 0$, $M_B = -18$ kN-m, as before. At $x = 3$, $M_E = -18 + 9 \times 3 - \dfrac{(3)^3}{27} = +8$ kN-m. Thus, the B.M. changes sign and is zero at x given by the cubic equation.

$$\frac{x^3}{27} - 9x + 18 = 0$$

This gives $x = 2.035$ m, by trial and error.

(iii) For ED : $M_x = -18 + 9x - 4.5\,(x - 3) - \dfrac{1}{2} \times \dfrac{2}{9} x \times x \times \dfrac{x}{9} = -4.5 + 4.5 x - \dfrac{x^3}{27}$

At $x = 3$ m, $M_E = -4.5 + 4.5 \times 3 - \dfrac{(3)^3}{27} = +8$ kN-m as before.

At $x = 6$ m, $M_D = M_{max} = -4.5 + 4.5 \times 6 - \dfrac{(6)^3}{27} = +14.5$ kN-m.

(iv) For DA : $M_x = -18 + 9x - 4.5\,(x - 3) - 3\,(x - 6) - \dfrac{x^3}{27}$

At $x = 9$, $M_A = -18 + 9 \times 9 - 4.5\,(9 - 3) - 3\,(9 - 6) - \dfrac{(9)^3}{27} = 0$, as expected.

The B.M.D. is shown in Fig. 9.65(c).

PROBLEMS

1. A beam, 6 m long is simply supported at the ends, and carries a uniformly distributed load of 15 kN/m (including its own weight) and three concentrated loads of 10 kN, 20 kN and 30 kN acting respectively at the left quarter point, centre point and right quarter point. Draw the S.F. and B.M. diagrams and determine the max. bending moment.

2. The intensity of loading on a simply supported beam of 5 m span increases gradually from 1 kN/m at one end to 2 kN/m. run on the other end. Find the position and amount of maximum bending moment. Also, draw the S.F. and B.M. diagrams.

3. Draw S.F. and B.M. diagrams for the beam shown in Fig. 9.66. Indicate numerical values at all important sections.

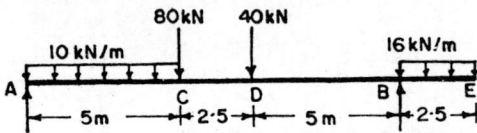

FIG. 9.66

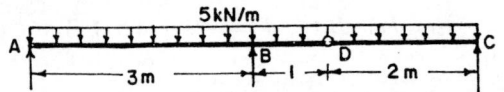

FIG. 9.67

4. Draw the S.F. and B.M. diagrams for the beam shown in Fig. 9.67 indicating principal values.

5. A horizontal beam, 30 m long, carries a uniformly distributed load of 10 kN/m over the whole length and a concentrated load of 30 kN at the right end. If the beam is freely supported at the left end, find the position of the second support so that the bending moment of the beam is as small as possible.

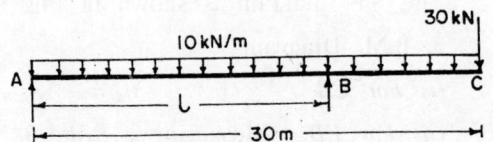

FIG. 9.68

6. A horizontal beam 10 m long is carrying uniformly distributed load of 1 kN/m (Fig. 9.69). The beam is supported on two supports 6 m apart. Find the position of the supports so that B.M. on the beam is as small as possible. Also, draw the S.F. and B.M. diagrams, indicating principal values.

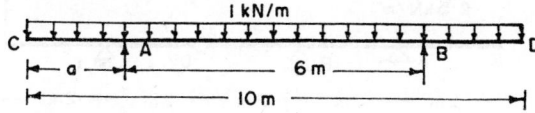

FIG. 9.69

7. For the beam shown in Fig. 9.70, draw the S.F. and bending moment diagrams, indicating principal values.

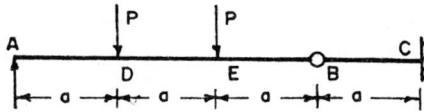

FIG. 9.70

8. Construct the S.F. and B.M. diagrams for the beam shown in Fig. 9.71 and mark the values of the important ordinates.

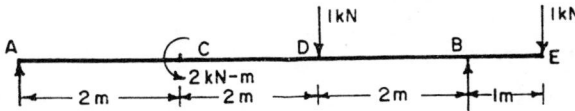

FIG. 9.71

9. The S.F. diagram for a beam ADE, supported at A and D and having an overhang DE is shown in Fig. 9.72. Determine the loading on the diagram and draw the B.M. diagram.

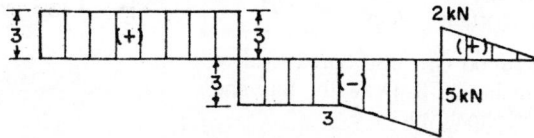

FIG. 9.72

10. A horizontal beam AB, 12 m long is hinged at A and freely supported at B. The beam is loaded as shown in Fig. 9.73. Draw the shear force, bending moment and thrust diagrams for the beam.

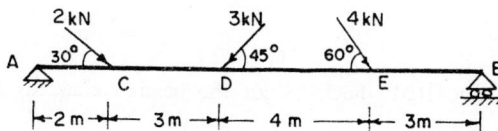

FIG. 9.73

11. For the beam loaded as shown in Fig. 9.74, draw the S.F. and B.M. diagrams, indicating values at important locations.

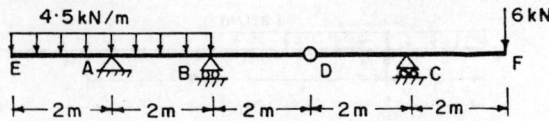

FIG. 9.74

12. A ladder AB, 5 m long, weighing 400 N/m, rests against a smooth wall and on a rough floor as shown in Fig. 9.75. A person weighing 600 N is standing at a distance of 1 m from the bottom. Find the reactions at A and B, and construct the shear force, bending moment and axial thrust diagrams for the ladder.

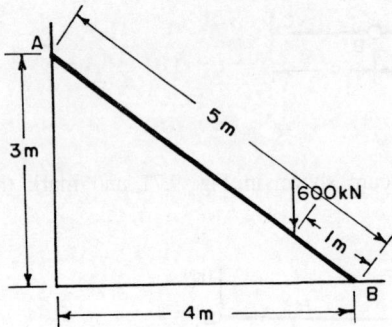

FIG. 9.75

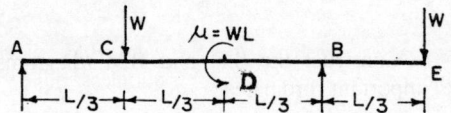

FIG. 9.76

13. Calculate the reactions at A and B for the beam shown in Fig. 9.76. Also draw the S.F. and B.M. diagrams, indicating the principal values.

14. A simple beam AB, shown in Fig. 9.77 is subjected to a concentrated load P and a couple $\mu = \dfrac{PL}{4}$ acting at the position indicated. Draw the S.F. and B.M. diagrams for the beam, indicating important values.

15. A beam $ABCD$ supports a distributed load of varying intensity, as shown in Fig. 9.78. Draw the S.F. and B.M. diagram, indicating principal values.

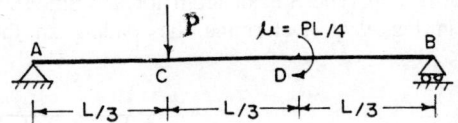

FIG. 9.77

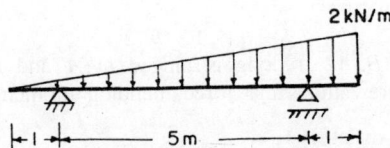

FIG. 9.78

16. Construct the S.F. and B.M. diagrams for the beam, loaded as shown in Fig. 9.79, indicating values at important locations.

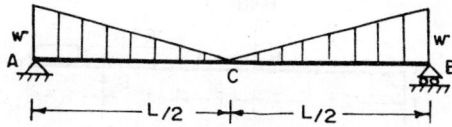

FIG. 9.79

17. A beam *ABCD*, shown in Fig. 9.80 has overhanging ends and carries a distributed load of linearly varying intensity. For what ratio a/L will the S.F. always be zero at the mid-point of the beam ?

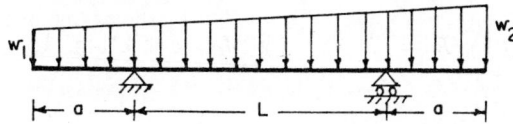

FIG. 9.80

18. Construct the S.F. and B.M. diagrams for the beam *ABC*, loaded as shown in Fig. 9.81. The cable passes over a small frictionless pulley in *C*, and supports a weight *W*.

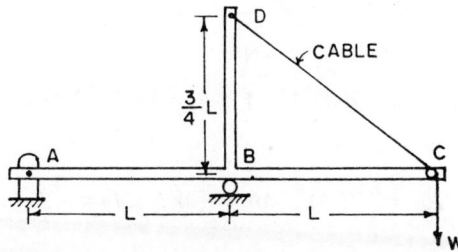

FIG. 9.81

ANSWERS

1. $M_{max} = 127.5$ kN-m

2. $M_{max} = 4.702$ kN-m at 2.638 m from one end.

3. $R_A = 100$ kN; $R_B = 110$ kN; $M_{max}(+) = 375$ kN-m at *C*; $M_{max}(-) = 50$ kN-m at *B*

4. $M_{max}(+) = 2.5$ kN-m at 1 m from either end

   $M_{max}(-) = 7.5$ kN-m at B.

5. $l = 22.96$ m; $M_{max} = 449$ kN-m

6. $a = 2.23$ m; $M_{max} = 2.49$ kN-m

7. $R_A = P$; $R_C = P$; $M_D = +Pa = M_E$; $M_C = -P.a$

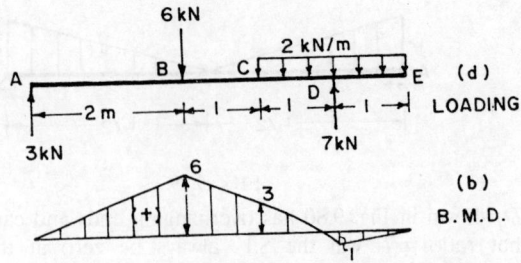

FIG. 9.82

8. $R_A = 0.5$ kN ($\uparrow$); $R_B = 1.5$ kN ($\uparrow$); $M_C = \pm 1$ kN-m; $M_D = 0$; $M_B = -1$ kN-m

9. Fig. 9.82

10. $V_A = 2.937$ ($\uparrow$); $H_A = 1.611$ ($\leftarrow$)

$V_B = 3.648$ ($\uparrow$) ; $H_B = 0$

$M_C = 5.874$; $M_D = 11.685$ kN-m

$M_E = 10.944$ kN-m

11. $R_A = 24$ kN ($\uparrow$), $R_B = 12$ kN ($\downarrow$)

$R_C = 12$ kN ($\uparrow$), $M_A = -9$ kN-m

$M_B = +12$ kN-m, $M_C = -12$ kN-m

12. $R_A = 1493.3$ ($\rightarrow$); $R_B = 2600$ N ($\uparrow$); $R_f = 1493.3$ N ($\leftarrow$)

$M_{max} = 1254.4$ N-m

13. $R_A = \dfrac{4}{3} W$ ($\uparrow$); $R_B = \dfrac{2}{3} W$ ($\uparrow$), $M_C = \dfrac{4}{9} WL$; $M_B = \dfrac{WL}{3}$

14. $R_A = \dfrac{7}{12} P$ ($\uparrow$); $R_B = \dfrac{5}{12} P$ ($\uparrow$); $M_{max} = \dfrac{7}{36} PL$

15. $F_{max}(-) = 3.276$ kN; $F_{max}(+) = 1.875$ kN; $M_{max}(+) = 2.633$ kN-m

16. $F_{max} = \dfrac{wL}{4}$; $M_{max} = \dfrac{wL^2}{24}$

17. $\dfrac{a}{L} = \dfrac{1}{4}$

18. $V_{max}(+) = 0.4 W$; $V_{max}(-) = W$; $M_{max}(-) = W.L.$

Bending Stresses in Beams

10.1. INTRODUCTION :

In the previous chapter, we have seen that when a straight beam carries lateral loads, the actions over any cross-section of a beam comprise (*i*) a bending moment, and (*ii*) shearing force. A beam section has to resist the action of bending moment and shearing force so induced, and under which the beam deforms. This bending is resisted by the internal resistance set up by the cross-section of the beam. The process of bending will stop when it has set up full resistance to the bending moment and the shearing force. The stresses produced at the section to resist the bending moment is known as the *bending stress* or the *longitudinal stress* and that to resist the action of the shearing force is known as *shear stress* or *transverse stress*. In fact the bending moment at any section represents the resultant moment, called the *moment of resistance*, of internal stresses distributed over the section. It is the purpose of this chapter to relate the bending moment to the stresses it causes in a beam. The shearing stresses have been dealt with in chapter 11.

10.2. EFFECT OF BENDING OF A BEAM

The section of a beam resists the bending moment by setting up *bending stresses*, also known as *longitudinal* stresses. Since the B.M. varies along the length of the beam, the magnitude of bending stresses also vary along the length. Also, the bending stresses vary along the depth of the section. As a simple instance, consider a cantilever carrying a concentrated load *W* at its free end, shown in Fig. 10.1 (*a*). At sections remote from the free end, the upper longitudinal fibres are

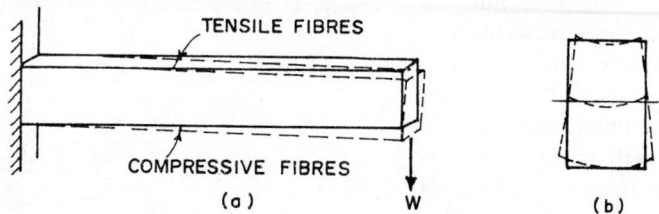

FIG. 10.1. BENDING STRAINS IN A LOADED CANTILEVER.

stretched, *i.e. tensile stresses* are induced while the lower fibres are compressed due to *compressive stresses* set up there. At any cross-section of the beam, as shown in Fig. 10.1 (*b*), the upper fibres, which are stretched longitudinally contract laterally owing to the Poisson's ratio effect while the lower fibres extend laterally. *Thus the whole cross-section of the beam is distorted.* In addition to longitudinal direct stresses in the beam, there are also shearing stresses over any cross-section of the beam. In most engineering problems, *shearing distortions* in the beam are relatively unimportant; this is not true, however of *shearing stresses*.

The bending moment at any section represents the resultant moment, called the *moment of resistance,* of internal forces distributed over the section. The equations of statics alone are not sufficient to establish the law of the distribution and the magnitude of the bending stress occurring at the section. We have to use the conditions of deformation of the beam.

10.3. THEORY OF SIMPLE BENDING

An elementary bending problem is that of a beam, having constant cross-sectional area with an axis of symmetry, under the action of end couples. Such a bending is known as *pure bending* in which the beam is subjected to a constant bending moment M, bending the beam into circular arc of radius R.

Let us consider two sections mn and $m_1 n_1$ along the length of the beam, spaced dx apart and subjected to a bending moment M, which bends the beam into a circular arc of radius R (Fig. 10.2 *a,b*).

If we examine various lines before and after bending, we make the following observations:

1. The two sections mn and $m_1 n_1$, which were parallel to each other before bending, rotate through an angle θ. However, they remain straight after the deformation.

2. The fibre *ab* towards the concave side *shortens*, while the fibre nn_1, towards the convex side *elongates*. However, there exists one fibre, such as *ef*, the length of which remains unchanged, indicating that this fibre neither elongates nor shortens. The layer *ef* is known as the *neutral layer* or the *neutral surface*. The line of intersection of the neutral layer with plane of cross-section of the beam is called the *neutral axis* as marked

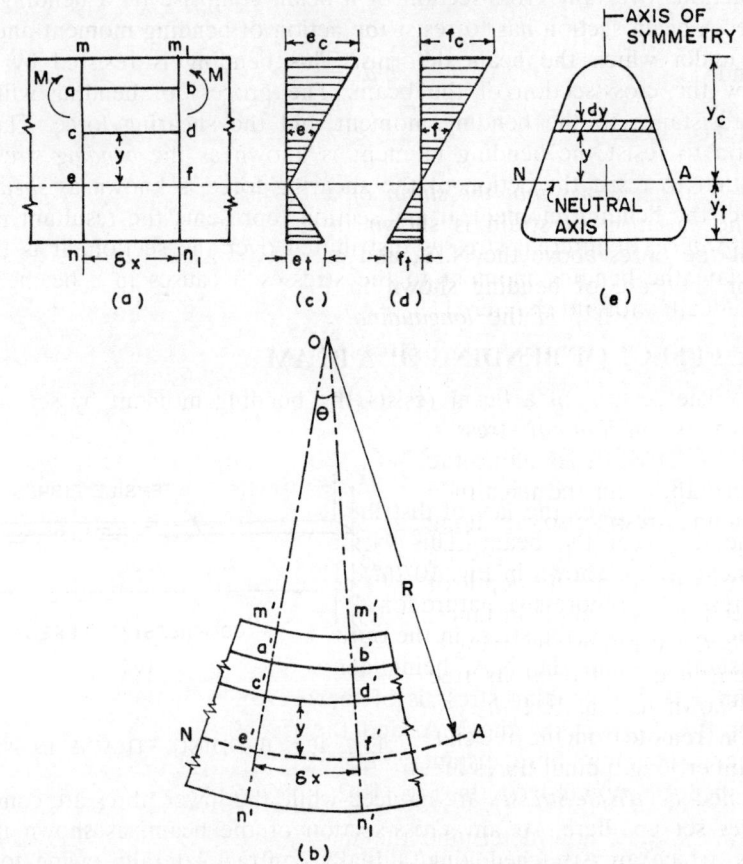

FIG. 10.2. BEAM IN PURE FLEXURE

in Fig. 10.2(e). Both the terms neutral surface as well as the neutral axis imply the location of *zero stress* in the member subjected to bending.

3. From the experimental results we observe that the amount of deformation (compressive or tensile) is greater for farther layers and smaller for those which are nearer to the neutral layer. We shall soon establish that the variation of the deformation is linear along the depth of the beam.

Let us consider an elementary layer cd, at a distance y from the neutral layer, and of thickness dy. This layer bends into shape $c'd'$, under the action the bending moment M.

Strain in the element   =   Change in length/original length

$$\therefore \qquad e = \frac{cd - c'd'}{cd} \text{ (compressive)}$$

Assuming the element to be bent into a circular arc and taking the radius of the neutral fibre to be R,

$$\theta = \frac{e'f'}{R} = \frac{ef}{R} = \frac{\delta x}{R}$$

$$\therefore \qquad \delta x = R \cdot \theta = cd$$

and

$$c'd' = (R - y)\,\theta$$

Hence strain

$$e = \frac{cd - c'd'}{cd} = \frac{R\theta - (R - y)\theta}{R\theta} = \frac{y}{R} \qquad \qquad ...(10.1)$$

This shows that the strain of a fibre is proportional to its distance from the neutral axis. The variation of strain is shown in Fig. 10.2(c). The strains are of compressive nature for all the fibres above the N.A., and are of tensile nature for the fibre below the neutral layer, for the case of bending shown in Fig.10.2(a).

Now, if f is the *longitudinal stress* (usually called the bending stress), we have :

stress = strain × elasticity

or

$$f = e \cdot E = \frac{y}{R} \cdot E$$

Hence we get

$$\frac{f}{y} = \frac{E}{R} \qquad \qquad ...(10.2)$$

This gives the law of distribution of the longitudinal stress (or the bending stress) along the depth of the beam. This variation is also linear, and is shown in Fig. 10.2(d). The bending stress is of compressive nature for all fibres above the neutral axis, the stress in the outer most fibre distant y_c from the N.A. being denoted by f_c. Similarly, the bending stress is of tensile nature for the fibres below the N.A. and the stress in the outer most fibre distant y_t from the N.A. is being denoted by f_t in Fig. 10.2(d).

Let us now determine the magnitude of the longitudinal or bending stress, from the equation of equilibrium. Let us consider the equilibrium of the section mn (say) subjected to external B.M. M, as internal stresses, as shown in Fig. 10.3.

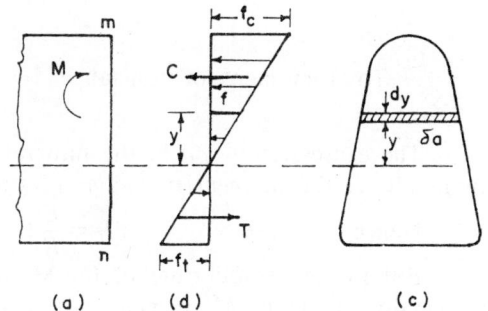

FIG. 10.3

Since there is no other external force, the sum of all the compressive forces above the neutral layer must be equal to the sum of all the tensile forces below the neutral layer.

Let us take a strip of dy thickness at a distance y from N.A. and let its area be δa (Fig. 10.3 c). Since the stress at this location is f, the compressive force exerted by this small area will be equal to $f . \delta a$. Hence the total compressive force C is

$$C = \sum_{y=0}^{y=yc} f . \delta a \quad . \text{ Similarly, the total tensile force is } \quad T = \sum_{y=0}^{y=yt} f \delta a.$$

Since $\qquad C + T = 0$, we have $\displaystyle\sum_{y=yt}^{y=yc} f \delta a = 0$. But $f = \dfrac{E}{R} y$

$$\therefore \qquad \sum_{y=yt}^{y=yc} \frac{E}{R} y \, \delta a \; = 0 \quad \left(\text{But } \frac{E}{R} \text{ is not equal to zero}\right)$$

Hence $\qquad \displaystyle\sum_{y=yt}^{y=yc} y \, \delta a \; = 0$ $\qquad\qquad\qquad\qquad\qquad$ ...(10.3 a)

In the above equation, the term $y . \delta a$ represents the *statical moment* of the elementary area about N.A. Hence $\displaystyle\sum_{y=yt}^{y=yc} y \, \delta a$ is the sum of the statical moments of all such elementary areas of the whole beam about the N.A., and its value is equal to $A \bar{y}$, where A is the total area of cross-section and $\bar{y}$ is the distance of the centroid from the N.A.

Thus we have $\qquad A \bar{y} = 0$ $\qquad\qquad\qquad\qquad\qquad$ ...(10.3)

But $\qquad\qquad A \neq 0$. Hence $\bar{y} = 0$

This shows that the N.A. passes through the centroid of the section. Hence the N.A. may be quickly and easily determined by simply finding the centroid of the cross-section.

Again, referring to Fig. 10.3, the bending moment M acting on section mn is resisted by the *internal moment* set up by the unbalanced forces C and T acting at some distance. This internal moment is known as the *moment of resistance M_r* of the cross-section. In order to find its magnitude, let us again consider the elementary strip of thickness dy, distant y from the N.A.

The elementary moment of resistance $\delta M_r = f \delta a . y = \dfrac{E}{R} . \delta a . y^2$

$$\therefore \text{ Total moment of resistance } M_r = \sum_{y=yt}^{y=yc} \frac{E}{R} . \delta a . y^2 = \frac{E}{R} \int_{yt}^{yc} y^2 \, \delta a \qquad \text{...(10.4)}$$

The expression $y^2 . \delta a$ in the integral is known as the second moment of area, and more commonly as the *moment of inertia* of the section about the N.A. and is represented by I.

Hence we have $\qquad M_r = \dfrac{E}{R} I$ $\qquad\qquad\qquad\qquad\qquad$ ...(10.5)

But for the equilibrium of the section, the moment of resistance M_r must be equal to the bending moment M. Hence

$$M = M_r = \frac{E}{R} I \text{ or } \frac{M}{I} = \frac{E}{R}$$

But from Eq. 10.2, $\dfrac{E}{R}$ is equal to $\dfrac{f}{y}$

Hence we have $$\frac{M}{I} = \frac{f}{y} = \frac{E}{R} \qquad \qquad ...(10.6)$$

The above equation is the well known *flexure formula*.

Also, from Eq. 10.6, we have $\dfrac{1}{R} = \dfrac{M}{E\,I}$. The term $\dfrac{1}{R}\,(=\rho)$ is known as the *curvature* of the section. *Hence the curvature of the axis of the beam is directly proportional to the bending moment and is inversely proportional to the flexural rigidity (EI) of the section.*

10.4. ASSUMPTIONS IN THE SIMPLE THEORY OF BENDING

The simple theory of bending discussed above is based on the following *assumptions*:

1. The beam is initially straight.

2. The beam has constant cross-sectional areas, *with an axis of symmetry*. This axis of symmetry is vertical. Several cross-sectional areas of beams satisfying this condition are shown in Fig. 10.4.

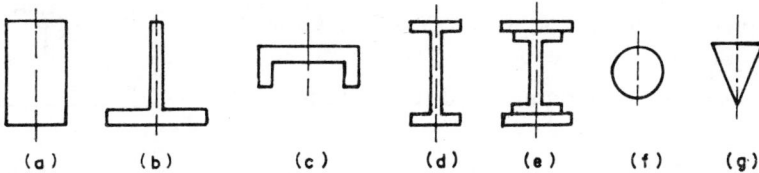

(a)   (b)   (c)   (d)   (e)   (f)   (g)

FIG. 10.4. BEAM CROSS-SECTIONS HAVING VERTICAL AXIS OF SYMMETRY

3. The material of the beam is *homogeneous*, *i.e.* of the same density throughout, and *isotropic*, *i.e.* equally elastic in all directions.

4. Hooke's law is obeyed at all points, *i.e.* stress is proportional to strain, and the stress to which the material is subjected does not exceed the elastic limit.

5. Plane transverse sections remain plane and normal after bending, *i.e.* there is no distortion of the cross-section.

6. Every layer of material is free to expand or contract longitudinally and laterally under stress, and do not exert pressure upon each other. Thus, the Poisson's effect and the interference of the adjoining differently stressed fibres are ignored.

7. The value of Young's modulus (E) for the material is the same in tension and in compression.

10.5. ORDINARY BENDING

The case of *pure bending* or simple bending discussed in Eq. § 10.3 is applicable only when the beam is subjected to *pure moments* (or couples) and the shearing forces are absent. In the ordinary bending commonly encountered, the beam section is subjected to both the bending moment as well as shearing force. In the presence of shearing force existing at the section, assumption No. 5, that the plane sections remain plane after bending will not be true, and the initial plane section will be distorted or warped after bending. The

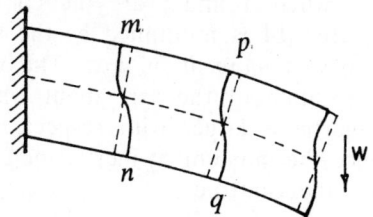

FIG. 10.5. WARPING OF THE CROSS SECTION DUE TO SHEAR

warping can be demonstrated by bending a beam on which vertical lines, such as lines *mn* and *pq* (Fig. 10.5) have been drawn. These lines will not remain straight, but will curve, with the maximum shear strain at the neutral surface. An elaborate investigation of the problem shows that the warping of cross-sections due to shear strains does not substantially affect the longitudinal strain even if a distributed load acts on the beam and the shear force varies contin ously along the beam. More over, in many cases of continuous loading the greatest bending moment occurs where the shearing force is zero. Hence the conditions correspond to those for *simple bending* and the theory and equations discussed above are quite sufficient and give results which enable the engineer to design beams and structures and calculate their stresses and strains with a reasonable degree of accuracy.

10.6. LOCATION OF CENTROID AND COMPUTATION OF *I*

The *centre of gravity* of a body is that point through which the resultant of system of parallel forces formed by the weights of all the particles of the body passes, for all positions of the body. The *plane areas*, like triangle, rectangle, quadrilateral, circle etc., has only *areas* and no mass. The *centre of area* of such figures is known as *centroid*.

Fig. 10.6 shows a plane area *A*, with its centroid *G* having its co-ordinates $\bar{x}$ and $\bar{y}$.

The *first moments* of area about *x* and *y* axes respectively are :

$$Q_x = \int y\,dA \text{ and } Q_y = \int x\,dA \qquad ...(10.7)$$

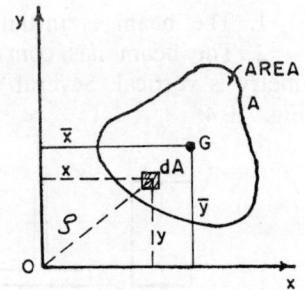

FIG. 10.6 CENTROID OF A PLANE AREA

The co-ordinates $\bar{x}$ and $\bar{y}$ of the centroid *G* are evidently equal to the first moment divided by the area itself.

Thus
$$\bar{x} = \frac{\int x.dA}{\int dA} = \frac{Q_y}{A} \text{ and } \bar{y} = \frac{\int y\,dA}{\int dA} = \frac{Q_x}{A} \qquad ...(10.8)$$

The axial (or equatorial) moment of inertia of a plane area (or of a cross-section) is the geometrical characteristic of the area (or the section) defined by the integrals

$$I_{xx} = \int y^2\,dA \text{ and } I_{yy} = \int x^2\,dA \qquad ...(10.9)$$

where *x* and *y* are the coordinates of the differential element of the area *dA*. Since this area *dA* is multiplied by the square of the distance, the *moment of inertia* is also called the *second moment of area*. The value of moment of inertia of a plane area will vary with the position of the axis about which we wish to find the moment of inertia. The moment of inertia is larger with respect to any axis *AA* than with respect to the centroidal *x*-axis. Hence the moment of inertia increases as the reference axis is moved parallel to it-self farther from the centroid.

A detailed treatment on the method of locating the centroid *G* and on the methods of computing the value of moment of inertia is given in Chapter 8. However, a summery of formulae for *I* for some common sections is given in Fig. 10.7.

$$I_{xx} = \frac{1}{12}bd^3$$

$$I_{yy} = \frac{1}{12}db^3$$

$$I_{xx} = \frac{1}{12}(BD^3 - bd^3)$$

$$I_{yy} = \frac{1}{12}(DB^3 - db^3)$$

$$I_{AB} = \frac{1}{12}bd^3$$

$$I_{xx} = \frac{1}{36}bd^3$$

$$I_{xx} = I_{yy} = \frac{\pi}{64}d^4 \qquad I_{xx} = I_{yy} = \frac{\pi}{64}(D^4 - d^4)$$

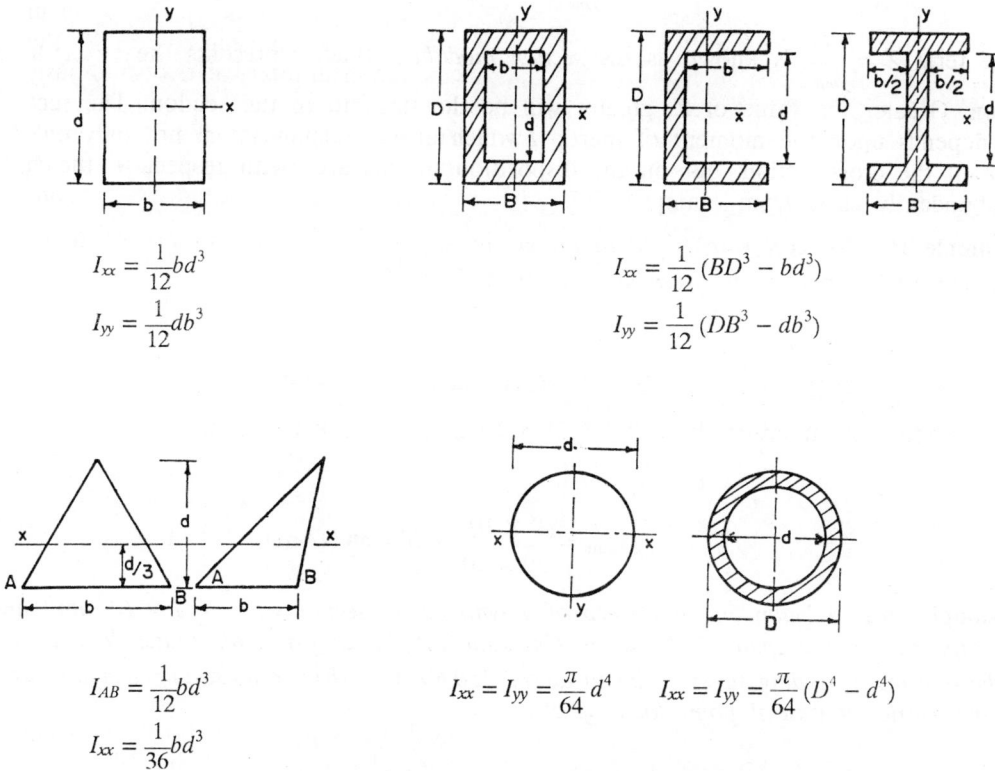

FIG. 10.7. VALUES OF I OF SOME COMMON SECTIONS.

10.7. DESIGN CRITERION : STRENGTH OF SECTION

The beam section should have sufficient strength to resist the external bending moment. To ensure strength of a beam, it is necessary that the greatest tensile and greatest compressive stresses at the critical section (*i.e.* at the section when B.M. is maximum) should not exceed their corresponding allowable stresses for the material.

Let y_t and y_c be the distances of the farthest tensile and compressive fibres respectively, from the N.A. Then we have

$$f_{t,max} = \frac{M}{I}y_t \text{ and } f_{c,max} = \frac{M}{I}y_c \qquad \qquad ...(10.10)$$

Hence the condition of strength or of design is

$$f_{t,max} \leq f_{t,allowable} \text{ and } f_{c,max} \leq f_{c,allowable} \qquad \qquad ...(10.11)$$

Again, $\qquad \qquad f_{t,max} = \frac{M}{I}y_t \text{ and } f_{c,max} = \frac{M}{I}y_c$

or In general $\qquad \qquad f_{max} = \frac{M}{I}y_{max}$

or
$$M = f_{max} \cdot \frac{I}{y_{max}} = f_{max} \cdot Z \qquad\qquad\qquad ...(10.12)$$

where the term $Z = \dfrac{I}{y_{max}}$ is known as the *section modulus*, which represents the strength of the section. Greater the value of Z, greater will be the strength of the section. The section modulus depends upon the moment of inertia I which again depends upon, not only on the total area of the cross-section, but on the disposition of this area with respect to the N.A. This is abundantly clear from example 10.7.

Example 10.1. *A steel wire of 10 mm diameter is bent into a circular arc of 20 metre radius. Determine the maximum stress induced in it. Take $E = 2 \times 10^5 N/mm^2$.*

Solution :

Diameter of wire = 10 mm. Hence $y_{max} = \dfrac{10}{2} = 5$ mm

Radius of curvature $R = 20$ m $= 20 \times 10^3$ mm ; $E = 2 \times 10^5$ N/mm^2

Now
$$\frac{f}{y} = \frac{E}{R}$$

$\therefore$
$$f_{max} = \frac{E}{R} y_{max} = \frac{2 \times 10^5}{20 \times 10^3} \times 5 = \textbf{50 N/mm}^2$$

Example 10.2. *A beam 500 mm deep of a symmetrical section has $I = 1 \times 10^8 mm^4$ and is simply supported over a span of 10 metres. Calculate (a) the uniformly distributed load it may carry if the maximum bending stress is not to exceed $150\,N/mm^2$. (b) the maximum bending stress if the beam carries a central point load of 25 kN.*

Solution :

We have
$$\frac{M_r}{I} = \frac{f}{y}$$

or
$$M_r = f \cdot \frac{I}{y} = f \left(\frac{1 \times 10^8}{250} \right) = 40 \times 10^4 f \ \text{N-mm}$$

(a) Let the U.D.L. by w kN/m

Then
$$M_{max} = \frac{w L^2}{8} = \frac{w\,(10)^2}{8} = 12.5\,w \ \text{kN-m}$$

But
$$1 \ \text{kN-m} = 1 \times 10^3 \times 10^3 = 10^6 \ \text{N-mm.}$$

$\therefore$
$$M_{max} = 12.5\,w \times 10^6 \ \text{N-mm.}$$

Equating this to the moment of resistance M_r, we get
$$12.5\,w \times 10^6 = 40 \times 10^4 f = 40 \times 40^4 \times 150$$

Hence we get
$$w = \frac{40 \times 10^4 \times 150}{12.5 \times 10^6} = \textbf{4.8 kN/m}$$

(b) For a central point load of 50 kN,
$$M_{max} = \frac{WL}{4} = \frac{25 \times 10}{4} = 62.5 \ \text{kN-m} = 62.5 \times 10^6 \ \text{N-mm}$$

$$\therefore \qquad f = \frac{M \cdot y}{I} = \frac{62.5 \times 10^6}{1 \times 10^8} \times 250 = \mathbf{156.25 \ N/mm^2}$$

Example 10.3. *A timber beam of rectangular section is to support a load of 20 kN over a span of 4 m. If the depth of the section is to be twice the breadth, and the stress in the timber is not to exceed 60 N/mm², find the dimensions of the cross-section.*

How would you modify the cross-section of the beam if it were a concentrated load placed at the centre with the same ratio of breadth to depth.

Solution :

Given $\qquad\qquad\qquad d = 2b, \ \text{Hence} \ y_{max} = \frac{d}{2} = b$

$$\therefore \qquad\qquad Z = \frac{b \, d^2}{6} = \frac{b \, (2 \, b)^2}{6} = \frac{2}{3} b^3$$

(a) When the load of 20 kN is uniformly distributed over a span of 4 m,

$$w = \frac{20}{4} = 5 \ \text{kN/m}$$

$$\therefore \qquad M_{max} = \frac{w \, L^2}{8} = \frac{5 \, (4)^2}{8} = 10 \ \text{kN-m} = 10 \times 10^6 \ \text{N-mm} \qquad \ldots(i)$$

Now $\qquad\qquad M_r = f Z = 60 \times \frac{2 \, b^3}{3} = 40 \, b^3 \ \text{N-mm} \qquad\qquad \ldots(ii)$

Equating the moment of resistance to the maximum B.M., we have

$$40 \, b^3 = 10 \times 10^6$$

From which we get $\qquad b = \left(\frac{10 \times 10^6}{40} \right)^{1/3} = 63 \ \text{mm}$

Hence $\qquad\qquad d = 2 \, b = \mathbf{126 \ mm}$

(b) When the load of 20 kN is placed at the mid span,

$$M_{max} = \frac{W L}{4} = \frac{20 \times 4}{4} = 20 \ \text{kN-m} = 20 \times 10^6 \ \text{N-mm}$$

$$M_r = 40 \, b^3 \ \text{N-mm as before}$$

$$\therefore \qquad\qquad 40 \, b^3 = 20 \times 10^6$$

From which $\qquad\qquad b = \left(\frac{20 \times 10^6}{40} \right)^{1/3} = 79.37 \ \text{mm} \approx 80 \ \text{mm}$

Hence $\qquad\qquad d = 2 \, b = 160 \ \text{mm}$

Example 10.4. *A 100 mm × 200 mm rolled steel joist of I-section has flanges 12 mm thick and web 10 mm thick. Find the safe uniformly distributed load that this section can carry over a span of 6 m if the permissible skin stress is limited to 160 N/mm².*

Solution :

For an *I*-section, $\qquad\qquad I = \frac{1}{12} \left(BD^3 - bd^3 \right)$

Here, $b = 100 - 10 = 90 \text{ mm}; d = 200 - 2 \times 12 = 176 \text{ mm}$

$\therefore$

$$I_{xx} = \frac{1}{12} \left[100 \, (200)^3 - 90 \, (176)^3 \right]$$

$$= 25.778 \times 10^6 \text{ mm}^4$$

$\therefore$

$$Z_{xx} = \frac{25.778 \times 10^6}{y_{max}} = \frac{25.778 \times 10^6}{100}$$

$$= 257.78 \times 10^3 \text{ mm}^3$$

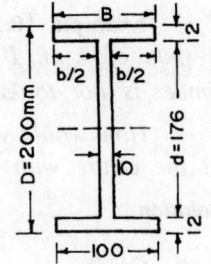

FIG. 10.8

Let w be the safe U.D.L. in kN/m

$\therefore$

$$M_{max} = \frac{wL^2}{8} = \frac{w \, (6)^2}{8} = 4.5 \, w \text{ kN-m} = 4.5 \, w \times 10^6 \text{ kN-m}$$

Now $f_{max} = \dfrac{M_{max}}{Z} = \dfrac{4.5 \, w \times 10^6}{257.78 \times 10^3} = 17.4567 \, w \text{ N/mm}^2$

But this is not to exceed 160 N/mm^2

$\therefore$ $17.4567 \, w = 160$

Giving $w = \mathbf{9.167 \text{ kN/m}}$

Example 10.5. *A cast iron pipe has 300 mm bore and 10 mm metal thickness, and is supported at two points 8 m apart. Find the maximum stress in the metal when it is running full. Take unit weight of cast iron as $70 \, kN/m^3$ and that of water as $9.81 \, kN/m^3$.*

Solution :

Internal area of pipe $= \dfrac{\pi}{4} \, (0.3)^2 = 0.07069 \text{ m}^2$

$\therefore$ Weight of water per m run of pipe $= 0.07069 \times 1 \times 9.81 = 0.6934 \text{ kN/m}$

Area of cross-section $= \dfrac{\pi}{4} \left(D^2 - d^2 \right) = \dfrac{\pi}{4} \left(0.320^2 - 0.300^2 \right) = 9.7389 \times 10^{-3} \text{ m}^2$

$\therefore$ Weight of pipe per m run $= 9.7389 \times 10^{-3} \times 1 \times 70 = 0.6817 \text{ kN/m}$

$\therefore$ Total weight per m run, $w = 0.6934 + 0.6817 = 1.3751 \text{ kN/m}$

Also, $I_{xx} = \dfrac{\pi}{64} \left(D^4 - d^4 \right)$

$$= \dfrac{\pi}{64} \left(320^4 - 300^4 \right) = 11.711 \times 10^8 \text{ mm}^4$$

$\therefore$

$$Z_{xx} = \dfrac{18.7377 \times 10^8}{160} = 731.942 \times 10^3 \text{ mm}^3$$

Now, $M = \dfrac{WL^2}{8} = \dfrac{1.3751 \, (8)^2}{8} = 11 \text{ kN-m} = 11 \times 10^6 \text{ N-mm}$

$\therefore$

$$f = \dfrac{M}{Z} = \dfrac{11 \times 10^6}{731.942 \times 10^3} = \mathbf{15.03 \text{ N/mm}^2}$$

Example 10.6. *For a given stress, compare the moments of resistance of a beam of square section placed (i) with two sides horizontal and (ii) with a diagonal horizontal.*

Solution :

Let b be the side of the square.

In case (i), $Z_1 = \dfrac{1}{6} bd^2 = \dfrac{1}{6} b^3$

In case (ii) shown in Fig. 10.9 (b).

$$I_{xx} = 2 \times \frac{1}{12} b \sqrt{2} \left(\frac{1}{2} b \sqrt{2} \right)^3$$

$$= \frac{b^4}{12}$$

$$y = \frac{1}{2} b \sqrt{2} = \frac{b}{\sqrt{2}}.$$

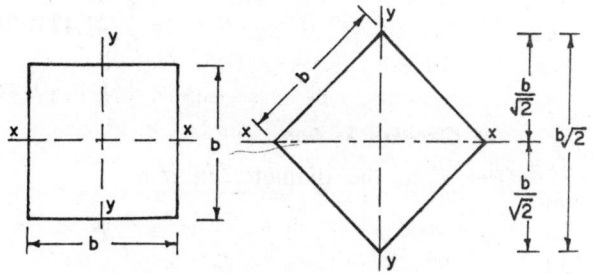

FIG. 10.9

Hence $Z_2 = \dfrac{b^4}{12} \div \dfrac{b}{\sqrt{2}} = \dfrac{b^3}{6\sqrt{2}}$

∴ $\dfrac{Z_1}{Z_2} = \sqrt{2} = 1.414$

Hence arrangement (i) is 41.4 % more strong than (ii).

Example 10.7. *Compare the flexural strength of the following three beams of equal weight.*

(1) I-section 100 mm × 200 mm having 10 mm flange thickness and 8 mm thickness.
(2) A rectangular section having depth equal to twice the width
(3) Solid circular section.

Solution :

(a) I-Section :

$$A_1 = 2 \times 100 \times 10 + 180 \times 8 = 3440 \text{ mm}^2$$

$$I_1 = \frac{1}{12} \left[BD^3 - bd^3 \right] = \frac{1}{12} \left[100\,(200)^3 - 92\,(180)^3 \right] \approx 2195 \times 10^4 \text{ mm}^4$$

$$Z_1 = \frac{2195 \times 10^4}{100} = 219.5 \times 10^3 \text{ mm}^3$$

(b) Rectangular Section :

$$A_2 = bd = b\,(2b) = 2b^2$$

But $A_2 = A_1$

∴ $2b^2 = 3440$

From which $b = 41.473$ mm

and $d = 82.946$ mm

∴ $Z_2 = \dfrac{1}{6} bd^2$

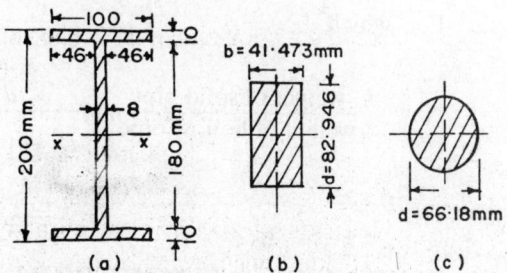

FIG. 10.10

$$= \frac{1}{6}(41.473)(82.946)^2$$

$$= 47.6 \times 10^3 \text{ mm}^3$$

(c) Circular Section

Let d be the diameter in mm.

$\therefore \qquad\qquad\qquad\qquad A_3 = \frac{\pi}{4}d^2$

But $\qquad\qquad\qquad\qquad A_3 = A_1$

$\therefore \qquad\qquad\qquad \frac{\pi}{4}d^2 = 3440$, from which $d = 66.18$ mm

$\therefore \qquad\qquad\qquad Z_3 = \frac{\pi}{32}d^3 = \frac{\pi}{32}(66.18)^3 = 28.5 \times 10^3 \text{ mm}^3$

$\therefore \qquad\qquad\qquad \frac{Z_1}{Z_2} = \frac{219.5}{47.6} = \mathbf{4.61}$ and $\frac{Z_1}{Z_3} = \frac{219.5}{28.5} = \mathbf{7.70}$

The disposition of the cross-sectional area with respect to the axis of bending for each of the three cases, is shown in Fig. 10.10. It is clear that an I-section is the most economical structural section and a circular section is very uneconomical for a beam.

Example 10.8. *Compare the weights of two beams of the same material and of equal strength, one being of circular section and solid and the other being of hollow circular section, the internal diameter being 3/4 of the external.*

Solution :

Let $d=$ diameter of solid section and D be the external diameter of hollow section.

Z for solid section $\qquad = \frac{\pi}{32}d^3$

Z for hollow section $\qquad = \frac{\pi}{32 D}\left[D^4 - \left(\frac{3}{4}D\right)\right]^4 = 0.6836 \times \frac{\pi}{32}D^3$

Hence for equal strength, we have $\frac{\pi}{32}d^3 = 0.6836 \frac{\pi}{32}D^3$

For which $\qquad\qquad \left(\frac{D}{d}\right)^3 = \frac{1}{0.6836} = 1.4629$ or $\frac{D}{d} = 1.1352$

Now $\quad \dfrac{\text{weight of solid pipe}}{\text{weight of hollow pipe}} = \dfrac{d^2}{D^2 - \left(\frac{3}{4}D\right)^2} = \left(\dfrac{d}{D}\right)^2 \times \dfrac{1}{0.4375}$

$$= \left(\frac{1}{1.1352}\right)^2 \frac{1}{0.4375} = \mathbf{1.774}$$

10.8. BENDING OF UNSYMMETRICAL SECTIONS

When the section is unsymmetrical about the axis of bending, we have to first find the position of centroid through which the axis will pass, and then to find the moment of inertia about this axis of bending. This can be done by dividing the section into different rectangles and triangles, as the case may be. The moment of inertia can first be found about an axis passing through the extreme edge of the section and then the moment of inertia can be found about the centroidal axis using the parallel axis theorem. This has been explained in § 8.6 and § 8.8, and illustrated in examples 8.9 to 8.12.

Since the section is unsymmetrical about the axis of bending passing through the centroid, the distance of extreme fibres in compression and tension, *i.e.* y_c and y_t will be *unequal.* Hence the section modulus Z, with respect to compression and tension will be different.

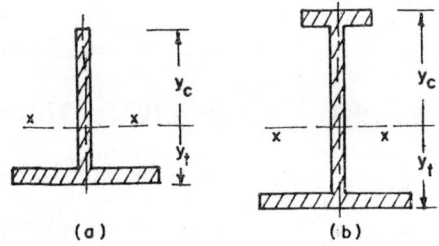

FIG. 10.11

Thus, $\dfrac{M}{I} = \dfrac{f}{y}$ is general.

Hence
$$M_{r_1} = \frac{f_c}{y_c}.I = f_c\, Z_c \ \text{ and } \ M_{r_2} = \frac{f_t}{y_t}.I = f_t.Z_t \qquad ...(10.13)$$

If f_c and f_t are the permissible values of compressive and tensile stresses in bending, the moment of resistance of the section will be the lesser of the two values of M_{r_1} and M_{r_2}.

Again, if M is the applied moment, the induced stresses f_c and f_t are related by the expression

$$M = \frac{f_c}{y_c}I = \frac{f_t}{y_t}I$$

or
$$\frac{f_c}{y_c} = \frac{f_t}{y_t} \qquad ...(10.14)$$

10.9. BENDING OF BUILT-UP SECTION

Many times, a beam section may be built-up of several basic sections; one has to first locate the position of the centroid through which the bending axis will pass. The moment of inertia about this axis can then be computed. This axis may not be symmetrically placed. In that case, y_c and y_t will be different, giving rise to different values of $Z_c\,(= I/y_c)$ and $Z_t\,(= I/y_t)$. The method of locating the centroid and then computing the moment of inertia of built-up section has been explained in example 8.18.

Example 10.8. *An unequal angle section shown in Fig. 10.13 (a) is used as a beam, simply supported over a span of 2 m, and is subjected to U.D.L. of 10 kN/m, inclusive of its own weight. Determine the maximum tensile and compressive stresses in the section.*

Solution :

The whole area can be splitted into two parts :

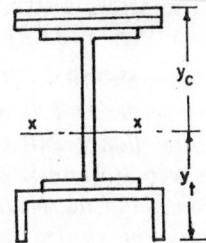

FIG. 10.12

(a) **Flange** : $A_1 = 100 \times 12.5 = 1250 \text{ mm}^2$

$y_1 = \dfrac{12.5}{2} = 6.25 \text{ mm from face } AC.$

(b) **Web** : $A_2 = 107.5 \times 12.5 = 1343.75 \text{ mm}^2$

$y_2 = \dfrac{107.5}{2} + 12.5 = 66.25 \text{ mm}$

Total $A = 1250 + 1343.75 = 2593.75 \text{ mm}^2$

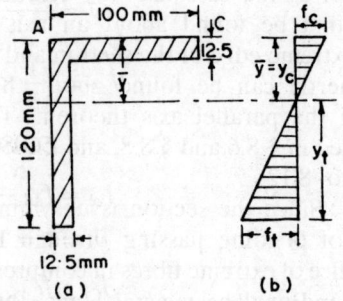

Taking moments about AC,

$$\bar{y} = \frac{A_1 y_1 + A_2 y_2}{A_1 + A_2} = \frac{1250 \times 6.25 + 1343.75 \times 66.25}{2593.75} = 37.33 \text{ mm}$$

FIG. 10.13

Now $I_{AC} = \left(\dfrac{1}{3} \times 87.5 \times 12.5^3 \right) + \left(\dfrac{1}{3} \times 12.5 \times 120^3 \right) = 725.7 \times 10^4 \text{ mm}^4$

∴ $I_{xx} = I_{AC} - A \bar{y}^2 = 725.7 \times 10^4 - 2593.75 (37.33)^2 = 364.3 \times 10^4 \text{ mm}^4$

Again, $y_c = \bar{y} = 37.33 \text{ mm}$ and $y_t = 120 - 37.33 = 82.67 \text{ mm}$

Now $M = \dfrac{w L^2}{8} = \dfrac{10 (2)^2}{8} = 5 \text{ kN-m} = 5 \times 10^6 \text{ N-mm}$

$$\frac{M}{I} = \frac{f}{y} \quad \text{ or } \quad f = \frac{M}{I} y$$

Hence, in top fibre, $f_c = \dfrac{M}{I} y_c = \dfrac{5 \times 10^6}{364.3 \times 10^4} \times 37.33 = \mathbf{51.24 \ N/mm^2}$

Also, in bottom fiber, $f_t = \dfrac{M}{I} y_t = \dfrac{5 \times 10^6}{364.3 \times 10^4} \times 82.67 = \mathbf{113.46 \ N/mm^2}$

The stress distribution across the section is shown in Fig. 10.13 (b).

Example 10.9. *The compression flange of a cast iron girder is 120 mm wide and 20 mm deep, the tension flange 240 mm wide and 40 mm deep and the web 300 mm × 20 mm. Find (a) the moment of inertia about the N.A. (b) the load per metre run which may be carried over a 4 m span by a beam simply supported at the ends, if the maximum permissible stresses are 90 N/mm² in compression and 30 N/mm² in tension.*

Solution :

(a) Total area
$$= 120 \times 20 + 300 \times 20 + 240 \times 40$$

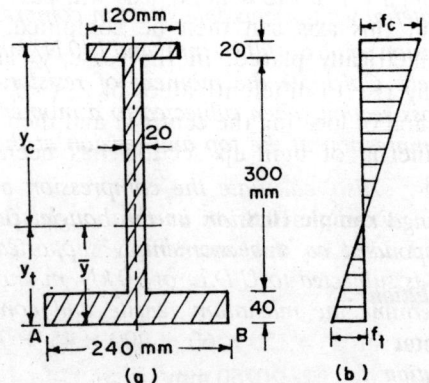

FIG. 10.14

$$= 2400 + 6000 + 9600 = 18000 \text{ mm}^2$$

$$\bar{y} = \frac{2400 \times 350 + 6000 \times 190 + 9600 \times 20}{18000} = 120.7 \text{ mm}$$

$$I_{AB} = \left(\frac{1}{3} \times 220 \times 40^3\right) + \left(\frac{1}{3} \times 20 \times 340^3\right) + \left\{\frac{1}{12} \times 120 \times 20^3 + 2400\,(350)^2\right\}$$

$$= 56080 \times 10^4 \text{ mm}^4$$

$\therefore \qquad I_{xx} = I_{AB} - A\,y^2 = 56080 \times 10^4 - 18000\,(120.7)^2 = 29857 \times 10^4 \text{ mm}^4$

(b) $\qquad y_t = \bar{y} = 120.7$ mm. Hence $y_c = 360 - 120.7 = 239.3$ mm

But $\qquad \dfrac{f_c}{y_c} = \dfrac{f_t}{y_t}$ or $f_c = \dfrac{f_t}{y_t} \times y_c = f_t \times \dfrac{239.3}{120.7} = 1.9826\,f_t$

When f_t reaches 30 N/mm^2, $f_c = 1.9826 \times 30 = 59.48$ N/mm^2, which is lower than the permissible limit. Should f_c be allowed to go upto 90 N/mm^2, f_t will evidently be more than 30 N/mm^2, which is not permissible. Hence the allowable tensile stress will be the criterion for the determination of strength. The corresponding stress distribution is shown in Fig. 10.13(b).

Hence $\qquad Z_t = \dfrac{I_{xx}}{y_t} = \dfrac{29857 \times 10^4}{120.7} = 2474 \times 10^3 \text{ mm}^3$

$\therefore \qquad M_r = f_t\,Z_t = 30 \times 2474 \times 10^3 = 74.22 \times 10^6 \text{ N-mm}$

Let w be the permissible load on the beam, in kN/m

$\therefore \qquad M = \dfrac{w\,L^2}{8} = \dfrac{w\,(4)^2}{8} = 2\,w \;\; \text{kN-m} = 2\,w \times 10^6 \text{ N-mm}$

Equating M_r and M, we get

$$2\,w \times 10^6 = 74.22 \times 10^6$$

From which $\qquad w = \textbf{37.11 kN/m}$

Example 10.10. *The cross-section of a beam is shown in Fig. 10.15. The beam is made of a material with permissible stress in compression and tension equal to 100 N/mm^2 and 140 N/mm^2 respectively. Calculate the moment of resistance of the cross-section, when subjected to a moment causing compression at the top and tension at the bottom.*

Also, calculate the compression in the top flange and the tension in the bottom flange corresponding to this moment.

Solution :

Total area $= 150 \times 60 + 200 \times 45 + 75 \times 30$
$= 20250 \text{ mm}^2$

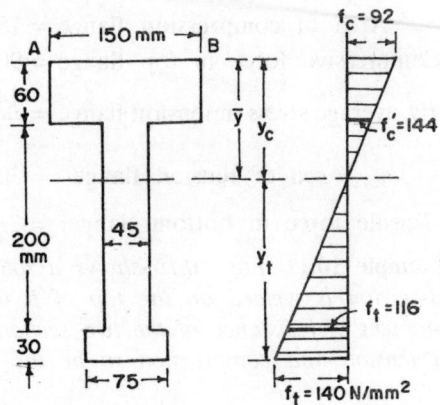

FIG. 10.15

$$\bar{y} = \frac{(150 \times 60 \times 30) + (200 \times 45 \times 160) + (75 \times 30 \times 275)}{20250}$$

$$= 115 \text{ mm}$$

$$I_{AB} = \frac{1}{3} \times 105 \ (60)^3 + \frac{1}{3} \times 45 \ (260)^3 + \left\{ \frac{1}{12} \times 75 \ (30)^3 + 30 \times 75 \ (275)^2 \right\}$$

$$= 44152 \times 10^4 \text{ mm}^4$$

$$\therefore \qquad I_{xx} = 44152 \times 10^4 - 20250 \ (115)^2 = 17372 \times 10^4 \text{ mm}^2$$

Now $y_c = \bar{y} = 115$ mm. Hence $y_t = 290 - 115 = 175$ mm

Moment of resistance $M_1 = \dfrac{f_c}{y_c} \times I = \dfrac{100}{115} \times 17372 \times 10^4 = 151 \times 10^6$ N-mm

Moment of resistance $M_2 = \dfrac{f_t}{y_t} \times I = \dfrac{140}{175} \times 17372 \times 10^4 = 139 \times 10^6$ N-mm

The moment of resistance of the section will be the lesser of the two.

Hence $M_r = 139 \times 10^6$ N-mm, which is based on $f_t = 140$ N/mm^2 which is the governing value. The corresponding value f_c is then given by $f_c = f_t \cdot \dfrac{y_c}{y_t} = 140 \times \dfrac{115}{175} = 92$ N/mm^2.

The corresponding stress distribution is shown in Fig. 10.15(b), from which we obtain the following values of stresses:

$$f_c' = \frac{f_c}{y_c} (y_c - 60) = \frac{92}{115} (115 - 60) = 44 \text{ N/mm}^2$$

and $$f_t' = \frac{f_t}{y_t} (y_t - 30) = \frac{140}{175} (175 - 30) = 116 \text{ N/mm}^2.$$

Now average stress in compression flange $= \dfrac{92 + 44}{2} = 68$ N/mm^2

Area of compression flange $= 150 \times 60 = 9000$ mm^2

$\therefore$ Compressive force in top flange $= 9000 \times 68 \times 10^{-3} = \textbf{612 kN}$

Similarly, average stress in tension flange $= \dfrac{140 + 116}{2} = 128$ N/mm^2

Area of tension flange $= 30 \times 75 = 2250$ mm^2

$\therefore$ Tensile force in bottom flange $= 2250 \times 128 \times 10^{-3} = \textbf{288 kN}$

Example 10.11. *Fig. 10.16 shows a rolled steel beam of an unsymmetrical I-section. If a similar I-section is welded on the top of it to form a symmetrical section, determine the ratio of the moment of resistance of the two sections to that of the single section. Assume permissible stress in tension and compression to be the same.*

Solution :

(a) *Single Section* : (Fig. 10.16)

Total area $= 40 \times 20 + 80 \times 20 + 80 \times 20 = 4000$ mm^2

$$\bar{y} = \frac{(40 \times 20 \times 110) + (80 \times 20 \times 50) + (80 \times 20 \times 10)}{4000} = 46 \text{ mm}$$

$$I_{AB} = \left(\frac{1}{3} \times 60 \times 20^3\right) + \left(\frac{1}{3} \times 20 \times 100^3\right)$$

$$+ \left\{\frac{1}{12} + 40 \times 20^3 + 40 \times 20 \,(110)^2\right\} = 1653 \times 10^4 \text{ mm}^4$$

$\therefore \qquad I_{xx} = 1653 \times 10^4 - 4000 \,(46)^2 = 807 \times 10^4 \text{ mm}^4$

$$y_t = \bar{y} = 46 \text{ mm} \,; y_c = 120 - 46 = 74 \text{ mm}$$

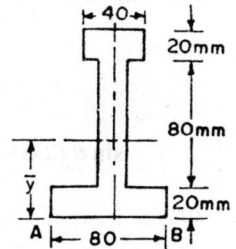

FIG. 10.16

Now $M_r = \dfrac{f}{y} I$, in general. Using the larger value of y to get minimum moment of resistance, we have

$$M_{r_1} = \frac{f}{y_c} I = \frac{f}{74} \times 807 \times 10^4 = 109045\,f \qquad \qquad ...(1)$$

(b) Double Section (Fig. 10.17)

The centroid of the section will be at the centre of the figure.

$\therefore \qquad\qquad I = 2\left[807 \times 10^4 + 4000 \,(74)^2\right]$

$$= 5994 \times 10^4 \text{ mm}^4$$

$$y = 120 \text{ mm}$$

$\therefore \qquad\qquad M_{r_2} = \dfrac{f}{y} \times I = \dfrac{f}{120} \times 5994 \times 4 = 499567\,f$

$\therefore \qquad\qquad \dfrac{M_{r_2}}{M_{r_1}} = \dfrac{499567}{109045} = \mathbf{4.58}$

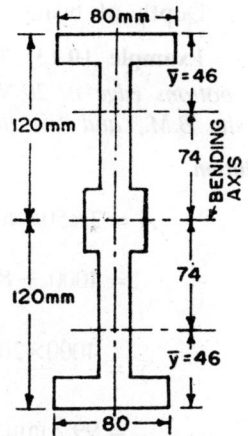

FIG. 10.17

Example 10.12. *Find the width and depth of the strongest beam that can be cut out of a cylindrical log of wood whose diameter is D. What is the ratio of depth to width of such a beam ?*

Solution :

OB = radius = R. Let OB be inclined at θ with the horizontal diameter. Let $ABCD$ be the rectangular beam to the cut out of the cylindrical log.

$$BC = d = 2 \cdot \frac{D}{2} \sin\theta = D \sin\theta$$

$$AB = b = 2 \cdot \frac{D}{2} \cos\theta = D \cos\theta$$

$$Z = \frac{b\,d^2}{6} = \frac{D \cos\theta \,(d \sin\theta)^2}{6} = \frac{D^3 \cos\theta \sin^2\theta}{6}$$

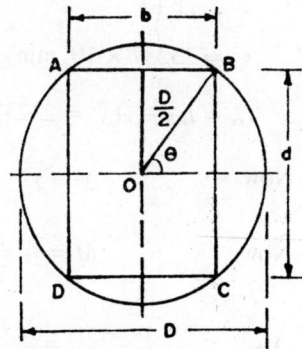

FIG. 10.18

For the beam to be the strongest, Z must be maximum. Hence $\dfrac{dZ}{d\theta} = 0$

$\therefore$ $\qquad\qquad\qquad\dfrac{dZ}{d\theta} = \dfrac{D^3}{6}\left[-\sin^3\theta + \cos\theta \cdot 2\sin\theta\cos\theta \right] = 0$

$\therefore$ $\qquad\sin\theta\,(2\cos^2\theta - \sin^2\theta) = 0,$

or $\qquad\qquad\qquad 2\cos^2\theta = \sin^2\theta,$ Hence $\tan^2\theta = 2$ or $\tan\theta = \sqrt{2}$

$\therefore$ $\qquad\qquad\qquad\sin\theta = \dfrac{\sqrt{2}}{\sqrt{3}}$ and $\cos\theta = \dfrac{1}{\sqrt{3}}$

$\therefore$ Width of beam, $\qquad b = D\cos\theta = \dfrac{D}{\sqrt{3}} = \mathbf{0.5774\,D}$

Depth of beam, $\qquad\qquad d = D\sin\theta = D\sqrt{2/3} = \mathbf{0.8165\,D}$

Example 10.13. *A cast iron beam section is shown in Fig. 10.19. The tensile stress at the bottom edge is 20 N/mm² when it is subjected to a bending moment. Determine (i) value of the B.M., and (ii) the value of stress at the top edge.*

Solution :

$A = 2\times50\times40 + 2\times20\times200 + 20\times140$

$\qquad = 4000 + 8000 + 2800 = 14800\ \text{mm}^2$

$\bar{y} = \dfrac{4000\times20 + 8000\times100 + 2800\times210}{14800}$

$\qquad = 99.2\ \text{mm}$

$I_{AB} = 2\times\dfrac{1}{3}\times50\,(40)^3 + 2\times\dfrac{1}{3}\times20\,(200)^3$

$\qquad + \left\{ \dfrac{1}{12}\times140\,(20)^3 + 2800\,(210)^2 \right\}$

$\qquad = 23237\times10^4\ \text{mm}^4$

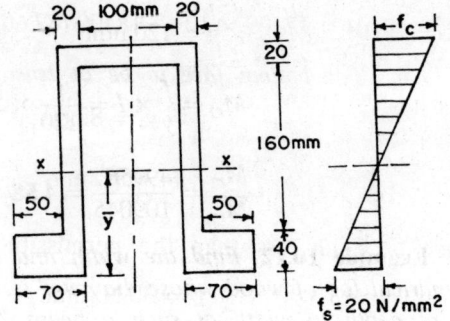

FIG. 10.19

$I_{xx} = I_{AB} - A\bar{y}^2 = 23237\times10^4 - 14800\,(99.2)^2 = 8673\times10^4\ \text{mm}^4$

Now $\qquad y_t = \bar{y} = 99.2\,;\, y_c = 220 - 99.2 = 120.8\ \text{mm}$

Now $\qquad M = f_t\cdot\dfrac{I}{y_t} = 20\times\dfrac{8673\times10^4}{99.2} = 17.486\times10^6\ \text{N-m} = \mathbf{17.486\ kN\text{-}m}$

Also, $\qquad\dfrac{f_c}{y_c} = \dfrac{f_t}{y_t}$

$$\therefore \qquad f_c = f_t \cdot \frac{y_c}{y_t} = 20 \times \frac{120.8}{99.2} = \textbf{24.35 N/mm}^2$$

Example 10.14. *The cross-section of a conveyer beam is shown in Fig. 10.20. The beam is subjected to a B.M. in the plane y-y. Determine the maximum permissible bending moment (a) for the bottom flange to be in tension (b) for the bottom flange in compression. The safe bending stress in tension and compression are 30 N/mm² and 120 N/mm² respectively.*

Solution :

$$A = 40 \times 80 + 80 \times 160 + 20 \times 120$$
$$= 3200 + 12800 + 2400 = 18400 \text{ mm}^2$$

$$\bar{y} = \frac{3200 \times 20 + 12800 \times 80 + 2400 \times 180}{18400}$$
$$= 82.60 \text{ mm}$$

$$\therefore \qquad y_1 = \bar{y} = 82.60 \text{ mm} ; y_2 = 240 - 82.6 = 157.4$$

$$I_{AB} = \frac{1}{3} \times 80 \, (40)^3 + \left\{ \frac{1}{12} \times 160 \times 80^3 + 12800 \, (80)^2 \right\}$$

$$+ \left\{ \frac{1}{12} \times 20 \, (120)^3 + 2400 \, (180)^2 \right\}$$

$$= 17109 \times 10^4 \text{ mm}^4$$

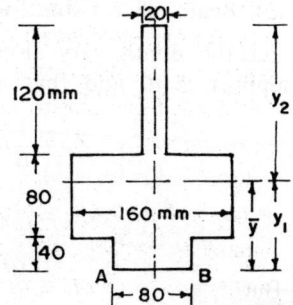

FIG. 10.20

$$\therefore \qquad I_{xx} = 17109 \times 10^4 - 18400 \, (82.60)^2 = 4555 \times 10^4 \text{ mm}^4$$

(a) For bottom face to be in tension

$$y_t = y_1 = 82.60 ; y_c = y_2 = 157.4 \text{ mm}$$

Taking $\qquad f_t = 30 \text{ N/mm}^2$, corresponding $f_c = \dfrac{f_t}{y_t} \cdot y_c = \dfrac{30}{82.6} \times 157.4 = 57.17 \text{ N/mm}^2$

which is much less than the permissible value of 120 N/mm^2.

Hence $\qquad f_t = 30 \text{ N/mm}^2$ is the governing stress.

Now $\qquad M = f_t \cdot \dfrac{I}{y_t} = 30 \times \dfrac{4555 \times 10^4}{82.6} = 16.55 \times 10^6 \text{ N-mm} = \textbf{16.55 kN-m}$

(b) For bottom face to be in compression :

Here $\qquad y_c = y_1 = 82.60 \text{ mm} ; y_t = y_2 = 157.4 \text{ mm}$

If f_c is allowed to reach the permissible value of 120 N/mm^2, corresponding f_t will be much higher than the permissible value of 30 N/mm^2. Hence max. f_t should be taken as 30 N/mm^2.

$$\therefore \qquad f_c = \frac{f_t}{y_t} \cdot y_c = \frac{30}{157.4} \times 82.6 = 15.74 \text{ N/mm}^2 \text{ only}$$

$$\therefore \qquad M = f_t \cdot \frac{I}{y_t} = 30 \times \frac{4555 \times 10^4}{157.4} = 8.68 \times 10^6 \text{ N-m} = \textbf{8.68 kN-m}$$

10.10. BEAM OF UNIFORM STRENGTH

In common practice, a beam of constant cross-section throughout the length is provided. This gives rise of constant section modulus and has constant or uniform moment of resistance. Since the actual moment generally varies along the length, such a section is not economical. Under heavy loads, a beam of *variable section* is designed to have *uniform strength*. There can be two such configurations : (*i*) beam of uniform width, and (*ii*) beam of uniform depth. We shall investigate both the configurations for the case of a beam with a concentrated load at the mid span *It is to be noted that a beam of uniform strength has the same maximum bending stress all along the length.*

(a) Beam of constant width

Let the depth vary along the length such that the depth at the distance x from the L.H. support is d_x and that at the mid-span is d.

$$\therefore \qquad Z_x = \frac{1}{6} b\, d_x^2$$

$$M_{rx} = f \cdot Z_x = f \cdot \frac{1}{6} b\, d_x^2$$

But $\qquad M_x = \frac{W}{2} x$

$$\therefore \qquad f \cdot \frac{1}{6} b\, d_x^2 = \frac{W}{2} x$$

or $\qquad d_x^2 = \frac{3\,W \cdot x}{f \cdot b},$

which gives $\qquad d_x = \sqrt{\dfrac{3\,W}{f\,b}} \sqrt{x} = c\sqrt{x}$ \qquad ...(10.13)

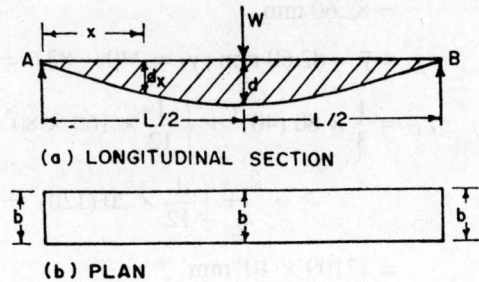

FIG. 10.21. BEAM OF UNIFORM STRENGTH : CONSTANT WIDTH

Thus, the depth will be proportional to $\sqrt{x}$ and the variation of depth will be parabolic, as shown in Fig. 10.21(*a*).

At the mid span, when $\quad x = \dfrac{L}{2}, d = \sqrt{\dfrac{3\,WL}{2\,fb}}$ \qquad ...(10.13 *a*)

(b) Beam of constant depth

Let the width of the beam vary along the length such that the width at a distance x from the support be b_x, and that at the mid-span be b.

$$\therefore \qquad Z_x = \frac{1}{6} b_x\, d^2$$

$$\therefore \qquad M_{rx} = f Z_x = f \cdot \frac{1}{6} b_x\, d^2$$

But $\qquad M_x = \frac{W}{2} x$

$$\therefore \qquad f \cdot \frac{1}{6} b_x\, d^2 = \frac{W}{2} x$$

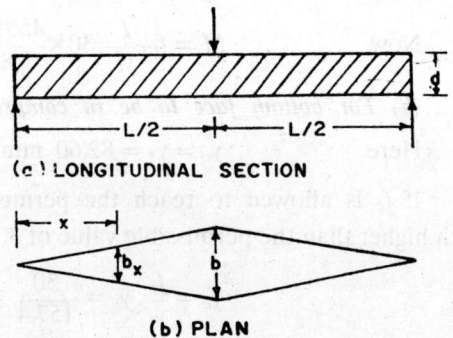

FIG. 10.22. BEAM OF UNIFORM STRENGTH : CONSTANT DEPTH

From which $$b_x = \frac{3\,W}{f\,d^2}\cdot x = c'\,x \qquad \qquad ...(10.14)$$

Thus the width b_x is proportional to the distance x and the variation is *linear*. The value of width is zero at the supports and $\dfrac{3\,WL}{2\,f\,d^2}$ at the mid-span, as shown in Fig. 10.22(b).

Example 10.15. *A beam of span L, simply supported at the ends, carries a point load which can be placed any where on the span. Design the beam having uniform strength, maintaining constant width throughout the length.*

Solution :

The greatest B.M. occurs at the mid-span when the point load is at mid-span. Let d be the depth at the mid span. Let f be the maximum stress at the mid-span.

$$M_{max} = \frac{WL}{4}\;;\; M_{r,\,max} = f\cdot\frac{1}{6}\,b\,d^2$$

Equating the two, we have

$$\frac{1}{6}f\,b\,d^2 = \frac{WL}{4}$$

FIG. 10.23

From which $$f = \frac{3}{2}\frac{WL}{b\,d^2} \qquad \qquad ...(i)$$

Now, let the point load W be placed at a distance x from the support. The maximum bending moment will occur under the load, and its value is

$$M_{max} = \frac{Wx\,(L-x)}{L}$$

Let d_x be the depth of the section at this location. Hence $Z_x = \dfrac{1}{6}\,b\,d_x^2$.

∴ Bending stress $$f_x = \frac{M_x}{Z_x} = \frac{Wx\,(L-x)}{L} \div \frac{1}{6}\,b\,d_x^2 = \frac{6\,Wx\,(L-x)}{L\,b\,d_x^2} \qquad \qquad ...(ii)$$

Since $f = f_x$ for the beam of uniform strength, we have

$$\frac{6\,Wx\,(L-x)}{L\,b\,d_x^2} = \frac{3}{2}\frac{WL}{b\,d^2}$$

or $$d_x^2 = \frac{4\,d^2}{L^2}\,x\,(d-x)$$

From which $$d_x = \frac{2\,d}{L}\sqrt{x\,(d-x)} \qquad \qquad ...(10.15)$$

which the required expression for the depth, the variation being parabolic.

Example 10.16. *A beam of span L carries a uniformly distributed load w per unit length on the whole span. Find the shape of the beam of uniform strength if (a) the breadth is to be maintained constant (b) depth is to be maintained constant.*

Solution :

(a) Beam of Constant width

Let the depth at the mid-span be d and that at any section distant x be d_x.

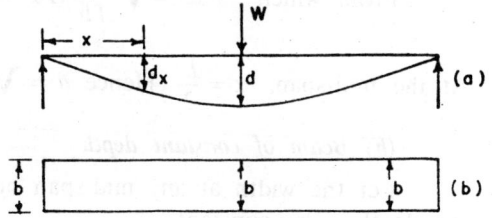

$$\therefore \qquad Z_x = \frac{1}{6}\, b\, d_x^2.$$

$$M_{rx} = f\,.\,Z_x = f\,.\,\frac{1}{6}\, b\, d_x^2$$

$$M_x = \frac{wL}{2}\, x - \frac{w\,x^2}{2} = \frac{w}{2}\,(Lx - x^2)$$

$$\therefore \qquad f\,.\,\frac{1}{6}\, b\, d_x^2 = \frac{w}{2}\,(Lx - x^2)$$

From which $\qquad d_x = \sqrt{\dfrac{3\,w}{f\,b}\,(Lx - x^2)} \quad ..(10.16)$

At the mid-span, $\; x = \dfrac{L}{2} \;$ Hence $\; d = \sqrt{\dfrac{3\,w}{f\,b}}\,.\,\dfrac{L}{2}$

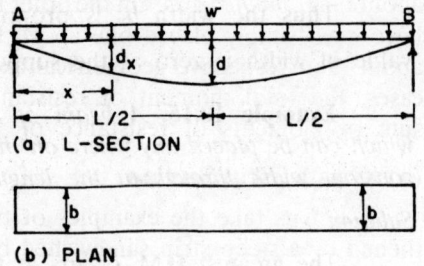

FIG. 10.24

(b) Beam of constant depth

Let the width at any mid-span be b and the width at any other distance x be b_x. Let the depth d be constant.

$$\therefore \qquad Z_x = \frac{1}{6}\, b_x\,.\,d^2$$

$$M_{rx} = f\,Z_x = f\,.\,\frac{1}{6}\, b_x\, d^2$$

$$M_x = \frac{wL}{2}\, x - \frac{w\,x^2}{2} = \frac{w}{2}\,(Lx - x^2)$$

$$\therefore \qquad f\,.\,\frac{1}{6}\, b_x\, d^2 = \frac{w}{2}\,(Lx - x^2)$$

From which $\qquad b_x = \dfrac{3\,w}{f\,d^2}\,(Lx - x^2), \quad ...(10.17)$

the variation being parabolic.

At the mid-span, $\qquad x = \dfrac{L}{2}.$ Hence $b = \dfrac{3}{4}\,\dfrac{w\,L^2}{f\,d^2}$

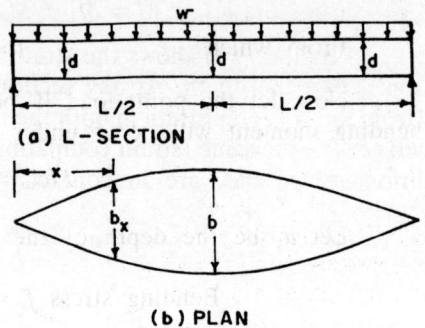

FIG. 10.25

10.11. BEAM OF COMPOSITE SECTION : FLITCHED BEAM

Beams that are made of more than one material are called *composite beams*. The common examples are (a) bimetallic beams (b) sandwich beams, (c) flitched beams, and (d) reinforced concrete beams, as shown in Fig. 10.26. Such composite beams can be analysed by the same bending theory because the assumption that cross-sections that are plane before bending remain plane after bending is valid in pure bending regardless of the material. The strain distribution along the depth of such a beam is linear. However, such structures are statically indeterminate, and *the position of the neutral axis is not the centroid of the section*. The criterion of *strain compatibility* has to be used, *i.e.* strain in the two materials, at a given vertical distance from the N.A., has to be the same.

If both the materials are rigidly joined together, they will behave like a unit piece and the bending will take place about the *combined axis*. On the other hand, if both the materials have been simply placed one above the other, they will bend about their respective geometrical axes. However, in both the cases, the total moment of resistance will be equal to the sum of moments of resistance of individual sections.

(a) Symmetrical Section

Let us take the examples of two timber pieces strengthened by a steep strip sandwiched between them (Fig. 10.27 *a*). Such a beam is commonly known as a *flitched beam*.

Let D be the depth of timber planks and d be the depth of steel strip. Similarly, let B be the total width of timber section and b be the width of steel strip. Let us use suffix 1 for timber and 2 for steel. Since the steel strip is symmetrically placed, the common axis of bending will remain the same as that of the timber.

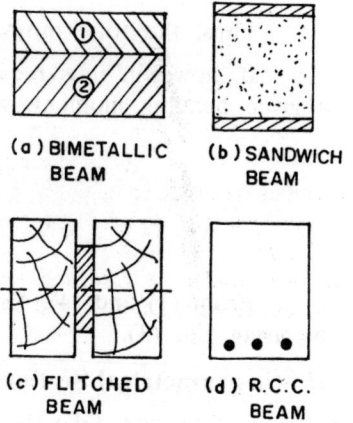

(a) BIMETALLIC BEAM (b) SANDWICH BEAM

(c) FLITCHED BEAM (d) R.C.C. BEAM

FIG. 10.26. COMPOSITE SECTIONS

From Statics, $M = M_1 + M_2$ ...(1)

Fig. 10.27 (*b*) shows the strain distribution across the depth. At any section distant y from the N.A., the strain in both the materials will remain the same (strain compatibility condition), since they are in contact.

Hence $e_1 = e_2$ or $\dfrac{f_1}{E_1} = \dfrac{f_2}{E_2}$

$\therefore \quad f_2 = f_1 \cdot \dfrac{E_2}{E_1} = m f_1 \,...(2)$

where $m = \dfrac{E_2}{E_1}$ is known as the *modular ratio*. Since E_2 is much more than E_1, m is

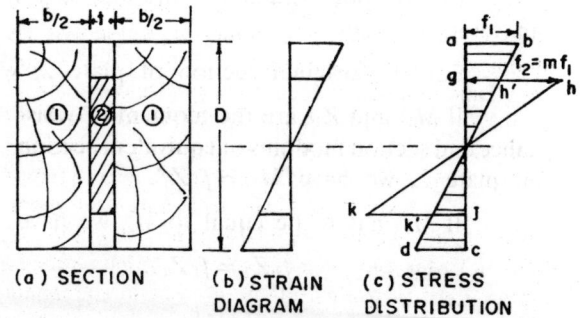

(a) SECTION (b) STRAIN DIAGRAM (c) STRESS DISTRIBUTION

FIG. 10.27. ANALYSIS OF A FLITCHED BEAM.

much greater than 1. Hence the bending stress f_2 will be much greater than f_1. The bending stress diagram is shown in Fig. 10.27(*c*) in which $f_2 = gh = m \cdot gh' = m f_1$.

The above relation can also be obtained by considering the fact that the radius of curvature at any level will be the same for both the materials. Thus,

or $$\dfrac{E_1 y}{f_1} = \dfrac{E_2 y}{f_2}$$

or $$f_2 = \dfrac{E_2}{E_1} \cdot f_1 = m f_1$$

Thus, if f_1 is given, f_2 can be found, and *vice-versa*.

If the geometry of the section is given, Z_1 and Z_2 can be calculated.

Hence $\qquad\qquad M_1 = f_1 Z_1 \ \text{and} \ M_2 = f_2 Z_2$ $\qquad\qquad$ ...(3)

$\therefore \qquad\qquad$ Total $M = M_1 + M_2 = f_1 Z_1 + f_2 Z_2$

Thus, the total moment of resistance can be calculated.

If, however, it is required to find the *stresses* induced in the section corresponding to a given bending moment, we have :

$$R_1 = R_2 \ \text{or} \ \frac{E_1 I_1}{M_1} = \frac{E_2 I_2}{M_2}$$

$\therefore \qquad\qquad$
$$\frac{M_1}{M_2} = \frac{E_1 I_1}{E_2 I_2}$$
$\qquad\qquad$ ...(4)

From (1) and (4), M_1 and M_2 can be found. Hence the stresses f_1 and f_2 can be found by using Eq. (3).

(b) Unsymmetrical Section

Let us now take the example of unsymmetrical section, consisting of strip of width b and depth d_1, of material 1 and strip of width b and depth d_2 of material 2. The first step will be to find the position of *new axis of bending*. This be best done by drawing what is known as the *equivalent section* (Fig 10.28 b).

Fig 10.28(a) shows the original section. Let us find the equivalent section of plate 2 in terms of plate 1.

For the original section of plate 2, we have $M_2 = f_2 Z_2$

If M_1' and Z_1' are the moment of resistance and section modulus of equivalent section of plate 2, we have $M_1' = f_1 Z_1'$.

If M_1' has to be equal to M_2, we have

$$f_2 Z_2 = f_1 Z_1'$$

or $\qquad\qquad$
$$Z_1' = \frac{f_2}{f_1} Z_2 = m Z_2$$

Hence $\qquad\qquad b' = m b$

(Since Z_1' and Z_2 are proportional to b)

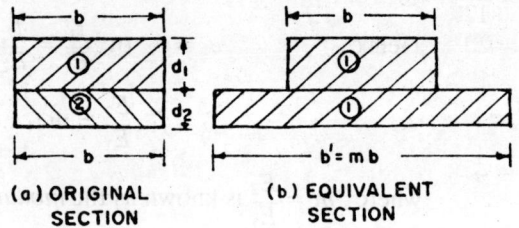

(a) ORIGINAL SECTION $\qquad$ (b) EQUIVALENT SECTION

FIG 10.28. COMPOSITE SECTION

Sandwich Beams

A sandwich beam consists of

(i) two thin layers of strong material, called *faces*, placed at top and bottom.

(ii) thick *core*, consisting of light weight, low strength material. The core simply serves as a *filler* or *spacer*. Sandwich construction is used where light weight combined with high strength and high stiffness are needed.

Sandwich beams can be analysed by two method :

(i) **Method 1** : Same as described for composite beam or flitched beam.

(*ii*) **Method 2** : An approximate theory for bending can be used, based on the assumption that the *faces* carry all the longitudinal bending stresses. Such an approximation is valid, specially when the core have very low modulus of elasticity in comparison to that of the faces.

If I_f is the moment of inertia of the faces about the bending axes, we have $\quad I_f = \dfrac{1}{12} b \, (d^3 - h^3)$

Hence $\quad f_f = \dfrac{M}{I_f} \cdot \dfrac{d}{2} = \dfrac{M d}{2 I_f}$ ...(10.18)

where f_f is the bending stress at the outermost edge of the beam.

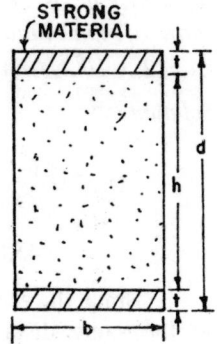

FIG. 10.29

Example 10.17. *A flitched timber beam consists of two joists each 80 mm wide and 240 mm deep, with a steel plate 160 mm deep and 12 mm thick placed symmetrically between and clamped to them. Calculate the total moment of resistance of the section if the allowable stress in joist is 9 N/mm². Take $E_S = 20\, E_T$.*

Solution :

Fig. 10.30(*a*) shows the arrangement while Fig 10.30(*b*) shows the stress diagram, both for timber as well as steel. Max. stress in timber $= 9 \, \text{N/mm}^2 = ab$. Hence stress in timber at the level of steel $= g h' = 9 \times \dfrac{80}{120} = 6 \, \text{N/mm}^2$. Modular ratio, $m = \dfrac{E_S}{E_T} = 20$. Hence max. stress in steel $= gh = m \times 6 = 120 \, \text{N/mm}^2$.

Z_T for timber

$= \dfrac{1}{6} \times 160 \, (240)^2 = 1536 \times 10^3 \, \text{mm}^3$

Z_S for steel

$= \dfrac{1}{6} \times 12 \times (120)^2 = 51.2 \times 10^3 \, \text{mm}^3$

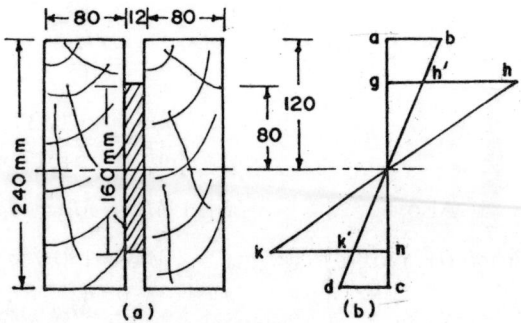

(a) (b)

$\therefore$ Moment of resistance of timber section,

FIG. 10.30

$$M_{rT} = f_T \cdot Z_T = 9 \times 1536 \times 10^3 = 13.824 \times 10^6 \ \text{N-mm}$$

Moment of resistance of steel section,

$$M_{rS} = f_S \, Z_S = 120 \times 51.2 \times 10^3 = 6.144 \times 10^6 \ \text{N-mm}$$

$\therefore$ Total moment of resistance of the composite section $= M_{rT} + M_{rS}$

$$= (13.824 + 6.144) \, 10^6 = 19.968 \times 10^6 \ \text{N-m} = \textbf{19.968 kN-m}$$

Example 10.18. *A 500 × 500 mm timber is strengthened by the addition of 500 mm × 8 mm steel plates secured to its top and bottom surfaces. The composite beam is simply supported at its ends and carries a uniformly distributed load of 100 kN/m run over an effective span of 6 m. Find the maximum bending stresses in steel and timber at the mid-span. Take $E_S = 2 \times 10^5 \, N/mm^2$ and $E_T = 0.1 \times 10^5 \, N/mm^2$.*

Solution :

$$M_{max} = \frac{w L^2}{8} = \frac{100 \, (6)^2}{8}$$

$$= 450 \ \ kN\text{-}m = 450 \times 10^6 \ \text{N-mm}$$

Since the section is composite, we have, at the same distance from N.A.,

$$e_S = e_T$$

$$\therefore \qquad \frac{f_S}{E_S} = \frac{f_T}{E_T}$$

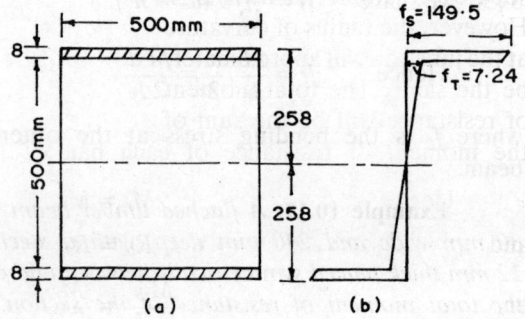

FIG. 10.31

or $\qquad\qquad \dfrac{M_{rs} \cdot y}{I_s E_s} = \dfrac{M_{rT} y}{I_T \cdot E_T}$ or $\dfrac{M_{rT}}{M_{rs}} = \dfrac{I_T \cdot E_T}{I_s E_s}$ ...(1)

Also, $\qquad\qquad\qquad M_r = M_{rT} + M_{rs}$ ...(2)

Now $\qquad\qquad\qquad I_S = \dfrac{1}{12} \times 500 \, (516^3 - 500^3) = 51617 \times 10^4 \ \text{mm}^4$

$$I_T = \frac{1}{12} \times 500 \, (500)^3 = 520833 \times 10^4 \ \text{mm}^4$$

$\therefore \qquad\qquad \dfrac{M_{rT}}{M_{rs}} = \dfrac{520833 \times 10^4}{51617 \times 10^4} \times \dfrac{0.1 \times 10^5}{2 \times 10^5} = 0.5045$ ...(i)

Also, $\qquad\qquad M_{rT} + M_{rs} = M_r = M_{max} = 450 \times 10^6$ N-mm ...(ii)

From (i) and (ii), we get $\quad M_{rT} = 150.9 \times 10^6$ and $M_{rs} = 299.1 \times 10^6$

$\therefore \qquad\qquad f_S = \dfrac{M_{rs}}{Z_S} = \dfrac{M_{rs}}{I_S} \cdot y_S = \dfrac{299.1 \times 10^6}{51617 \times 10^4} \times 258 = \textbf{149.5 N/mm}^2$

and $\qquad\qquad f_T = \dfrac{M_{rT}}{Z_T} = \dfrac{M_{rT}}{I_T} \cdot y_T = \dfrac{150.9 \times 10^6}{520833 \times 10^4} \times 250 \approx \textbf{7.24 N/mm}^2$

Example 10.19. *Two rectangular bars, one of brass and the other of steel, each of 80 mm × 20 mm are placed together, to form a beam of 80 mm wide and 40 mm deep, on two supports 2 m apart, the brass being on the top of steel. Determine the maximum central load which can be applied to the beam if the bars are (a) separate and can bend independently, and (b) firmly secured to each other throughout their length. Take the following values :*

$$E_s = 2 \times 10^5 \, N/mm^2 ; f_{s, \, max} = 120 \, N/mm^2$$

$$E_b = 0.8 \times 10^5 \, N/mm^2 ; f_{b, \, max} = 75 \, N/mm^2$$

Solution :

(a) Each bar bending separately

When the bars are not rigidly jointed, each bar will bend separately about its own axis. However, the radius of curvature at the junction will approximately be the same. The total moment of resistance will be the sum of the moment of resistance of each bar.

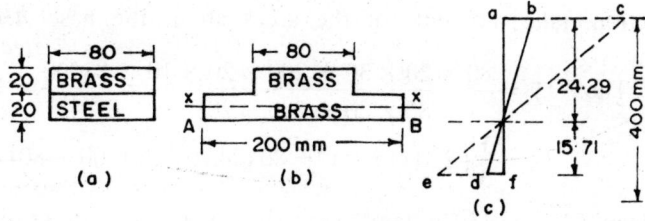

FIG. 10.32

Hence
$$M_r = M_{rs} + M_{rb}, \text{ for equilibrium} \qquad ...(1)$$

and
$$R_b = R_s, \text{ for compatibility}$$

or
$$\frac{M_{rb}}{E_b I_b} = \frac{M_{rs}}{E_s I_s} \text{ which gives } \frac{M_{rs}}{M_{rb}} = \frac{E_s I_s}{E_b I_b} \qquad ...(2)$$

Since
$$I_s = I_b, \text{ we get } \frac{M_{rs}}{M_{rb}} = \frac{2}{0.8} \times 1 = 2.5$$

Substituting in (i), we get $M_r = M_{rb} + 2.5\,M_{rb} = 3.5\,M_{rb}$

But
$$M_r = M = \frac{W \times L}{4} = \frac{W \times 2}{4} = 0.5\,W \text{ N-m (when } W \text{ is in } N)$$

$\therefore$
$$3.5\,M_{rb} = 0.5\,W \times 1000, \text{ from which } M_{rb} = 142.86\,W \text{ N-mm } ...(3)$$

Again,
$$\frac{f_b}{f_s} = \frac{M_{rb}}{M_{rs}} \cdot \frac{Z_s}{Z_b} = \frac{M_{rb}}{M_{rs}} = \frac{1}{2.5}$$

Taking
$$f_s = 120 \text{ N/mm}^2, \text{ we get } f_b = \frac{120}{2.5} = 48 \text{ N/mm}^2$$

Hence when the stress in steel has reached a value of 120 N/mm², the stress in brass will be only 48 N/mm². Should the stress in brass be allowed to go upto its max. permissible value of 70 N/mm², the corresponding stress in steel will be $70 \times 2.5 = 175$ N/mm² which is much above its permissible value. Hence $f_s = 120$ N/mm² and $f_b = 48$ N/mm².

Also
$$Z_b = Z_s = \frac{1}{6} \times 80\,(20)^2 = 5333.3 \text{ mm}^3$$

$\therefore$
$$M_{rb} = f_b \cdot Z_b = 48 \times 5333.3 = 255998 \text{ N-mm}$$

But
$$M_{rb} = 142.86\,W, \text{ from (3)}.$$

Hence
$$142.86\,W = 255998, \text{ from which } W = \textbf{1792 N}$$

(b) Both bars composite

When the bars are composite, they cannot bend about their own axis, but will bend about the common axis. In order to locate the common axis, let us convert the original section into an *equivalent section* in terms of brass, as shown in Fig. 10.32(b). In that case, equivalent length of brass strip $= 80 \times \dfrac{E_s}{E_b} = 80 \times \dfrac{2}{0.8} = 200$ mm. To find the centroid of the equivalent section, take moments of the areas about the base AB.

The $\quad \bar{y} = \dfrac{80 \times 20 \times 30 + 200 \times 20 \times 10}{80 \times 20 + 200 \times 20} = \dfrac{88000}{5600} = 15.71$

$\therefore \quad I_{xx} = \dfrac{1}{3} \left\{ 200 \, (15.71)^3 + 80 \, (24.29)^3 + (200 - 80) \, (4.29)^3 \right\} = 64.38 \times 10^4 \text{ mm}^4$

Taking $f_{s,max} = 120 \text{ N/mm}^2$, corresponding stress in brass in $f_b = 120 \times \dfrac{E_b}{E_s} = \dfrac{120}{2.5} = 48 \text{ N/mm}^2$.

which is less than the permissible value of 75 N/mm^2. The stress diagram is shown in Fig. 10.32(c), in which $e\,c = 120 \text{ N/mm}^2$; $cd = 48 \text{ N/mm}^2$; $ab = \dfrac{48 \times 24.29}{15.71} = 74.22$, which is less than the permissible value of 75 N/mm^2.

M_r of transformed section $= f_b Z = 74.22 \times \dfrac{64.38 \times 10^4}{24.29} = 1.967 \times 10^6 \text{ N-mm}$

(Alternatively, $M_r = 48 \times \dfrac{64.38 \times 10^4}{15.71} = 1.967 \times 10^6$). But $M_r = M = 0.5\,W \times 1000$ N-mm

$\therefore \qquad\qquad 0.5\,W \times 1000 = 1.967 \times 10^6$, from which $W = \mathbf{3934\,N}$

Example 10.20. *Find the moment of resistance of a flitched beam section shown in Fig. 10.33(a), if the stresses in steel and timber are not to exceed 160 N/mm² and 8 N/mm² respectively. Take $E_s = 2 \times 10^5 \text{ N/mm}^2$ and $E_w = 1 \times 10^7$ N/mm².*

Solution :

$$m = \dfrac{E_s}{E_T} = \dfrac{2 \times 10^5}{1 \times 10^4} = 20$$

The original section is shown in Fig. 10.33(a), which can be replaced by an equivalent section in terms of steel, as shown in Fig. 10.33(b). The 200×160 mm timber section can be replaced by steel section having depth equal to 200 mm, but width $= \dfrac{160}{20} = 8$ mm.

In order to find $\bar{y}$ of the equivalent section, take moments about base AB.

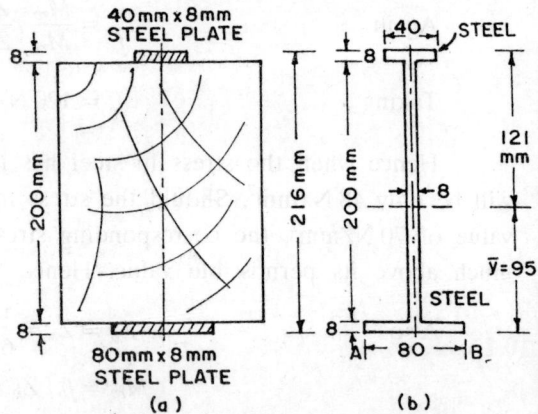

FIG. 10.33

$$\therefore \qquad \bar{y} = \dfrac{40 \times 8 \times 212 + 200 \times 8 \times 108 + 80 \times 8 \times 4}{40 \times 8 + 200 \times 8 + 80 \times 8} = \dfrac{243200}{2560} = 95 \text{ mm}$$

$$I_{AB} = \dfrac{1}{3} \times 72 \, (8)^3 + \dfrac{1}{3} \times 8 \, (208)^3 + \left\{ \dfrac{1}{12} \times 40 \, (8)^3 + 40 \times 8 \, (212)^2 \right\} = 3839 \times 10^4 \text{ mm}^4$$

$$\therefore \qquad I_{xx} = 3839 \times 10^4 - 2560 \, (95)^2 = 1529 \times 10^4 \, \text{mm}^4.$$

Taking $f_{s,\,max} = 160 \, \text{N/mm}^2$, extreme stress in timber $= \dfrac{1}{20} \times \dfrac{160}{121} \times 113 = 7.47 \, \text{N/mm}^2$.

which is less than the permissible value of $8 \, \text{N/mm}^2$.

$$\therefore \qquad M_r = \frac{f}{y} \times I = \frac{160}{121} \times 1529 \times 10^4 = 20.22 \times 10^6 \, \text{N-m} = \textbf{20.22 \, kN-m}$$

Example 10.21. *A solid rod of bronze 20 mm in diameter is surrounded by a fitting steel cylinder of external diameter 28 mm. If the permissible bending stress in bronze and steel are 100 and 150 N/mm², find the moment of resistance of the composite section. The Young's modulus for steel may be taken as 1.75 times that of bronze.*

Solution :

Given : $m = \dfrac{E_s}{E_b} = 1.75$

Let the maximum stress in steel reach its permissible value of $150 \, \text{N/mm}^2$. Hence corresponding maximum stress reached in bronze

$$= 150 \times \frac{10}{14} \times \frac{1}{m} = \frac{150 \times 10}{14 \times 1.75}$$

$= 61.22 \, \text{N/mm}^2$, which is less than the permissible value of $100 \, \text{N/mm}^2$.

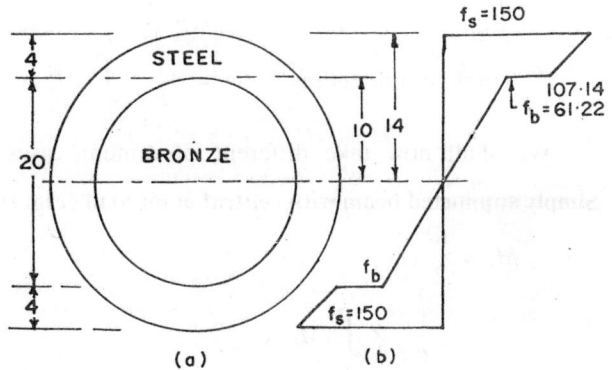

For bronze component,

$$Z_b = \frac{\pi}{32} (20)^3 = 785.4 \, \text{mm}^3$$

FIG. 10.34

For steel component, $\qquad Z_s = \dfrac{\pi}{32} \dfrac{(28^4 - 20^4)}{28} = 1594.1 \, \text{mm}^3$

$$\therefore \qquad M_{rb} = f_b Z_b = 61.22 \times 785.4 = 48082 \, \text{N-mm}$$

$$M_{rs} = f_s Z_s = 150 \times 1594.1 = 239120 \, \text{N-mm}$$

$\therefore$ Total $\qquad M_r = 48082 + 239120 = 287202 \, \text{N-m} \approx \textbf{0.287 \, kN-m}$

10.12. STRAIN ENERGY DUE TO BENDING

In chapter 6, we have seen that strain energy per unit volume $= \dfrac{f^2}{2E}$. In order to find strain energy due to bending, consider two transverse sections at a small distance δx apart. Let δA be the small transverse area over which the direct stress f is acting at a height h above the N.A. If M_x is the B.M. at the section, we have

$$f = \frac{M_x y}{I}$$

$\therefore$ Strain energy of the elementary volume of length δx and area δA is

$$= \frac{f^2}{2E} \times \delta x \,.\, \delta A = \frac{M_x^2 y^2}{2\,I^2\,E} \delta x \,.\, \delta A$$

Strain energy of the whole piece of length δx between the transverse sections

$$= \delta U \;=\; \Sigma \; \frac{M_x^2 y^2}{2\,I^2\,E} \,.\, \delta x \, \delta A = \frac{M_x^2 \,\delta x}{2\,I^2\,E} \, \Sigma \, \delta A \,.\, y^2 = \frac{M_x^2 \,\delta x}{2\,I^2\,E} \times I$$

Hence $\qquad\qquad\qquad \delta U = \dfrac{M_x^2 \,\delta x}{2\,E\,I}$ (Since $\Sigma \; \delta A \,.\, y^2 = I$) $\qquad\qquad$ ...(10.19)

The above expression can also be derived with reference to Fig. 10.2.

$$\delta U = \text{work done by bending} = \text{average B.M.} \times \text{Change in angle}$$

$$= \frac{1}{2} M_x \,.\, \delta\theta = \frac{1}{2} M_x \,.\, \frac{\delta x}{R} = \frac{1}{2} M_x \,.\, \delta x \,.\, \frac{M_x}{E\,I} = \frac{M_x^2 \,\delta x}{2\,E\,I}$$

$\therefore$ Total strain energy $\qquad U = \dfrac{1}{2\,E\,I} \displaystyle\int_0^L M_x^2 \, dx.$ $\qquad\qquad\qquad$ ..(10.20)

We shall now take different prominent cases.

1. Simply supported beam with central point load (Fig. 10.35 a)

$$M_x = \frac{W}{2} x$$

$$\therefore \qquad U = \frac{1}{2\,E\,I} \times \int_0^L M_x^2 \, dx$$

$$= \frac{1 \times 2}{2\,E\,I} \int_0^{L/2} \left(\frac{W}{2} x \right)^2 dx$$

$$= \frac{1}{E\,I} \left(\frac{W^2 x^3}{12} \right)_0^{L/2} = \frac{W^2 L^3}{96\,E\,I} \qquad ...(10.21)$$

2. Simply supported beam with U.D.L. w
   (Fig. 10.35 b)

$$M_x = \frac{w\,L}{2} x - \frac{w\,x^2}{2}$$

$$U = \frac{1}{2\,E\,I} \int_0^L M_x^2 \, dx$$

$$= \frac{1}{2\,E\,I} \int_0^L \left(\frac{w\,L}{2} x - \frac{w\,x^2}{2} \right)^2 dx$$

$$= \frac{1}{2\,E\,I} \int_0^L \left[\frac{w}{2} (Lx - x^2) \right]^2 dx$$

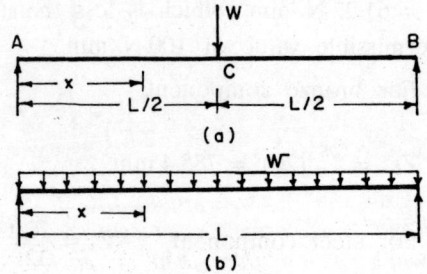

FIG. 10.35

$$= \frac{w^2}{8EI} \int_0^L \left(L^2 x^2 + x^4 - 2Lx^3 \right) dx = \frac{w^2 L^5}{240 EI} \qquad \dots(10.22)$$

3. Cantilever with U.D.L. w

$$M_x = \frac{w x^2}{2}$$

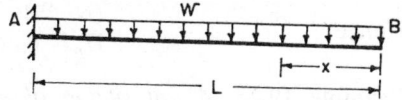

$$U = \frac{1}{2EI} \int_0^L M_x^2 \, dx$$

FIG. 10.36

$$= \frac{1}{2EI} \int_0^L \frac{w^2 x^4}{4} \, dx = \left(\frac{w^2 x^5}{40 EI} \right)_0^L$$

$$= \frac{w^2 L^5}{40 EI} \qquad \dots(10.23)$$

4. Simply supported beam with constant M throughout

$$M_x = M$$

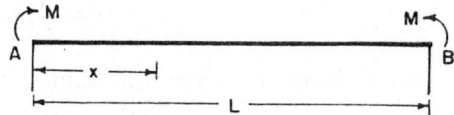

$$U = \frac{1}{2EI} \int_0^L M_x^2 \, dx$$

FIG. 10.37

$$= \frac{1}{2EI} \int_0^L M^2 \, dx = \frac{M^2 L}{2 EI} \qquad \dots(10.24)$$

Example 10.22. *Compare the strain energies of two equal uniform beams, simply supported at the ends, one carrying a concentrated central load and the other carrying a uniformly distributed load when (a) the total load on each beam is the same, and (b) the maximum stress due to bending in each beam is the same.*

Solution :

For a simply supported beam loaded with a central point load W_1

$$U_1 = \frac{W_1^2 L^3}{96 EI} \qquad \dots(1)$$

Similarly, for a simply supported beam loaded with U.D.L. w per unit length

$$U_2 = \frac{w^2 L^5}{240 EI} = \frac{W_2^2 L^3}{240 EI} \text{ , where } W_2 = w L \qquad \dots(2)$$

(a) If the total load for both the beams is the same,

$$W_1 = W_2 = W$$

$$\therefore \qquad \frac{U_1}{U_2} = \frac{W^2 L^3}{96 EI} \times \frac{240 EI}{W^2 L^3} = \frac{240}{96} = \textbf{2.5}$$

(b) If the stresses for both the beams are the same

For $\qquad\qquad\qquad\qquad f_1 = f_2$, we must have $M_1 = M_2$

$\therefore \qquad\qquad\qquad \dfrac{W_1 L}{4} = \dfrac{W_2 L}{8}$, from which $W_2 = 2\, W_1$

Hence $\qquad\qquad \dfrac{U_1}{U_2} = \dfrac{W_1^2 L^3}{96\, E I} \times \dfrac{240\, E I}{(2\, W_1)^2 L^3} = \dfrac{240}{96 \times 4} = \mathbf{0.625}$

Example 10.23. *A flat ribbon of steel, 6 mm wide and 0.6 mm thick is wound round a cylinder 600 mm in diameter. Find the maximum stress in the steel and the energy stored per metre length of the ribbon. Take $E = 2 \times 10^5\ N/mm^2$.*

Solution :

$$f = \frac{E}{R} y = \frac{2 \times 10^5}{300} \times 0.3 = 200\ \text{N/mm}^2$$

When the ribbon is wound round the drum, it has a constant radius of curvature and hence it is subjected to a constant bending moment M, where $M = E I/R$.

$$\therefore \qquad U = \frac{M^2 L}{2 E I} = \left(\frac{E I}{R}\right)^2 \cdot \frac{L}{2 E I} = \frac{E I L}{2 R^2}$$

Substituting the numerical values, we have

$$U = \frac{2 \times 10^5 \times 6\,(0.6)^3 \times \pi \times 600}{12 \times 2\,(300)^2} = 226.2\ \text{mm-N}$$

$\therefore$ Strain energy stored per m length $= \dfrac{226.2 \times 1000}{\pi \times 600} = \mathbf{120\ mm\text{-}N/m}$

10.13. FORCE ON A PARTIAL AREA OF A BEAM SECTION AND ITS MOMENT ABOUT N.A.

Fig 10.38(*a*) shows a beam section subjected to bending at a given location. Let f_{max} be the maximum bending stress at the extreme fiber distant y_{max} from the N.A. Let us now develop an expression for force P acting on a partial area A (shown shaded) of the beam section, and the moment of this force about the N.A.

Let us consider an elementary area dA of the shaded area, at a distance y from the N.A. The stress at this location is given by

$$f = \frac{f_{max}}{y_{max}} . y$$

$\therefore$ Force δP on the elementary area

$$= f\,\delta A = \frac{f_{max}}{y_{max}} . y . \delta A$$

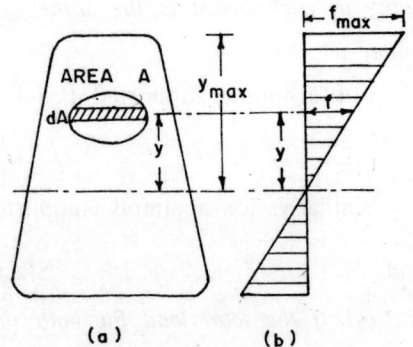

FIG. 10.38

$\therefore$ Total force P_A on the shaded area $= \dfrac{f_{max}}{y_{max}} \Sigma \, y \, dA$

$\therefore$ $$P_A = \dfrac{f_{max}}{y_{max}} . A \, \bar{y} \qquad \qquad ...(10.25)$$

where $\bar{y}$ is the distance of the centroid of the shaded area from the N.A., and A is the total shaded area.

Also, the moment of the elementary force δP about N.A. is

$$\delta M = \delta P . y = \dfrac{f_{max}}{y_{max}} . y^2 . dA$$

Hence total moment $\qquad M_A = \dfrac{f_{max}}{y_{max}} \Sigma \, y^2 \, dA = \dfrac{f_{max}}{y_{max}} I_A \qquad \qquad ...(10.26)$

where M_A is the total moment of the force on area A, and I_A is the moment of inertia of the shaded area about the neutral axis.

Example 10.24. *Fig. 10.39(a) shows a rectangular section, 200 mm × 300 mm, subjected to a sagging B.M. of 150 kN-m acting about its horizontal axis. Find (a) the compressive force, and its moment about the N.A., acting on the shaded area of the section, and (b) the tensile force and its moment about the N.A., acting on the cross-hatched area of the section.*

Solution :

For the whole section, $\qquad I = \dfrac{1}{12} \times 200 \, (300)^3 = 45000 \times 10^4 \, mm^4$

Hence $\qquad f_{max} = \dfrac{M}{I} y_{max} = \dfrac{150 \times 10^6}{45000 \times 10^4} \times 150 = 50 \, N/mm^2$

(a) Compressive force on the shaded area

$P_c = \dfrac{f_{max}}{y_{max}} A \, \bar{y}$

$= \dfrac{50}{150} (120 \times 100)(50 + 50)$

$= 666667 \, kN = \mathbf{666.667 \; kN}$

Moment of this force about N.A. is

$M_c = \dfrac{f_{max}}{y_{max}} . I_A$

and $\qquad I_A = $ moment of inertia of the shaded area about the N.A.

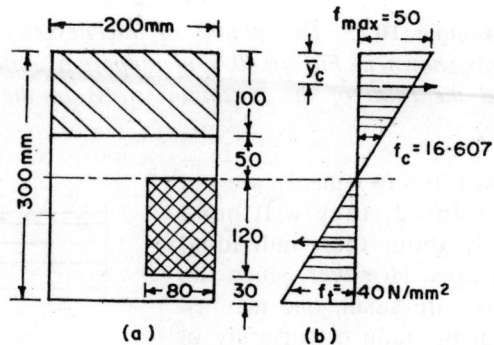

FIG. 10.39

$= \dfrac{1}{12} \times 200 \, (100)^3 + 200 \times 100 \, (100)^2 = 21667 \times 10^4 \, mm^4$

$M_c = \dfrac{50}{150} \times 21667 \times 10^4 = 72.222 \times 10^6 \, N\text{-}mm = \mathbf{72.222 \;\; kN\text{-}m}$

Alternatively : $f_{max} = 50 \text{ N/mm}^2$. Hence $f_c = \dfrac{50}{150} \times 50 = 16.667 \text{ N/mm}^2$

$\therefore$ Average stress on shaded area $= \dfrac{50 + 16.667}{2} = 33.333 \text{ N/mm}^2$

$\therefore$ $P_c =$ average stress $\times$ area $= 33.333 \times 200 \times 100 = 666667 \text{ N} = \textbf{666.667 kN}$ and distance

of centroid of this force from top fibre, $\bar{y}_c = \dfrac{100}{3}\left[\dfrac{2 \times 16.667 + 50}{16.667 + 50}\right] = 41.67 \text{ mm}$

$\therefore$ $M_c = 666.667 \times (150 - \bar{y}_c) = 666.667 \,(150 - 41.67) \times 10^{-3} = \textbf{72.222 kN-m}$

(b) Tensile force on the cross-hatched area

$$P_T = \dfrac{f_{max}}{y_{max}} A\,\bar{y} = \dfrac{50}{150}\,(80 \times 120) \times 60 = 19200 \text{ N} = \textbf{192 kN}$$

$$I_A = \dfrac{1}{3} \times 80\,(120)^3 = 4608 \times 10^4 \text{ mm}^4$$

$\therefore$ $$M_T = \dfrac{f_{max}}{y_{max}} I_A = \dfrac{50}{150} \times 4608 \times 10^4 = 15.36 \times 10^6 \text{ N-m} = \textbf{15.36 kN-m}$$

Alternatively : Stress $f_t = \dfrac{50}{150} \times 120 = 40 \text{ N/mm}^2$

$$P_T = \text{Average Stress} \times \text{area} = \dfrac{0 + 40}{2}\,(80 \times 120) = 192000 \text{ N} = 192 \text{ kN}$$

and $$M_T = P_T \,.\, \bar{y} = 192\left(\dfrac{2}{3} \times 120\right) = 15.36 \times 10^6 \text{ N-m} = \textbf{15.36 kN-m}$$

10.14. ADDITIONAL ILLUSTRATIVE EXAMPLES

Example 10.25. *Two planks of thicknesses t_1 and t_2 rest just one above another forming a beam as shown in Fig. 10.40, and support a uniformly distributed load of w Newton per metre run. Find the ratio of the maximum stress in the two beams.*

Solution :

Since the two planks are not rigidly jointed, they will bend separately about their individual bending axes. However, since the thicknesses are small, one may assume that the radii of curvature of neutral layer of each plank is the same.

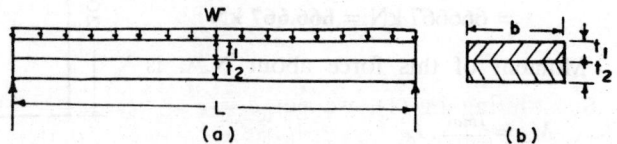

FIG. 10.40

Let maximum B.M. for the first layer of thickness $t_1 = M_1$

Let maximum B.M. for the second layer of thickness $t_2 = M_2$

Radius of curvature for each plank $= R$

$$\therefore \qquad \frac{1}{R} = \frac{M_1}{E\,I_1} = \frac{M_2}{E\,I_2} \quad \text{or} \quad \frac{M_1}{M_2} = \frac{I_1}{I_2} = \frac{b\,t_1^3/12}{b\,t_2^3/12} = \frac{t_1^3}{t_2^3} \qquad \ldots(1)$$

If f_1 and f_2 are the maximum bending stresses in the two planks at mid span,

$$M_1 = f_1\,Z_1 = f_1 \cdot \frac{1}{6} b\,t_1^2 \quad \text{and} \quad M_2 = f_2\,Z_2 = f_2 \cdot \frac{1}{6} b\,t_2^2$$

$$\therefore \qquad \frac{M_1}{M_2} = \frac{f_1}{f_2} \cdot \frac{t_1^2}{t_2^2} \qquad \ldots(2)$$

Hence from (1) and (2), we get $\dfrac{t_1^3}{t_2^3} = \dfrac{f_1}{f_2} \dfrac{t_1^2}{t_2^2}$

From which $\qquad \dfrac{f_1}{f_2} = \dfrac{t_1}{t_2}$ (Answer)

Example 10.26. *A long rod of uniform rectangular section and thickness t originally straight is bent into the form of circular arc and the displacement d of the midpoint of length L is measured by means of dial gauge. The displacement d may be regarded as small compared with the length L. Show that the longitudinal surface strain in the rod is given by $e = 4td/L^2$.* (U.L.)

Solution :

At any height y from the N.A.,

$$\frac{f}{y} = \frac{E}{R} = \frac{M}{I}$$

$$\therefore \qquad \frac{f}{E} = e = \frac{y}{R} = \frac{t}{2R} \qquad \ldots(1)$$

From the properties of chord of a circle,

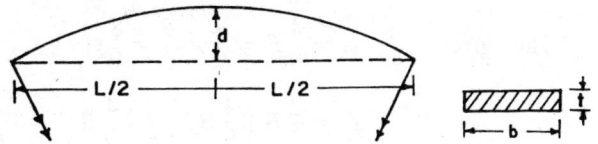

FIG. 10.41

$$d\,(2R - d) = \frac{L^2}{4}$$

or $\qquad 2Rd - d^2 = \dfrac{L^2}{4}$

Neglecting d^2 in comparison to $2Rd$, we get

$$2Rd = \frac{L^2}{4}$$

or $\qquad 2R = \dfrac{L^2}{4d} \qquad \ldots(2)$

Substituting in (1), we get $e = \dfrac{t}{2R} = t \div \dfrac{L^2}{4d} = \dfrac{4\,t\,d}{L^2}$ (Proved).

Example 10.27. *Prove that the moment of resistance of a beam of square section with the diagonal in the plane of bending is increased by flattening the top and bottom corners as shown in Fig. 10.42 and that the moment of resistance is maximum when $y = \dfrac{8}{9}y_1$.*

Solution :

Let us take an elementary strip of width b and thickness δd at a distance d from the N.A.

δI_{xx} of elemental strip $= b \cdot \delta d \cdot d^2$

or $\qquad \delta I_{xx} = (B - 2d) \, \delta d \cdot d^2 = (B d^2 - 2 d^3) \, \delta d$

$\therefore \qquad I_{xx}$ of whole section $= 2 \int_0^y \left(B d^2 - 2 d^3 \right) \delta d = \dfrac{y^3}{3} (2B - 3y) = I_1 \quad$ (say) ...(1)

When $\qquad y = \dfrac{B}{2}, I_{xx} = \dfrac{B^3}{24} \left(2B - \dfrac{3B}{2} \right) = \dfrac{B^4}{48} = I_x$ (say) $\qquad\qquad$ ...(2)

Now $\qquad M_1 = f_1 Z_1 \text{ and } M_2 = f_2 Z_2$

$\therefore \qquad M_1 > M_2, \text{ if } Z_1 > Z_2 \text{ for the same value of } f.$

$\therefore \qquad Z_2 = \dfrac{I_2}{B/2} = \dfrac{B^4}{48} \times \dfrac{2}{B} = \dfrac{B^3}{24}$

and $\qquad Z_1 = \dfrac{I_1}{y} = \dfrac{y^2}{3} (2B - 3y) = \dfrac{2}{3} B y^2 - y^3$

For Z_1 to be maximum, $\dfrac{dZ_1}{dy} = \dfrac{4By}{3} - 3 y^2 = 0$

This gives $\qquad y = \dfrac{4}{9} B = \dfrac{8}{9} \times \dfrac{B}{2} = \dfrac{8}{9} y_1$

$\therefore \qquad Z_1 = \dfrac{2}{3} B \left(\dfrac{4}{9} B \right)^2 - \left(\dfrac{4}{9} B \right)^3 = \dfrac{32 B^3}{729}$

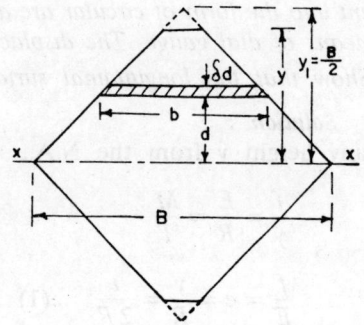

FIG. 10.42

Since $\qquad Z_2 = \dfrac{B^3}{24}, Z_1$ is greater than Z_2.

Hence $\qquad M_1 > M_2$

The reason for this increase in moment of resistance is quite obvious : the removal of small corner areas decreases the extreme fibre distance in greater proportion than it reduces the moment of inertia of the section.

Example 10.28. *Find the condition at which any further decrease of depth H of the beam section shown in Fig. 10.43 will result in an increase in section modulus.*

Solution :

$$I_{xx} = \dfrac{1}{12} b d^3 + \dfrac{1}{12} a H^3$$

$\therefore \qquad Z = \dfrac{I}{H/2} = \dfrac{2I}{H} = \dfrac{b d^3}{6H} + \dfrac{a H^2}{6}$

Rate of change of Z with respect to H is given by

$$\dfrac{dZ}{dH} = -\dfrac{b d^3}{6 H^2} + \dfrac{a H}{3}$$

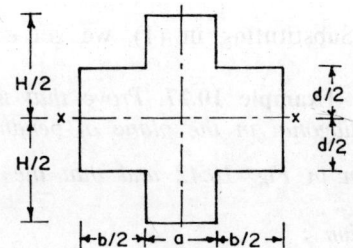

FIG. 10.43

The condition for Z to increase when H decreases is

$$\frac{b\,d^3}{6\,H^2} > \frac{a\,H}{3}$$

or $$\frac{b}{2\,a} > \frac{H^3}{d^3}$$ (Answer)

Example 10.29. *A box beam is made from $50\,mm \times 150\,mm$ pieces screwed together as shown in Fig. 10.44. If the maximum flexural stress is $8\,N/mm^2$, compute (a) force acting on the shaded portion, and (b) moment of this force about N.A.*

Solution :

Area of shaded portion, $A = 50 \times 150 = 7500$ mm^2

$$\bar{y} = 25 \text{ mm}, \text{ from N.A.}$$

$\therefore$ $$P = \frac{f_{max}}{y_{max}} \cdot A\,\bar{y}$$

$$= \frac{8}{100} \times 7500\,(25) = 15000 \text{ N}$$

$$= \textbf{15 kN}$$

Moment of this force about N.A. is

$$M = \frac{f_{max}}{y_{max}} \cdot I_A$$

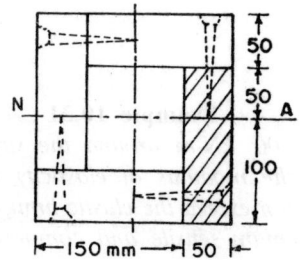

FIG. 10.44

where $$I_A = \frac{1}{12} \times 50\,(150)^3 + 50 \times 150\,(25)^2 = 1875 \times 10^4 \text{ mm}^4$$

$\therefore$ $$M = \frac{8}{100} \times 1875 \times 10^4 = 1.5 \times 10^6 \text{ N-m} = \textbf{1.5 kN-m}$$

Example 10.30. *A uniformly tapering vertical post of height H having diameter D at the base and a diameter d at the top is fixed at the base. A horizontal force P is applied at the top of the post. Determine the maximum bending stresses for the post and state where it occurs.*

Solution :

Let us take a horizontal section at a distance x from the top. Its diameter d_x is given by

$$d_x = d + \frac{D-d}{H}x = d + k\,x$$

where $$k = \frac{D-d}{H}$$

$\therefore$ $$Z = \frac{\pi\,d_x^3}{32} \text{ and } M = P\,.\,x$$

Stress $$f = \frac{M}{Z} = \frac{P\,.\,x}{\pi\,d_x^3/32} = \frac{32\,P}{\pi} \cdot \frac{x}{d_x^3} = \frac{32\,P}{\pi} \cdot \frac{x}{(d+k\,x)^3}$$

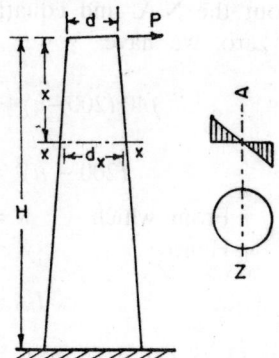

FIG. 10.45

For $\qquad\qquad f_{max}, \dfrac{df}{dx} = 0 = \dfrac{32\,P}{\pi} \dfrac{(d + kx)^3 - x\,(3)\,(d + kx)^2\,.\,k}{(d + kx)^3}$

or $\qquad\qquad (d + kx)^2\,(d + kx - 3\,kx) = 0$

or $\qquad\qquad\qquad d - 2\,kx = 0$

$\therefore \qquad\qquad\qquad\qquad x = \dfrac{d}{2\,k} = \dfrac{d}{2\,(D - d)}\,H,$

which gives the location of maximum stress.

Again, $\qquad\qquad f_{max} = \dfrac{32\,P}{\pi}\,.\,\dfrac{d/2\,k}{\left(d + \dfrac{d}{2}\right)^3} = \dfrac{32\,P}{\pi} \times \dfrac{8}{27}\,.\,\dfrac{d}{2\,k\,d^3}$

$\qquad\qquad\qquad\qquad = \dfrac{32 \times 8\,P}{27 \times 2\,\pi}\,.\,\dfrac{1}{d^2}\,.\,\dfrac{H}{D - d} = \dfrac{128}{27\,\pi}\,\dfrac{PH}{(D - d)\,d^2}$ $\qquad$ (Answer)

Example 10.31. *A 100 × 200 rectangular section is subjected to a sagging B.M. of 100 kN-m around the strong axis. The material of the beam is non-isotropic and is such that the modulus of elasticity in tension is 1.4 times as great as in compression. If the stresses do not exceed the elastic limit, find the maximum tensile and compressive stress in the beam.*

Solution :

$\qquad$ Modular ratio $\quad = \dfrac{E_t}{E_c} = 1.4.$

$\qquad$ Fig. 10.46(a) shows the original non-isometric section in which n is the depth of N.A. below the top compression fibre. Fig. 10.46(b) shows the equivalent isotropic section in which the width of tension portion= 1.4 × 100= 140 mm.

$\qquad$ Taking the moments of the area about the N.A. and equating the sum to zero, we have

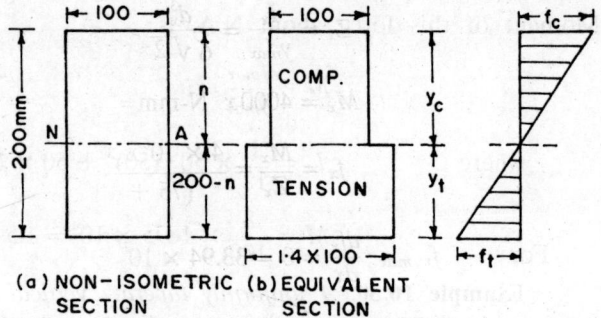

(a) NON-ISOMETRIC (b) EQUIVALENT
SECTION   SECTION

FIG. 10.46

$$140\,(200 - n)\left(\dfrac{200 - n}{2}\right) - 100 \times n \times \dfrac{n}{2} = 0$$

or $\qquad\qquad (200 - n)^2 = 0.7143\,n^2 \quad$ or $\quad 200 - n = 0.8452\,n$

From which $\quad n = 108.4$ mm.

Hence $\qquad\quad y_c = n = 108.4$ mm and $y_t = 200 - 108.4 = 91.6$ mm

$\therefore \qquad\qquad I_{NA} = \dfrac{1}{3} \times 100\,(108.4)^3 + \dfrac{1}{3} \times 140\,(91.6)^3 = 7832.6 \times 10^4 \text{ mm}^4$

$\therefore \qquad\qquad f_c = \dfrac{M}{I}\,y_c = \dfrac{100 \times 10^6}{7832.6 \times 10^4} \times 108.4 = \mathbf{138.4 \text{ N/mm}^2}$

and
$$f_t = \frac{M}{I} y_t = \frac{100 \times 10^6}{7832.6 \times 10^4} \times 91.6 = \mathbf{116.9 \ N/mm^2}$$

Example 10.32. *A vertical flag staff standing 7.5 m above the ground is of square section throughout, the dimensions being 75 mm × 75 mm at the top, tapering uniformly to 150 mm × 150 mm at the ground. A horizontal pull of 4000 N is applied at the top, the location of loading being along a diagonal of the section. Find the maximum stress due to bending, and the position where it acts.*

Solution :

Let the dimensions of the column at a distance x m below the top be d_x so that

$$d_x = 75 + \frac{x}{7.5}(150 - 75)$$

$$= 75 + 10x \text{ mm}$$

$$I_x = \frac{d_x^4}{12} \text{ and } y_{max} = \frac{d_x}{\sqrt{2}} \text{ mm}$$

$$\therefore \qquad Z_x = \frac{I_x}{y_{max}} = \frac{d_x^3}{6\sqrt{2}} = \frac{(75 + 10x)^3}{6\sqrt{2}}$$

$$M_x = 4000x \text{ N-mm} = 4 \times 10^6 x \text{ N-mm}$$

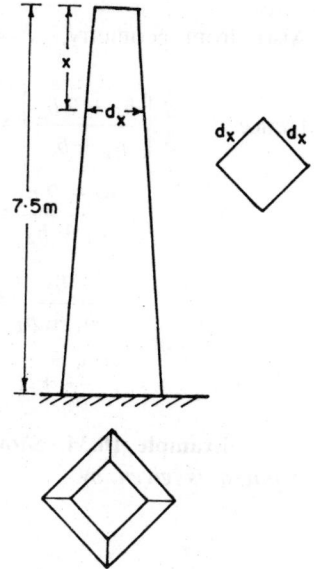

FIG. 10.47

$$\therefore \qquad f_x = \frac{M_x}{Z_x} = \frac{4 \times 10^6 x \times 6\sqrt{2}}{(75 + 10x)^3} = \frac{33.94 \times 10^6 x}{(75 + 10x)^3}$$

For $f_{x,max}$, $\dfrac{df_x}{dx} = 0 = 33.94 \times 10^6 \left[\dfrac{(75 + 10x)^3 - 3x(75 + 10x)^2 \, 10}{(75 + 10x)^6} \right]$

$$\therefore \qquad (75 + 10x)^2 (75 + 10x - 30x) = 0$$

or $\qquad 75 - 20x = 0$, which gives $x = \mathbf{3.75 \ m}$

$$\therefore \qquad f_{max} = \frac{33.94 \times 10^6 x}{(75 + 10x)^3} = \frac{33.94 \times 10^6 \times 3.75}{(75 + 10 \times 3.75)^3} = \mathbf{89.4 \ N/mm^2}$$

Example 10.33. *A prismatic beam of trapezoidal section shown in Fig. 10.48 is subjected to sagging B.M. Calculate the ratio of b_1 to b_2 for maximum economy if the allowable stresses in tension and compression are 40 N/mm² and 50 N/mm² respectively.*

Solution :

Let the depth of the N.A. be n below the top compressive fibre.

$$\therefore \qquad f_c = \frac{M}{I} n = 50 \qquad\qquad\qquad ...(i)$$

and
$$f_t = \frac{M}{I}(d - n) = 40 \qquad\qquad\qquad ...(ii)$$

From (i) and (ii), $\quad \dfrac{d-n}{n} = \dfrac{40}{50} = \dfrac{4}{5}$

or $\quad \dfrac{d}{n} - 1 = \dfrac{4}{5}$ from which $n = \dfrac{5}{9}d$ $\qquad$ ...(1)

Also, from geometry, $\quad n = \dfrac{d}{3} \left[\dfrac{b_1 + 2b_2}{b_1 + b_2} \right]$ $\qquad$ ...(2)

Hence $\quad \dfrac{d}{3} \left[\dfrac{b_1 + 2b_2}{b_1 + b_2} \right] = \dfrac{5}{9}d$

or $\qquad \dfrac{b_1 + 2b_2}{b_1 + b_2} = \dfrac{5}{3}$ or $\dfrac{b_1 + 2b_2}{b_1 + b_2} - 1 = \dfrac{5}{3} - 1$

$\therefore \qquad \dfrac{b_2}{b_1 + b_2} = \dfrac{2}{3}$ or $\dfrac{b_1 + b_2}{b_2} = \dfrac{3}{2}$

$\therefore \qquad \dfrac{b_1}{b_2} + 1 = \dfrac{3}{2}$ from which $\dfrac{b_1}{b_2} = \dfrac{1}{2}$

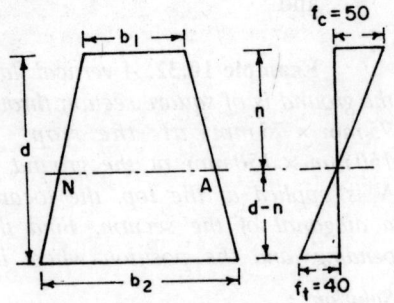

FIG. 10.48

Example 10.34. *Show that the maximum bending stress in beam of rectangular section of depth d is given by*

$$f_{max} = \frac{M \cdot d}{6 I n} (2n + 1)$$

if instead of Hooke's law, the stress-strain relation is $f^n = E \cdot \varepsilon$, where n is a number dependent on the properties of the material.

Solution :

Consider an elementary area $dA \ (= b \cdot dy)$, located at y from the N.A.

Then, $\qquad dM = f_y \cdot dA \cdot y = (E \cdot \varepsilon)^{1/n} \cdot b \cdot dy \cdot y$

$\therefore \qquad M = 2 \displaystyle\int_0^{d/2} (E\varepsilon)^{1/n} b\, y \cdot dy$

But $\qquad \varepsilon = \dfrac{\varepsilon_{max}}{d/2} y = \dfrac{f_{max}^n}{E} \cdot \dfrac{2y}{d}$

$\therefore \qquad M = 2 \displaystyle\int_0^{d/2} \left(f_{max}^n \cdot \dfrac{2y}{d} \right)^{1/n} b\, y\, dy$

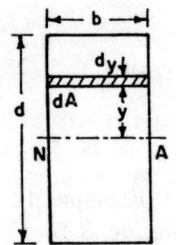

FIG. 10.49

or $\qquad M = 2 \left(\dfrac{d}{2} \right)^{-1/n} \cdot b \cdot f_{max} \left[\dfrac{y^{2 + \frac{1}{n}}}{2 + \dfrac{1}{n}} \right]_0^{\frac{d}{2}}$

or $\qquad M = f_{max} \cdot b \cdot 2 \left(\dfrac{d}{2} \right)^2 \dfrac{n}{2n + 1}$

or
$$f_{max} = \frac{2n+1}{n} \cdot \frac{M}{2b\left(\dfrac{d}{2}\right)^2} = \frac{2n+1}{n} \cdot \frac{M}{b\,d^2/2}$$

But
$$I = \frac{1}{12} b\,d^3$$

or
$$\frac{b\,d^2}{2} = \frac{6\,I}{d}$$

$\therefore$
$$f_{max} = \frac{2n+1}{n} \cdot \frac{M}{6\,I/d} = \frac{M\,d}{6\,I\,n}(2n+1) \quad \text{(Proved)}$$

Example 10.35. *A flitched beam of span 6 m consists of two timber joists each of 80 mm × 160 mm with a 12 mm thick and 120 mm deep steel plate bolted between them as shown in Fig. 10.50(a). The beam carries a U.D.L. of 2000 N/m over the whole span.*

Determine the extreme bending stresses in both the materials. Take $E_s = 2 \times 10^5$ N/mm^2 and $E_T = 1 \times 10^4$ N/mm^2.

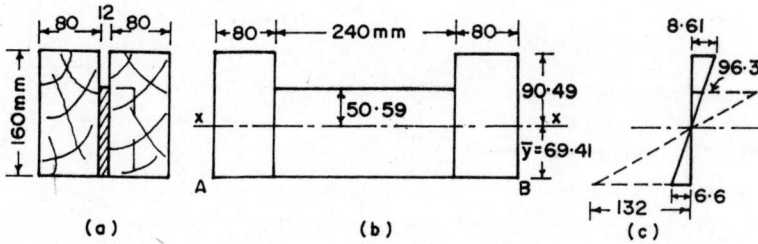

FIG. 10.50

Solution :

Modular ratio
$$m = \frac{2 \times 10^5}{1 \times 10^4} = 20$$

$\therefore$ Width of timber equivalent to steel plate $= 12 \times 20 = 240$ mm.

The equivalent section is shown in Fig. 10.50(b).

Total area $= 2 \times 80 \times 160 + 240 \times 120 = 54400$ mm^2

$$\bar{y} = \frac{2 \times 80 \times 160 \times 80 + 240 \times 120 \times 60}{54400} = 69.41 \text{ mm}$$

$\therefore$
$$I_{AB} = \frac{2}{3} \times 80\,(160)^3 + \frac{1}{3} \times 240\,(120)^3 = 35669 \times 10^4 \text{ mm}^4$$

$$I_{xx} = 35669 \times 10^4 - 54400\,(69.41)^2 = 9461 \times 10^4 \text{ mm}^4$$

$$M = \frac{w\,L^2}{8} = \frac{200\,(6)^2}{8} = 9000 \text{ N-m} = 9 \times 10^6 \text{ N-mm}$$

$\therefore f_{b,max}$ (in timber) $= \dfrac{9 \times 10^6}{9461 \times 10^4} \times 69.41 = \mathbf{6.60\ N/mm^2}$

$$f_{c,max} \text{ (in timber)} = \frac{9 \times 10^6}{9461 \times 10^4} \times 90.49 = \mathbf{8.61 \ N/mm^2}$$

$$f_{t,max} \text{ (in steel)} = 6.60 \times 20 = \mathbf{132 \ N/mm^2}$$

$$f_{c,max} \text{ (in steel)} = \frac{9 \times 10^6}{9461 \times 10^4} \times 50.59 \times 20 = \mathbf{96.3 \ N/mm^2}$$

Example 10.36. *A composite beam having cross-sectional dimensions shown in Fig. 10.51(a) is subjected to a bending moment of 30 kN-m. Materials are fastened so that the beam acts as a unit. Determine the maximum bending stress in each material.*
Take $E_s = 2 \times 10^5 \ N/mm^2$, $E_A = 0.667 \times 10^5 \ N/mm^2$ and $E_c = 1 \times 10^5 \ N/mm^2$.

Solution :

$$m_1 = \frac{E_s}{E_A} = \frac{2}{0.667} = 3$$

$$m_2 = \frac{E_c}{E_A} = \frac{1}{0.667} = 1.5$$

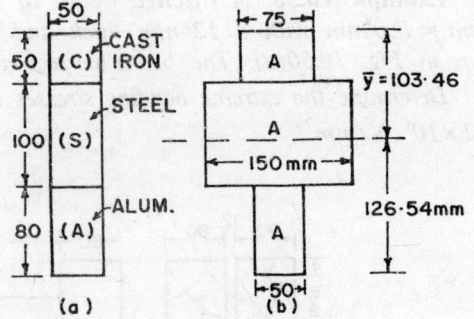

The equivalent section in terms of aluminum is shown in Fig. 10.51(b).

FIG. 10.51

Let the N.A. be at a distance of $\bar{y}$ below the top.

Total area $A = 75 \times 50 + 150 \times 100 + 80 \times 50 = 22750 \ mm^2$

$$\bar{y} = \frac{(75 \times 50 \times 25) + (150 \times 100 \times 100) + (80 \times 50 \times 190)}{22750} = 103.46 \ mm$$

$$I_{xx} = \left[\frac{1}{12} \times 75 \times 50^3 + 75 \times 50 (103.46 - 25)^2 \right] + \left[\frac{1}{12} \times 150 (100)^3 + 100 \times 150 (103.46 - 100)^2 \right]$$
$$+ \left[\frac{1}{12} \times 50 \times (80)^3 + 50 \times 80 (126.54 - 40)^2 \right]$$

$$= 6863.4 \times 10^4 \ mm^4$$

$$\therefore \quad f_A = \frac{M}{I} y_{A,max} = \frac{30 \times 10^6}{6863 \times 10^4} \times 126.54 = \mathbf{55.31 \ N/mm^2}$$

$$f_c = 1.5 \cdot \frac{M}{I} y_{c,max} = \frac{1.5 \times 30 \times 10^6}{6863 \times 10^4} \times 103.46 = \mathbf{67.83 \ N/mm^2}$$

$$f_s = 3 \cdot \frac{M}{I} y_{s,max} = \frac{3 \times 30 \times 10^6}{6863 \times 10^4} \times (103.46 - 50) = \mathbf{70.1 \ N/mm^2}$$

Example 10.37. *In a laboratory test of a beam loaded by end couples, the fibres at layer ABC (Fig. 10.52a) are found to lengthen by 0.004 mm and fibres at CD shorten by 0.012 mm* *in the 20 mm gauge length. Locate the N.A. and determine the flexural stresses at top and bottom fibres. What is the nature of end couples ? Take* $E = 2 \times 10^5 \, N/mm^2$.

Solution :

The top fibres are stretched while the bottom fibres are shortened; hence the moment is of *hogging* nature.

Now $\qquad \varepsilon_{AB} = \dfrac{0.004}{20} = 2 \times 10^{-4}$

and $\qquad \varepsilon_{CD} = \dfrac{0.012}{20} = 6 \times 10^{-4}$

$\therefore \qquad f_{AB} = \varepsilon_{AB} \cdot E = 2 \times 10^{-4} \times 2 \times 10^5 = 40 \, \text{N/mm}^2$

$\qquad f_{CD} = \varepsilon_{CD} \cdot E = 6 \times 10^{-4} \times 2 \times 10^5 = 120 \, \text{N/mm}^2$

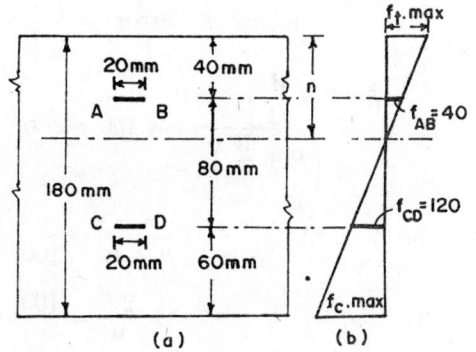

FIG. 10.52

The stress distribution is shown in Fig. 10.52(b). Let the depth of the N.A. be n below the top tensile fibres. From the geometry of the stress distribution diagram, we have

$$\frac{40 + 120}{80} = \frac{40}{n - 40}, \text{ From which } n = 60 \text{ mm}$$

$\therefore \qquad$ Stress at top fibre $= f_{t, max} = \dfrac{160}{80} \times 60 = \textbf{120 N/mm}^2$ (tensile)

$\qquad$ Stress at bottom fibre $= f_{c, max} = \dfrac{160}{80} (180 - 60) = \textbf{240 N/mm}^2$ (Comp.)

Example 10.38. *A simple beam weigh W and supports a concentrated load P at its midspan. If the error in calculating the bending stress is e % when the weight W is neglected, what is the ratio of P/W ? Find its numerical value when e = 4.*

Solution :

Neglecting the self weight W,

$$M_{max} = \frac{PL}{4}$$

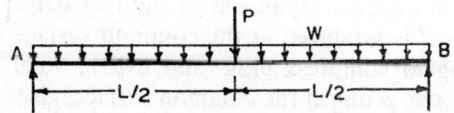

FIG. 10.53

$\therefore \qquad f_1 = \dfrac{M_{max}}{I} y_{max} = \dfrac{PL}{4} \cdot \dfrac{y_{max}}{I} = k P \qquad \qquad ...(1)$

where $\qquad k = \dfrac{L \, y_{max}}{4 \, I}$

If, however, self weight is considered, $M_{max} = \dfrac{PL}{4} + \dfrac{WL}{8}$

$\therefore \qquad f_2 = \left(\dfrac{PL}{4} + \dfrac{WL}{8} \right) \dfrac{y_{max}}{I} = \left(P + \dfrac{W}{2} \right) \dfrac{L \, y_{max}}{4 \, I} = k \left(P + \dfrac{W}{2} \right) \qquad \qquad ...(2)$

Hence % error $= \dfrac{f_2 - f_1}{f_2} \times 100$

$\therefore$ $\dfrac{k\left(P + \dfrac{W}{2}\right) - kP}{k\left(P + \dfrac{W}{2}\right)} \times 100 = e$ or $\dfrac{\dfrac{W}{2}}{P + \dfrac{W}{2}} = \dfrac{e}{100}$

or $\dfrac{W}{2P + W} = \dfrac{e}{100}$ or $\dfrac{2P + W}{W} = \dfrac{100}{e}$

$\therefore$ $\dfrac{2P}{W} = \dfrac{100}{e} - 1$ or $\dfrac{P}{W} = \dfrac{1}{2}\left(\dfrac{100}{e} - 1\right)$ Answer.

When $e = 4, \dfrac{P}{W} = \dfrac{1}{2}\left(\dfrac{100}{4} - 1\right) = \mathbf{12}$

Example 10.39. *A straight bimetallic strip of brass of rectangular section of width b and thickens t is joined along its length by a strip of steel of the same dimension thus forming a composite bar of width b and thickness 2t. If the bar is uniformly heated and is quite free to bend, show that it bends to a radius.*

$$R = \frac{E_B^2 + E_S^2 + 14\,E_B\,E_S}{12\,E_B\,E_S\,(\alpha_B - \alpha_S)} \cdot \frac{t}{T}$$

where α_B and α_S are the coefficients of linear expansion and T is the rise in temperature.

Such a strip 200 mm long with the steel and brass each 1.5 mm thick rests on a level surface with brass upper most. If the strip is initially straight, find the maximum clearance between it and surface due to a rise in temperature of $100°$ C. Take $\alpha_B = 19 \times 10^{-6}\,per\,°C$, $\alpha_S = 11 \times 10^{-6}\,per\,°C$, $E_B = 95000\,N/mm^2$ and $E_S = 205000\,N/mm^2$.   *(U.L.)*

Solution :

Brass will expand more than steel. Because of unequal expansion of the two strips, a force P is produced at the common surface, tending to compress brass and extend steel. This force, acting at the common surface, gives rise to a direct force P at the centre of each section along with a bending moment in each strip as marked in Fig. 10.54. The combined unit will bend into a radius R at the common surface

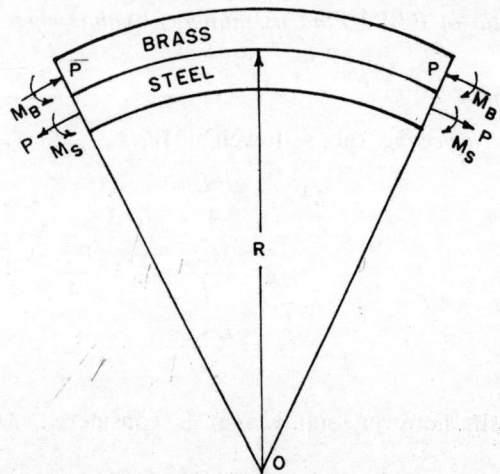

FIG. 10.54

Now $M_B = \left(\dfrac{E_B}{R}\right) I_B = \dfrac{b\,t^3}{12} \cdot \dfrac{E_B}{R}$ ...(i)

and $M_S = \left(\dfrac{E_S}{R}\right) I_s = \dfrac{b\,t^3}{12} \cdot \dfrac{E_S}{R}$ ...(ii)

Also, for equilibrium of the section,

$M_B + M_S = P \cdot t$

Hence
$$P \cdot t = \frac{b\,t^3}{12\,R}\left(E_B + E_S\right) \qquad \qquad ...(a)$$

The difference in linear strains at the central axis of each strain
$$= \frac{t/2}{R} - \left(-\frac{t/2}{R}\right) = \frac{t}{R}$$

Hence allowing for force P and temperature, the compatibility equation is
$$\frac{t}{R} = \left(\alpha_B\,T - \frac{P}{b\,t\,E_B}\right) - \left(\alpha_S\,T + \frac{P}{b\,t\,E_S}\right)$$

or
$$\left(\alpha_b - \alpha_S\right)T = \frac{P}{b\,t}\left(\frac{1}{E_B} + \frac{1}{E_S}\right) + \frac{t}{R} \qquad \qquad ...(b)$$

Substituting the value of $\dfrac{P}{b\,t}$ from (a), we get

$$\left(\alpha_B - \alpha_S\right)T = \frac{t}{12\,R}\frac{\left(E_B + E_S\right)^2}{E_B \cdot E_S} + \frac{t}{R}$$

or
$$\left(\alpha_B - \alpha_S\right)T = \frac{t}{12\,R}\left[\frac{E_B^2 + E_S^2 + 14\,E_B\,E_S}{E_B\,E_S}\right]$$

From which
$$R = \frac{E_B^2 + E_S^2 + 14\,E_B\,E_S}{12\,E_B\,E_S\left(\alpha_B - \alpha_S\right)} \cdot \frac{t}{T}$$

Substituting the numerical values,
$$R = \frac{95000^2 + 205000^2 + 14 \times 95000 \times 205000}{12 \times 95000 \times 205000\,(8 \times 10^{-6})} \times \frac{1.5}{100} = 2597 \ \text{mm}$$

The clearance h is given by the property of the circle :
$$(2R - h)\,h = \frac{L}{2} \times \frac{L}{2}.$$

Taking
$$2R - h \approx 2R$$

$$2Rh = \left(\frac{L}{2}\right)^2 = (100)^2$$

$\therefore$
$$h = \frac{(100)^2}{2R} = \frac{(100)^2}{2 \times 2597} = 1.93 \ \text{mm}$$

Example 10.40. *A composite beam is made by bolting on a steel channel 50 mm × 150 mm × 6 mm to a 150 mm × 150 mm timber beam as shown in Fig. 10.55(a). The composite beam is freely supported over a span of 4 m. Find the maximum uniformly distributed load that the beam can carry safely, if the allowable bending stresses in timber and steel are 8 N/mm² and 160 N/mm² respectively. Take E for steel = 2 × 10⁵ N/mm² and E for timber = 0.1 × 10⁵ N/mm².*

Solution :

Modular ratio
$$m = \frac{2}{0.1} = 20$$

$\therefore$ Width of steel component equivalent to timber section $= \dfrac{150}{20} = 7.5$ mm

The equivalent section is shown in Fig. 10.55(b).

Total area $= 2 \times 50 \times 6 + 138 \times 6 + 150 \times 7.5 = 2553$ mm^2

$$\bar{y} = \frac{2 \times 50 \times 6 \times 175 + 138 \times 6 \times 153 + 150 \times 7.5 \times 75}{2553} = 123.8 \text{ mm}$$

$$I_{xx} = \left[\frac{2}{12} \times 6 \,(50)^3 + 2 \times 50 \times 6 \,(26.2 + 25)^2 \right] + \left[\frac{1}{12} \times 138 \,(6)^3 + 138 \times 6 \,(26.2 + 3)^2 \right]$$

$$+ \left[\frac{1}{12} \times 7.5 \,(150)^3 + 150 \times 7.5 \,(123.8 - 75)^2 \right] = 719.5 \times 10^4 \text{ mm}^4$$

Let us permit the stress in steel to reach a value of 160 N/mm^2. Hence stress in steel at 76.2 mm from N.A. $= 160$ N/mm^2

$\therefore$ Stress in timber at 23.8 mm from N.A.

$= \dfrac{123.8}{76.2} \times \dfrac{160}{20}$

$= 13$ N/mm^2

This is more than the permissible value of 8 N/mm^2 in timber.

Hence maximum stress in timber $= 8$ N/mm^2.

Corresponding stress in steel $= \dfrac{76.2}{123.8} \times 8 \times 20$

$= 98.48$ N/mm^2

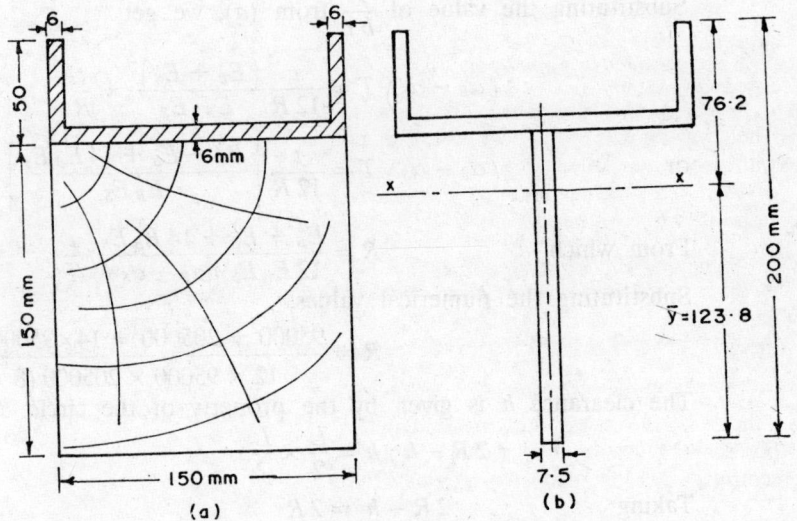

FIG. 10.55

$$M_{max} = \frac{wL^2}{8} = \frac{w\,(4)^2}{8} = 2w \;=\; 2w \times 1000 \ \text{N-mm}$$

Now $\dfrac{M}{I} = \dfrac{f}{y}$ or $\dfrac{2000\,w}{719.5 \times 10^4} = \dfrac{98.48}{76.2}$

From which $w = 4649 \text{ N/m} = \mathbf{4.649\ kN/m}$

PROBLEMS

1. The compression flange of a cast iron girder is 100 mm wide and 30 mm deep, the tension flange 300 mm wide and 50 mm deep and the web 250 mm × 30 mm. Find (a) moment of inertia about N.A. (b) load per metre run which may be carried over a 3 m span by a beam simply supported at its ends if the maximum permissible stresses are 95 N/mm^2 in compression and 25 N/mm^2 in tension.

2. The cross-section of a beam is shown in Fig. 10.57. The beam is made of a material with permissible stress in compression and tension equal to 100 N/mm^2 and 140 N/mm^2 respectively. Calculate the moment of resistance of the cross-section, when subjected to a moment causing compression at the top and tension at the bottom.

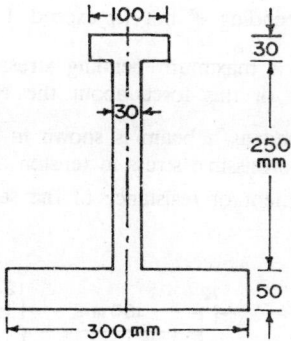

FIG. 10.56

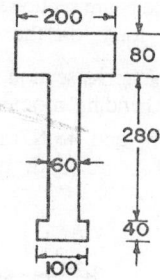

FIG. 10.57

3. Three beams have the same length, the same allowable stress and the same bending moment. The cross-sections of the beam are, a square, a rectangle with depth twice the width and a circle. Find the ratios of weight of circular and the rectangular beams with respect to the square beam.

4. Fig. 10.58 shows the section of a steel beam in the shape of an inverted semi-circular channel with flanges. Determine the position of the neutral axis and the second moment of area of the section about x-x..

Calculate the moment of resistance of the beam if the maximum stress due to bending is 125 N/mm². For semi-circular area of radius r, the distance of the centroid from the diameter is $0.4244\, r$.

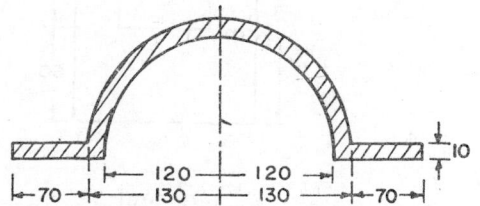

FIG. 10.58

5. A horizontal cantilever 3 m long is of rectangular cross-section 60 mm wide throughout its length and depth varying uniformly from 60 mm at free end to 180 mm at the fixed end. A load of 4 kN acts at the free end. Find the position of the highest stressed section, and the value of the maximum bending stress induced. Neglect the weight of the cantilever itself.

6. A tube of uniform thickness 2.5 mm has section in the shape of regular hexagon, as shown in Fig. 10.59, the outside hexagon having a side of 40 mm. Find the value of I_{xx} for the hollow hexagon. A length of the above tube rests in a horizontal position on two supports 2 m apart. The tube carries

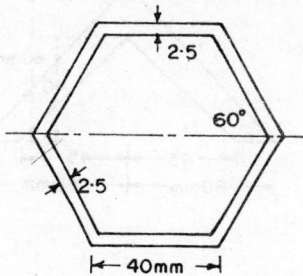

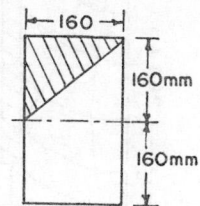

FIG.10.60

two loads of 2 kN situated between the supports and at equal distance from the ends of the tube. Find the least distance between the loads if the stresses due to bending is not to exceed 110 N/mm^2.

7. The beam section shown in Fig. 10.60 is subjected to a maximum bending stress of 12 N/mm^2. Find (i) the force on the area shaded, and (ii) the moment of this force about the N.A.

8. The cross-section of a cast iron machine element used as a beam is shown in Fig. 10.61. The beam resists bending moment about the horizontal N.A. The permissible stress in tension and compression are 40 N/mm^2 and 48 N/mm^2 respectively. Determine the moment of resistance of the section about the horizontal N.A. for both positive and negative B.M.

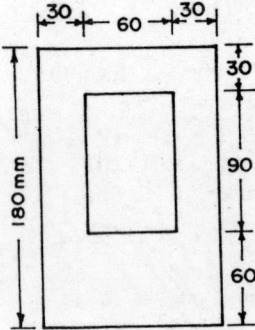

FIG. 10.61

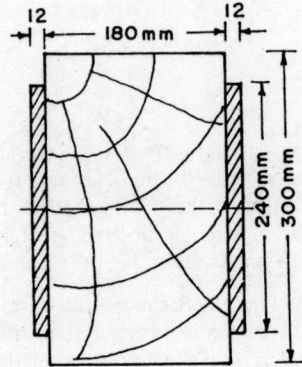

FIG. 10.62

9. A flitched beam consists of a wooden joist 180 mm wide and 300 mm deep strengthened by steel plates 12 mm thick and 240 mm deep one on either side of the joist (Fig. 10.62). If the stresses in wood and steel are not to exceed 8.75 N/mm^2 and 150 N/mm^2, find the moment of resistance of the section taking $E_S = 20 E_T$.

10. A flitched beam is made up of two timber joists 120 mm wide and 264 mm deep with a 20 mm thick steel plate 192 mm deep placed symmetrically between them and firmly attached to both. The plate is recessed into grooves cut in the inner faces of the joists so that the overall dimension of

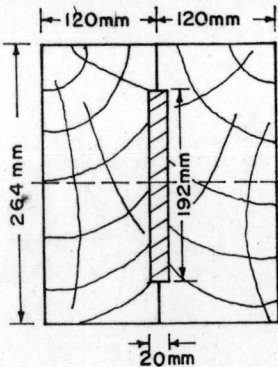

FIG. 10.63

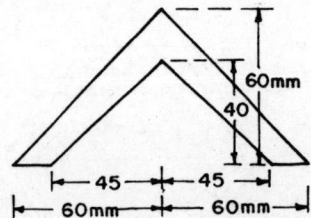

FIG. 10.64

the built up section may be taken as 240 mm × 264 mm. Calculate the moment of resistance of the combined section when the maximum bending stress in timber is 8 N/mm². What is then the maximum stress in steel ? Take $E_s = 20 E_T$.

11. A beam, simply supported over a span of 2 m is subjected to a central point load W. The beam section is symmetrical about y-axis as shown in Fig. 10.64. Determine the magnitude of W if the maximum compressive and tensile stresses are not to exceed 100 N/mm² and 90 N/mm² respectively.

12. A bar of steel 120 mm in diameter is encased in an aluminum tube 160 mm outer diameter. Assuming no slip between the components, find the maximum stresses induced in each material when the beam section is subjected to bending moment of 50 kN-m. Take $E_s = 3 E_A$.

FIG. 10.65

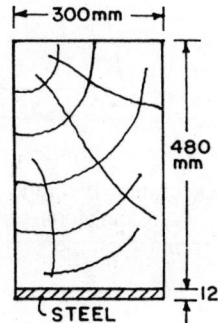

FIG. 10.66

13. A timber beam 300 mm wide and 480 mm deep is strengthened by a steel plate 300 mm wide and 12 mm thick connected to its lower face as shown in Fig. 10.66. Determine the stress in steel and timber when the beam section is subjected to a sagging moment of 90 kN-m. Assume that the Young's modulus for steel is 20 times that for timber.

14. A steel wire of diameter d is bent over a drum of radius r (Fig. 10.67). Calculate the maximum bending stress and the bending moment in the wire.

FIG. 10.67

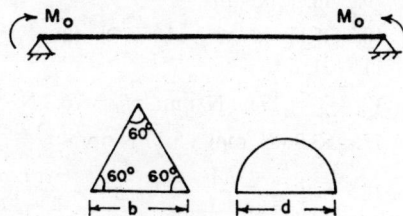

FIG. 10.68

15. The beam shown in Fig. 10.68 in subjected to pure bending by couples M_o. Determine the ratio $\dfrac{f_t}{f_c}$ of the maximum tensile and compressive stresses if the cross-section is (a) the equilateral triangle and (b) a semicircle.

16. A beam in pure bending has a trapezoidal cross-section (Fig. 10.69) with the top of the beam in compression. The allowable stresses in tension and compression are in the ratio $f_t/f_c = \alpha$. Determine the ratio b_1/b_2 of the base dimensions (in terms of α) in order that the stresses at both the top and bottom of the beam have the maximum allowable values. What is the permissible range of values of α for the trapezoidal cross-section ?

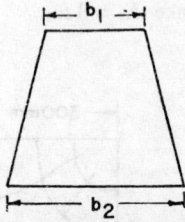

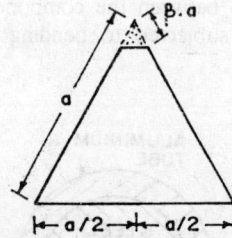

FIG. 10.69   FIG. 10.70

17. Determine the ratio β defining the small area that should be removed from a cross-section in the form of an equilateral triangle (Fig. 10.70) in order to obtain the strongest cross-section in bending. By what percentage is the section modulus increased when the area is removed ?

ANSWERS

1. 66.23 kN/m
2. 350.3 kN-m
3. 1.26 ; 0.895
4. 20.65 kN-m
5. 41.7 N/mm^2
6. 0.564 m
7. 15.36 kN-m
8. 24.9 kN-m ; 22.28 kN-m
9. 46.77 kN-m
10. 35.62 kN-m ; 116.36 N/mm^2
11. 2156 N
12. $f_s = 171.4$ N/mm^2 ; $f_a = 76.2$ N/mm^2
13. 53.96 N/mm^2 ; 5.17 N/mm^2
14. $f_{max} = \dfrac{E\,d}{2r + d}$; $M_{max} = \dfrac{\pi\,E\,d^4}{32\,(2\,r + d)}$
15. 0.5 ; 0.7373
16. $\dfrac{b_1}{b_2} = \dfrac{2\,\alpha - 1}{2 - \alpha}$; $\dfrac{1}{2} < \alpha < 2$
17. $\beta = 0.1304$; 9.23 %

11

Shearing Stresses in Beams

11.1. INTRODUCTION

In the previous chapter, we have studied the effect of bending moment in inducing bending or longitudinal stress. While discussing the simple theory of bending, we neglected the presence of shear and the distortion of plane section due to it. In the presence of shearing force existing at the section, the assumption that the plane sections remain plane after bending will not be true and the initial plane section will be distorted or warped after bending. An elaborate investigation of the problem shows that the warping of cross-section due to shearing strains does not substantially affect the longitudinal strains even if a distributed load acts on the beam and shearing force varies continuously along the beam. Due to this, we stated that the results of the simple theory of bending could be applied with sufficient accuracy to the cases where shear is present. This does not imply that the shearing stresses can be neglected altogether. *The effect of shear on bending stresses is not of practical importance, but the shearing stresses must be considered for their own importance.* In this chapter, we shall discuss the distribution of shearing stresses (q) associated with shear force F at any section. In the elementary treatment that follows, we shall consider only the shearing stresses in transverse planes parallel to the shearing force and the complimentary shear stresses in longitudinal planes parallel to the axis of the beam. The presence of other shear stresses is neglected.

11.2. EXISTENCE OF VERTICAL AND HORIZONTAL SHEAR STRESSES

In order to appreciate the existence of vertical and horizontal shearing stresses at any layer of the beam cross-section, let us consider a beam of rectangular cross-section of width b and depth d, subjected to a vertical shear force F. Let us reasonably assume that (*i*) the shear stress q act parallel to the S.F. (*i.e.* parallel to the vertical sides of the cross-section, and that (*ii*) the distribution of shear stress is *uniform* across the width b of the beam. Let us consider a small element mn, cut between two adjacent cross-sections and between

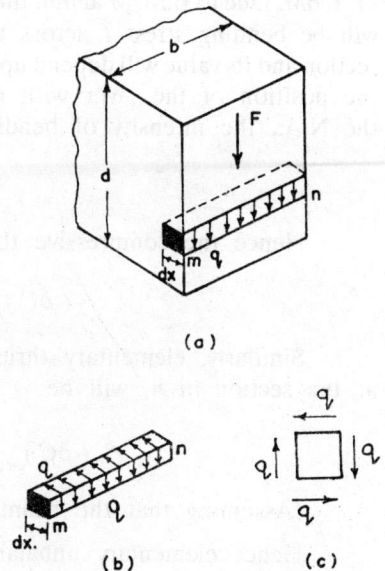

(a)

(b)   (c)

FIG. 11.1. VERTICAL AND HORIZONTAL SHEAR STRESSES

(395)

two adjacent planes that are parallel to the neutral surface. The vertical shear stress q is uniformly distributed on the vertical faces of the element. However, we know that shear stresses on one side of the element are accompanied by complimentary shear stresses of equal magnitude acting on the perpendicular faces of the element. Hence there will be *horizontal shear stresses*, between horizontal layers, as well as *transverse* or *vertical shear stresses* on the vertical faces.

Let us now consider the top and bottom faces of the cross-section. The horizontal shear stresses on the top and bottom faces must vanish because there are no stresses on the outer faces of the beam. Since the horizontal and vertical shearing stresses at any level must be equal, we arrive at a very interesting and important conclusion that the vertical shear stress q must also vanish at the top and bottom, *i.e.* $q = 0$ at $y = \pm d/2$.

11.3. DISTRIBUTION OF SHEAR STRESSES

In order to evaluate the shear stresses, let us consider the equilibrium of an element abm_1m (Fig. 11.2a) cut out from a beam between two adjacent cross-sections mn and m_1n_1 separated by a distance dx. The top face of this element is the upper face of the beam and is free from stress, but the bottom face ab is parallel to the neutral surface and at an arbitrary distance y_1 from that surface. This face ab is acted upon by the horizontal shear stress q existing at this level in the beam, and we have to find an expression for the same.

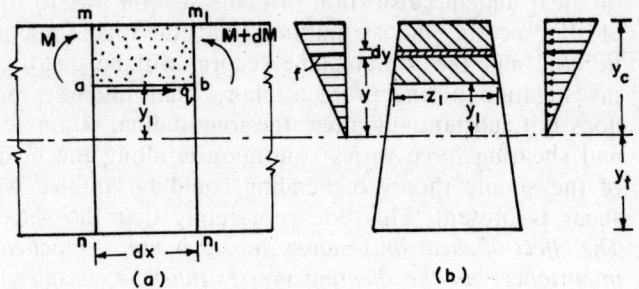

Let the B.M. at section mn be M and that at m_1n_1 be $M + \delta M$. Due to B.M. M at mn, there will be bending stress f across the section and its value will depend upon

FIG. 11.2

the position of the layer with respect to the neutral surface. For any layer distant y from the N.A., the intensity of bending stress f is given by

$$f = \frac{M}{I} y$$

Hence the compressive thrust on the strip of area δa at this height is

$$(\delta C)_{mn} = f \cdot \delta a = \frac{M}{I} \cdot y \cdot \delta a$$

Similarly, elementary thrust on the strip of area δa at the height y from the N.A. at the section m_1n_1 will be

$$(\delta C)_{m_1n_1} = \frac{M + \delta M}{I} \cdot y \cdot \delta a$$

(Assuming that the beam section is constant from mn to m_1n_1)

Hence elementary unbalanced horizontal thrust between mn and m_1n_1 is

$$\delta H = \frac{M + \delta M}{I} y \, \delta a - \frac{M}{I} y \, \delta a = \frac{\delta M}{I} y \, \delta a$$

The total unbalanced horizontal thrust for the layers between $y = y_1$ to $y = y_c$ will be

$$H = \sum_{y=y_1}^{y=y_c} \frac{\delta M}{I} y \, \delta a$$

Now, for the equilibrium of the element abm_1m, a horizontal shear force at ab must act to counter-balance this, since no other horizontal force is acting. Let the intensity of balancing shear at ab be q_1. If z_1 is the width of the beam section at this layer distant y_1 and N.A., the horizontal shear force at $ab = q_1 . \delta x . z_1$, assuming that the distribution is uniform.

Hence

$$q_1 . \delta x . z_1 = \sum_{y=y_1}^{y=y_c} \frac{\delta M}{I} y \, \delta a$$

or

$$q_1 = \frac{\delta M}{\delta x . I . z_1} \sum_{y=y_1}^{y=y_c} y \, \delta a$$

But $\dfrac{\delta M}{\delta x} = F$ and $y \, \delta a$ is the *moment of area above ab* (*i.e.* the shaded area) about the N.A.

$\therefore$

$$q_1 = \frac{F}{I z_1} (A \bar{y})$$

Dropping the suffixes,

$$q = \frac{F}{I z} . A \bar{y} \qquad \qquad \text{...(11.1)}$$

Assumptions : The above analysis is based on the following assumptions :

1. For all values of y, q is uniform across the width of the cross-section, irrespective of its shape.

2. $F = \dfrac{dM}{dx}$ is derived from the assumption that bending stress varies linearly across the section and is zero at the centroid.

3. The material is homogeneous and isotropic and the value of E is the same for tension as well as compression.

Assumption No. 1 is not strictly correct because the tangential value must be zero at the boundaries of the section. Hence it is understood that q is the *average value* across the section. Regarding assumption No. 2, the stress curve is not a straight line passing through the centroid of the section.

11.4. SHEAR STRESS DISTRIBUTION OVER RECTANGULAR SECTION

Fig. 11.3 (*a*) shows the rectangular cross-section of the beam, over which we have to determine the distribution of shear stress. Consider a layer ab at any height y above the N.A. The intensity of shear stress at this level is given by Eq. 11.1

$$q = \frac{F}{I z} (A \bar{y})$$

where
$\quad I$ = moment of inertia of the whole section
$\quad z$ = width of section at $ab = b$
$\quad A \bar{y}$ = moment of area above ab, about N.A.
$\quad\quad$ = moment of shaded area *about* N.A.

$$\therefore \qquad q = \frac{F}{Ib} \left\{ b \left(\frac{d}{2} - y \right) \right\} \left\{ y + \frac{1}{2} \left(\frac{d}{2} - y \right) \right\}$$

$$= \frac{F}{Ib} \left\{ b \left(\frac{d}{2} - y \right) \right\} \left\{ \frac{1}{2} \left(\frac{d}{2} + y \right) \right\}$$

or $\qquad q = \frac{F}{Ib} \times \frac{b}{2} \left(\frac{d^2}{4} - y^2 \right) = \frac{F}{2I} \left(\frac{d^2}{4} - y^2 \right)$ ...(11.2)

Thus, we find that the variation of q over the cross-section is parabolic.

At $\quad y = \pm \frac{d}{2}, q = 0$, as expected.

At $\quad y = 0, q = q_{max} = \frac{Fd^2}{8I}, = \frac{Fd^2}{8 \times \frac{1}{12} b d^3} = \frac{3}{2} \frac{F}{bd}$

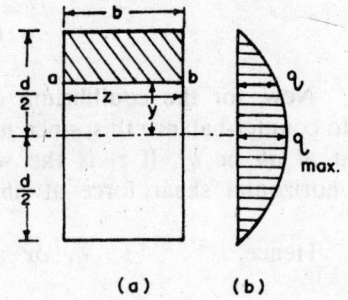

(a)   (b)

FIG. 11.3

...(11.3)

Mean shear stress on the section $q_{mean} = \dfrac{F}{\text{area}} = \dfrac{F}{bd}$

$$\therefore \qquad \frac{q_{max}}{q_{mean}} = \frac{3}{2} = 1.5 \qquad\qquad\qquad ...(11.3\ a)$$

Hence we observe that in the case of rectangular cross-section, the maximum shear stress at the N.A. is 50% more than the mean value.

11.5. SHEAR STRESS DISTRIBUTION OVER SOLID CIRCULAR SECTION

Fig. 11.4(a) shows the beam of a solid circular section of diameter d(or radius r). Consider a layer ab at a distance y from the N.A. The intensity of shear stress q is given by

$$q = \frac{F}{Iz} (A\bar{y})$$

where $\quad I = $ moment of inertia of the whole section.

$\qquad z = $ width ab of the section at height $y = 2 \left(r^2 - y^2 \right)^{\frac{1}{2}}$

$\qquad A\bar{y} = $ moment of the shaded area, situated above ab, about N.A.

To find the value of $A\bar{y}$, consider an elementary strip of thickness δy at height y ($h > y$). The area δa of the strip $= z . \delta y$. The moment of the elementary area $= \delta a . y = z . \delta y . y$. Hence the moment of the shaded area about the N.A. is

$$A\bar{y} = \int_{y=y}^{y=r} zy . \delta y$$

where $\qquad\qquad z = 2 \left(r^2 - y^2 \right)^{1/2}$ or $z^2 = 4 \left(r^2 - y^2 \right)$

$\therefore \qquad\qquad 2 z dz = 4 \left(-2y \right) dy = -8y \, dy$

$\therefore \qquad\qquad y \, dy = -\frac{1}{4} z \, dz$

when $\qquad\qquad y = r, z = 0; \text{ when } y = y, z = z$

$$\therefore \quad A\bar{y} = \int_{z}^{0} \left(-\frac{z^2}{4} \right)^2 dz = \frac{1}{4}\int_{0}^{z} z^2\, dz = \frac{z^3}{12}$$

$$\therefore \quad q = \frac{F}{Iz}A\bar{y} = \frac{F}{Iz} \times \frac{z^3}{12} = \frac{Fz^2}{12\,I}$$

or $\quad q = \frac{F}{12\,I}\{4(r^2 - y^2)\} = \frac{F}{3\,I}(r^2 - y^2) \quad$ ...(11.4)

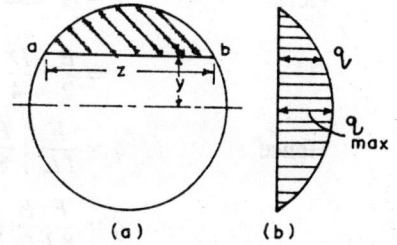

FIG. 11.4

The variation of q with y is again parabolic, as shown in Fig. 11.3(b).

At $\qquad\qquad y = 0, q = 0$. At $y = 0, q = q_{max} = \frac{F}{3\,I}r^2 = \frac{Fd^2}{12\,I}$. $\qquad$ ...(11.5)

$$\therefore \qquad q_{max} = \frac{Fd^2}{12\,\dfrac{\pi d^4}{64}} = \frac{4}{3}\frac{F}{\dfrac{\pi d^2}{4}} = \frac{4}{3}\frac{F}{\text{area}} = \frac{4}{3}q_{mean}$$

Hence q_{max} is 33.33% greater than the mean shear stress.

11.6. SHEAR STRESS DISTRIBUTION OVER I-SECTION

Fig. 11.5(a) shows an I-section or a flanged beam with (i) flange width B (ii) flange thickness t_f (iii) overall depth D (iv) depth of web, $d = D - 2t_f$ and (v) web thickness t_w. Let us find the shear stress distribution across the section.

(i) Distribution in flange

Let us consider a layer in the flange, at any distance y from the N.A. In general

$$q = \frac{F}{Iz}(A\bar{y})$$

Here $\qquad z = B \quad$ and

$$A\bar{y} = \left\{ B\left(\frac{D}{2} - y\right) \right\}\left\{ \frac{1}{2}\left(\frac{D}{2} + y\right) \right\} = \frac{B}{2}\left(\frac{D^2}{4} - y^2\right)$$

$$\therefore \qquad q = \frac{F}{IB}\cdot\frac{B}{2}\left(\frac{D^2}{4} - y^2\right) = \frac{F}{2\,I}\left(\frac{D^2}{4} - y^2\right) \text{...(11.6)}$$

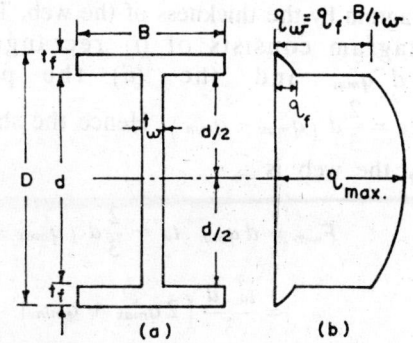

(a)   (b)

FIG. 11.5

The variation is parabolic. At $y = D/2, q = 0$, as expected.

At the junction with the web, $y = d/2$ and $q = q_f$ (say)

Hence $\qquad\qquad q_f = \frac{F}{8\,I}(D^2 - d^2) \qquad\qquad$ ...(11.7)

(ii) Distribution in the web

In general the shear stress intensity at height y is $q = \frac{F}{Iz}(A\bar{y})$

Here $z = t_w$ and $A\bar{y} = B \left(\dfrac{D}{2} - \dfrac{d}{2} \right) \left(\dfrac{D}{2} + \dfrac{d}{2} \right) \dfrac{1}{2} + t_w \left(\dfrac{d}{2} - y \right) \left(\dfrac{d}{2} + y \right) \dfrac{1}{2}$

$$= \frac{B}{2} \left(\frac{D^2}{4} - \frac{d^2}{4} \right) + \frac{t_w}{2} \left(\frac{d^2}{4} - y^2 \right) = \frac{B}{8} \left(D^2 - d^2 \right) + \frac{t_w}{8} \left(d^2 - 4y^2 \right)$$

Hence $\qquad q = \dfrac{F}{I\, t_w} \left\{ \dfrac{B}{8} \left(D^2 - d^2 \right) + \dfrac{t_w}{8} \left(d^2 - 4y^2 \right) \right\}$

or $\qquad q = \dfrac{F}{8I} \dfrac{B}{t_w} \left(D^2 - d^2 \right) + \dfrac{F}{8I} \left(d^2 - 4y^2 \right)$ ...(11.8)

The variation is parabolic. At the junction with the flange, $y = \dfrac{d}{2}$

Hence $\qquad q = q_w = \dfrac{F}{8I} \cdot \dfrac{B}{t_w} \left(D^2 - d^2 \right)$ ...(11.9)

or $\qquad q_w = \dfrac{B}{t_w} q_f$ ...(11.9a)

This shows that at the junction, the shear stress intensity suddenly shoots up and becomes B/t_w times that in the flange.

Again, at the N.A., $y = 0$ and $q = q_{max} = \dfrac{F}{8I} \left[\dfrac{B}{t_w} \left(D^2 - d^2 \right) + d^2 \right]$ ...(11.10)

Fig. 11.6 shows the shear stress distribution in the web. The maximum shear stress q_{max} occurs at the N.A. while the minimum shear stress q_{min} occurs at the junction in the flange. Depending upon the beam dimensions, q_{max} in the web typically is from 10 % to 60 % greater than q_{min}. The total shear force carried by the web may be computed by multiplying the area of shear stress diagram by the thickness of the web. The area of stress diagram consists of (i) rectangular area abcd $= d \cdot q_{min}$ and the (ii) the parabolic area $bce = \dfrac{2}{3} d \left(q_{max} - q_{min} \right)$. Hence the shear force carried by the web is

$$F_{web} = d\, q_{min} \cdot t_w + \frac{2}{3} d \left(q_{max} - q_{min} \right) t_w$$

$$= \frac{t_w \cdot d}{3} \left(2 q_{max} + q_{min} \right) \qquad ...(11.11)$$

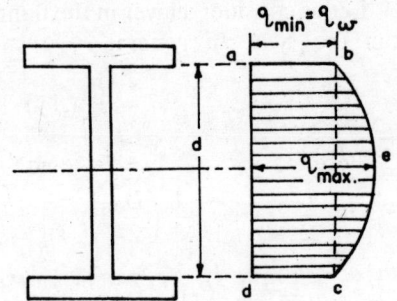

FIG. 11.6. SHEAR STRESS DISTRIBUTION IN THE WEB

For typical beam proportions, the shear stresses in web account for 90 % to 98 % of total S.F., the remainder being carried by shear in flanges. See example 11.8.

11.7. SHEAR STRESS DISTRIBUTION OVER OTHER SECTIONS

Proceeding similarly, one can find the shear stress distribution over other sections, such as hollow circular section, T-section, L-section, built-up section etc. Fig. 11.7 gives the summary of shear stress distribution over some common sections.

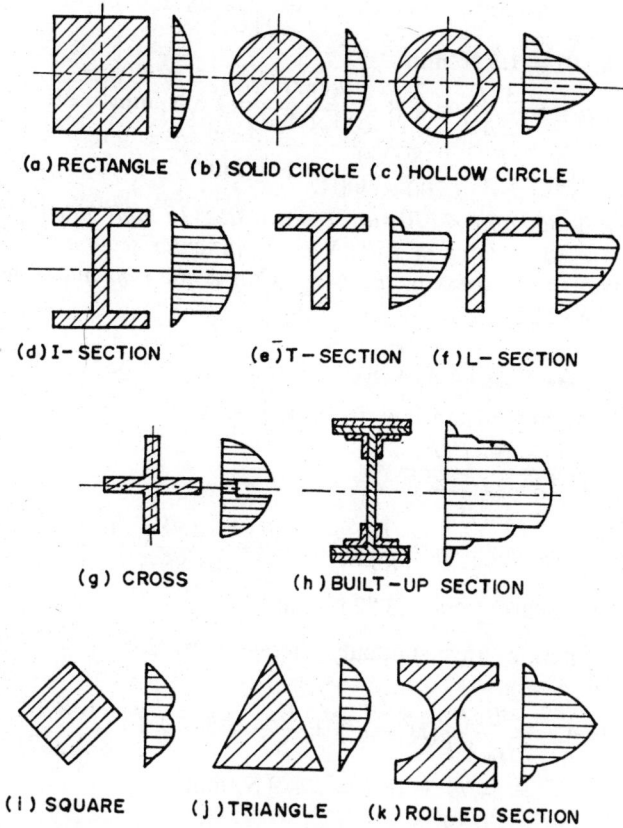

FIG. 11.7. SHEAR STRESS DISTRIBUTION OVER COMMON SECTIONS

Example 11.1 *A wooden beam supports U.D.L. of 40 kN/m run over a simply supported span of 4 m. It is of rectangular cross-section, 200 mm wide and 400 mm deep. Sketch the shear stress distribution, and determine (i) maximum shear stress (ii) average shear stress.*

Solution :

In general
$$q = \frac{F}{I\,b}\,(A\,\bar{y})$$

where
$$b = 200 \text{ mm}$$

$$I = \frac{1}{12} \times 200(400)^3 = 106667 \times 10^4 \text{ mm}^4$$

$$A\,\bar{y} = 200\,(200 - y)\left\{\frac{1}{2}\,(200 + y)\right\}$$

$$= 100\,(200^2 - y^2) = 100\,(40000 - y^2)$$

$$\therefore \quad F = \frac{w\,L}{2} = \frac{40 \times 4}{2} = 80 \text{ kN} = 80000 \text{ N}$$

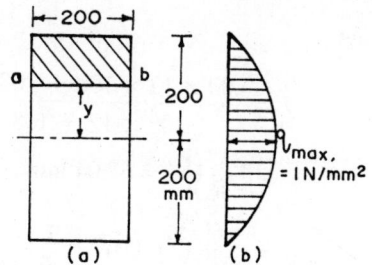

FIG. 11.8

$$\therefore \qquad q = \frac{80000}{106667 \times 10^4 \times 200} \times 100 \,(40000 - y^2) = 3.75 \times 10^{-5} \,(40000 - y^2)$$

which gives the law of variation of shear stress across the depth.

q_{max} (at $y = 0$) = **1.5 N/mm^2**

Alternatively, $\quad q_{max} = \dfrac{3}{2}\dfrac{F}{b\,d} = \dfrac{3}{2} \times \dfrac{80000}{200 \times 400} = $ **1.5 N/mm^2**

$$q_{av} = \frac{F}{b\,d} = \frac{80000}{200 \times 400} = 1 \text{ N/mm}^2$$

Example 11.2. *A 300 mm × 150 mm I-girder has 12 mm thick flanges and 8 mm thick web. It is subjected to a shear force of 150 kN at a particular section. Find the ratio of maximum shear stress to minimum shear stress in the web. What is the maximum shear stress in the flange?*

Solution :   (Refer Fig. 11.5)

$$I_{xx} = \frac{1}{12}\left[150 \times 300^3 - 142 \times 276^3 \right] = 8871 \times 10^4 \text{ mm}^4$$

In the flange, at any distance y from the N.A.

$$q = \frac{F}{2I}\left(\frac{D^2}{4} - y^2 \right)$$

At the junction with the web, $q_f = \dfrac{F}{8I}(D^2 - d^2) = \dfrac{150 \times 10^3}{8 \times 8871 \times 10^4}\left[300^2 - 276 \right]^2 = 2.92 \text{ N/mm}^2$

$\therefore$ Maximum shear stress = **2.92 N/mm^2**

In *the web*, at the junction, this suddenly increases to $2.92 \times \dfrac{150}{8} = 54.79 \text{ N/mm}^2 = q_{min}$.

q_{max} at the N.A. $\quad = \dfrac{B}{t_w}\dfrac{F}{8I}(D^2 - d^2) + \dfrac{F\,d^2}{8I} = 54.79 + \dfrac{150 \times 10^3\,(276)^2}{8 \times 8871 \times 10^4}$

$$= 54.79 + 16.1 = 70.89 \text{ N/mm}^2$$

$\therefore \qquad \dfrac{q_{max}}{q_{min}} = \dfrac{70.89}{54.79} = \mathbf{1.294}$

Example 11.3. *The cross-section of a joist is a T-section, 120 mm × 200 mm × 12 mm, with 120 mm side horizontal. Sketch the shear stress distribution and hence find the maximum shear stress if it has to resist a shear force of 200 kN.*

Solution :

$$\bar{y} = \frac{200 \times 12 \times 100 + 108 \times 12 \times 6}{200 \times 12 + 108 \times 12}$$

$$= \frac{247776}{3696} = 67.04 \text{ mm}$$

$$I_{AB} = \frac{1}{3} \times 12\,(200)^3 + \frac{1}{3} \times 108\,(12)^3$$

$$= 3206 \times 10^4 \text{ mm}^4$$

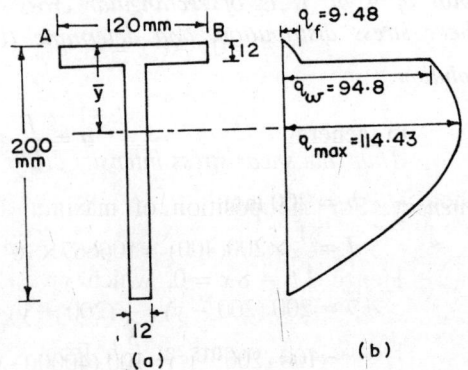

FIG. 11.9

$$I_{xx} = 3206 \times 10^4 - 3696\,(67.04)^2 = 1545 \times 10^4\,\text{mm}^4$$

q_f (at the junction with the web) $= \dfrac{F}{I \times 20}\,[\,120 \times 12\,(67.04 - 6)\,] = \dfrac{732.48\,F}{I}$

$$= \dfrac{732.48 \times 200 \times 10^3}{1545 \times 10^4} = 9.48\,\text{N/mm}^2$$

q_w at the junction with flange $= 9.48 \times \dfrac{120}{12} = 94.8\,\text{N/mm}^2$

$q_{w,max}$ at the centroid $= \dfrac{F}{I \times 12}\left[\,120 \times 12\,(67.04 - 6) + \dfrac{12\,(67.04 - 12)^2}{2}\,\right] = \dfrac{8840\,F}{I}$

$$= \dfrac{200 \times 10^3 \times 8840}{1545 \times 10^4} = \mathbf{114.43\,N/mm^2}$$

The variation of shear stress is shown in Fig. 11.9 (b).

Example 11.4. *A beam of square section is used as a beam with one diagonal horizontal. Find the magnitude and location of maximum shear stress in the beam. Also, sketch the shear stress distribution across the section.*

Solution : Let $\qquad B = $ length of side

$$b = \text{length of diagonal} = \sqrt{2}\,B$$

$$I_{AB} = 2 \times \dfrac{1}{12}\,(b)\left(\dfrac{b}{2}\right)^3 = \dfrac{b^4}{48}$$

At any distance x from the apex C, width $ab = 2x$

$\therefore \qquad\qquad q = \dfrac{F}{I\,(2x)} \times$ moment of the shaded area about N.A. AB

$$= \dfrac{F}{I\,(2x)}\left[\dfrac{1}{2} \times 2x \times x\left(\dfrac{b}{2} - \dfrac{2}{3}x\right)\right] = \dfrac{F}{\left(\dfrac{b^4}{48}\right) \times 2x}\left[\dfrac{x^2\,(3b - 4x)}{6}\right] = \dfrac{4\,Fx}{b^4}\,(3\,b - 4x).$$

The variation is parabolic. In the above expression, the first term $\dfrac{4\,Fx}{b^4}$ increases with the increasing value of x, while the second term decrease with the increasing value of x.

At $x = 0, q = 0$. At $x = \dfrac{b}{2}, q_{na} = \dfrac{2\,F}{b^3}\,(3\,b - 2\,b)$

$$= \dfrac{2\,F}{b^2} = \dfrac{F}{\text{area}} = q_{mean}$$

Thus, the shear stress intensity at the N.A. is the mean intensity. For the position of maximum shear, $\dfrac{dq}{dx} = 0$

Hence $3\,b - 8x = 0$, which gives $x = \dfrac{3}{8}\,b$

Hence q_{max} occurs at $\dfrac{3}{8}\,b$ from C, or at $\dfrac{1}{8}\,b$ from the N.A.

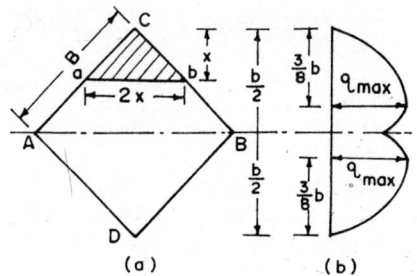

FIG. 11.10

$$q_{max} = \frac{4F}{b^4} \left(\frac{3}{8}b\right) \left[3b - 4 \times \frac{3}{8}b\right] = \frac{9F}{4b^2} = \frac{9F}{8B^2} \qquad ...(11.12)$$

$$q_{mean} = \frac{F}{area} = \frac{F}{B^2} = \frac{2F}{b^2}$$

$$\therefore \qquad \frac{q_{max}}{q_{mean}} = \frac{9}{8} = 1.125$$

Example 11.5. *A beam of triangular cross-section with base b and height h, is used with the base horizontal. Calculate the intensity of maximum shear stress and plot the variation of shear stress intensity over the section.*

Solution :

We know that $I_{xx} = \frac{1}{36}bh^3$

Now, at any distance x from the apex C,

$$q = \frac{F}{Iz}(A\bar{y})$$

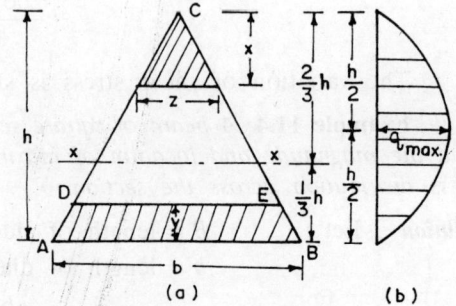

where $z = b \cdot \dfrac{x}{h}$ and

$$A\bar{y} = \left(\frac{1}{2}zx\right)\left(\frac{2}{3}h - \frac{2}{3}x\right) = \frac{1}{3}zx(h-x)$$

FIG. 11.11

$$\therefore \qquad q = \frac{F}{Iz} \times \frac{1}{3}zx(h-x) = \frac{F}{3I}x(h-x) \qquad ...(11.13)$$

The variation is parabolic, giving $q = 0$ at $x = 0$

At the N.A., $\quad q_n = \dfrac{F}{3I}\left(\dfrac{2}{3}h\right)\left(h - \dfrac{2}{3}h\right) = \dfrac{2}{27}\dfrac{F}{I}h^2 = \dfrac{2}{27}\dfrac{36F}{bh^3}h^2 = \dfrac{72}{27}\dfrac{F}{bh} = \dfrac{8}{3}\dfrac{F}{bh} \qquad ...(11.14)$

$$= \frac{4}{3}\frac{F}{area} = \frac{4}{3}q_{mean}$$

Hence the intensity of shear stress at the N.A. is 4/3 of the mean intensity.

For maximum intensity above the N.A., $\dfrac{dq}{dx} = 0 = h - 2x$.

This gives $x = h/2$. Hence the maximum shear stress occurs at the mid-height.

$$q_{max} = \frac{F}{3I}\frac{h}{2} \cdot \frac{h}{2} = \frac{F}{12I}h^2 = \frac{3F}{bh^3} \cdot h^2 = \frac{3F}{bh} \qquad ...(11.15)$$

$$= \frac{3F}{2\,area} = \frac{3}{2}q_{mean}$$

Similarly, to plot the shear stress distribution below the N.A., consider a section DE distant y from the base, where the shear stress intensity is given by

$$q = \frac{F}{Iz'}(A\bar{y}) \text{ where } z' = DE = \frac{b}{h}(h-y)$$

and
$$A\bar{y} = \frac{1}{2}(b + z')y\left[\frac{h}{3} - \frac{y}{3}\left(\frac{b + 2z'}{b + z'}\right)\right]$$

$$= \frac{y}{6}\left[b + \frac{b}{h}(h - y)\right]\left[h - y\left\{\frac{b + \frac{2b}{h}(h - y)}{b + \frac{b}{h}(h - y)}\right\}\right] = \frac{by}{6h}(2h - y)\left[h - y\left(\frac{3h - 2y}{2h - y}\right)\right] = \frac{by}{3h}(h - y)^2$$

$$\therefore \quad q = \frac{F}{I\frac{b}{h}(h - y)} \cdot \frac{by}{3h}(h - y)^2 = \frac{Fy}{3I}(h - y) \qquad \ldots(11.16)$$

This variation is also parabolic, similar to Eq. 11.13, giving $q = 0$ at $y = 0$.

Also, at $\quad y = \frac{h}{3}$, $q_n = \frac{F}{3I}\frac{h}{3} \times \frac{2h}{3} = \frac{2}{27}\frac{F}{I}h^2 = \frac{8F}{3bh}$, which is the same as found earlier.

Example 11.6. *A cast iron bracket, subjected to bending has a cross-section of I-shape with unequal flanges, as shown in Fig. 11.12(a). If the section is subjected to a shear force of 1600 kN, draw the shear stress distribution over the depth of the section, indicating the principal values.*

Solution :

Let $\bar{y}$ the distance of the N.A. from the top fibre.

Total Area $= 300 \times 50 + 300 \times 50$
$\qquad + 200 \times 50 = 40000 \text{ mm}^2$

$\bar{y} = \frac{1}{40000}[250 \times 50 \times 25 + 350 \times 50$
$\qquad \times 175 + 200 \times 50 \times 375]$

$\qquad = 178.125 \text{ mm}$

$I_{AB} = \frac{1}{3} \times 250 \times 50^3 + \frac{1}{3} \times 50 \times 350^3$

$+ \left[\frac{1}{12} \times 200\,(50)^3 + 200 \times 50\,(375)^2\right]$

$= 213333 \times 10^4 \text{ mm}^4$

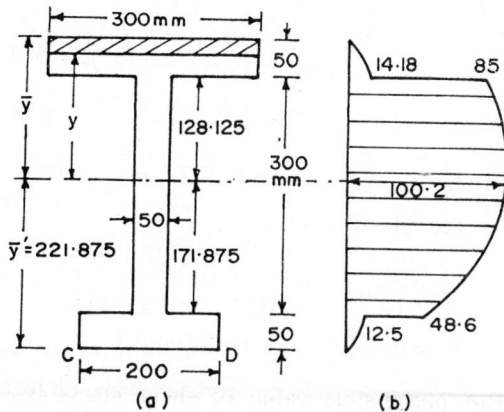

FIG. 11.12

$\therefore \qquad I_{xx} = 213333 \times 10^4 - 40000\,(178.125)^2 = 86419 \times 10^4 \text{ mm}^4$

Now, at any distance y from the N.A., $q = \frac{F}{Iz}(A\bar{y})$

where $\qquad z = 300$ mm and $A\bar{y} = 300\,(\bar{y} - y)\,(\bar{y} + y)\frac{1}{2}$

$\qquad = 150\,(\bar{y}^2 - y^2) = 150\,(178.125^2 - y^2) = 150\,(31729 - y^2)$

$\therefore \qquad q = \frac{F}{Iz}(A\bar{y}) = \frac{1600 \times 10^3}{86419 \times 10^4 \times 300} \times 150\,(31729 - y^2) = 9.257 \times 10^{-4}\,(31729 - y^2)$

The variation is parabolic, giving $q = 0$ at $y = 178.125$ mm.

At the junction with the web, $q_f = 9.257 \times 10^{-4}\,(31729 - 128.125^2) = 14.18 \text{ N/mm}^2$

At the junction with the web, $q_f = 14.18 \times \dfrac{300}{50} = 85 \text{ N/mm}^2$

At the N.A., $q_n = \dfrac{F}{Iz}(A\bar{y}) = \dfrac{1600 \times 10^3}{86419 \times 10^4 \times 50}\left[300 \times 50\,(178.125 - 25) + 50 \times 128.125 \times \dfrac{128.125}{2}\right]$

$$= 85 + 15.2 = 100.2 \text{ N/mm}^2$$

Similarly, at the junction of web with lower flange,

$$q_f = \dfrac{1600 \times 10^3}{86419 \times 10^4 \times 300}[200 \times 50\,(221.875 - 25)] = 12.15 \text{ N/mm}^2$$

and $\qquad q_w = 12.15 \times \dfrac{200}{50} = 48.6 \text{ N/mm}^2$

The shear stress distribution is shown in Fig. 11.12 (b).

Example 11.7. *A laminated wooden beam 120 mm wide and 180 mm deep in made of three 120 mm × 60 mm planks glued together to resist longitudinal shear. The beam is simply supported over a span of 2.5 m. If the allowable shearing stress in the glued joint is 0.5 N/mm², find the safe U.D.L. the beam can carry.*

Solution :

$$I_{xx} = \dfrac{1}{12} \times 120\,(180)^3 = 5832 \times 10^4 \text{ mm}^4$$

$$F = \dfrac{wL}{2} = \dfrac{w \times 2.5}{2} = 1.25\,w \text{ kN}$$

(where w is the safe U.D.L. in N/m)

At the glued joint ab,

$$q = \dfrac{F}{Iz}(A\bar{y}) = \dfrac{1.25\,w}{5832 \times 10^4 \times 120}[\,120 \times 60 \times 60\,]$$

$$= 0.7716 \times 10^{-4}\,w \text{ N/mm}^2$$

FIG. 11.13

But permissible value of shear stress is 0.5 N/mm^2

$\therefore \qquad 0.7716 \times 10^{-4}\,w = 0.5$

From which $\qquad w = \textbf{6480 N/m}$

Example 11.8. *A rolled steel joist 300 mm deep and 200 mm wide has flange 16 mm thick and web 12 mm thick. Calculate the proportion in which the flange and web resist (a) B.M. (b) shear force.*

Solution : $\qquad I = \dfrac{1}{12}\left[200\,(300)^3 - 188\,(268)^3\right] = 14843 \times 10^4 \text{ mm}^4$

(a) Resistance to B.M. : Consider a section of δy thickness in the web at a distance y from the N.A. Stress $f = \dfrac{M}{I}y$ at the section.

Elementary force offered by the strip $= f \cdot \delta a = \dfrac{M}{I}y\,(12\,\delta y)$

Moment of elementary force, about N.A. $= \delta M = \dfrac{M}{I}y^2\,(12\,\delta y)$

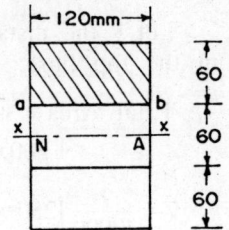

$$\therefore \quad M_r \text{ offered by the web} = M_{rw} = \sum_{y=-134}^{y=+134} \delta M$$

or
$$M_{rw} = \int_{-134}^{+134} 12 \frac{M}{I} d^2 \, dy = \frac{24M}{I} \int_{0}^{134} y^2 \, dy = \frac{24M}{3I} \left(y^3\right)_{0}^{134}$$

or
$$M_{rw} = \frac{24M}{3 \times 14843 \times 10^4} (134)^3 = \mathbf{0.1297\,M}$$

Hence moment of resistance offered by the flange $= M - 0.1297\,M = \mathbf{0.8703\,M}$

Hence the flange takes up 87.03 % of B.M. while the web takes up only 12.97 %.

(b) Resistance to S.F. : Consider an elementary strip of δy thickness in the flange, at a distance y from the N.A. The elementary area $\delta a = 200 \, \delta y$.

$$\text{Shear stress intensity } q = \frac{F}{2I} \left(\frac{D^2}{4} - y^2 \right) = \frac{F}{2I} (22500 - y^2)$$

$$\text{Shear resistance offered by the strip} = q\,\delta a = \frac{F}{2I} (22500 - y^2)\,200\,\delta y$$

$$\therefore \quad \text{Shear resistance offered by one flange} = \int_{134}^{150} \frac{100F}{I} (22500 - y^2)\,dy$$

$$\therefore \quad \text{Shear resistance of both the flanges} = \frac{200F}{I} \left(22500\,y - \frac{y^3}{3} \right)_{134}^{150}$$

$$= \frac{200F}{I} \left[\left\{ 22500 \times 150 - \frac{(150)^3}{3} \right\} - \left\{ 22500 \times 134 - \frac{(134)^3}{3} \right\} \right]$$

$$= \frac{7406933\,F}{I} = \frac{7406933}{14843 \times 10^4} F \approx \mathbf{0.05\,F}$$

$\therefore$ Shear resistance offered by the web $= F - 0.05\,F = \mathbf{0.95\,F}$

Hence web takes 95 % of shear while the flanges take only 5 % of shear.

Example 11.9. *A steel beam of I-section, 200 mm deep and 160 mm wide has 16 mm thick flanges and 10 mm thick web. The beam is subjected to a shear force of 200 kN. Determine the shear stress distribution over the beam section if the web of the beam is kept horizontal.*

Solution :

$$I_{xx} = 2 \times \frac{1}{12} \times 16\,(160)^3 + \frac{1}{12} \times 168\,(10)^3$$
$$= 1094 \times 10^4 \text{ mm}^4$$

Shear stress in the flange, just above the web

$$q_f = \frac{F}{Iz} (A\bar{y}) \text{ where } z = 2 \times 16 = 32 \text{ mm}$$

$$A\bar{y} = 2 \times 16 \times 75\,(37.5 + 5) = 102000 \text{ mm}^3$$

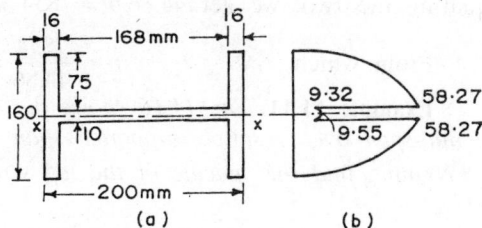

$$\therefore \qquad q_f = \frac{200 \times 10^3}{1094 \times 10^4 \times 32} \times 102000 = \mathbf{58.27\ N/mm^2}$$

Shear stress in the web, just at the junction

$$q_w = q_f \times \frac{32}{200} = 58.27 \times \frac{32}{200} = \mathbf{9.32\ N/mm^2}$$

Shear stress at N.A.

$$q_n = \frac{F}{I\,z}\,(A\,\bar{y}),\ \text{where}\ z = 200\ \text{mm}$$

$$A\,\bar{y} = 2 \times 16 \times 75\,(37.5 + 5) + 200 \times 5 \times 2.5 = 104500\ \text{mm}^3$$

$$\therefore \qquad q_n = \frac{200 \times 10^3}{1094 \times 10^4 \times 200} \times 104500 = \mathbf{9.55\ N/mm^2}$$

The shear stress distribution is shown in Fig. 11.14 (*b*).

Example 11.10. *Three planks, each of 150 mm × 50 mm are bolted together by 10 mm diameter bolts to form an I-section, as shown in Fig. 11.15. The beam carries a central point load of 20 kN. If the shear stress in the bolt is not to exceed 100 N/mm² find the pitch of the bolts.*

Solution :

$$I_{xx} = \frac{1}{12}\left[150\,(250)^3 - 100\,(150)^3\right] = 16719 \times 10^4\ \text{mm}^4$$

$$F = \frac{20 \times 10^3}{2} = 1000\ \text{N}$$

At the level *ab*, the junction of the flange with the web

$$q = \frac{F}{I\,z}\,(A\,\bar{y})$$

$\therefore$ Horizontal shear load per mm length of the beam is given

by

$$Q = \frac{F}{I}\,A\,\bar{y}) = \frac{10000}{16719 \times 10^4}\,(150 \times 50 \times 100) = 44.86\ \text{N/mm}$$

Let *p* be the pitch of the bolts, in mm.

$\therefore$ Horizontal shear load per pitch length $= 44.86\,p$ N …(*i*)

Also, safe shear load per bolt $= f_s \dfrac{\pi}{4}\,d^2 = 100 \times \dfrac{\pi}{4}\,(10)^2 = 7854\ \text{N}$ …(*ii*)

Equating the two, we get $44.86\,p = 7854$

From which $\qquad p = \dfrac{7854}{44.86} = \mathbf{175\ mm}$

Example 11.11. *Fig. 11.16 shows the cross-section of beam, carrying a vertical load W at the mid-span over a simply supported span of 2 m. If the allowable working stress in bending in 8 N/mm², find the spacing of the lag screws. Each lag screw can transmit a shear force of 300 N.*

Solution : Let the spacing of the lag screws be *s*.

$$I = \frac{1}{12} \times 2 \times 50\,(240)^3 + 2\left[\frac{1}{12} \times 300\,(30)^3 + 30 \times 300\,(135)^2\right] = 44460 \times 10^4\ \text{mm}^4$$

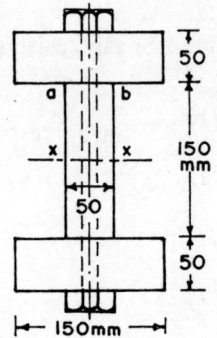

FIG. 11.15

$$Z = \frac{44460 \times 10^4}{150}$$
$$= 2964 \times 10^3 \text{ mm}^3$$
$$M = fZ = 8 \times 2964 \times 10^3$$
$$= 23.712 \times 10^6 \text{ N-mm}$$
$$= 23712 \text{ N-m}$$

But $\quad M = \dfrac{WL}{4}$. Hence

$$W = \frac{4M}{L} = \frac{4 \times 23712}{2}$$
$$= 47424 \text{ N}$$

Hence $\quad F = \dfrac{W}{2} = \dfrac{47424}{2} = 23712 \text{ N}$

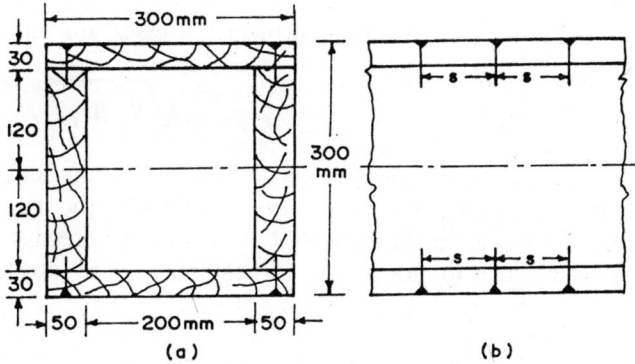

FIG. 11.16

Now, shear stress at the junction, 30 mm from the top (or the bottom) is

$$q' = \frac{F}{Iz}(A\bar{y}) = \frac{23712}{44460 \times 10^4 (2 \times 50)} (30 \times 300 \times 135) = 0.648 \text{ N/mm}^2$$

Since there are two screws in each row, total shear transmitted by each screw $= \dfrac{1}{2}(100 \times s \times 0.648) = 32.4\, s$ N. Equating this to shear value of each screw, we have

$$32.4\, s = 3000, \text{ from which } s = \mathbf{92.6\ mm}$$

Example 11.12. *A box section, having dimensions shown in Fig. 11.17 is used for a beam on simple supports. In a certain region along the beam, there is a constant linear change in bending moment of 80 kN-m per m along the axis of the beam. Determine the maximum shearing stress at a section in this region.*

Solution :

$$I = \frac{1}{12}\left[240\,(360)^3 - 180\,(300)^3\right] = 52812 \times 10^4 \text{ mm}^4$$
$$F = \frac{\Delta M}{\Delta x} = \frac{80 \text{ kN–m}}{1 \text{ m}} = 80 \text{ kN}$$

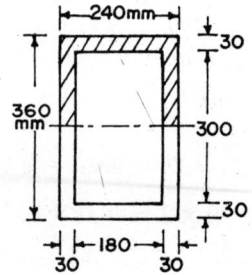

The maximum shear stress occurs at the N.A.

FIG. 11.17

$$\therefore \quad q_{max} = \frac{F}{Iz}(A\bar{y}) = \frac{80000}{52812 \times 10^4 (2 \times 30)}\left[30 \times 240 \times 165 + 2 \times 150 \times 30 \times 75\right] = \mathbf{4.7\ N/mm^2}$$

11.8. PRINCIPAL STRESSES AND PRINCIPAL PLANES AT A POINT IN A BEAM SECTION

We have seen that when a beam is subjected to transverse loading, bending moment and shear force are induced at a given section. Due to this, the bending stress f and shear stress q at a given point in the cross-section is given by

$$f = \frac{M}{I} y \qquad \text{and} \qquad q = \frac{F}{I z} (A \bar{y})$$

Because of the f and q, principal stresses are induced, the magnitude of which is given by Eq.

$$\sigma = \frac{f}{2} \pm \sqrt{\frac{f^2}{4} + q^2} .$$

The major principal stress σ_1 will be of the same sign as that of f (*i.e.* compressive above N.A. and tensile below the N.A.) while the minor principal stress σ_2 will be of the opposite sign (*i.e.* tensile above the N.A. and compressive below N.A.), for the simply supported beams subjected to downward vertical loads. The position of principal plane is given by

$$\tan 2\theta = 2q/f$$

where θ = inclination of the principal plane with the direction of f.

At the top fibre, $q = 0$. Hence $\theta_1 = 0$

As we go towards the N.A., q increases and hence θ_1 also increases.

At the N.A., $f = 0, 2\theta_1 = 90°$ and hence $\theta_1 = 45°$. Hence at the N.A. there exists a state of simple shear.

The maximum shear stress any where in the beam section will be equal to $\sqrt{\dfrac{f^2}{4} + q^2}$, its plane being inclined at 45° to that of σ_1. The variation of principal stresses along the depth are shown in Fig. 11.18 and 11.19 for beams of rectangular and I-section respectively.

Example 11.13. *A beam simply supported over a span of 5 m, is loaded with a central point load of 80 kN. The section of the beam is a rectangle, 200 mm wide and 400 mm deep. At a cross-section distant 2 m from the support, calculate the bending and shearing stresses at points 200, 150, 75 and 0 mm from the N.A. of the section. Also, find the principal stresses and locate principal planes at these points.*

Solution :

$I = \dfrac{1}{12} \times 200 (400)^3 = 106667 \times 10^4 \text{ mm}^4$

$M = 40 \times 2 = 80 \text{ kN-m} = 80 \times 10^6 \text{ N-mm}$

$F = 40 \text{ kN} = 40000 \text{ N}$

(a) *At a point 200 mm from N.A.*

$$f = \frac{M}{I} y = \frac{80 \times 10^6}{106667 \times 10^4} \times 200$$

$$= 15 \text{ N/mm}^2 \text{ (comp.)}$$

$q = 0$

$\therefore \qquad \sigma_1 = f = 15 \text{ N/mm}^2 \text{ (Comp.) and } \sigma_2 = 0 ; \theta_1 = 0$

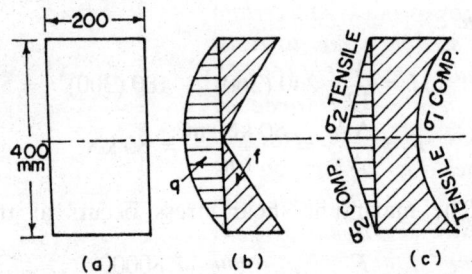

FIG. 11.18

(b) *At a point 150 mm from the N.A.*

$$f = \frac{80 \times 10^6}{106667 \times 10^4} \times 150 = 11.25 \text{ N/mm}^2 \text{ (Compressive)}$$

$$q = \frac{F}{2I}\left(\frac{d^2}{4} - y^2\right) = \frac{40000}{2 \times 106667 \times 10^4}\left(\frac{400^2}{4} - 150^2\right) = 0.328 \text{ N/mm}^2$$

$$\sigma = \frac{11.25}{2} \pm \sqrt{\left(\frac{11.25}{2}\right)^2 + (0.328)^2} = 5.625 \pm 5.635$$

$$\therefore \qquad \sigma_1 = \textbf{11.26 N/mm}^2 \text{ (Comp.)} \text{ and } \sigma_2 = \textbf{0.01 N/mm}^2 \text{ (tensile)}$$

(c) At a point 75 mm from the N.A.

$$f = \frac{80 \times 10^6}{106667 \times 10^4} \times 75 = 5.625 \text{ N/mm}^2$$

$$q = \frac{400000}{2 \times 106667 \times 10^4}\left(\frac{400^2}{4} - 75^2\right) = 0.645 \text{ N/mm}^2$$

$$\therefore \qquad \sigma = \frac{5.625}{2} \pm \sqrt{\left(\frac{5.625}{2}\right)^2 + (0.645)^2} = 2.813 \pm 2.886$$

$$\therefore \qquad \sigma_1 = \textbf{5.699 N/mm}^2 \text{ (Comp.)} \text{ and } \sigma_2 = \textbf{0.073 N/mm}^2$$

(d) At the N.A.

$$f = 0 \, ; q = \frac{40000}{2 \times 106667 \times 10^4}\left(\frac{400^2}{4}\right) = 0.75 \text{ N/mm}^2$$

$$\theta_1 = \theta_2 = 45° \, ; \sigma_1 = \sigma_2 = 0.75 \text{ N/mm}^2$$

At the N.A., there is a state of simple shear and principal stresses are 0.75 N/mm^2 (Comp.) along one diagonal plane and 0.75 N/mm^2 tensile along the other diagonal plane. Fig. 11.18 (*b*) shows the variation of bending and shearing stresses, while Fig. 11.18 (*c*) shows the variations of σ_1 and σ_2.

Example 11.14. *A 200 mm × 400 mm R.S.J. has flange 20 mm thick and web 16 mm thick. At a certain cross-section it has to resist a bending moment of 160 kN-m and a shear force of 300 kN. Find the principal stresses (a) at the top (b) in the flange at 180 mm from the N.A. (c) in the web at 180 mm from the N.A., and (d) at the N.A. Plot the variation of q, f and σ along the depth of the section.*

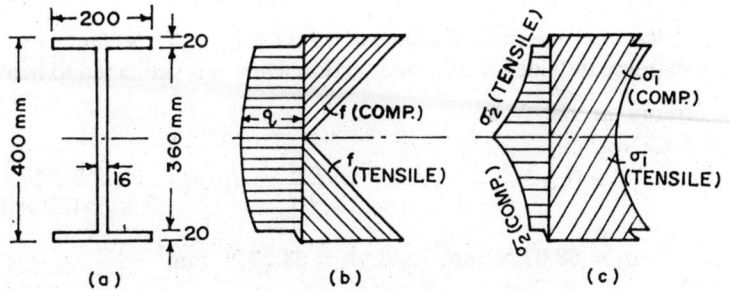

FIG. 11.19

Solution :

$$I = \frac{1}{12}\left[200 \times 400^3 - 184 \times 360^3\right]$$

$$= 35127 \times 10^4 \text{ mm}^4$$

(a) Stresses at the top

$$f = \frac{M}{I} y = \frac{160 \times 10^6}{35127 \times 10^4} \times 200$$

$$= 91.1 \text{ N/mm}^2 \text{ (Comp.)}$$

$$q = 0$$

$$\therefore \qquad \sigma_1 = \textbf{91.1 N/mm}^2 \text{ (Comp.)}$$

$$\sigma_2 = 0$$

(b) Stresses in the flange at 180 mm from the N.A.

$$f = \frac{160 \times 10^6}{35127 \times 10^4} \times 180 = 81.99 \text{ N/mm}^2 \text{ (Comp.)}$$

$$q = \frac{F}{8I}(D^2 - d^2) = \frac{300000}{8 \times 35127 \times 10^4}(400^2 - 360^2) = 3.25 \text{ N/mm}^2$$

$$\therefore \qquad \sigma = \frac{81.99}{2} \pm \sqrt{\left(\frac{81.99}{2}\right)^2 + (3.25)^2} = 40.99 \pm 41.12$$

$$\therefore \qquad \sigma_1 = \textbf{82.11 N/mm}^2 \text{ (comp.) and } \sigma_2 = \textbf{0.13 N/mm}^2 \text{ (tensile)}$$

(c) Stresses in the web at 180 mm from the N.A.

$$f = 81.99 \text{ N/mm}^2 \text{ (Comp.)} \; ; \; q = 3.25 \times \frac{200}{16} = 40.63 \text{ N/mm}^2$$

$$\sigma = \frac{81.99}{2} \pm \sqrt{\left(\frac{81.99}{2}\right)^2 + (40.63)^2} = 40.99 \pm 57.72$$

$$\therefore \qquad \sigma_1 = \textbf{98.71 N/mm}^2 \text{ (Comp.) and } \sigma_2 = \textbf{16.73 N/mm}^2 \text{ (tensile)}$$

Thus the intensity of principal stress (i.e. 98.71 N/mm^2) at the junction may exceed that at the extreme outside layers of the section when it is subjected to heavy B.M. and S.F. simultaneously.

(d) Stresses at the N.A.

$$f = 0; q = \frac{B}{t} \cdot \frac{F}{8I}(D^2 - d^2) + \frac{Fd^2}{8I} = 40.99 + \frac{300000}{8 \times 35127 \times 10^4}(400)^2 = 40.99 + 17.08 = 58.07$$

$$\therefore \quad \sigma_1 = \textbf{58.07 N/mm}^2 \text{ and } \sigma_2 = \textbf{58.07 N/mm}^2$$

The variation of f and q are plotted in Fig. 11.19 (b) while the variation of σ_1 and σ_2 are shown in Fig. 11.19 (c).

11.9. CURVES OF PRINCIPAL STRESSES

At any point in the beam, the longitudinal bending stress and the shearing stress give rise to principal stresses the magnitude and direction of which can be found as explained in the previous para. Curves or envelopes of principal stresses may be obtained by finding the direction of principal stresses at various points in several cross-sections of the beam, and joining up the directions of the principal stresses. Such curves are shown in Fig. 11.20, drawn on a longitudinal section of a beam. The curves are such that the tangent and normal at any point give the directions of the two principal stresses at the point. As shown, there are two systems of curves, one normal to the other.

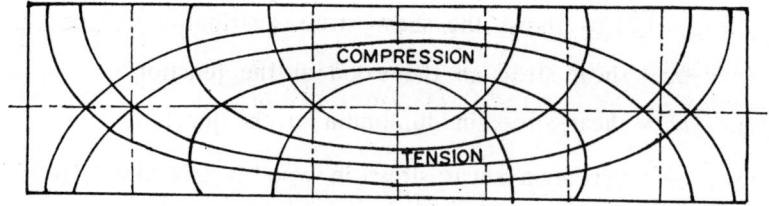

FIG. 11.20. CURVES OF PRINCIPAL STRESSES

Properties of the curves

A close study of the two systems of the principal stress envelopes give rise to the following properties:

1. Both the systems of the curve cross each other at right angles.

2. Each system crosses the N.A. at $45°$

3. At any point of a curve, the tangent and normal give the directions of the two principal stresses.

4. The intensity of stress along each curve is the greatest when it is parallel to the length of the beam and diminishes along the curve to zero, where it cuts a face of beam at right angles.

11.10. COMPOSITE AND BUILT UP BEAMS

The composite and built up beams can be analysed for shearing stresses in the same manner adopted for bending stresses. In each case, the centroid of the section is first determined, to locate the position of the bending axis. The moment of inertia of the section is then computed, using the parallel axis theorem. The shearing stress at any location can then be computed using the relation $q = \dfrac{F}{Iz}(A\bar{y})$. In the case of composite section made up of two materials, it may be convenient to analyse the beam by first determining the *equivalent section* in terms of any one material. Examples 11.15 and 11.16 illustrate the procedure.

Example 11.15. *A composite beam is made by bonding duralumin sheets to the upper and lower surfaces of a rectangular wooden spar. The wooden spar is 160 mm deep and 80 mm wide and duralumin sheets 80 mm by 2 mm. Calculate the greatest load which the beam can carry when loaded as cantilever if the maximum shearing stress in the wood is limited to* $6 N/mm^2$. *For duralumin, $E = 7700 N/mm^2$ and for wood $E = 700 N/mm^2$.*

Solution :

Let us use suffix D for duralumin and W for wood.

$$\text{Now} \quad \frac{\text{Shear stress}}{\text{Shear strain}} = N$$

$$\therefore \qquad q \propto N$$

At any point, $\dfrac{q_D}{q_w} = \dfrac{N_D}{N_W} = \dfrac{E_D}{E_W} = \dfrac{7700}{700} = 11$

Fig. 11.21(b) shows the shear stress distribution diagram in which

    bc = shear stress in the wood at the junction

    bd = shear stress in duralumin at the junction

    fe = maximum shear stress in wood = 6 N/mm^2 (given)

Let us first determine the value of bc and bd. The distribution of shear stress in wood will be parabolic, as for a rectangular beam (Fig. 11.21 c).

Let the equation of the parabola be

$x = ky^2$ where y is measured from N.A., upwards towards the top, and x is the ordinate of the parabola.

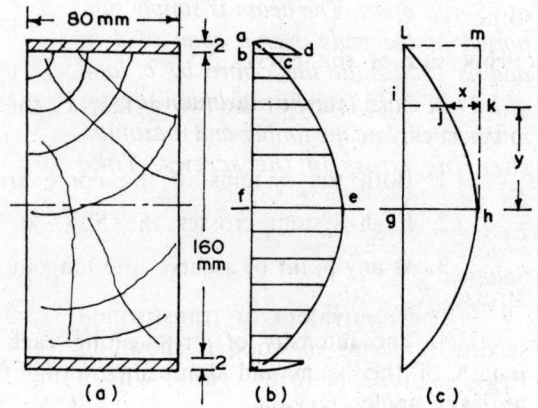

FIG. 11.21

$\therefore$ $ij = lm - jk = k\,(82)^2 - ky^2$

$\therefore$ $\dfrac{ij}{gh} = \dfrac{ij}{lm} = \dfrac{6724 - y^2}{6724}$

$\therefore$ $ij = \dfrac{6724 - y^2}{6724} \times gh$

Thus, at any distance y above N.A., the ordinate is given by the above equation. For the parabolic shear stress diagram of Fig 11.21 (b), we have

$$bc = q_w = \frac{6724 - (80)^2}{6724} \times fe = \frac{6724 - 6400}{6724} \times 6 = 0.289 \text{ N/mm}^2$$

$\therefore$ $bd = q_D = 11\,q_w = 11 \times 0.289 = 3.18 \text{ N/mm}^2$

Thus, the stresses are completely known.

Now W = Total load taken $= W_D + W_W = F_D + F_W$

Now $q = \dfrac{F}{Iz}(A\bar{y})$, and hence $F = \dfrac{qIz}{A\bar{y}}$ with usual symbols.

$\therefore$ $F_D = \dfrac{q_D \cdot I_D \cdot z_D}{(A\bar{y})_D}$ and $F_W = \dfrac{q_W \cdot I_W \cdot z_W}{(A\bar{y})_W}$

Here $I_D = \dfrac{1}{12} \times 80\,(164^3 - 160^3) \approx 210 \times 10^4 \text{ mm}^4$ and $I_W = \dfrac{1}{12} \times 80\,(160)^3 = 2731 \times 10^4 \text{ mm}^4$

$(A\bar{y})_D = 80 \times 2 \times 81 = 12960 \text{ mm}^3$ and $(A\bar{y})_W = 80 \times 80 \times 40 = 256000$

$z_D = z_W = 80 \text{ mm}$; $q_D = 3.18 \text{ N/mm}^2$; $q_W = 6 \text{ N/mm}^2$

$$\therefore \qquad F_D = \frac{3.18 \times 210 \times 10^4 \times 80}{12960} = 41222 \text{ N}$$

and
$$F_W = \frac{6 \times 2731 \times 10^4 \times 80}{256000} = 51206 \text{ N}$$

Total $\qquad W = F = F_D + F_W = 41222 + 51206 = 92428 \text{ N} = \textbf{92.428 kN}$

Example 11.16. *A rectangular wooden beam 60 mm wide and 160 mm deep is reinforced by screwing a steel plate 10 mm thick and 60 mm wide on to the bottom. The screws are 6 mm in diameter and pitched at 75 mm apart. The beam is simply supported at the ends over a span of 4 m and is loaded at the centre by a load of 1.2 kN. Calculate the maximum stresses in the steel plate the timber and maximum shearing stress in the screws. Take* $\dfrac{E_S}{E_T} = 15$.

Solution :

The equivalent or transformed section in terms of wood is shown in Fig. 11.22 (b) in which $AB = 15 \times 60 = 900$ mm.

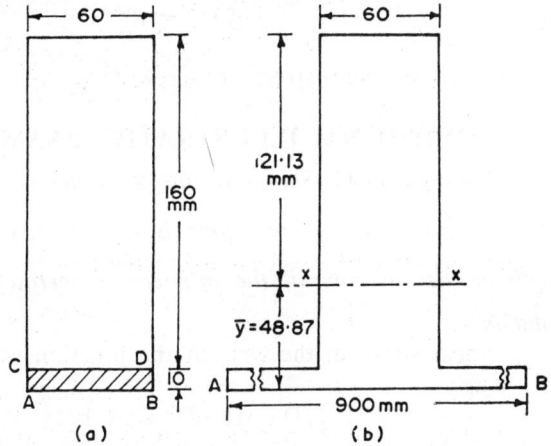

FIG. 11.22

Total $A = 60 \times 160 + 900 \times 10$
$\qquad = 18600 \text{ mm}^2$

$$\therefore \qquad \bar{y} = \frac{60 \times 160 \times 90 + 900 \times 10 \times 5}{18600} = 48.87 \text{ mm}^2$$

$$I_{AB} = \frac{1}{3} \times 60 \times 170^3 + \frac{1}{3} \times 840 \times 10^3 = 9854 \times 10^4 \text{ mm}^4$$

$$\therefore \qquad I_{xx} = 9854 \times 10^4 - 18600 \,(48.87)^2 = 5412 \times 10^4 \text{ mm}^4$$

$$M_{max} = \frac{WL}{4} = \frac{1.2 \times 4}{4} = 1.2 \text{ kN-m} = 1.2 \times 10^6 \text{ N-mm}$$

$$\therefore \qquad (f_c)_{max} = \frac{M}{I} y_{max} = \frac{1.2 \times 10^6}{5412 \times 10^4} \times 121.13 = \textbf{2.686 N/mm}^2$$

Also, $(f_t)_{max}$ is timber $= \dfrac{1.2 \times 10^6}{5412 \times 10^4} \times (48.87 - 10) = \textbf{0.862 N/mm}^2$

$(f_t)_{max}$ in steel $= \left[\dfrac{1.2 \times 10^6}{5412 \times 10^4} \times 48.87 \right] \times 15 = \textbf{16.254 N/mm}^2$

Shear stress in screws

Area of screws $= \dfrac{\pi}{4}(6)^2 = 28.274 \text{ mm}^2$; Pitch $= 75$ mm

Let $\qquad q = $ maximum horizontal stress in screws.

$\therefore$ Maximum horizontal force F_{max} in each end screw $= q \times b \times$ pitch.

$$= 75\, bq = 75\, b \cdot \frac{F}{I\,b}\,(A\,\bar{y})$$

$$= \frac{75\,F}{I}\,(A\,\bar{y})$$

Here $F = \dfrac{1.2}{2} = 0.6\ \text{kN} = 600\ \text{N}\,;\quad A\bar{y}$ at $CD = 900 \times 10\,(48.87 - 5) = 394830$

$\therefore$ $F_{max} = \dfrac{75 \times 600}{5412 \times 10^4}\,(394830) = 328.3\ \text{N}$

$\therefore$ Max. shear stress in screw $= \dfrac{328.3}{28.274} = \mathbf{11.61\ N/mm^2}$

11.11. ADDITIONAL ILLUSTRATIVE EXAMPLES

Example 11.17. *Show that the difference between the maximum and mean shear stress down the rectangular web of an I-joist is* $\dfrac{F\,d^2}{24\,I}$, *where F is the shear force at the section, d is the depth of the web and I, the moment of inertia of the section about the N.A.*

Solution :

Shear stress in the web, at the junction with the flange

$$ab = \frac{F}{I\,b}\left[\, B\,\frac{(D-d)}{2}\left(\frac{D}{2}+\frac{d}{2}\right)\frac{1}{2}\,\right]$$

$$= \frac{F\,B}{8\,I\,b}\left(D^2 - d^2\right)$$

Max. shear stress in the web

$$cd = \frac{F}{I\,b}\left[\, B\,\frac{(D-d)}{2}\left(\frac{D}{2}+\frac{d}{2}\right)\frac{1}{2} + b \times \frac{d}{2} \times \frac{d}{4}\,\right]$$

$$= \frac{F\,B}{8\,I\,b}\left(D^2 - d^2\right) + \frac{F\,d^2}{8\,I}$$

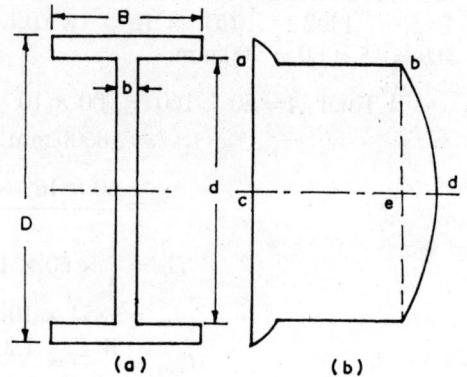

Hence shear stress changes in the web from ab to cd, parabolically,

FIG. 11.23

$\therefore$ $\left(q_{mean}\right)_{web} = ab + \dfrac{2}{3}\,ed$

But $ed = cd - cd = ce - ab = \dfrac{F\,d^2}{8\,I}$

$\therefore$ $\left(q_{mean}\right)_{web} = \dfrac{F\,B}{8\,I\,b}\left(D^2 - d^2\right) + \dfrac{2}{3}\dfrac{F\,d^2}{8\,I} = \dfrac{F\,B}{8\,I\,b}\left(D^2 - d^2\right) + \dfrac{F\,d^2}{12\,I}$

Also, $\left(q_{max}\right)_{web} = cd = \dfrac{F\,B}{8\,I\,b}\left(D^2 - d^2\right) + \dfrac{F\,d^2}{8\,I}$

$$\therefore \qquad (q_{max})_{web} - (q_{mean})_{web} = \frac{Fd^2}{8I} - \frac{Fd^2}{12I} = \frac{Fd^2}{24I} \quad \text{(Proved)}$$

Example 11.18. *A rod of circular section is subjected to a shearing force on a plane perpendicular to its axis. Find the maximum shearing stress in terms of shearing force and rod diameter.*

If the rod is used as a beam with free ends and a central concentrated load, express the free length in terms of diameter for which the maximum shearing stress, due to shearing force, is half the maximum direct stress.

Solution :

For a circular section, we have, $q_{max} = \dfrac{16 F}{3 \pi D^2}$

For simply supported beam, $M_{max} = \dfrac{WL}{4}$

$$\therefore \qquad \pm f_b = \frac{WL}{4Z} = \frac{32\,WL}{4\,\pi\,D^3} = \frac{8\,WL}{\pi\,D^3} \qquad \qquad ...(i)$$

$$q_{max} = 16 \times \frac{W}{2} \cdot \frac{1}{3\,\pi\,D^2} = \frac{8\,W}{3\,\pi\,D^2} \qquad \qquad ...(ii)$$

But $\qquad q_{max} = \dfrac{f_b}{2}$

$$\therefore \qquad \frac{8\,W}{3\,\pi\,D^2} = \frac{1}{2} \cdot \frac{8\,WL}{\pi\,D^3}$$

which gives $\qquad L = \dfrac{8\,W}{3\,\pi\,D^2} \times \dfrac{2\,\pi\,D^3}{8\,W} = \dfrac{2}{3}\,D$

Example 11.19. *A beam is made up of four 60 mm × 120 mm full sized Douglas fir pieces which are glued to a 30 mm × 600 mm Douglas fir plywood web, as shown in Fig. 11.24. Determine the maximum allowable shear force and maximum allowable bending moment which the section can carry if the allowable bending stress is 12 N/mm², the allowable shear stress is 1.2 N/mm² and the allowable shearing stress in the glued joint is 0.24 N/mm².*

Solution :

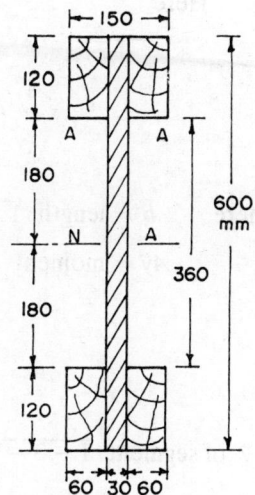

FIG. 11.24

$$I = \frac{1}{12}\left[150 \times 600^3 - 120 \times 360^3 \right]$$

$$= 223344 \times 10^4 \text{ mm}^4$$

$$M = \frac{f}{y_{max}} \cdot I = \frac{12}{300} \times 223344 \times 10^4$$

$$= 89.34 \times 10^6 \text{ N-mm} = 89.34 \text{ kN-m}$$

The maximum shear stress occurs at the N.A. for which the maximum allowable shear force is given by

$$F = \frac{q\,I z}{(A\,\overline{y})} = \frac{1.2 \times 223344 \times 10^4 \times 30}{2 \times 60 \times 120 \times 240 + 30 \times 300 \times 150} = 16730 \text{ N} = 16.73 \text{ kN}$$

The maximum shear stress in the glue occurs at level A–A, for which S.F. is given by

$$F = \frac{q\,I z}{(A\,\overline{y})} = \frac{0.24 \times 223344 \times 10^4 \times (2 \times 60)}{2 \times (60 \times 120 \times 240)} = 18612 \text{ N} = 18.612 \text{ kN}$$

Hence the allowable B.M. = **89.34 kN-m** and allowable S.F. = **16.73 kN**

Example 11.20. *A steel bar rolled to the section shown in Fig. 11.25 (a) is subjected to shearing force of 200 kN applied in the direction YY. Making the usual assumptions, determine the average shearing stress at section A, B, C and D, and find the ratio of the maximum to the mean shearing stress in the section. Draw a diagram to show the variation of the average shearing stress across the section.*

Solution :

Fig. 11.25 (b) shows the equivalent section. At any layer distant y from the N.A. :

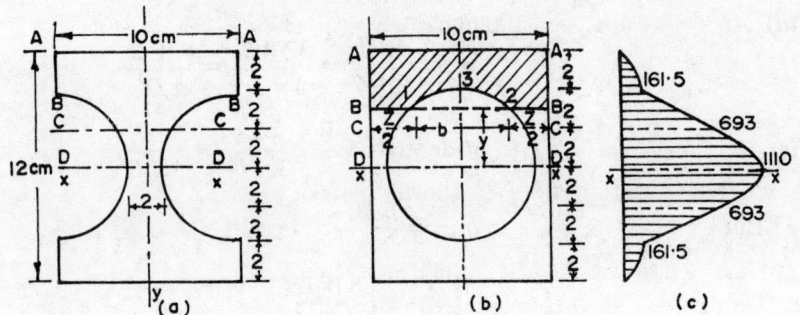

FIG. 11.25

$$q = \frac{F}{I z}\,(A\,\overline{y})$$

Here

$$I = \frac{1}{12} \times 100 \times 120^3 - \frac{\pi}{64}\,(80^4)$$

$$= 1239 \times 10^4 \text{ mm}^4$$

$$F = \text{S.F.} = 200 \text{ kN} = 200000 \text{ N}$$

$$z = \text{Solid width of resisting layer} = 100 - b = 100 - 2\,(r^2 - y^2)^{1/2}$$

where $\quad b = $ length $\overline{1-2} = 2\,(r^2 - y^2)^{1/2}$; $\quad r = $ radius of circle $= 40$ mm

$A\overline{y} = $ moment of the shaded portion, about the N.A.

$$= \left[100\,(60 - y)\,(60 + y)\,\frac{1}{2} - A\,\overline{y}\,\text{of segment } \overline{1-3-2} \right]$$

$$= \left[50\,(3600 - y^2) - A\,\overline{y}\,\text{of segment } \overline{1-3-2} \right]$$

$A\,\overline{y}$ of segment $\overline{1-3-2} = \dfrac{b^3}{12} = \dfrac{2}{3}\,(r^2 - y^2)^{3/2}$

$\therefore\;\; A\,\overline{y}$ of shaded portion $= 50\,(3600 - y^2) - \dfrac{2}{3}\,(1600 - y^2)^{3/2}$

(i) At y = 0 : $z = 100 - 40 \times 2 = 20$ mm

and $A\bar{y} = 50(3600 - 0) - \dfrac{2}{3}(1600 - 0)^{3/2} = 180000 - 42667 = 137333$ mm^3

∴ $q_D = q_{max} = \dfrac{F}{Iz}(A\bar{y}) = \dfrac{200000}{1239 \times 10^4 \times 20} \times 137333 = \mathbf{110.8\ N/mm^2}$

(ii) At y = 20 mm : $z = 100 - 2(1600 - 400)^{1/2} = 30.72$ mm

$A\bar{y} = 50(3600 - 400) - \dfrac{2}{3}(1600 - 400)^{3/2} = 132287$ mm^3

∴ $q_c = \dfrac{F}{Iz}(A\bar{y}) = \dfrac{200000}{1239 \times 10^4 \times 30.72} \times 132287 = \mathbf{69.5\ N/mm^2}$

(iii) At y = 40 mm: $z = 100$ mm ; $A\bar{y} = 50(3600 - 1600) = 100000$ mm^3

$q_D = \dfrac{F}{Iz}(A\bar{y}) = \dfrac{200000}{1239 \times 10^4 \times 100} \times 100000 = \mathbf{16.14\ N/mm^2}$

(iv) At y = 60 mm : q_A is evidently zero

The variation of q is shown in Fig. 11.25 (c).

Mean $q = \dfrac{200000}{12000 - 1600\,\pi} = 28.68$ N/mm^2

Ratio $\dfrac{q_{max}}{q_{mean}} = \dfrac{110.8}{28.68} = \mathbf{3.86}$

Example 11.21. *Fig. 11.26 shows a built-up beam section consisting of two ISLB 150, placed one above the other, and connected by 16 mm dia. rivets spaced at 100 m centers along the length of the beam. The beam, when uniformly loaded over a span of 2.5 m, carries a maximum bending stresses of 140 N/mm². Calculate the average shear stress developed in the rivets near the end of the beam. For each ISLB section, $I_{xx} = 688.2\ cm^4$ and $A = 18.08\ cm^2$.*

Solution :

For ISLB 150, width of flange = 80 mm, depth of section = 150 mm.

For the built-up section,

$$I_{NA} = 2\left[688.2 \times 10^4 + 1808(75)^2\right]$$

$$= 3410.4 \times 10^4\ \text{mm}^4$$

$$Z = \dfrac{3410.4 \times 10^4}{150} = 227360\ \text{mm}^3$$

∴ $M = fZ = 140 \times 227360 = 31.83 \times 10^6$ N-mm

$$= 31.83\ \text{kN-m}$$

Now $M = \dfrac{wL^2}{8} = 31.83$

∴ $F = \dfrac{wL}{2} = \dfrac{31.83 \times 4}{L} = \dfrac{31.83 \times 4}{2.5} = 50.928$ kN

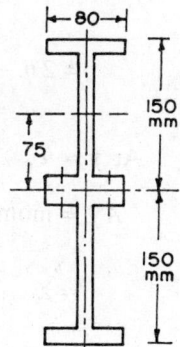

FIG. 11.26

Now, at the rivet level (*i.e.* at N.A.)

$$q_{max} = \frac{F}{Iz}(A\bar{y}) = \frac{50.928 \times 10^3 (1808 \times 75)}{3410.4 \times 10^4 \times 80} = 2.531 \text{ N/mm}^2$$

$\therefore$ Horizontal shear $= q_{max} \times b \times s$

where b = width of section at N.A. = 80 mm
             s = spacing of the rivet = 100 mm

$\therefore$ Horizontal shear force $= 2.531 \times 80 \times 100 = 20251$ N

This is borne by two rivets.

$\therefore$ Average shear stress in rivet cross-section $= \dfrac{20251}{2 \times \dfrac{\pi}{4}(16)^2} = \mathbf{50.4 \text{ N/mm}^2}$

Example 11.22. *A bar of hexagonal cross-section of side length b mm is used as cantilever, one diagonal being horizontal. Plot the shear stress distribution diagram if it is subjected to a shear force of 8 kN and if b = 25 mm.*

Solution :

At any layer distant $\pm y$ from the N.A., $q = \dfrac{F}{Iz}(A\bar{y})$

where $I = I_x$ of rectangle $+ I_x$ of triangles.

$$= 2\left[\frac{1}{3}bd^3 + \frac{1}{12}bd^3\right]$$

$$= \frac{5}{6}bd^3 = \frac{5}{6}b\frac{3\sqrt{3}}{8}b^3 = 0.54 b^4$$

$$z = b + 2\left(\frac{b}{2}\right)\left(\frac{d-y}{d}\right)$$

$$= b + \frac{2}{\sqrt{3}}\left(\frac{\sqrt{3}}{2}b - y\right)$$

$$= 2b - \frac{2}{\sqrt{3}}y = \frac{2}{\sqrt{3}}\left(\sqrt{3}\,b - y\right)$$

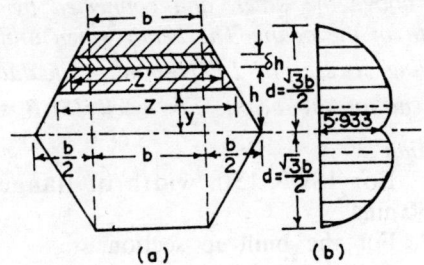

FIG. 11.27

At $y = h$, $z' = \dfrac{2}{\sqrt{3}}(\sqrt{3}\,b - h)$

$A\bar{y}$ = moment of the shaded area about the N.A.

$$= \sum_{h=y}^{h=d}\left[\frac{2}{\sqrt{3}}\left(\sqrt{3}\,b - h\right)\delta h\right)\right]h = \frac{2}{\sqrt{3}}\left(\frac{\sqrt{3}\,bh^2}{2} - \frac{h^3}{3}\right)_y^d$$

$$= \frac{2}{\sqrt{3}}\left[\left(\frac{\sqrt{3}\,bd^2}{2} - \frac{d^3}{3}\right) - \left(\frac{\sqrt{3}\,by^2}{2} - \frac{y^3}{3}\right)\right]$$

$$= \frac{2}{\sqrt{3}} \left[\left(\frac{\sqrt{3}}{2} \frac{3}{4} b^3 - \frac{1}{3} \frac{3\sqrt{3}}{8} b^3 \right) - \left(\frac{\sqrt{3}}{2} b y^2 - \frac{y^3}{3} \right) \right]$$

$$= \frac{2}{\sqrt{3}} \left[\frac{\sqrt{3}}{4} b^3 - \left(\frac{\sqrt{3}}{2} b y^2 - \frac{y^3}{3} \right) \right]$$

$$\therefore \quad q = \frac{F}{Iz}(A \bar{y}) = \frac{F\sqrt{3}}{(0.54\, b^4)\, 2\, (\sqrt{3}\, b - y)} \times \frac{2}{\sqrt{3}} \left[\frac{\sqrt{3}}{4} b^3 - \left(\frac{\sqrt{3}}{2} b y^2 - \frac{y^3}{3} \right) \right]$$

or $\qquad q = \dfrac{F}{0.54\, b^4\, (1.73\, b - y)} \left[0.433\, b^3 - y^2\, (0.865\, b - 0.333\, y) \right]$

This is the required equation for the shear stress.

When $b = 25$ mm and $F = 8$ kN $= 8000$ N

$$d = \frac{\sqrt{3}\, b}{2} = \frac{\sqrt{3} \times 25}{2} = 21.65 \text{ mm}$$

$$\therefore \qquad q = \frac{8000}{0.54\, (25)^4\, (1.73 \times 25 - 4)} \left\{ 0.433\, (25)^3 - y^2\, (0.865 \times 25 - 0.333\, y) \right\}$$

$$= \frac{0.03793}{43.25 - y} \left[6765.6 - y^2\, (21.625 - 0.333\, y) \right]$$

Area of hexagon $= (b \times 2d) + 4 \left[\dfrac{1}{2} \times \dfrac{b}{2} \cdot d \right]$

$$= 2\, bd + bd = 3\, bd = 3\, b \times \frac{\sqrt{3}}{2} b = \frac{3\sqrt{3}}{2} b^2$$

$$= \frac{3\sqrt{3}}{2} (25)^2 = 1623.8 \text{ mm}^2$$

$$q_{mean} = \frac{8000}{1623.8} = 4.927 \text{ N/mm}^2$$

At $\qquad y = 0, q_{na} = \dfrac{0.03793}{43.25} \times 6765.6 = \mathbf{5.933 \text{ N/mm}^2}$

The shear stress distribution can be plotted, as shown in Fig. 11.27 (b).

Example 11.23. *Find the ratio of maximum to mean intensity of vertical shear in the cross-section of a beam ·of hollow circular section, the outside diameter being twice the inside diameter.*

Solution :

Fig. 11.28 shows a hollow circular section. Take a strip of thickness dy at a distance y from the N.A., so that

$$y = \frac{D}{2} \sin \theta = \frac{d}{2} \sin \varphi$$

$$dy = \frac{D}{2} \cos \theta \, d\theta = \frac{d}{2} \cos \varphi \, d\varphi$$

Now $q = \dfrac{F}{Iz}(A\bar{y})$

where $z = 2\left[\dfrac{D}{2}\cos\theta - \dfrac{d}{2}\cos\varphi\right]$

$\qquad\qquad = D\cos\theta - d\cos\varphi$

Area of strip $= (D\cos\theta - d\cos\varphi)\,dy$

$\qquad\qquad = D\cos\theta.\dfrac{D}{2}\cos\theta\,d\theta - d\cos\varphi.\dfrac{d}{2}\cos\varphi\,d\varphi$

$\qquad\qquad = \dfrac{D^2}{2}\cos^2\theta\,d\theta - \dfrac{d^2}{2}\cos^2\varphi\,d\varphi.$

Also, $A\bar{y} = \displaystyle\int_0^{\frac{\pi}{2}} \dfrac{D^2}{2}\cos^2\theta\,d\theta\,.\,y - \int_0^{\frac{\pi}{2}} \dfrac{d^2}{2}\cos^2\varphi\,d\varphi\,.\,y$

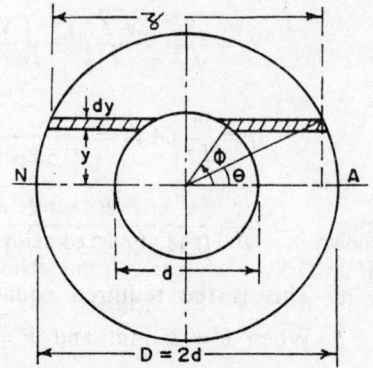

FIG. 11.28

$\qquad\qquad = \displaystyle\int_0^{\frac{\pi}{2}} \dfrac{d^2}{2}\cos^2\theta\,d\theta\,.\,\dfrac{D}{2}\sin\theta - \int_0^{\frac{\pi}{2}} \dfrac{d^2}{2}\cos^2\varphi\,d\varphi\,.\,\dfrac{d}{2}\sin\varphi$

$\qquad\qquad = \dfrac{D^3}{4}\displaystyle\int_0^{\frac{\pi}{2}} \cos^2\theta\sin\theta\,d\theta - \dfrac{d^3}{4}\int_0^{\frac{\pi}{2}} \cos^2\varphi\sin\varphi\,d\varphi$

$\qquad\qquad = \dfrac{D^3}{4}\,.\,\dfrac{\cos^3\theta}{4} - \dfrac{d^3}{4}\dfrac{\cos^3\varphi}{3}$

$\therefore\qquad q = \dfrac{F \times \dfrac{1}{12}\left[D^3\cos^3\theta - d^3\cos^3\varphi\right]}{\dfrac{\pi}{64}(D^4 - d^4) \times (D\cos\theta - d\cos\varphi)}$

Now shear stress will be maximum at the N.A. where $\theta = \varphi = 0$

$\therefore\qquad q_{max} = \dfrac{\dfrac{F}{12}(D^3 - d^3)}{\dfrac{\pi}{64}(D^4 - d^4)(D - d)}$

Also, $q_{av} = \dfrac{F}{\dfrac{\pi}{4}(D^2 - d^2)}$

$\therefore\qquad \dfrac{q_{max}}{q_{av}} = \dfrac{\dfrac{F}{12}(D^3 - d^3)}{\dfrac{\pi}{64}(D^4 - d^4)(D - d)} \times \dfrac{\dfrac{\pi}{4}(D^2 - d^2)}{F} = \dfrac{4(D^3 - d^3)}{3(D^2 + d^2)(D - d)}$

For the present problem, $d = D/2$

$$\therefore \quad \frac{q_{max}}{q_{av}} = \frac{4 \left[D^3 - \left(\frac{D}{2} \right)^3 \right]}{3 \left[D^2 + \left(\frac{D}{2} \right)^2 \right] \left[D - \frac{D}{2} \right]} = \frac{4 \times \frac{7}{8} D^3}{3 \times \frac{5}{4} D^2 \times \frac{1}{2} D} = \frac{28}{15}$$

PROBLEMS

1. A cast iron bracket, subjected to bending, has a cross-section of I-shape with unequal flange as shown in Fig. 11.29. If the compressive stress in top flange is not to exceed 17.5 N/mm², what is the B.M. the section can take ? If the section is subjected to a S.F. of 100 kN, draw the shear stress distribution over the depth of the section.

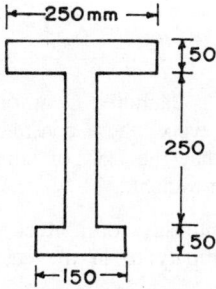

FIG. 11.29

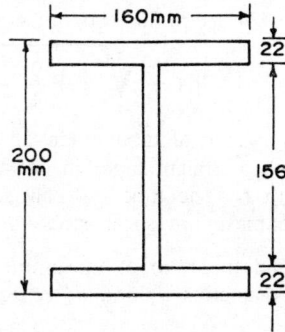

FIG. 11.30

2. A rolled steel joist 200 mm × 160 mm wide has flanges 22 mm thick and web 12 mm thick. Find the proportion in which the flanges and the web resist (*i*) B.M. (*ii*) S.F..

3. A beam *AB* of 4 m span is loaded with a central point load of 60 kN. The section of the beam is a rectangle 150 mm wide and 300 mm deep. At a cross-section distant 2 m from the support, calculate the bending and shear stresses at point 150 mm, 100 mm, 40 mm and 0 mm from the N.A. of the section. Find also the principal planes and principal stresses at these points.

4. A 300 mm × 150 mm RSJ has flanges 20 mm thick and web 13 mm thick. At a certain cross-section, it has to resist a B.M. of 100 kN-m and a S.F. of 200 kN. Find the principal stresses (*a*) at the top, (*b*) in the flange at 130 mm from the N.A., (*c*) in the web at 130 mm from the N.A., and (*d*) at the N.A. Plot the variation of the principal stresses along the section.

5. Show that for all values of D/d of a hollow circular section of outer diameter D and inner diameter d, the ratio of maximum to average shear stress intensities lies between 4/3 to 2.

6. A water main of diameter D and thickness t is subjected at a particular cross-section to a B.M. M and S.F. F. Show that, at a point in the cross-section where the radius is inclined at an angle φ to the neutral axis, the principal stress are given by

$$\frac{2}{\pi D^2 t} \left[M \sin \varphi \pm \sqrt{M^2 \sin^2 \varphi + F^2 D^2 \cos^2 \varphi} \right]$$

7. A bar of regular hexagonal section of side a is subjected to a shearing force F which acts at right angles to one of the diagonals of the hexagon. Derive a formula for the shearing stress q at a distance x from the diagonal, and hence find the ratio of q to the mean shearing stress for the particular values

424 MECHANICS OF MATERIALS

$x = 0$ and $x = a/2$. Indicate by means of sketch how the shearing stress varies across the depth of the section.

8. In the loaded beam as shown in Fig. 11.31, locate the point of maximum principal stress. Give the magnitude of principal stress at this point.

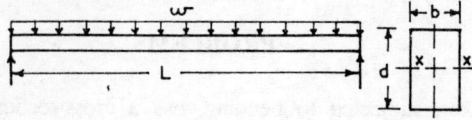

FIG. 11.31

9. A rectangular beam of height d, breadth b and length l is supported at the ends and carries a concentrated load P at the middle. Show that the principal stress at a point in the central cross-section and distance $d/4$ from the top are :

$$\frac{3}{8}\frac{Pl}{bd^2}\left(1 + \sqrt{q + \frac{9}{4}\frac{d^2}{l^2}}\right)$$

10. A cylindrical tube made of an alloy of density ρ has a diameter D at one end and $D/2$ at the other; with a straight taper in between. The wall thickness is every where constant, and is very small compared with D. The tube is freely supported at the ends so that the axis, of length L, is horizontal. Calculate the maximum shear stress in the tube due to its own weight.

11. Find the ratio of maximum to average shear stress intensity for a thick cylinder of external and internal diameters d_1 and d_2 respectively. What does this simplify to in the case of simple tube ?

ANSWERS

1. $M = 57.792$ kN-m; $q_{max} = 7.33$ N/mm^2

2. $M_w = 6.35\ \%$; $M_f = 93.65\ \%$; $S_w = 87.85\ \%$ $S_f = 12.15\ \%$

3.   (i) $y = 150 : f = 26.7 ; q = 0 ; \sigma_1 = 0 ; \theta_1 = 0$
     (ii) $y = 100 : f = 17.8 ; q = 0.56 ; \sigma_1 = 17.82 ; \theta_1 = 1°\ 48'$
     (iii) $y = 40 : f = 7.11 ; q = 0.93 ; \sigma_1 = 7.23 ; \theta_1 = 7°18'$
     (iv) $y = 0 : f = 0 ; q = 1 ; \sigma_1 = 1 ; \theta_1 = 45°$

4   (a) $\sigma_1 = 110.3 ; \sigma_2 = 0$ (b) $\sigma_1 = 95.8 ; \sigma_2 = 0.2$
     (c) $\sigma_1 = 115.2 ; \sigma_2 = 19.6$ (d) $\sigma_1 = 59.9 ; \sigma_2 = 59.9$

7.   (a) $q = \dfrac{4S(9a^3 - 18ax^2 + 4x^2 + 4x^3\sqrt{3})}{15a^4\sqrt{3}(3a - x\sqrt{3})}$

     (b) At $x = 0 ; q/q_{mean} = 1.20$ (c) At $x = \dfrac{a}{2}, q/q_{mean} = 1.008$

8. $\dfrac{3}{4}\dfrac{wL^2}{bd^2}$

10. $\dfrac{4\rho L}{3}$

11. $\dfrac{q_{max}}{q_{av}} = \dfrac{4}{3}\left[\dfrac{d_1^2 + d_1 d_2 + d_2^2}{d_1^2 + d_2^2}\right] ; 2$

Deflection of Beams : I
Double Integration Method

12.1. INTRODUCTION

In chapters 10 and 11, we have considered two effects of bending : (*i*) bending or longitudinal stress, and (*ii*) shearing or transverse stress. Both these effects are connected with the *strength* aspect of the beam. For design purpose, a beam should be so designed that it is *strong* enough to resist the bending moment and shearing force. But there is yet another important effect of bending : the deflection of the beam. This is the *stiffness* aspect of the beam. For design purpose, a beam should be so designed that it has adequate *stiffness* so that the deflections are within the permissible limits. In other words, the *stiffness* of the beam, which is inversely proportional to the deflection, is the second criterion of beam design.

In the case of statically indeterminate beams, such as propped cantilevers, fixed beams and continuous beams, the study of deflection is not only important as a design criterion, but also as only means of determining bending moment and shear force along its length. The end reactions, and consequently the B.M. and S.F. cannot be determined for such beams without studying the deformation of the axis of the beam. In addition to this, deflection often must be calculated in order to verify that they do not exceed the maximum permissible value, because large deflections are associated with poor appearance and with too much flexibility in the structure.

12.2. METHODS OF DETERMINING DEFLECTION OF BEAMS

Following are the principal methods of computing the deflection of beams.
1. Double integration method.
2. Moment area method.
3. Strain energy method.
and 4. Conjugate beam method.

The first method, also known as integration method, uses the equation of the deflection curve in terms of bending moment. Since the differential equation is of second order, two integrations (*i.e.* double integration) are required. The *moment area method* (also known as area moment method) or Mohr's method utilizes the properties of the area of the bending moment diagram. The method is specially suitable when the deflection or angle of rotation at only one point of the beam is desired. The deflection of beam can also be computed from the consideration of strain energy due to bending. The *conjugate beam method*, also known as the *method of elastic weights*, is specially useful to simply supported beams. This chapter deals with the first method while the remaining methods have been discussed in subsequent chapters.

12.3. DIFFERENTIAL EQUATION OF THE DEFLECTION CURVE OF BEAM

Fig. 12.1 shows the deflected shape or the deflection curve of a loaded beam. When a beam is subjected to pure bending couple M, it is bent into a circular arc the radius of curvature of which is given by Eq. 10.5 :

$$\frac{1}{R} = \frac{M}{EI} \quad ...(i)$$

However, when the beam is not subjected to a pure bending couple, as is generally the case, its radius of curvature will not be constant, but will change from point to point. The first step will therefore be to find an expression for the radius of curvature of the deflection curve at any given point.

Let m and n be two points at a very small distance δs along the deflection curve. Let x and y be the coordinates of point m and $(x + \delta x)$ and $(y + \delta y)$ be the coordinates of the point n. We

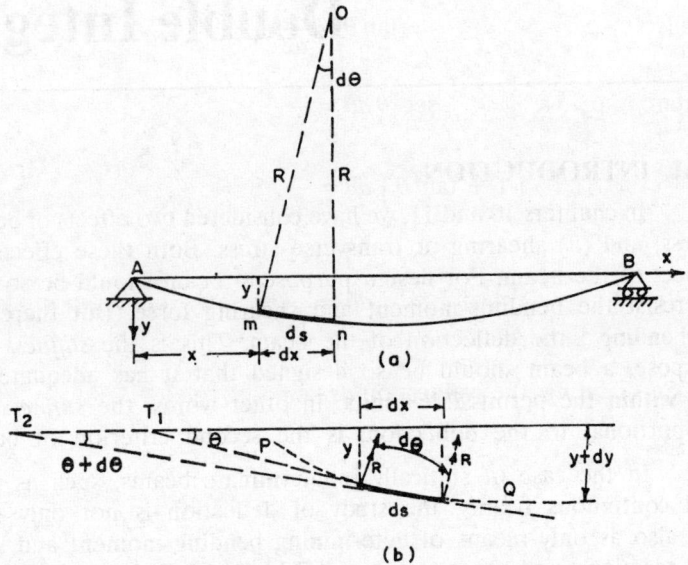

FIG. 12.1. DEFLECTION CURVE OF A BEAM

take the origin of the coordinates at the end, with x axis directed to the right and the y axis directed downwards. Thus xy plane is the *plane of bending*. The deflection y of the beam at any point m at a distance x from the origin is the translation (or displacement) of that point in the y-direction, measured from the x-axis to the deflection curve. We will consider *downward* deflection as *positive* and *upward* deflection as *negative*. The equation of the deflection curve is obtained when y is expressed as the function of x.

In Fig. 12.1(b), let the tangent $m\,T_1$ to the curve at m be making an angle θ and the tangent $n\,T_2$ at n be making an angle $\theta + d\theta$ with the x-axis. Let R be the radius of the curve at m. Since δs is extremely small, we have

$$ds = R\,d\theta \qquad \text{and} \qquad \frac{1}{R} = \left| \frac{d\theta}{ds} \right| \qquad \qquad ...(ii)$$

The bars in the above expression indicate that we consider here only the numerical value of curvature. Regarding sign, it should be clearly borne in mind that B.M. is taken positive in Eq. (*i*) if it produces concavity. *Hence curvature is positive when the centre of curvature is above the curve*, as in Fig. 12.1. By close inspection of Fig. 12.1(*b*), we observe that for such a curvature, the angle θ decreases as the point m moves along the curve from point P to Q. Thus, we have proper sign for Eq. (*ii*), which must be written as

$$\frac{1}{R} = -\frac{d\theta}{ds} \qquad \qquad ...(iii)$$

Also, $$ds = \sqrt{dx^2 + dy^2} \qquad \text{or} \quad ds = dx\sqrt{1 + \left(\frac{dy}{dx}\right)^2} \qquad ...(iv)$$

Now $$\tan\theta = \frac{dy}{dx}$$

Differentiating, we get $$\sec^2\theta\, d\theta = \frac{d^2y}{dx^2}\, dx$$

or $$\left(1 + \tan^2\theta\right) d\theta = \frac{d^2y}{dx^2}\, dx$$

or $$d\theta = \frac{\dfrac{d^2y}{dx^2}\, dx}{1 + \left(\dfrac{dy}{dx}\right)^2} \qquad \qquad ...(v)$$

Substituting the values of ds and $d\theta$ in Eq. (*iii*), we have

$$\frac{1}{R} = -\frac{\dfrac{d^2y}{dx^2}\, dx}{1 + \left(\dfrac{dy}{dx}\right)^2} \times \frac{1}{dx\sqrt{1 + \left(\dfrac{dy}{dx}\right)^2}}$$

or $$\frac{1}{R} = -\frac{\dfrac{d^2y}{dx^2}}{\left[1 + \left(\dfrac{dy}{dx}\right)^2\right]^{3/2}} \qquad \qquad ...(vi)$$

But $$\frac{1}{R} = \frac{M}{EI} \quad \text{where } M \text{ is the B.M. at } m.$$

Hence $$\frac{M}{EI} = -\frac{\dfrac{d^2y}{dx^2}}{\left[1 + \left(\dfrac{dy}{dx}\right)^2\right]^{3/2}}$$

or $$EI\frac{d^2y}{dx^2} = -M\left[1 + \left(\frac{dy}{dx}\right)^2\right]^{3/2} \qquad \qquad ...(12.1)$$

Since $\dfrac{dy}{dx}$ (*i.e.* the slope of the tangent to the curve at any point m) is extremely small, $\left(\dfrac{dy}{dx}\right)^2$ will be still smaller and hence $\left[1 + \left(\dfrac{dy}{dx}\right)^2\right]$ will be very nearly equal to unity.

Hence we have, $\qquad EI\dfrac{d^2y}{dx^2} = -M$ $\qquad\qquad\qquad$ ...(12.2)

This is the basic differential equation for the deflected shape of the beam. This should be clearly borne in mind that the above equation takes into account the effect of bending moment only. The effect of shear on deflection is extremely small and may be neglected. However, the effect of shear has been considered in chapter 14.

The basic differential equation can also be written as follows :

$$\dfrac{d^2y}{dx^2} = \dfrac{d}{dx}\left(\dfrac{dy}{dx}\right) = \dfrac{d\theta}{.dx} = -\dfrac{M}{EI} \qquad\qquad ...(12.2\ a)$$

This equation can be integrated in each particular case to find the angle of rotation θ (usually called the slope) or the deflection y, provided the bending moment M is known.

Sign Conventions : We adopt the following sign conventions :

(i) x is positive when measured towards the right.

(ii) y is positive when measured downwards.

(iii) θ is positive when the rotation is clockwise from the x-axis.

(iv) M is positive when sagging, i.e. when it produces compression in the upper part of the beam.

12.4. DOUBLE INTEGRATION METHOD

We have the basic differential equation for the deflection curve :

$$EI\dfrac{d^2y}{dx^2} = -M$$

(where M is positive when it is of sagging nature)

Integrating once, we have $EI\dfrac{dy}{dx} = EI.\theta = -\displaystyle\int M$ $\qquad\qquad$ ...(12.3)

Integrating again, we have $EIy = -\displaystyle\int\int M$ $\qquad\qquad$ ...(12.4)

Thus, integrating the basic differential equation once, we get the slope at a given point, while integrating it again, we get the value of deflection at the given point. Since the deflection is obtained by integrating the basic differential equation twice, the method is known as the *double integration method.* In the process of double integration, two constants of integration C_1 and C_2 will be obtained, the values of which can be determined by using the conditions at the two ends of the beam. We shall now apply this method by taking different cases of beam bending.

Case 1 : Cantilever with uniformly distributed load.

Fig. 12.2 shows a cantilever AB, of length L, loaded with uniformly distributed load w per unit length. The dotted line shows the deflected shape of the beam. Consider a point

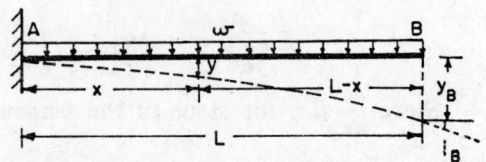

FIG. 12.2

X, distant x from the fixed end A. We have from Eq. 12.2

$$EI\frac{d^2y}{dx^2} = -M = -\left[-\frac{w(L-x)^2}{2}\right] = \frac{w(L-x)^2}{2}$$

Integrating once, $\qquad EI\frac{dy}{dx} = -\frac{w(L-x)^3}{6} + C_1$

At $\quad x = 0$, $\quad \frac{dy}{dx} = 0$, since the beam is fixed at A. $\qquad \therefore \quad C_1 = \frac{wL^3}{6}$

Hence $\qquad EI\frac{dy}{dx} = -\frac{w(L-x)^3}{6} + \frac{wL^3}{6}$ $\qquad$ ...(1)

Integrating again, $\qquad EIy = +\frac{w(L-x)^4}{24} + \frac{wL^3}{6}x + C_2$

Again at $\quad x = 0$, $\qquad\qquad y = 0$. $\quad \therefore \qquad C_2 = -\frac{wL^4}{24}$

Hence $\qquad EIy = \frac{w(L-x)^4}{24} + \frac{wL^3}{6}x - \frac{wL^4}{24}$ $\qquad$ ...(2)

Eq. (1) gives the value of slope at any point X, while Eq. (2) gives the value of deflection at that point.

At fixed end A, where $x = 0$, we get $EI\frac{dy}{dx} = EI(i_A) = -\frac{wL^3}{6} + \frac{wL^3}{6} = 0$, as expected.

At the free end B, where $x = L$, we get $EI(i_B) = -\frac{w(L-L)^3}{6} + \frac{wL^3}{6} = +\frac{wL^3}{6}$

Hence $\qquad\qquad i_B = \frac{wL^3}{6EI}$ radians $\qquad$ ...(12.5)

and $\qquad\qquad EI(y_B) = \frac{w(L-L)^4}{24} + \frac{wL^3}{6}\cdot L - \frac{wL^4}{24} = \frac{wL^4}{8}$

Hence $\qquad\qquad y_B = +\frac{wL^4}{8EI}$ $\qquad$ ...(12.6)

Case 2 Cantilever partially loaded with w over a length L_1 from fixed end

Fig. 12.3 shows a cantilever AB, of length L, partially loaded with U.D.L. from fixed end A to a point C, distant L_1 from A. The dotted line shows the deflected shape of the beam. Evidently, the beam will be curved from point A to C, and then straight for the remaining length from C to B since there is no load between point C and B. Hence i_B will be equal to i_C.

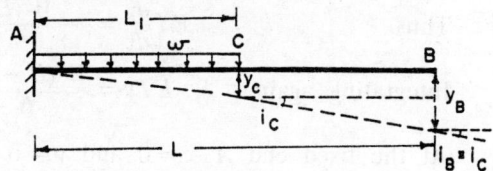

FIG. 12.3

Applying Eqs. 12.5 and 12.6 for the length AC, we get

$$i_c = \frac{wL_1^3}{6EI} \qquad \text{and} \qquad y_c = \frac{wL_1^4}{8EI}$$

Hence $\qquad i_B = i_C = \dfrac{w L_1^3}{6 E I}$ $\qquad\qquad\qquad$ ...(12.7)

and $\qquad y_B = y_C + i_C (L - L_1) = \dfrac{w L_1^4}{8 E I} + \dfrac{w L_1^3}{6 E I} (L - L_1)$ $\qquad$ ...(12

Case 3. Cantilever partially loaded with w from the free end

Fig. 12.4 (a) shows the loaded beam with the dotted line as the deflected shape. The slope and deflection may be looked upon as the difference between the slopes and deflections with (a) entire span loaded from A to B (Fig. 12.4 b) and (b) upward U.D.L. from A to C (Fig. 12.4 (c)).

Thus, $i_B = \dfrac{w L^3}{6 E I} - \dfrac{w L_1^3}{6 E I} = \dfrac{w}{6 E I} (L^3 - L_1^3)$ ...(12.9)

and $y_B = \dfrac{w L^4}{8 E I} - \left[\dfrac{w L_1^4}{8 E I} + \dfrac{w L_1^3}{6 E I} (L - L_1) \right]$

$= \dfrac{w}{8 E I} (L^4 - L_1^4) - \dfrac{w L_1^3}{6 E I} (L - L_1)$ ...(12.10)

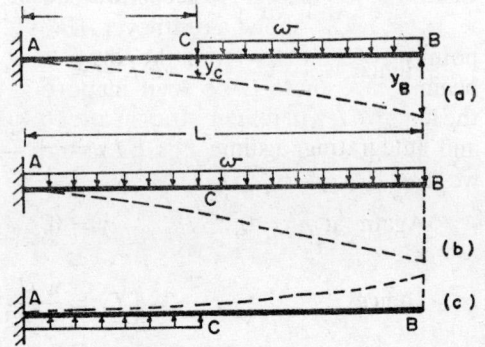

FIG. 12.4

Case 4. Cantilever with point load at the free end

Fig. 12.5 shows a cantilever AB of length L, loaded with a point load W at the free end B. Consider a section X, distant x from the fixed end. Then we have

$$E I \frac{d^2 y}{dx^2} = -M = -[- W (L - x)] = W (L - x)$$

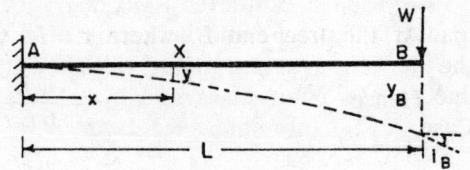

FIG. 12.5

Integrating once, $\qquad E I \dfrac{dy}{dx} = - \dfrac{W (L - x)^2}{2} + C_1$

At fixed end A, $\qquad x = 0 \qquad$ and $\qquad \dfrac{dy}{dx} = 0.$ $\qquad$ Hence $C_1 = \dfrac{W L^2}{2}$

Thus, $\qquad E I \dfrac{dy}{dx} = - \dfrac{W (L - x)^2}{2} + \dfrac{W L^2}{2}$ $\qquad\qquad$ ...(1)

Integrating again, $\qquad E I y = \dfrac{W (L - x)^3}{6} + \dfrac{W L^2}{2} x + C_2$

At the fixed end A, $x = 0$ and $y = 0$. Hence $C_2 = - \dfrac{W L^3}{6}$

Hence $\qquad E I y = \dfrac{W (L - x)^3}{6} + \dfrac{W L^2}{2} x - \dfrac{W L^3}{6}$ $\qquad\qquad$ ...(2)

Eqs (1) and (2) give slope and defection, respectively, at any point X.

At the free end, $\qquad x = L.$ $\qquad$ Hence $\qquad E I (i_B) = - \dfrac{W (L - L)^2}{2} + \dfrac{W L^2}{2}$

or
$$i_B = \frac{WL^2}{2EI} \text{ radians} \qquad \qquad ...(12.11)$$

Also,
$$EIy_B = \frac{W(L-L)^3}{6} + \frac{WL^2}{2} \cdot L - \frac{WL^3}{6} = \frac{WL^3}{3}$$

∴
$$y_B = \frac{WL^3}{3EI} \qquad \qquad ...(12.12)$$

Case 5. Cantilever with point load at intermediate point

Fig. 12.6 shows a cantilever AB of length L, loaded with a point load W at some intermediate point C, distant L_1 from the fixed end A. The dotted line shows the deflected shape of the beam. Since there is no load in portion CB, the length CB will remain straight after bending, and hence $i_B = i_C$. From Eqs. 12.11 and 12.12, we have

$$i_C = \frac{WL_1^2}{2EI} \text{ and } y_C = \frac{WL_1^3}{6EI}$$

Hence
$$i_B = i_C = \frac{WL_1^2}{2EI} \qquad ...(12.13)$$

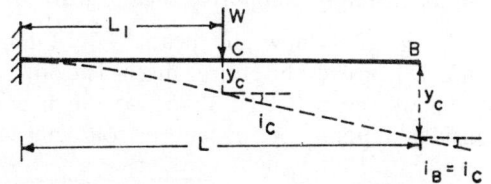

FIG. 12.6

and
$$y_B = y_C + i_C(L - L_1) = \frac{WL_1^3}{6EI} + \frac{WL_1^2}{2EI}(L - L_1) \qquad \qquad ...(12.14)$$

Case 6. Cantilever with several point loads and cantilever with U.D.L. and point loads

When a cantilever is loaded with several point loads, or with some U.D.L. and point load (s), the slope and deflection at a point can be found by *method of super position.* Thus, the deflection at any point will be equal to the algebraic sum of deflections at that point due to the point loads and/or U.D.L. acting individually.

Case 7. Simply supported beam with central point load W

Fig. 12.7 shows a beam AB, of length L, simply supported at the ends, and loaded with a point load W at the mid span. Consider a point X, distant x from A, in length AC.

Thus, $EI\dfrac{d^2y}{dx^2} = -M = -\left[\dfrac{W}{2}x\right] = -\dfrac{W \cdot x}{2}$

Integrating once, $EI\dfrac{dy}{dx} = -\dfrac{Wx^2}{4} + C_1$

Due to symmetry, at $x = \dfrac{L}{2},\ \dfrac{dy}{dx} = i_c = 0.$

Hence $C_1 = \dfrac{WL^2}{16}$

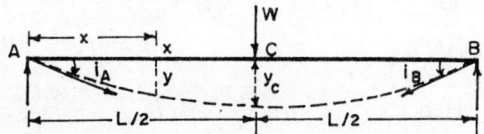

FIG. 12.7

∴ $EI\dfrac{dy}{dx} = -\dfrac{Wx^2}{4} + \dfrac{WL^2}{16} \qquad \qquad ...(1)$

Integrating again, $EIy = -\dfrac{Wx^3}{12} + \dfrac{WL^2}{16}x + C_2$

At $x = 0, y = 0.$ Hence $C_2 = 0$

$$\therefore \qquad E I y = -\frac{W x^3}{12} + \frac{W L^2}{16} x \qquad\qquad\qquad ...(2)$$

Eqs (1) and (2) give, respectively, the slope and deflection at any point

$$\text{At} \quad x = 0, \qquad i_A = +\frac{1}{E I}\left(\frac{W L^2}{16}\right) = +\frac{W L^2}{16 E I} \qquad\qquad ...(12.15)$$

By symmetry, $\quad i_B = -\dfrac{W L^2}{16 E I}$

Also, at $x = \dfrac{L}{2}$, $\quad y_c = y_{\max} = \dfrac{1}{E I}\left[-\dfrac{W}{12}\left(\dfrac{L}{2}\right)^3 + \dfrac{W L^2}{16}\left(\dfrac{L}{2}\right)\right] = \dfrac{W L^3}{48 E I} \qquad ...(12.16)$

Case 8. Simply Supported beam with U.D.L. over the entire length

Fig. 12.8 show the beam AB of length L, simply supported at the ends, and loaded with U.D.L. w over the entire length. The dotted
line shows the deflected shape of the beam.
Consider a point X, distant x from end A.

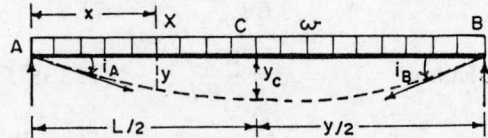

FIG. 12.8

$$\therefore \quad E I \frac{d^2 y}{dx^2} = -M = -\left[\frac{w L}{2} x - \frac{w x^2}{2}\right]$$

$$= -\frac{w L}{2} x + \frac{w x^2}{2}$$

Integrating, $\qquad E I \dfrac{dy}{dx} = -\dfrac{w L}{2}\cdot\dfrac{x^2}{2} + \dfrac{w x^3}{6} + C_1$

Due to symmetry, $i_c = 0$ at $x = \dfrac{L}{2}$. Hence $C_1 = \dfrac{w L}{4}\left(\dfrac{L}{2}\right)^2 - \dfrac{w}{6}\left(\dfrac{L}{2}\right)^3 = \dfrac{w L^3}{24}$

$$\therefore \qquad E I \frac{dy}{dx} = -\frac{w L}{4} x^2 + \frac{w}{6} x^3 + \frac{w L^3}{24} \qquad\qquad ...(1)$$

Integrating again, $\qquad E I y = -\dfrac{w L x^3}{12} + \dfrac{w x^4}{24} + \dfrac{w L^3}{24} x + C_2$

At $\qquad\qquad\qquad\qquad x = 0, \; y = 0 \qquad \therefore \qquad C_2 = 0$

Hence $\qquad\qquad E I y = -\dfrac{w L x^3}{12} + \dfrac{w x^4}{24} + \dfrac{w L^3}{24} x \qquad\qquad ...(2)$

Eqs. (1) and (2) give slope and deflection, respectively, at any point X.

Now at A, $x = 0$. Hence $i_A = \dfrac{w L^3}{24 E I} \qquad\qquad\qquad\qquad ...(12.17)$

By symmetry, $\qquad\qquad i_B = -i_A = -\dfrac{w L^3}{24 E I}$

At $\qquad x = \dfrac{L}{2}, y_c = y_{\max} = \dfrac{1}{E I}\left[-\dfrac{w L}{12}\left(\dfrac{L}{2}\right)^3 + \dfrac{w}{24}\left(\dfrac{L}{2}\right)^4 + \dfrac{w L^3}{24}\left(\dfrac{L}{2}\right)\right] = \dfrac{5}{384}\dfrac{w L^4}{E I} \qquad ...(12.18)$

Case 9. Simply supported beam with eccentric point load

Fig. 12.9 shows a beam AB of length L, simply supported at the ends, and loaded with a point load W at point C, distant a from end A and b from end B,

Naturally, $R_A = \dfrac{Wb}{L}$ and $R_B = \dfrac{Wa}{L}$

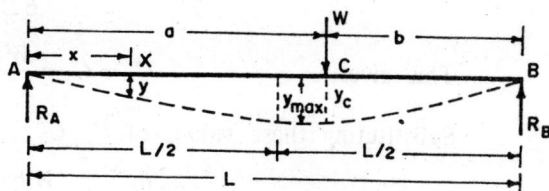

FIG. 12.9

For $x < a$: $EI\dfrac{d^2y}{dx^2} = -M = -\left[\dfrac{Wb}{L}x\right]$

$$= -\dfrac{Wb}{L}x$$

Integrating once $\qquad EI\dfrac{dy}{dx} = -\dfrac{Wb}{L}\cdot\dfrac{x^2}{2} + C_1$ ...(1)

Integrating further $\qquad EIy = -\dfrac{Wbx^3}{6L} + C_1x + C_2$ ...(2)

Eqs. (1) and (2) give the values of slope and deflection for the portion AC only.

For $x > b$: $\qquad EI\dfrac{d^2y}{dx^2} = -\dfrac{Wb}{L}x + W(x-a)$

Integrating once, $\qquad EI\dfrac{dy}{dx} = -\dfrac{Wbx^2}{2L} + \dfrac{W}{2}(x-a)^2 + C_3$ ...(3)

Integrating further, $\qquad EIy = -\dfrac{Wbx^3}{6L} + \dfrac{W}{6}(x-a)^3 + C_3x + C_4$ ...(4)

Eqs (3) and (4) give the values of slope and deflection for the portion CB only. The constant of integration appearing in the above four equations can be found from the following conditions : (1) at $x = a$, the slope $dy/dx\,(= i_c)$ for the two parts of the beam should be equal; (2) at $x = a$, the deflection $y\,(= y_c)$ for the two parts of the beam should be equal; (3) at $x = 0$, the deflection y_A is zero and (4) at $x = L$, the deflection y_B is zero.

For the first condition, the slopes determined by Eqs (1) and (3) is equal when $x = a$.

$\therefore \qquad -\dfrac{Wba^2}{2L} + C_1 = -\dfrac{Wba^2}{2L} + C_3$

This gives $\qquad C_1 = C_3$

For the second condition, the deflections determined by Eqs. (2) and (4) should be equal when $x = a$.

$\therefore \qquad -\dfrac{Wba^3}{6L} + C_1a + C_2 = -\dfrac{Wba^3}{6L} + C_3a + C_4$ (where $C_1 = C_3$)

This gives $\qquad C_2 = C_4$

Again, applying the third conditions, *i.e.* at $x = 0, y = 0$ we get from Eq. (2)

$$0 = C_2. \qquad \text{Hence } C_4 = 0$$

Lastly, applying the fourth condition, *i.e.* at $x = L, y = 0$, we get from (4).

$$0 = -\frac{WbL^3}{6L} + \frac{W}{6}(L-a)^3 + C_3 L + 0$$

This gives $$C_3 = C_1 = \frac{Wb(L^2 - b^2)}{6L}$$

Substituting these values of C_1, C_2, C_3 and C_4 in Eqs. (1) to (4), we get

For $x < a$: $$EI\frac{dy}{dx} = -\frac{Wbx^2}{2L} + \frac{Wb(L^2 - b^2)}{6L} = \frac{Wb}{6L}(L^2 - b^2 - 3x^2) \qquad \text{...(I)}$$

$$EIy = -\frac{Wbx^3}{6L} + \frac{Wb(L^2 - b^2)}{6L}x = \frac{Wb}{6L}x(L^2 - b^2 - x^2) \qquad \text{...(II)}$$

For $x > a$: $$EI\frac{dy}{dx} = -\frac{Wbx^2}{2L} + \frac{Wb(L^2 - b^2)}{6L} + \frac{W}{2}(x-a)^2 = \frac{Wb}{6L}(L^2 - b^2 - 3x^2) + \frac{W}{2}(x-a)^2 \qquad \text{...(III)}$$

and $$EIy = -\frac{Wbx^3}{6L} + \frac{Wb(L^2 - b^2)}{6L}x + \frac{W}{6}(x-a)^3 = \frac{Wbx}{6L}(L^2 - b^2 - x^2) + \frac{W}{6}(x-a)^3 \qquad \text{...(IV)}$$

From the above four equations, the slope and deflection at any point can be found.

Slopes at the ends

At $x = 0$, we get from Eq. (I), $i_A = \dfrac{Wb}{6EIL}(L^2 - b^2) = \dfrac{Wab}{6EIL}(L+b)$ ...(12.19 *a*)

At $x = L$, we get from Eq. (III) $i_B = -\dfrac{Wa}{6EIL}(L^2 - a^2) = -\dfrac{Wab}{6EIL}(L+a)$ ...(12.19 *b*)

Maximum deflection

Eqs. (I) and (II) give slope and deflection for the portion AC. Maximum deflection will occur in AC, if $a > b$. For maximum deflection, $\dfrac{dy}{dx} = 0$

Hence from (I), $$0 = \frac{Wb}{6L}(L^2 - b^2 - 3x^2)$$

This gives $$x = \sqrt{\frac{L^2 - b^2}{3}} \qquad \text{...(12.20)}$$

Hence from (II), $$y_{max} = \frac{Wb}{6EIL}\sqrt{\frac{L^2 - b^2}{3}}\left[L^2 - b^2 - \left(\frac{L^2 - b^2}{3}\right)\right]$$

or $$y_{max} = \frac{Wb}{3EIL}\left(\frac{L^2 - b^2}{3}\right)^{3/2} = \frac{Wb(L^2 - b^2)^{3/2}}{9\sqrt{3}\,EIL} \qquad \text{...(12.21)}$$

Deflection under the load

From (II), at $x = a$, $$y_c = \frac{Wab}{6EIL}(L^2 - b^2 - a^2) = \frac{Wa^2 b^2}{3EIL} \qquad \text{...(12.22)}$$

Deflection at mid-span

From Eq. (II), $\left[y\right]_{x=L/2}^{a>b} = \dfrac{Wb}{6EIL} \cdot \dfrac{L}{2}\left(L^2 - b^2 - \dfrac{L^2}{4}\right) = \dfrac{Wb}{48EI}(3L^2 - 4b^2)$ ...(12.23)

Deflection at mid-span versus maximum deflection

From Eq. 12.20, we find that when $b = L/2$, $x = 0.5L$. In the most unfavourable case, when b is extremely small (*i.e.* when W is very near to the support), we get $x \approx L/\sqrt{3} = 0.577L$ from Eq. 12.20. Thus the point of maximum deflection is only $0.077L$ (or $L/13$) away from the centre.

Also, the difference between Eqs. 12.21 and 12.23, in the most unfavorable case (when b approaches zero) is only 2.5% of the maximum deflection.

Hence we conclude that the deflection at the mid-span is a close approximation to the maximum deflection.

Central point load : If the load W is applied at the mid-span (*i.e.* if $a = b = L/2$) the maximum deflection will evidently be at the mid-span and its magnitude is given by Eq. 12.22.

$$\left[y\right]_{x=L/2}^{a=b} = \frac{W}{3EIL}\left(\frac{L}{2}\right)^2\left(\frac{L}{2}\right)^2 = \frac{WL^3}{48EI} \qquad ...(12.24)$$

12.5. CONSIDERATION OF UNITS

While computing the numerical values of slope and deflection, proper consideration of units must be made. Generally, span is expressed in metres while E and I are expressed in mm units. Various formulae developed in the previous article, for various standard cases, can't give correct results unless proper care is taken for units.

(*a*) **Computation of deflection** : We find from various equations for deflection that L appears in third power, *i.e.* $y = \dfrac{k_1 L^3}{EI}$. Hence for working out the numerical value of deflection in mm, the value of L must be substituted in metres and then the whole expression must be multiplied by $(1000)^3$. Thus, $y = \dfrac{k_1 L^3}{EI} \times 10^9$ mm, when L is substituted in metres and E and I are expressed in mm units. However, W and E must have the same units of force (*i.e.* N or kN).

(*b*) **Computation of Slope** : We find from various equations for slope that L appears in second power, *i.e.* $i = \dfrac{k_2 L^2}{EI}$. Hence for working out the numerical value of slope in radians, L must be substituted in metres and then the whole expression must be multiplied by $(1000)^2$. Thus $i = \dfrac{k_2 L^2}{EI} \times 10^6$ radians, when L is substituted in metres and E and I are expressed in mm units. However, W and E must have the same units of force.

Example 12.1. *A horizontal cantilever of uniform section of length L, carries two point loads, W at the free end and 2W at a distance L_1 from the free end. Find the maximum deflection due to this loading.*

Solution :

Maximum deflection evidently occurs at end B. We will use method of superposition, while using Eqs. 12.11 and 12.12.

Due to W acting at B, $y_{B1} = \dfrac{WL^3}{3EI}$

Due to $2W$ acting at C,

$$y_{B2} = \frac{2W(L-L_1)^3}{3EI} + \frac{2W(L-L_1)^2}{2EI}L_1$$

$\therefore$ Total $\;y_B = \dfrac{WL^3}{3EI} + \dfrac{2W(L-L_1)^3}{3EI}$

$$+ \frac{W(L-L_1)^2}{EI}L_1$$

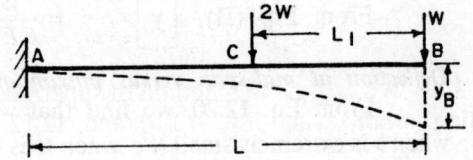

FIG. 12.10

$$= \frac{W}{3EI}\left[L^3 + 2(L^3 - 3L^2L_1 + 3LL_1^2 - L_1^3) + 3(L^2 + L_1^2 - 2LL_1)L_1 \right]$$

$$= \frac{W}{3EI}\left[L^3 + 2L^3 - 6L^2L_1 + 6LL_1^2 - 2L_1^3 + 3L^2L_1 + 3L_1^3 - 6LL_1^2 \right]$$

$$= \frac{W}{3EI}\left[3L^3 - 3L^2L_1 + L_1^3 \right] = \frac{W}{3EI}\left[3L^2(L - L_1) + L_1^3 \right]$$

$\therefore \qquad y_B = \dfrac{W}{3EI}\left[3L^2(L - L_1) + L_1^3 \right]$

Example 12.2. *A simply supported beam of span L carries a U.D.L. w per unit length over the left half of the span. Find the deflection at the mid-span.*

Solution :

Let y_{c1} be the deflection at mid-span when the left half of the span is loaded. If the right hand half of the span only is loaded (Fig. 12.11 (b)) the deflection y_{c2} at the centre will also be equal to y_{c1}. Hence if the left hand half as well as right hand half are loaded (*i.e.* if the entire span is loaded) the deflection y_c at C will evidently be equal to $2y_{c1}$. Hence

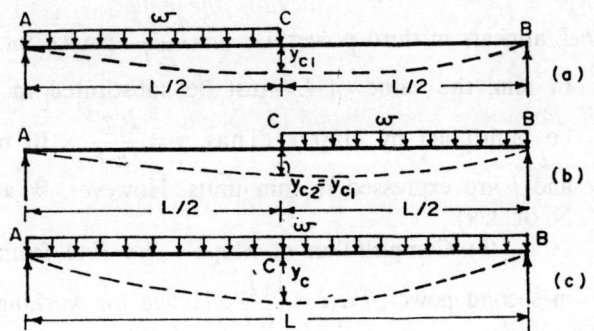

$$y_{c1} = \frac{1}{2}y_c$$

But $\qquad\qquad y_c = \dfrac{5}{384}\dfrac{wL^4}{EI}$

FIG. 12.11

$\therefore \qquad\quad y_{c1} = \dfrac{1}{2}y_c = \dfrac{5}{768}\dfrac{wL^4}{EI}$

Example 12.3. *A cantilever 2.4 m long is loaded as shown in Fig. 12.12. Calculate the deflection at the end if the section is rectangular, 150 mm × 300 mm.*

Take E = 0.2 × 10⁵ N/mm².

Solution :

$$I = \frac{1}{12} \times 150 \,(300)^2 = 33750 \times 10^4 \text{ mm}^4$$

We will use the method of super position, while using Eqs. 12.10 and 12.12.

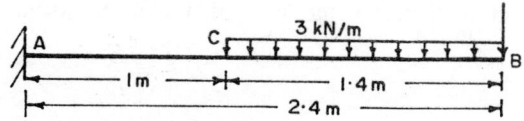

FIG. 12.12

Due to U.D.L.,

$$y_{B1} = \frac{w L^4}{8 E I} - \left[\frac{w L_1^4}{8 E I} + \frac{w L_1^3}{6 E I} (L - L_1) \right]$$

or

$$y_{B1} = \frac{3000}{E I} \left[\frac{(2.4)^4}{8} - \frac{(1)^4}{8} - \frac{(1)^3 (2.4 - 1)}{6} \right] \times (1000)^3$$

$$= \frac{11.3666 \times 10^{12}}{E I}, \text{ where } E \text{ and } I \text{ are in mm units.}$$

$$\therefore \qquad y_{B1} = \frac{11.3666 \times 10^{12}}{0.2 \times 10^5 \times 33750 \times 10^4} = 1.684 \text{ mm}$$

Due to point load, $\quad y_{B2} = \frac{W L^3}{3 E I} = \frac{2000 \,(2.4)^3 \times (1000)^3}{3 \times 0.2 \times 10^5 \times 33750 \times 10^4} = 1.365 \text{ mm}$

$$\therefore \text{ Total} \qquad y_B = 1.684 + 1.365 = \mathbf{3.049 \text{ mm}}$$

Example 12.4. *A girder of uniform section and constant depth of 400 mm is freely supported over a span of 6 m. Calculate the deflection for a uniformly distributed load on it such that the maximum bending stress induced is 120 N/mm². Take E = 2 × 10⁵ N/mm².*

If, for the above girder, the flanges are so proportioned that there is a uniform flange stress of 120 N/mm² throughout the beam, calculate the central deflection.

Solution :

Let w be the U.D.L. in N/m length.

$$M = \frac{w L^2}{8} = \frac{w \,(6)^2}{8} = 4.5 \, w \text{ N-m} = 4500 \, w \text{ N-mm}$$

Max. stress

$$f = \frac{M}{I} y$$

$$\therefore \qquad 120 = \frac{4500 \, w}{I} \times 200$$

$$\therefore \qquad \frac{w}{I} = \frac{120}{4500 \times 200} = 1.333 \times 10^{-4}$$

The maximum deflection $y_c = \frac{5}{384} \frac{w L^4}{E I} = \frac{5}{384} \cdot \frac{w}{I} \times \frac{(6)^4 (1000)^3}{2 \times 10^5}$

$$= 8.4375 \times 10^4 \frac{w}{I} = 8.4375 \times 10^4 \,(1.333 \times 10^{-4}) = \mathbf{11.25 \text{ mm}}$$

If the girder is of constant depth and uniform strength, it will bend to a circular arc of radius R the value of which can be found from the relation.

$$\frac{f}{y} = \frac{E}{R}$$

$$\therefore \qquad \frac{1}{R} = \frac{f}{yE} = \frac{120}{200 \times 2 \times 10^5}$$

For a circular arc, the central deflection is given by

$$y_c = \frac{L^2}{8R} = \frac{(6)^2 (1000)^2}{8} \times \frac{1200}{200 \times 2 \times 10^5} = \mathbf{13.5\ mm}$$

Example 12.5. *A cantilever of uniform section has a length $AB = L$. End B is free end and carries a point load W, while end A is fixed end. Find the slope and deflection at a point C, distant $L/4$ from the free end A.*

Solution :

For any point X distant x from A, we have

$$E I \frac{d^2 y}{dx^2} = - M = -[- W(L - x)] = W(L - x)$$

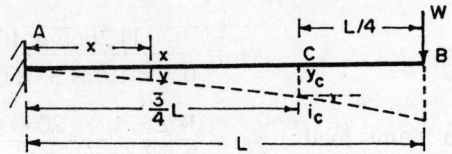

FIG. 12.13

Integrating once, $E I \dfrac{dy}{dx} = W \left(L x - \dfrac{x^2}{2} \right) + C_1$

At A, $\qquad x = 0$ and $\dfrac{dy}{dx} = 0$. Hence $C_1 = 0$

$$\therefore \qquad E I \frac{dy}{dx} = W \left(L x - \frac{x^2}{2} \right) \qquad \qquad \dots(1)$$

Integrating again, $E I y = W \left(\dfrac{L x^2}{2} - \dfrac{x^3}{6} \right) + C_2$

At A, $\qquad x = 0$ and $y = 0$. $\qquad$ Hence $C_2 = 0$

Hence $E I y = W \left(\dfrac{L x^2}{2} - \dfrac{x^3}{6} \right)$ ...(2), which is the equation for deflection at any point.

At C, $\qquad x = \dfrac{3}{4} L$

Hence $\qquad i_c = \dfrac{1}{E I} . W \left[L \times \dfrac{3}{4} L - \dfrac{1}{2} \left(\dfrac{3}{4} L \right)^2 \right] = \dfrac{15}{32} \dfrac{W L^2}{E I}$

and $\qquad y_c = \dfrac{1}{E I} . W \left[\dfrac{L}{2} \left(\dfrac{3}{4} L \right)^2 - \dfrac{1}{6} \left(\dfrac{3}{4} \right)^3 \right] = \dfrac{27}{128} \dfrac{W L^3}{E I}$

Example 12.6 (a). *A uniform beam of length L is simply and symmetrically supported over of span L. Find the ratio L/l so that the upward deflection at each end equals the downward deflection at the mid-span due to a central point load.*

Solution :

The dotted line represents the deflected shape of the beam.

Due to a central point load W, the slope at the ends of a simply supported beam are each $\dfrac{W l^2}{16 E I}$ and the deflection at mid-span is $\dfrac{W l^3}{48 E I}$.

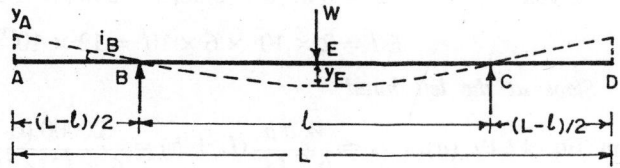

FIG. 12.14

∴ $$i_B = \frac{W l^2}{16 E I}$$

Since this angle is very small, $y_A = i_B\,(AB) = \dfrac{W l^2}{16 E I} \cdot \left(\dfrac{L - l}{2}\right)(\uparrow)$ ...(1)

Also, $$y_E = \frac{w L^3}{48 E I}\ (\downarrow)$$ ...(2)

Equating the two, we get $\dfrac{W l^2}{16 E I}\left(\dfrac{L - l}{2}\right) = \dfrac{W l^3}{48 E I}$

∴ $$L - l = \frac{2}{3} l$$

or $$\frac{L}{l} = \frac{2}{3} + 1 = \frac{5}{3}$$

Example 12.6 (b). *A beam 3 m long, simply supported at its ends, is carrying a point load W at its mid-span. If the slope at the ends of the beam is not to exceed 1°, find the deflection at the mid-span.*

Solution :

For a simply supported beam with central point load W, we have

$$i_A = \frac{W L^2}{16 E I} \quad \text{and } y_c = \frac{W L^3}{48 E I}$$

Here $$i_A = 1° = \frac{1 \times \pi}{180} = 0.01745 \ \text{radian}$$

Now $$y_c = \frac{W L^3}{48 E I} = \frac{W L^2}{16 E I} \times \frac{L}{3} = i_A \times \frac{L}{3}$$

$$= 0.01745 \left(\frac{3000}{3}\right) = \mathbf{17.45\ mm}$$

Example 12.7. *A simply supported beam of span 8 m carries a point load of 20 kN at a distance of 6 m from the left end. Compute (a) the slope at the left end (b) the deflection under the load (c) the deflection at the mid-span and (d) the maximum deflection and its location. Take $E = 2 \times 10^5 N/mm^2$ and $I = 6 \times 10^8 mm^4$.*

Solution :

Given : $L = 8\,m ; a = 6\,m ; b = 2\,m ; W = 20\,kN$

$EI = 2 \times 10^5 \times 6 \times 10^8 = 12 \times 10^{13}$ N-mm² units.

(a)   Slope at the left hand

From Eq. 12.19 (a), $i_A = \dfrac{Wab}{6\,EIL}\,(L + b) = \dfrac{20000\,(6 \times 2)}{6 \times 12 \times 10^3 \times 8}\,(8 + 2) \times (1000)^2$

$= 4.167 \times 10^{-4}$ radian = **0.0004167 radian**

(b)   Deflection under the load

From Eq. 12.22, $y_c = \dfrac{Wa^2b^2}{3\,EIL} = \dfrac{20000}{3 \times 12 \times 10^{13} \cdot \times 8}\,(6)^2\,(2)^2\,(1000)^3 =$ **1 mm**

(c)   Deflection at mid-span

From Eq. 12.23, $\left[y\right]_{x = L/2}^{a > b} = \dfrac{Wb}{48\,EI}\,(3L^2 - 4b^2) = \dfrac{20000 \times 2}{48 \times 12 \times 10^{13}}\left[3\,(8)^2 - 4\,(2)^2\right](1000)^3$

$= \textbf{1.222 mm}$

(d)   Maximum deflection

Maximum deflection occurs at $x = \sqrt{\dfrac{L^2 - b^2}{3}} = \sqrt{\dfrac{(8)^2 - (2)^2}{3}} = \textbf{4.472 m}$

$y_{max} = \dfrac{Wb\,(L^2 - b^2)^{3/2}}{9\sqrt{3}\,EIL} = \dfrac{20000 \times 2}{9\sqrt{3}\,(12 \times 10^{13})\,8}\left[(8)^2 - (2)^2\right]^{3/2} \times (1000)^3$

$= \textbf{1.242 mm}$

Example 12.8. *A uniform circular bar of length L extends by an amount δ under a tensile pull P. Show that if the bar is used as a beam simply supported at its ends and carrying a central load W, the maximum deflection is given by* $y = \dfrac{W\delta L^2}{3\,P\,d^2}$ *where d is the diameter of the beam.*

If L = 80 d, and maximum bending stress due to W is equal to 0.9 times the tensile stress due to pull P, find the ratio y/δ.

Solution :

Due to tensile load P, the extension δ of the circular bar is given by

$$\delta = \frac{PL}{AE} = \frac{PL}{\frac{\pi}{4}d^2 E} = \frac{4PL}{\pi d^2 E}$$

From which $E = \dfrac{4PL}{\pi d^2 \delta}$ ...(1)

Due to central point load, the central deflection is given by

$$y = y_{max} = \frac{WL^3}{48EI} = \frac{WL^3}{48E\frac{\pi}{64}d^4} = \frac{4WL^3}{3E\pi d^4} \qquad ...(2)$$

Substituting the value of E in (2), we get

$$y = \frac{4WL^3}{3\pi d^4} \times \frac{\pi d^2 \delta}{4PL} = \frac{W\delta L^2}{3Pd^2} \qquad ...(3)$$

Now, maximum bending stress $= f_{max} = \dfrac{M}{Z} = \dfrac{WL}{4} \times \dfrac{32}{\pi d^3}$

or $\qquad\qquad\qquad\qquad f_{max} = \dfrac{8W}{\pi} \times \dfrac{80d}{d^3} = \dfrac{640W}{\pi d^2} \qquad$ (since $L = 80d$)

Max. tensile stress $\qquad p = \dfrac{P}{\frac{\pi}{4}d^2} = \dfrac{4P}{\pi d^2} \qquad\qquad\qquad ...(5)$

Since $f = 0.9P$, we have, from (4) and (5)

$$\frac{640W}{\pi d^2} = 0.9 \times \frac{4P}{\pi d^2}$$

or $\qquad\qquad\qquad\qquad \dfrac{P}{W} = \dfrac{640}{3.6} \qquad\qquad\qquad ...(6)$

But from (3), $\qquad\qquad \dfrac{P}{W} = \dfrac{\delta L^2}{3yd^2} = \dfrac{\delta(80d)^2}{3yd^2} = \dfrac{6400\delta}{3y} \qquad ...(7)$

Equating (6) and (7), we get $\dfrac{6400\delta}{3y} = \dfrac{640}{3.6}$

or $\qquad\qquad\qquad\qquad \dfrac{y}{\delta} = \dfrac{6400}{3} \times \dfrac{3.6}{640} = \dfrac{36}{3} = 12$

12.6. USE OF DISCONTINUITY FUNCTION : MACAULAY'S METHOD

In the case of a simply supported beam with an eccentric point load (case 9) discussed in the previous article, we had to write four equations (two equations for portion AC and two equations for the portion CB) to represent slope and deflection at various points in the two segments. Also, the process of integration gave rise to four constants of integration which were determined from the conditions $y = 0$ at each end and the conditions that y and $\dfrac{dy}{dx}$ should be continuous at the point C where the point load acts. Due to this, the procedure became very cumbersome, even for a single point load. When the beam is subjected to several point loads, or a combination of point loads and U.D.L. for some portion, and/or a moment, the procedure described earlier becomes highly cumbersome. However, the complication can be avoided by the use of *discontinuity functions* for different segments of the beam. Two kinds of discontinuity functions are used : (*i*) Macaulay's function, and (*ii*) singularity function. Since Macaulay's function is more popular, we will discuss the use of this function in this article.

The method using Macaulay's discontinuous function is known as Macaulay's method. The unique feature of Macaulay's method is that it permits the writing of Macaulay's discontinuous function by a single expression, where as the more conventional approach requires that a discontinuous function be described by a series of expressions, one for each region in which the function is distinct. The use of special brackets for discontinuity function was introduced by the English mathematician W.H. Macaulay, and hence the brackets are called *Macaulay's brackets* of the type { } as originally used by him. Later, pointed brackets of the type < > were introduced; however many workers use simply vertical line, called the separation line such as | to identify the function. Macaulay's method essentially consists of the *manner of successive integration* for the expression for the bending moment. Though the law of bending moment varies from section to section, the constants of integration are valid for all the sections of the beam. Let us describe the method by taking the case of a simply supported beam subjected to an eccentric point load (Fig. 12.9).

The expression for the B.M. can be written as

$$EI\frac{d^2y}{dx^2} = -\frac{Wb}{L}x \ \Big| \ + W(x-a) \qquad \qquad ...(1)$$

In the above expression, the quantities to left of the separation line are valid for the portion AC only, while both the quantities are valid for the portion CB. The function $(x-a)$ is the Macaulay's discontinuous function. The function has the zero value when x is less than or equal to a (*i.e.* when the expression within the bracket is negative or zero) and a value equal to $x-a$ when x is greater than a.

Integrating the above expression.

$$EI\frac{dy}{dx} = -\frac{Wbx^2}{2L} + C_1 \ \Big| \ + \frac{W(x-a)^2}{2} \qquad \qquad ...(2)$$

It is to be noted that the integration of $(x-a)$ has been made *as a whole* and not for the individual terms. This *manner* of integration makes Macaulay's method *effective*, because the constant of integration C_1 is valid for the slopes at all sections of the beam and not for AC alone.

Integrating once more the above expression

$$EIy = -\frac{Wbx^3}{6L} + C_1x + C_2 \ \Big| \ + \frac{W(x-a)^3}{6} \qquad \qquad ...(3)$$

Now at $x=0$, $y=0$. Hence $C_2=0$

Also, at $x=L$, $y=0$. Substituting this in (3) and including all terms,

$$0 = -\frac{WbL^3}{6L} + C_1L + \frac{W(L-a)^3}{6} = C_1L - \frac{Wb}{6}(L^2-b^2)$$

or $$C_1 = \frac{Wb}{6L}(L^2-b^2)$$

Substituting this value of C_1 in Eqs. (2) and (3), we get

$$EI\frac{dy}{dx} = -\frac{Wbx^2}{2L} + \frac{Wb}{6L}(L^2-b^2) \ \Big| \ + \frac{W(x-a)^2}{2}$$

or
$$E I \frac{dy}{dx} = \frac{Wb}{6L}(L^2 - b^2 - 3x^2) \Bigg| + \frac{W(x-a)^2}{2} \qquad \text{...(I)}$$

and
$$E I y = -\frac{Wbx^3}{6L} + \frac{Wb}{6L}(L^2 - b^2)x \Bigg| + \frac{W(x-a)^3}{6}$$

or
$$E I y = \frac{Wbx}{6L}(L - b^2 - x^2) \Bigg| + \frac{W(x-a)^3}{6} \qquad \text{...(II)}$$

Eqs. (I) and (II) are the standard equations for slope and deflection at any point, applicable for the whole length of the beam.

To write the equations for slope and deflection for the portion AC only, we have to neglect the terms to the right hand side of the Macaulay's line. Thus, for the portion AC, we have

$$E I \frac{dy}{dx} = \frac{Wb}{6L}(L^2 - b^2 - 3x^2) \qquad \text{...(Ia)}$$

and
$$E I y = \frac{Wbx}{6L}(L^2 - b^2 - x^2) \qquad \text{...(IIa)}$$

which are exactly the same as found earlier in the previous article.

The rest of the procedure for finding the maximum deflection and its position, and for finding slopes at the ends is the same as described in the previous article.

Example 12.9. *A horizontal beam of uniform section and length L rests on supports at its ends. It carries a U.D.L. w per unit length which extends over a length l from the right hand support. Determine the value of l in order that the maximum deflection may occur at the left hand end of the load, and if the maximum deflection is $\frac{wL^4}{kEI}$, determine the value of k.*

Solution : (Fig. 12.15)

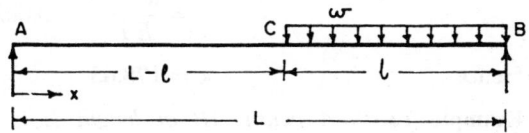

FIG. 12.15

Taking moments about B, we get

$$R_A = \frac{wl^2}{2L}$$

At any section distant x from A,

$$E I \frac{d^2y}{dx^2} = -\frac{wl^2}{2L}x \Bigg| + \frac{w}{2}\{x - (L-l)^2\} \qquad \text{...(1)}$$

Integrating once,
$$E I \frac{dy}{dx} = -\frac{wl^2}{2L}\cdot\frac{x^2}{2} + C_1 \Bigg| + \frac{w}{6}\{x - (L-l)\}^3 \qquad \text{...(2)}$$

Integrating again,
$$E I y = -\frac{wl^2}{12L}x^3 + C_1 x + C_2 \Bigg| + \frac{w}{24}\{x - (L-l)\}^4 \qquad \text{...(3)}$$

At $x = 0$, $\quad y = 0$ hence $C_2 = 0$

At $x = L$, $\quad y = 0 = -\frac{wl^2}{12L}(L)^3 + C_1 L + \frac{w}{24}\{L - (L-l)\}^4$

From which we obtain $\quad C_1 = \dfrac{w\,l^2\,L}{12} - \dfrac{w\,l^4}{24\,L}$ $\qquad$ ...(4)

Substituting in (2), we get

$$E\,I\frac{dy}{dx} = \left. -\frac{w\,l^2\,x^2}{4\,L} + \frac{w\,l^2\,L}{12} - \frac{w\,l^4}{24\,L}\ \right| + \frac{w}{6}\{x - (L - l)\}^3 \qquad ...(2a)$$

Again, if y is to be maximum at C, $\dfrac{dy}{dx} = 0\quad$ when $x = (L - l)$

Hence from 2 (a), $\qquad 0 = -\dfrac{wl^2}{4L}(L - l)^2 + \dfrac{wl^2 L}{12} - \dfrac{wl^4}{24L}$

Simplifying the above, we get $7\,l^2 - 12\,L\,l + 4\,L^2 = 0$

From this, we get $\qquad l = L \times \dfrac{12 \pm \sqrt{144 - 4 \times 4 \times 7}}{2 \times 7} = \dfrac{12 \pm 5.657}{14}L = \mathbf{0.453\,L}$

Substituting in (4), we get $C_1 = \dfrac{w\,(0.453\,L)^2\,L}{12} - \dfrac{w\,(0.453\,L)^4}{24\,L} = 0.01535\,w\,L^3$

Substituting $x = (L - l) = 0.547\,L$ and $C_1 = 0.01535\,w\,L^3$ in 3, we get

$$y_{\text{max}} = \frac{1}{E\,I}\left[-\frac{w\,(0.453\,L)^2}{12\,L}(0.547\,L)^3 + 0.01535\,w\,L^3\,(0.547\,L) \right\}$$

$$= \frac{w\,L^4}{E\,I}\left[-0.0028 + 0.0084 \right] = 0.0056\,\frac{w\,L^4}{E\,I} = \frac{w\,L^4}{178.65\,E\,I}$$

Hence $\qquad\qquad k = \mathbf{178.65}$

Example 12.10. *A beam AB of length L is loaded as shown in Fig. 12.16(a). Deduce standard expressions for slope and deflection at any point.*

Solution :

Here the load does not extend to the end support. However, the problem can be solved by supposing the load to extend further from D to support B, and then superimposing the effect of an upward load w from D to B, as shown in Fig. 12.16(b). R_A can be found by taking moments about B. Thus

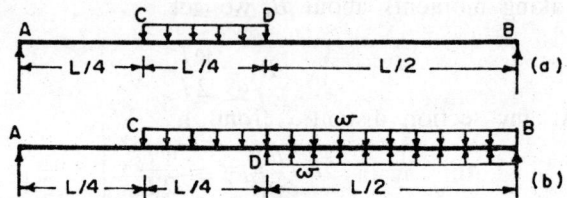

FIG. 12.16

$$R_A = \frac{1}{L}\left\{ w\,\frac{L}{4}\left(\frac{L}{2} + \frac{L}{8} \right) \right\} = \frac{5}{32}\,w\,L$$

Hence for any point distant x from A,

$$E\,I\frac{d^2 y}{dx^2} = \left. -\frac{5}{32}\,w\,L\,x\ \right| + \frac{w}{2}\left(x - \frac{L}{4} \right)^2 \left| -\frac{w}{2}\left(x - \frac{L}{2} \right)^2 \right.$$

$$\therefore \qquad EI\frac{dy}{dx} = -\frac{5}{64}wLx^2 + C_1 \;\Big|\; +\frac{w}{6}\left(x-\frac{L}{4}\right)^3 \;\Big|\; -\frac{w}{6}\left(x-\frac{L}{2}\right)^3 \qquad ...(1)$$

and
$$EIy = -\frac{5}{192}wLx^3 + C_1x + C_2 \;\Big|\; +\frac{w}{24}\left(x-\frac{L}{4}\right)^4 \;\Big|\; -\frac{w}{24}\left(x-\frac{L}{2}\right)^4 \quad ...(2)$$

At $\qquad x = 0\,, y = 0.$ Hence $C_2 = 0$

At $\qquad x = L\,, y = 0 = -\frac{5}{192}wL\,(L)^3 + C_1L + \frac{w}{24}\left(L-\frac{L}{4}\right)^4 - \frac{w}{24}\left(L-\frac{L}{2}\right)^4$

From which we obtain $\quad C_1 = \frac{95}{6144}wL^3$

Hence the equations for slope and deflection at any point are

$$EI\frac{dy}{dx} = -\frac{5}{64}wLx^2 + \frac{95}{6144}wL^3 \;\Big|\; +\frac{w}{6}\left(x-\frac{L}{4}\right)^3 \;\Big|\; -\frac{w}{6}\left(x-\frac{L}{2}\right)^3 \quad ...(I)$$

and
$$EIy = -\frac{5}{192}wLx^3 + \frac{95}{6144}wL^3x \;\Big|\; +\frac{w}{24}\left(x-\frac{L}{4}\right)^4 \;\Big|\; -\frac{w}{24}\left(x-\frac{L}{2}\right)^3 ...(II)$$

Example 12.11. *A beam, simply supported at ends A and B is loaded with two points loads of 30 kN each at a distance of 2 m and 3 m respectively from end A. Determine the position and magnitude of the maximum deflection. Take $E=2\times10^5\,N/mm^2$ and $I = 7200\,cm^4$.*

Solution :

Taking moments about B, we get

$$R_A = \frac{1}{6}\Big[\,30 \times 3 + 30 \times 4\,\Big] = 35 \text{ kN}$$

Measuring x from A, we have the differential equation

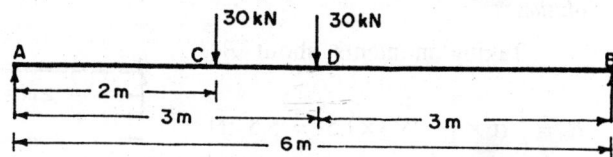

FIG. 12.17

$$EI\frac{d^2y}{dx^2} = -M = -35x \;\Big|\; +30\,(x-2) \;\Big|\; +30\,(x-3)$$

Integrating, $\qquad EI\frac{dy}{dx} = -\frac{35x^2}{2} + C_1 \;\Big|\; +\frac{30\,(x-2)^2}{2} \;\Big|\; +\frac{30\,(x-3)^2}{2} \qquad ...(1)$

Integrating again, $\quad EIy = -\frac{35x^3}{6} + C_1x + C_2 \;\Big|\; +\frac{30\,(x-2)^3}{6} \;\Big|\; +\frac{30\,(x-3)^3}{6} \quad ...(2)$

At $\;x = 0,$ $\qquad\qquad y = 0.$ Hence $C_2 = 0$

At $\;x = 6$ m, $\qquad\quad y = 0 = -\frac{35\,(6)^3}{6} + (C_1 \times 6) + \frac{30}{6}(6-2)^3 + \frac{30}{6}(6-3)^3$

From which $C_1 = 134.17$. Hence the slope and deflection equations are :

$$EI\frac{dy}{dx} = -\frac{35}{2}x^2 + 134.17 \;\Big|\; +15\,(x-2)^2 \;\Big|\; +15\,(x-3)^2 \qquad ...(I)$$

and
$$EIy = -\frac{35}{6}x^3 + 134.17x \;\Big|\; +5\,(x-2)^3 \;\Big|\; +5\,(x-3)^3 \qquad ...(II)$$

Now, for maximum deflection, $\frac{dy}{dx} = 0$. Also, the maximum deflection always occurs near the midspan. Hence by inspection, maximum deflection will occur between C and D region where maximum loading is there. Therefore, including all the corresponding terms of Eq. (I), we have

$$0 = -\frac{35}{2}x^2 + 134.17 + 125\,(x - 2)^2$$

or $x^2 + 12x - 77.67 = 0$

From which we get $x = \textbf{4.662 m}$ from A.

Substituting this value of x and including first three terms, we get

$$E\,I\,y_{max} = -\frac{35}{6}(4.662)^3 + 134.17\,(4.662) + 5\,(4.662 - 2)^3 = 128.81 \text{ kN-m}^3$$

$$= 128.81\,(1000)\,(1000)^3 = 128.81 \times 10^{12} \text{ N-mm}^3$$

$\therefore$ $y_{max} = \dfrac{128.81 \times 10^{12}}{(2 \times 10^5)\,(7200 \times 10^4)} = \textbf{8.95 mm}$

Example 12.12. *A beam AB of 6 m span is simply supported at the ends and is loaded as shown in Fig. 12.18. Determine (i) deflection at C (ii) maximum deflection and (iii) slope at end A. Take $E = 2 \times 10^5 \text{ N/mm}^2$ and $I = 2000 \text{ cm}^4$.*

Solution :

Taking moments about B,

$$R_A = \frac{1}{6}(6 \times 4 + 2 \times 3 \times 1.5) = 5.5 \text{ kN}$$

Measuring x from A, we have

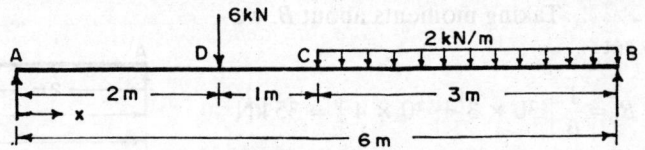

FIG. 12.18

$$E\,I\,\frac{d^2y}{dx^2} = -5.5x \;\Big|\; +6\,(x - 2) \;\Big|\; +\frac{2\,(x - 3)^2}{2}$$

$\therefore$ $E\,I\,\dfrac{dy}{dx} = -\dfrac{5.5\,x^2}{2} + C_1 \;\Big|\; +\dfrac{6\,(x - 2)^2}{2} \;\Big|\; +\dfrac{2\,(x - 3)^3}{6}$ ...(1)

and $E\,I\,y = -\dfrac{5.5\,x^3}{6} + C_1 x + C_2 \;\Big|\; +\dfrac{6\,(x - 2)^3}{6} \;\Big|\; +\dfrac{2\,(x - 3)^4}{24}$ ...(2)

At $x = 0$, $y = 0$. Hence $C_2 = 0$

At $x = 6$ m, $y = 0 = -\dfrac{5.5}{6}(6)^3 + C_1\,(6) + \dfrac{6\,(6 - 2)^3}{6} + \dfrac{2}{24}(6 - 3)^4$

which gives $C_1 = 21.21$

Hence the slope and deflection equations are :

$$E\,I\,\frac{dy}{dx} = -2.75\,x^2 + 21.21 \;\Big|\; +3\,(x - 2)^2 \;\Big|\; +\frac{2}{6}(x - 3)^3$$ ...(I)

and
$$E\,Iy = -\frac{5.5}{6}x^3 + 21.21\,x \;\bigg|\; + (x-2)^3 \;\bigg|\; + \frac{2}{24}(x-3)^4 \qquad\qquad \ldots(I)$$

For maximum deflection, $\frac{dy}{dx} = 0$. However, the maximum deflection will be very near to the mid-point C, say in the sector DC. Hence from (2), including the terms upto point C, we get

$$0 = -2.75\,x^2 + 21.21 + 3\,(x-2)^2$$

or $\qquad x^2 + 24\,x - 82.16 = 0$ from which $x = 2.9486$ m.

Hence from II, $\quad E\,I y_{max} = -\dfrac{5.5}{6}(2.9486)^3 + 21.21\,(2.9486) + (2.9486-2)^3 = 39.89$ kN-m^3 units

$\therefore \qquad\qquad E\,I y_{max} = 39.89\,(1000)\,(1000)^3$ N-mm^3 = 39.89×10^{12} N-mm^3

$\therefore \qquad\qquad y_{max} = \dfrac{39.89 \times 10^{12}}{2 \times 10^5 \times 2000\,(10^4)} = \mathbf{9.973\ mm}$

For deflection at C, put $x = 3$ m in Eq. II, in terms upto point C.

$\therefore \qquad\qquad E\,I y_c = -\dfrac{5.5}{6}(3)^3 + 21.21\,(3) + (3-2)^3 = 39.88$ kN-m^3 units

$\therefore \qquad\qquad y_c = \dfrac{39.88 \times 10^{12}}{2 \times 10^5\,(2000)\,(10^4)} = \mathbf{9.97\ mm}$

Thus, we note that the deflection at the mid-span is very nearly equal to the maximum deflection.

Also, putting, $\quad x = 0$ in Eq. (I), we get

$$E\,I i_A = 21.21\ \text{kN-m}^2 = 21.21 \times 1000\,(1000)^2\ \text{N-mm}^2$$

$\therefore \qquad\qquad i_A = \dfrac{21.21 \times 10^9}{2 \times 10^5 \times 2000\,(10^4)} = \mathbf{5.3 \times 10^{-3}\ radian}$

Example 12.13. *A simply supported beam AB is loaded with a couple μ at the right hand end B, as shown in Fig. 12.19. Determine (i) equation for the elastic curve (ii) the maximum deflection and (iii) slopes at the ends. Take EI constant along the length of the beam.*

Solution :

Since there is no external vertical load, the reactions (R) at A and B will be equal and opposite, so as to form a clockwise couple to resist the external anticlockwise couple.

Hence $R = \dfrac{\mu}{L}(\uparrow)$ at A and $R = \dfrac{\mu}{L}(\downarrow)$ at B.

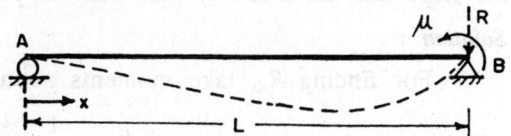

FIG. 12.19

Measuring x from A, $\qquad E\,I\dfrac{d^2y}{dx^2} = -M = -\dfrac{\mu}{L}x$

Hence $\qquad\qquad E\,I\dfrac{dy}{dx} = -\dfrac{\mu}{L}\dfrac{x^2}{2} + C_1 \qquad\qquad \ldots(1)$

and
$$E I y = - \frac{\mu}{L} \frac{x^3}{6} + C_1 x + C_2 \qquad \qquad ...(2)$$

At $x = 0$, $y = 0$. Hence $C_2 = 0$

At $x = L$, $y = 0 = - \frac{\mu}{L} \cdot \frac{L^3}{6} + C_1 L$

This gives $C_1 = \frac{\mu L}{6}$

Hence the slope and deflection equations are as follows

$$E I \frac{dy}{dx} = - \frac{\mu}{2L} x^2 + \frac{\mu L}{6} \qquad \qquad ...(I)$$

and
$$E I y = - \frac{\mu}{6L} x^3 + \frac{\mu L}{6} x \qquad \qquad ...(II)$$

Hence the equation for the elastic curve is

$$y = \frac{\mu}{6 E I} \left(L x - \frac{x^3}{L} \right) \text{ Ans}$$

For maximum deflection, $\frac{dy}{dx} = 0$. Hence from (I)

$$0 = - \frac{\mu}{2L} x^2 + \frac{\mu L}{6}$$

which gives $x = \frac{L}{\sqrt{3}}$. Substituting this value of x in (II)

$$E I y_{max} = - \frac{\mu}{6L} \left(\frac{L}{\sqrt{3}} \right)^3 + \frac{\mu L}{6} \left(\frac{L}{\sqrt{3}} \right) = \frac{\mu L^2}{9 \sqrt{3}}$$

Hence $y_{max} = \frac{\mu L^2}{9 \sqrt{3} E I}$ **Ans.**

Again, putting $x = 0$ in (I), we get $i_A = \frac{\mu L}{6 E I}$ **(Ans.)**   ...(12.24 a)

Also, putting $x = L$ in (I), we get $i_B = \frac{1}{E I} \left[- \frac{\mu}{2L} L^3 + \frac{\mu L}{6} \right] = - \frac{\mu L}{3 E I}$ ...(12.24 b)

Example 12.14. *An over hanging beam ABC is loaded as shown in Fig. 12.29(a). Determine the slope and deflection of the beam at point C, in terms of E, I, W and L.*

Solution :

For finding R_A, take moments about B (Fig. 12.20 a)

$$\therefore \qquad R_A = \frac{1}{2I} \left[\frac{WL}{2} - WL \right] = - \frac{W}{4} \quad (i.e. \ \frac{W}{4} \downarrow)$$

Hence $R_B = W + \frac{W}{4} + W = \frac{9}{4} W (\uparrow)$

Total   U.D.L. $= W$

$$\therefore \qquad w = \frac{W}{L}$$

In order to effectively apply Macaulay's method, extend U.D.L. from B to C, and apply upward load from B to C, as shown in Fig. 12.20 (b). Measuring x from A, we have

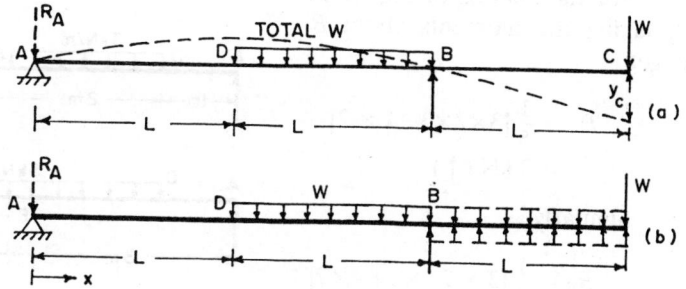

FIG. 12.20

$$EI\frac{d^2y}{dx^2} = \frac{W}{4}x \;\bigg|\; + \frac{W}{L}\frac{(x-L)^2}{2}\;\bigg|$$
$$-\frac{9W}{4}(x-2L) - \frac{W}{L}\frac{(x-2L)^2}{2}$$

Hence

$$EI\frac{dy}{dx} = \frac{Wx^2}{8} + C_1 \;\bigg|\; + \frac{W}{6L}(x-L)^3 \;\bigg|\; -\frac{9}{8}W(x-2L)^2 - \frac{W}{6L}(x-2L)^3 \qquad ...(1)$$

and

$$EIy = \frac{Wx^3}{24} + C_1 x + C_2 \;\bigg|\; + \frac{W}{24L}(x-L)^4 \;\bigg|\; - \frac{9}{24}W(x-2L)^3 - \frac{W}{24L}(x-2L)^4 \qquad ...(2)$$

At $x=0$, $y=0$. Hence $C_2 = 0$

Also, at $x = 2L$, $y = 0 = \frac{W}{24}(2L)^3 + C_1(2L) + \frac{W}{24L}(2L-L)^4$

From which $\qquad C_1 = -\frac{3}{16}WL^2$

Substituting the value of C_1 in Eqs. (1) and (2)

$$EI\frac{dy}{dx} = \frac{Wx^2}{8} - \frac{3}{16}WL^2 \;\bigg|\; + \frac{W}{6L}(x-L)^3 \;\bigg|\; -\frac{9}{8}W(x-2L)^2 - \frac{W}{6L}(x-2L)^3 \qquad ...(I)$$

$$EIy = \frac{Wx^3}{24} - \frac{3}{16}WL^2 x \;\bigg|\; + \frac{W}{24L}(x-L)^4 \;\bigg|\; - \frac{9}{24}(x-2L)^3 - \frac{W}{24L}(x-2L)^4 \qquad ...(II)$$

At C, $\quad x = 3L$; hence from (I), including all the terms, we get

$$EI\,i_c = \frac{W(3L)^2}{8} - \frac{3}{16}WL^2 + \frac{W}{6L}(3L-L)^3 - \frac{9}{8}(3L-2L)^2 - \frac{W}{6L}(3L-2L)^3$$

From which $\qquad i_c = \frac{47}{48}\frac{WL^2}{EI}$ **(Ans.)**

Also, at C, $x = 3L$. Hence from (II), including all the terms, we get

$$EI\,y_c = \frac{W}{24}(3L)^3 - \frac{3}{16}WL^2(3L) + \frac{W}{24L}(3L-L)^4 - \frac{9}{24}W(3L-2L)^3 - \frac{W}{24L}(3L-2L)^4$$

From which $\qquad y_c = \frac{13}{16}\frac{WL^3}{EI}$ **(Ans.)**

Example 12.15. *An over hanging beam ABC, supported at A and B is loaded as shown in Fig. 12.21(a). Determine the deflection at the free end, and maximum deflection between A and B. Take $I = 600\,cm^4$ and $E = 2 \times 10^5\,N/mm^2$.*

Solution :

Macaulay's method can be applied only if the U.D.L is continuous upto the end of the beam. Hence extend the U.D.L. from E to end C, and apply an upward U.D.L. from C to E, as shown in Fig. 12.21(b).

For the loading of Fig. 12.21
(a), taking the moments about B,
we get

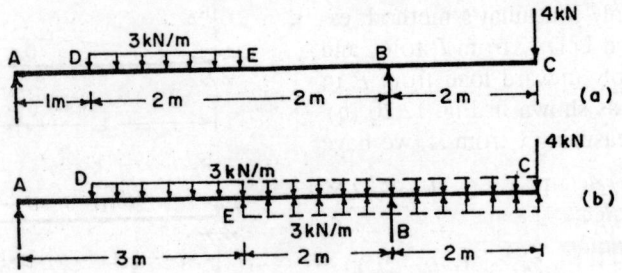

$$R_A = \frac{1}{5}[3\times2\times3-4\times2]$$
$$= 2 \text{ kN } (\uparrow)$$

Similarly,

$$R_B = \frac{1}{5}[3\times2\times2+4\times7]$$
$$= 8 \text{ kN } (\uparrow)$$

FIG. 12.21

Measuring x from A,

$$E I \frac{d^2y}{dx^2} = -M_x = -2x \left| + \frac{3(x-1)^2}{2} \right| - \frac{3(x-3)^2}{2} \left| \right| -8(x-5)$$

$$\therefore \quad E I \frac{dy}{dx} = -\frac{2x^2}{2} + C_1 \left| + \frac{3(x-1)^3}{6} \right| - \frac{3(x-3)^3}{6} \left| \right| - \frac{8(x-5)^2}{2} \qquad \text{...(1)}$$

and $\quad E I y = -\frac{x^3}{3} + C_1 x + C_2 \left| + \frac{3(x-1)^4}{24} \right| - \frac{3(x-3)^4}{24} \left| \right| - \frac{8(x-5)^3}{6} \qquad \text{...(2)}$

At $\qquad\qquad x = 0, y = 0.$ Hence $C_2 = 0$

At $\qquad\qquad x = 5 \text{ m}, y = 0.$ Hence from Eq. (2), including appropriate terms,

$$0 = -\frac{(5)^3}{3} + C_1(5) + \frac{3(5-1)^4}{24} - \frac{3(5-3)^4}{24}$$

From which $\quad C_1 = 2.333$

Hence the slope and deflection equations are as follows.

$$E I \frac{dy}{dx} = -x^2 + 2.333 \left| + \frac{(x-1)^3}{2} \right| - \frac{(x-3)^3}{2} \left| \right| -4(x-5)^2 \qquad \text{...(I)}$$

and $\quad E I y = -\frac{x^3}{3} + 2.333x \left| + \frac{(x-1)^4}{8} \right| - \frac{(x-3)^4}{8} \left| \right| - \frac{4}{3}(x-5)^3 \qquad \text{...(II)}$

Deflection at C : For deflection at C, put $x = 7$ m in (II)

$$\therefore \qquad E I y_c = -\frac{(7)^3}{3} + 2.333(7) + \frac{(7-1)^4}{8} - \frac{(7-3)^4}{8} - \frac{4}{3}(7-5)^3 = 21.331 \text{ kN-m}^2$$

$$\therefore \qquad y_c = \frac{21.331(10^3)(1000)^3}{(2\times10^5)(600\times10^4)} = \textbf{1.78 mm}$$

For maximum deflection, $dy/dx = 0$. Maximum deflection will evidently occur in range DE. Putting $dy/dx = 0$ in Eq. (I) and including all terms upto E, we have

$$0 = -x^2 + 2.333 + \frac{(x-1)^3}{2} \quad \text{or} \quad (x-1)^3 - 2x^2 + 4.666 = 0$$

Solving this by trial, we get $x = 1.555$ m

Substituting in (II), we get $E I y_{max} = -\dfrac{(1.555)^3}{3} + 2.333\,(1.555) - \dfrac{(1.555)^4}{8}$

$$= 1.644 \quad \text{kN-m}^3 = 1.644 \times 10^3 \,(1000)^3 \text{ N-mm}^3$$

$\therefore \qquad y_{max} = \dfrac{1.644 \times 10^3 \,(1000)^3}{2 \times 10^5 \,(600 \times 10^4)} = \mathbf{1.37 \text{ mm}} (\downarrow)$

Example 12.16. *A beam ABC is loaded as shown. Find (i) slopes at A and B and C (ii) deflection at C and (iii) maximum deflection between the supports.*

Solution :

$R_A = \dfrac{1}{L}\,(Wa) = \dfrac{Wa}{L}(\downarrow)$

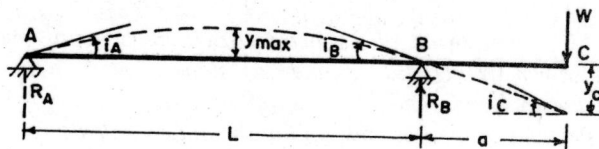

FIG. 12.22

$R_B = \dfrac{1}{L}\,W\,(a+L) = \dfrac{W(a+L)}{L}(\uparrow)$

$$E I \dfrac{d^2 y}{dx^2} = -M_x = \dfrac{Wa}{L}\,x \;\bigg|\; -\dfrac{W(a+L)}{L}\,(x-L)$$

$\therefore \qquad EI \dfrac{dy}{dx} = \dfrac{Wax^2}{2L} + C_1 \;\bigg|\; -\dfrac{W(a+L)}{L}\dfrac{(x-L)^2}{2} \qquad \text{...(1)}$

and $\qquad E I y = \dfrac{Wax^3}{6L} + C_1 x + C_2 \;\bigg|\; -\dfrac{W(a+L)}{L}\dfrac{(x-L)^3}{6} \qquad \text{...(2)}$

At $x = 0$, $\qquad\qquad y = 0$. Hence $C_2 = 0$

At $x = L$, $\qquad\qquad y = 0$. Hence from (2), including appropriate terms

$$0 = \dfrac{Wa\,(L)^3}{6L} + C_1 L, \text{ from which } C_1 = -\dfrac{WaL}{6}$$

Hence the slope and deflection equations are as follows :

$$E I \dfrac{dy}{dx} = \dfrac{Wax^2}{2L} - \dfrac{WaL}{6} \;\bigg|\; -\dfrac{W(a+L)}{L}\dfrac{(x-L)^2}{2} \qquad \text{...(I)}$$

and $\qquad E I y = \dfrac{Wax^3}{6L} - \dfrac{WaL}{6}\,x \;\bigg|\; -\dfrac{W(a+L)}{L}\dfrac{(x-L)^3}{6} \qquad \text{...(I)}$

Slopes at A and B and C : From (I), we get

$i_A = \dfrac{1}{EI}\left[-\dfrac{WaL}{6} \right] = -\dfrac{WaL}{6EI}$

$i_B = \dfrac{1}{EI}\left[\dfrac{WaL^2}{2L} - \dfrac{WaL}{6} \right] = \dfrac{WaL}{3EI}$

$i_C = \dfrac{1}{EI}\left[\dfrac{Wa}{2L}\,(a+L)^2 - \dfrac{WaL}{6} - \dfrac{W(a+L)}{L}\dfrac{(a+L-L)^2}{2} \right] = \dfrac{Wa}{6EI}\,(2L+3a)$

Deflection at C : From (II), at $x = a + L$, we get

$y_c = \dfrac{1}{EI}\left[\dfrac{Wa}{6L}\,(a+L)^3 - \dfrac{WaL}{6}\,(a+L) - \dfrac{W(a+L)}{6L}\,(a+L-L)^3 \right]$

or $\qquad y_c = \dfrac{1}{EI}\dfrac{Wa}{6L}\left[a^3 + L^3 + 3a^3L + 3L^2 a - L^2 \cdot a - L^3 - a^3 - a^2 L \right] = \dfrac{Wa^2}{3EI}\,(a+L)$

Maximum deflection between A and B : Putting $\dfrac{dy}{dx} = 0$ in (I), we get

$$0 = \frac{Wax^2}{2L} - \frac{WaL}{6}, \text{ from which we get } x = \frac{L}{\sqrt{3}}$$

Hence $EIy_{max} = \dfrac{Wa}{6L}\left(\dfrac{L}{\sqrt{3}}\right)^3 - \dfrac{WaL}{6}\left(\dfrac{L}{\sqrt{3}}\right) = -\dfrac{WaL^2}{9\sqrt{3}}$

or $y_{max} = -\dfrac{WaL^2}{9\sqrt{3}\,EI}$

Example 12.17. *A beam ABCD has equal over hangs to both the sides and is loaded as shown in Fig. 12.23. Find (a) slopes at the free ends and at the supports (b) deflections at the free ends and at the mid-span.*

Solution :

$$R_B = R_C = \frac{4W}{2} = 2W$$

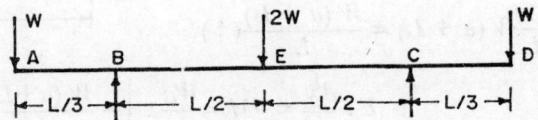

FIG. 12.23

Measuring x from A, we have

$$EI\frac{d^2y}{dx^2} = -M_x = W.x\ \Big|\ -2W\left(x-\frac{L}{3}\right), \text{ for portion upto point } E.$$

$\therefore$ $EI\dfrac{dy}{dx} = \dfrac{Wx^2}{2} + C_1\ \Bigg|\ -\dfrac{2W\left(x-\dfrac{L}{3}\right)^2}{2}$ ...(1)

and $EIy = \dfrac{Wx^3}{6} + C_1 x + C_2\ \Bigg|\ -\dfrac{2W\left(x-\dfrac{L}{3}\right)^3}{6}$ ...(2)

Due to symmetry, at $x = \left(\dfrac{L}{3} + \dfrac{L}{2}\right) = \dfrac{5}{6}L, \ \dfrac{dy}{dx} = 0$

$\therefore$ $0 = \dfrac{W}{2}\left(\dfrac{5}{6}L\right)^2 + C_1 - W\left(\dfrac{5}{6}L - \dfrac{L}{3}\right)^2$, which gives $C_1 = -\dfrac{7}{72}WL^2$

Also, at $x = \dfrac{L}{3}$, $y = 0$. Hence from (2)

$$0 = \frac{W}{6}\left(\frac{L}{3}\right)^3 - \frac{7}{72}WL^2\left(\frac{L}{3}\right) + C_2, \text{ from which } C_2 = +\frac{17}{648}WL^3$$

Hence the slope and deflection equations are :

$$EI\frac{dy}{dx} = \frac{Wx^2}{2} - \frac{7}{72}WL^2\ \Big|\ -W\left(x - \frac{L}{3}\right)^2 \qquad ...(I)$$

and $EIy = \dfrac{Wx^3}{6} - \dfrac{7}{72}WL^2 x + \dfrac{17}{648}WL^3\ \Bigg|\ -\dfrac{W}{3}\left(x - \dfrac{L}{3}\right)^3$ ...(II)

Slope at free end : Substituting $x = 0$, in (I), we get

$$i_A = \frac{1}{EI}\left(-\frac{7}{72}WL^2\right) = -\frac{7WL^2}{72EI}$$

Slopes at supports : Substituting $x = L/3$, in (I), we get

$$i_B = \frac{1}{EI}\left[\frac{W}{2}\left(\frac{L}{3}\right)^2 - \frac{7}{72}WL^2\right] = -\frac{WL^2}{24\,EI}$$

Deflection at free end : Substituting $x = 0$ in (I), we get

$$y_A = \frac{1}{EI}\left(+\frac{17}{648}WL^3\right) = +\frac{17}{648}\frac{WL^3}{EI}$$

Deflection at mid-span : Substituting $x = \frac{5}{6}L$ in (II), we get

$$y_E = \frac{1}{EI}\left[\frac{W}{6}\left(\frac{5}{6}L\right)^3 - \frac{7}{72}WL^2\left(\frac{5}{6}L\right) + \frac{17}{648}WL^3 - \frac{W}{3}\left(\frac{5}{6}L - \frac{L}{3}\right)^3\right]$$

From which $\quad y_E = 0$

Example 12.18. *A beam AB of length L, hinged at the ends, carries a couple μ at a distance a from the left end. Find the slope at each end and the deflection at the point of application of the couple*

Solution :
$$R_A = \frac{\mu}{L}(\downarrow)$$

$$R_B = \frac{\mu}{L}(\uparrow)$$

Measuring x from A, we have

$$EI\frac{d^2y}{dx^2} = -M_x = \frac{\mu}{L}x\ \bigg|\ -\mu(x-a)^0$$

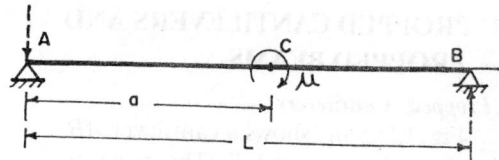

FIG. 12.24

Integrating, $\qquad EI\frac{dy}{dx} = \frac{\mu}{2L}x^2 + C_1\ \bigg|\ -\mu(x-a)$ ...(1)

and $\qquad\qquad EIy = \frac{\mu}{L}\frac{x^3}{6} + C_1x + C_2\ \bigg|\ -\mu\frac{(x-a)^2}{2}$ ...(2)

At $x = 0$, $\qquad y = 0$. Hence from (2), $C_2 = 0$

At $x = L$, $\qquad y = 0 = \frac{\mu}{L}\left(\frac{L^3}{6}\right) + C_1L - \mu\frac{(L-a)^2}{2}$

From which $\qquad C_1 = \frac{\mu}{6L}(2L^2 - 6aL + 3a^2)$

Hence the slope and deflection equations are as follows

$$EI\frac{dy}{dx} = \frac{\mu x^2}{2L} + \frac{\mu}{6L}(2L^2 - 6aL + 3a^2)\ \bigg|\ -\mu(x-a)$$ ...(I)

$$EI\frac{dy}{dx} = \frac{\mu x^3}{6L} + \frac{\mu}{6L}(2L^2 - 6aL + 3a^2)x\ \bigg|\ -\frac{\mu}{2}(x-a)^2$$ ...(II)

Slope at end A : Putting $x = 0$ in (I), we get

$$i_A = \frac{1}{EI}\left[\frac{\mu}{6L}(2L^2 - 6aL + 3a)\right] = \frac{\mu}{6EIL}(2L^2 - 6aL + 3a^2)$$

Slope at end B : Putting $x = L$ in (II), we get

$$i_B = \frac{1}{EI}\left[\frac{\mu L^2}{2L} + \frac{\mu}{6L}(2L^2 - 6aL + 3a^2) - \mu(L-a)\right] = \frac{\mu}{6EIL}(3a^2 - L^2)$$

Deflection at C : Putting $x = a$ in (II), we get

$$y_C = \frac{1}{EI}\left[\frac{\mu a^3}{6L} + \frac{\mu a}{6L}(2L^2 - 6aL + 3a^2)\right] = \frac{\mu a}{3EIL}(2a^2 + L^2 - 3aL)$$

$$= \frac{\mu a}{3EIL}(L - a)(L - 2a)$$

Special case :   When $a = b = \dfrac{L}{2}$

$$i_A = \frac{\mu}{6EIL}\left[2L^2 - 6\frac{L}{2}L + 3\left(\frac{L}{2}\right)^2\right] = -\frac{\mu L}{24EI}$$

$$i_B = \frac{\mu}{6EIL}\left[3\left(\frac{L}{2}\right)^2 - L^2\right] = -\frac{\mu L}{24EI}$$

Hence both the slopes are equal and are in anti-clockwise direction.

Also, $y_c = \dfrac{\mu}{3EIL}\left(\dfrac{L}{2}\right)\left(L - \dfrac{L}{2}\right)\left(L - 2 \times \dfrac{L}{2}\right) = 0$

12.7. PROPPED CANTILEVERS AND PROPPED BEAMS

(a) Propped Cantilevers

Fig. 12.25 (*a*) shows a cantilever *AB*, propped at the free and *B*. The reaction *P* at the prop can be easily found from the consideration of deflection of the point *B* where the prop has been placed. *The prop is rigid.*

Fig. 12.25(*b*), shows the deflected position of the cantilever, when the prop is removed. In that case, the free end *B* will deflect by an amount y_B due to external loading. The effect of the prop is to exert an upward force *P* (equal to the prop reaction) to cancel the downward deflection due to the external load. If $y_B{}'$ is the upward deflection of the free end *B* when subjected to an upward load *P* (Fig. 12.25 c), we have the following compatibility equation.

$$y_B = y_B{}' \qquad ...(12.25)$$

If, however, the prop is *not rigid*, but yields by an amount δ, we have the following compatibility equation

$$y_B = y_B{}' + \delta \quad ...(12.26)$$

Again, consider a simply supported beam *AB*, propped at an intermediate point *C* (Fig. 12.26). The effect of providing a prop at *C* is to exert an upward force *P* to cancel the downward deflection of *C* due to the external loading.

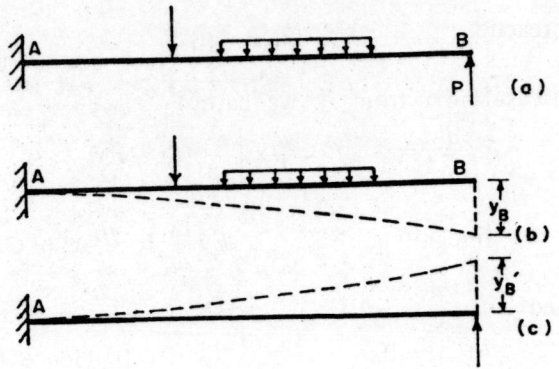

FIG. 12.25

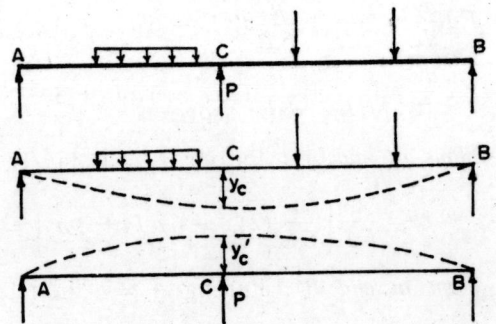

FIG. 12.26

Thus, if the prop is rigid, we have

$$y_c = y_c'$$ ...(12.25a)

If, however, the prop is not rigid, but deflects or settles by an amount δ, we have

$$y_c = y_c' + \delta$$ ...(12.26a)

Example 12.19. *A cantilever of length L, propped at the free end carries a uniformly distributed load w throughout its length. Calculate the prop reaction if (a) the prop is rigid, and (b) the prop yields by an amount λ under unit load.*

Also, plot the B.M. and S.F. diagrams for the first case and derive general equations for slope and deflection.

Solution (a) Rigid Prop

The downward deflection of B due to U.D.L., in absence of the prop, is

$$y_B = \frac{w L^4}{8 E I}$$

Upward deflection of B due to the prop reaction P, in absence of the load, is

$$y_B' = \frac{P L^3}{3 E I}$$

Equating the two, we get

$$\frac{P L^3}{3 E I} = \frac{w L^4}{8 E I}$$

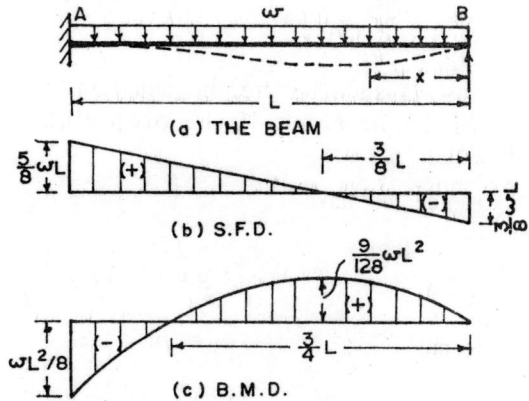

(a) THE BEAM

(b) S.F.D.

(c) B.M.D.

FIG. 12.27

From which $\qquad P = \frac{3}{8} w L$

Measuring x from B, the B.M. at any point is given by

$$M_x = + P . x - \frac{w x^2}{2} = \frac{3}{8} w L x - \frac{w x^2}{2} \quad \text{(Parabolic variation)}$$

At $x = 0$, $\qquad M_B = 0$. At $x = L , M_A = \frac{3}{8} w L^2 - \frac{w L^2}{2} = -\frac{w L^2}{8}$

The point of contraflexure is given by $\frac{3}{8} w L x - \frac{w x^2}{2} = 0$

which gives $x = \frac{3}{4} L$. The B.M. diagram is shown in Fig. 12.27(c).

S.F. at any point is given by $F_x = -P + w x = -\frac{3}{8} w L + w x$ (linear)

At $x = 0$, $\qquad F_B = -\frac{3}{8} w L$. At $x = L , F_A = -\frac{3}{8} w L + w L = +\frac{5}{8} w L$

S.F. is zero at $x = \frac{3}{8} L$. Hence maximum $+$ve B.M. occurs at this location, its value being given by

$$M_{\max} = \frac{3}{8} w L \left(\frac{3}{8} L \right) - \frac{w}{2} \left(\frac{3}{8} L \right)^2 = +\frac{9}{128} w L^2$$

Again, we have $E I \dfrac{d^2 y}{dx^2} = \dfrac{3}{8} w L x - \dfrac{w x^2}{2}$

Integrating, we get $E I \dfrac{dy}{dx} = \dfrac{3}{8} w L \dfrac{x^2}{2} - \dfrac{w x^3}{6} + C_1$

At $x = L$, $\dfrac{dy}{dx} = 0$ Hence $C_1 = \dfrac{w L^3}{6} - \dfrac{3}{16} w L (L^2) = -\dfrac{w L^3}{48}$

$\therefore$ $E I \dfrac{dy}{dx} = \dfrac{3}{8} w L \dfrac{x^2}{2} - \dfrac{w x^3}{6} - \dfrac{w L^3}{48}$ ...(I)

Integrating further, $E I y = \dfrac{3}{48} w L x^3 - \dfrac{w x^4}{24} - \dfrac{w L^3}{48} x + C_2$

At $x = 0$, $y = 0$ Hence $C_2 = 0$

$\therefore$ $E I y = \dfrac{1}{16} w L x^3 - \dfrac{w x^4}{24} - \dfrac{w L^3}{48} x$ ...(II)

Eqs (I) and (II) are the equations for slope and deflection at any point

(b) **Elastic Prop** : If the prop sinks, the sinking of the prop will be equal to $\delta = P . \lambda$

Hence we have $y_B = y_B' + \delta$

or $\dfrac{w L^4}{8 E I} = \dfrac{P L^3}{3 E I} + P \lambda = P \left(\dfrac{L^3}{3 E I} + \lambda \right)$

Hence $P = \dfrac{w L^4}{8 E I} \times \dfrac{3 E I}{(L^3 + 3 E I \lambda)} = \dfrac{3}{8} \times \dfrac{w L^4}{L^3 + 3 E I \lambda}$ **(Ans.)**

Example 12.20. *A cantilever of length L carries a concentrated load W at the mid-span. If the free end is supported on a rigid prop, find the reaction at the prop. Also, draw S.F. and B.M. diagrams for the cantilever.*

Solution :

Let P = prop reaction.

Downward deflection of end B due to load W, in the absence of the prop

$= \dfrac{W \left(\dfrac{L}{2} \right)^3}{3 E I} + \dfrac{W \left(\dfrac{L}{2} \right)^2}{2 E I} \cdot \dfrac{L}{2}$

$= \dfrac{5}{48} \dfrac{W L^3}{E I}$ ...(i)

Upward deflection of B, due to prop reaction P, in absence of the load $= \dfrac{P L^3}{3 E I}$ ...(ii)

Equating the two we get, $\dfrac{P L^3}{3 E I} = \dfrac{5}{48} \dfrac{W L^3}{E I}$

From which we get $P = \dfrac{5}{16} W$ **(Ans.)**

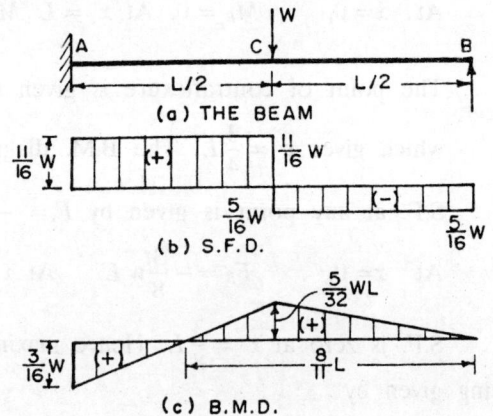

FIG. 12.28

Reaction $R_A = W - P = W - \dfrac{5}{16} W = \dfrac{11}{16} W.$

S.F.D. : For BC, $F_x = - P = - \dfrac{5}{16} W$ (constant between B and C)

For CA, $F_x = - P + W = - \dfrac{5}{16} W + W = + \dfrac{11}{16} W$, which is constant from C to A. The S.F. changes sign at C. The S.F.D. is shown in Fig. 12.28 (b).

B.M.D. For BC, $M_x = \dfrac{5}{16} W x$ (linear variation)

At $x = 0$, $M_B = 0$. At $x = \dfrac{L}{2}$, $M_C = + \dfrac{5}{16} w \cdot \dfrac{L}{2} = + \dfrac{5}{32} w L$

For CA, $M_x = \dfrac{5}{16} W x - W \left(x - \dfrac{L}{2} \right)$

At $x = L/2$, $M_c = \dfrac{5}{32} W L$, as before

At $x = L$, $M_A = \dfrac{5}{16} w L - W \left(L - \dfrac{L}{2} \right) = - \dfrac{3}{16} W L$

B.M. is zero at x given by $0 = \dfrac{5}{16} W x - W (x - L/2)$

which gives $x = \dfrac{8}{11} L$. The B.M.D. is given in Fig. 12.28(c).

Example 12.21. *A cantilever AB of length L carries a point load W at its free end. If the cantilever is propped at C, distant 3 L/4 from the fixed and, find the prop reaction, assuming that there is no deflection at C. Also, draw the B.M and S.F. diagrams for the propped cantilever.*

Solution :
Let the prop reaction be P.
Let us remove the prop. In order to find the deflection at C due to downward load W acting at B, we proceed as follows

$$E I \frac{d^2 y}{dx^2} = - M_x = W (L - x)$$

Integrating, $E I \dfrac{dy}{dx} = W \left(L x - \dfrac{x^2}{2} \right) + C_1$

At $x = 0$, $\dfrac{dy}{dx} = 0$; Hence $C_1 = 0$

Hence $E I \dfrac{dy}{dx} = W \left(L x - \dfrac{x^2}{2} \right)$

Integrating further,

$$E I y = W \left(\frac{L x^2}{2} - \frac{x^3}{6} \right) + C_2$$

At $x = 0$, $y = 0$ Hence $C_2 = 0$

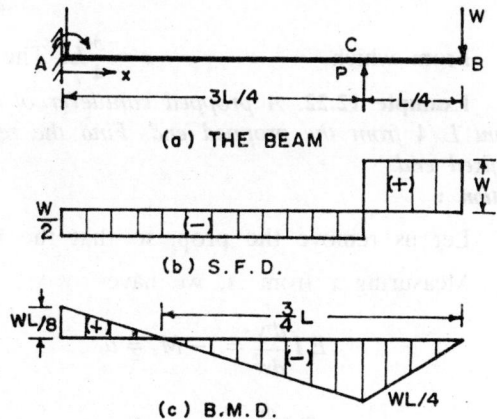

(a) THE BEAM

(b) S.F.D.

(c) B.M.D.

FIG. 12.29

$\therefore$ $E I y = W \left(\dfrac{L x^2}{2} - \dfrac{x^3}{6} \right)$, which is the equation for deflection at any point.

At $x = \dfrac{3L}{4}$, we get $y_c = \dfrac{1}{EI} W \left[\dfrac{L}{2} \left(\dfrac{3L}{4} \right)^2 - \dfrac{1}{6} \left(\dfrac{3L}{4} \right)^3 \right] = \dfrac{27}{128} \dfrac{W L^3}{EI}$ ...(i)

Now remove the external load. The upward deflection of C due to upward load P at C

$$= y_c' = \dfrac{P \left(\dfrac{3}{4} L \right)^3}{3 E I} = \dfrac{9}{64} \dfrac{P L^3}{EI} \qquad \qquad ...(ii)$$

Equating the two, we get $\dfrac{9}{64} \dfrac{P L^3}{EI} = \dfrac{27}{128} \dfrac{W L^3}{EI}$

From which we get $P = \dfrac{3}{2} W$ (Ans.)

$$R_A = W - P = W - \dfrac{3}{2} W = - \dfrac{W}{2} . \ \ (i.e. \ \dfrac{W}{2} \downarrow)$$

S.F.D. : For BC, $F_x = + W$ (constant from B to C)

For CA, $F_x = W - P = W - \dfrac{3}{2} W = - \dfrac{W}{2}$ (constant from C to A)

The S.F.D. is shown in Fig. 12.29 (b).

B.M.D. : For BC, measuring x from B,

$$M_x = - W . x \text{ which gives } M_B = 0 \text{ and } M_C = - \dfrac{W L}{4}$$

For CA, $M_x = - W x + \dfrac{3}{2} W (x - L/4)$

At $x = L$, $M_A = - W L + \dfrac{3}{2} W \left(L - \dfrac{L}{4} \right) = + \dfrac{W L}{8}$

B.M. is zero at x given by $0 = - W x + \dfrac{3}{2} W \left(x - \dfrac{L}{4} \right)$

From which $x = \dfrac{3}{4} L$. The B.M.D. is shown in Fig. 12.29(c).

Example 12.22. *A propped cantilever of span L is subjected to a couple μ at a section distant L/4 from the propped end. Find the reaction at the prop and the bending moment at the fixed end.*

Solution :

Let us remove the prop, so that the beam is subjected to only a couple at C.

Measuring x from A, we have

$$E I \dfrac{d^2 y}{dx^2} = - M_x = \mu$$

$$E I \dfrac{dy}{dx} = \mu x + C_1$$

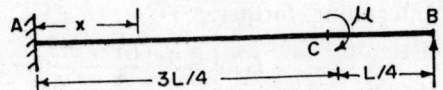

FIG. 12.30

At $\qquad x = 0, \dfrac{dy}{dx} = 0$ Hence $C_1 = 0$

$\therefore \qquad\qquad EI \dfrac{dy}{dx} = \mu x$

Integrating further, $\quad EIy = \dfrac{\mu x^2}{2} + C_2 \qquad\qquad ...(i)$

At $\quad x = 0, \qquad y = 0$ Hence $C_2 = 0$

$\therefore \qquad\qquad EIy = \dfrac{\mu x^2}{2} \qquad\qquad ...(ii)$

Hence deflection at B due to μ acting at C is given by

$$ y_B = \mu \left(\dfrac{3}{4}L\right)^2 \dfrac{1}{2EI} + \mu \left(\dfrac{3}{4}L\right) \dfrac{1}{EI} \times \dfrac{L}{4} = \dfrac{15}{32}\mu L^2 \qquad\qquad ...(a) $$

Now remove μ and put an upward force P at B. The upward deflection at B is given by,

$$ y_B' = \dfrac{PL^3}{3EI} \qquad\qquad ...(b) $$

Equating the two, we get

$$ \dfrac{PL^3}{3EI} = \dfrac{15}{32}\mu L^2 $$

From which $\qquad\qquad P = \dfrac{45}{32}\dfrac{\mu}{L} \qquad\qquad$ (Ans.)

B.M. at $A = M_A = PL - \mu = \dfrac{45}{32}\dfrac{\mu}{L}\cdot L - \mu = \dfrac{13}{32}\mu \qquad\qquad$ (Ans.)

Example 12.23. *A beam AB of length L is simply supported on two props at the ends and carries on U.D.L. of w per unit length. A prop is introduced in the middle of the beam. Calculate the beam reactions and plot the B.M.D. if the prop is rigid. Also, find the position and magnitude of the maximum deflection.*

If all the props are elastic having σ as the stiffness, calculate the reaction of the central prop.

Solution :

(a) Rigid Props

Let P be the reaction at the rigid prop. The reactions at the end will be $\dfrac{wL - P}{2}$ each.

Remove the prop. The downward deflection of C due to U.D.L. is

$$ y_c = \dfrac{5}{384}\dfrac{wL^4}{EI} \qquad ...(i) $$

Remove the U.D.L. and place upward force P at C. The upward deflection at C due to prop reaction is $y_c' = \dfrac{PL^3}{48EI} \quad ...(ii)$

Equating the two,

$$ \dfrac{PL^3}{48EI} = \dfrac{5}{384}\dfrac{wL^4}{EI} $$

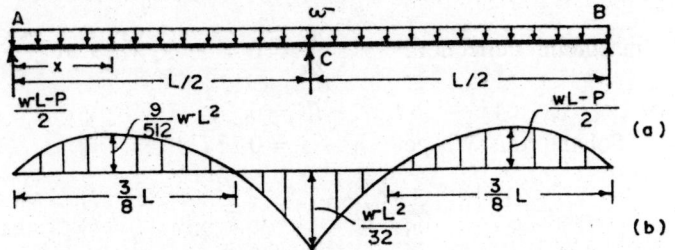

FIG. 12.31

From which $\qquad\qquad\qquad P = \dfrac{5}{8}wL$ (Ans.)

At any distance x from A, for the portion AC, we have

$$M_x = +\left(\frac{wL-P}{2}\right)x - \frac{wx^2}{2} = +\frac{3}{16}wLx - \frac{wx^2}{2}$$

This is zero at $x = 0$ and at $x = 3/8\,L$, the latter being the point of contraflexure. Maximum B.M. occurs where dM_x/dx is zero.

$\therefore\qquad\qquad\qquad \dfrac{dM_x}{dx} = 0 = \dfrac{3}{16}wL - wx$, which gives $x = \dfrac{3}{16}L$

$\therefore\qquad\qquad M_{max} = +\dfrac{3}{16}wL\left(\dfrac{3}{16}L\right) - \dfrac{w}{2}\left(\dfrac{3}{16}L\right)^2 = +\dfrac{9}{512}wL^2$

Also, at $x = \dfrac{L}{2}$, $\qquad M_c = \dfrac{3}{16}wL\left(\dfrac{L}{2}\right) - \dfrac{w}{2}\left(\dfrac{L}{2}\right)^2 = -\dfrac{wL^2}{32}$

The B.M.D. is shown in Fig. 12.31(b).

Again, $\qquad\qquad EI\dfrac{d^2y}{dx^2} = -M_x = -\left(\dfrac{wL-P}{2}\right)x + \dfrac{wx^2}{2} = -\dfrac{3}{16}wLx + \dfrac{wx^2}{2}$

Integrating $\qquad\qquad EI\dfrac{dy}{dx} = -\dfrac{3}{16}wL\dfrac{x^2}{2} + \dfrac{wx^3}{6} + C_1$ $\qquad\qquad$ ...(i)

and $\qquad\qquad EIy = -\dfrac{3}{32}\dfrac{wLx^3}{3} + \dfrac{wx^4}{24} + C_1x + C_2$ $\qquad\qquad$ ...(ii)

At $x = 0$, $\qquad\qquad y = 0$. Hence $C_2 = 0$

At $x = L/2$, $\qquad\qquad y = 0 = -\dfrac{3}{96}wL\left(\dfrac{L}{2}\right)^3 + \dfrac{w}{24}\left(\dfrac{L}{2}\right)^4 + C_1\left(\dfrac{L}{2}\right)$

From which $\qquad\qquad C_1 = \dfrac{2}{L}\left[+\dfrac{3}{96\times8}wL^4 - \dfrac{1}{24\times16}wL^4\right] = +\dfrac{wL^3}{384}$

Hence the slope and deflection equations are as follows.

$$EI\frac{dy}{dx} = -\frac{3}{32}wLx^2 + \frac{wx^3}{6} + \frac{wL^3}{384} \qquad\qquad ...(I)$$

and

$$EIy = -\frac{3}{96}wLx^3 + \frac{wx^4}{24} + \frac{wL^3}{384}x \qquad\qquad ...(II)$$

For maximum deflection, $\qquad \dfrac{dy}{dx} = 0 = -\dfrac{3}{32}wLx^2 + \dfrac{wx^3}{6} + \dfrac{wL^3}{384}$

or $\qquad\qquad\qquad 64x^3 - 36Lx^2 + L^3 = 0$

Solving this we get $\qquad\qquad x = 0.27L$

$\therefore\qquad y_{max} = \dfrac{1}{EI}\left[-\dfrac{3}{96}wL(0.27L)^3 + \dfrac{w}{24}(0.27L)^4 + \dfrac{wL^3}{384}(0.27L)\right] = \dfrac{3.095\times10^{-4}}{EI}wL^4$

or $\qquad\qquad y_{max} = \dfrac{0.0003095\,wL^4}{EI} = \dfrac{wL^4}{3231\,EI}$ $\quad$ (Ans.)

(b) *Elastic props* : Let all the three props be elastic. Now stiffness is defined as the force required to depress it by unity. The yielding of end supports $= \dfrac{wL - P}{2\sigma}$ and that of the central prop $= \dfrac{P}{\sigma}$.

Hence difference in levels of central prop and the end props is given by

$$\delta = \frac{P}{\sigma} - \frac{wL - P}{2\sigma}$$

Now for the central point C, we have the compatibility equation

$$y_c = y_c' + \delta$$

$$\therefore \qquad \frac{5}{384} \frac{wL^4}{EI} = \frac{PL^3}{48EI} + \frac{P}{\sigma} - \frac{wL - P}{2\sigma}$$

or $\qquad P \left[1 + \dfrac{48EI}{L^3\sigma} + \dfrac{48EI}{L^3 2\sigma} \right] = \dfrac{5}{384} \dfrac{wL^4}{EI} \times \dfrac{48EI}{L^3} + \dfrac{wL}{2\sigma} \times \dfrac{48EI}{L^3}$

or $\qquad P \left(1 + \dfrac{72EI}{\sigma L^3} \right) = \dfrac{5}{8} wL + \dfrac{24 wLEI}{\sigma L^3}$

$$\therefore \qquad P = \frac{wL \left[\dfrac{5}{8} + \dfrac{24EI}{\sigma L^3} \right]}{\left[1 + \dfrac{72EI}{\sigma L^3} \right]} \quad \text{Ans.}$$

Example 12.24. *A bridge across a river has a span of 2L and is constructed with beam resting on the banks and supported at the middle on a pontoon. When the bridge is unloaded, the three supports are all at the same level and the pontoon is such that the vertical displacement is equal to the load on it multiplied by a constant λ. Show that the load on the pontoon due to a concentrated load placed one quarter of the way along the bridge, is given by*

$$\frac{11\,W}{16 \left(1 + \dfrac{6EI\lambda}{L^3} \right)},$$ *where I is the moment of inertia of the section of the beam.*

Solution :

Remove the prop at C, so that only the point load is acting. From Eq. 12.23, the deflection at mid-point C due to the point load is given by

$$y_c = \frac{Wb}{48EI}(3l^2 - 4b^2), \text{ where } l = \text{span} = 2L \text{ and } b = \frac{L}{2}$$

$$\therefore \qquad y_c = \frac{W}{48EI} \left(\frac{L}{2} \right) \left[3(2L)^2 - 4 \left(\frac{L}{2} \right)^2 \right] = \frac{11\,WL^3}{96EI} \,(\downarrow) \qquad \qquad ...(i)$$

Now remove the load W and place upward load $= P$ at C. The deflection at C is given

by $y_c' = \dfrac{Pl^3}{48EI} = \dfrac{P}{48EI}(2L)^3 = \dfrac{PL^3}{6EI} \quad ...(ii)$

Downward displacement of prop $= \delta = P\lambda$

Hence $\qquad y_c = y_c' + P\lambda$

or $\qquad \dfrac{11\,WL^3}{96EI} = \dfrac{PL^3}{6EI} + P\lambda$

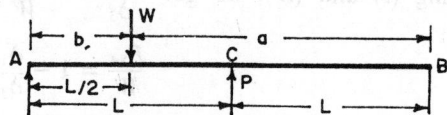

FIG. 12.32

or $\qquad P\left[1 + \dfrac{6EI\lambda}{L^3}\right] = \dfrac{11\,WL^3}{96\,EI} \times \dfrac{6EI}{L^3} = \dfrac{11}{16}\,W$

From which $\qquad P = \dfrac{11\,W}{16\left(1 + \dfrac{6EI\lambda}{L^3}\right)}$. Hence proved.

Example 12.25 (a). *Fig. 12.33 shows two cantilevers, the end of one being vertically above the other, and its connected to it by a spring AB.*

Initially, the system is unstrained. A weight W, placed at A, causes a vertical deflection at A of δ_1 and a vertical deflection at B of δ_2. When the spring is removed, the weight W at A causes a deflection at A of δ_3. Find the extension of the spring, when it is replaced and the weight W is transferred to B.

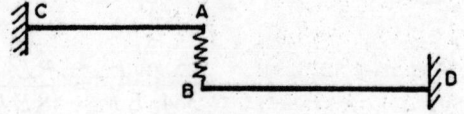

FIG. 12.33

Solution :

Let $\qquad L_1$ = length of cantilever CA ; L_2 = length of cantilever DB,

δ_4 = deflection of A with load at B ; δ_5 = deflection of B with load at B.

Given : δ_1 = deflection of A with load at A, with spring in position.

δ_2 = deflection of B with load at A, with spring in position

δ_3 = deflection of A with load at A, without spring.

When the load is at A, let P_{SA} be the force in the spring. When the load is at B, let P_{SB} be the force in the spring.

$\therefore \qquad \delta_1 = \dfrac{(W - P_{SA})\,L_1^3}{3EI}$ $\qquad\qquad$ ...(i)

and $\qquad \delta_2 = \dfrac{P_{SA}\,L_2^3}{3EI}$ $\qquad$ or $\qquad \dfrac{\delta_2}{P_{SA}} = \dfrac{L_2^3}{3EI}$ $\qquad$ ...(ii)

Compression of spring $\qquad AB = \delta_1 - \delta_2$

$\therefore \qquad$ Stiffness of spring $= s = \dfrac{\text{force}}{\text{compression}} = \dfrac{P_{SA}}{\delta_1 - \delta_2}$ $\qquad$ ...(iii)

Again, when the spring is removed, and load W is placed at A,

Deflection of $A =$ $\qquad \delta_3 = \dfrac{WL_1^3}{3EI}$ $\qquad$ or $\qquad \dfrac{\delta_3}{W} = \dfrac{L_1^3}{3EI}$ $\qquad$ ...(iv)

Dividing (i) and (iv), we get $\dfrac{\delta_1}{\delta_3} = \dfrac{W - P_{SA}}{W} = 1 - \dfrac{P_{SA}}{W}$

or $\qquad \dfrac{P_{SA}}{W} = 1 - \dfrac{\delta_1}{\delta_3} = \dfrac{\delta_3 - \delta_1}{\delta_3}$

or $\qquad P_{SA} = \dfrac{W(\delta_3 - \delta_1)}{\delta_3}$ $\qquad\qquad$ ...(v)

Substituting this value of P_{SA} in Eq. (iii), we get

$$s = \frac{W (\delta_3 - \delta_1)}{\delta_3 (\delta_1 - \delta_2)} \qquad \qquad ...(vi)$$

When the cantilever BD is loaded with W at B, the deflection of B is given by

$$\delta_5 = \frac{(W - P_{SB}) L_2^3}{3 E I}$$

and deflection of A is given by $\delta_4 = \dfrac{P_{SB} L_1^3}{3 E I} = \dfrac{P_{SB} \delta_3}{W}$ (from iv).

Substituting the values of $\dfrac{L_2^3}{3 E I}$ (from ii), and P_{SA} (from v), we get

$$\delta_5 = \frac{(W - P_{SB}) \delta_2}{P_{SA}} = \frac{(W - P_{SB}) \delta_2 \delta_3}{W (\delta_3 - \delta_1)} \qquad \qquad ...(vii)$$

Now stiffness $\qquad\qquad s = \dfrac{\text{force}}{\text{extension}} = \dfrac{P_{SB}}{\delta_5 - \delta_4}$

$\therefore \qquad\qquad \delta_5 - \delta_4 = \dfrac{P_{SB}}{s} = \dfrac{P_{SB} \cdot \delta_3 (\delta_1 - \delta_2)}{W (\delta_3 - \delta_1)}$ (from vi) $\qquad ...(I)$

But $\qquad \delta_5 - \delta_4 = \dfrac{(W - P_{SB}) \delta_2 \delta_3}{W (\delta_3 - \delta_1)} - \dfrac{P_{SB} \delta_3}{W} = \dfrac{\delta_3}{W} \left[\dfrac{(W - P_{SB}) \delta_2}{\delta_3 - \delta_1} - P_{SB} \right] \qquad ...(II)$

Equating (I) and (II), we get

$$\frac{P_{SB} \cdot \delta_3 (\delta_1 - \delta_2)}{W (\delta_3 - \delta_1)} = \frac{\delta_3}{W} \left[\frac{(W - P_{SB}) \delta_2}{\delta_3 - \delta_1} - P_{SB} \right]$$

or $\qquad\qquad \dfrac{P_{SB} (\delta_1 - \delta_2)}{\delta_3 - \delta_1} = \dfrac{(W - P_{SB}) \delta_2 - P_{SB} (\delta_3 - \delta_1)}{\delta_3 - \delta_1}$

or $\qquad\qquad P_{SB} \delta_1 - P_{SB} \delta_2 = W \delta_2 - P_{SB} \cdot \delta_2 - P_{SB} \delta_3 + P_{SB} \delta_1$

or $\qquad W \delta_2 = P_{SB} \cdot \delta_3$ from which $P_{SB} = \dfrac{W \delta_2}{\delta_3}$. Substituting the value of P_{SB} in (I), we get

$$\delta_5 - \delta_4 = \frac{\dfrac{W \delta_2}{\delta_3} \cdot \delta_3 (\delta_1 - \delta_2)}{W (\delta_3 - \delta_1)} = \frac{\delta_2 (\delta_1 - \delta_2)}{\delta_3 - \delta_1} \text{ (Ans.)}$$

Example 12.25 (b). *A cantilever AB, loaded at the end B is supported by a short cantilever CD of the same cross-section as cantilever AB (Fig. 12.34). Prove that pressure X between the two beams at C is given by*

$$X = \frac{3 P}{4} \left(\frac{L}{L_1} - \frac{1}{3} \right)$$

Solution :

When the two cantilevers bend due to load P, the upper cantilever will have large angular. deflection than the lower one. Due to this, both the cantilevers will have contact only at points D and C. Let the pressure between the two cantilevers at point C be X.

For the cantilever AB : A point load P acts downward at B and a pressure X acts upwards at point C (Fig. 12.34 b). Let y_{c_1} be the downward deflection of C due to load P and y_{c_2} be the upward deflection of C due to force X. In order to find y_{c_1} (*i.e.* deflection of C due to load P), let us measure x from A.

Then $E I \dfrac{d^2 y}{dx^2} = - M_x = P(L-x)$

$\therefore \qquad E I \dfrac{dy}{dx} = P\left(Lx - \dfrac{x^2}{2}\right) + 0$

(since $\dfrac{dy}{dx} = 0$ at $x = 0$)

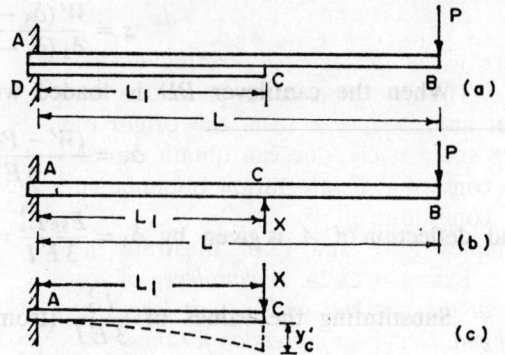

FIG. 12.34

and $\qquad E I y = P\left(\dfrac{Lx^2}{2} - \dfrac{x^3}{6}\right) + 0$, since $y = 0$ at $x = 0$

Hence $\qquad E I y_{c_1} = P\left(\dfrac{L L_1^2}{2} - \dfrac{L_1^3}{6}\right)$ $\;(\downarrow)$ ...(i)

Also, deflection y_{c_2} of C due to upward pressure X on cantilever AB is

$$y_{c_2} = \frac{X L_1^3}{3 E I} \;(\uparrow) \qquad\qquad\qquad ...(ii)$$

$\therefore \qquad$ Net deflection of $C = y_c = y_{c_1} - y_{c_2} = \dfrac{P}{E I}\left(\dfrac{L L_1^2}{2} - \dfrac{L_1^3}{6}\right) - \dfrac{X L_1^3}{3 E I}$ (downwards)

For the cantilever AC : A force X acts downwards at C (Fig. 12.34 c)

$\therefore \qquad$ Downward deflection of $C = y_c' = \dfrac{X L_1^3}{3 E I}$ $\;(\downarrow)$

Since both the cantilevers are in contact at C, we have

$$\frac{P}{E I}\left(\frac{L L_1^2}{2} - \frac{L_1^3}{6}\right) - \frac{X L_1^3}{3 E I} = \frac{X L_1^3}{3 E I}$$

or $\qquad\qquad\qquad \dfrac{2 X L_1^3}{3 E I} = \dfrac{P L_1^3}{2 E I}\left(\dfrac{L}{L_1} - \dfrac{1}{3}\right)$

From which $\qquad X = \dfrac{3 P}{4}\left(\dfrac{L}{L_1} - \dfrac{1}{3}\right)$...(Proved)

12.8. VARIABLE LOADING ON BEAM OF UNIFORM SECTION

We have the differential equation

$$E I \frac{d^2 y}{dx^2} = - M_x$$

Differentiating it, we get $\qquad E I \dfrac{d^3 y}{dx^3} = - \dfrac{d M_x}{dx} = - F_x$ ...(12.27)

Differentiating it Further, $EI\dfrac{d^4y}{dx^4} = -\dfrac{dF_x}{dx} = w_x$ ...(12.28)

where w_x is the rate of loading at the point.

Thus, when a beam is loaded with non-uniformly distributed load, the rate of loading w_x at any distance x from the origin can be written and Eq. 12.28 obtained. Integrating Eq. 12.28 successively, one can obtain expressions for S.F., B.M., slope and deflection at any point. The constants of integration obtained in this process can be easily evaluated by knowing the end conditions.

Examples 12.26 and 12.27 illustrate the procedure.

Example 12.26. *A cantilever of length L is loaded with uniformly varying load of intensity zero at the free end and w/unit length at the fixed end. Derive an expression for the deflection at any point. Find also the slope and deflection of the free end.*

Solution :

At any distance x from the free end B,

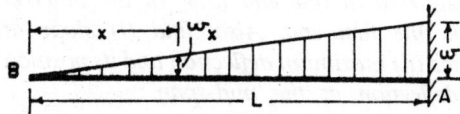

FIG. 12.35

$$EI\dfrac{d^4y}{dx^4} = \text{rate of loading, } w_x = \dfrac{w \cdot x}{L}$$

Integrating, $\qquad EI\dfrac{d^3y}{dx^3} = -F_x = \dfrac{w x^2}{2L} + C_1$

At $x=0$, $\qquad F_B = 0$. Hence $C_1 = 0$

$\therefore \qquad EI\dfrac{d^3y}{dx^3} = -F_x = \dfrac{w x^2}{2L}$

Integrating further, $\quad EI\dfrac{d^2y}{dx^2} = -M_x = \dfrac{wx^3}{6L} + C_2$

At $x=0$, $\qquad M_B = 0$. Hence $C_2 = 0$

$\therefore \qquad EI\dfrac{d^2y}{dx^2} = \dfrac{w x^3}{6L}$ ...(1)

Alternatively, from Fig. 12.35, $\quad M_x = -\dfrac{1}{2}w_x \cdot x \cdot \dfrac{x}{3} = -\dfrac{w_x \cdot x^2}{6} = -\dfrac{w x^3}{6L}$

Hence $\qquad EI\dfrac{d^2y}{dx^2} = -M_x = \dfrac{w x^3}{6L}$ ...(1)

Integrating further, $\quad EI\dfrac{dy}{dx} = \dfrac{w x^4}{24L} + C_3$

At $x=L$, $\qquad \dfrac{dy}{dx} = 0 = \dfrac{wL^4}{24L} + C_3$, from which $C_3 = -\dfrac{wL^3}{24}$

Hence $\qquad EI\dfrac{dy}{dx} = \dfrac{w x^4}{24L} - \dfrac{w L^3}{24}$ ...(I)

Integrating further, $\quad EIy = \dfrac{w x^5}{120L} - \dfrac{w L^3}{24}x + C_4$

At $x=L$, $\qquad y = 0 = \dfrac{w L^5}{120L} - \dfrac{w L^3}{24}L + C_4$, from which $C_4 = \dfrac{wL^4}{30}$

Hence
$$E I y = \frac{w x^5}{120 L} - \frac{w L^3}{24} x + \frac{w L^4}{30} \qquad \qquad \text{...(II)}$$

Eqs. (I) and (II) are the required expressions.
For slope at free end, put $x = 0$ in (I)

Hence
$$i_B = \frac{1}{E I} \left[- \frac{w L^3}{24} \right] = - \frac{w L^3}{24 E I}$$

Also, for deflection at the free end, put $x = 0$ in (II)

$$\therefore \qquad y_B = \frac{1}{E I} \left(\frac{w L^4}{30} \right) = \frac{w L^4}{30 E I}$$

Example 12.27. *A simply supported beam of length L carries uniformly varying load of intensity zero at one end to w at the other end. Derive an expression of the deflection at a point x from the first end. Also, find (i) slope at the ends (ii) maximum deflection and its position (iii) deflection at the mid-span.*

Solution :

$$R_A = \frac{1}{L} \left(\frac{w L}{2} \times \frac{L}{3} \right) = \frac{w L}{6}$$

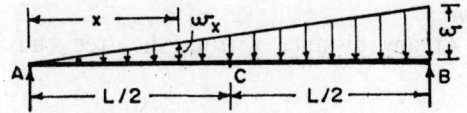

FIG. 12.36

Measuring x from end A,

$$E I \frac{d^4 y}{dx^4} = w_x = \frac{w x}{L}$$

Integrating,
$$E I \frac{d^3 y}{dx^3} = - F_x = \frac{w x^2}{2 L} + C_1$$

At $x = 0$,
$$F_x = R_A = \frac{w L}{6}. \quad \text{Hence } C_1 = - \frac{w L}{6}$$

$$\therefore \qquad E I \frac{d^3 y}{dx^3} = \frac{w x^2}{2 L} - \frac{w L}{6}$$

Integrating further,
$$E I \frac{d^2 y}{dx^2} = - M_x = \frac{w x^3}{6 L} - \frac{w L x}{6} + C_2$$

At $x = 0$,
$$M_x = M_A = 0. \quad \text{Hence } C_2 = 0$$

$$\therefore \qquad E I \frac{d^2 y}{dx^2} = \frac{w x^3}{6 L} - \frac{w L x}{6} \qquad \qquad \text{...(1)}$$

Alternatively, we can also obtain Eq. (1) directly as under :

$$E I \frac{d^2 y}{dx^2} = - M_x = - \left(\frac{w L}{6} x - \frac{1}{2} \frac{w x}{L} \cdot x \cdot \frac{x}{3} \right) = \frac{w x^3}{6 L} - \frac{w L x}{6} \qquad \text{...(1)}$$

Integrating,
$$E I \frac{dy}{dx} = \frac{w x^4}{24 L} - \frac{w L x^2}{12} + C_3 \qquad \qquad \text{...(2)}$$

and
$$E I y = \frac{w x^5}{120 L} - \frac{w L x^3}{36} + C_3 x + C_4 \qquad \qquad \text{...(3)}$$

At $x = 0$,
$$y = 0. \quad \text{Hence } C_4 = 0$$

At $x = L$,
$$y = 0 = \frac{w L^5}{120 L} - \frac{w L \cdot L^3}{36} + C_3 L \quad \text{from which } C_3 = \frac{7}{360} w L^3$$

Hence the slope and deflection equations are as under :

$$E I \frac{dy}{dx} = \frac{w x^4}{24 L} - \frac{w L x^2}{12} + \frac{7}{360} w L^3 \qquad \qquad ...(I)$$

and

$$E I y = \frac{w x^5}{120 L} - \frac{w L x^3}{36} + \frac{7}{360} w L^3 x \qquad \qquad ...(II)$$

Substituting $x = 0$ in (I), we get $i_A = \dfrac{7 w L^3}{360 E I}$

Substituting $x = L$ in (II), we get $i_B = \dfrac{1}{E I} \left[\dfrac{w L^4}{24 L} - \dfrac{w L . L^2}{12} + \dfrac{7}{360} w L^3 \right] = - \dfrac{w L^3}{45 E I}$

Again, substituting $x = L/2$ in II, we get

$$E I y_c = \frac{w}{120 L} \left(\frac{L}{2} \right)^5 - \frac{w L}{36} \left(\frac{L}{2} \right)^3 + \frac{7}{360} w L^3 \left(\frac{L}{2} \right)$$

or

$$y_c = \frac{1}{E I} \left[\frac{w L^4}{120 \times 32} - \frac{w L^4}{36 \times 8} + \frac{7 w L^4}{360 \times 2} \right] = \frac{5}{768} \frac{w L^4}{E I} = 0.00651 \frac{w L^4}{E I}$$

To find maximum deflection, equate (I) to zero.

$$\therefore \quad \frac{w x^4}{24 L} - \frac{w L x^2}{12} + \frac{7}{360} w L^3 = 0$$

The solution of which gives $x = \mathbf{0.519 L}$

Substituting this value of x in (I), we get

$$E I y_{max} = \frac{w}{120 L} (0.519 L)^5 - \frac{w L}{36} (0.519 L)^3 + \frac{7}{360} w L^3 (0.519 L)$$

which gives $\qquad y_{max} = 0.00652 \dfrac{w L^4}{E I}$

Again, we find that y_{max} and y_c are almost equal. The same observation was made while dealing with an eccentric point load on a simply supported beam. *Hence in simply supported beam, the central deflection is a close approximation of maximum deflection, irrespective of type and location of loading.*

12.9. BEAM OF VARIABLE CROSS-SECTION

If the beam is of variable cross-section and its moment of inertia I_x at any point x can be expressed by some law, the usual differential equation $E I \dfrac{d^2 y}{dx^2} = - M_x$ can be rearranged in the following form :

$$E \frac{d^2 y}{dx^2} = - \frac{M_x}{I_x} \qquad \qquad ...(12.29)$$

In the above expression, both M_x and I_x are the functions of x.

The expression can be integrated successively to get slope and deflection at any point.

If, however, the moment of inertia does not vary according to some law, but its value is different for different segment, the expression can be used separately for separate portions of its length, I being constant for a particular segment of the beam. In this procedure, the origin is selected at one end of a beam and integrations are completed until i and y are obtained for first segment. These values of i and y at the *end* of the first segment become *initial constants* for the next segment. This process is repeated until the far end of the beam is reached, where the unknown constants are determined from the boundary conditions. *A new origin of x is used at every juncture of the segments.* However, the problem can be solved more conveniently by the area moment method discussed in the next chapter.

Example 12.28. *A cantilever L carries a point load W at the free end. If the moment of inertia of the section increases uniformly from I at the free end to 2 I at the fixed end, calculate the deflection of the free end.*

Solution :

At any distance x from the free end,

$$I_x = I\left(1 + \frac{x}{L}\right)$$

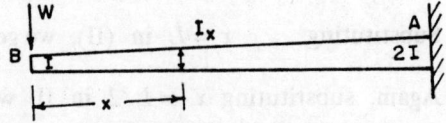

FIG. 12.37

Now

$$E\frac{d^2y}{dx^2} = -\frac{M_x}{I_x} = \frac{W.x}{I\left(1 + \frac{x}{L}\right)} = \frac{wL}{I}\frac{\dfrac{x}{L}}{\left(1 + \dfrac{x}{L}\right)}$$

or

$$E\frac{d^2y}{dx^2} = \frac{WL}{I}\left[1 - \frac{1}{1 + \dfrac{x}{L}}\right] = \frac{WL}{I} - \frac{WL}{I}\frac{1}{1 + \dfrac{x}{L}}$$

Integrating,

$$E\frac{dy}{dx} = \frac{WL}{I}x - \frac{WL^2}{I}\log_e\left(1 + \frac{x}{L}\right) + C_1$$

At $x = L$,

$$E\frac{dy}{dx} = 0 = \frac{WL}{I}.L - \frac{WL^2}{I}\log_e 2 + C_1$$

From which

$$C_1 = -\frac{WL^2}{I}\left(1 - \log_e 2\right)$$

Hence

$$E\frac{dy}{dx} = \frac{WL}{I}x - \frac{WL^2}{I}\log_e\left(1 + \frac{x}{L}\right) - \frac{WL^2}{I}\left(1 - \log_e 2\right)$$

Integrating again, $E y = \dfrac{WLx^2}{2I} - \dfrac{WL^2}{I}\left[x\log_e\left(1 + \dfrac{x}{L}\right) - \int \dfrac{x}{L}\dfrac{1}{1 + \dfrac{x}{L}}dx\right] - \dfrac{WL^2}{I}(1 - \log_e 2)x + C_2$

or $E y = \dfrac{WLx^2}{2I} - \dfrac{WL^2}{I}\left[x\log_e\left(1 + \dfrac{x}{L}\right) - \int\left\{1 - \dfrac{1}{1 + \dfrac{x}{L}}\right\}dx\right] - \dfrac{WL^2}{I}\left(1 - \log_e 2\right)x + C_2$

or $E y = \dfrac{WLx^2}{2I} - \dfrac{WL^2}{I}\left[x\log_e\left(1 + \dfrac{x}{L}\right) - x + L\log_e\left(1 + \dfrac{x}{L}\right)\right] - \dfrac{WL^2}{I}\left(1 - \log_e 2\right)x + C_2$

At the fixed end (*i.e.* $x = L$), deflection $y = 0$. Hence

$$0 = \frac{WL^3}{2I} - \frac{WL^2}{I}\left[L\log_e 2 - L + L\log_e 2\right] - \frac{WL^3}{I}\left(1 - \log_e 2\right) + C_2$$

From which $C_2 = -\dfrac{WL^3}{2I} + \dfrac{WL^2}{I}\left[L\log_e 2 - L + L\log_e 2 + L - L\log_e 2\right]$

or $$C_2 = -\frac{WL^3}{2I} + \frac{WL^3}{I} \log_e 2 = \frac{WL^3}{I} (\log_e 2 - 0.5)$$

Hence $$E y = \frac{WLx^2}{2I} - \frac{WL^2}{I}\left[x \log_e \left(1 + \frac{x}{L}\right) - x + L \log_e \left(1 + \frac{x}{L}\right)\right]$$

$$-\frac{WL^2}{I}(1 - \log_e 2) x + \frac{WL^3}{I}(\log_e 2 - 0.5)$$

At the free end B, $x = 0$. Hence deflection of end B is given by

$$y_B = \frac{1}{E}\left[\frac{WL^3}{I}(\log_e 2 - 0.5)\right] = \frac{WL^3}{EI}(\log_e 2 - 0.5) = \mathbf{0.1931}\frac{WL^3}{EI} \text{ (Ans.)}$$

Example 12.29. *A freely supported beam of span L carries a central load W. The sectional area of the beam is so designed that the moment of inertia of section increases uniformly from I at the ends to 1.5 I at the middle. Calculate the central deflection.*

Solution :

At any section x from A,

$$I_x = I + 0.5 I \frac{2x}{L} = I\left(1 + \frac{x}{L}\right)$$

Hence $$E\frac{d^2y}{dx^2} = -\frac{M_x}{I_x} = -\frac{\dfrac{W}{2}x}{I\left(1 + \dfrac{x}{L}\right)}$$

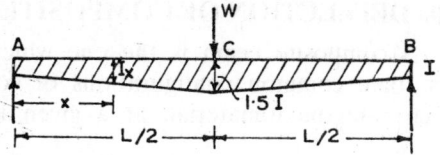

FIG. 12.38

$$= -\frac{W}{2I}\left[\frac{L\left(1 + \dfrac{x}{L}\right) - L}{1 + \dfrac{x}{L}}\right]$$

or $$E\frac{d^2y}{dx^2} = -\frac{WL}{2I} + \frac{WL}{2I\left(1 + \dfrac{x}{L}\right)}$$

Integrating, $$E\frac{dy}{dx} = -\frac{WLx}{2I} + \frac{WL^2}{2I}\log_e\left(1 + \frac{x}{L}\right) + C_1$$

At $$x = \frac{L}{2}, \frac{dy}{dx} = 0 = -\frac{WL}{2I}\left(\frac{L}{2}\right) + \frac{WL^2}{2I}\log_e\left(1 + \frac{x}{L}\right) + C_1,$$

from which $$C_1 = \frac{WL^2}{4I} - \frac{wL^2}{2I}\log_e 1.5$$

Hence $$E\frac{dy}{dx} = -\frac{WLx}{2I} + \frac{WL^2}{4I} + \frac{WL^2}{2I}\log_e\frac{2}{3}\left(1 + \frac{x}{L}\right) \qquad \dots(I)$$

Integrating again, $$E y = -\frac{WLx^2}{4I} + \frac{WL^2 x}{4I} + \frac{WL^2}{2I}\left[x \log_e\frac{2}{3}\left(1 + \frac{x}{L}\right) - \int \frac{\dfrac{2}{3}\dfrac{x}{L}}{\dfrac{2}{3}\left(1 + \dfrac{x}{L}\right)}dx\right] + C_2$$

or $\qquad Ey = -\dfrac{WLx^2}{4I} + \dfrac{WL^2x}{4I} + \dfrac{WL^2}{2I}\left[x\log_e\dfrac{2}{3}\left(1+\dfrac{x}{L}\right) - \int\left\{1 - \dfrac{1}{1+\dfrac{x}{L}}\right\}dx\right] + C_2$

or $\qquad Ey = -\dfrac{WLx^2}{4I} + \dfrac{WL^2x}{4I} + \dfrac{WL^2}{2I}\left[x\log_e\dfrac{2}{3}\left(1+\dfrac{x}{L}\right) - x + L\log_e\left(1+\dfrac{x}{L}\right)\right] + C_2$

At $x = 0$, $y = 0$. Hence $C_2 = 0$

Hence $\qquad Ey = -\dfrac{WLx^2}{4I} + \dfrac{WL^2x}{4I} + \dfrac{WL^2}{2I}\left[x\log_e\dfrac{2}{3}\left(1+\dfrac{x}{L}\right) - x + L\log_e\left(1+\dfrac{x}{L}\right)\right]$

Hence the central deflection at $x = L/2$ is given by

$$Ey_c = -\frac{WL}{4I}\left(\frac{L}{2}\right)^2 + \frac{WL^2}{4I}\left(\frac{L}{2}\right) + \frac{WL^2}{2I}\left[\frac{L}{2}\log_e\frac{2}{3}\left(1+\frac{1}{2}\right) - \frac{L}{2} + L\log_e\left(1+\frac{1}{2}\right)\right]$$

$$= -\frac{WL^3}{16I} + \frac{WL^3}{8I} - \frac{WL^3}{4I} + \frac{WL^3}{2I}\log\frac{3}{2} = -\frac{3}{16}\frac{WL^3}{I} + 0.2075\frac{WL^3}{I}$$

Hence $\qquad y_c = 0.02\dfrac{WL^3}{EI}$ **(Ans.)**

12.10. DEFLECTION OF COMPOSITE BEAMS

A composite beam is the one which is made up of two or more materials. Fig. 12.39 shows some common configurations of composite beams. For such a section, the deflection of each component/material, at a given location, will be the same.

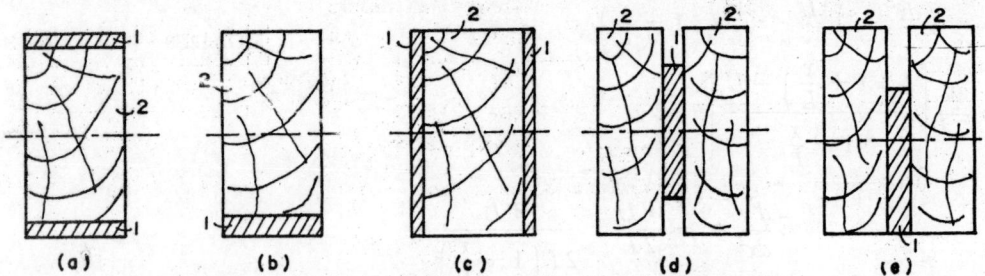

FIG. 12.39. BEAMS OF COMPOSITE SECTION

The method of finding the slope and deflection of such beams is exactly the same as used for beam of one single material. However, the *flexural rigidity* (*EI*) of such a composite beam is found by adding the flexural rigidities of each individual material. Thus, for the beam shown in Fig. 12.39,

$$\Sigma\,EI = E_1I_1 + E_2I_2 \qquad\qquad ...(12.30)$$

Example 12.30. *A composite beam consists of a timber section 120 mm wide and 240 mm deep. It is strengthened with steel plate 120 mm wide and 20 mm thick, fixed at the top and the bottom. The composite beam is simply supported over a span of 5 metres and carries a concentrated load of 100 kN at the midspan. Compute the maximum deflection of the beam under the load. Take E for steel and timber as $2 \times 10^5\,N/mm^2$ and $0.1 \times 10^5\,N/mm^2$ respectively.*

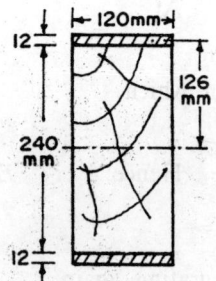

FIG. 12.40

Solution :

$$(E\,I)_{timber} = 0.1 \times 10^5 \left[\frac{1}{12} \times 120 \,(240)^3 \right] = 138.2 \times 10^{10} \text{ N-mm}^2$$

$$(E\,I)_{steel} = 2 \times 10^5 \left[2 \left\{ \frac{1}{12} \times 120 \,(12)^3 + 120 \times 12 \,(126)^2 \right\} \right] = 915.1 \times 10^{10} \text{ N-mm}^2$$

$$\therefore \qquad \Sigma E\,I = 138.2 \times 10^{10} + 915.1 \times 10^{10} = 1053.3 \times 10^{10} \text{ N-mm}^2$$

Now, for a beam with central point load, the maximum deflection occurs at the mid-span and its magnitude is given by

$$y_c = \frac{W L^3}{48\,\Sigma E\,I} = \frac{(100 \times 1000)\,(5)^3}{48 \times 1053.3 \times 10^{10}} \times (1000)^3 = \mathbf{24.72 \text{ mm}}$$

12.11. RELATION BETWEEN MAXIMUM STRESS AND MAXIMUM DEFLECTION

Example 12.31. *A simply supported beam of span L carries a uniformly distributed load W. Find the ratio of maximum deflection to maximum stress.*

Solution : Both maximum B.M. and maximum deflection will occur at the mid span C. Let δ be the maximum deflection and f be the maximum stress.

Now M_{max} (at C) $= \dfrac{w L^2}{8} = \dfrac{W L}{8}$

$$\therefore \qquad f = \frac{M}{Z} = \frac{W L}{8} \times \frac{y_{max}}{I} = \frac{W L}{8} \times \frac{d}{2\,I}$$

$$= \frac{W L\,d}{16\,I} \qquad \dots(i)$$

Also, $\qquad \delta = \dfrac{5}{384} \dfrac{w L^4}{E\,I} = \dfrac{5}{384} \times \dfrac{W L^3}{E\,I} \quad \dots(ii)$

$$\therefore \qquad \frac{\delta}{f} = \frac{5}{384} \frac{W L^3}{E\,I} \times \frac{16\,I}{W L\,d} = \frac{5 L^2}{24\,E\,d} \quad \text{(Ans.)}$$

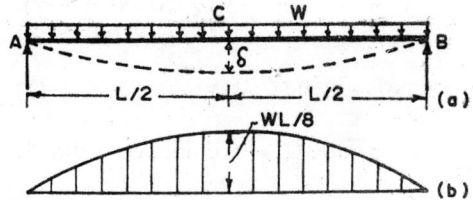

FIG. 12.41

Example 12.32. *A beam of uniform section, span L, is subjected to a constant bending moment M. Find the ratio of the maximum deflection to the maximum stress.*

Solution :

When the beam is subjected to constant bending moment M, it bends into a circular arc of radius R, which is constant all along its length, as shown in Fig. 12.42. From the property of the circle, the central deflection δ is given by

$$\delta \cdot 2 R = \frac{L}{2} \cdot \frac{L}{2} \qquad \text{or} \quad \delta = \frac{L^2}{2 R}$$

But $\dfrac{1}{R} = \dfrac{M}{E\,I}$. Hence $\delta = \dfrac{L^2}{8} \cdot \dfrac{M}{E\,I} \qquad \dots(i)$

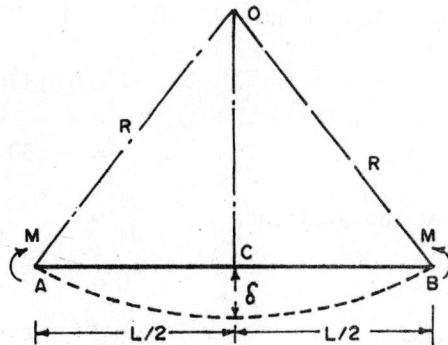

FIG. 12.42

Also, $$f = \frac{M}{Z} = \frac{M}{I} \cdot \frac{d}{2} = \frac{Md}{2I}$$ ...(ii)

$\therefore$ $$\frac{\delta}{f} = \frac{L^2 M}{8EI} \times \frac{2I}{Md} = \frac{L^2}{4Ed} \quad \textbf{(Ans.)}$$

12.12. ADDITIONAL ILLUSTRATIVE EXAMPLES

Example 12.33. *A cantilever of uniform length is to be turned from a mild steel bar 60 mm in diameter. A load of 10 kN is to be supported from the free end, and the maximum stress is to be limited to 150 N/mm². Determine the maximum permissible length of the cantilever and the deflection at the end, when it is loaded. Take $E = 2 \times 10^5 \, N/mm^2$.*

Solution :

At any distance x from the fixed end,

$$M_x = W(L - x) = f Z_x = f \frac{\pi}{32} D_x^3$$

$\therefore$ $$D_x^3 = \frac{32 \, W (L - x)}{\pi f} = \frac{32 \times 10000 \, (L - x)}{\pi \times 150}$$

or $$D_x^3 = 679 \, (L - x) \qquad ...(1)$$

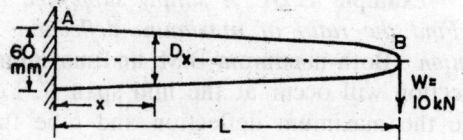

FIG. 12.43

At $x = 0, D_A = 60$. Hence from 1, $(60)^3 = 679 \, (L - 0)$, from which $L = \textbf{318.1 mm}$

Now $$E \frac{d^2 y}{dx^2} = -\frac{M_x}{I_x} = \frac{W(L - x) \, 64}{\pi D_x^4} = \frac{64 \, W (L - x)}{\pi \times 679 \, (L - x) \, D_x}$$

or $$E \frac{d^2 y}{dx^2} = 0.03 \, W D_x^{-1} \qquad ...(2)$$

Now from (1), $$L - x = \frac{D_x^3}{679} = \frac{8 u^3}{679} \quad \text{where } u = \frac{D_x}{2}$$

$\therefore$ $$x = L - \frac{8 u^3}{679} \quad \text{and} \quad \frac{dx}{du} = -\frac{24 u^2}{679} = -0.0353 \, u^2 \qquad ...(3)$$

Integrating (2) we have $$E \frac{dy}{dx} = \int 0.03 \, W D_x^{-1} dx = 0.03 \, W \int \frac{1}{2u} dx$$

$$= 0.015 \, W \int \frac{1}{u} \cdot \frac{dx}{du} \cdot du = 0.015 \, W \int \frac{1}{u} \left(-0.0353 \, u^2 \right) dx$$

$$= -530 \times 10^{-6} \, W \int u \, du = -530 \times 10^{-6} \, W \left(\frac{u^2}{2} \right) + C_1$$

At the fixed end, $$\frac{dy}{dx} = 0, \quad \text{and} \quad u = \frac{D_x}{2} = \frac{60}{2} = 30$$

$\therefore$ $$0 = -\frac{530 \times 10^{-6}}{2} \, W (30)^2 + C_1, \text{ from which } C_1 = 0.2386 \, W$$

Hence $$E \frac{dy}{dx} = -265 \times 10^{-6} \, W u^2 + 0.2386 \, W$$

Integrating, $$Ey = -265 \times 10^{-6} \, W \int (u^2 - 900.4) \frac{dx}{du} \cdot du$$

$$= -265 \times 10^{-6} W \int (u^2 - 900.4)(-0.0353\,u^2)\,du$$

$$= 9.3545 \times 10^{-6} W \int (u^4 - 900.4\,u^2)\,du$$

$$= 9.3545 \times 10^{-6} W \left[\frac{u^5}{5} - \frac{900.4\,u^3}{3} \right] + C_2$$

At fixed end A, $y = 0$ and $u = \dfrac{D_x}{2} = 30$

$\therefore \qquad 0 = 9.3545 \times 10^{-6} W \left[\dfrac{(30)^5}{5} - \dfrac{900.4}{3}(30)^3 \right] + C_2$, from which $C_2 = 30.34\,W$

Hence $\qquad Ey = 9.3545 \times 10^{-6} W \left(\dfrac{u^5}{5} - \dfrac{900.4\,u^3}{3} \right) + 30.34\,W$

At the free end, $u = 0$

Hence $\qquad E\,y_B = 30.34\,W$

From which $\qquad y_B = \dfrac{30.34\,W}{E} = \dfrac{30.34 \times 10000}{2 \times 10^5} = \mathbf{1.52\ mm}$

Example 12.34. *A beam ACB, supported at the ends, has moment of inertia 4I for the length AC and I for the length CB, and is loaded with a point load W at C. Determine (i), slope at the end A (ii) deflection at mid-span and (iii) maximum deflection.*
Compute the numerical values if $W = 16\,kN$, $a = 1.5\,m$, $I = 2500\,cm^4$ and $E = 2 \times 10^5\,N/mm^2$

Solution :

$$R_A = \frac{Wa}{5a} = \frac{W}{5} \qquad \text{and} \qquad R_B = \frac{4aW}{5a} = \frac{4}{5}W$$

For portion AC :
Measuring x from A,

$$E\frac{d^2y}{dx^2} = -\frac{1}{4I}\left(\frac{W}{5}x \right)$$

Integrating,

$$E\frac{dy}{dx} = -\frac{W}{20I}\frac{x^2}{2} + C_1 \qquad \text{...(1a)}$$

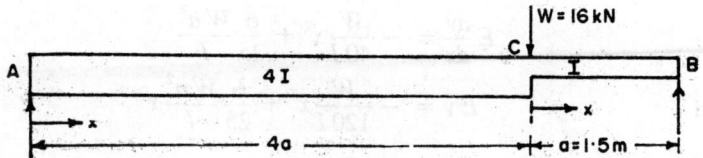

FIG. 12.44

and $\qquad Ey = -\dfrac{Wx^3}{120I} + C_1 x + C_2 \qquad\qquad \text{...(2a)}$

At $x = 0$, $\qquad y = 0$. Hence $C_2 = 0$

Also, at $x = 4a$, $\left(E\dfrac{dy}{dx} \right)_c = E\,i_c = -\dfrac{W}{40I}(16\,a^2) + C_1 \qquad \text{...(1b)}$

and $\qquad E\,y_c = -\dfrac{W}{120I}(4a)^3 + 4a\,C_1 \qquad\qquad \text{...(2b)}$

These values of i_c and y_c are evidently the initial constants for portion CB.

For Portion CB : Measuring x from C

$$E \frac{d^2y}{dx^2} = \frac{1}{I} \left[-\frac{W}{5}(4a+x) + Wx \right]$$

$\therefore$
$$E \frac{dy}{dx} = -\frac{4}{5} \frac{wax}{I} - \frac{Wx^2}{10I} + \frac{Wx^2}{2I} + C_3 \qquad \qquad ...(1c)$$

and
$$E y = -\frac{2}{5} \frac{Wax^2}{I} - \frac{Wx^3}{30I} + \frac{Wx^3}{6I} + C_3 x + C_4 \qquad \qquad ...(2c)$$

At $x = 0$,
$$E \frac{dy}{dx} = E i_c = -\frac{W}{40I}(16a^2) + C_1$$

Hence from 1(c),
$$C_3 = -\frac{2Wa^2}{5I} + C_1$$

Also, at $x = 0$,
$$E y_c = -\frac{W}{120I}(4a)^3 + 4aC_1$$

Hence from 2(c), $\quad -\frac{W}{120I}(4a)^3 + 4aC_1 = C_4$

$\therefore \quad E y = -\frac{2}{5}\frac{Wax^2}{I} - \frac{Wx^3}{30I} + \frac{Wx^3}{6I} + \left(C_1 - \frac{2Wa^2}{5I} \right)x + \left(4aC_1 - \frac{8}{15}\frac{Wa^3}{I} \right) \qquad ...(3)$

This is the expression for deflection at any point in CB. At $x = a$, $y = y_B = 0$

Hence $\quad 0 = -\frac{2}{5}\frac{Wa(a)^2}{I} - \frac{W(a^3)}{30I} + \frac{Wa^3}{6I} + C_1 a - \frac{2}{5}\frac{Wa^3}{I} + 4aC_1 - \frac{8}{15}\frac{Wa^3}{I}$

This gives $\quad C_1 = \frac{6}{25}\frac{Wa^2}{I}$

Substituting this value of C_1 in Eq. 1(a) and 2(a) we get equations for slope and deflection for the portion AC. Thus

$$E \frac{dy}{dx} = -\frac{W}{40I}x^2 + \frac{6}{25}\frac{Wa^2}{I} \qquad \qquad ...(I)$$

and
$$E y = -\frac{W}{120I}x^3 + \frac{6}{25}\frac{Wa^2}{I}x \qquad \qquad ...(II)$$

Maximum deflection :

Maximum deflection will evidently occur in portion on AC. Putting $\frac{dy}{dx} = 0$,

we get $\quad 0 = -\frac{W}{40I}x^2 + \frac{6}{25}\frac{Wa^2}{I}$, from which $x = 3.098a$

Hence $\quad E y_{max} = -\frac{W}{120I}(3.098a)^3 + \frac{6}{25}\frac{Wa^2}{I}(3.098a)$

From which $\quad y_{max} = 0.4957 \frac{Wa^3}{EI}$ **(Answer)**

Deflection at mid-span : At mid span $x = 2.5a$. Hence from (II)

$$E y_{centre} = -\frac{W}{120I}(2.5a)^3 + \frac{6}{25}\frac{Wa^2}{I}(2.5a)$$

$\therefore$
$$y_{centre} = 0.4695 \frac{W a^3}{E I} \text{ (Ans.)}$$

This again shows that the deflection at mid-span is very near to the maximum deflection.
Slope at end A : At end A, $x = 0$ Hence from (I)

$$i_A = \frac{6}{25} \frac{W a^2}{E I} \text{ (Ans.)}$$

Numerical Values : Substituting $a = 1.5$ m and $W = 16$ kN, we have

$$\frac{W a^2}{E I} = \frac{16000 \, (1.5)^2}{(2 \times 10^5) \, (2500 \times 10^4)} \times (1000)^2 = 7.2 \times 10^{-3}$$

and
$$\frac{W a^3}{E I} = 7.2 \times 10^{-3} \, (1.5 \times 1000) = 10.8$$

Hence
$$y_{max} = 0.4957 \frac{W a^3}{E I} = 0.4957 \times 10.8 = \textbf{5.354 mm}$$

$$y_{center} = 0.4695 \frac{W a^3}{E I} = 0.4695 \times 10.8 = \textbf{5.07 mm}$$

$$i_A = \frac{6}{25} \frac{W a^2}{E I} = \frac{6}{25} \times 7.2 \times 10^{-3} = \textbf{1.73} \times \textbf{10}^{-3}\textbf{radian}$$

Note : The solution of this problem, using conjugate beam method is extremely easy, as illustrated in Example 14.13. This problem has also been solved by area-moment method at example 13.18.

Example 12.35. *Two equal steel beams are encastered at one end and connected by a steel rod as shown in Fig. 12.45. Show that the pull in the rod is*

$$P = \frac{5 W L^3}{32 \left(\dfrac{6 a I}{\pi d^2} + L^3 \right)}$$

where d is the diameter of the rod and I is the moment of inertia of the section of each beam about its neutral axis.

Solution :

Let the tensile force in the tie rod be P. Due to external load W, end B will deflect downwards by y_B, end D will also deflect down wards by y_D and the rod will extend by δ. Hence we have the compatibility equation,

FIG. 12.45

$$y_B = y_D + \delta \qquad \qquad ...(i)$$

For cantilever AB : A point load W acts down wards at E while a load P acts upwards at B. Hence

$$y_B = \frac{W \left(\dfrac{L}{2} \right)^3}{3 E I} + \frac{W}{2 E I} \left(\frac{L}{2} \right)^2 \times \frac{L}{2} - \frac{P L^3}{3 E I}$$

$$= \frac{W L^3}{24 E I} + \frac{W L^3}{16 E I} - \frac{P L^3}{3 E I} = \frac{5}{48} \frac{W L^3}{E I} - \frac{P L^3}{3 E I} \qquad ...(ii)$$

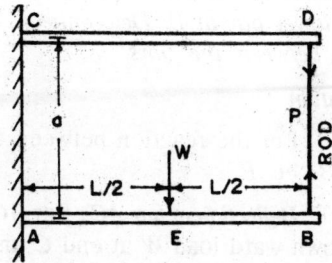

For Cantilever CD : A point load P act downwards at D.

$$\therefore \qquad y_D = \frac{PL^3}{3EI} \qquad \qquad \qquad ...(iii)$$

For rod DB : Tensile force P acts along its axis.

Hence elongation $\qquad \delta = \dfrac{Pa}{\frac{\pi}{4}d^2 E} = \dfrac{4Pa}{\pi d^2 E} \qquad \qquad \qquad ...(iv)$

Now, we have $\qquad \qquad y_B = y_D + \delta$

$$\therefore \qquad \frac{5}{48}\frac{WL^3}{EI} - \frac{PL^3}{3EI} = \frac{PL^3}{3EI} + \frac{4Pa}{\pi d^2 E}$$

or $\qquad \qquad P\left[\dfrac{2L^3}{3I} + \dfrac{4a}{\pi d^3}\right] = \dfrac{5WL^3}{48I}$

From which $\qquad P = \dfrac{5WL^3}{48I\left(\dfrac{2}{3}\dfrac{L^3}{I} + \dfrac{4a}{\pi d^2}\right)} = \dfrac{5WL^3}{48I\dfrac{2}{3I}\left(L^3 + \dfrac{4a}{\pi d^2}\times\dfrac{3I}{2}\right)}$

or $\qquad \qquad P = \dfrac{5WL^3}{32\left(L^3 + \dfrac{6aI}{\pi d^2}\right)}$ (Proved)

Example 12.36. *Two uniform steel bars of the same rectangular section are built-in together with the longer bar immediately over the shorter bar to form a cantilever as shown in Fig. 12.46. Before loading, the bars are in contact from A to B, but after loading it may be assumed that separation takes place with contact occurring only in the built-in part at A, and at the tip of the lower bar at B. Determine (a) the reaction at B (b) the deflection at C and (c) the maximum gap between the bars.*

Solution :

Let the reaction between the two bars, at B, be P.

Deflection of bar AC : Bar AC is subjected a down ward load W at end C and an upward load P at point B.

Measuring x from A, we have, for the portion AB

$$EI\frac{d^2y}{dx^2} = -M_x = W(L-x) - P\left(\frac{3}{4}L-x\right)$$

Integrating, $EI\dfrac{dy}{dx} = W\left(Lx - \dfrac{x^2}{2}\right)$

$$-P\left(\frac{3}{4}Lx - \frac{x^2}{2}\right) + C_1$$

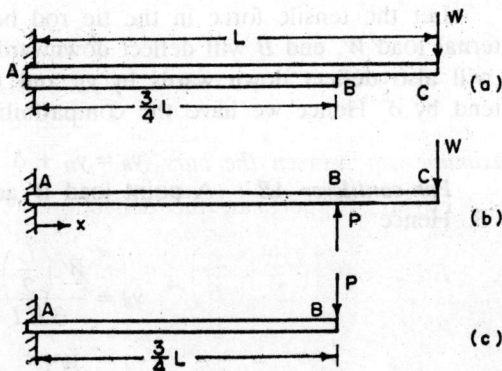

FIG. 12.46

At $\quad\quad\quad x = 0, \dfrac{dy}{dx} = 0.$ Hence $C_1 = 0$

$\therefore\quad\quad EI\dfrac{dy}{dx} = W\left(Lx - \dfrac{x^2}{2}\right) - P\left(\dfrac{3}{4}Lx - \dfrac{x^2}{2}\right)$ ...(i)

Integrating, $\quad EIy = W\left(\dfrac{Lx^2}{2} - \dfrac{x^3}{6}\right) - P\left(\dfrac{3}{4}\dfrac{Lx^2}{2} - \dfrac{x^3}{6}\right) + C_2$ ...(ii)

At $\quad x = 0,\quad\quad y = 0.$ Hence $C_2 = 0$

$\therefore\quad\quad EIy = W\left(\dfrac{Lx^2}{2} - \dfrac{x^3}{6}\right) - P\left(\dfrac{3}{8}Lx^2 - \dfrac{x^3}{6}\right)$ ...(iii)

From point $B,\quad x = \dfrac{3}{4}L$ and $y = y_B$

$\therefore\quad EIy_B = W\left[\dfrac{L}{2}\left(\dfrac{3}{4}L\right)^2 - \dfrac{1}{6}\left(\dfrac{3}{4}L\right)^3\right] - P\left[\dfrac{3}{8}L\left(\dfrac{3}{4}L\right)^2 - \dfrac{1}{6}\left(\dfrac{3}{4}L\right)^3\right]$

or $\quad\quad y_B = \dfrac{1}{EI}\left[\dfrac{9}{32}WL^3 - \dfrac{27}{6\times 64}WL^3 - \dfrac{27}{32\times 4}PL^3 + \dfrac{27}{6\times 64}PL^3\right]$

or $\quad\quad\quad\quad y_B = \dfrac{9L^3}{128\,EI}[3W - 2P]$ ...(a)

Deflection of bar AB : Bar AB is subjected to a downward load P at B.

Hence $\quad\quad\quad\quad y_B{}' = \dfrac{P\left(\dfrac{3}{4}L\right)^3}{3EI} = \dfrac{9PL^3}{64\,EI}$ ...(b)

Equating (a) and (b), we have $\dfrac{9PL^3}{64\,EI} = \dfrac{9L^3}{128\,EI}[3W - 2P]$

From which we get $\quad P = \dfrac{3}{4}W$

Deflection at C :

$$y_c = \dfrac{WL^3}{3EI} - \left[\dfrac{P\left(\dfrac{3}{4}L\right)^3}{3EI} + \dfrac{P\left(\dfrac{3}{4}L\right)^2}{2EI}\cdot\dfrac{L}{4}\right] = \dfrac{WL^3}{3EI} - \dfrac{81}{384}\dfrac{PL^3}{EI}$$

$$= \dfrac{WL^3}{3EI} - \dfrac{81}{384}\left(\dfrac{3}{4}W\right)\dfrac{L^3}{EI} = \dfrac{269\,WL^3}{1536\,EI} \text{ (Ans.)}$$

Maximum gap between the bars :

For the upper bar, the deflection curve is given by Eq. (ii)

$$EIy_u = W\left(\dfrac{Lx^2}{2} - \dfrac{x^3}{6}\right) - P\left(\dfrac{3}{8}Lx^2 - \dfrac{x^3}{6}\right) = W\left(\dfrac{Lx^2}{2} - \dfrac{x^3}{6}\right) - \dfrac{3}{4}W\left(\dfrac{3}{8}Lx^2 - \dfrac{x^3}{6}\right)$$

or $\quad\quad\quad\quad EIy_u = \dfrac{7}{32}WLx^2 - \dfrac{Wx^3}{24}$ ...(I)

The differential equation for the lower cantilever is

$$E I \frac{d^2y}{dx^2} = \frac{3}{4} W \left(\frac{3}{4} L - x \right) = \frac{9}{16} W L - \frac{3}{4} W x$$

$$E I \frac{dy}{dx} = \frac{9}{16} W L x - \frac{3}{8} W x^2 \quad \text{(constant of integration being zero)}$$

and
$$E I y_l = \frac{9}{32} W L x^2 - \frac{3}{24} W x^3 = \frac{9}{32} W L x^2 - \frac{1}{8} W x^3 \qquad ...(II)$$

(The constant of integration being zero)

Hence, at any distance x from A, the gap δ between the two beams is given by

$$E I \delta = y_l - y_u = \left(\frac{9}{32} W L x^2 - \frac{1}{8} W x^3 \right) - \left(\frac{7}{32} W L x^2 - \frac{W x^3}{24} \right)$$

or
$$E I \delta = \frac{1}{16} W L x^2 - \frac{1}{12} W L x^3$$

For maximum gap, $\quad \dfrac{d\delta}{dx} = 0$

$$\therefore \qquad 0 = \frac{1}{8} W L x - \frac{1}{4} W x^2$$

which gives
$$x = \frac{L}{2}$$

$$\therefore \qquad E I \delta_{max} = W L^3 \left(\frac{1}{64} - \frac{1}{96} \right)$$

or
$$\delta_{max} = \frac{W L^3}{192 E I} \quad \text{(Ans.)}$$

Example 12.37. *A rigid beam ABC is pinned to a wall at C and supported by two springs A and B shown in Fig. 12.47. Determine the slope of the beam when it carries load W at a distance c from C. The springs at A and B stretch δ_1 and δ_2 respectively under unit load. The unloaded beam is horizontal.*   *(U.L.)*

Solution :

Let $P_1 = $ force in spring at A

           $\delta_1 = $ stretch of spring at A

           $P_2 = $ force in spring at B

           $\delta_2 = $ stretch of spring at B.

Now $\Delta_1 = P_1 \delta_1$ or $P_1 = \dfrac{\Delta_1}{\delta_1}$

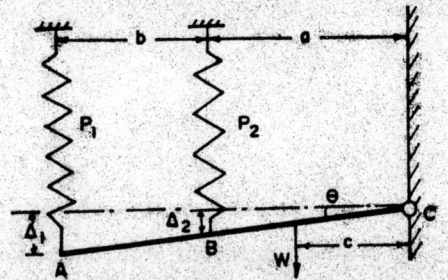

and $\Delta_2 = P_2 . \delta_2$ or $P_2 = \dfrac{\Delta_2}{\delta_2}$

FIG. 12.47

Taking moments at hinge C, where $\Sigma M = 0$, we get

$$W . c = P_1 (a + b) + P_2 . a = \frac{\Delta_1}{\delta_1} (a + b) + \frac{\Delta_2}{\delta_2} a \qquad ...(i)$$

Since there are two unknowns (*i.e.* Δ_1 and Δ_2), another equation is necessary, which can be obtained from the deformation of rigid beam *ABC*, as under :

$$\frac{\Delta_1}{\Delta_2} = \frac{a+b}{a} \qquad \text{or} \qquad \Delta_1 = \frac{a+b}{a}\,\Delta_2$$

Substituting in (*i*), we get

$$W.c = \left(\frac{a+b}{a}\right)\frac{\Delta_2}{\delta_1}(a+b) + \frac{\Delta_2}{\delta_2}.a = \Delta_2\left[\frac{(a+b)^2}{a\,\delta_1} + \frac{a}{\delta_2}\right]$$

or

$$\Delta_2 = \frac{W.c.a\,\delta_1\delta_2}{(a+b)^2\,\delta_2 + a^2\,\delta_1}$$

$\therefore$ Slope of the beam $= \theta = \dfrac{\Delta_2}{a} = \dfrac{W.c.\delta_1.\delta_2}{(a+b)^2\,\delta_2 + a^2\,\delta_1}$

Example 12.38. *A cantilever of length L carries a point load W at its free end. The member is circular in section, having diameter D for a distance L/2 from the fixed end and a diameter D/2 for the remaining length. Find the deflection at the free end.*

Solution :

For the portion *AC*

$$I_{AC} = \frac{\pi D^4}{64}$$

For the portion *CB*,

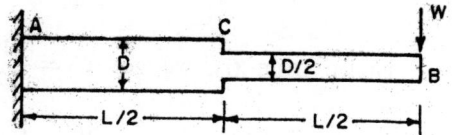

FIG. 12.48

$$I_{CB} = \frac{\pi}{64}\left(\frac{D}{2}\right)^4 = \frac{\pi D^4}{64 \times 16}$$

Hence if $I_{CB} = I$, $I_{AC} = 16\,I$

For portion *AC* : Measuring x from *A*, we get

$$E\frac{d^2y}{dx^2} = -\frac{M_x}{I_{AC}} = \frac{W(L-x)}{16\,I}$$

Integrating,

$$E\frac{dy}{dx} = \frac{W}{16\,I}\left(Lx - \frac{x^2}{2}\right) + C_1$$

At $x = 0$, $\dfrac{dy}{dx} = 0$. Hence $C_1 = 0$

$\therefore$

$$E\frac{dy}{dx} = \frac{W}{16\,I}\left(Lx - \frac{x^2}{2}\right) \qquad \qquad \dots(\text{I})$$

Integrating further, $E y = \dfrac{W}{16\,I}\left(\dfrac{Lx^2}{2} - \dfrac{x^3}{6}\right) + C_2$

At $x = 0$, $y = 0$. Hence $C_2 = 0$

$\therefore$

$$E y = \frac{W}{16\,I}\left(\frac{Lx^2}{2} - \frac{x^3}{6}\right) \qquad \qquad \dots(\text{II})$$

Eqs. (I) and (II) are the equations of slope and deflection for portion AC. At $x = \dfrac{L}{2}$, the slope and deflection at C are as under :

$$i_c = \frac{W}{16\,E\,I}\left[L \cdot \frac{L}{2} - \frac{1}{2}\left(\frac{L}{2}\right)^2\right] = \frac{3\,W L^2}{128\,E\,I} \qquad \ldots(a)$$

and

$$y_c = \frac{W}{16\,E\,I}\left[\frac{L}{2}\left(\frac{L}{2}\right)^2 - \frac{1}{6}\left(\frac{L}{2}\right)^3\right] = \frac{5\,W L^3}{16 \times 48\,E\,I} \qquad \ldots(b)$$

For portion CB : Measuring x from C, we have

$$E\frac{d^2 y}{dx^2} = -\frac{M_x}{I_{CB}} = \frac{W\left(\dfrac{L}{2} - x\right)}{I}$$

Integrating

$$E\frac{dy}{dx} = \frac{W}{I}\left(\frac{L}{2}x - \frac{x^2}{2}\right) + C_3 \qquad \ldots(i)$$

At $x = 0$,

$$\frac{dy}{dx} = i_C = \frac{3\,W L^2}{128\,E\,I}$$

Hence from (i), we get $C_3 = \dfrac{3\,W L^2}{128\,I}$

$\therefore$

$$E\frac{dy}{dx} = \frac{W}{I}\left(\frac{L}{2}x - \frac{x^2}{2}\right) + \frac{3\,W L^2}{128\,I} \qquad \ldots(III)$$

Integrating further,

$$E y = \frac{W}{I}\left(\frac{L x^2}{4} - \frac{x^3}{6}\right) + \frac{3\,W L^2}{128\,I}x + C_4 \qquad \ldots(ii)$$

At $x = 0$,

$$y = y_c = \frac{5\,W L^2}{16 \times 48\,E\,I}$$

Hence from (iii), we get $C_4 = \dfrac{5\,W L^3}{16 \times 48\,I}$

$\therefore$

$$E y = \frac{W}{I}\left(\frac{L x^2}{4} - \frac{x^3}{6}\right) + \frac{3\,W L^2}{128\,I}x + \frac{5\,W L^3}{16 \times 48\,I} \qquad \ldots(IV)$$

Eqs. (III) and (IV) are the equations for slope and deflection for the portion CB.

At the free end, $x = \dfrac{L}{2}$. Hence from IV, we get

$$E y_B = \frac{W}{I}\left[\frac{L}{4}\left(\frac{L}{2}\right)^2 - \frac{1}{6}\left(\frac{L}{2}\right)^3\right] + \frac{3\,W L^2}{128\,I}\left(\frac{L}{2}\right) + \frac{5\,W L^3}{16 \times 48\,I}$$

From which we get $\quad y_B = \dfrac{23}{384}\dfrac{W L^3}{E\,I}$ (Answer).

The solution of this problem (or similar problem) by area moment method, and by strain energy method is relatively easier. See examples 13.12 and 15.14 respectively. Also see example 14.11 for solution by conjugate beam method.

Example 12.39 *An experimental beam of steel of uniform section* $I = 5000\ cm^4$ *is simply supported in a horizontal position by rigid supports 4 m apart. An elastic prop is placed under the beam at the mid-span with initial clearance between the top of the prop and the under side of the beam. The beam is centrally loaded with a series of increasing loads. The observed central deflection is 8 mm for a concentrated load of 100 kN, and when the results are plotted, the slope of the load deflection line is 27.3 kN per mm after the contact with the prop has occurred. Determine the stiffness of the prop and the initial clearance. Take* $E = 2.04 \times 10^5\ N/mm^2$.

Solution :

Let $\quad \sigma_b$ = stiffness of the beam

σ_p = stiffness of the prop.

The stiffness of the whole structure (*i.e.* that of the beam and the prop) is equal to the slope of load deflection curve.

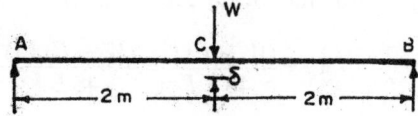

FIG. 12.49

Hence $\qquad \sigma_b + \sigma_p = 27.3$ (kN/mm)

But $\qquad \sigma_B = \dfrac{\text{load}}{\text{deflection}} = \dfrac{W}{y} = \dfrac{W}{\dfrac{WL^3}{48EI}} = \dfrac{48EI}{L^3}$

$$= \frac{48 \times 2.04 \times 10^5 \times 50 \times 10^6}{(4)^3 (1000)^3} = 7650\ \text{N/mm} = 7.65\ \text{kN/mm}$$

$\therefore \qquad \sigma_p = 27.3 - 7.65 = \mathbf{19.65\ kN/mm}$

Let $\qquad \delta$ = initial clearance, in mm

$\therefore \qquad$ Deflection of prop = $8 - \delta$

Force on prop = (stiffness of prop) × (deflection of prop)

$\therefore \qquad P = \sigma_p (8 - \delta) = 19.65 (8 - \delta)$ kN

Also, deflection of beam $= \dfrac{\text{Net load on the beam}}{\text{Stiffness of the beam}}$

$\therefore \qquad 8 = \dfrac{100 - P}{\sigma_b} = \dfrac{100 - P}{7.65} = \dfrac{100 - 19.65 (8 - \delta)}{7.65}$

Simplifying and rearranging, we get

$$19.65\ \delta = 61.2 - 100 + 157.2 = 117.4$$

$\therefore \qquad \delta = \dfrac{117.4}{19.65} = \mathbf{5.97\ mm}$

Example 12.40. *A beam AB of span 5 m is simply supported at A and B. A cantilever DC of length 3 m, which is fixed at D, meets the beam AB at the mid-point C, thereby forming a rigid joint at C. Find out the reactions at A and B, if a vertical load W = 17 kN is applied at the end C of the cantilever. Both the beam and the cantilever have the same moment of inertia, and are made of the same material. What will be the values of the reactions at A and B, if the cantilever and the beam have equal span ?*

Solution :

(a) *Let the load shared by the cantilever be P.*

$\therefore$ Load shared by beam
$= W - P$

For the cantilever DC,.

$$y_c = \frac{P(L)^3}{3EI} = \frac{P(3)^3}{3EI} = \frac{9P}{EI} \qquad ...(i)$$

For the beam AB,

$$y_c = \frac{(W-P)l^3}{48EI} = \frac{(W-P)(5)^3}{48EI}$$

$$= \frac{125}{48}\frac{(W-P)}{EI} \qquad ...(ii)$$

Equating the two, we have
$$\frac{9P}{EI} = \frac{125}{48}\frac{(W-P)}{EI}$$

FIG. 12.50

From which $\quad P = \frac{125}{557}W = \frac{125}{557} \times 17 = 3.815$ kN

Load shared by the beam $= W - P = 17 - 3.815 = 13.185$ kN

Hence reactions $\quad R_A = R_B = \frac{1}{2} \times 13.185 = \textbf{6.5925 kN}$

(b) *Let the beam and cantilever have equal span of L.*

For the cantilever, $\qquad y_c = \frac{PL^3}{3EI}$ ...(iii)

For the beam, $\qquad y_c = \frac{(W-P)L^3}{48EI}$ ...(iv)

Equating the two, $\qquad \frac{PL^3}{3EI} = \frac{(W-P)L^3}{48EI}$

From which $\qquad P = \frac{1}{17}W = \frac{17}{17} = 1$ kN

Hence load shared by the beam $= W - P = 17 - 1 = 16$ kN

$\therefore$ Reactions $\qquad R_A = R_B = \frac{1}{2} \times 16 = \textbf{8 kN}$

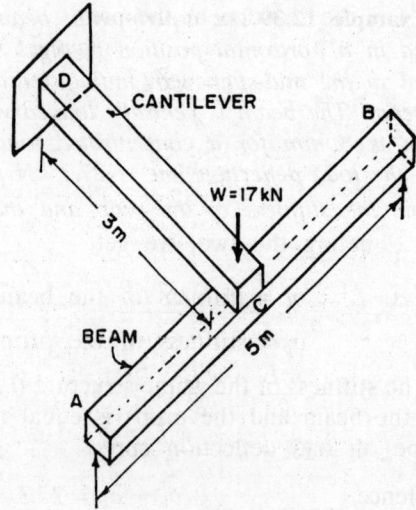

Example 12.41. *A horizontal cantilever of uniform section and length L carries a uniformly distributed load w per unit length throughout its length. The cantilever is supported by a rigid prop at a distance kL from the fixed end, the level of the beam at prop being the same as that at the fixed end. Determine the value of k which will make the bending moment at the prop the same as that at the fixed end. Also, sketch the S.F. and B.M. diagrams for the propped cantilever.*

Solution :

Let the reaction at the prop be P.

$$\therefore \quad M_c = -\frac{w(1-k)^2 L^2}{2} \quad ...(i)$$

Also, $\quad M_A = P.kL - \dfrac{wL^2}{2} \quad ...(ii)$

Equating the two, we get

$$PkL - \frac{wL^2}{2} = -\frac{w(1-k)^2 L^2}{2}$$

or $\quad Pk = \dfrac{wL}{2} - \dfrac{wL}{2}(1-k)^2$

$$=\frac{wL}{2}\left[1-1+2k-k^2\right]=\frac{wL}{2}k(2-k)$$

$$\therefore \qquad P = \frac{wL}{2}(2-k) \qquad\qquad ...(iii)$$

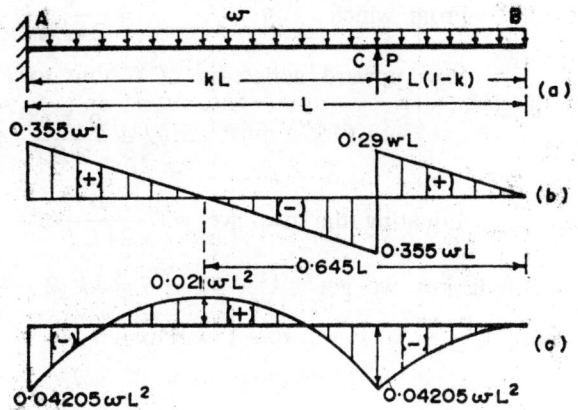

FIG. 12.51

Thus, we know the value of prop reaction P in terms of k. In order to find the value of k, we use the compatibility conditions at C. Since the deflection at C is zero, the downward deflection due to load w, in absence of the prop, should be equal to the upward deflection (y_c') of C due to upward force P alone, applied at C.

Hence $\qquad\qquad y_c = y_c'$

In order to find the y_c due to U.D.L., in absence of the prop, consider a section distant x from A. Then we have

$$EI\frac{d^2y}{dx^2} = -M_x = \frac{w}{2}(L-x)^2 = \frac{w}{2}(L^2+x^2-2Lx)$$

Integrating, $\qquad EI\dfrac{dy}{dx} = \dfrac{w}{2}(L^2x+\dfrac{x^3}{3}-Lx^2)+C_1$

At $\quad x=0, \qquad\qquad \dfrac{dy}{dx}=0.$ Hence $C_1=0$

$$\therefore \qquad EI\frac{dy}{dx} = \frac{w}{2}\left[L^2x+\frac{x^3}{3}-Lx^2\right]$$

Integrating further, $\quad EIy = \dfrac{w}{2}\left[\dfrac{L^2x^2}{2}+\dfrac{x^4}{12}-\dfrac{Lx^3}{3}\right]+C_2$

At $\quad x=0,\qquad\qquad y=0.$ Hence $C_2=0$

$$\therefore \qquad EIy = \frac{w}{2}\left[\frac{L^2x^2}{2}+\frac{x^4}{12}-\frac{Lx^3}{3}\right]$$

At $\quad x=kL,\qquad\qquad y=y_c$

$$\therefore \qquad EIy_c = \frac{w}{2}\left[\frac{L^2}{2}(kL)^2+\frac{1}{12}(kL)^4-\frac{L}{3}(kL)^3\right]$$

From which $\qquad y_c = \dfrac{w}{24\,E\,I}\,k^2\,(k^2 - 4\,k + 6)$ $\qquad\qquad$ ...(a)

Now upward deflection of C due to P alone, is

$$y_c' = \frac{P\,(k\,L)^3}{3\,E\,I} = \frac{w\,L}{2}\,(2 - k)\,\frac{k^3\,L^3}{3\,E\,I} = \frac{w\,L^4\,(2 - k)\,k^3}{6\,E\,I} \qquad\qquad ...(b)$$

Equating the two, we get $\dfrac{w}{24\,E\,I}\,k^2\,(k^2 - 4\,k + 6) = \dfrac{w\,L^4\,(2 - k)\,k^3}{6\,E\,I}$

Simplifying, we get $\quad k^2 - 4\,k + 6 = 4\,k\,(2 - k)$

or $\qquad\qquad\qquad 5\,k^2 - 12\,k + 6 = 0 \qquad\qquad$ From which $k = \mathbf{0.71}$

Hence $\qquad\qquad\qquad P = \dfrac{w\,L}{2}\,(2 - k) = \dfrac{w\,L}{2}\,(2 - 0.71) = 0.645\,w\,L$

and $\qquad\qquad\qquad R_A = w\,L - P = w\,L - 0.645\,w\,L = 0.355\,wL$

Length $AC = k\,L = 0.71\,L$; Length $CB = L\,(1 - k) = 0.29\,L$

S.F. Diagram : $\qquad\qquad F_B = 0\,; F_c\,(right) = \;+ w\,L\,(1 - k) = \;+ 0.29\,w\,L$

$$F_c\,(left) = 0.29\,w\,L - P = 0.29\,w\,L - 0.645\,w\,L = \;- 0.355\,w\,L$$

$$F_A = \;+ R_A = \;+ 0.355\,w\,L$$

Evidently, S.F. is zero at $\qquad \dfrac{k\,L}{2} = \dfrac{0.71\,L}{2} = 0.355\,L$ from A.

The S.F. diagram is shown in Fig. 12.50 (b).

B.M. Diagram : $\qquad M_c = \;- \dfrac{w\,(0.29\,L)^2}{2} = \;- 0.04205\,w\,L^2$

For CA, measuring x from B,

$$M_x = \;- \frac{w\,x^2}{2} + P\,(x - 0.29\,L) = \;- \frac{w\,x^2}{2} + 0.645\,w\,L\,(x - 0.29\,L) \qquad ...(I)$$

Maximum positive B.M. occurs at $k\,L/2$ from C, where S.F. is zero.

At this location, $x = 0.29\,L + 0.71\,\dfrac{L}{2} = 0.645\,L$

$\therefore \qquad\qquad M_{max} = \;- \dfrac{w}{2}\,(0.645\,L)^2 + 0.645\,w\,L\,(0.645\,L - 0.29\,L) = 0.021\,w\,L^2$

Also, putting $\quad x = L$ in (I), we get

$$M_A = \;- \frac{w\,L^2}{2} + 0.645\,w\,L\,(L - 0.29\,L) = \;- 0.04205\,w\,L^2$$

The complete B.M. diagram is shown in Fig. 12.50(c).

Example 12.42. *A cantilever of a circular section tapers uniformly from a diameter d at the free end to 2d at the fixed end. It carries a concentrated load W at the free end. Calculate the diameter of a cantilever of uniform cross-section which would have the same deflection.*

Solution : Extend the upper and lower faces of the cantilever to meet at C, as shown in Fig. 12.51. By inspection, we get $BC = AB = L$

At any section x from C $(x > L)$,

Diameter $d_x = \dfrac{x}{L} d$ $\qquad \therefore \quad I_x = \dfrac{\pi}{64}\left(\dfrac{x^4 d^4}{L^4}\right)$

Now $\quad E\dfrac{d^2y}{dx^2} = -\dfrac{M_x}{I_x} = \dfrac{W(x-L)}{\dfrac{\pi}{64}\dfrac{x^4 d^4}{L^4}}$

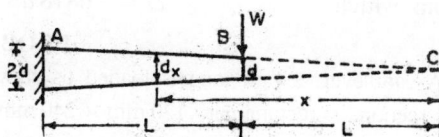

FIG. 12.52

$\qquad\qquad = \dfrac{64}{\pi d^4} WL^4 \left(\dfrac{x-L}{x^4}\right)$

or $\qquad\qquad E\dfrac{d^2y}{dx^2} = k\,(x^{-3} - Lx^{-4})$ where $k = \dfrac{64\,WL^4}{\pi d^4}$ ...(i)

Integrating, $\qquad E\dfrac{dy}{dx} = k\left(\dfrac{x^{-2}}{-2} - \dfrac{Lx^{-3}}{-3}\right) + C_1 = k\left(-\dfrac{x^{-2}}{2} + \dfrac{Lx^{-3}}{3}\right) + C_1$

At $\quad x = 2L$, $\qquad \dfrac{dy}{dx} = 0 = k\left[-\dfrac{1}{2}(2L)^{-2} + \dfrac{L}{3}(2L)^{-3}\right] + C_1$

From which $\qquad C_1 = \dfrac{kL^{-2}}{12}$

Hence $\qquad E\dfrac{dy}{dx} = k\left(-\dfrac{x^{-2}}{2} + \dfrac{Lx^{-3}}{3}\right) + \dfrac{kL^{-2}}{12}$

Integrating further, $\qquad Ey = k\left(\dfrac{x^{-1}}{2} - \dfrac{Lx^{-2}}{6}\right) + \dfrac{kL^{-2}}{12}x + C_2$

At $\quad x = 2L$, $\qquad y = 0 = k\left[\dfrac{1}{2}(2L)^{-1} - \dfrac{L}{6}(2L)^{-2} + \dfrac{L^{-2}}{12}(2L)\right] + C_2$

From which $\qquad C_2 = -\dfrac{3}{8}\dfrac{k}{L}$

$\therefore \qquad Ey = k\left[\dfrac{1}{2x} - \dfrac{L}{6x^2} + \dfrac{x}{12L^2} - \dfrac{3}{8}L\right]$

For the free end $x = L$, hence $y_B = \dfrac{k}{E}\left[\dfrac{1}{2L} - \dfrac{L}{6L^2} + \dfrac{L}{12L^2} - \dfrac{3}{8}L\right] = \dfrac{k}{24\,E\,L}$

Substituting the value of k, we get

$$y_B = \dfrac{1}{24\,E\,L}\left(\dfrac{64\,WL^4}{\pi d^4}\right) = \dfrac{64}{24\,\pi}\dfrac{WL^3}{E\,d^4} \qquad ...(a)$$

For a cantilever of uniform diameter D, $I = \dfrac{\pi}{64}D^4$

$\therefore \qquad\qquad y_B = \dfrac{WL^3}{3\,EI} = \dfrac{WL^3}{3E\left(\dfrac{\pi}{64}D^4\right)} = \dfrac{64}{3\pi}\dfrac{WL^3}{E\,D^4} \qquad ...(b)$

Equating the two, we get $\quad \dfrac{64}{3\pi}\dfrac{WL^3}{E\,D^4} = \dfrac{64}{24\,\pi}\dfrac{WL^3}{E\,d^4}$

or $D^4 = 8\,d^4$

From which $D = 1.6818\,d$

PROBLEMS

1. A cantilever, 2.4 m long is loaded as shown in Fig. 12.53. Calculate the deflection at the free end if the section is rectangular, 120 mm × 240 mm. Take $E = 0.11 \times 10^5$ N/mm².

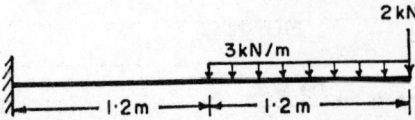

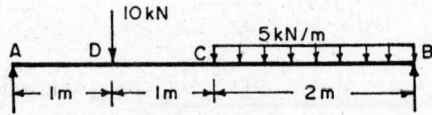

FIG. 12.53   FIG. 12.54

2. A beam AB of 8 m span is simply supported at the ends and is loaded as shown in Fig. 12.54. Determine (*i*) deflection at C (*ii*) maximum deflection, and (*iii*) slope at end A. Take $E = 2 \times 10^5$ N/mm² and $I = 1000$ cm⁴.

3. An overhanging beam ABC is supported at A and B and is loaded with point load W at end C (Fig. 12.55). Determine (*i*) deflection at C and (*ii*) Maximum deflection between A and B..

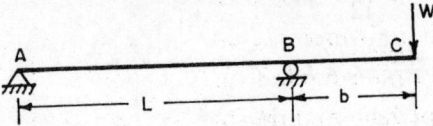

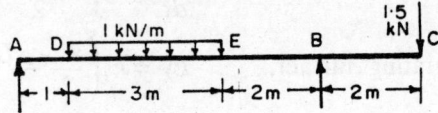

FIG. 12.55   FIG. 12.56

4. An overhanging beam ABC, supported at A and B is loaded as shown in Fig. 12.56. Determine (*i*) deflection at free end C and (*ii*) maximum deflection between A and B. Take $E = 2 \times 10^5$ N/mm² and $I = 450$ cm⁴.

5. A horizontal steel beam $I = 6000$ cm⁴ carries a uniformly distributed load of 50 kN over its length of 4 m. The beam is supported by three vertical steel tie rods, each 1.5 m long, one at each end and one in the middle, the diameter of each rod being 20 mm. Calculate the deflection of the centre of the beam below the end points and the stress in each rod. Take $E = 2 \times 10^5$ N/mm².

6. A simply supported beam of span L carries a central load W. Find the ratio of the maximum deflection to the maximum skin stress.

7. A beam $PQRS$ is initially horizontal. A load W is then applied at R. In order to bring the position of the beam at Q, back to the original level $PQRS$, a vertical force W_1 is placed at Q (Fig. 12.57) Find W_1.

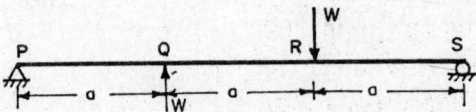

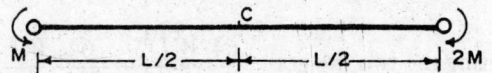

FIG. 12.57   FIG. 12.58

8. A horizontal beam of uniform section is pinned at its ends which are at the same level and is loaded at the left hand pin with an anticlockwise moment M and at the right hand pin with a clockwise moment $2M$ both in the same vertical plane (Fig. 12.58). The length between the pins is L. Find the angles of slope at each end and the deflection of the mid point of the span.

9. A cantilever of uniform section has a length $AB = L$, and carries a point load W at its free end B. Find the deflection at a point C distant $L/4$ from the free end B. If the cantilever is propped at C, find the reaction of the prop, assuming that there is no deflection at C (Fig. 12.59). Also, draw the B.M. and S.F. diagrams for the propped cantilever.

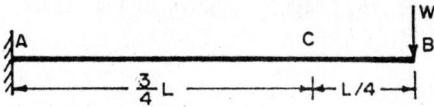

FIG. 12.59

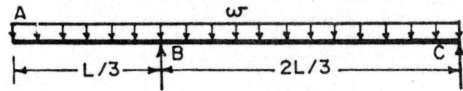

FIG. 12.60

10. A beam ABC of length L carries a uniformly distributed load w per unit run over the whole length. It has one support at $L/3$ from A and the other support at C (Fig. 12.60). Find the slope and deflection at A.

11. A horizontal beam AB is freely supported at A and B, 8 m apart, and carries a uniformly distributed load of 15 kN/m (including its own weight). A clockwise moment of 160 kN-m is applied to the beam at a point C, 3 m from the left hand support A (Fig. 12.61). Calculate the slope of the beam at C, if $EI = 40$ MN–m^2.

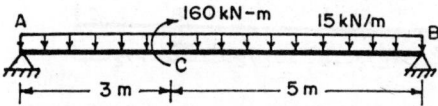

FIG. 12.61

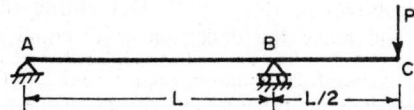

FIG. 12.62

12. Determine the equations of the deflection curve for a simple beam with an overhang subjected to a concentrated load P (Fig. 12.62). Also find the deflection of the free end C.

13. Find the deflection of the free end B of the cantilever AB, loaded as shown in Fig. 12.63.

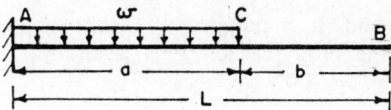

FIG. 12.63

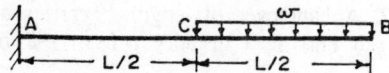

FIG. 12.64

14. Find the deflection of the free end B, of the cantilever AB, loaded as shown in Fig. 12.64.

15. Find (a) the rotation of end A and (b) deflection at the mid point C, for a simply supported beam, loaded by a triangularly distributed load shown in Fig. 12.65.

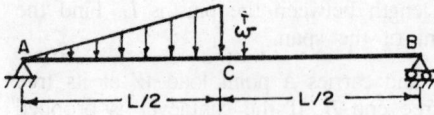

FIG. 12.65

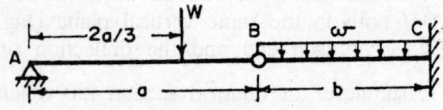

FIG. 12.66

16. Determine the deflection at the hinge B of the compound beam shown in Fig. 12.66.

17. Determine the deflection of the free end B of a cantilever AB, loaded as shown in Fig. 12.67.

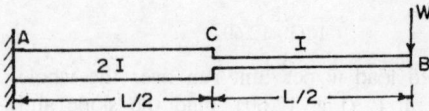

FIG. 12.67

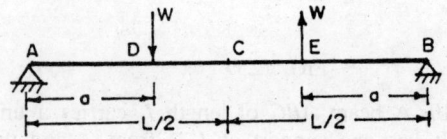

FIG. 12.68

18. A simple beam AB shown in Fig. 12.68 supports two concentrated loads W, one acting downward and the other upward. Determine (*i*) angle of rotations at A (*ii*) deflection under the downward load, and (*iii*) deflection at the mid-point.

19. A beam with an overhang supports loads P and Q as shown in Fig. 12.69. Determine the ratio P/Q that will make the deflection at C equal to zero.

20. A beam of uniform section and length $2\,l$ is simply supported at its ends and carries two point loads each of magnitude W situated at equal distance a on either side of mid-span. Show that the maximum deflection δ is given by the formula.

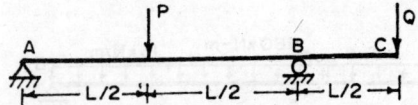

FIG. 12.69

$$\delta = \frac{W(2\,l^3 - 3\,l\,a^2 + a^3)}{3\,E\,I}$$ (U.L.)

21. A uniform beam of length $4L$ is simply and symmetrically supported over a span of $2L$. It carries a load W_1 at each end and a total uniformly distributed load of W_2 on the span between the supports. Find the ratio of W_1 to W_2 if the deflection at the mid-span is equal to that at each end.

22. A cantilever of length L carries a load W at the free end. It is propped at the same level as the fixed end at a distance l from the fixed end. Show that the prop reaction P is given by

$$P = \frac{W(3L - l)}{2l}$$

Show also that the deflection under the load is given by $y = \dfrac{W(L - l)^2\,(4L - l)}{12\,E\,I}$

23. A load W acts at the free end of a cantilever of constant depth h but of variable width b as shown in Fig. 12.70. Find the deflection of the free end.

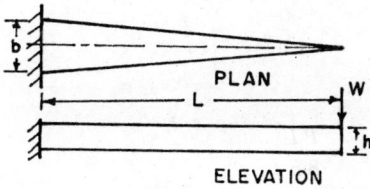

FIG. 12.70.

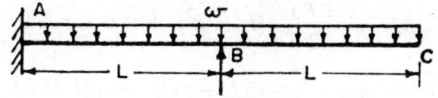

FIG. 12.71

24. A beam of length $2L$ and uniform flexural stiffness EI is supported at A and B (Fig. 12.71). The support A is completely rigid while that at B is a knife edge which sinks a depth equal to k times, the load on the support. If the beam carries a uniformly distributed vertical load of intensity w over the whole length, prove that the load on the support B is equal to

$$\frac{17\,w\,L^4}{8\,(L^3 + 3\,E\,I\,k)}$$

25. A beam $ABCD$ is simply supported at B and C and is loaded by force W at A and D, as shown in Fig. 12.72. Determine (a) the angles of rotations at supports B and C (b) Deflections at free ends A and D (c) deflection at the midpoint E of the beam.

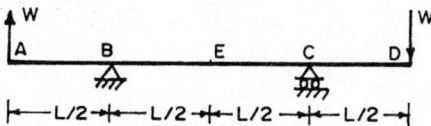

FIG. 12.72

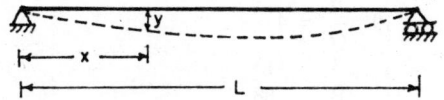

FIG. 12.73

26. The equation of deflection curve for a simple beam AB, shown in Fig. 12.73 is

$$y = \frac{w\,x}{360\,L\,E\,I}(7\,L^4 - 10\,L^2 x^2 + 3\,x^4)$$

What is the load of the beam ?

ANSWERS

1. 13.16 mm
2. (i) 8.747 mm (ii) 8.75 mm (iii) 7.29×10^{-3} radian
3. (i) $y_c = \dfrac{W b^2}{3\,E I}(L + b)$ ($\downarrow$) (ii) $y_{max} = \dfrac{W b L^3}{9\sqrt{3}\,E I}$ ($\uparrow$)
4. (i) $y_c = 4.95$ mm ($\downarrow$) (ii) $y_{max} = 5.7$ mm ($\downarrow$)
5. (i) 0.76 mm (ii) 108.6 N/mm^2 and 101.09 N/mm^2
6. $\dfrac{L^2}{6\,E\,d}$
7. $W_1 = \dfrac{7}{8}W$
8. $i_A = -\dfrac{2}{3}\dfrac{ML}{EI}$; $i_B = +\dfrac{5}{6}\dfrac{ML}{EI}$; $y_c = -\dfrac{3}{16}\dfrac{ML^2}{EI}$
9. $y_c = \dfrac{27}{128}\dfrac{WL^3}{EI}$; $P = \dfrac{3}{2}W$

10. $i_A = -\dfrac{wL^3}{162\,EI}$; $y_A = \dfrac{wL^4}{648\,EI}$

11. 0.0061 radian

12. $y = \dfrac{Px}{12\,EI}(L^2 - x^2)$, for $0 \le x \le L$

$y = \dfrac{P}{12\,EI}(3L - x)(L - x)(L - 2x)$ for $0 \le x \le \dfrac{3L}{2}$; $y_c = \dfrac{PL^3}{8\,EI}$

13. $\dfrac{wa^3}{24\,EI}(4L - a)$

14. $\dfrac{41\,wL^4}{384\,EI}$

15. $i_A = \dfrac{41\,wL^3}{2880\,EI}$; $y_c = \dfrac{wL^4}{240\,EI}$

16. $y_A = \dfrac{wb^4}{8\,EI} + \dfrac{2Pb^3}{9\,EI}$

17. $\dfrac{3PL^3}{16\,EI}$

18. $i_A = \dfrac{Wa}{6\,LEI}(L - a)(L - 2a)$; $y_D = \dfrac{Wa^2}{6\,LEI}(L - 2a)^2$; $y_c = 0$

19. $\dfrac{P}{Q} = 4$

21. $\dfrac{W_1}{W_2} = \dfrac{13}{88}$

23. $\dfrac{6\,WL^3}{E\,b\,h^3}$

25. $i_B = \dfrac{WL^2}{12\,EI}$; $y_A = \dfrac{WL^3}{12\,EI}$; $y_E = 0$

26. $w_x = w\,\dfrac{x}{L}$

Deflection of Beams : II
Area Moment Method

13.1. INTRODUCTION :

Area moment method, also known as *moment area method*, is a very useful and simple method for finding slopes and deflections of the beams. The method utilises the properties of the area of the bending moment diagram and also the moment of that area. Depending as it does on the geometry of the elastic curve, the area moment method emphasizes the physical significance of slope and deflection. The method is especially suited when the deflection and angle of rotation at only one point of the beam is required, because it is possible to find these quantities directly without first finding the complete equation for the deflection curve. The method is also known as *Mohr's method* because it is based on two theorems given by Mohr and discussed in § 13.3. The area moment method is subject to the same limitations as the double integration method.

13.2. DEVIATION, DEFLECTANCE AND DEFLECTION

Fig. 13.1 shows the elastic curve ACB of a beam AB, subject to external loading. AB_2 is the tangent to the elastic curve at point A. Point C is deflected position of any point on the beam, while C_1 is the original position of the point. Line $A C_1 B$ is the original position of the centre line of the beam, before loading. The interval $C_1 C$ is therefore the *deflection* of the point and is abbreviated as y_C^A in the area moment method.

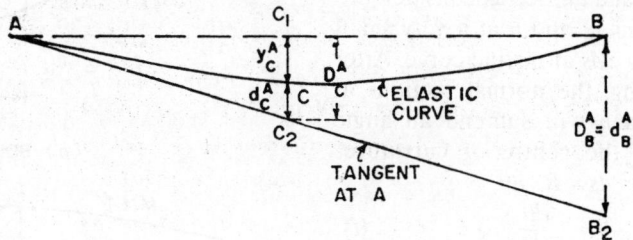

FIG. 13.1 BASIC DEFINITIONS.

Here, the lower suffix to y denote the deflection of the *point* under consideration and the upper suffix to y will mean the point with respect to which the deflection is being calculated. The interval $C C_2$ is called the *deviation* of the point C from the tangent at A and is abbreviated as d_C^A. The lower suffix to d will mean the deviation of the point under consideration and the upper suffix to d will mean the point with respect to which deviation is being calculated.

Thus, the *deviation* of point B with respect to the tangent at A is abbreviated as d_B^A. Naturally, the deviation of a point on the elastic curve may have infinite number of values depending upon the reference point chosen for the tangent.

The total interval $C_1 C_2$ is called the *deflectance* of point C and is abbreviated as D_C^A. Here again, the lower suffix to D will mean the point under consideration and the upper suffix to D will mean the point with respect to which the *deflectance* is being calculated.

Study of Fig. 13.1 shows that the relation between the deflection, deviation and deflectance of a point can be expressed by the equation :

$$y_C^A = D_C^A - d_C^A \qquad \qquad ...(13.1)$$

Evidently, if the horizontal line through the *point of reference passes through the point where deflection is required (such as point A and B)*, we have

$$D_B^A = d_B^A \qquad \qquad ...(13.1a)$$

Hence
$$y_B^A = D_B^A - d_B^A = 0.$$

In order to determine the deflection of a point, it is first required to find the *deviation*, which in turn can be found from the Mohr's theorems discussed in the next article.

13.3. MOHR'S THEOREMS : AREA MOMENT EQUATIONS

(*a*) **Rotation :** Fig. 13.2 shows the elastic curve $AmnB$ of a beam. AB' is the tangent to the curve at A and BB'' is the tangent to the curve at B. Evidently, BB' is the *deviation* (d_B^A) of B with respect to tangent at A. The angle between the two tangents is θ_B^A. If θ_A is the rotation of tangent at A and θ_B is the rotation of tangent at B, we have, in general,

$$\theta_B^A = \theta_B - \theta_A \qquad ...(13.2)$$

In Fig. 13.2, θ_B is negative (since the rotation is anticlockwise)

Hence $\theta_B^A = (-\theta_B) - \theta_A$

$$= -(\theta_B + \theta_A) \ ...(13.2a)$$

In order to find the values of θ_B^A and d_B^A, let us consider two sections m and n at a very small distance ds along the curve. After bending, the normal sections at m and n will subtend an angle $d\theta$ at the centre of curvature. Hence $ds = R \cdot d\theta$

and $\dfrac{1}{R} = \left| \dfrac{d\theta}{ds} \right| \qquad ...(i)$

The bars in the above expression indicate that we consider here only the numerical value of curvature. Regarding sign, B.M. is taken positive if it produces concavity. *Hence curvature is positive when the centre of curvature*

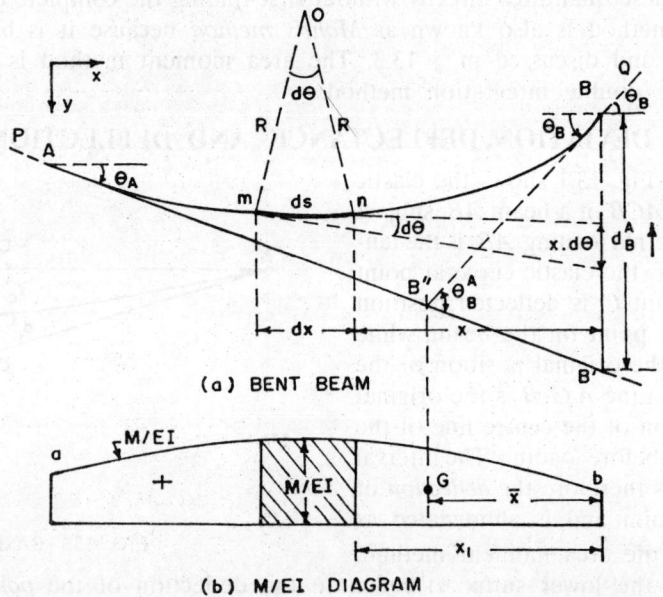

FIG. 13.2

is above the curve, as in Fig. 13.2. By close inspection of Fig. 12.1(*b*), we observe that for such a curvature, the angle θ decreases as the point m moves along the curve from point P to Q. Thus we have proper sign for Eq. (*i*) which must be written as

$$\frac{1}{R} = -\frac{d\theta}{ds}$$

But

$$\frac{1}{R} = \frac{M}{EI}$$

Hence

$$d\theta = -\frac{M}{EI} ds$$

Since the curvature is very small, we can take ds equal to dx.

Hence

$$d\theta = -\frac{M}{EI} dx \qquad \qquad ...(13.3)$$

The term $\dfrac{M}{EI} dx$ has a simple geometric interpretation. Directly below the deflection curve is shown the $\dfrac{M}{EI}$ diagram. It should be noted that the $\dfrac{M}{EI}$ diagram will have the same shape as the M-diagram, only if EI is constant along the entire length of the beam. The ordinate of the (M/EI) diagram is equal to the ordinate of the B.M. diagram (*i.e.* M-diagram) divided by the *flexural* rigidity EI at that point. The term $\dfrac{M}{EI} dx$ is the area of the shaded strip (Fig. 13.2 *b*) within the M/EI diagram.

Since the angle $\left(\theta_B^A\right)$ between the two tangents at A and B consists of such small angles of elemental sections, we have :

$$\theta_B^A = \sum_B^A d\theta = -\int_A^B \frac{M\,dx}{EI} \qquad \qquad ...(13.4)$$

In the above expression, $\dfrac{M}{EI} dx$ is the area of the $\dfrac{M}{EI}$ diagram between m and n. The term $\displaystyle\int_B^A \frac{M}{EI} dx$ is therefore the total area of $\dfrac{M}{EI}$ diagram between B and A, say $\Sigma A_{M/EI}$.

Hence

$$\theta_B^A = -\int_B^A \frac{M\,dx}{EI} = -\sum_B^A A_{M/EI} \qquad \qquad ...(13.5)$$

If, however EI is constant along the length of the beam, we have

$$EI\,\theta_B^A = -\sum_B^A A_M \qquad \qquad ...(13.5\ a)$$

where A_M is the area of the B.M. diagram between B and A.

The use of bending moment diagram for calculating the slope and deflection of beam was developed by Mohr. Hence Eq. 13.5 can be stated by the following *first theorem* by Mohr:

Mohr's First Theorem : *The angle θ_B^A between the tangents to the deflection curve at two points A and B is equal to the negative of the area of M/EI diagram between the points.*

(*b*) **Deviation :** Let us now determine the deviation d_B^A of B from the tangent at A. Multiplying Eq. 13.3 by x', we have

$$x' \, d\theta = - \frac{M . x'}{E I} dx$$

Since the deviation d_B^A consists of summation of each $x' . d\theta$ of elementary sections, we

have
$$d_B^A = \sum_B^A x' \, d\theta = - \int_B^A \frac{M x'}{E I} dx \qquad \qquad ...(13.6)$$

In the above expression, $\frac{M}{E I} dx . x'$ is the moment of the elementary area of the

$\frac{M}{E I}$ diagram about the point B.

Hence
$$d_B^A = - \sum_B^A A_{M/EI} . \bar{x} \quad \text{(where } x' = 0 \text{ at } B) \qquad ...(13.7)$$

It must be remembered that the variable x' has its origin at the point at which deviation is being computed. Eq. 13.7 can be stated by Mohr's second theorem :

Mohr's Second Theorem : *The deviation of B from tangent at A is equal to the negative of the statical moment (or the first moment) with respect to B, of the $\frac{M}{E I}$ diagram area between A and B.*

If however, $E I$ is constant along the length of the beam, we have
$$E I \, d_B^A = - \sum_B^A A_M \bar{x} \qquad \qquad ...(13.6 \ a)$$

where A_M is the area of B.M. diagram between B and A.

Mohr's second theorem is useful is finding the deflection because it relates the position of a point of the beam to the tangent at some other point.

13.4. SIGN CONVENTIONS

The following sign conventions are followed in the area-moment method :

1. B.M. is taken *positive* when it causes *concavity* at the upper side (*i.e.* if it causes compression in the upper fibres).

2. Area of M/EI diagram is taken *positive* if M is *positive*.

3. The rotation θ at any point is taken *positive* if the rotation is *clockwise*.

4. The deflection y at any point is *positive* if it is *downwards* with respect to the original axis of the beam.

5. The angle θ_B^A is *positive* if the tangent at B rotates *clockwise* with respect to tangent at A. Thus θ_B^A in Fig. 13.2(a) is negative since the rotation of tangent at B is anticlockwise with respect to tangent AB' at A.

6. The deviation d_B^A is taken *positive* when it is measured *downward* from the tangent at A. Thus, is Fig 13.2(a), d_B^A is *negative* since it is measured *upward* from the tangent at A.

7. $\bar{x}$ is taken positive when it is measured from point B towards point A.

In the above sign conventions, point B must be to the right of A.

If the area of B.M. diagram is *positive*, the first moment is also positive; hence the *deviation* comes out to be negative from Eq. 13.6 and the point B is above the tangent at A. This situation is illustrated in Fig. 13.2. If, however, as we move from A to B in the direction, the area of B.M. diagram is negative, then the first moment of the area is also negative; then the deviation comes out to be *positive* from Eq. 13.6 which means that point B is below the tangent at A. This situation is illustrated in Fig. 13.3.

Note : The above sign conventions may seem complicated at the first instance. In many practical cases, one can find by inspection itself whether the beam deflects upwards or downwards and whether the angle of rotation is clockwise or anticlockwise. Hence, for such obvious cases, it may not be necessary to follow the above sign conventions. Instead, we can calculate the absolute values and determine the direction by inspection.

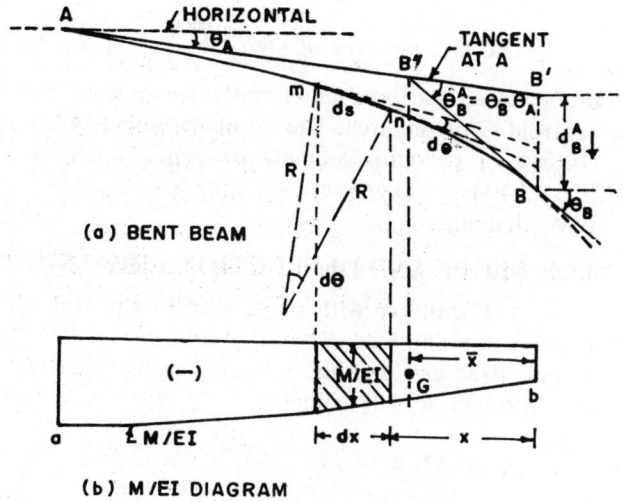

(a) BENT BEAM

(b) M/EI DIAGRAM

FIG. 13.3

13.5. GEOMETRICAL PROPERTIES OF *M/EI* DIAGRAM

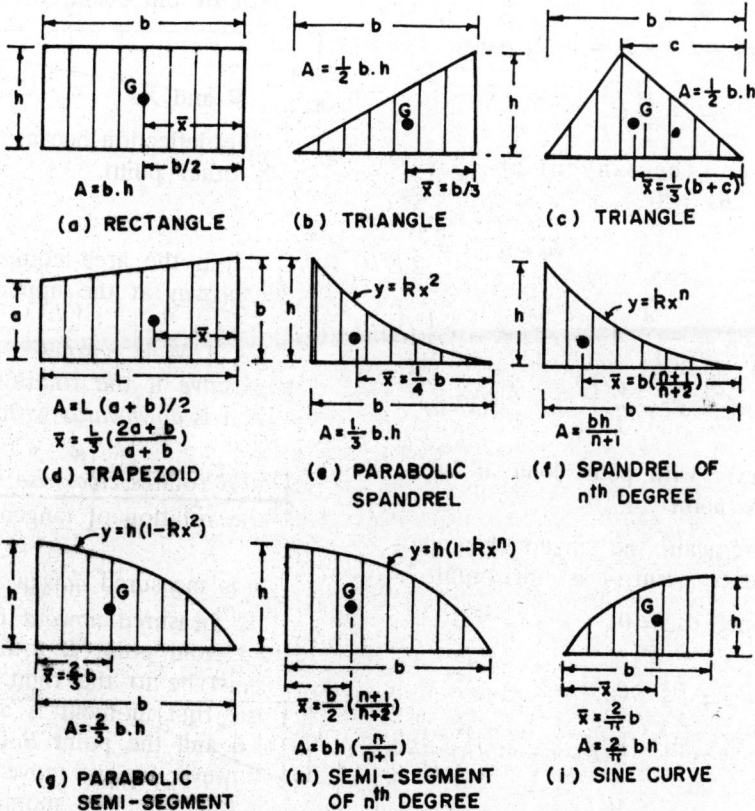

FIG. 13.4. GEOMETRICAL PROPERTIES OF FAMILIAR SEGMENTS

The *first moment of area* $\left(\dfrac{M x'}{E I}\right)$ *of the M/EI diagram can be found either by integration or by taking the product of the area of the diagram and the distance* $\bar{x}$ *from point B to the* centroid G of the area. The latter method is more convenient because the M/EI diagram usually consists of common geometrical figures such as rectangles, triangles and parabolic segments. Fig. 13.4 shows expression for area A and centroidal distance $\bar{x}$ for some common and familiar B.M. diagrams.

13.6. SLOPE AND DEFLECTION FROM MOHR'S THEOREMS

1. Cantilever with point load at the free end : Fig. 13.5 shows a cantilever AB of span L, with a point load W at the free end B. The B.M. diagram is shown in Fig. 13.5(b). Let us take fixed end A as the reference point. Hence the tangent at the fixed end and the horizontal line through it will coincide.

Area $\displaystyle\sum_{B}^{A} A_{M/EI}$

$$= \frac{1}{2}(L)(-WL)\left(\frac{1}{EI}\right) = -\frac{WL^2}{2EI}$$

From Eq. 13.5,

$$\theta_B^A = \theta_B - \theta_A = -\sum_{B}^{A} A_{M/EI}$$

$$= +\frac{WL^2}{2EI}$$

Since the tangent at A is horizontal, $\theta_A = 0$

Hence $\qquad\qquad \theta_B \text{ (or } i_B) = \dfrac{WL^2}{2EI}$ ...(13.7)

Also, $\quad d_B^A = -\displaystyle\sum_{B}^{A} A_{M/EI}\cdot\bar{x} = -\left[\frac{1}{2}(L)(-WL)\left(\frac{2}{3}L\right)\frac{1}{EI}\right] = \frac{WL^3}{3EI}$

$\therefore\qquad\qquad y_B^A = d_B^A = \dfrac{WL^3}{3EI}$ ...(13.8)

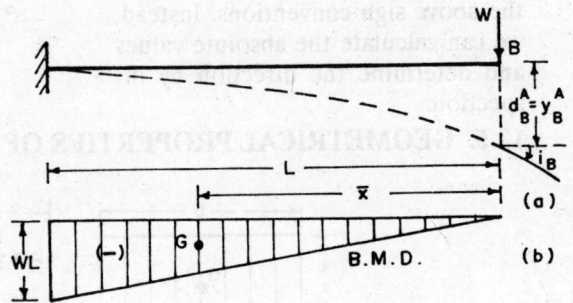

FIG. 13.5

2. Cantilever with point load at intermediate point

Here again, the tangent through the reference point A is horizontal.

Hence $\theta_A = 0$.

$\therefore\qquad \theta_B^A = \theta_B - \theta_A = -\displaystyle\sum_{B}^{A} A_{M/EI}$

$$= -\left[\frac{1}{2}(L_1)(-WL_1)\frac{1}{EI}\right]$$

$\therefore\qquad i_B = \theta_B = \dfrac{WL_1^2}{2EI}$

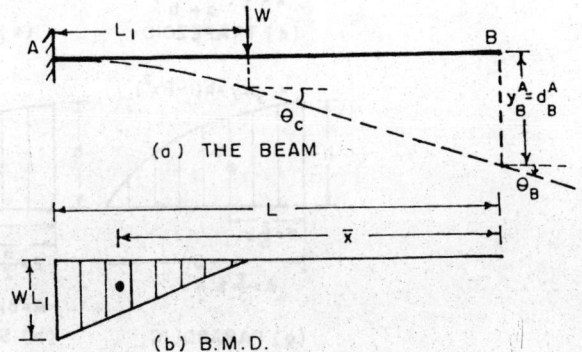

(a) THE BEAM

(b) B.M.D.

FIG. 13.6

Also, by inspection $y_B^A = d_B^A$

$$\therefore \qquad y_B^A = d_B^A = -\overset{A}{\underset{B}{\Sigma}} A_{M/EI} . \bar{x}$$

$$= -\left[\frac{1}{2}(L_1)(-WL_1)\left(L - L_1 + \frac{2}{3}L_1\right)\frac{1}{EI} \right] = \frac{WL_1^2}{2EI}(L - L_1) + \frac{WL_1^3}{3EI}$$

Hence $\qquad y_B^A = \dfrac{WL_1^3}{3EI} + \dfrac{WL_1^2}{2EI}(L - L_1)$ $\hspace{2cm}$ ...(13.9)

3. Cantilever with uniformly distributed load over the whole span

The B.M. diagram, shown in Fig. 13.7 has a maximum ordinate of $wL^2/2$.

Here, $\hspace{3cm} A_M = \dfrac{1}{3}(L)\left(-\dfrac{wL^2}{2}\right) = -\dfrac{wL^3}{6}$

$$\bar{x} = \frac{3}{4}L$$

$$\therefore \qquad \theta_B^A = -\overset{A}{\underset{B}{\sum}} A_{M/EI}$$

$$i_B = \theta_B^A = -\left[-\frac{wL^3}{6}\left(\frac{1}{EI}\right)\right]$$

$$= \frac{wL^3}{6EI}$$

Also, $\quad y_B^A = d_B^A = -\overset{A}{\underset{B}{\sum}} A_{M/EI} . \bar{x}$

$$= -\left[-\frac{wL^3}{6}\left(\frac{3}{4}L\right)\left(\frac{1}{EI}\right)\right]$$

$$\therefore \qquad y_B = y_B^A = \frac{wL^4}{8EI} \hspace{2cm} ...(13.11)$$

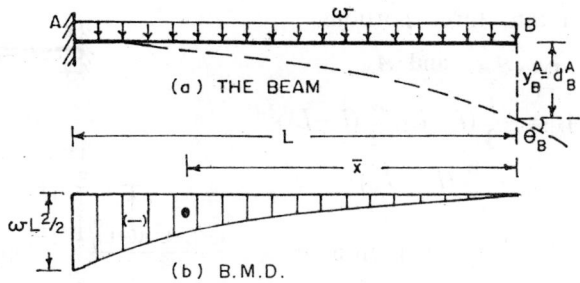

(a) THE BEAM

(b) B.M.D.

FIG. 13.7

4. Cantilever, partially loaded with w over a length L_1 from fixed end

$$A_M = \frac{1}{3}(L_1)\left(-\frac{wL_1^2}{2}\right) = -\frac{wL_1^3}{6}$$

$$\bar{x} = (L - L_1) + \frac{3}{4}L_1$$

$$\therefore \quad \theta_B^A = -\overset{A}{\underset{B}{\Sigma}} A_{M/EI} = -\left[-\frac{wL_1^3}{6} . \frac{1}{EI}\right]$$

$$\therefore \quad i_B = \theta_B = \theta_B^A = \frac{wL_1^3}{6EI} \hspace{1cm} ...(13.12)$$

and $\qquad y_B = y_B^A = d_B^A = -\overset{A}{\underset{B}{\Sigma}} A_{M/EI} . \bar{x}$

$$= -\left[-\frac{wL_1^3}{6}\left\{(L - L_1) + \frac{3}{4}L_1\right\}\right]\frac{1}{EI}$$

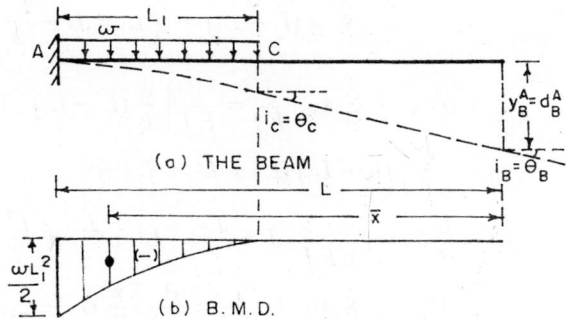

(a) THE BEAM

(b) B.M.D.

FIG. 13.8

$$\therefore \qquad y_B = \frac{w L_1^4}{8EI} + \frac{w L_1^3}{6EI}(L - L_1) = \frac{w L_1^3}{24EI}(4L - L_1) \qquad \dots(13.13)$$

when $\qquad L_1 = L$, we get $y_B = \dfrac{w L^4}{8EI}$, which is the same as Eq. 13.11.

5. Cantilever partially loaded with w from the free end

The B.M. diagram is shown in Fig. 13.9(b). The variation of B.M. is parabolic from B to C, and linear from C to A.

Ordinate $\qquad\qquad c\,c_1 = \dfrac{w(L - L_1)^2}{2} = a\,a_1$

Ordinate $\qquad\qquad a\,a_2 = w(L - L_1)\left(L_1 + \dfrac{L - L_1}{2}\right) = \dfrac{w}{2}(L - L_1)(L + L_1)$

$\therefore \qquad\qquad a_1 a_2 = \dfrac{w}{2}(L - L_1)(L + L_1) - \dfrac{w}{2}(L - L_1)^2 = w L_1(L - L_1)$

The total area can be splitted into three portions :

A_{M1}, A_{M2} and A_{M3}

Area $A_{M1} = -\dfrac{1}{3}(L - L_1)\cdot\dfrac{w}{2}(L - L_1)^2$

$\qquad = -\dfrac{w}{6}(L - L_1)^3$

$\bar{x}_1 = \dfrac{3}{4}(L - L_1)$, from b

Area $A_{M2} = -L_1 \cdot \dfrac{w}{2}(L - L_1)^2$

$\qquad = -\dfrac{w L_1}{2}(L - L_1)^2$

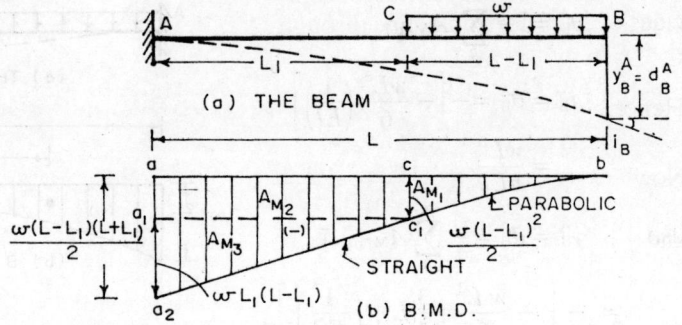

(a) THE BEAM

(b) B.M.D.

FIG. 13.9

$$\bar{x}_2 = \frac{L_1}{2} + (L - L_1) = L - \frac{L_1}{2}, \text{ from } b$$

Area $\qquad A_{M3} = -\dfrac{1}{2}\cdot L_1 \cdot w L_1(L - L_1) = -\dfrac{w L_1^2}{2}(L - L_1)$

$$\bar{x}_3 = (L - L_1) + \frac{2}{3}L_1 = L - \frac{L_1}{3} \text{ from } b$$

Now $\qquad i_B = \theta_B^A = -\sum_B^A A_M \cdot \dfrac{1}{EI} = \dfrac{1}{EI}\left[\dfrac{w}{6}(L - L_1)^3 + \dfrac{w L_1}{2}(L - L_1)^2 + \dfrac{w L_1^2}{2}(L - L_1)\right]$

or $\qquad i_B = \dfrac{w}{6EI}(L - L_1)(L^2 + L_1^2 + L L_1)$ $\qquad\qquad\dots(13.14)$

when $\qquad L_1 = \dfrac{L}{2}, \; i_B = \dfrac{w}{6EI}\left(L - \dfrac{L}{2}\right)\left(L^2 + \dfrac{L^2}{4} + \dfrac{L^2}{2}\right) = \dfrac{7 w L^3}{48 EI}$ $\qquad\dots(13.14\,a)$

Also, $\qquad y_B = d_B^A = -\sum_B^A A_M \cdot \bar{x} \cdot \dfrac{1}{EI} = \dfrac{1}{EI}\left[\dfrac{w}{6}(L - L_1)^3 \times \dfrac{3}{4}(L - L_1) + \dfrac{w L_1}{2}(L - L_1)^2 \times\right.$

$$\left. \left\{L - \frac{L_1}{2}\right\} + \frac{w L_1^2}{2}(L - L_1)\left(L - \frac{L_1}{3}\right)\right]$$

or $\qquad y_B = \dfrac{1}{EI}\left[\dfrac{w}{8}(L-L_1)^4 + \dfrac{wL_1}{2}(L-L_1)^2\left(L-\dfrac{L_1}{2}\right) + \dfrac{w}{2}L_1^2(L-L_1)\left(L-\dfrac{L_1}{3}\right)\right]$

Expanding, rearranging and simplifying, we get

$$y_B = \dfrac{wL^4}{8EI} - \left\{\dfrac{wL_1^4}{8EI} + \dfrac{wL_1^3}{6EI}(L-L_1)\right\} \qquad\qquad ...(13.15)$$

When $\quad L_1 = \dfrac{L}{2}, y_B = \dfrac{wL^4}{8EI} - \left\{\dfrac{w}{8EI}\left(\dfrac{L}{2}\right)^4 + \dfrac{w}{6EI}\left(\dfrac{L}{2}\right)^3\left(L-\dfrac{L}{2}\right)\right\} = \dfrac{11}{384}\dfrac{wL^4}{EI} \quad ...(13.15\,a)$

6. Simply supported beam with U.D.L.

Because of symmetrical loading, the tangent at C will be horizontal, as shown in Fig. 13.10(a). Hence the central deflection y_C^A is given by

$$y_C^A = -y_A^C$$

Since the tangent at C coincides with the horizontal line through C, D_A^C will be zero.

Hence $\quad y_A^C = d_A^C = -\overset{C}{\underset{A}{\Sigma}}\dfrac{A_M}{EI}.\bar{x}$

Now $\quad A_M = \dfrac{2}{3}\times\dfrac{L}{2}\times\dfrac{wL^2}{8} = \dfrac{wL^3}{24}$

and $\quad \bar{x} = \dfrac{5}{8}\left(\dfrac{L}{2}\right) = \dfrac{5}{16}$

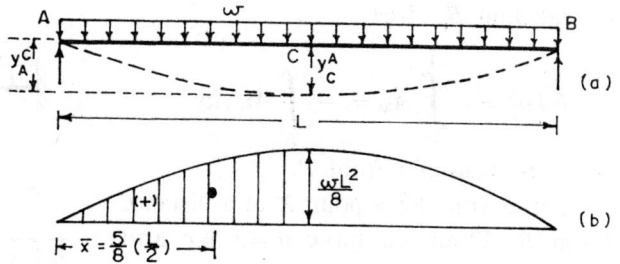

FIG. 13.10

$\therefore \qquad\qquad y_A^C = -\left[\dfrac{wL^3}{24}\times\dfrac{5}{16}\times\dfrac{1}{EI}\right] = -\dfrac{5}{384}\dfrac{wL^4}{EI}$

Hence $\qquad\qquad y_C^A = -y_A^C = \dfrac{5}{384}\dfrac{wL^4}{EI} \qquad\qquad ...(13.16)$

7 . Simply supported beam with central point load

Here also, because of symmetrical loading, the tangent at C will be horizontal, as shown in Fig. 13.11(a). Hence the central deflection is given by

$$y_C^A = -y_A^C$$

Since the tangent at C coincides with the horizontal line through C, D_A^C will be zero.

Hence $\quad y_A^C = d_A^C = -\overset{C}{\underset{A}{\Sigma}}\dfrac{A_M}{EI}.\bar{x}$

Here $\quad A_M = $ shaded area between A and C

$= \dfrac{1}{2}\times\dfrac{L}{2}\times\dfrac{WL}{4} = \dfrac{WL^2}{16}$

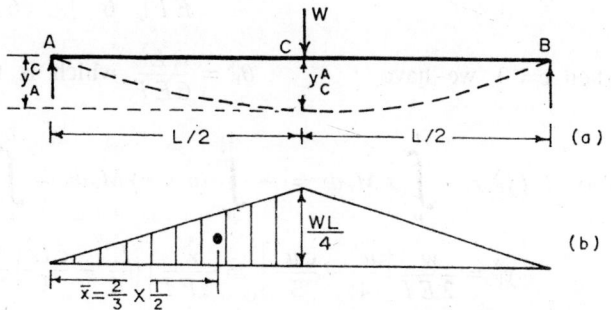

FIG. 13.11

$\bar{x}$ = distance of the C.G. of the shaded area from $A = \dfrac{2}{3} \times \dfrac{L}{2} = \dfrac{L}{3}$

$$y_A^C = -\left[\frac{WL^2}{16} \times \frac{L}{3} \times \frac{1}{EI}\right] = -\frac{WL^3}{48\,EI}$$

$\therefore$ $$y_C = y_C^A = -y_A^C = +\frac{WL^3}{48\,EI} \qquad\qquad\qquad ...(13.17)$$

8. Simply supported beam with general loading: See § 13.8

Example 13.1 *(a). A cantilever AB, of length L is loaded with U.D.L. throughout its length. Find the slope and deflection at any point P, distant c from the free end.*

(b) If the end B is propped, find (i) reaction at the prop, and (ii) slope at the propped end.

Solution :

(a) End B free

$$EI\,\theta_P^A = -\int_P^A A_M = -\int_P^A M_x \cdot dx$$

where x is measured from P.

Let us consider a point X at a distance u from B. Then we have $u = x + c$ and $du = dx$.

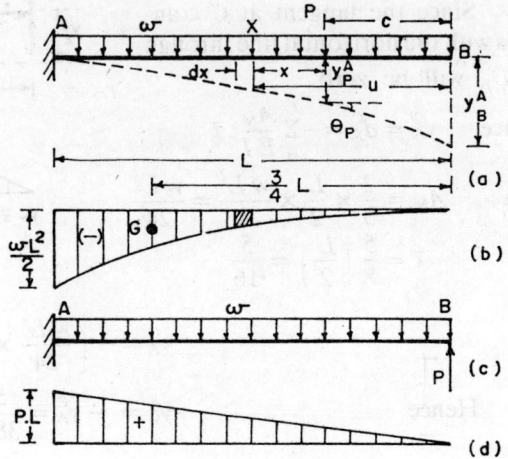

FIG. 13.12

Also $\quad M_x = -\dfrac{w u^2}{2}$

Hence $EI\,\theta_P^A = -\displaystyle\int_P^A \left(-\frac{w u^2}{2}\right) du$

$\qquad\qquad = -\displaystyle\int_0^L \left(-\frac{w u^2}{2}\right) du$

$\therefore$ $$\theta_P^A = \frac{1}{EI}\left[\frac{w u^3}{6}\right]_C^L = \frac{w}{6\,EI}\left[L^3 - c^3\right]$$

When $c = 0$, we have $\quad \theta_B^A = \dfrac{wL^3}{6\,EI}$, which is the same as Eq. 13.10.

Also, $EI\,y_P^A = -\displaystyle\int_P^A x\,M_x\,dx = -\int_P^A (u - c)\,M_x\,du = \int_C^L (u - c)\frac{w u^2}{2}\,du$

or $\quad y_P^A = \dfrac{w}{2\,EI}\left[\dfrac{u^4}{4} - \dfrac{c u^3}{3}\right]_C^L = \dfrac{w}{2\,EI}\left[\left(\dfrac{L^4}{4} - \dfrac{c L^3}{3}\right) - \left(\dfrac{c^4}{4} - \dfrac{c^4}{3}\right)\right] = \dfrac{w}{24\,EI}\left(3 L^4 - 4 c L^3 + c^4\right)$

When $c = 0$, we have $\quad y_B^A = \dfrac{wL^4}{8\,EI}$ which is the same as Eq. 13.11.

(b) **End B propped :** Let P be the prop reaction. The component bending moment diagrams are shown in Fig. 13.12(b) and (d) respectively.

Now
$$y_B^A = \overset{A}{\underset{B}{\Sigma}} (A_1 \bar{x}_1)_{M/EI} + \overset{A}{\underset{B}{\Sigma}} (A_2 \bar{x}_2)_{M/EI} = 0$$

where A_1 is the area of B.M. diagram due to external load and A_2 is the B.M. diagram due to prop reaction.

$$\therefore \quad -\frac{1}{3}\frac{wL^2}{2}L \cdot \frac{3}{4}L + \frac{1}{2}PL \cdot L \cdot \frac{2}{3}L = 0$$

or
$$\frac{wL^4}{8} = \frac{PL^3}{3} \quad \text{from which} \quad P = \frac{3}{8}wL$$

Also,
$$EI\,\theta_B^A = -\overset{A}{\underset{B}{\Sigma}} (A_1 + A_2)_M = -\left[-\frac{1}{3} \cdot \frac{wL^2}{2} \cdot L + \frac{3}{8}wL \cdot \frac{L^2}{2} \right] = \frac{wL^3}{48}$$

Hence
$$\theta_B^A = \frac{wL^3}{48\,EI}$$

Example 13.2. *A cantilever beam AB, supporting a triangularly distributed load of maximum intensity w is shown in Fig. 13.13. Find the slope and deflection at the free end.*

Solution :

At any distance x from B,

$$w_x = \frac{w}{L}x \quad \text{and} \quad M_x = -\frac{1}{2}\left(\frac{w}{L}x\right)x \cdot \frac{x}{3}$$

$$= -\frac{wx^3}{6L}$$

Hence
$$M_A = -\frac{w}{6L} \cdot L^3 = -\frac{wL^2}{6}$$

The B.M. diagram will be a third degree curve, as shown in Fig. 13.13(b), and will be of the form $y = kx^n$ where $n = 3$ and $k = -\frac{w}{6L}$.

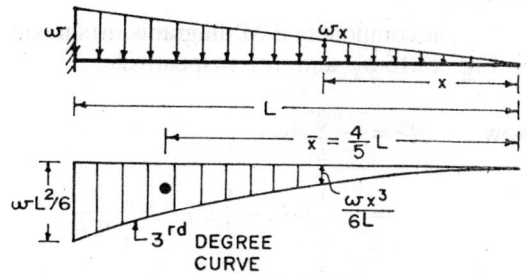

FIG. 13.13

Hence
$$A_M = \frac{bh}{n+1} = \frac{L}{3+1}\left(-\frac{wL^2}{6}\right) = -\frac{wL^3}{24}$$

Also,
$$\bar{x} = b\left(\frac{n+1}{n+2}\right) = L\left(\frac{3+1}{3+2}\right) = \frac{4}{5}L$$

Now,
$$\theta_B^A = -\overset{A}{\underset{B}{\Sigma}} \frac{A_M}{EI} = \frac{wL^3}{24\,EI}$$

Also,
$$y_B^A = -\overset{A}{\underset{B}{\Sigma}} \frac{A_M}{EI} \cdot \bar{x} = \frac{1}{EI}\left(\frac{wL^3}{24} \times \frac{4}{5}L\right) = \frac{wL^4}{30\,EI}$$

Example 13.3. *A cantilever AB of length L, is subjected to a couple μ in the clockwise direction at the free end. Determine the slope and deflection of the free end.*

Solution :

The B.M. diagram is shown in Fig. 13.14(b). Evidently, it will be a rectangle of height equal to μ, since B.M. at any section is $-\mu$, which is constant all along the length of the cantilever.

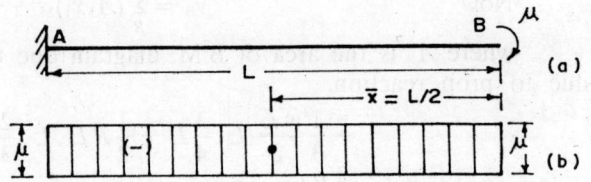

FIG. 13.14

Now $\qquad \theta_B^A = -\sum\limits_B^A A_{M/EI}$

$$= -\left[-\frac{\mu}{EI}.L \right] = \frac{\mu L}{EI} \quad \text{(Ans.)}$$

Also, $\qquad y_B^A = -\sum\limits_B^A A_{M/EI}.\bar{x} = -\left[-\frac{\mu L}{EI}.\frac{L}{2} \right] = \frac{\mu L^2}{2EI} \quad \text{(Ans.)}$

Example 13.4. *A cantilever AB of length L is subjected to a concentrated load W and a couple μ acting at the free end, as shown in Fig. 13.15. Determine the slope and deflection at the free end.*

Solution :

The component B.M. diagrams are shown in Fig. 13.15(b) and (c) respectively.

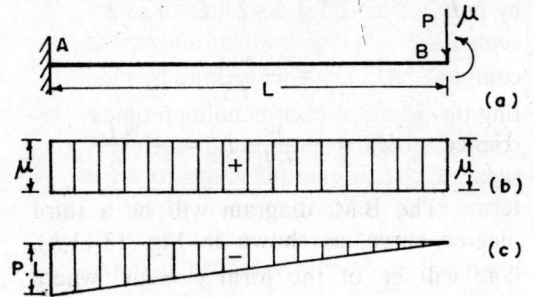

Now $\qquad \theta_B^A = -\sum\limits_B^A A_{M/EI}$

$$= -\left[\mu L - \frac{1}{2}PL.L \right] \frac{1}{EI}$$

$$= \frac{1}{2EI}[PL - 2\mu]$$

and $\qquad y_B^A = -\sum\limits_B^A A_{M/EI}.\bar{x}$

$$= -\frac{1}{EI}\left[\mu L.\frac{L}{2} - \frac{1}{2}.PL.L.\frac{2L}{3} \right]$$

FIG. 13.15

or $\qquad y_B^A = \frac{PL^3}{3EI} - \frac{\mu L^2}{2EI} = \frac{L^2}{6EI}[2PL - 3\mu]$

Example 13.5. *A beam of length L is simply supported at the ends and carries a load W at a distance a from the left support. Calculate the deflection at the centre.*

Solution :

In order to produce symmetry, so that slope at C becomes zero, add a load W at a distance a from B. Evidently, the deflection at C will be *doubled*. The corresponding bending moment diagram is shown in Fig. 13.16(b).

Now, from Fig. 13.16(a), $y_C^A = -y_A^C = -d_A^C$

But $\qquad y_A^C = d_A^C = -\overset{C}{\underset{A}{\Sigma}} A_{M/EI} \cdot \bar{x}$

$\therefore \quad y_C^A = \overset{C}{\underset{A}{\Sigma}} A_{M/EI} \cdot \bar{x} = \dfrac{1}{EI} \left[\dfrac{1}{2} \times a \times Wa. \times \right.$

$\dfrac{2}{3} a + \left(\dfrac{L}{2} - a \right) . Wa . \dfrac{1}{2} \left. \left(a + \dfrac{L}{2} \right) \right]$

or $\quad y_C^A = \dfrac{1}{EI} \left[\dfrac{Wa^3}{3} + \dfrac{Wa}{8} (L - 2a) \times \right.$

$\left. (L + 2a) \right]$

or $\quad y_C^A = \dfrac{Wa}{24 EI} \left[8 a^2 + 3 L^2 - 12 a^3 \right]$

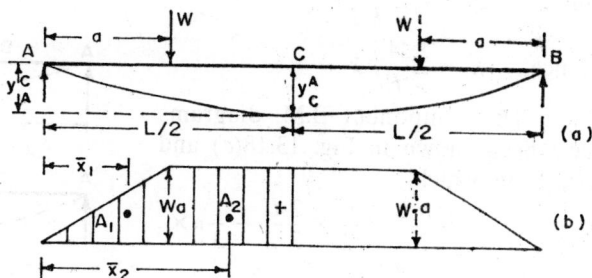

FIG. 13.16

Hence $\qquad y_C = \dfrac{1}{2} y_C^A = \dfrac{Wa}{48 EI} \left[3 L^2 - 4 a^3 \right]$

13.7. USE OF MOMENT DIAGRAMS BY PARTS

When a beam is subjected to several loads of various types, it is more convenient to use the moment diagrams by parts, sometimes also known as the *component bending moment diagram* to compute $\int M.x.dx$. This is done by plotting the graph of each bending moment component corresponding to each load separately, *i.e.* separate graph for each term of the bending moment equation.

For example, let us take the simply supported beam AB, loaded as shown in Fig. 13.17(a). The equation of B.M. at any point P, distant x from A is

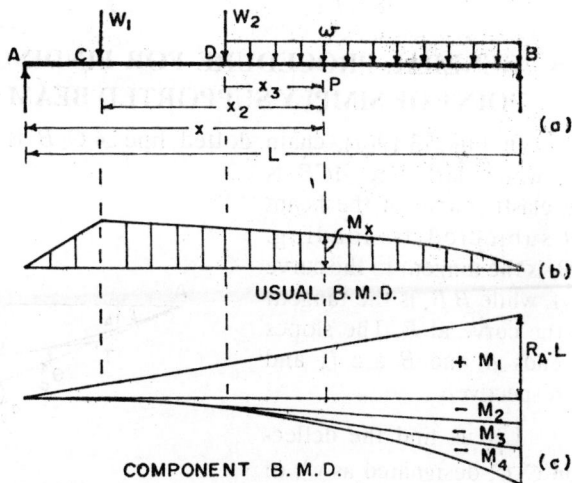

FIG. 13.17

$M_x = + R_A . x - W_1 x_1 - W_2 x_2 - \dfrac{w x_2^2}{2}$

$= M_1 + M_2 + M_3 + M_4$

Fig. 13.17(b) shows the usual B.M. diagram. In Fig. 13.17(c), the terms M_1, M_2, M_3 and M_4 have been plotted *separately*. It is very clear that Fig. 13.17(c) is more convenient for calculating $A_1 \bar{x}_1, A_2 \bar{x}_2, A_3 \bar{x}_3, A_4 \bar{x}_4$ etc.

Example 13.6. *A beam AB of span L is loaded with U.D.L. w per unit length, extending from the centre towards the left end for a length a. Compute the central deflection.*
Solution :

In order to produce symmetry, so that tangent at C becomes horizontal, add U.D.L for a length a from the centre towards right hand end. Then $R_A = R_B = w a$. The deflection at C will then be doubled.

Also, $y_C^A = -y_A^C = -d_A^C$

But $d_A^C = -\sum\limits_{A}^{C} \dfrac{A_M}{EI}\,\bar{x}$

Hence $y_C^A = \sum\limits_{A}^{C} \dfrac{A_M}{EI}\,\bar{x}$

The component B.M. diagrams have been shown in Fig. 13.18(c) and (d), from which

$y_C^A = \dfrac{1}{EI}\left[\dfrac{1}{2}\cdot\dfrac{waL}{2}\times\dfrac{L}{2}\times\dfrac{2}{3}\dfrac{L}{2} - \dfrac{1}{3}\,a\times\right.$

$\left. \cdot\dfrac{wa^2}{2}\left(\dfrac{L}{2}-a+\dfrac{3}{4}a\right)\right]$

or $y_A^C = \dfrac{wa}{24EI}\left[L^3 - a^2(2L - a)\right]$

$= \dfrac{wa}{24EI}\left[L^3 - 2La^2 + a^3\right]$

Hence actual

$y_C = \dfrac{1}{2}y_A^C = \dfrac{wa}{48EI}\left[L^3 - 2La^2 + a^3\right]$

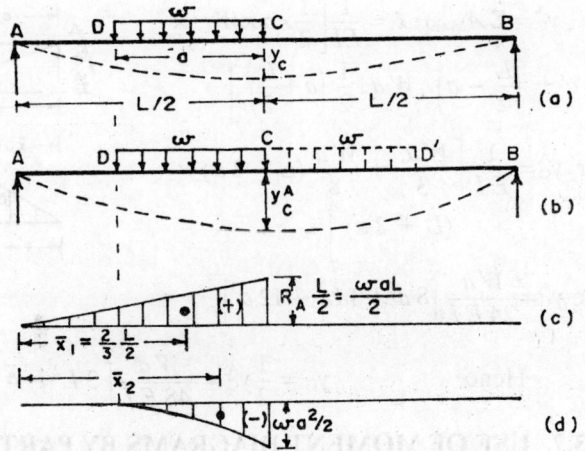

FIG. 13.18

13.8. GENERAL PROCEDURE FOR FINDING SLOPE AND DEFLECTION AT ANY POINT OF SIMPLY SUPPORTED BEAM

In Fig. 13.19(a), chain dotted line AC_1B is the original axis (horizontal) of the beam AB, while dark line ACB is the elastic curve of the beam AB subjected to loading. AB_2 is the tangent to the curve at A, while BB_1 is the tangent to the curve at B. The slopes at ends A and B are i_A and i_B respectively.

Let us find the deflection C_1C, designated as y_C^A, of the point C. Note that this deflection is positive, since it is in the *downward* direction from the original horizontal axis. The distance C_2C is the *deviation* of point C. *This deviation is negative since it is in the upward direction measured from the tangent at A to the curve.*

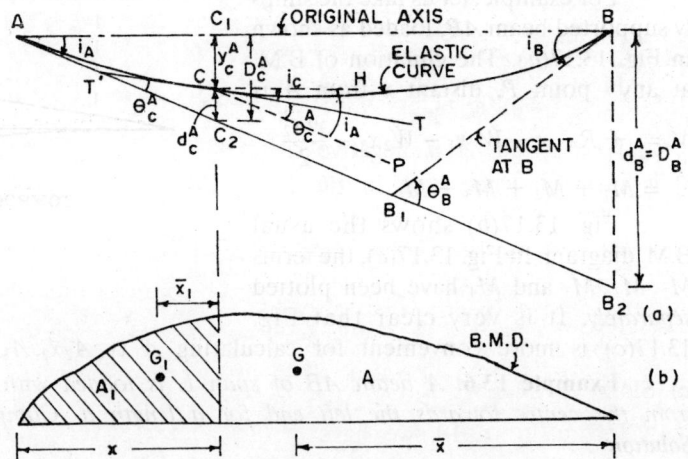

FIG. 13.19

(a) **Deflection at C :** Let us find deflection $C_1 C$ of the point C located at a distance x from the left hand support A. From the geometry of Fig. 13.19(a),

$$C_1 C_2 = \frac{x}{L} BB_2. \text{ But } BB_2 = D_B^A = d_B^A$$

Hence
$$C_1 C_2 = \frac{x}{L} d_B^A$$

Now deflection of $C = C_1 C = C_1 C_2 - CC_2 = \frac{x}{L} d_B^A - d_C^A$

Hence
$$y_C = \frac{x}{L} d_B^A - d_C^A \qquad ...(13.18)$$

It should be very clearly noted that both $d_B^A (= B_2 B)$ and $d_C^A (= C_2 C)$ are *negative* since they are in *upward direction* when measured from the tangent at A to the elastic curve.

$\therefore$
$$d_B^A = \sum_B^A \frac{A_M \bar{x}}{EI} \text{ and } d_C^A = \sum_B^A \frac{A_{M1} \bar{x}_1}{EI}$$

Hence
$$y_C = \frac{x}{L} \sum_B^A \frac{A_M \bar{x}}{EI} - \sum_B^A \frac{A_{M1} \bar{x}_1}{EI} \qquad ...(13.18a)$$

(b) **Slope at C :**

Through C, draw horizontal line CH, tangent line CT and line CP parallel to the tangent at A. Evidently, we have.

$$\angle HCT = i_C = \text{ slope at } C$$

$$\angle CT'B_2 = \angle TCP = \theta_C^A = \text{rotation of tangent at } C \text{ with respect to tangent at } A$$

$$\angle HCP = i_A = \text{ slope at } A.$$

Now slope at $C = i_C = i_A - \theta_C^A$ (From Fig. 13.19a)

But
$$i_A \approx \tan i_A = \frac{1}{L} d_B^A$$

Hence
$$i_C = \frac{1}{L} d_B^A - \theta_C^A \qquad ...(13.19)$$

Here again d_B^A is negative since it is measured upwards from the tangent at A. Also, θ_C^A is negative since it is in the anticlockwise direction.

$\therefore$
$$d_B^A = \sum_B^A \frac{A_M \bar{x}}{EI} \text{ and } \theta_C^A = \sum_C^A \frac{A_{M1}}{EI}$$

Hence
$$i_C = \frac{1}{L} \sum_B^A \frac{A_M \bar{x}}{EI} - \sum_C^A \frac{A_{M1}}{EI} \qquad ...(13.19a)$$

(c) **Slope at support B :**

From Eq. 13.19, we have

$$i_B = \frac{1}{L} d_B^A - \theta_B^A \qquad ...(13.19c)$$

where
$$d_B^A = \sum_B^A \frac{A_M \bar{x}}{EI} \quad \text{and} \quad \theta_B^A = \sum_B^A \frac{A_M}{EI}$$

Example 13.7. *A beam of length L is simply supported at the ends and carries a point load W at a distance a from end A. Find (a) expression for elastic curve of the beam (b) central deflection (c) maximum deflection and (d) slopes at the ends.*

Solution :

Consider a section P at a distance x from A. The component bending moment diagram for the length AB are shown in Fig. 13.20 (b) and (c), while that of the length AP is shown in in Fig. 13.20(d). The deviation d_B^A is *negative* since it is in the *upward* direction from the tangent at A.

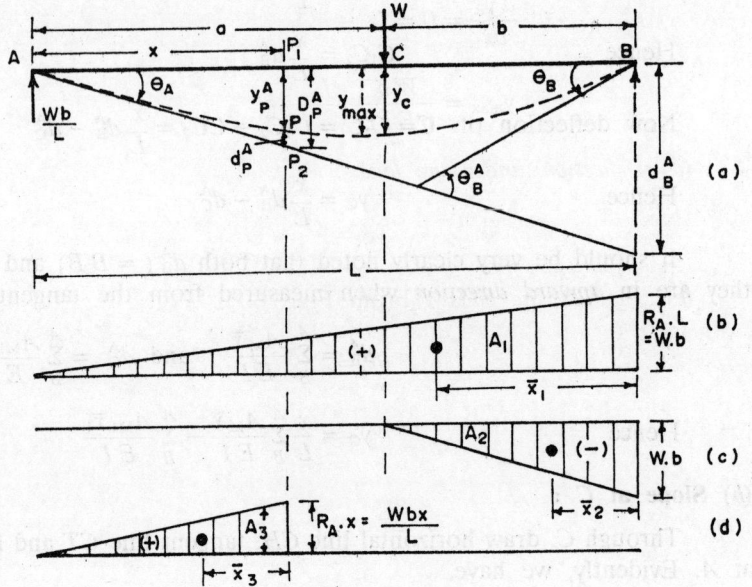

FIG. 13.20

Hence
$$d_B^A = \frac{1}{EI} \sum_B^A A_M \bar{x} = \frac{1}{EI} \sum_B^A \left(A_1 \bar{x}_1 + A_2 \bar{x}_2 \right)$$

$$= \frac{1}{EI} \left[\frac{1}{2} Wb \cdot L \cdot \frac{L}{3} - \frac{1}{2} Wb \cdot b \cdot \frac{b}{3} \right] = \frac{Wb}{6EI} \left[L^2 - b^2 \right] \qquad ...(1)$$

Similarly
$$d_P^A = \frac{1}{EI} \sum_P^A A_M \bar{x} = \frac{1}{EI} \left[\frac{1}{2} \cdot x \cdot \frac{Wbx}{L} \cdot \frac{x}{3} \right] = \frac{Wbx^3}{6EIL} \qquad ...(2)$$

(a) Expression for the elastic curve :

From Fig. 13.20(a),
$$D_P^A = P_1 P_2 = d_B^A \cdot \frac{x}{L} = \frac{Wbx}{6EIL} \left[L^2 - b^2 \right]$$

Hence
$$y_P^A = D_P^A - d_P^A = \frac{Wbx}{6EIL} \left[L^2 - b^2 \right] - \frac{Wbx^3}{6EIL}$$

or
$$y_P^A = \frac{Wbx}{6EIL} \left[L^2 - b^2 - x^2 \right] \qquad ...(3)$$

which is the required expression for the elastic curve.

(b) Central deflection :

At $x = \dfrac{L}{2}$, central deflection $= \dfrac{Wb}{6EIL} \cdot \dfrac{L}{2} \left[L^2 - b^2 - \dfrac{L^2}{4} \right] = \dfrac{Wb}{48EI} \left[3L^2 - 4b^2 \right]$

This is the same as Eq. 12.23.

(c) **Maximum deflection :**

For maximum deflection, we obtain from Eq. (3)

$$\frac{d y_P^A}{dx} = 0 = L^2 - b^2 - 3x^2, \text{ from which } x = \sqrt{\frac{L^2 - b^2}{3}}$$

$\therefore$
$$y_{max} = \frac{Wb}{6EIL}\left(\frac{L^2 - b^2}{3}\right)^{1/2}\left[L^2 - b^2 - \left(\frac{L^2 - b^2}{3}\right)\right] = \frac{Wb(L^2 - b^2)^{3/2}}{9\sqrt{3}\,EIL}$$

(d) **Deflection under the load :** Putting $x = a$ in Eq. 3

$$y_C = \frac{Wba}{6EIL}\left[L^2 - b^2 - a^2\right] = \frac{Wab}{6EIL}\cdot 2ab = \frac{Wa^2b^2}{3EIL}$$

(e) **Slope at the ends :** From Fig. 13.20, θ_B^A is negative. Hence

$$\theta_B^A = \sum_B^A \frac{A_M}{EI} = \left[\frac{1}{2}Wb\cdot L - \frac{1}{2}Wb\cdot b\right]\frac{1}{EI} = \frac{Wb}{2EI}(L - b)$$

$\therefore$
$$\theta_B^A = \frac{Wab}{2EI}$$

Now
$$\theta_A = \frac{d_B^A}{L} = \frac{Wb}{6EIL}\left[L^2 - b^2\right] = \frac{Wab}{6EIL}(L + b)$$

Numerically we have
$$\theta_B = \theta_B^A - \theta_A = \frac{Wab}{2EI} - \frac{Wab}{6EIL}\left[L + b\right] = \frac{Wab}{6EIL}\left[L + a\right]$$

Example 13.8. *A beam AB, simply supported at the ends is subjected to a point load at C, as shown in Fig. 13.21. Using area moment method, compute (i) deflection at C (ii) slope at A (iii) slope at B and (iv) slope at C. Take $I = 6 \times 10^8 \, mm^4$ and $E = 2 \times 10^5 \, N/mm^2$.*
Solution :

$$M_C = \frac{Wab}{L} = \frac{20 \times 6 \times 2}{8} = 30 \text{ kN-m} = 30 \times 10^6 \text{ N-mm}$$

Now $EI\,d_B^A = \sum_B^A A_M\bar{x}$

$= \frac{1}{2} \times 8000 \times 30 \times 10^6 \times \frac{1}{3} \times$

$(8000 + 2000) = 4 \times 10^{14}$

(The values have been substituted in N-mm units)

Similarly,

$EI\,d_C^A = \sum_C^A A_M\bar{x} = \frac{1}{2} \times 6000 \times 30$

$\times 10^6 \times \frac{1}{3} \times 6000 = 1.8 \times 10^{14}$

From Fig. 13.21 (a),

$$y_C^A = \frac{x}{L}d_B^A - d_C^A.$$

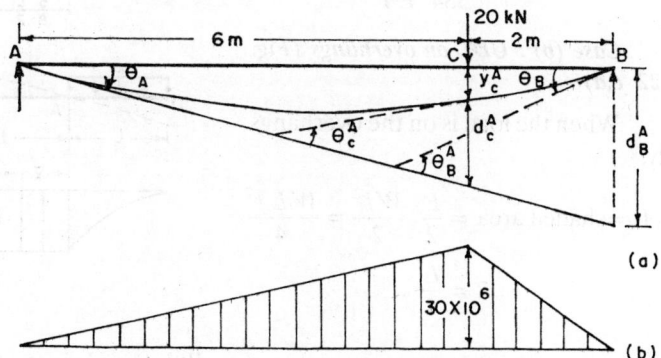

FIG. 13.21

$$\therefore \qquad y_C^A = \frac{1}{EI}\left[4 \times 10^{14} \times \frac{6}{8} - 1.8 \times 10^{14} \right] = \frac{1.2}{EI} \times 10^{14}$$

$$= \frac{1.2 \times 10^{14}}{2 \times 10^5 \times 6 \times 10^8} = 1 \text{ mm}$$

Also, $\qquad \theta_A = \dfrac{d_B^A}{L} = \dfrac{4 \times 10^{14}}{8000\, EI} = \dfrac{4 \times 10^{14}}{8000 \times 2 \times 10^5 \times 6 \times 10^8} = \mathbf{0.4167 \times 10^{-3}}$ **radian**

$$\theta_B^A = \sum_B^A \frac{A_M}{EI} = \frac{\frac{1}{2} \times 8000 \times 30 \times 10^6}{2 \times 10^5 \times 6 \times 10^8} = 1 \times 10^{-3} \text{ radian}$$

$\therefore \qquad \theta_B$ (numerically) $= \theta_B^A - \theta_A = 1 \times 10^{-3} - 0.4167 \times 10^{-3} = \mathbf{0.5833 \times 10^{-3}}$ **radian**

Also, $\qquad \theta_C^A = \sum_C^A \dfrac{A_M}{EI} = \dfrac{\frac{1}{2} \times 6000 \times 30 \times 10^6}{2 \times 10^5 \times 6 \times 10^8} = \mathbf{0.75 \times 10^{-3}}$ **radian**

$\therefore \qquad \theta_C$ (numerically) $= \theta_C^A - \theta_A = (0.75 - 0.4167) \times 10^{-3} = \mathbf{0.3333 \times 10^{-3}}$ **radian**

Example 13.9. *A beam of uniform section and length $(L + 2\,l)$ is simply supported over a span L with two equal over hanging lengths L. Derive expression for the deflection at mid-span due to a uniformly distributed load covering (a) the length L between the supports (b) the two overhanging lengths. If the beam carries uniformly distributed load on the whole length, find the ratio l/L so that the beam at the mid-span is just level with the supports.*

Solution :

Case (a) : UDL on mid-span (Fig. 13.22 a,b)

$$EI y_C^A = -EI y_A^C = -EI d_A^C$$

$\therefore \qquad EI y_C^A = + \sum_A^C A_M \bar{x}$

$$= \frac{2}{3}\left(\frac{wL^2}{8} \right)\left(\frac{L}{2} \right)\left(\frac{5}{8}\frac{L}{2} \right)$$

or $\qquad y_C^A = y_1 = \dfrac{5}{384} \dfrac{wL^4}{EI} \ (\downarrow) \quad \dots(1)$

Case (b) : UDL on overhangs (Fig. 13.22 c,d)

When the load is on the overhangs only,

$$A_M = \text{shaded area} = \frac{L}{2} \cdot \frac{Wl^2}{2} = \frac{WLl^2}{4}$$

$$\bar{x} = \frac{L}{4}$$

$\therefore \qquad EI y_C^A = -EI d_A^C = \sum_A^C A_M \bar{x} = \dfrac{WLl^2}{4} \times \dfrac{L}{4}$

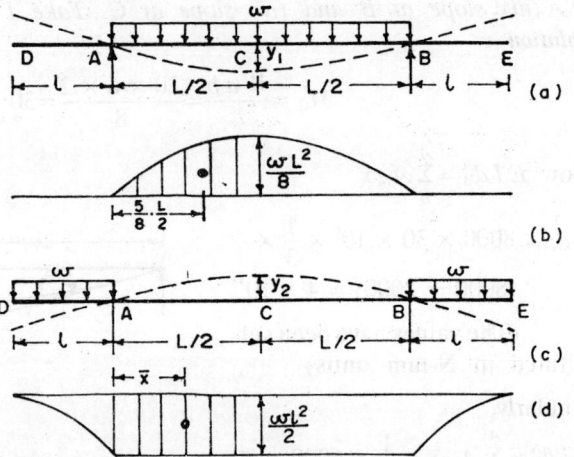

FIG. 13.22

$$\therefore \qquad y_C^A = y_2 = \frac{w L^2 l^2}{16 E I} \ (\uparrow) \qquad \qquad ...(ii)$$

Case (c) UDL over the whole span

When the U.D.L. is over the whole span

$$y_C^A = y_1 + y_2 = \frac{5}{384} \frac{w L^4}{E I} - \frac{w L^2 l^2}{16 E I}$$

But $\qquad\qquad y_C^A = 0$ (given condition)

$$\therefore \qquad \frac{5}{384} \frac{w L^4}{E I} = \frac{w L^2 l^2}{16 E I}$$

or $\qquad\qquad\qquad \dfrac{5}{24} L^2 = l^2$

From which $\qquad\qquad \dfrac{l}{L} = \sqrt{\dfrac{5}{24}} = \mathbf{0.4564}$

Example 13.10. *A uniform section straight edge of length L is loaded by its own weight only and is freely supported two points. Find the distance between the two supports:*

(a) so that, with the supports at the same level, the two ends of the beam remain horizontal.

(b) so that the deviation, from the straight line is as small as possible.

Solution :

(a) Required Condition :
$i_A = i_B = 0$

Also, by symmetry $i_C = 0$

$$\therefore \qquad E I \theta_C^A = - \sum_C^A A_M = 0$$

$$\therefore \qquad \frac{1}{2} a . w l a - \frac{1}{3} . l \frac{w l^2}{2} = 0$$

From which $a^2 = \dfrac{l^2}{3}$.

or $\quad a = \dfrac{l}{\sqrt{3}} = 0.5774\, l$

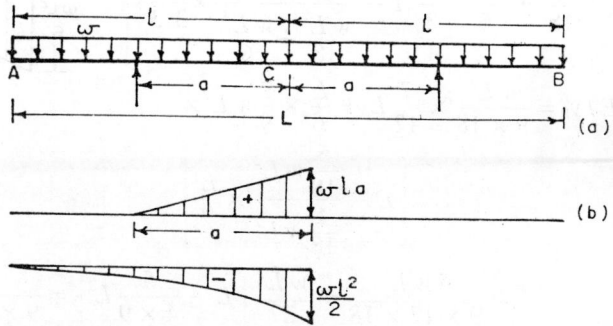

FIG. 13.23

$\therefore$ Distance between the supports $= 2\, a = 0.5774\,(2\, l) = \mathbf{0.5774\, L}$

(b) For the deviation to be as small as possible, $y_A = y_B = y_C$

$$\therefore \qquad E I y_A^C = \sum_A^C A_M \bar{x} = 0$$

Hence $\dfrac{1}{2} a . w l a \left(l - \dfrac{a}{3} \right) - \dfrac{1}{3} \times l \times \dfrac{w l^2}{2} \times \dfrac{3}{4} l = 0$

or $\qquad \dfrac{w}{2}\left(a^2 l - \dfrac{a^3}{3}\right) - \dfrac{w\,l^3}{8} = 0$

or $\qquad 4\,a^2 l - \dfrac{4\,a^3}{3} - l^3 = 0$

or $\qquad 4\,a^3 - 12\,a^2 l + 3\,l^3 = 0$

Let $\qquad\qquad\qquad\qquad a = n\,l$

Then $\qquad\qquad 4\,n^3 - 12\,n^2 + 3 = 0$

Solving this by trial or by plotting, we get $n = 0.554$

$\therefore \qquad\qquad\qquad\qquad a = 0.554\,l$

$\therefore$ Distance between the supports $= 2\,a = 0.554\,(2\,l) = 0.554\,L$

Example 13.11 *Determine the angle of rotation and deflection at the free end of a cantilever beam AB with a uniform load w acting over the middle third of the length.*

Solution :

$$E\,I\,\theta_B^A = -\sum_B^A A_M = \left[\frac{1}{3}\times\frac{w\,L^2}{18}\times\frac{L}{3} + \frac{1}{2}\left(\frac{w\,L^2}{18}+\frac{w\,L^2}{6}\right)\frac{L}{3}\right] = \frac{7}{162}\,w\,L^3$$

$\therefore\qquad i_B = \theta_B^A = \dfrac{7}{162}\dfrac{w\,L^3}{E\,I}$

Also, $\ E\,I\,y_B^A = E\,I\,d_B^A = -\sum_B^A A_M\,.\,\bar{x}$

$$= \left[\frac{1}{3}\times\frac{w\,L^2}{18}\times\frac{L}{3}\left(\frac{L}{3}+\frac{3}{4}\cdot\frac{L}{3}\right)\right]$$

$$+ \left[\frac{1}{2}\left(\frac{w\,L^2}{18}+\frac{w\,L^2}{6}\right)\frac{L}{3}\left\{L - \frac{\dfrac{2\,w\,L^2}{18}+\dfrac{w\,L^2}{6}}{\dfrac{w\,L^2}{18}+\dfrac{w\,L^2}{6}}\times\frac{1}{3}\frac{L}{3}\right\}\right]$$

or $E\,I\,y_B^A = \dfrac{w\,L^3}{9\times 18}\times\dfrac{7}{12}L + \dfrac{L}{6}\times\dfrac{2}{9}\,w\,L^2\times$

$$\left\{L - \frac{\dfrac{5}{18}\,w\,L^2}{\dfrac{4}{18}\,w\,L^2}\times\frac{L}{9}\right\}$$

$$= \frac{7\,w\,L^4}{9\times 12\times 18} + \frac{w\,L^3}{27}\left[L - \frac{5}{4\times 9}L\right] = \frac{7}{9\times 12\times 18}\,w\,L^4 + \frac{31}{27\times 36}\,w\,L^4$$

Hence $\quad y_B^A = \dfrac{23}{648}\dfrac{w\,L^4}{E\,I}$

FIG. 13.24

Example 13.12. *A cantilever beam AB with two different moments of inertia I and 2I supports a uniformly distributed load w. Determine the slope and deflection at the free end.*

Solution :

M diagram is shown in Fig .13.25(b) while $\dfrac{M}{E\,I}$ diagram is shown in Fig. 13.25(c). In

Fig. 13.25(c), ordinate at C (right) $= \dfrac{w\,L^2}{8}\times\dfrac{1}{E\,I} = \dfrac{w\,L^2}{8\,E\,I}$, ordinate at C (left) $= \dfrac{w\,L^2}{8}\times\dfrac{1}{2\,E\,I} = \dfrac{w\,L^2}{16\,E\,I}$

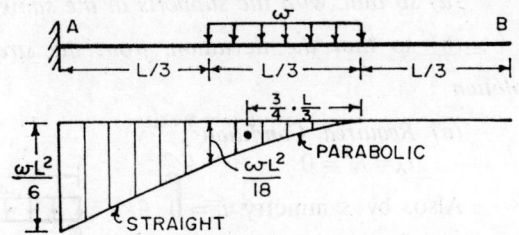

and ordinate at $A = \dfrac{wL^2}{2} \times \dfrac{1}{2EI}$

$= \dfrac{wL^2}{4EI}$. The complete $\dfrac{M}{EI}$ diagram can be splitted into two parts A_1 and A_2

(i) Area A_1 : Parabolic variation

$$A_1 = \frac{1}{3} \frac{wL^2}{8EI} \cdot \frac{L}{2} = \frac{wL^3}{48EI}$$

$$\bar{x}_1 = \frac{3}{4}\left(\frac{L}{2}\right) = \frac{3}{8}L \quad \text{(from } B\text{)}$$

(ii) Area A_2 : This is *parabolic sector*. Fig. 13.25(*d*) shows the details of the sector. Measuring x from C, towards A, the equation of the curve is

$$y = \frac{M_x}{EI_x} = \frac{w}{2}\left(\frac{L}{2}+x\right)^2 \times \frac{1}{2EI}$$

$$= \frac{w}{4EI}\left(\frac{L}{2}+x\right)^2$$

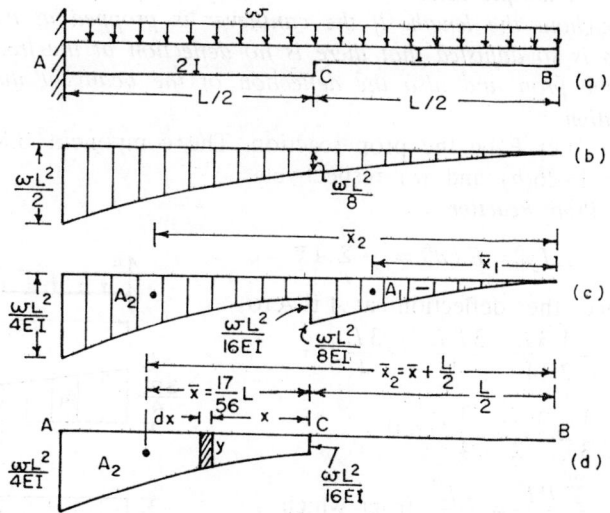

FIG. 13.25

$$dA = y \, . \, dx$$

$$\therefore \quad A_2 = \int_0^{L/2} dA = \int_0^{L/2} y \, . \, dx = \int_0^{L/2} \frac{w}{4EI}\left(\frac{L}{2}+x\right)^2$$

$$= \frac{w}{4EI}\int_0^{L/2}\left(\frac{L^2}{4}+x^2+Lx\right)dx = \frac{w}{4EI}\left[\frac{L^2}{4}x+\frac{x^3}{3}+\frac{Lx^2}{2}\right]_0^{L/2} = \frac{7wL^3}{96EI}$$

Also, $\quad Q = \int_0^{L/2} x \, dA = \frac{w}{4EI}\int_0^{L/2}\left(\frac{L^2}{4}x+x^3+Lx^2\right)dx = \frac{w}{4EI}\left[\frac{L^2}{4}\cdot\frac{x^2}{2}+\frac{x^4}{4}+\frac{Lx^3}{3}\right]_0^{L/2}$

$$= \frac{17wL^4}{4 \times 192 EI}$$

$$\therefore \quad \bar{x} = \frac{Q}{A_2} = \frac{17wL^4}{4\times192EI}\times\frac{96EI}{7wL^3} = \frac{17}{56}L$$

Now $\quad \theta_B^A = -\sum_B^A A_{M/EI} = \frac{wL^3}{48EI}+\frac{7wL^3}{96EI} = \frac{9wL^3}{96EI} = \frac{3wL^3}{32EI}$ (Ans.)

Also, $\quad y_B^A = -\sum_B^A A_{M/EI}\,.\,\bar{x} = \frac{wL^3}{48EI}\times\frac{3}{8}L+\frac{7wL^3}{96EI}\left(\frac{17}{56}L+\frac{L}{2}\right) = \frac{17}{256}\frac{wL^4}{EI}$ (Ans.)

13.9. ADDITIONAL ILLUSTRATIVE EXAMPLES

Example 13.13. *A cantilever of effective length L carries a total load wL uniformly distributed throughout the length. If the cantilever is propped at a point L/4 from the free end and the prop is so adjusted that there is no deflection at the free end, derive a formula for the reaction at the prop and also the deflection of the beam at the prop.*

Solution :

Let P be the prop reaction. The component B.M. diagram for P and w are shown in Fig. 13.26(b) and (c) respectively.

(a) Prop Reaction :

$$E I y_B^A = E I d_B^A = - \sum_B^A A \bar{x} = 0$$

(since the deflection at A is zero)

$$\therefore \quad -\frac{1}{2}\frac{3L}{4}\left(\frac{3PL}{4}\right)\left(\frac{3L}{4}\right) +$$

$$\frac{1}{3}L.\frac{wL^2}{2}.\frac{3}{4}L = 0$$

or $\dfrac{27\,P L^3}{128} = \dfrac{wL^4}{8}$ from which

$$P = \frac{16}{27}\,wL \quad \text{(Ans.)}$$

(b) Deflection of the beam at the prop

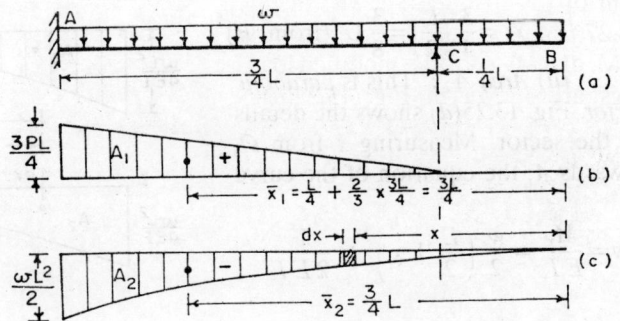

FIG. 13.26

$$E I y_C^A = E I d_C^A = - \sum_C^A A \bar{x} \qquad \qquad ...(i)$$

(i) $A\bar{x}$ due to P :

$$(A\bar{x})_C^A \text{ due to } P = \frac{1}{2}\times\frac{3}{4}L\times\frac{3PL}{4}\left(\frac{2}{3}.\frac{3}{4}L\right) = \frac{9PL^3}{64}$$

$$= \frac{9}{64}\left(\frac{16}{27}wL\right)L^3 = \frac{wL^4}{12}$$

(ii) $A\bar{x}$ due to w :

To find $(A\bar{x})_C^A$ due to w, consider an elementary strip dx at a distance x from A.

Ordinate $\qquad y = \dfrac{wx^2}{2}$. Hence $dA = y\,dx = \dfrac{wx^2}{2}\,dx$

$\bar{x}$ of this strip, from $C = x - L/4$

$$\delta(A\bar{x}) = \frac{wx^2}{2}\,dx\,(x - L/4)$$

$$\therefore \quad \sum_C^A (A\bar{x})_w = \int_{L/4}^{L} \frac{wx^2}{2}\left(x-\frac{L}{4}\right)dx = \frac{w}{2}\int_{L/4}^{L}\left(x^3-\frac{Lx^2}{4}\right)dx$$

$$= \frac{w}{2}\left[\frac{x^4}{4}-\frac{Lx^3}{12}\right]_{L/4}^{L} = \frac{171\,wL^4}{2048}$$

Substituting the values in (i), we get

$$E I y_C^A = -\left[\frac{w L^4}{12} - \frac{171 \, w \, L^4}{2048}\right] = \frac{w \, L^4}{6144 \, E \, I} \quad \text{(Ans.)}$$

Example 13.14. *Compute the maximum slope and deflection for a cantilever beam, shown in Fig. 13.27, that carries varying load from zero at the wall to w_0 at the free end.*

Solution :

The elastic curve in Fig. 13.27(a) shows that the maximum slope and maximum deflection occurs at the free end B. Also, the given loading shown in Fig. 13.27(a) is equivalent to the sum of the loadings shown in Fig. 13.27(b) and (c). The corresponding B.M. diagrams for the modified loadings are shown in Fig. 13.27(d).

Now $i_B = \theta_B^A = -\dfrac{1}{E \, I} \sum\limits_B^A A_M$

$= -\dfrac{1}{E \, I}\left[\dfrac{1}{4} \times \dfrac{w_0 L^2}{6} \times L - \dfrac{1}{3} \dfrac{w_0 L^2}{2} \times L\right]$

$= \dfrac{w_0 L^2}{8 E \, I}$ (Ans.)

Also, $y_B = d_B^A = -\dfrac{1}{E \, I} \sum\limits_B^A A_M \cdot \bar{x}$

$= -\dfrac{1}{E \, I}\left[\dfrac{1}{4} \times \dfrac{w_0 L^2}{6} \times L \times \dfrac{4}{5}L\right.$

$\left. - \dfrac{1}{3} \cdot \dfrac{w_0 L^2}{2} \cdot L \times \dfrac{3}{4}L\right]$

$= \dfrac{11}{120} \dfrac{w_0 L^4}{E \, I}$ (Ans.)

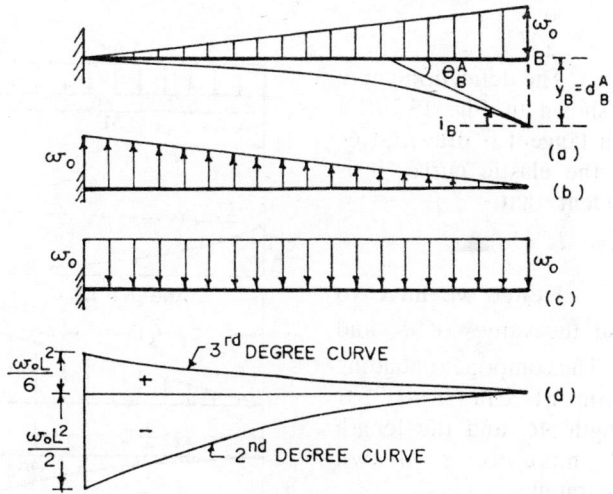

FIG. 13.27

Example 13.15. *A cantilever is acted on by a uniformly distributed moment of intensity m per unit distance along the axis of the beam. Find the slope and deflection at the free end.*

Solution :

$$M_B = 0 \, ; \, M_A = m \, L$$

The B.M. diagram is shown in Fig. 13.28(b), the variation being linear.

Now $\qquad i_B = \theta_B^A = -\sum\limits_B^A \dfrac{A_M}{E \, I}$

$= -\dfrac{1}{E \, I}\left[-\dfrac{1}{2} \times m \, L \times L\right] = \dfrac{m \, L^2}{2 \, E \, I}$ (Ans.)

Also, $\qquad y_B = d_B^A = -\sum\limits_B^A \dfrac{A_M}{E \, I} \cdot \bar{x}$

$= -\dfrac{1}{EI}\left[-\dfrac{1}{2} \times m \, L \times L \times \dfrac{2}{3}L\right] = \dfrac{m \, L^3}{3 \, E \, I}$ (Ans.)

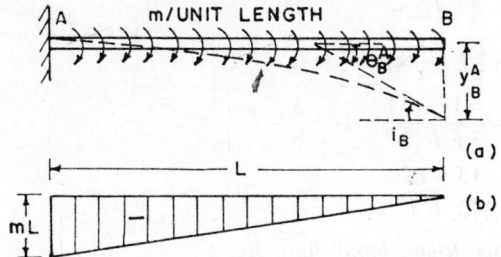

FIG. 13.28

Example 13.16. *A simply supported beam of span $2L$ has a second moment of area of $3I$ for the left half of the span and $2I$ for the right hand half. The beam carries a load of intensity $3w$ uniformly distributed over the left hand half of the span and of intensity $2w$ uniformly distributed over the right hand half. Obtain an expression for the deflection at the centre of the span. If the prop is now placed at the centre of the span to restore the beam to its original level at this point, find the force in the prop.*

Solution :

(a) Beam without prop :

$$R_A = \left(3wL \times \frac{3}{2}L + 2wL \times \frac{L}{2}\right)\frac{1}{2L} = \frac{11}{4}wL.$$

$$R_B = (3wL + 2wL) - \frac{11}{4}wL$$

$$= \frac{9}{4}wL$$

The deflection curve is shown in Fig. 13.29(b). If a tangent is drawn at C, to the elastic curve, it is evident that

$$y_C = \left(d_A^C + d_B^C\right)\frac{1}{2}$$

Hence we have to find the values of d_A^C and d_B^C. The component bending moment diagrams for length AC and the length BC have been drawn separately.

(i) Left hand half AC :

Since the deviation d_A^C is *negative*, we have

$$d_A^C = \frac{1}{3EI}\sum_A^C A\bar{x}$$

$$= \frac{1}{3EI}\left[\frac{1}{2} \times L \times \frac{11}{4}wL^2 \times \frac{2}{3}L - \frac{1}{3} \times L \times \frac{3}{2}wL^2 \times \frac{3}{4}L\right]$$

$$= \frac{1}{3EI}\left[\frac{11}{12}wL^4 - \frac{3}{8}wL^4\right]$$

$$= \frac{13}{72}\frac{wL^4}{EI} \qquad \dots(i)$$

(ii) Right hand half BC :

Here also, the deviation d_B^C is *negative*. Hence we have

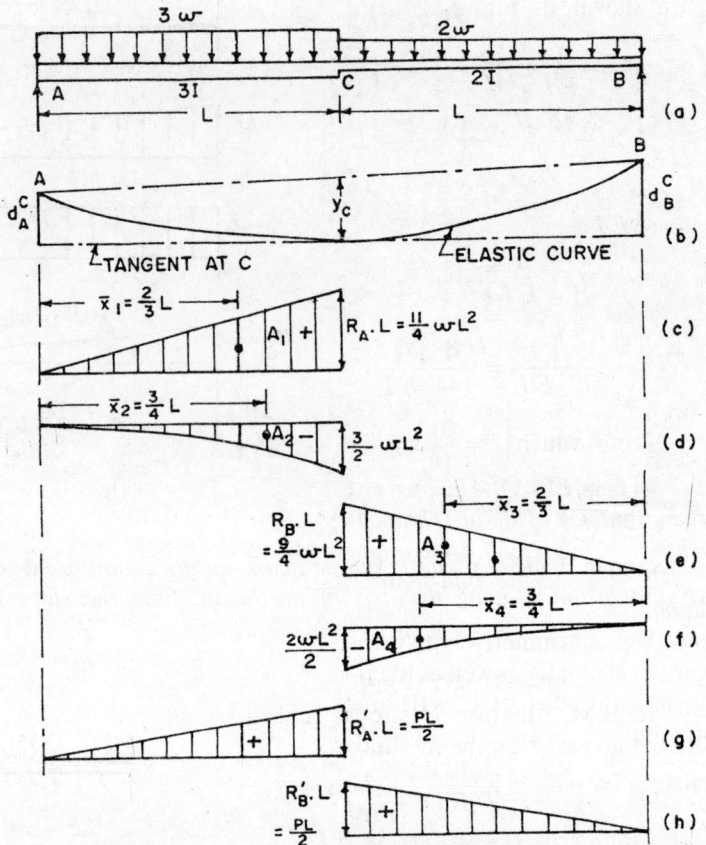

FIG. 13.29

$$d_B^C = \frac{1}{2EI}\sum_B^C A\bar{x} = \frac{1}{2EI}\left[\frac{1}{2}\times L\times\frac{9}{4}wL^2\times\frac{2}{3}L - \frac{1}{3}L.wL^2\times\frac{3}{4}L\right]$$

$$= \frac{1}{2EI}\left[\frac{3}{4}wL^4 - \frac{wL^4}{4}\right] = \frac{wL^4}{4EI} \qquad ...(ii)$$

Hence $\qquad y_C = \frac{1}{2}\left[d_A^C + d_B^C\right] = \frac{1}{2}\left[\frac{13}{72}\frac{wL^4}{EI} + \frac{1}{4}\frac{wL^4}{EI}\right] = \frac{31}{144}\frac{wL^4}{EI}$ (Ans.)

(b) Beam with prop at C

Let P be the force in prop. Due to the prop force P, let y_C' be the upward deflection of C. The condition equation is : $y_C = y_C'$.

Let us now calculate the upward deflection y_C' due to prop force P acting upwards. Evidently, $R_A' = R_B' = \frac{1}{2}P$. The component B.M. diagrams for AC and BC due to this loading are shown in Fig. 13.29(g) and (h) respectively.

Evidently $y_C' = \frac{1}{2}\left[d_A^{C'} + d_B^{C'}\right]$

For AC, $d_A^{C'} = \frac{1}{3EI}\sum_A^C A'\bar{x}' = \frac{1}{3EI}\left[\frac{1}{2}\times L\times\frac{PL}{2}\times\frac{2}{3}L\right] = \frac{PL^3}{18EI}$ $\qquad ...(iii)$

For BC, $d_B^{C'} = \frac{1}{2EI}\sum_B^C A'\bar{x}' = \frac{1}{2EI}\left[\frac{1}{2}\times L\times\frac{PL}{2}\times\frac{2}{3}L\right] = \frac{PL^3}{12EI}$ $\qquad ...(iv)$

$\therefore \qquad y_C' = \frac{1}{2}\left[d_A^{C'} + d_B^{C'}\right] = \frac{1}{2}\left[\frac{PL^3}{18EI} + \frac{PL^3}{12EI}\right] = \frac{5}{72}\frac{PL^3}{EI}$

Now $\qquad y_C' = y_C$

$\therefore \qquad \frac{5}{72}\frac{PL^3}{EI} = \frac{31}{144}\frac{wL^4}{EI}$

From which $P = \dfrac{31}{10}wL$

Example 13.17. *A beam with variable moment of inertia is loaded as shown in Fig. 13.30. Determine the deflection at the mid-span.*

Solution :

Due to symmetry, both with regard to geometry as well as loading, the tangent at C will be horizontal.

Hence $y_C^A = -d_A^C = \sum_A^C \dfrac{A_M\bar{x}}{EI}$

Fig. 13.30 (b) shows M-diagram. Fig. 13.30(c) shows M/EI diagram, which can be splitted into three parts.

$\sum_A^C \dfrac{A_M\bar{x}}{EI} = \left[\frac{1}{2}\times a\times\frac{Pa}{EI}\times\frac{2}{3}a\right]$

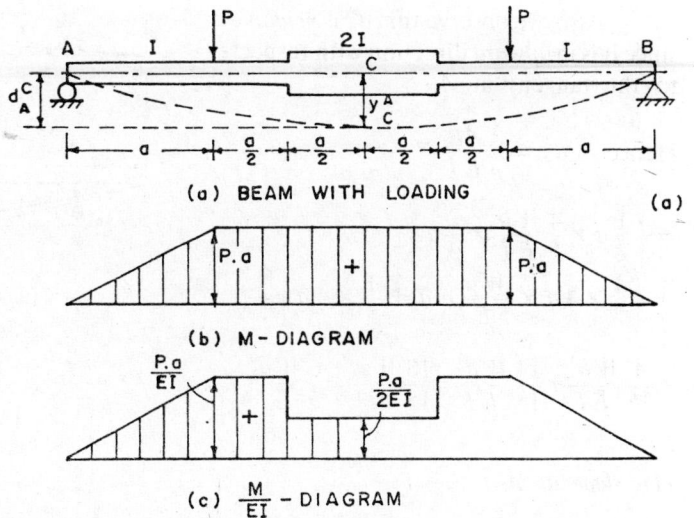

(a) BEAM WITH LOADING

(b) M- DIAGRAM

(c) $\frac{M}{EI}$ – DIAGRAM

FIG. 13.30

$$+ \left[\frac{P a}{E I} \times \frac{a}{2} \left(a + \frac{a}{4} \right) \right] + \left[\frac{P a}{2 E I} \times \frac{a}{2} \left(a + \frac{a}{2} + \frac{a}{4} \right) \right]$$

$$= \frac{P a^3}{3 E I} + \frac{5 P a^3}{8 E I} + \frac{7 P a^3}{16 E I} = \frac{67}{48} \frac{P a^3}{E I}$$

Hence $y_C^A = \frac{67}{48} \frac{P a^3}{E I}$ (Ans.)

Example 13.18. *A beam ACB, simply supported at the ends, has moment of inertia 4 I for the length AC and I for the length CB, and is loaded with point load W at C. Determine (i) slope at end A (ii) Deflection at mid-span and (iii) Maximum deflection.*

Solution :

Fig. 13.31(*b*) shows the *M* diagram, while Fig. 13.31(*c*) shows $\frac{M}{E I}$ diagram which is self explanatory.

Fig. 13.31(*d*) shows the geometry of the deflection curve from which we find that

$$i_A = \theta_A = \frac{1}{L} d_B^A \qquad ...(1)$$

Also, for any point *X*, distant *x* from *A*, we have

$$y_X^A = \frac{x}{L} d_B^A - d_X^A \qquad ...(ii)$$

Also, we observe that d_B^A is *negative* since it is in *upward* direction with respect to the tangent at *A*.

Hence $d_B^A = \overset{A}{\underset{B}{\Sigma}} \frac{A_M}{E I} . \bar{x}$

$$= \left[\frac{1}{2} a \times \frac{4}{5} \frac{W a}{E I} \times \frac{2}{3} a \right]$$

$$+ \left[\frac{1}{2} \times 4 a \times \frac{W a}{5 E I} \left(a + \frac{1}{3} \times 4 a \right) \right]$$

$$= \frac{4}{15} \frac{W a^3}{E I} + \frac{14}{15} \frac{W a^3}{E I} = \frac{18}{15} \frac{W a^3}{E I} = \frac{6}{5} \frac{W a^3}{E I}$$
$$...(iii)$$

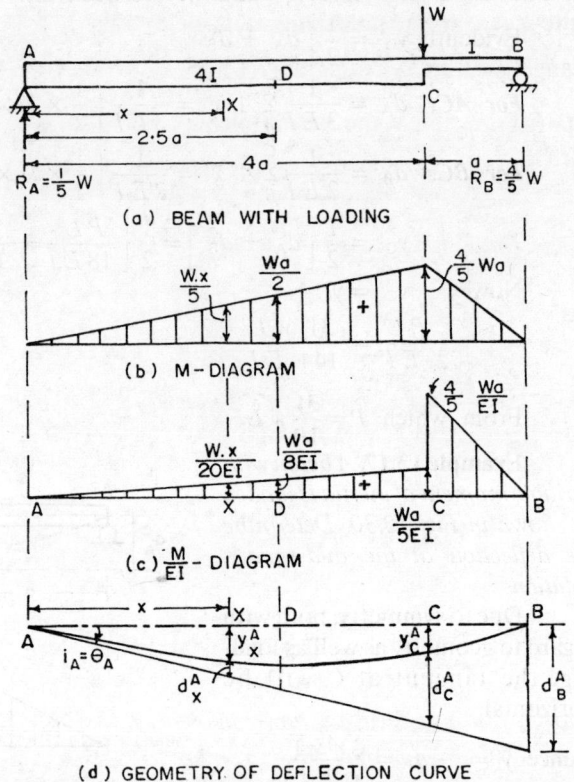

(a) BEAM WITH LOADING

(b) M – DIAGRAM

(c) $\frac{M}{E I}$ – DIAGRAM

(d) GEOMETRY OF DEFLECTION CURVE

FIG. 13.31

(1) Slope at A :

$$i_A = \theta_A = \frac{1}{L} d_B^A = \frac{1}{5 a} \times \frac{6}{5} \frac{W a^3}{E I} = \frac{6}{25} \frac{W a^2}{E I} \text{ (Ans.)}$$

(ii) Deflection at mid-span (i.e. at point D)

From Eq. (ii)
$$y_D^A = \frac{2.5\,a}{5\,a}\,d_B^A - d_D^A = \frac{1}{2}\,d_B^A - d_D^A \qquad \ldots(iv)$$

Here, d_D^A is *negative* since it is also in the upward direction.

$$\therefore \qquad d_D^A = \overset{A}{\underset{D}{\Sigma}} \frac{A_M \cdot \bar{x}}{EI} = \frac{1}{2} \times 2.5\,a \times \frac{W\,a}{8\,EI}\left(\frac{1}{3} \times 2.5\,a\right) = \frac{25}{192}\frac{W\,a^3}{EI}$$

Substituting the values of d_B^A and d_D^A in (iv), we get

$$y_D^A = \frac{1}{2}\left(\frac{6}{5}\frac{W\,a^3}{EI}\right) - \frac{25}{192}\frac{W\,a^3}{EI} = \frac{902}{1920}\frac{W\,a^3}{EI} = \mathbf{0.4698}\frac{W\,a^3}{EI}$$

(iii) Maximum deflection

Maximum deflection occurs at point X, distant x from A. Since its location is *always* quite near to the midspan, it is definitely to the left of point C. Hence only the left hand triangle of the $\frac{M}{EI}$ diagram (Fig. 13.31 c) will be considered. The deflection y_X^A is given by Eq. (ii) in which the deviations d_X^A is negative since it is in the upward direction. Hence

$$d_X^A = \overset{A}{\underset{X}{\Sigma}} \frac{A_M \cdot \bar{x}}{EI} = \frac{1}{2}x \cdot \frac{W\,x}{20\,EI}\left(\frac{x}{3}\right) = \frac{W\,x^3}{120\,EI}$$

Hence
$$y_X^A = \frac{x}{L}\,d_B^A - d_X^A = \frac{x}{5\,a} \times \frac{6}{5}\frac{W\,a^3}{EI} - \frac{W\,x^3}{120\,EI} = \frac{6}{25}\frac{W\,x\,a^2}{EI} - \frac{W\,x^3}{120\,EI}$$

For maxima,
$$\frac{d\,y_X^A}{d\,x} = 0 = \frac{6}{25}\frac{W\,a^2}{EI} - \frac{3\,W\,x^2}{120\,EI}$$

From which, we get $\qquad x = 3.0984\,a$

Hence
$$y_{max} = y_{X = 3.0984\,a}^A = \frac{6}{25}\frac{W\,a^2}{EI}(3.0984\,a) - \frac{W}{120\,EI}(3.0984\,a)^3$$

or
$$y_{max} = \mathbf{0.4957}\frac{W\,a^3}{EI}$$

Note : This problem has also been solved by double integration method at example 12.34. For solution of this problem by the conjugate beam method, see example 14.13.

Example 13.19. *A beam ABC is simply supported at A and B, and it overhangs from B to C, and is loaded as shown in Fig. 13.29(a). Calculate (a) slopes at A, B and C (b) deflection y_C at the free end, and (c) maximum deflection in the span AB. Take $E = 2 \times 10^5\,N/mm^2$ and $I = 1.5 \times 10^9\,mm^4$.*

Solution :

Fig. 13.32(b) shows the deflection curve, in which AB_1 is the tangent to the curve at A and A_1BC_1 is the tangent to the curve at support B. As marked in Fig. 13.32(b), angles i_A, i_B and i_C are all positive. The B.M. diagram is shown in Fig. 13.32(c). For CB, the B.M. varies parabolically, with $M_B = -\frac{6\,(3)^2}{2} = -27$ kN-m.

Reaction $\quad R_A = \dfrac{1}{7.5}(48 \times 4.5 - 6 \times 3 \times 1.5) = 25.2 \text{ kN}(\uparrow).$

Also, $\quad\quad R_B = 48 + 18 - 25.2 = 40.8 \;\; \text{kN}(\uparrow)$

Hence

$M_D = 25.2 \times 3 = +75.6$ kN-m. The variation of B.M in AD is linear. For B.M. in DB, measuring x from B, we have $M_x = -6 \times 3\,(x + 1.5) + 40.8\,x = 22.8\,x - 27.$ This variation is linear, which gives $M_D = 22.8 \times 4.5 - 27 = 75.6$ kN-m, as found earlier. The point of contraflexure occurs at $x = 27/22.8 = 1.1842$ m from B. This point of inflexion has been marked by a dark dot on the deflection curve.

The component bending moment diagrams for span AB and span CB are shown in Fig. 13.32(d).

(a) Rotations at A, B and C

Now $i_A = \theta_A = \dfrac{d_B^A}{AB}$

$\quad = \dfrac{d_B^A}{7.5} \quad\quad ...(i)$

Note that $d_B^A = B_1 B$ is negative since it is in upward direction from the tangent $A\,B_1$.

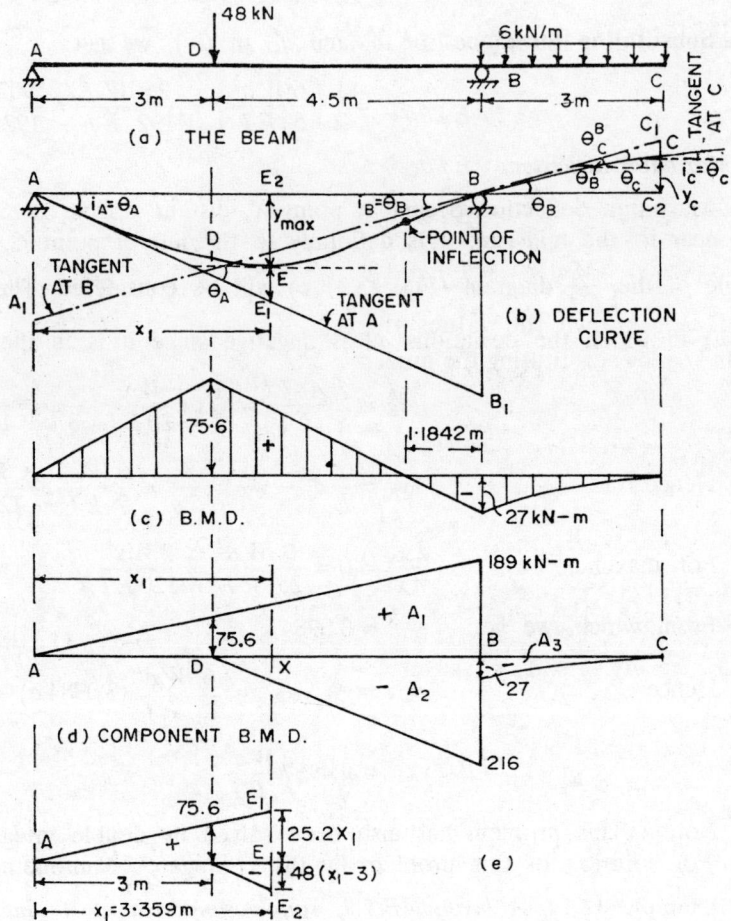

FIG. 13.32

$\therefore \quad\quad E\,I\,d_B^A = \overset{A}{\underset{B}{\sum}} A\,\bar{x} = \left(A_1 \bar{x}_1 + A_2 \bar{x}_2\right)_B^A$

$= \left[\dfrac{1}{2} \times 7.5 \times 189 \times \dfrac{1}{3} \times 7.5 - \dfrac{1}{2} \times 4.5 \times 216 \times \dfrac{1}{3} \times 4.5\right] = 1042.9 \;\; \text{kN-m}^3$

$$\therefore \qquad EI\theta_A = \frac{EId_B^A}{7.5} = \frac{1042.9}{7.5} = 139.05 \ \text{kN-m}^2 = 139.05 \times 10^9 \ \text{N-mm}^2 \qquad ...(ii)$$

Similarly, $\qquad i_B = \theta_B = \dfrac{d_A^B}{BA} = \dfrac{d_A^B}{7.5}$ $\qquad\qquad\qquad\qquad\qquad\qquad ...(iii)$

Here also, d_A^B is negative since it is in upward direction from the tangent BA_1.

$$\therefore \qquad EId_A^B = \sum_A^B A\bar{x} = \left(A_1\bar{x}_1 + A_2\bar{x}_2 \right)_A^B$$

$$= \left(\frac{1}{2} \times 7.5 \times 189 \times \frac{2}{3} \times 7.5 \right) - \left(\frac{1}{2} \times 4.5 \times 216 \right) \left(3 + \frac{2}{3} \times 4.5 \right) = 627.75 \ \text{kN-m}^3$$

$$\therefore \qquad EI\theta_B = \frac{627.75}{7.5} = 83.7 \ \text{kN-m}^2 = 83.7 \times 10^9 \ \text{N-mm}^2$$

Now algebraically, $\qquad EI\theta_C = EI\theta_B + EI\theta_C^B$

or $\qquad\qquad\qquad\qquad EI\theta_C = EI\theta_B + \sum_C^B A_3$

or $\qquad\qquad\qquad\qquad EI\theta_C = 83.7 - \left(\frac{1}{3} \times 3 \times 27 \right) = 56.7 \ \text{kN-m}^2 = 56.7 \times 10^9 \ \text{N-mm}^2$

Having known the values of $EI\theta_A, EI\theta_B$ and $EI\theta_C$, let us find the values of θ_A, θ_B and θ_C, by substituting the numerical values of $EI = 2 \times 10^5 \times 1.5 \times 10^9 = 3 \times 10^{14} \ \text{N-mm}^2$.

$$\therefore \qquad i_A = \theta_A = \frac{139.05 \times 10^9}{3 \times 10^{14}} = 46 \times 10^{-5} \ \text{rad.}$$

$$i_B = \theta_B = \frac{83.7 \times 10^9}{3 \times 10^{14}} = 27.9 \times 10^{-5} \ \text{rad.}$$

$$i_C = \theta_C = \frac{56.7 \times 10^9}{3 \times 10^4} = 18.9 \times 10^{-5} \ \text{rad.}$$

(b) Deflection of free end C

From Fig. 13.32, we have $\because y_C = C_2C = C_1C_2 - C_1C$

But $\qquad\qquad EI(C_1C_2) = EI\theta_B(BC_2) = 83.7 \times 3 = 251.1 \ \text{kN-m}^3$

Also, $\qquad\qquad EI(C_1C) = -\sum_C^B A_3\bar{x}_3 = -\left[-\frac{1}{3} \times 3 \times 27 \times \left(\frac{3}{4} \times 3 \right) \right] = 60.75 \ \text{kN-m}^3$

$$\therefore \qquad EI(C_2C) = EI(C_1C_2) - EI(C_1C) = 251.1 - 60.75 = 190.35 \ \text{kN-m}^3$$
$$= 190.35 \times 10^2 \ \text{N-mm}^3$$

$$\therefore \qquad y_C = C_2C = \frac{190.35 \times 10^{12}}{3 \times 10^{14}} = \textbf{0.6345 mm}$$

This deflection is upward as shown in Fig. 13.32(b).

(c) Maximum deflection in AB

The maximum downward deflection in AB occurs at a point E, the location of which is to be found. Let us assume that point E is between D and B, and is at a distance x, from A. If this is not, the calculations will indicate so, and then we will assume that E is between A and D.

Note that at point E, the point of maximum deflection, the tangent will be horizontal. Hence the area of M/EI diagram will be equal to the angle of rotation θ_A.

Hence $E I \theta_A = \overset{E}{\underset{A}{\Sigma}} A$ ...(iv)

The component M-diagram between A and E is shown separately in Fig. 13.32(e). In this diagram, ordinate $E E_1 = R_A . x_1 = + 25.3 x_1$ kN-m while ordinate $E E_2 = - 48 (x_1 - 3)$.

Hence $\overset{E}{\underset{A}{\Sigma}} A = \frac{1}{2} x_1 (25.2 x_1) - \frac{1}{2} (x_1 - 3) 48 (x_1 - 3)$

$\qquad\qquad = 12.6 x_1^2 - 24 x_1^2 + 144 x_1 - 216 = - 11.4 x_1^2 + 144 x_1 - 216$

In the above expression x_1 has units of metres. Hence substituting the value of $E I \theta_A$ in kN-m^2 in (iv), we get

$$139.05 = - 11.4 x_1^2 + 144 x_1 - 216$$

or $11.4 x_1^2 - 144 x_1 + 355.05 = 0$, from which we get $x_1 = 3.359$ m.

The maximum deflection y_{max} is numerically equal to the offset of point A from the horizontal tangent at E.

Hence $E I y_{max} = \overset{E}{\underset{A}{\Sigma}} A \bar{x} = \left[\frac{1}{2} x_1 \times 25.2 x_1 \left(\frac{2}{3} x_1 \right) \right] - \left[\frac{1}{2} (x_1 - 3) 48 (x_1 - 3) \left\{ 3 + \frac{2}{3} (x_1 - 3) \right\} \right]$

Substituting $x_1 = 3.359$ m, we get

$$E I y_{max} = 308.26 \text{ kN-m}^3 = 308.26 \times 10^{12} \text{ N-mm}^3$$

$\therefore \qquad\qquad y_{max} = \dfrac{308.26 \times 10^{12}}{3 \times 10^4} = \mathbf{1.028 \text{ mm}}$

PROBLEMS

1. A cantilever beam AB is subjected to a concentrated load W and a couple μ acting at the free end (Fig. 13.33). Determine the slope and the deflection at the free end.

2. Determine the deflection at points B and C, of the cantilever beam shown in Fig. 13.34.

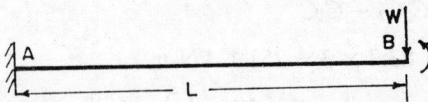

FIG. 13.33

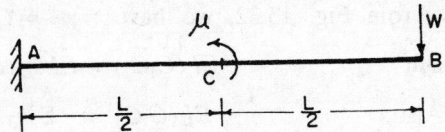

FIG. 13.34

3. Determine the deflections at points B and C of the cantilever beam shown in Fig. 13.35.

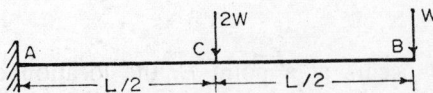

FIG. 13.35

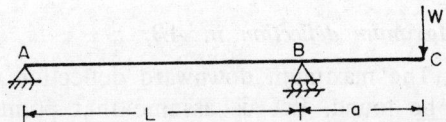

FIG. 13.36

4. Determine the deflection at the end of the overhang for the beam, loaded as shown in Fig. 13.36.

5. Determine the deflection at the free end B of the cantilever beam AB shown in Fig. 13.37.

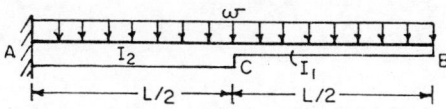

FIG. 13.37

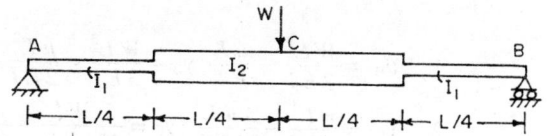

FIG. 13.38

6. A simple beam AB, shown in Fig. 13.38 has two different moments of inertia I_1 and I_2. Determine (a) slope at end A, and (b) deflection at the mid-span.

7. Determine the deflection at the midspan of an overhanging beam, loaded as shown in Fig. 13.39.

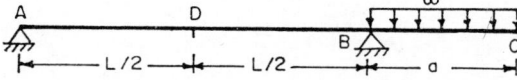

FIG. 13.39

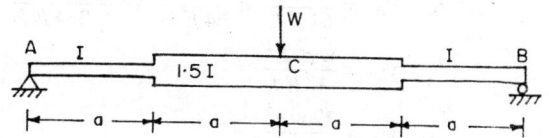

FIG. 13.40

8. The middle half of the beam shown in Fig. 13.40 has a moment of inertia 1.5 times, that of the rest of the beam. Find the mid- span deflection.

9. A simple beam with overhang is loaded as shown in Fig. 13.41. Find (i) the slope at B, and (ii) the deflection at C.

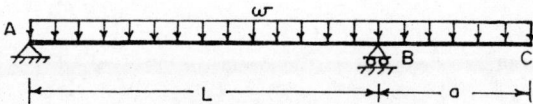

FIG. 13.41

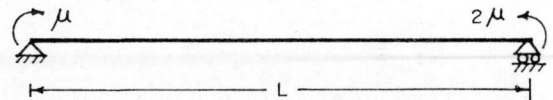

FIG. 13.42

10. A simple beam AB is acted upon by couples μ and 2μ at the ends, as shown in Fig. 13.42. Determine (i) slopes at A and B, and (ii) the deflections at the mid-span.

11. Find the slopes at the ends and central deflection for a simply supported beam shown in Fig. 13.43.

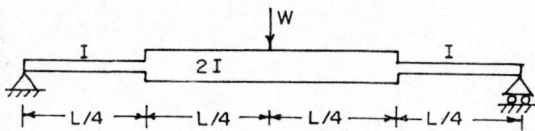

FIG. 13.43

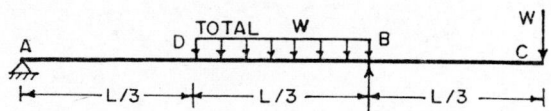

FIG. 13.44

12. An overhanging beam ABC is loaded as shown in Fig. 13.44. Determine the slope and deflection of the beam at point C.

ANSWERS

1. $\theta_B \doteq \dfrac{WL^2}{2EI} - \dfrac{\mu_0 L}{EI}$; $y_B = \dfrac{WL^3}{3EI} - \dfrac{\mu L^2}{2EI}$

2. $y_B = \dfrac{wL^3}{3EI} - \dfrac{3}{8}\dfrac{\mu L^2}{EI}$; $y_C = \dfrac{5}{48}\dfrac{WL^3}{EI} - \dfrac{\mu L^2}{8EI}$

3. $y_B = \dfrac{13}{24}\dfrac{WL^3}{EI}$; $y_C = \dfrac{3}{16}\dfrac{WL^3}{EI}$

4. $y_C = \dfrac{Wa^2}{3EI}(L + a)$

5. $y_B = \dfrac{wL^4}{128EI_1}\left(1 + \dfrac{15I_1}{I_2}\right)$

6. $\theta_A = \dfrac{WL^2}{64EI_1} + \dfrac{3WL^2}{64EI_2}$; $y_C = \dfrac{WL^3}{384EI_1} + \dfrac{7WL^3}{384EI_2}$

7. $y_D = \dfrac{wa^2L^2}{32EI}$

8. $y_C = \dfrac{17wa^3}{18EI}$

9. $\theta_B = \dfrac{wL(4a^2 - L^2)}{24EI}$; $y_C = \dfrac{wa}{24EI}(3a^3 + 4a^2L - L^3)$

10. $\theta_A = \dfrac{2\mu L}{3EI}$; $\theta_B = \dfrac{5\mu L}{6EI}$; $y_C = \dfrac{3\mu L^2}{16EI}$

11. $\theta_A = +\dfrac{5WL^2}{128EI}$; $\theta_B = -\dfrac{5WL^2}{128EI}$; $y_C = \dfrac{3WL^3}{256EI}$

12. $\theta_C = -\dfrac{47}{48}\dfrac{WL^2}{EI}$; $y_C = \dfrac{13}{16}\dfrac{WL^3}{EI}$

14

Deflection of Beams : III
Conjugate Beam Method

14.1. INTRODUCTION :

In chapter 12 and 13, we have found the slope and deflection at any point in a beam using double integration method (including Macaulay's method) and the area moment method respectively. These methods of determining slope and deflection are suitable only for simple cases, where the beam is having uniform flexural rigidity. If, however, the flexural rigidity, $E I$, is not uniform, the methods become quite laborious. In such cases conjugate beam method presents an easy approach. It is an ingenious method and the student will find its application very interesting. A *conjugate beam is an imaginary secondary beam*, which when loaded with the M/EI diagram of the real beam, yield directly the slope and deflection of the real beam in the form of shear force and bending moment of the conjugate beam. Evidently, a *conjugate beam* is a mirror image of the real beam, but with support conditions changed so as to meet the boundary conditions. *Conjugate beam method* is also known as the *method of elastic weight*.

14.2. THE CONJUGATE BEAM

We start with the deflection equation, the *successive differentiation* of which give the following relations :

$$E I y = \text{Deflection} \qquad \qquad ...(1)$$

$$E I \frac{dy}{dx} = \text{slope} \qquad \qquad ...(2)$$

$$E I \frac{d^2y}{dx^2} = -M \ (i.e. \text{ bending moment}) \qquad \qquad ...(3)$$

$$E I \frac{d^3y}{dx^3} = -\frac{dM}{dx} = -F \ (i.e. \text{ shear force}) \qquad \qquad ...(4)$$

$$E I \frac{d^4y}{dx^4} = -\frac{d^2M}{dx^2} = -\frac{dF}{dx} = w \ (i.e. \text{ rate of loading}) \qquad \qquad ...(5)$$

From the above equations, we observe that there is similarity of relations among load, shear and moment (Eq. 5, 4 and 3) and among moment, slope and deflection (Eqs. 3, 2 and 1). This similarity directly suggests us a method of calculating slope and deflection using the usual method of calculating shear and bending moment in a beam.

The method, therefore, uses a *fictitious secondary beam*, known as *conjugate beam*, which is loaded with not the actual loads, but with the *elastic weight* M/EI corresponding to the actual loads. Then, the *shear force at any point* on the *conjugate beam* will give the *slope* at the *corresponding point* of the *real beam*. Similarly, the *B.M.* at any point on the *conjugate beam* will give the *deflection* at the *corresponding point* of the *real beam*. In order to show this, we will consider two propositions.

Proposition 1 : *Similarity between S.F. of conjugate beam and slope of real beam.*

We have *load on conjugate beam* $= w' = \dfrac{M}{EI}$ of real beam

$\therefore$ Shear force $\qquad F'_x = -\displaystyle\int_0^x w'\,dx = -\int_0^x \dfrac{M}{EI}\,dx$

But $-\dfrac{M}{EI} = \dfrac{d^2y}{dx^2}$, from $\quad$ (3)

$\therefore \qquad\qquad\qquad F'_x = \displaystyle\int \dfrac{d^2y}{dx^2}\,dx = \dfrac{dy}{dx} = \text{slope}$ $\qquad\qquad\qquad$ ...(14.1)

This shows that the slope at any point of a real beam, relative to the original axis of the beam, is equal to the shear force at the the corresponding point of the conjugate beam.

Proposition 2 : *Similarity between B.M. of conjugate beam and deflection of real beam*

Shear force $\qquad F'_x = -\displaystyle\int_0^x w'\,dx = -\int_0^x \dfrac{M}{EI}\,dx = \int_0^x \dfrac{d^2y}{dx^2}$

$\therefore \qquad M'_x = \displaystyle\int_0^x F'_x \cdot dx = -\int_0^x \int_0^x w'\,dx = -\int_0^x \int_0^x \dfrac{M}{EI}\,dx = \int \int \dfrac{d^2y}{dx^2}\,dx.$

$\qquad\qquad\qquad = \displaystyle\int_0^x \dfrac{dy}{dx}\,dx = y = \text{deflection}$ $\qquad\qquad\qquad$ ...(14.2)

This shows that the deflection at any point of a real beam, relative to the original axis of the beam, is equal to the bending moment at the corresponding point of the conjugate beam.

Before we apply this method to simply supported beams, cantilevers and propped cantilevers, we shall consider the sign conventions.

14.3. SIGN CONVENTIONS

The following sign conventions will be adopted.

1. Loading on the conjugate beam : The loading on the conjugate beam is equal to the M/EI diagram of the real beam. This loading is also known as the *elastic weight*. The loading or the elastic weight acts *downwards* if the M/EI diagram is *positive* and *upwards* if M/EI diagram is *negative*. If however, M/EI diagram is partly positive and partly negative, the elastic weight or the loading will act downward for the positive portion of the diagram and upward for the negative portion of the M/EI diagram.

2. Slope of the real beam : The slope of the real beam will be *clockwise* if the S.F. is positive and anticlockwise is the S.F. is negative.

3. Deflection of the real beam : The deflection of the *real beam* will be *downward* (or positive) if the B.M. at the corresponding point of the conjugate beam is *positive* and *upward* if the B.M. is *negative*.

14.4. SIMPLY SUPPORTED BEAMS

Fig. 14.1 (*a*) shows a simply supported beam *AB*, called the real beam, with loading, along with the B.M. diagram. Fig. 14.1(*b*) shows the *conjugate beam, A' B'* with the loading equal to the M/EI diagram of the real beam. Corresponding to a simply supported real beam, the conjugate beam will also be simply supported. This is so because the bending moment at the ends of the conjugate beam have to be zero so as to give zero deflection at the ends of the real beam. *Hence the conjugate beam of a simply supported real beam will also be simply supported at the ends.* The application of the conjugate beam method to simply supported beam is illustrated in Example 14.1 to 14.4.

Example 14.1. *Determine the slopes at the ends and the deflection at the mid-span of a simply supported beam carrying a central point load W. Also, plot the slope and deflection diagrams for the beam.*

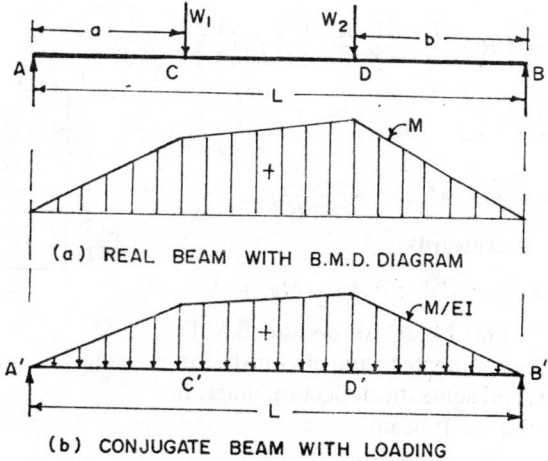

(a) REAL BEAM WITH B.M.D. DIAGRAM

(b) CONJUGATE BEAM WITH LOADING

FIG. 14.1

Solution :

Fig. 14.2(*a*) shows the real beam with the loading, while Fig. 14.2(*b*) shows the B.M.D. having a maximum ordinate of $WL/4$ under *C*. Fig. 14.2(*c*) shows the conjugate beam $A' B' C'$ with loading (*i.e.* elastic weight) having maximum ordinate of $WL/4EI$ at *C'*. Ends *A'* and *B'* of the conjugate beam will be simply supported. Since M/EI is *positive*, the loading on the conjugate beam acts downwards.

$$\text{Reaction } R_{A'} = \frac{1}{2}\left[\frac{1}{2}L\frac{WL}{4EI}\right] = \frac{WL^2}{16EI}(\uparrow) = R_{B'}$$

$$\therefore \text{ S.F. at } A' = F_{A'} = +R_{A'} = +\frac{WL^2}{16EI}$$

But shear at any point of the conjugate beam is equal to slope of the real beam at the corresponding point.

$$\therefore \qquad i_A = F_{A'} = +\frac{WL^2}{16EI} \text{ (i.e. clockwise), which is the same as Eq. 12.15. Similarly,}$$

$$i_B = F_B' = -R_B' = -\frac{WL^2}{16EI}$$

(*i.e.* anticlockwise)

Fig. 14.2 (*d*) shows the S.F.D. for the conjugate beam; obviously this also represents the slope diagram of the real beam. Since F_C is zero, the slope at the centre of the real beam (*i.e.* i_C) is zero. Also, for the conjugate beam,

$$M_C' = +R_A' \cdot \frac{L}{2} - \left(\frac{1}{2} \cdot \frac{L}{2} \cdot \frac{WL}{4EI}\right)\left(\frac{1}{3}\frac{L}{2}\right)$$

$$= \frac{WL^2}{16EI} \cdot \frac{L}{2} - \frac{WL^3}{96EI} = +\frac{WL^3}{48EI}$$

Hence $y_C = M_C' = +\dfrac{WL^3}{48EI}$

(*i.e.* downward)

Also, $y_A = M_A' = 0$; $y_B = M_B' = 0$.

Fig. 14.2(*e*) shows the B.M.D. for the conjugate beam; obviously, this also represents the deflection diagram for the real beam.

Example 14.2. *Determine the slopes at the ends and the deflection at the mid-span of a simply supported beam carrying U.D.L. w throughout its length. Also, plot the slope and deflection diagrams for the beam.*

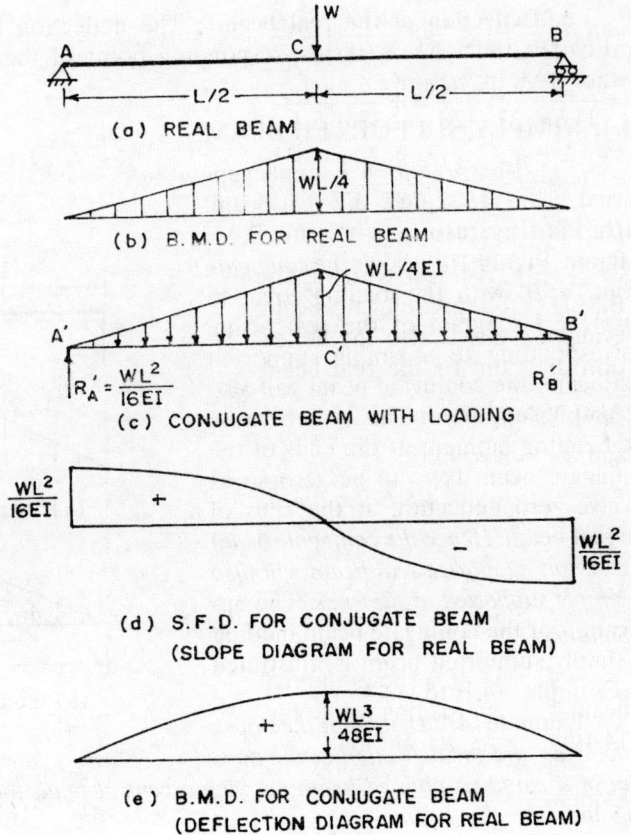

(a) REAL BEAM

(b) B.M.D. FOR REAL BEAM

(c) CONJUGATE BEAM WITH LOADING

(d) S.F.D. FOR CONJUGATE BEAM
(SLOPE DIAGRAM FOR REAL BEAM)

(e) B.M.D. FOR CONJUGATE BEAM
(DEFLECTION DIAGRAM FOR REAL BEAM)

FIG. 14.2

Solution :

Fig. 14.3(*a*) shows the real beam *ACB* with loading, while Fig. 14.3(*b*) shows its B.M.D. having a maximum ordinate of $+wL^2/8$ under *C*. Fig. 14.3(*c*) shows the conjugate beam with loading M/EI. The loading on the conjugate beam is thus parabolic, having maximum ordinate of $wL^2/8EI$.

$$R_A' = R_B' = \frac{1}{2}\left[\frac{2}{3} \times L \times \frac{wL^2}{8EI}\right] = \frac{wL^3}{24EI} \;(\uparrow)$$

Hence $\qquad i_A = F_A' = +\dfrac{wL^3}{24EI}$

Similarly $\qquad i_B = F_B' = -\dfrac{wL^3}{24EI}$

Fig. 14.3(*d*) shows the S.F.D. for the conjugate beam, which is also the slope of diagram for the real beam.

Evidently, $\qquad i_C = F_{C'} = 0$

Again $M_{C'}$

$$= R_{A'} \cdot \frac{L}{2} - \left[\frac{2}{3} \times \frac{L}{2} \times \frac{wL^2}{8EI} \left(\frac{3}{8} \cdot \frac{L}{2} \right) \right]$$

$$= \frac{wL^3}{24EI} \frac{L}{2} - \frac{wL^4}{128} = + \frac{5}{384} \frac{wL^4}{EI}$$

$\therefore \quad y_C = M_{C'} = + \dfrac{5}{384} \dfrac{wL^4}{EI}$

(*i.e.* downwards)

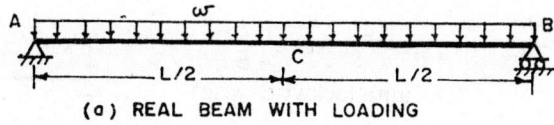

(a) REAL BEAM WITH LOADING

Fig. 14.3(*e*) shows the B.M.D. for the conjugate beam; evidently, this is also the deflection diagram for the real beam.

Also $y_A = M_{A'} = 0$

and $y_B = M_{B'} = 0$

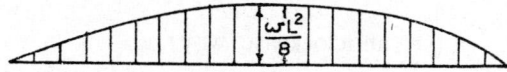

(b) B.M.D. FOR REAL BEAM

Example 14.3. *Calculate the slope at the ends and deflection at the centre of a beam loaded with a couple μ at the centre.*

Solution :

Fig. 14.4(*a*) shows the real beam with the loading, while Fig. 14.4(*b*) shows its B.M.D.

Evidently, $\qquad R_A = \dfrac{\mu}{L} (\downarrow)$

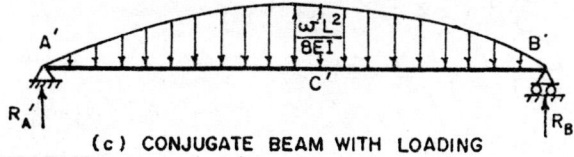

(c) CONJUGATE BEAM WITH LOADING

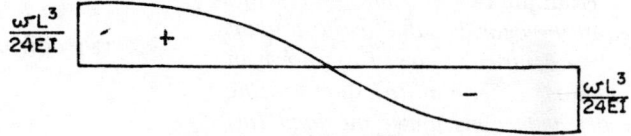

(d) S.F.D. FOR CONJUGATE BEAM
(SLOPE DIAGRAM FOR REAL BEAM)

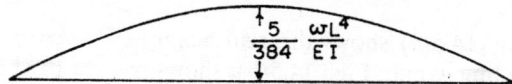

(e) B.M.D FOR CONJUGATE BEAM
(DEFLECTION DIAGRAM FOR REAL BEAM)

and $\qquad R_B = \dfrac{\mu}{L} (\uparrow)$

FIG. 14.3

$\therefore \qquad M_A = 0 \; ; M_C \text{ (left)} = -\dfrac{\mu}{L} \times \dfrac{L}{2} = -\dfrac{\mu}{2}$

$\qquad M_C \text{ (right)} = -\dfrac{\mu}{L} \times \dfrac{L}{2} + \mu = + \dfrac{\mu}{2}$

$\qquad M_B = 0$

Fig. 14.4(*c*) shows the conjugate beam with M/EI loading.

For the conjugate beam (Fig. 14.4 *c*),

$$R_{A'} = \frac{1}{L} \left[\frac{1}{2} \times \frac{L}{2} \times \frac{\mu}{2EI} \left(\frac{L}{2} + \frac{1}{3} \frac{L}{2} \right) - \frac{1}{2} \times \frac{L}{2} \times \frac{\mu}{2EI} \left(\frac{2}{3} \cdot \frac{L}{2} \right) \right]$$

$$= \frac{\mu L}{12EI} - \frac{\mu L}{24EI} = \frac{\mu L}{24EI} \; (\downarrow)$$

$$R_B' = \frac{\mu L}{24 E I} \ (\uparrow)$$

For $\qquad i_A = F_A' = -\dfrac{\mu L}{24 E I}$

(*i.e.* anticlockwise wise)

Similarly, $\qquad i_B = F_B' = -\dfrac{\mu L}{24 E I}$

(*i.e.* anticlockwise wise)

Also, M_C'

$$= - R_A' \cdot \frac{L}{2} + \left(\frac{1}{2} \times \frac{L}{2} \times \frac{\mu}{2 E I} \times \frac{1}{3} \frac{L}{2} \right)$$

$$= - \frac{\mu L}{24 E I} \cdot \frac{L}{2} + \frac{\mu L^2}{48 E I} = 0$$

$$\therefore \ y_C = M_C' = 0$$

Example 14.4. *A beam, simply supported at the ends, is subjected to a point load W, eccentrically placed as shown in Fig. 14.5(a). Determine (a) slopes at the ends (ii) deflections under the load (iii) central deflection, and (iv) maximum deflection and its location.*

Solution :

Fig. 14.5(a) shows the real beam with loading while Fig. 14.5(b) shows its B.M.D. having a maximum ordinate of $W a b/L$ under the point load. Fig. 14.5(c) shows the conjugate beam with $M/E I$ loading. Ordinate of loading at $C' = W a b/L E I$.

Ordinate of loading at D'

$$= \frac{W a b}{L E I} \cdot \frac{1}{a} \cdot \frac{L}{2} = \frac{W b}{2 E I}$$

Ordinate of loading at X', distant

x from $A' = \dfrac{W a b}{L E I} \cdot \dfrac{1}{a} \cdot x = \dfrac{W b x}{L E I}$

$$R_A' = \frac{1}{L} \left(\frac{1}{2} \times L \times \frac{W a b}{L E I} \right) \left[\frac{1}{3} (L + b) \right]$$

$$= \frac{W b}{6 E I L} (L^2 - b^2)$$

$$R_B' = \frac{1}{L} \left(\frac{1}{2} \times L \times \frac{W a b}{L E I} \right) \left[\frac{1}{3} (L + a) \right]$$

$$= \frac{W a}{6 E I L} (L^2 - a^2)$$

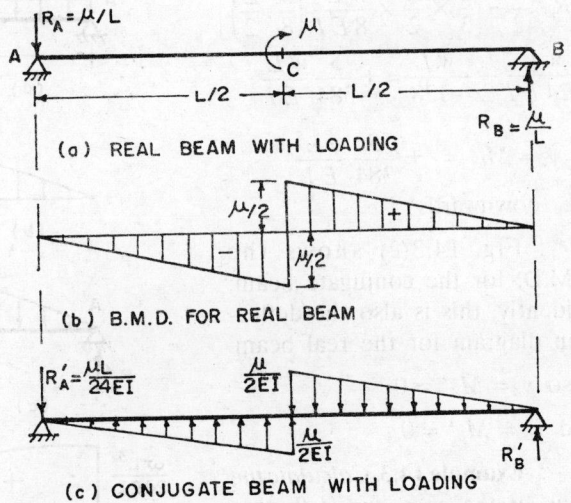

(a) REAL BEAM WITH LOADING

(b) B.M.D. FOR REAL BEAM

(c) CONJUGATE BEAM WITH LOADING

FIG. 14.4

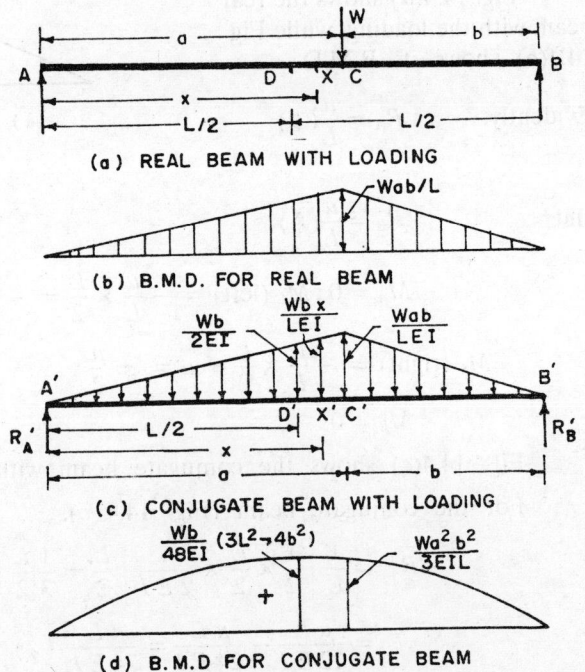

(a) REAL BEAM WITH LOADING

(b) B.M.D. FOR REAL BEAM

(c) CONJUGATE BEAM WITH LOADING

(d) B.M.D FOR CONJUGATE BEAM

FIG. 14.5

(i) Slope at ends :

Slope at A of real beam $= i_A = F_A' = +\dfrac{Wb}{6EIL}(L^2 - b^2)$ *(i.e.* clockwise)

Slope at B of real beam $= i_B = F_B' = -\dfrac{Wa}{6EIL}(L^2 - a^2)$ *(i.e.* anticlockwise)

(ii) Deflection under the load :

We have $\qquad y_C = M_C'$

Now, $\qquad\qquad M_C' = R_A' \cdot a - \dfrac{1}{2} a \times \dfrac{Wab}{LEI}\left(\dfrac{1}{3}a\right)$

$$= \dfrac{Wab}{6EIL}(L^2 - b^2) - \dfrac{Wab}{6EIL}(a^2) = \dfrac{Wab}{6EIL}(L^2 - b^2 - a^2)$$

$$= \dfrac{Wab}{6EIL}\left(a^2 + b^2 + 2ab - b^2 - a^2\right) = \dfrac{Wa^2b^2}{3EIL}$$

$\therefore\qquad\qquad y_C = M_C' = \dfrac{Wa^2b^2}{3EIL}$

(iii) Central deflection : We have $y_D = M_D'$

Now $\qquad M_D' = R_A' \cdot \dfrac{L}{2} - \dfrac{1}{2} \cdot \dfrac{L}{2} \cdot \dfrac{Wb}{2EI}\left(\dfrac{1}{3} \cdot \dfrac{L}{2}\right) = \dfrac{Wb}{6EIL}(L^2 - b^2) \cdot \dfrac{L}{2} - \dfrac{WbL^2}{48EI}$

$$= \dfrac{Wb}{6EIL} \cdot \dfrac{L}{2}\left[L^2 - b^2 - \dfrac{L^2}{4}\right] = \dfrac{Wb}{48EI}(3L^2 - 4b^2)$$

(iv) Maximum deflection :

Let maximum deflection occurs at point X, between D and C, distant x from A.

Maximum deflection at X occurs where B.M. is maximum at X' of the conjugate beam. Naturally $(M_x')_{max}$ occurs where S.F. is zero, *i.e.* where $F_x' = 0$.

Hence $\qquad F_x' = 0 = R_A' - \dfrac{1}{2}x\left(\dfrac{Wbx}{LEI}\right) = \dfrac{Wb}{6EIL}(L^2 - b^2) - \dfrac{Wbx^2}{2EIL}$

This gives $\qquad x = \left(\dfrac{L^2 - b^2}{3}\right)^{\frac{1}{2}}$

Now $\qquad M_x' = R_A' \cdot x - \dfrac{1}{2}x\left(\dfrac{Wbx}{LEI}\right)\dfrac{x}{3} = \dfrac{Wbx}{6EIL}(L^2 - b^2) - \dfrac{Wb}{6EIL}x^3$

$\therefore \qquad (M_x')_{max} = \dfrac{Wb}{6EIL}(L^2 - b^2)\left(\dfrac{L^2 - b^2}{3}\right)^{\frac{1}{2}} - \dfrac{Wb}{6EIL}\left(\dfrac{L^2 - b^2}{3}\right)^{\frac{3}{2}}$

$$= \dfrac{Wb}{6EIL}\left(\dfrac{L^2 - b^2}{3}\right)^{\frac{1}{2}}\left[L^2 - b^2 - \left(\dfrac{L^2 - b^2}{3}\right)\right]$$

$\therefore \qquad y_{max} = (M_x')_{max} = \dfrac{Wb}{3EIL}\left(\dfrac{L^2 - b^2}{3}\right)^{\frac{3}{2}} = \dfrac{Wb(L^2 - b^2)^{\frac{3}{2}}}{9\sqrt{3}\,EIL}$

14.5. CANTILEVERS :

In the case of cantilevers, the B.M. diagram is negative for the usual down ward loading, as shown in Fig. 14.6(b). Hence the loading on the conjugate beam will be in the upward direction, as shown in Fig. 14.6(c). Also, since the S.F. at any point in the conjugate beam gives the slope of the corresponding point of the real beam, the conjugate beam will have free end at A', corresponding to the fixed end A of the real beam, so as to give $y_A = M_A' = 0$. Again, the end B of the real beam deflects downward by some finite amount. To satisfy this condition, end B' of the conjugate beam should have some bending moment. This is possible only if end B' of the conjugate beam is *fixed* instead of being free. *Thus in the case of a cantilever beam, the conjugate beam is also a cantilever, but with fixed support on the opposite end.*

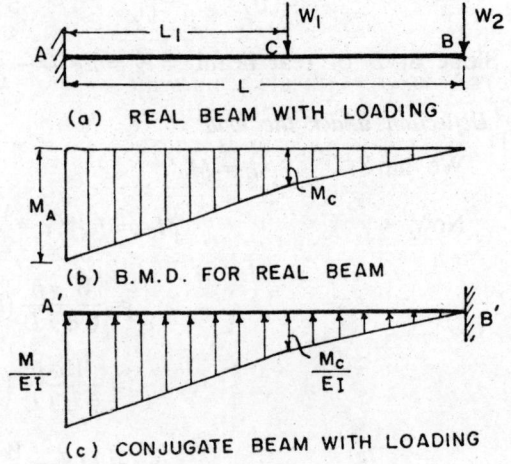

(a) REAL BEAM WITH LOADING

(b) B.M.D. FOR REAL BEAM

(c) CONJUGATE BEAM WITH LOADING

FIG. 14.6

Examples 14.5 to 14.8 illustrate the method of application.

Example 14.5. *A cantilever AB is subjected to point load W at the free end. Determine the slope and deflection of the free end.*

Solution :

Fig. 14.7(a) shows the real beam with loading while Fig. 14.7(b) shows its B.M. diagram. Fig. 14.7(c) shows the conjugate beam with loading M/EI. Since B.M.D. is negative, the loading on the conjugate beam will act upward. The conjugate beam will have end A' free (corresponding to the fixed end A) while end B' will be fixed, corresponding to the free end A of the real beam.

Now $\qquad F_{B'} = +\dfrac{1}{2} \times L \times \dfrac{WL}{EI} = +\dfrac{WL^2}{2EI}$

$\therefore \qquad i_B = F_{B'} = +\dfrac{WL^2}{2EI}$ (*i.e.* clockwise)

Again $M_{B'} = +\dfrac{1}{2} \times L \times \dfrac{WL}{EI}\left(\dfrac{2}{3}L\right) = +\dfrac{WL^3}{3EI}$

$\therefore \qquad y_B = M_{B'} = +\dfrac{WL^3}{3EI}$ (*i.e.* downwards)

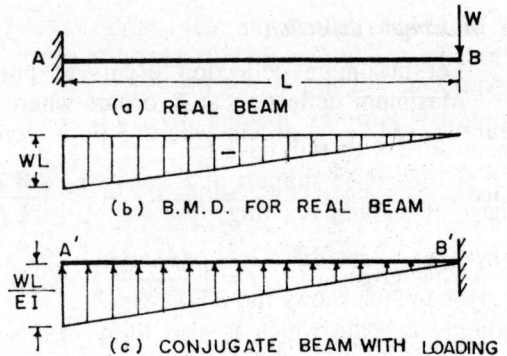

(a) REAL BEAM

(b) B.M.D. FOR REAL BEAM

(c) CONJUGATE BEAM WITH LOADING

FIG. 14.7

Example 14.6. *A cantilever AB is subjected to uniformly distributed load w throughout its length. Determine the slope and deflection at the free end.*

Solution :

Fig. 14.8(a) shows real beam with loading, while 14.8(b) shows its B.M. diagram having max. ordinate $= -wL \cdot \dfrac{L}{2} = -\dfrac{wL^2}{2}$. Fig. 14.8(c) shows the conjugate beam, with loading M/EI. The loading acts upwards, since the B.M.D. for the real beam is negative.

Now $F_B' = +\dfrac{1}{3} \times L \times \dfrac{wL^2}{2EI} = +\dfrac{wL^3}{6EI}$

$\therefore \qquad i_B = F_B' = +\dfrac{wL^3}{6EI}$ (*i.e.* clockwise)

Also, $M_B' = +\dfrac{1}{3} \times L \times \dfrac{wL^2}{2EI}\left(\dfrac{3}{4}L\right) = +\dfrac{wL^4}{8EI}$

$\therefore \qquad y_B = M_B' = +\dfrac{wL^4}{8EI}$ (*i.e.* downwards)

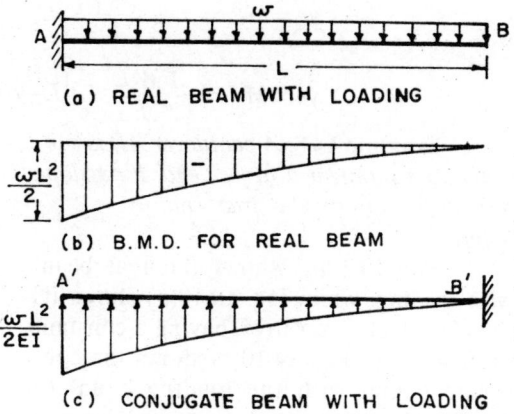

(a) REAL BEAM WITH LOADING

(b) B.M.D. FOR REAL BEAM

(c) CONJUGATE BEAM WITH LOADING

FIG. 14.8

Example 14.7. *A cantilever AB is loaded as shown in Fig. 14.9(a). Draw the slope and deflection diagram for the cantilever. Hence find the slope and deflection of (a) point under the loading, and (b) free end.*

Solution :

Fig. 14.9(a) shows the real beam with loading, while Fig. 14.9(b) shows its B.M.D. Fig. 14.9(c) shows the conjugate beam with the loading M/EI. The conjugate beam will have free support at A' and fixed support at B' and will have the loading acting upwards.

(a) Slopes at C and B :

Fig. 14.9(d) shows the S.F.D. for the conjugate beam which is also the slope diagram for the real beam. The diagram will be parabolic from A' to C', and constant shear from C' to B'. This shows that $i_C = i_B$.

Now $F_C' = F_B' = \dfrac{1}{2} \times L_1 \times \dfrac{WL_1}{EI} = \dfrac{WL_1^2}{2EI}$

$\therefore \qquad i_C = i_B = F_C' = F_B' = \dfrac{WL_1^2}{2EI}$

(*i.e.* clockwise)

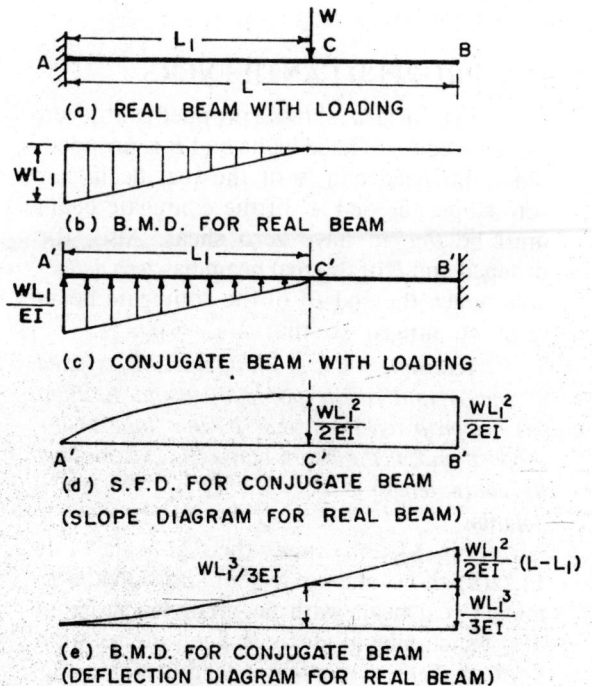

(a) REAL BEAM WITH LOADING

(b) B.M.D. FOR REAL BEAM

(c) CONJUGATE BEAM WITH LOADING

(d) S.F.D. FOR CONJUGATE BEAM
(SLOPE DIAGRAM FOR REAL BEAM)

(e) B.M.D. FOR CONJUGATE BEAM
(DEFLECTION DIAGRAM FOR REAL BEAM)

FIG. 14.9

(b) Deflection at C and B : Fig. 14.9(e) shows the B.M.D. for the conjugate beam, which is also the deflection diagram for the real beam.

$$y_C = M_C' = +\frac{1}{2} \cdot \frac{WL_1}{EI} \cdot L_1 \cdot \frac{2}{3} L_1 = +\frac{WL_1^3}{3EI} \ (i.e. \ \text{downwards})$$

$$y_B = M_B' = -\frac{1}{2} \cdot \frac{WL_1}{EI} L_1 \left[L - L_1 + \frac{2L_1}{3} \right] = \frac{WL_1^3}{3EI} + \frac{WL_1^2}{2EI}(L - L_1) \ (i.e. \ \text{downwards})$$

Example 14.8. *A cantilever AB is subjected to a moment μ at free end. Find slope and deflection of the free end.*

Solution :

Fig. 14.10(a) shows the real beam with loading, while Fig. 14.10(b) shows its B.M.D. which is positive, having a constant ordinate of μ. Fig. 14.10(c) shows the conjugate beam, with the loading equal to M/EI. The conjugate beam will have end A' free and end B' fixed.

Now $\quad i_B = F_B' = -\dfrac{\mu}{EI} \cdot L = -\dfrac{\mu L}{EI}$

(*i.e.* anticlockwise)

$$y_B = M_B' = -\frac{\mu}{EI} \cdot L \cdot \frac{L}{2} = -\frac{\mu L^2}{2EI}$$

(*i.e.* upwards).

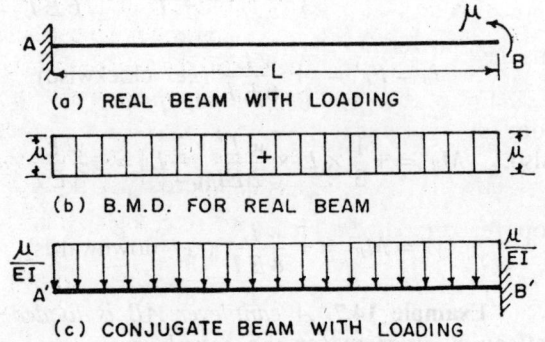

(a) REAL BEAM WITH LOADING

(b) B.M.D. FOR REAL BEAM

(c) CONJUGATE BEAM WITH LOADING

FIG. 14.10

14.6. PROPPED CANTILEVERS

Fig. 14.11(a) shows a propped cantilever, in which end A is fixed while end B is propped. Since the fixed end A of the real beam has zero slope, the end A' of the conjugate beam must be *free* to have zero shear. Also, the propped end B of the real beam has *zero deflection*; hence the end B' of the conjugate beam must be hinged so that $M_B' = 0 = y_B$.

Example 14.9. *A cantilever AB is fixed at end A and rigidly propped at end B. Find (a) the prop reaction, and (b) the slope at the propped end, if the beam carries U.D.L. w over its entire length.*

Solution :

Fig. 14.12(a) shows the real beam while 14.12(b) shows the equivalent statically determinate real beam with an unknown moment M_A of such magnitude as to keep the rotation i_A of end A of the real beam to zero. Fig. 14.12(c) shows the component B.M.D., showing

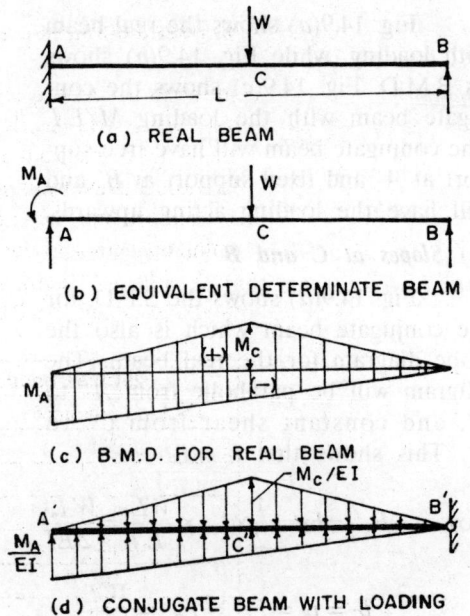

(a) REAL BEAM

(b) EQUIVALENT DETERMINATE BEAM

(c) B.M.D. FOR REAL BEAM

(d) CONJUGATE BEAM WITH LOADING

FIG. 14.11

the effects of w and M_A separately. Note that M_A' is negative since it causes convexity upwards. Fig. 14.12(d) shows the conjugate beam along with the loading M/EI in appropriate directions. The end B of the real beam does not deflect; hence end B' of the conjugate beam should have zero B.M., which is possible by providing at hinge at end B' of the conjugate beam. For the conjugate beam,

$$M_B'=0=-\frac{2}{3}\cdot\frac{wL^2}{8EI}\times L\times\frac{L}{2}+\frac{1}{2}\frac{M_A\cdot L}{EI}\cdot\frac{2}{3}L$$

This gives $\qquad M_A=\dfrac{wL^2}{8}$

From Fig. 14.12(b), taking moments about A, we have

$$M_A+P\cdot L-\frac{wL^2}{2}=0, \text{ where } P \text{ is the}$$

prop reaction at B. Hence,

$$P=\frac{wL}{2}-\frac{M_A}{L}=\frac{wL}{2}-\frac{wL^2}{8L}=\frac{3}{8}wL(\text{Ans.})$$

Now $\quad i_B=F_{B'}=\dfrac{1}{2}\dfrac{M_A}{EI}\cdot L-\dfrac{2}{3}\dfrac{wL^2}{8EI}L$

$$=\frac{wL^3}{16EI}-\frac{wL^3}{12EI}=-\frac{wL^3}{48EI}$$

(i.e. anticlockwise)

Example 14.10. *If the prop at B (Fig. 14.13 a) sinks by λ under unit load, determine the prop reaction.*

Solution :

Let $P=$ prop reaction.
The condition equation is
$$y_B = P\cdot\lambda$$

The end B' of the conjugate beam is *partially fixed* such that

$$M_B' = y_B = P\lambda \qquad ...(i)$$

But $\quad M_B'=\dfrac{1}{2}\dfrac{M_A}{EI}L\cdot\dfrac{2}{3}L-\dfrac{2}{3}\dfrac{wL^2}{8EI}\cdot L\cdot\dfrac{L}{2}$

$$=\frac{M_AL^2}{3EI}-\frac{wL^4}{24EI} \qquad ...(ii)$$

Substituting in (i), we get

$$\frac{M_AL^2}{3EI}-\frac{wL^4}{24EI}=P\lambda \qquad ...(a)$$

Also, taking moments about end A of the real beam (Fig. 14.13 b)

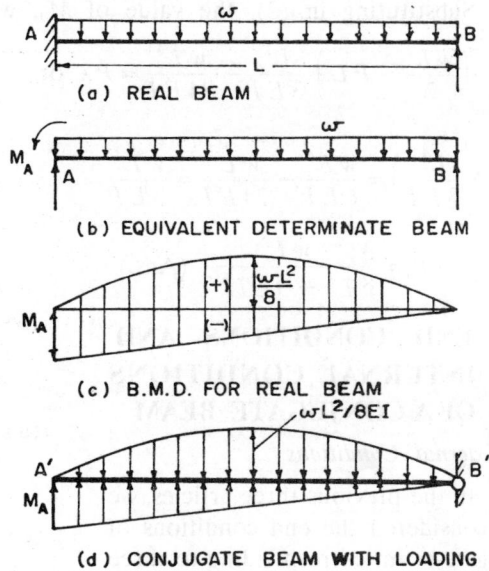

(a) REAL BEAM

(b) EQUIVALENT DETERMINATE BEAM

(c) B.M.D. FOR REAL BEAM

(d) CONJUGATE BEAM WITH LOADING

FIG. 14.12

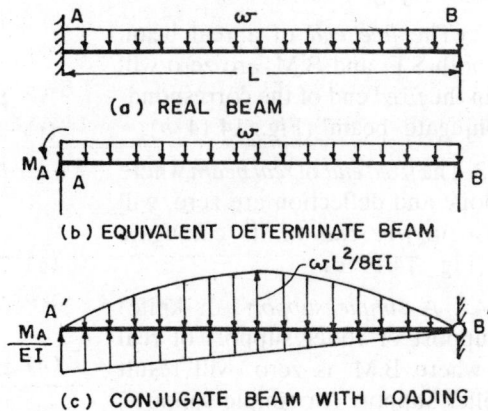

(a) REAL BEAM

(b) EQUIVALENT DETERMINATE BEAM

(c) CONJUGATE BEAM WITH LOADING

FIG. 14.13

$$M_A + P L - \frac{w L^2}{2} = 0$$

$$\therefore \qquad\qquad M_A = \frac{w L^2}{2} - P L \qquad\qquad ...(b)$$

Substituting in (2), the value of M_A, we get

$$\left(\frac{w L^2}{2} - P L \right) \frac{L^2}{3 E I} - \frac{w L^4}{24 E I} = P \lambda \quad \text{or}$$

$$P \left(\lambda + \frac{L^3}{3 E I} \right) = \frac{w L^4}{6 E I} - \frac{w L^4}{24 E I} = \frac{w L^4}{8 E I}$$

$$\therefore \qquad P = \frac{3}{8} \frac{w L^4}{L^3 + 3 E I \lambda} \quad \text{(Ans.)}$$

14.7. END CONDITIONS AND INTERNAL CONDITIONS OF A CONJUGATE BEAM

(a) External Conditions

In the previous three articles, we have considered the end conditions of conjugate beam corresponding to three types of ends of a real beam : (i) simple or hinged end (ii) free end, and (iii) fixed end. In that process, we have drawn the following conclusions with regard to the *external conditions*:

1. The *hinged end* of a real beam, where B.M. is zero, will result in a *hinged end* of the conjugate beam (Fig. 14.14 a).

2. The *free end* of a real beam where both S.F. and B.M. are zero will result in the *fixed* end of the corresponding conjugate beam (Fig. 14.14 b).

3. The *fixed end* of *real beam* where both slope and deflection are zero, will give rise to *free end* of its conjugate beam (Fig. 14.14 c).

4. A *simple support* (or knife) edge support or roller support of real beam, where B.M. is zero, will result in a roller support (or simple support) of the corresponding conjugate beam (Fig. 14.14 d).

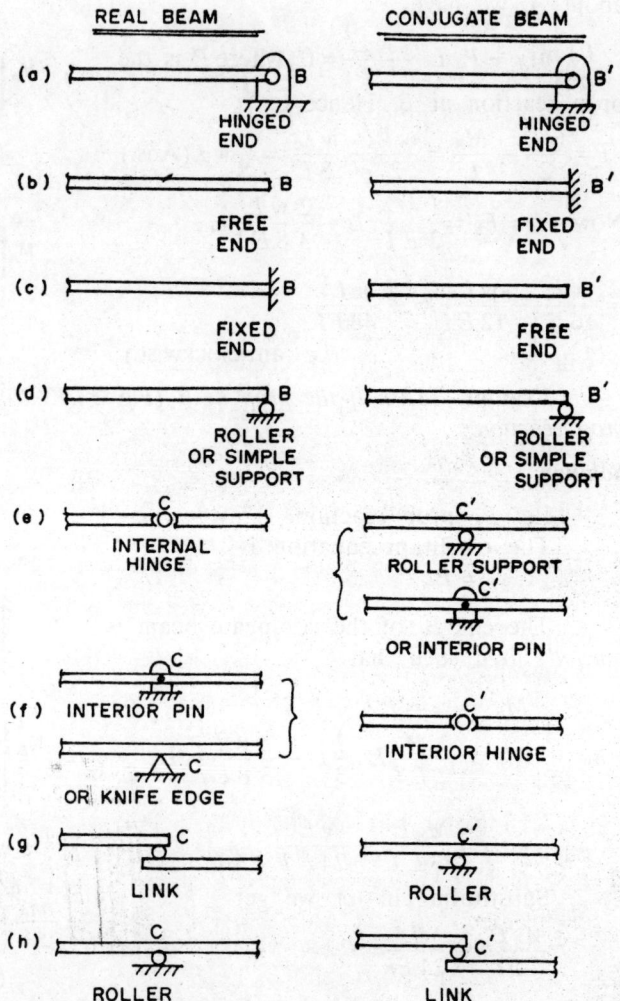

FIG. 14.14 EXTERNAL AND INTERNAL CONDITIONS

(b) Internal Conditions

Let us now take the internal conditions of a real beam.

1. *Internal hinge* : Consider an internal hinge at intermediate point C of the real beam, where B.M. is zero (Fig. 14.14 *e*). Also, the deflection to the left of the hinge is equal to the deflection to the right of the hinge. In addition to this, the shear to the left of the hinge is equal to the shear to the right of the hinge. These conditions are represented by the following equations for the real beam :

$$y_L = y_R \quad ...(i) \; ; \; F_L = F_R \quad ...(ii) \text{ and } \quad M_L = M_R = 0 \quad\quad\quad\quad ...(iii)$$

These conditions are satisfied by providing a *roller support* or *interior pin* at C' of the conjugate beam, where the following equations are applicable.

$$M_L' = M_R' \quad ...(i) \; ; \quad i_L' = i_R' \quad \text{ and } y_L' = y_R' = 0 \quad\quad\quad\quad ...(iii)$$

2. *Interior pin or knife edge* (Fig. 14.14 *f*): For such an internal condition of a real beam, (*i*) the deflection is zero, (*ii*) the slope at the left is equal to the slope at the right and (*iii*) the moment at the left is equal to the moment at the right. These are represented by the following equations for the *real beam*.

$$y_L = y_R = 0 \quad ...(i); \quad i_L = i_R ...(ii); \quad M_L = M_R \quad\quad\quad\quad ...(iii)$$

The conjugate beam must have the following conditions for the corresponding point C'.

$$M_L' = M_R' = 0 \quad ...(i); \quad F_L' = F_R' \quad ...(ii) \quad \text{ and } \quad y_L' = y_R' \quad\quad\quad\quad ...(iii)$$

These conditions are satisfied by providing an *interior hinge* at C'.

3. *Internal Link* (Fig. 14.14 *g*) : For an internal link at point C in a real beam, there will be an roller at the corresponding point C' of the conjugate beam.

4. *Internal roller* : (Fig. 14.14 *h*) : For an internal roller at point C in a real beam, there will be an internal link at corresponding point C' of the conjugate beam.

Important points : In addition to the above support conditions and internal conditions, the following points should be carefully noted.

1. A *stable* and *statically determinate real beam* will have a conjugate beam which is also stable and statically determinate.

2. An *unstable real beam* will have *statically indeterminate* conjugate beam. Hence if a conjugate beam is found to be statically indeterminate, it is concluded that the real beam is unstable, and further analysis is not appropriate.

3. A *statically indeterminate* real beam will have *unstable* conjugate beam. Hence its conjugate load must be such that it maintains equilibrium.

14.8. ADDITIONAL ILLUSTRATIVE EXAMPLES

Example 14.11. *A cantilever of length L carries a point load W at its free end. The member is circular in section having diameter D for a distance L/2 from the fixed end and a diameter D/2 for the remaining length. Find the slope and deflection at point C and B.*
Solution :

For the portion AC, $\quad I_{AC} = \dfrac{\pi D^4}{64}.$ $\quad$ Similarly, $\quad I_{CB} = \dfrac{\pi}{64} \left(\dfrac{D}{2} \right)^4 = \dfrac{\pi D^4}{64 \times 16}$

Hence if $I_{CB} = I, I_{AC} = 16 I$

Fig. 14.15(a) shows the real beam, while Fig. 14.15(b) shows the BMD for the real beam. Fig. 14.15(c) shows the conjugate beam, with the end A' free and end B' fixed; Fig. 14.15(d) shows loading M/EI for the conjugate beam. Thus, loading at end $A' = (WL)\left(\dfrac{1}{16EI}\right) = \dfrac{WL}{16EI}$; Loading at C' (left) $= \dfrac{WL}{2}\left(\dfrac{1}{16EI}\right) = \dfrac{WL}{32EI}$

Loading at C' (right)

$$= \frac{WL}{2}\left(\frac{1}{EI}\right) = \frac{WL}{2EI}$$

Loading at $B' = 0$

(a) **Slopes at C and B**

$$i_C = F_{C'} = +\frac{1}{2}\left(\frac{WL}{16EI} + \frac{WL}{32EI}\right)\frac{L}{2}$$

$$= +\frac{3WL^2}{128EI} \quad (i.e.\ \text{clockwise})$$

$$i_B = F_{B'} = +\frac{1}{2}\left(\frac{WL}{16EI} + \frac{WL}{32EI}\right)\frac{L}{2} + \frac{1}{2}\left(\frac{WL}{2EI}\right)\times\frac{L}{2}$$

$$= \frac{3WL^2}{128EI} + \frac{WL^2}{8EI} = \frac{19}{128}\frac{WL^2}{EI} \quad \text{(clockwise)}$$

(b) **Deflections at C and B**

$$y_C = M_{C'} = \frac{1}{2}\left(\frac{WL}{16EI} + \frac{WL}{32EI}\right)\frac{L}{2}\left[\frac{1}{3}\frac{L}{2}\frac{\dfrac{2WL}{16EI} + \dfrac{WL}{32EI}}{\dfrac{WL}{16EI} + \dfrac{WL}{32EI}}\right]$$

$$= \frac{3}{128}\frac{WL^2}{EI}\left[\frac{1}{3}\cdot\frac{L}{2}\frac{5}{3}\right] = \frac{3}{128}\frac{WL^2}{EI}\left(\frac{5L}{18}\right) = \frac{5}{768}\frac{WL^3}{EI} \quad \text{(Ans.)}$$

$$y_B = M_{B'} = \frac{3}{128}\frac{WL^2}{EI}\left[\frac{L}{2} + \frac{5L}{18}\right] + \frac{1}{2}\left(\frac{WL}{2EI}\right)\frac{L}{2}\left(\frac{2}{3}\frac{L}{2}\right)$$

$$= \frac{3}{128}\frac{WL^2}{EI}\times\frac{7}{9}L + \frac{WL^3}{24EI} = \frac{23}{384}\frac{WL^3}{EI} \quad \text{(Ans.)}$$

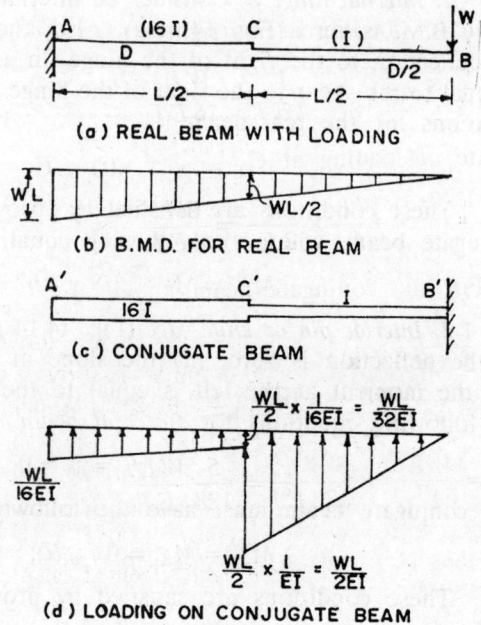

(a) REAL BEAM WITH LOADING

(b) B.M.D. FOR REAL BEAM

(c) CONJUGATE BEAM

(d) LOADING ON CONJUGATE BEAM

FIG. 14.15

Example 14.12. *Using conjugate beam method, find slopes at the ends and central deflection for a simply supported beam shown in Fig. 14.16(a).*

Solution : For the real beam, $M_C = \dfrac{WL}{4}$

$$M_D = \frac{W}{2}\cdot\frac{L}{4} = \frac{WL}{8} = M_E. \quad \text{Also,}\ M_A = M_B = 0$$

Fig. 14.16(b) shows the conjugate beam with its loading, $\dfrac{M}{EI}$.

Ordinate of loading at D (left)

$$= \frac{WL}{8} \cdot \frac{1}{EI} = \frac{WL}{8EI}$$

Ordinate of loading at D (right)

$$= \frac{WL}{8} \cdot \frac{1}{2EI} = \frac{WL}{16EI}$$

Ordinate of loading at C

$$= \frac{WL}{4} \times \frac{1}{2EI} = \frac{WL}{8EI}$$

For the conjugate beam,

$$R_A{'} = \left(\frac{1}{2} \frac{WL}{8EI} \times \frac{L}{4} \right)$$

$$+ \frac{1}{2} \left(\frac{WL}{16EI} + \frac{WL}{8EI} \right) \frac{L}{4}$$

$$= \frac{WL^2}{64EI} + \frac{3WL^2}{128EI} = \frac{5}{128} \frac{WL^2}{EI}$$

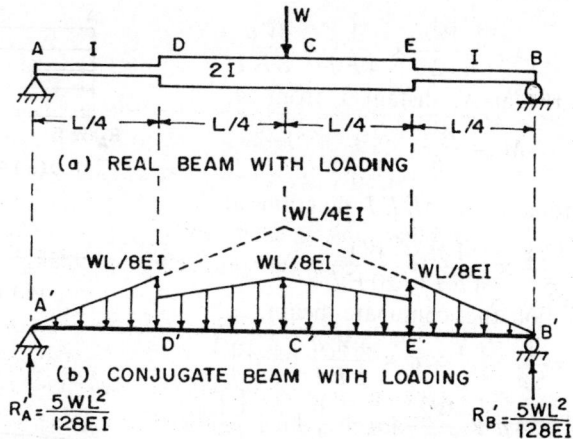

FIG. 14.16

Hence

$$i_A = F_A{'} = + R_A{'} = \frac{5}{128} \frac{WL^2}{EI} \text{ (clockwise)}$$

By symmetry,

$$i_B = F_B{'} = -- \frac{5}{128} \frac{WL^2}{EI} \text{ (i.e. anticlockwise)}$$

Also,

$$y_C = M_C{'} = R_A{'} \left(\frac{L}{2} \right) - \frac{WL^2}{64EI} \left(\frac{L}{4} + \frac{1}{3} \frac{L}{4} \right) - \frac{3}{128} \frac{WL^2}{EI} \left[\frac{1}{3} \frac{L}{4} \frac{\frac{2WL}{16EI} + \frac{WI}{8EI}}{\frac{WL}{16EI} + \frac{WL}{8EI}} \right]$$

$$= \frac{5}{128} \frac{WL^2}{EI} \cdot \frac{L}{2} - \frac{WL^3}{192EI} - \frac{1}{128 \times 3} \frac{WL^3}{EI} = \frac{3}{256} \frac{WL^3}{EI} \text{ (Ans.)}$$

Example 14.13. *A beam ACB, simply supported at the ends, has moment of inertia 4 I for the length AC and I for the length CB, and is loaded with point load W at C. Determine (i) Slope at end A, (ii) deflection at mid-span, and (iii) maximum deflection. Compute the numerical values taking* $W = 8\,kN$, $a = 2.5\,m$, $I = 5000\,cm^4$ *and* $E = 2 \times 10^5\,N/mm^2$.

Solution : Fig. 14.17(a) shows the real beam ABC, while Fig. 14.17(b) shows the B.M.D. for the real beam, with salient values. Fig. 14.17(c) shows the conjugate beam $A'C'B'$ with the loading diagram (M/EI diagram). For the real beam,

$$R_A = \frac{Wa}{5a} = \frac{W}{5}(\uparrow); \qquad R_B = \frac{4Wa}{5a} = \frac{4}{5}W(\uparrow) \qquad M_C = \frac{W(4a)(a)}{5a} = \frac{4}{5}Wa$$

$\therefore$ Ordinate of M/EI diagram just to the left of $C' = \frac{4}{5}Wa \left(\frac{1}{4EI} \right) = \frac{Wa}{5EI}$

Ordinate of M/EI diagram just to the right of $C' = \frac{4}{5}Wa \left(\frac{1}{EI} \right) = \frac{4}{5}\frac{Wa}{EI}$

Also, $M_D = R_A (2.5\,a) = \dfrac{W}{5} \times 2.5\,a = \dfrac{Wa}{2}$

$\therefore$ Ordinate of M/EI diagram at D'

$$= \frac{Wa}{2} \times \frac{1}{4\,EI} = \frac{Wa}{8\,EI}$$

Similarly, at X, distant x from A,

$$M_x = \frac{Wx}{5}.$$

$\therefore$ Ordinate of M/EI diagram at

$X' = \dfrac{W \cdot x}{5} \times \dfrac{1}{4\,EI} = \dfrac{Wx}{20\,EI}$

For the conjugate beam,

$R_A' = \dfrac{1}{5\,a} \left[\left\{ \dfrac{1}{2} \times a \times \dfrac{4\,Wa}{5\,EI} \left(\dfrac{2}{3}\,a \right) \right\} \right.$

$\left. + \left\{ \dfrac{1}{2} \times 4\,a \times \dfrac{Wa}{5\,EI} \left(a + \dfrac{1}{3}\,4\,a \right) \right\} \right]$

$= \dfrac{6}{25} \dfrac{Wa^2}{EI}$

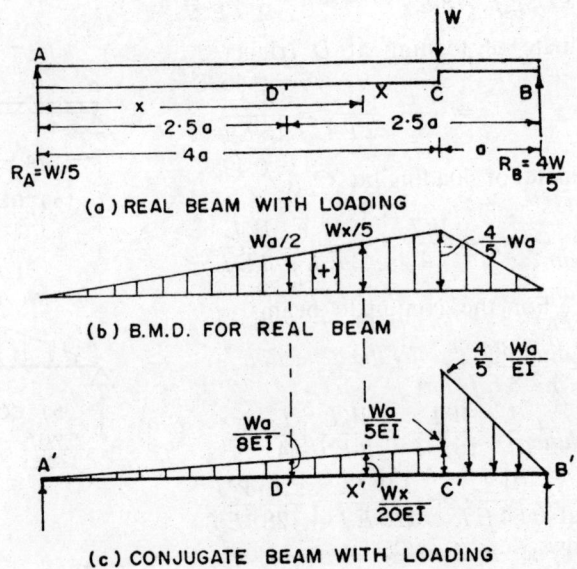

(a) REAL BEAM WITH LOADING

(b) B.M.D. FOR REAL BEAM

(c) CONJUGATE BEAM WITH LOADING

FIG. 14.17

$R_B' = \dfrac{1}{5\,a} \left[\left\{ \dfrac{1}{2} \times 4\,a \times \dfrac{Wa}{5\,EI} \left(\dfrac{2}{3}\,4\,a \right) \right\} \right.$

$\left. + \left\{ \dfrac{1}{2} \times a \times \dfrac{4\,Wa}{5\,EI} \left(4\,a + \dfrac{1}{3}\,a \right) \right\} \right] = \dfrac{14}{25} \dfrac{Wa^2}{EI}$

$\therefore \qquad i_A = F_A' = + R_A' = + \dfrac{6\,Wa^2}{25\,EI}$

Again, $\qquad M_D' = \dfrac{6}{25} \dfrac{Wa^2}{EI} \times 2.5\,a - \left\{ \dfrac{1}{2} \times 2.5\,a \times \dfrac{Wa}{8\,EI} \left(\dfrac{1}{3} \times 2.5\,a \right) \right\}$

$$= \frac{6}{10} \frac{Wa^3}{EI} - \frac{6.25}{48} \frac{Wa^3}{EI} = 0.4698 \frac{Wa^3}{EI}$$

$\therefore \qquad y_D = M_D' = \mathbf{0.4698} \dfrac{Wa^3}{EI} \text{ (Ans.)}$

Also, the maximum B.M. in the conjugate beam occurs at x', some where between D and C, where S.F. is zero.

$\therefore \qquad F_{X'} = 0 = R_A' - \dfrac{1}{2} \dfrac{Wx}{20\,EI} \cdot x$

or $\qquad \dfrac{Wx^2}{40\,EI} = R_A' = \dfrac{6}{25} \dfrac{Wa^2}{EI}$, which gives $x = \mathbf{3.098\,a}$

$\therefore \qquad (M_{X'})_{max} = \dfrac{6}{25} \dfrac{Wa^2}{EI} (3.098\,a) - \left[\dfrac{1}{2} \dfrac{W}{20\,EI} (3.098\,a)(3.098\,a) \left(\dfrac{1}{3} \times 3.098\,a \right) \right]$

$$= 0.7436 \frac{Wa^3}{EI} - 0.2479 \frac{Wa^3}{EI} = 0.4957 \frac{Wa^3}{EI}$$

$\therefore \qquad y_{max} = \left(M_{X'} \right)_{max} = \mathbf{0.4957} \dfrac{Wa^3}{EI}$

Substituting the *numerical values*, we get

$$i_A = \frac{6}{25} \frac{W a^2}{E I} = \frac{6}{25} \frac{8000 \, (2.5)^2}{(2 \times 10^5) \, (5000 \times 10^4)} \, (1000)^2 = 1.2 \times 10^{-3} \text{ radian}$$

$$y_D = 0.4698 \frac{W a^3}{E I} = 0.4698 \times \frac{8000 \, (2.5)^3}{(2 \times 10^5) \, (5000 \times 10^4)} \, (1000)^3 = 5.87 \text{ mm} (\downarrow)$$

$$y_{\max} = 0.4957 \frac{W a^3}{E I} = 0.4957 \times \frac{8000 \, (2.5)^3}{(2 \times 10^5) \, (5000 \times 10^4)} \, (1000)^2 = 6.20 \text{ mm} (\downarrow)$$

Example 14.14. *A simple beam AB is acted upon by couples μ and 2μ at the ends as shown in Fig. 14.18. Determine the slope at A and B, and (ii) the deflection at the mid-span.*

Solution :

Fig. 14.18(*a*) shows the real beam while Fig. 14.18(*c*) shows the conjugate beam with the loading $M/E I$. Load at $A' = \mu/E I$ while the load at $B' = 2\mu/E I$.

For the conjugate beam,

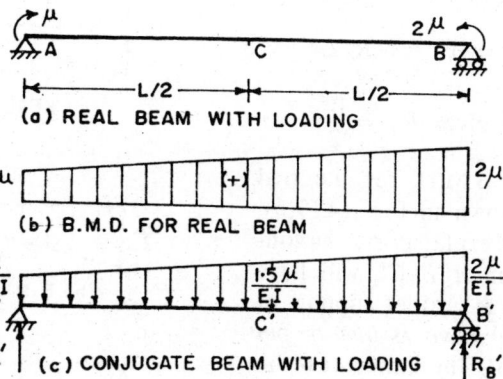

FIG. 14.18

Reaction $R_A' = \dfrac{1}{L} \left[\dfrac{1}{2} \left(\dfrac{\mu}{EI} + \dfrac{2\mu}{E I} \right) \times L \left\{ \dfrac{L}{3} \dfrac{\frac{2\mu}{EI} + \frac{2\mu}{EI}}{\frac{\mu}{EI} + \frac{2\mu}{EI}} \right\} \right] = \dfrac{1}{L} \left[\dfrac{3\mu L}{2 E I} \times \dfrac{4L}{9} \right] = \dfrac{2\mu L}{3 E I}$

$R_B' = \dfrac{1}{L} \left[\dfrac{1}{2} \left(\dfrac{\mu}{E I} + \dfrac{2\mu}{E I} \right) L \left\{ \dfrac{L}{3} \dfrac{\frac{2 \times 2\mu}{E I} + \frac{\mu}{E I}}{\frac{2\mu}{E I} + \frac{\mu}{E I}} \right\} \right] = \dfrac{1}{L} \left[\dfrac{3\mu L}{2 E I} \times \dfrac{5}{9} L \right] = \dfrac{5\mu L}{6 E I}$

Now

$$i_A = F_A' = + R_A' = + \frac{2}{3} \frac{\mu L}{E I}$$

$$i_B = F_B' = - R_B' = - \frac{5}{6} \frac{\mu L}{E I}$$

$$y_C = M_C' = R_A' \cdot \frac{L}{2} - \left[\frac{1}{2} \left(\frac{\mu}{E I} + \frac{1.5\mu}{E I} \right) \frac{L}{2} \left\{ \frac{1}{3} \cdot \frac{L}{2} \frac{\frac{2\mu}{E I} + \frac{1.5\mu}{E I}}{\frac{\mu}{E I} + \frac{1.5\mu}{E I}} \right\} \right]$$

$$= \frac{2}{3} \frac{\mu L}{E I} \cdot \frac{L}{2} - \left[\frac{5}{8} \frac{\mu L}{E I} \times \frac{7}{30} L \right] = \frac{\mu L^2}{3 E I} - \frac{7}{48} \frac{\mu L^2}{E I} = \frac{3}{16} \frac{\mu L^2}{E I}$$

Example 14.15. *A beam ABC is fixed at end A, and has a roller support at end C. It is also provided with an internal hinge at B. Determine the slope and deflection at the hinge B, when loaded with a point load W as shown in Fig. 14.18(a).*

Solution :

Fig. 14.19(a) shows the real beam ABC. There are three reaction components: R_A, M_A and R_C. Against this, there are three condition equations available from statical equilibrium:

$\Sigma V = 0$, $M_C = 0$ and $M_B = 0$ (because of internal hinge at B). Hence the beam is statically determinate. For reaction at C, take moments about B.

$\therefore M_B = 0 = W \cdot \dfrac{L}{2} - R_A L$

This gives $R_A = \dfrac{W}{2}$.

The B.M.D. for the real beam is shown in Fig. 14.19(b), which is self explanatory. The conjugate beam $A' B' C'$, will have *free* end at A', roller support at C' and will have as *interior pin support* at B'. The conjugate beam with the elastic loading equal to M/EI is shown in Fig. 14.19(c). For reaction R_B' at B' of the conjugate beam, take moment about C'.

$R_B' \times L + \left(\dfrac{WL}{4EI} \times \dfrac{L}{2} \right) \left(\dfrac{L}{2} \right)$

$- \left(\dfrac{1}{2} \times L \times \dfrac{WL}{2EI} \right) \left(L + \dfrac{2}{3}L \right) = 0$

Which gives

$R_B' = \dfrac{1}{L} \left[\dfrac{WL^3}{EI} \times \dfrac{5}{12} - \dfrac{WL^3}{16EI} \right]$

$= \dfrac{17}{48} \dfrac{WL^2}{EI} (\downarrow)$

Hence R_C'

$= \dfrac{1}{2} \times L \times \dfrac{WL}{4EI} + \dfrac{17}{48} \dfrac{WL^2}{EI}$

$- \dfrac{1}{2} \times L \times \dfrac{WL}{2EI} = \dfrac{11}{48} \dfrac{WL^2}{EI} (\uparrow)$

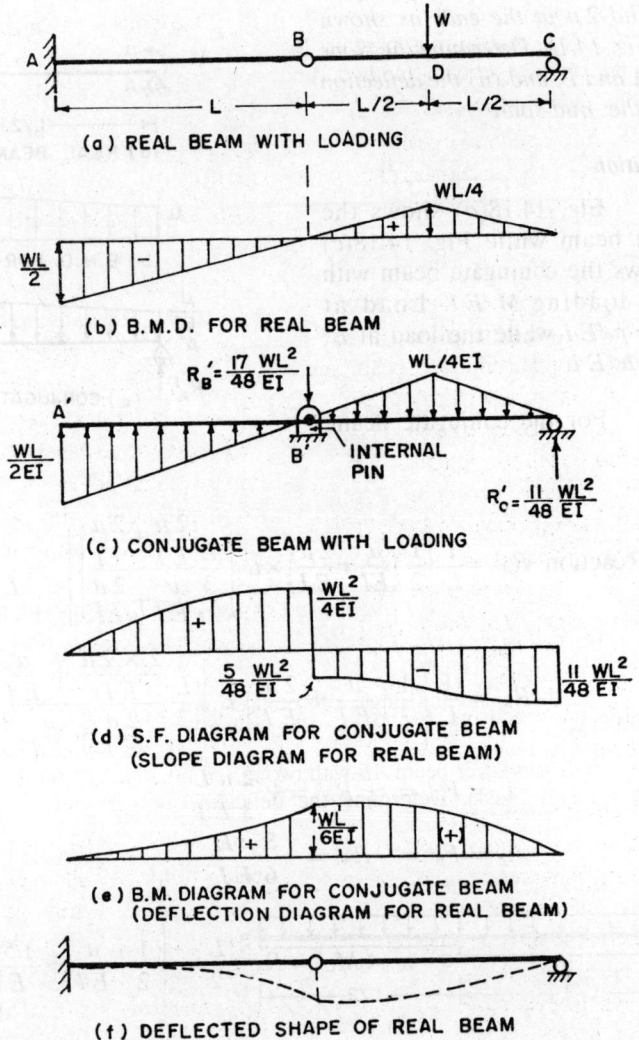

(a) REAL BEAM WITH LOADING

(b) B.M.D. FOR REAL BEAM

(c) CONJUGATE BEAM WITH LOADING

(d) S.F. DIAGRAM FOR CONJUGATE BEAM
(SLOPE DIAGRAM FOR REAL BEAM)

(e) B.M. DIAGRAM FOR CONJUGATE BEAM
(DEFLECTION DIAGRAM FOR REAL BEAM)

(f) DEFLECTED SHAPE OF REAL BEAM

FIG. 14.19

The S.F. diagram for the conjugate beam is shown in Fig. 14.19(d).

Now
$$\left(i_B \right)_{left} = \left(F_B{}' \right)_{left} = +\frac{1}{2} \times L \times \frac{WL}{2EI} = +\frac{WL^2}{4EI} \text{ (i.e. clockwise)}$$

$$\left(i_B \right)_{right} = \left(F_B{}' \right)_{right} = \frac{1}{2} \times L \times \frac{WL}{2EI} - \frac{17}{48} \frac{WL^2}{EI} = -\frac{5}{48} \frac{WL^2}{EI} \text{ (i.e. anticlockwise)}$$

Also,
$$y_B = M_B{}' = +\frac{1}{2} \times L \times \frac{WL}{2EI} \left(\frac{2}{3} L \right) = +\frac{WL^3}{6EI} \text{ (i.e. } \downarrow \text{)}$$

Also,
$$y_A = M_A{}' = 0 \,;\, y_C = M_C{}' = 0$$

The B.M.D. for the conjugate beam is shown in Fig. 14.19(e). Fig. 14.19(f) shows the deflected shape of the real beam.

PROBLEMS

1. A cantilever is partially loaded with U.D.L. w over a length L_1, from the fixed end (Fig. 14.20). Using conjugate beam method, find slope and deflection at the end.

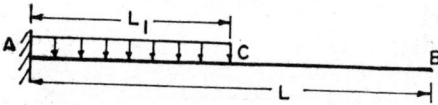

FIG. 14.20

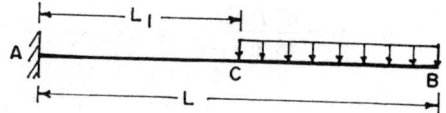

FIG. 14.21

2. A cantilever is partially loaded with U.D.L. w over a length $(L_1 - L)$ from the free end (Fig. 14.21). Using conjugate beam method, find the deflection at the free end.

3. A cantilever AB of length L is subjected to a concentrated load W and a couple μ acting at the free end (Fig. 14.22). Determine the slope and deflections at the free end.

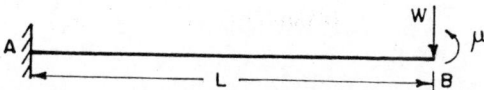

FIG. 14.22

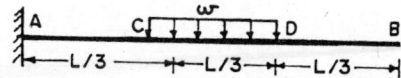

FIG. 14.23

4. Determine the angle of rotation and deflection at the free end of a cantilever beam AB with uniform load w acting over the middle third of the beam (Fig. 14.23).

5. A cantilever beam AB with two different moments of inertia I and $2I$ supports a uniformly distributed load w (Fig. 14.24). Determine the deflection at the free end.

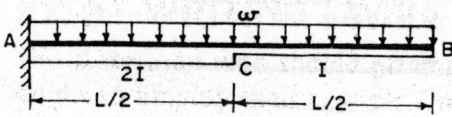

FIG. 14.24

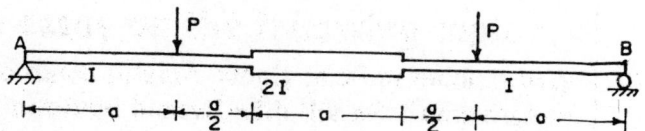

FIG. 14.25

6. A beam with variable moment of inertia at is loaded as shown in Fig. 14.25. Determine the deflection at the mid-span.

ANSWERS

1. $i_B = \dfrac{w L_1^3}{6 E I}$; $y_B = \dfrac{w L_1^4}{8 E I} + \dfrac{w L_1^3}{6 E I}(L - L_1)$

2. $\dfrac{w L^4}{8 E I} - \left\{ \dfrac{w L_1^4}{8 E I} + \dfrac{w L_1^3}{6 E I}(L - L_1) \right\}$

3. $\dfrac{W L^2}{2 E I} - \dfrac{\mu L}{E I}$; $\dfrac{W L^3}{3 E I} - \dfrac{\mu L^2}{2 E I}$

4. $i_B = \dfrac{7 w L^3}{162 E I}$; $y_B = \dfrac{23 w L^4}{648 E I}$

5. $y_B = \dfrac{17 w L^4}{256 E I}$

6. $y_C = \dfrac{67}{48} \dfrac{P a^3}{E I}$

15

Deflection of Beams : IV
Strain Energy Method

15.1. STRAIN ENERGY OF BENDING

In chapter 6, the concept of strain energy was discussed with respect to the axially loaded members. We have seen there that the strain energy per unit volume is equal to $\frac{f^2}{2E}$, where f is the axial stress. We shall now apply the concept of strain energy to the bending of beams. To start with, consider a beam to span L, subjected to couples M at the ends (*i.e.* pure bending). The resulting deflection curve will be a circular arc of constant curvature the radius of curvature R being given by

$$\frac{1}{R} = \frac{M}{EI} \qquad ...(i)$$

If θ is the angle substended at the centre,

$$\theta = L/R \qquad ...(ii)$$

Hence $\qquad \theta = ML/EI \qquad ...(15.1)$

Thus, there is linear relationship between M and θ. This linear relationship is shown in Fig. 15.1(b), usually known as *moment rotation diagram*. Assuming that moment M is applied gradually in magnitude from zero to its maximum value M, the work (W) done in the process is represented by the shaded area. The work is stored in the form of strain energy in the beam given by $U = W = \frac{M\theta}{2} \qquad ...(15.2)$

Hence from 15.1 and 15.2,

$$U = \frac{M^2 L}{2EI} \qquad ...(15.3\,a)$$

Also, $\qquad U = \frac{EI\theta^2}{2L} \qquad ...(15.3\,b)$

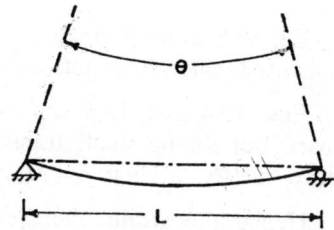

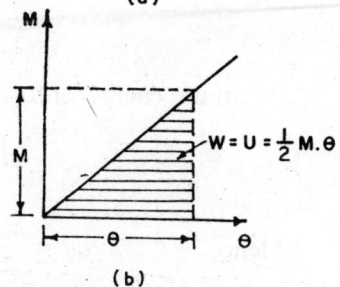

(a)

(b)

FIG. 15.1

Let us now take the usual case of beam bending in which the bending moment varies along the length of the beam. Let the bending moment at any section X, distant x from the origin, be M_x. Consider another section distant dx from the previous one. Such an element, of length dx, of the beam is shown in Fig. 15.2.

Let $d\theta$ be the angle between the sides of the element. Then the angle $d\theta$ is given by

$$d\theta \approx \frac{d^2y}{dx^2} dx = \frac{M_x\, dx}{E\,I}$$

Hence strain energy stored in the element is

$$du = \frac{1}{2} M_x . d\theta = \frac{M_x^2\, dx}{2\,E\,I} \qquad ...(15.4)$$

Also,

$$du = \frac{E\,I}{2} \left(\frac{d^2y}{dx^2}\right)^2 dx \qquad ...(15.4\,a)$$

Hence total strain energy stored in the whole beam is given by

$$U = \int_0^L \frac{M_x^2\, dx}{2\,E\,I} \qquad ...(15.5)$$

Also,

$$U = \int_0^L \frac{E\,I}{2} \left(\frac{d^2y}{dx^2}\right)^2 dx \qquad ...(15.5a)$$

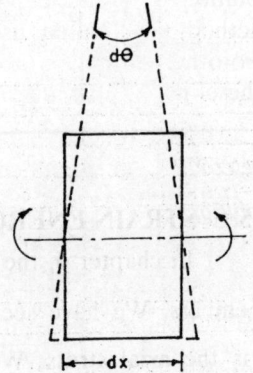

FIG. 15.2

Eq. 15.5 is used when the B.M. is known while Eq. 15.5(a) can be used when the deflection curve is known.

Eqs. 15.4 and 15.5 can be derived *alternatively* by considering two transverse sections dx apart. Let dA be small transverse area over which the direct stress f is acting at a height h above the N.A. Then $f = M_x . y/I$

Hence the strain energy of the elementary volume of length dx and area dA is

$$= \frac{f^2}{2\,E} . dx . dA = \frac{M_x^2 y^2}{2\,I^2\,E} . dx . dA$$

$\therefore$ Strain energy of the whole piece of length dx between the transverse sections

$$= du = \frac{\Sigma M_x^2 y^2}{2\,I^2\,E} . dx\, dA = \frac{M_x^2\, dx}{2\,I^2\,E} \Sigma\, dA . y^2 = \frac{M_x^2 . dx}{2\,I^2\,E} \;(I)$$

Hence

$$du = \frac{M_x^2\, dx}{2\,E\,I} \quad (\text{Since } \Sigma\, dA . y^2 = I) \qquad ...(15.4)$$

and

$$U = \int_0^L \frac{M_x^2\, dx}{2\,E\,I} \qquad ...(15.5)$$

15.2. DEFLECTION OF BEAMS FROM STRAIN ENERGY CONSIDERATION

When a beam is subjected to a point load, the deflection under the point load can be found by equating the total strain energy of the beam, using Eq. 15.5, to the work(W)

done by load P, which is equal to $\frac{1}{2}P \cdot y$ where y is the required deflection. This is illustrated in Example 15.1. It is important to observe that the only deflection we can find is the *deflection under the load*, and not the deflection else where, by this direct method. Similarly, when a beam is subjected to a couple μ, the rotation θ at the point of application can be found by equating the total strain energy of the beam (using Eq. 15.5) to the work done by couple μ, which is equal to $\frac{1}{2}\mu\theta$. This is illustrated in example 15.2. Here also, we can find the rotation only at the point where the couple is applied, and not else where. Thus, the direct method has limited use. However we can find the deflection at *any point* of the beam by two other methods : (*i*) unit load method, and (*ii*) fictitious load method or Castigliano's method. These have been discussed in subsequent articles.

Example 15.1. *A cantilever AB of length L is loaded with a point load W at its free end. Determine (a) strain energy of the beam and (b) the deflection of the free end.*

Solution :

At any section X, distant x from B,

$$M_x = -Wx$$

$$\therefore \quad U = \int \frac{M_x^2 \, dx}{2EI} = \int_0^L \frac{(-W \cdot x)^2 \, dx}{2EI}$$

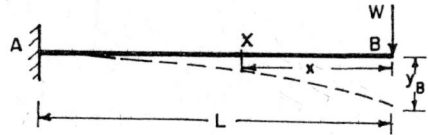

FIG. 15.3

$$= \frac{W^2}{2EI}\left(\frac{x^3}{3}\right)_0^L = \frac{W^2 L^3}{6EI} \qquad \qquad ...(1)$$

It is to be noted that strain energy is always a *positive* quantity, and that the load appears in the second power.

$$\text{Work done by load} = \frac{1}{2}Wy_B \qquad \qquad ...(2)$$

Equating the two, $\quad \frac{1}{2}Wy_B = \frac{W^2 L^3}{6EI}$

From which $\qquad \qquad y_B = \frac{WL^3}{3EI}$ **(Ans.)**

Example 15.2. *A cantilever AB of length L is subjected to a couple μ acting at the free end. Determine (a) the strain energy of the beam, and (b) rotation of the free end.*

Solution :

At any section X, distant x from B, we have

$$M_x = -\mu$$

$$\therefore \quad U = \int \frac{M_x^2 \, dx}{2EI} = \int_0^L \frac{(-\mu)^2 \, dx}{2EI}$$

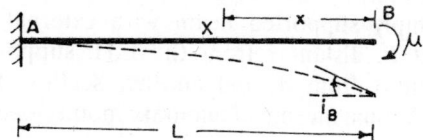

$$= \frac{\mu^2}{2EI}\left[x\right]_0^L = \frac{\mu^2 L}{2EI}$$

FIG. 15.4

If i_B is the rotation at the free end, work done by during loading of the beam is $\frac{1}{2}\mu\, i_B$

Hence $\dfrac{1}{2}\mu\, i_B = \dfrac{\mu^2 L}{2EI}$.

From which $i_B = \dfrac{\mu L}{EI}$ (Clockwise)

Example 15.3. *A cantilever AB of length L is subjected simultaneously to both a concentrated load W and a couple μ, as shown in Fig. 15.5. Determine the strain energy of the beam. Is the method of super position applicable ? Can you find the slope and deflection of the beam?*

Solution :

At any distance x from the free end,

$M_x = -W.x - \mu$

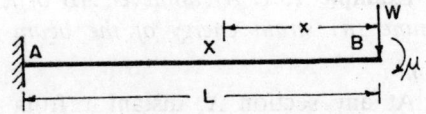

FIG. 15.5

$\therefore \qquad U = \int \dfrac{M_x^2\, dx}{2EI} = \dfrac{1}{2EI}\int_0^L (-Wx-\mu)^2\, dx$

$= \dfrac{1}{2EI}\left[\dfrac{W^2 x^3}{3} + \mu^2 x + \dfrac{2W\mu x^2}{2}\right]_0^L = \dfrac{1}{2EI}\left[\dfrac{W^2 L^3}{3} + W\mu L^2 + \mu^2 L\right]$

$= \dfrac{W^2 L^3}{6EI} + \dfrac{W\mu L^2}{2EI} + \dfrac{\mu^2 L}{2EI}$ ...(1) (Ans.)

The above expression for U contains three terms. The first terms gives the strain energy due to *W acting alone* while the last term gives the value of strain energy due to μ acting alone. However, when both W and μ acts together, the term in the middle also appears. *This shows that the strain energy due to two or more loads cannot be found by method of super position.* This is because the strain energy U is a quadratic function of loads and not a linear function.

Again work done $= \dfrac{W y_b}{2} + \dfrac{\mu\, i_B}{2}$ ...(2)

When (1) and (2) are equated, there appear two unknowns y_B and i_B. Hence slope and deflection cannot be found by this method.

15.3. DEFLECTION BY UNIT LOAD METHOD

In the previous article, we have seen that we can find the deformation of the beam only at the point of application of the load/moment, by the direct method. For finding the deflection of the beam at any other point, we will use the *unit load method.* Fig. 15.6(a) shows a simply supported beam with external loading. It is required to find the deflection at any point P, distant x from the L.H. support, due to the external loading. Consider a section X, distant x from A, and another section distant dx from the previous one. Let M be the B.M. there. Imagine an elementary point load dW at point P where the deflection is desired. Due to the addition of this load, the work supplied $= \frac{1}{2}dW.y_P$ ...(1)

where y_P is the desired deflection at P.

Again, due to the addition of dW at P, the B.M. at X will be increased to $(M+dM)$ where dM is the increment due to dW. If m is the B.M. at X due to unit load at P, the incremental B.M. $dM = m\,dW$.

The change in slope of the tangent at X, due to dW at P, is given by

$$E\,I\frac{di}{dx} = dM = m\,dW$$

$$\therefore \quad di = \frac{m\,dW.dx}{E\,I} \qquad \qquad ...(2)$$

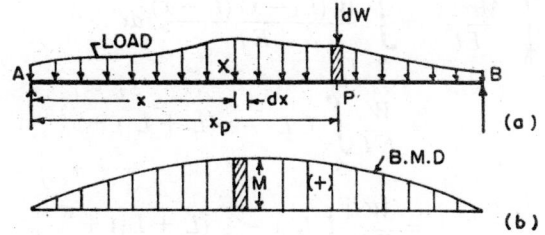

FIG. 15.6

Work stored in the strip of length $dx = \frac{1}{2}(M + m\,dW).di = \frac{1}{2}\left(M + m\,dW\right).\frac{m\,dW.dx}{E\,I}$

$\therefore$ Work stored in the whole beam due to dW at P

$$= \frac{1}{2E\,I}\int_0^L M.m.dW.dx \qquad \qquad ...(3)$$

(neglecting the small quantities of higher order). Equating (1) and (3), we get

$$\frac{1}{2}dW.y_P = \frac{1}{2E\,I}\int_0^L M\,m\,dW.dx$$

or

$$y_P = \int_0^L \frac{M.m.dx}{E\,I} \qquad \qquad ...(15.6)$$

Procedure : In order to find the deflection at any point P, proceed as follows.

1. Find the B.M. at any section X, distant x from the support due to external loading. Thus M is known in terms of x.

2. Put unit load at point P under consideration and find the B.M. m at the section X. Thus m is also known in terms if x.

3. Integrate Eq. 15.6 between limits $x = 0$ to $x = L$ and get the value of deflection y_P at the point under consideration.

Example 15.4. *A cantilever AB of length L is loaded with a point load W at distance L_1 from the support. Calculate the deflection at the free end.*

Solution :

Apply unit load at B. Measuring x from A, we have

$$y_B = \int_0^L \frac{M\,m\,dx}{E\,I} = \int_0^{L_1} \frac{M\,m\,dx}{E\,I} + \int_{L_1}^L \frac{M\,m\,dx}{E\,I}$$

For AC $M = -W(L_1 - x)$ and $m = -1(L - x)$

$$\therefore \int_0^{L_1} \frac{Mmdx}{EI} = \int_0^{L_1} \frac{W(L_1 - x)(L - x)}{EI} dx$$

$$= \frac{W}{EI} \int_0^{L_1} L L_1 - x(L + L_1) + x^2$$

$$= \frac{W}{EI} \left[L L_1 x - \frac{x^2}{2}(L + L_1) + \frac{x^3}{3} \right]_0^{L_1}$$

$$= \frac{W}{EI} \left[L L_1^2 - \frac{L_1^2}{2}(L + L_1) + \frac{L_1^3}{3} \right]$$

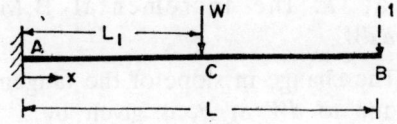

FIG. 15.7

$$= \frac{W}{EI} \left[\frac{L L_1^2}{2} - \frac{L_1^3}{6} \right] = \frac{W}{EI} \left[\frac{3 L L_1^2 - 3 L_1^3 + 2 L_1^3}{6} \right] = \frac{WL_1^3}{3EI} + \frac{WL_1^2}{2EI}(L - L_1) \qquad ...(1)$$

For CB : $M = 0$ and $m = -1(L - x)$

Hence $\displaystyle\int_{L_1}^{L} \frac{M m dx}{EI} = 0$

$$\therefore \qquad y_B = \int_0^{L} \frac{M m dx}{EI} = \frac{WL_1^3}{3EI} + \frac{WL_1^2}{2EI}(L - L_1)$$

This is the same as Eq. 12.14.

Example 15.5. *A cantilever is loaded with uniformly distributed load throughout its length. Calculate (a) the deflection at the free end. (b) deflection of a point C distant c from the free end.*

Solution :

(a) **Deflection at B**: Apply a unit load at B, as shown in Fig. 15.8(b).

Then $\displaystyle y_B = \int_0^{L} \frac{M m dx}{EI}$

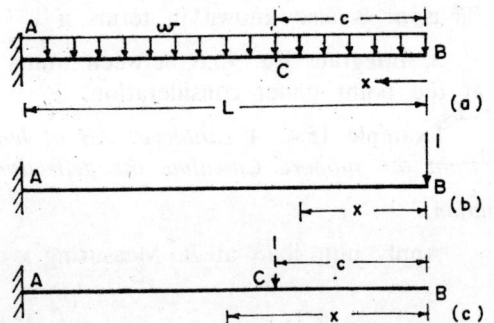

Here $M = -\dfrac{w x^2}{2}$ and $m = -1x = -x$

$$y_B = \frac{1}{EI} \int_0^{L} -\frac{w x^2}{2}(-x)\, dx$$

$$= \frac{1}{EI} \int_0^{L} \frac{w x^3}{2} = \frac{wL^4}{8EI} \quad \text{(Ans.)}$$

(b) **Deflection at C** : Apply the unit load at C, as shown in Fig. 15.8(c).

FIG. 15.8

Then $$y_C = \int_0^L \frac{M\,m\,dx}{E\,I} = \int_0^C \frac{M\,m\,dx}{E\,I} + \int_C^L \frac{M\,m\,dx}{E\,I}$$

For BC $$M = -\frac{w\,x^2}{2}; m = 0 \quad \therefore \quad \int_0^C \frac{M\,m\,dx}{E\,I} = \text{zero}$$

For CA $$M = -\frac{w\,x^2}{2}; m = -1\,(x - c)$$

$$\therefore \quad \int_C^L \frac{M\,m\,dx}{E\,I} = \frac{1}{E\,I}\int_C^L \frac{w\,x^2}{2}(x - c)\,dx = \frac{1}{E\,I}\left[\frac{w\,x^4}{8} - \frac{w\,c\,x^3}{6}\right]_c^L$$

$$= \frac{w}{E\,I}\left[\left\{\frac{L^4}{8} - \frac{c\,L^3}{6}\right\} - \left\{\frac{c^4}{8} - \frac{c^4}{6}\right\}\right] = \frac{w}{24\,E\,I}\left[3\,L^4 - 4\,c\,L^3 + c^4\right]$$

Hence $$y_C = \int_0^L \frac{M\,m\,dx}{E\,I} = \frac{w}{24\,E\,I}\left[3\,L^4 - 4\,c\,L^3 + c^4\right]\ \text{Ans.}$$

Example 15.6. *Find the central deflection of a simply supported beam loaded with a point load W distant a from A and b from B.*

Solution :

Apply additional load W at a distance b from A. Due to this application, the deflection at C will be *doubled*. Now apply unit load at C, where deflection is desired.

Then $$y_C = \int_0^L \frac{M\,m\,dx}{E\,I} = 2\int_0^{\frac{L}{2}} \frac{M\,m\,dx}{E\,I}, \text{ due to symmetry.}$$

For AE, $M = W.x$ and $m = \frac{1}{2}.x$

$$\therefore \quad \int_0^b \frac{M\,m\,dx}{E\,I} = \frac{1}{E\,I}\int_0^b \frac{W\,x^2}{2}\,dx = \frac{W\,b^3}{6\,E\,I}\ \ ...(i)$$

For EC, $M = Wx - W(x - b)$

and $m = \frac{1}{2}x$

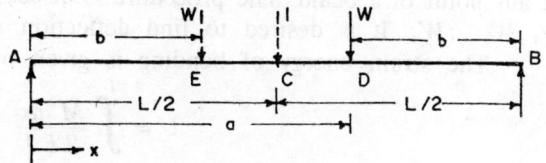

FIG. 15.9

$$\therefore \quad \int_b^{L/2} \frac{M\,m\,dx}{E\,I} = \int_b^{L/2} \frac{1}{E\,I}\left[\frac{W\,x^2}{2} - \frac{W\,x}{2}(x - b)\right]dx = \frac{1}{E\,I}\left[\frac{W\,x^3}{6} - \frac{W\,x^3}{6} + \frac{W\,b\,x^2}{4}\right]_b^{\frac{L}{2}}$$

$$= \frac{W\,b}{4\,E\,I}\left[\frac{L^2}{4} - b^2\right] = \frac{W\,b}{16\,E\,I}\left(L^2 - 4\,b^2\right)\ \ ...(ii)$$

Now
$$y_c = 2 \int_0^{\frac{L}{2}} \frac{M\,m\,dx}{E\,I} = 2 \left[\int_0^b \frac{M\,m\,dx}{E\,I} + \int_b^{\frac{L}{2}} \frac{M\,m\,dx}{E\,I} \right]$$

$$= \frac{2}{E\,I} \left[\frac{W\,b^3}{6} + \frac{W\,b}{16} (L^2 - 4\,b^2) \right] = \frac{2\,W\,b}{48\,E\,I} \left[8\,b^2 + 3\,L^2 - 12\,b^2 \right]$$

$$= \frac{W\,b}{24\,E\,I} (3\,L^2 - 4\,b^2)$$

Hence the central deflection due to single point load

$$= \frac{W\,b}{48\,E\,I} (3\,L^2 - 4\,b^2)$$

15.4. DEFLECTION BY FICTITIOUS LOAD METHOD USING CASTIGLIANO'S FIRST THEOREM

The concept of elastic strain energy can be very useful in the study of deflections of various points of a structure under load. Instead of directly equating the *external work* to the internal strain energy, considerable simplification is obtained by *Castigliano's first theorem*, which states that deflection caused by any external force is equal to the partial derivative of the strain energy with respect of that force. A generalised statement of the theorem* is as follows:

"If there is any elastic system in equilibrium under the action of a set of forces $W_1, W_2, W_3 \ldots W_n$ and corresponding displacements $\delta_1, \delta_2, \delta_3 \ldots \delta_n$, and a set of moments $M_1, M_2, M_3 \ldots M_n$ and the corresponding rotations $\varphi_1, \varphi_2, \varphi_3 \ldots \varphi_n$, then the partial derivative of the total strain energy U with respect to any one of the forces or moments, taken individually would yield its corresponding displacement in its direction of action"

Expressed mathematically,

$$\frac{\partial U}{\partial W_1} = \delta_1 \quad \text{and} \quad \frac{\partial U}{\partial M_1} = \varphi_1 \qquad \qquad ...(15.7)$$

The above theorem of Castigliano can be used for computing the deflection and slope at any point of a beam. The procedure is discussed below. Consider a beam subjected to loads $W_1, W_2 \ldots W_n$. It is desired to find deflection under load W_1.

The strain energy of bending is given by

$$U = \int_0^L \frac{M^2\,dx}{2\,E\,I} \quad \text{(where } M \text{ is a function of } W_1) \qquad ...(15.5)$$

$$\therefore \qquad \delta_1 = \frac{\partial U}{\partial W_1} = \int_0^L M \left(\frac{\partial M}{\partial W_1} \right) \frac{dx}{E\,I} \qquad \qquad ...(15.8)$$

In the above expression, $\partial M / \partial W_1$ is evaluated by differentiating *inside the integral sign, before integrating.* If no load is acting at a point where the deflection is desired, a *fictitious load W* is applied at the point, in the direction the deflection is required. Then, *after differentiating,* but *before integrating,* the fictitious load is set to zero. The method is also sometimes known

*For the proof of the theorem, see Author's book THEORY OF STRUCTURES

as the *fictitious load method*. If, however, the rotation φ_1 is required in the direction of M_1, Eq. 15.8 is modified as follows :

$$\varphi_1 = \frac{\partial U}{\partial M_1} = \int_0^L M \left(\frac{\partial M}{\partial M_1} \right) \frac{dx}{E\,I} \qquad \qquad ...(15.9)$$

where M is a function of M_1.

Example 15.7. *Calculate the central deflection, and the slope at ends of a simply supported beam carrying a U.D.L. w per unit length over the whole span.*

Solution :

    (a) Central deflection :

Since no point load is acting at the centre where the deflection is required, apply a *fictitious load* W there, as shown in Fig. 15.10 (*a*). The reactions at A and B will be $\left(\dfrac{WL}{2} + \dfrac{W}{2} \right)(\uparrow)$ each.

$$\therefore \ \ y_C = \frac{\partial U}{\partial W} = \frac{1}{E\,I} \int_0^L M_x \frac{\partial M_x}{\partial W}\, dx$$
$$...(1)$$

where M_x is the B.M. at any section distant x from A.

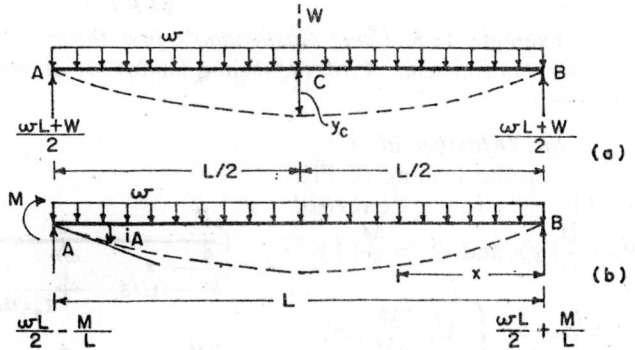

FIG. 15.10

$$M_x = \left(\frac{wL}{2} + \frac{W}{2} \right) x - \frac{wx^2}{2} \ ; \quad \frac{\partial M_x}{\partial W} = \frac{x}{2}$$

Hence $\qquad \qquad y_C = \dfrac{2}{E\,I} \displaystyle\int_0^{\frac{L}{2}} \left[\left(\dfrac{wL}{2} + \dfrac{W}{2} \right) x - \dfrac{wx^2}{2} \right] \dfrac{x}{2}\, dx$

Putting $\qquad \qquad W = 0$, we get

$$y_C = \frac{2}{E\,I} \int_0^{\frac{L}{2}} \left(\frac{wL}{2} x - \frac{wx^2}{2} \right) \frac{x}{2}\, dx = \frac{2}{E\,I} \left[\frac{wL\,x^3}{12} - \frac{wx^4}{16} \right]_0^{\frac{L}{2}} = \frac{5}{384} \frac{wL^4}{E\,I}$$

(b) Slope at ends :

To obtain slope at end A, apply *fictitious moment* M at A, as shown in Fig. 15.10(*b*). The reactions at A and B will be respectively $\left(\dfrac{wL}{2} - \dfrac{M}{L} \right)$ and $\left(\dfrac{wL}{2} + \dfrac{M}{L} \right)$.

Measuring x from B, we have, $i_A = \dfrac{\partial U}{\partial M} = \dfrac{1}{E\,I} \displaystyle\int_0^L M_x \cdot \dfrac{\partial M_x}{\partial M} \cdot dx$ $\qquad ...(2)$

where M_x is the B.M at any point distant x from B, and is a function of M.

$$M_x = \left(\frac{wL}{2} + \frac{M}{L} \right) x - \frac{wx^2}{2} \ ; \quad \frac{\partial M_x}{\partial M} = \frac{x}{L}$$

Substituting in Eq. (2), we get

$$i_A = \frac{1}{EI} \int_0^L \left\{ \left(\frac{wL}{2} + \frac{M}{L} \right) x - \frac{wx^2}{2} \right\} \frac{x}{L} dx$$

Putting $M = 0$, we get

$$i_A = \frac{1}{EI} \int_0^L \left(\frac{wL}{2} x - \frac{wx^2}{2} \right) \frac{x}{L} dx = \frac{1}{EI} \left[\frac{wx^3}{6} - \frac{wx^4}{8L} \right]_0^L$$

$$= + \frac{wL^3}{24EI} \quad (i.e. \text{ clockwise})$$

Example 15.8. *Using Castigliano's first theorem, determine the deflection and rotation of the over hanging end A of the beam loaded as shown in Fig. 15.11(a).*

Solution :

(a) Deflection at A :

For the loading of Fig. 15.11, the reaction $R_B = \frac{M}{L}(\downarrow)$ and $R_C = \frac{M}{L}(\uparrow)$

$$i_A = \frac{\partial U}{\partial M} = \frac{1}{EI} \int_A^B M_x \cdot \frac{\partial M_x}{\partial M} \cdot dx$$

$$+ \frac{1}{EI} \int_C^B M_x \cdot \frac{\partial M_x}{\partial M} dx \quad ...(i)$$

For AB : Measuring x from A,

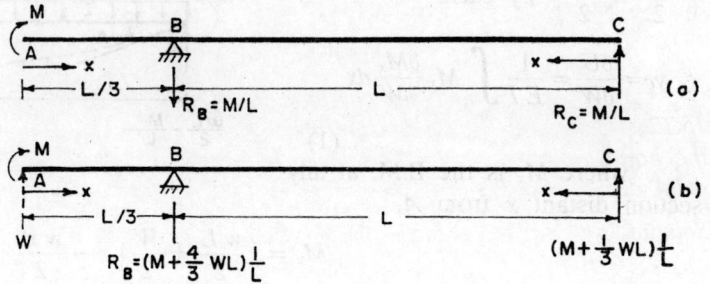

FIG. 15.11

$$M_x = M ; \frac{\partial M_x}{\partial M} = 1$$

$$\therefore \quad \frac{1}{EI} \int_A^B M_x \frac{\partial M_x}{\partial M} dx = \frac{1}{EI} \int_0^{\frac{L}{3}} (M \times 1) \, dx = \frac{M}{EI} \left[x \right]_0^{L/3} = \frac{ML}{3EI} \quad ...(ii)$$

For CB, Measuring x from C, $M_x = \frac{M}{L} x ; \frac{\partial M_x}{\partial M} = \frac{x}{L}$

$$\therefore \quad \frac{1}{EI} \int_C^B M_x \frac{\partial M_x}{\partial M} dx = \frac{1}{EI} \int_0^L \left(\frac{M}{L} x \right) \left(\frac{x}{L} \right) dx = \frac{M}{EIL^2} \left[\frac{x^3}{3} \right]_0^L = \frac{ML}{3EI} \quad ...(iii)$$

Hence from (i), $i_A = \frac{ML}{3EI} + \frac{ML}{3EI} = \frac{2ML}{3EI}$ (clockwise)

(b) Deflection at A : To find the deflection at A, apply a fictitious load W at A, in upward direction, as shown in Fig. 15.11(b).

$$R_B = \left(M + \frac{4}{3} WL \right) \frac{1}{L} (\downarrow) \text{ and } R_C = \left(M + \frac{1}{3} WL \right) \frac{1}{L} (\uparrow)$$

Now
$$y_A = \frac{\partial U}{\partial W} = \frac{1}{EI}\int_A^B M_x \frac{\partial M_x}{\partial W} dx + \frac{1}{EI}\int_C^B M_x \cdot \frac{\partial M_x}{\partial W} \cdot dx \qquad ...(iv)$$

For AB, Measuring x from A,
$$M_x = M + Wx \ ; \ \frac{\partial M_x}{\partial W} = x$$

For CB, Measuring x from C,
$$M_x = \left(M + \frac{1}{3}WL\right)\frac{1}{L}x \ ; \ \frac{\partial M_x}{\partial W} = \frac{x}{3}$$

Substituting the values in (iv), we get
$$y_A = \frac{1}{EI}\int_0^{L/3}(M + Wx)x\, dx + \frac{1}{EI}\int_0^L \left(M + \frac{1}{3}WL\right)\frac{x}{L}\cdot\frac{x}{3}\, dx$$

Putting $W = 0$, $\quad y_A = \frac{1}{EI}\int_0^{L/3} Mx\, dx + \frac{1}{EI}\int_0^L \frac{Mx^2}{3L}dx = \frac{M}{EI}\left[\frac{x^2}{2}\right]_0^{\frac{L}{3}} + \frac{M}{3EIL}\left[\frac{x^3}{3}\right]_0^L$

$$= \frac{ML^2}{18EI} + \frac{ML^2}{9EI} = \frac{ML^2}{6EI}(\uparrow)$$

Example 15.9. *A vertical load W is applied to the rigid cantilever frame shown in Fig. 15.12. Assuming E I to be constant throughout the frame, determine the horizontal and vertical displacement of the point C. Neglect axial deformations.*

Solution : **(a) Vertical deflection of C**

$$y_{CV} = \frac{\partial U}{\partial W} = \frac{1}{EI}\int M_x \frac{\partial M_x}{\partial W} dx \qquad ...(1)$$

For CB : Measuring x from C,
$$M_x = -Wx; \frac{\partial M_x}{\partial W} = x$$

For BA : Measuring x from B,
$$M_x = -\frac{WL}{2}; \frac{\partial M_x}{\partial W} = -L/2$$

Substituting in (1), we get

FIG. 15.12

$$y_{CV} = \frac{1}{EI}\left[\int_0^{L/2} Wx\cdot x\, dx + \int_0^L \frac{WL}{2}\cdot\frac{L}{2}dx\right] = \frac{1}{EI}\left[\frac{Wx^3}{3}\right]_0^{L/2} + \frac{1}{EI}\left[\frac{WL^2}{4}x\right]_0^L$$

$$= \frac{1}{EI}\left[\frac{WL^3}{24} + \frac{WL^3}{4}\right] = \frac{7WL^3}{24EI}\ (\downarrow)$$

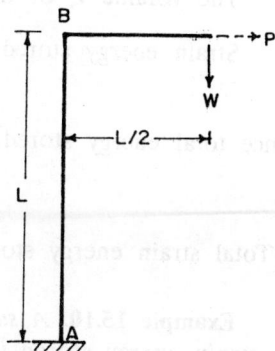

(b) Horizontal deflection of C: Apply a fictitious horizontal load P at C. Then

$$y_{CH} = \frac{\partial U}{\partial P} = \frac{1}{EI}\int M_x \frac{\partial M_x}{\partial P} dx \qquad ...(2)$$

For CB : Measuring x from C, $M_x = -Wx$; $\partial M_x / \partial P = 0$

For BA : Measuring x from B, $M_x = -\dfrac{WL}{2} - P.x$; $\partial M_x / \partial P = -x$

Substituting the values in (2),

$$y_{CH} = \frac{1}{EI} \left[\int_0^{L/2} (-Wx)(0)\, dx + \int_0^L \left(\frac{WL}{2} + Px \right) x\, dx \right]$$

Putting $P = 0$, $y_{CH} = \dfrac{1}{EI} \displaystyle\int_0^L \dfrac{WL}{2} x\, dx = \dfrac{1}{EI} \cdot \dfrac{WL}{2} \left[\dfrac{x^2}{2} \right]_0^L = \dfrac{WL^3}{4EI} (\rightarrow)$.

15.5. STRAIN ENERGY DUE TO SHEAR

Let us now determine the strain energy due to shear at any section of a beam subjected to external loading. Taking an elementary strip of length dx of a beam, distant x from the support, the shear stress at the layer distant y from the neutral axis of the section is given by

$$q = \frac{F}{Iz}(A\bar{y})$$

where I = moment of inertia of the whole section
z = width of the section at that layer
$A\bar{y}$ = moment of the area *above* that layer, about N.A.

The volume V of the strip of thickness $dy = dx \cdot z \cdot dy$

Strain energy stored in the elementary strip$= dU = \dfrac{q^2}{2N} \times V = \dfrac{q^2}{2N} \cdot z \cdot dx \cdot dy$

Hence total energy stored in section of length $dx = \displaystyle\int_{y_t}^{y_c} \dfrac{q^2}{2N} z\, dx \cdot dy$

$\therefore$ Total strain energy stored in the whole beam$= U_s = \displaystyle\int_0^L \int_{y_t}^{y_c} \dfrac{q^2}{2N} z \cdot dx \cdot dy \ldots (15.10)$

Example 15.10. *A simply supported beam of span L carries a central load W. Calculate the strain energy stored in the beam due to shear, if the beam is a rectangular section, $b \times d$.*

Solution :

At any distance x from the support, $F_x = \dfrac{W}{2}$

Also, for the rectangular beam section, $I = \dfrac{1}{12} b d^3$

$\therefore$ $$q = \frac{F}{2I} \left(\frac{d^2}{4} - y^2 \right) = \frac{3W}{b d^3} \left(\frac{d^2}{4} - y^2 \right)$$

or $$q^2 = \frac{9W^2}{b^2 d^6} \left(\frac{d^4}{16} + y^4 - \frac{d^2 y^2}{2} \right)$$

The total strain energy in the beam, due to shear, is given by Eq. 15.10

$$U_s = 2 \int_0^{L/2} \int_{y_t}^{y_c} \frac{q^2}{2N} z \, dx \, dy = 2 \int_0^{\frac{L}{2}} \int_{-\frac{d}{2}}^{+\frac{d}{2}} \frac{b}{2N} \cdot \frac{9W^2}{b^2 d^6} \left(\frac{d^4}{16} + y^4 - \frac{d^2 y^2}{2} \right) dx \, dy$$

$$= \frac{9W^2}{N b d^6} \int_0^{\frac{L}{2}} \left(\frac{d^4}{16} y + \frac{y^5}{5} - \frac{d^2 y^3}{6} \right)_{-\frac{d}{2}}^{+\frac{d}{2}} dx = \frac{9W^2}{N b d^6} \int_0^{\frac{L}{2}} \left(\frac{d^4}{16} d + \frac{1}{5} \frac{d^5}{16} - \frac{d^2}{6} \cdot \frac{d^3}{4} \right) dx$$

$$= \frac{9W^2}{N b d^6} \cdot \frac{d^5}{30} \int_0^{\frac{L}{2}} dx = \frac{9W^2}{30 N b d} \cdot \frac{L}{2} = \frac{3}{20} \frac{W^2 L}{N b d} \qquad ...(15.11)$$

15.6. DEFLECTION DUE TO SHEAR

Upto this stage (*i.e.* in Chapters 12, 13 and 14), only the effects of bending deformations were considered in finding deflections. *Shear* deformations produce additional deflection. The shear deformations, for a beam of rectangular cross-section cause an element of the beam of length dx to be deformed as shown in Fig. 15.13(*a*). Since the shear stresses vary over the depth of the beam, the cross-sections become curved surfaces. The line *ab* represents the original axis of the beam, while the line *ac* shows the position of the line after the shear deformations have occurred. Let angle γ_c between the lines *ab* and *ac* be the value of shear strain at the N.A. The value of γ_c is maximum at the N.A., and it decreases in the outer layers. At the outer most layers, γ_c becomes zero; hence the sides of this layer are at right angles.

Fig. 15.13(*c*) shows the curvature of the beam axis produced by shear deformation *alone*. The plane sections do not remain plane after bending, but are warped due to shearing strain. Small rectangular elements on the central axis become rhombus, the vertical edges of which remain vertical during deformations. The exact method of calculating the deflection curve due to shear in based on the fact that the slope of the deflection curve at any cross-section is simply equal to the shear strain at the N.A. However, we will find an approximate formula for deflection y_s due to shear. In the approximate method, the strain energy stored due to shear in the beam is equated to the work done by the load in producing shear.

Now, strain energy U of the whole beam due to shear is

$$U = \int_0^L \int_{y_t'}^{y_c} \frac{q^2}{2N} z \cdot dy \cdot dx \qquad ...(i)$$

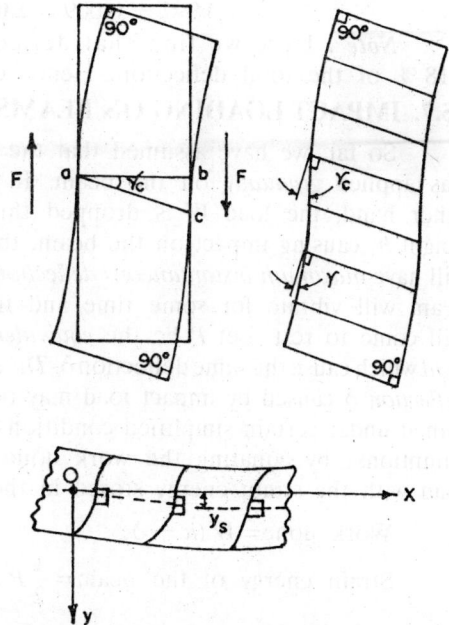

FIG. 15.13. SHEAR DEFORMATIONS

Also, work done by the load $= \frac{1}{2} P \cdot y_s$. (where y_s is the deflection due to shear)

Equating the two, $\frac{1}{2} P \cdot y_s = \int\limits_0^L \int\limits_{y_t}^{y_c} \frac{q^2}{2N} z \, dy \, dx$ ...(15.12)

Thus, Eq. 15.11 gives the *additional deflection* y_s due to shear.

Example 15.11. *Calculate the deflection due to shear and the total deflection for the beam of example 15.10. Take $W = 50\,kN$, $L = 4\,m$, $b = 100\,mm$, $d = 200\,mm$, $E = 2 \times 10^5\,N/mm^2$ and $N = 0.82 \times 10^5\,N/mm^2$.*

Solution :

As computed in example 15.10, strain energy due to shear is given by

$$U = \frac{3}{20} \frac{W^2 L}{N b d}$$ ...(15.11)

Also, work done due to deflection due to shear $= \frac{1}{2} W \cdot y_s$

Equating the two, $\frac{1}{2} W y_s = \frac{3}{20} \frac{W^2 L}{N b d}$ $\therefore$ $y_s = \frac{3}{10} \frac{WL}{N b d}$ ...(15.13)

Hence the total central deflection is $y = \frac{WL^3}{48 EI} + \frac{3}{10} \frac{WL}{N b d}$ (Ans.)

Substituting the numerical values, noting that $I = \frac{1}{12}(100)(200)^3 = 6.67 \times 10^7$

$$y = \frac{50000\,(4)^3}{48 \times 2 \times 10^5 \times 6.67 \times 10^7}(1000)^3 + \frac{3}{10} \frac{50000\,(4 \times 1000)}{0.82 \times 10^5 \times 200 \times 400}$$

$$= 4.997 + 0.009 = \mathbf{5.006}$$

Note : Here we find that deflection due to shear is only 0.009 mm which is only 0.18 % of the total deflection. Hence deflection due to shear is usually neglected.

15.7. IMPACT LOADING ON BEAMS

So far, we have assumed that the load W was applied *gradually* on the beam. If, on the other hand, the load W is dropped through a height h, causing impact on the beam, the beam will have *maximum instantaneous deflection* δ. The beam will vibrate for some time and finally it will come to rest. Let P be the *equivalent static load* which cause the same deflection δ. *The dynamic deflection* δ caused by impact load may be determined under certain simplified conditions (or assumptions) by equating the work done by the load with the strain energy stored in the beam.

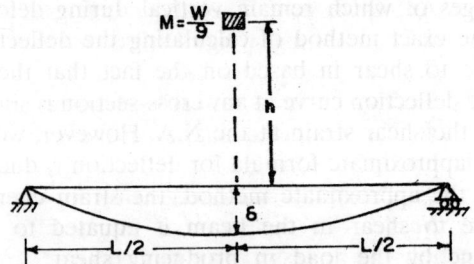

Work done $= W (h + \delta)$

Strain energy of the beam $= \frac{1}{2} P \cdot \delta$

Equating the two, we get $W (h + \delta) = \frac{1}{2} P \delta$ ...(1)

FIG. 15.14

Since P is the equivalent static load exerted on the beam when its deflection is maximum (*i.e.* δ), we have

$$\delta = \frac{PL^3}{48EI} \qquad \text{or} \qquad P = \frac{48EI\delta}{L^3} \qquad \qquad ...(2)$$

From (1) and (2), the values of P and δ can be easily found. Substituting the value of P in (i), we get

$$W(h + \delta) = \frac{24EI\delta^2}{L^3} \qquad \qquad ...(3)$$

This is a quadratic equation in δ, and can be solved for its positive root:

$$\delta = \frac{WL^3}{48EI} + \left[\left(\frac{WL^3}{48EI} \right)^2 + 2h \left(\frac{WL^3}{48EI} \right) \right]^{\frac{1}{2}} \qquad \qquad ...(15.14\,a)$$

Denotating the *static deflection* of the beam due to W as δ_{st} :

$$\delta_{st} = \frac{WL^3}{48EI} \, , \text{ Eq. 15.14}(a) \text{ takes the form}$$

$$\delta = \delta_{st} + \left(\delta_{st}^2 + 2h\,\delta_{st} \right)^{\frac{1}{2}} \qquad \qquad ...(15.14)$$

From Eq. 15.14, we find that the dynamic deflection δ is always much higher than the static deflection.

Case (i) : $h = 0$: If $h = 0$, *i.e.* when the load is *applied suddenly* but without any free fall, we get from Eq. 15.14 :

$$\delta = \delta_{st} + \delta_{st} = 2\,\delta_{st}$$

Hence dynamic deflection is twice the static deflection.

Case (ii) : h very large : When h is very large compared to δ, then the term containing h predominates and hence Eq. 15.12 can be written as

$$\delta = \sqrt{2h\,\delta_{st}} \qquad \qquad ...(15.15)$$

Assumptions : The above analysis is based on the following assumptions :
1. The falling weight sticks to the beam and moves/vibrates with it.
2. No energy loss take place.
3. The beam is linearly elastic.
4. The deflected shape of the beam is the same under a dynamic load as under the static load.
5. The potential energy of the beam due to change in the position is disregarded.

Note : The deflection δ found from Eq. 15.14, represents its upper limit. The actual deflection will be lesser than this because of (i) local deformation of contact surfaces (ii) tendency of falling mass to bounce upward, and (iii) mass of the beam itself. All these tend to cause loss of energy, due to which the actual deformations will be lesser than the one given by Eq. 15.14.

Example 15.12. *A rectangular beam 200 mm × 300 mm is freely supported over a span of 4 m. A load of 50 kN is dropped on to the middle of the beam from a height of 20 mm. Find the maximum instantaneous deflection and the stress induced in the beam. Take $E = 2 \times 10^5$ N/mm².*

Solution :

$$I = \frac{1}{12}(200)(300)^3 = 45 \times 10^7 \text{ mm}^4$$

Let $P = $ equivalent static load in N ; $W = 50000$ N

Now $\quad W(h + \delta) = \frac{1}{2}P\delta \quad$ or $\quad P\delta = 2 \times 50000(20 + \delta)$ ...(1)

where $\quad \delta = \dfrac{PL^3}{48EI} = \dfrac{P(4)^3(1000)^3}{48 \times 2 \times 10^5 \times 45 \times 10^7} = 1.481 \times 10^{-5} P$ mm ...(2)

Substituting δ in (1), we have.

$$P(1.481 \times 10^{-5} P) = 100000(20 + 1.481 \times 10^{-5} P)$$

or $\quad\quad P^2 = 13.5 \times 10^{10} + 100000 P$

This is a quadratic equation in P, solving which we get $P = 4.208 \times 10^5$ N $= 420.8$ kN

$$\therefore \quad \delta = 1.481 \times 10^{-5} P = 1.48 \times 10^{-5}(4.208 \times 10^5) = 6.231 \text{ mm}$$

Alternatively, $\quad \delta_{st} = \dfrac{WL^3}{48EI} = \dfrac{50000(4)^3(1000)^3}{48 \times 2 \times 10^5 \times 45 \times 10^7} = 0.74$ mm

$$\therefore \quad \delta = \delta_{st} + \left(\delta_{st} + 2h\,\delta_{st}\right)^{\frac{1}{2}} = 0.74 + \left[(0.74)^2 + 2 \times 20 \times 0.74\right]^{\frac{1}{2}}$$
$$= 6.231 \text{ mm}$$

$$M_{max} = \frac{PL}{4} = \frac{4.208 \times 10^5 \times 4000}{4} = 1.052 \times 10^8 \text{ N-mm}$$

$$\therefore \quad f_{max} = \frac{M}{I}y = \frac{1.052 \times 10^8}{45 \times 10^7} \times 150 = \mathbf{35.07 \text{ N/mm}^2}$$

15.8. ADDITIONAL ILLUSTRATIVE EXAMPLES

Example 15.13. *A simply supported beam of span L has an overhang of length a on the left. The vertical load W is applied at the end of the overhang. Calculate the deflection of the point of application of the load by (i) Unit load method (ii) Castigliano's first theorem.*

Solution :

(a) **Unit load method**

Apply unit load at C. Then

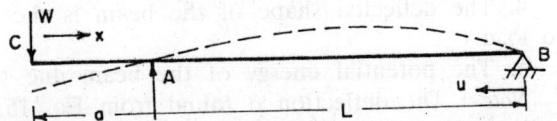

$$y_c = \int\limits_{x=0}^{a+L} \frac{M m \, dx}{EI}$$

FIG. 15.15

$$= \int\limits_0^a \frac{M m \, dx}{EI} + \int\limits_a^{a+L} \frac{M m \, dx}{EI}$$

$$= \int_0^a \frac{M\,m\,dx}{EI} + \int_0^L \frac{M\,m\,du}{EI} \quad \text{(where } u \text{ is measured from } B\text{)}$$

For CA, $\qquad M = -W.x \quad$ and $\quad m = -1.x$

$$\therefore \qquad \int_0^a \frac{M\,m\,dx}{EI} = \int_0^a \frac{Wx^2}{EI}.dx = \frac{Wa^3}{3EI}$$

For BA : $\qquad R_B = \dfrac{Wa}{L}(\downarrow)$ due to point load and $R_B' = \dfrac{a}{L}(\downarrow)$ due to unit load

$$\therefore \qquad M = -\frac{Wa}{L}u \quad \text{and} \quad m = -\frac{a}{L}u$$

$$\therefore \qquad \int_0^L \frac{M\,m\,du}{EI} = \frac{1}{EI}\int_0^L \frac{Wa}{L}u\left(\frac{a}{L}u\right)du = \frac{Wa^2}{L^2 EI}\int_0^L u^2\,du = \frac{Wa^2 L}{3EI}$$

Hence $\qquad y_C = \dfrac{Wa^3}{3EI} + \dfrac{Wa^2 L}{3EI} = \dfrac{Wa^2}{3EI}(a+L)$ Ans.

(b) Castigliano's first theorem

$$y_C = \frac{\partial U}{\partial W} = \frac{1}{EI}\int M_x \frac{\partial M_x}{\partial W}dx = \frac{1}{EI}\left[\int_0^a M_x \frac{\partial M_x}{\partial W}dx + \int_0^L M_u \frac{\partial M_u}{\partial W}du\right]$$

For CA, $\qquad M_x = -W.x$ and $\dfrac{\partial M_x}{\partial W} = -x$

$$\therefore \qquad \int_0^a M_x \frac{\partial M_x}{\partial W}dx = \int_0^a (Wx)\,x\,dx = \frac{Wa^3}{3}$$

For BA $\qquad M_u = -\dfrac{Wa}{L}u \quad$ and $\dfrac{\partial M_u}{\partial W} = -\dfrac{a}{L}u$

$$\therefore \qquad \int_0^L M_u \frac{\partial M_u}{\partial W}du = \int_0^L \frac{Wau}{L}\left(\frac{a}{L}u\right)du = \frac{Wa^2}{L^2}\left(\frac{u^3}{3}\right)_0^L = \frac{Wa^2 L}{3}$$

Hence $\qquad y_c = \dfrac{1}{EI}\left[\dfrac{Wa^3}{3} + \dfrac{Wa^2 L}{3}\right] = \dfrac{Wa^2}{3EI}(a+L)$

Example 15.14. *A cantilever of length L carries a point load W at its free end. The member is circular in section having diameter D for a distance L/2 from the fixed end and a diameter D/2 for the remaining length. Find the deflection at the free end.*

Solution :

Let us solve this problem by the direct method.

$U = \int\limits_0^L \dfrac{M_x^2\, dx}{2\,E\,I_x}$ where x is measured from B.

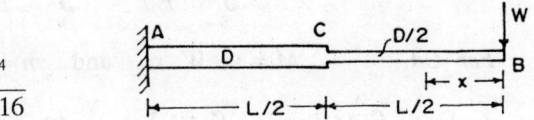

FIG. 15.16

For the portion $BC = I_{BC} = \dfrac{\pi}{64}\left(\dfrac{D}{2}\right)^4 = \dfrac{\pi D^4}{64 \times 16}$

For the portion CA, $I_{CA} = \dfrac{\pi}{64} D^4$

Hence if $I_{BC} = I \, , I_{CA} = 16\,I$

$\therefore$ $U = \int\limits_0^{\frac{L}{2}} \dfrac{M_x^2\, dx}{2\,E\,I} + \int\limits_{\frac{L}{2}}^{L} \dfrac{M_x^2\, dx}{2\,E\,(16\,I)}$ ...(1)

For BC, $U_{BC} = \int\limits_0^{\frac{L}{2}} \dfrac{(Wx)^2}{2\,E\,I}\, dx = \dfrac{W^2}{2\,E\,I}\left[\dfrac{x^3}{3}\right]_0^{\frac{L}{2}} = \dfrac{W^2 L^3}{48\,E\,I}$

For CA, $U_{CA} = \int\limits_{\frac{L}{2}}^{L} \dfrac{(Wx)^2}{2\,E\,(16\,I)} = \dfrac{W^2}{32\,E\,I}\left[\dfrac{x^3}{3}\right]_{\frac{L}{2}}^{L} = \dfrac{7\,W^2 L^3}{96 \times 8\,E\,I}$

$\therefore$ $U = U_{BC} + U_{CA} = \dfrac{W^2 L^3}{48\,E\,I} + \dfrac{7\,W^2 L^3}{96 \times 8\,E\,I} = \dfrac{23}{768}\dfrac{W^2 L^3}{E\,I}$

Now, work supplied $= \dfrac{1}{2} W \cdot y_B$

$\therefore$ $\dfrac{1}{2} W \cdot y_B = \dfrac{23}{768}\dfrac{W^2 L^3}{E\,I}$

From which $y_B = \dfrac{23}{384}\dfrac{W L^3}{E\,I}$

Example 15.15. *A freely supported beam of span L carries a central load W. The sectional area of the beam is so designed that the moment of inertia of the section increases uniformly from I at the ends to 1.5 I in the middle. Calculate the central deflection.*

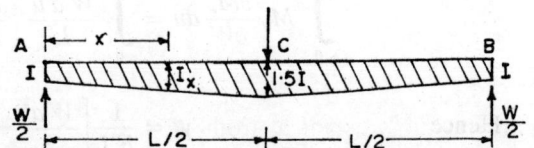

FIG. 15.17

Solution :

The central deflection is given by

$$y_C = \dfrac{\partial U}{\partial W} = \dfrac{1}{E}\int\limits_0^{L} \dfrac{M_x}{I_x}\dfrac{\partial M_x}{\partial W}\, dx = \dfrac{2}{E}\int\limits_0^{\frac{L}{2}} \dfrac{M_x}{I_x}\cdot\dfrac{\partial M_x}{\partial W}\, dx, \text{ due to symmetry.}$$

At any distance x from A, $\qquad I_x = I + \dfrac{I}{2} \cdot \dfrac{2}{L} x = I\left(1 + \dfrac{x}{L}\right);$

$$M_x = \dfrac{W}{2} x \quad \text{and} \quad \dfrac{\partial M_x}{\partial W} = \dfrac{x}{2}$$

$$\therefore \qquad y_C = \dfrac{2}{E} \int_0^{\frac{L}{2}} \dfrac{1}{I\left(1 + \dfrac{x}{L}\right)} \dfrac{W}{2} x \cdot \dfrac{x}{2} \, dx = \dfrac{W}{2EI} \int_0^{\frac{L}{2}} \dfrac{x^2}{\left(1 + \dfrac{x}{L}\right)} \, dx$$

Putting $x + L = t$ in the above integral and simplifying, we get

$$y_c = \dfrac{WL}{2EI} \int_L^{\frac{3L}{2}} \left(t - 2L + \dfrac{L^2}{t}\right) dt = \dfrac{WL}{2EI} \left[\dfrac{t^2}{2} - 2Lt + L^2 \log_e t\right]_L^{\frac{3L}{2}} = \mathbf{0.015} \, \dfrac{WL^3}{EI}$$

Example 15.16. *A beam of uniform section and of length $2L$ is freely supported by rigid supports at its ends and by an elastic prop at its centre. If the prop deflects by an amount λ times the load it carries, and if the beam carries a total distributed load of W, show that the load carried by the prop is $\dfrac{5W}{8\left(1 + \dfrac{6EI\lambda}{L^3}\right)}$.* *(U.L.)*

Solution :

Let the prop reaction $= P$
Total load on the beam $= W$

$\therefore$ U.D.L. $\qquad w = \dfrac{W}{2L}$

Reactions at ends $= R = \dfrac{1}{2}(W - P)$

The deflection at the prop is given by

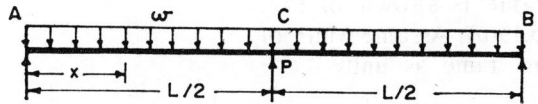

FIG. 15.18

$$y_C = \dfrac{\partial U}{\partial P} = \dfrac{1}{EI} \int M_x \dfrac{\partial M_x}{\partial P} \cdot dx$$

Since the prop deflects by an amount λ times the load it carries, we have

$$y_C = -P\lambda$$

The minus sign has been used since the deflection is in a direction opposite to the line of action of P.

Hence $\qquad -P . \lambda = \dfrac{2}{EI} \int_0^L M_x \dfrac{\partial M_x}{\partial P} \cdot dx \qquad$ or $\quad P = -\dfrac{2}{EI\lambda} \int_0^L M_x \dfrac{\partial M_x}{\partial P} \cdot dx \qquad$ ...(1)

For any section distant x from A, $\quad M_x = \dfrac{1}{2}(W - P)x - \dfrac{W}{2L} \dfrac{x^2}{2}; \dfrac{\partial M_x}{\partial P} = -\dfrac{x}{2}$

Hence $\qquad P = \dfrac{2}{EI\lambda} \int_0^L \left[\dfrac{1}{2}(W - P)x - \dfrac{W}{2L} \cdot \dfrac{x^2}{2}\right] \dfrac{x}{2} \, dx$

or $\qquad P . \dfrac{EI\lambda}{2} = \left[\dfrac{1}{12}(W - P)x^3 - \dfrac{W}{32L}x^4\right]_0^L = \dfrac{WL^3}{12} - \dfrac{PL^3}{12} - \dfrac{WL^3}{32} = \dfrac{5WL^3}{96} - \dfrac{PL^3}{12}$

or $$P\left(\frac{6EI\lambda}{L^3} + 1\right) = \frac{5W}{8}$$

From which $$P = \frac{5W}{8\left(1 + \frac{6EI\lambda}{L^3}\right)}$$

Example 15.17. *Obtain an expression for vertical displacement of point A in the bent cantilever shown in Fig. 15.19(a).*

Solution :

The vertical displacement of A is given by

$$y_A = \frac{\partial U}{\partial W} = \frac{1}{E}\int \frac{M_x}{I_x}\frac{\partial M_x}{\partial W}\,dx$$
...(1)

where the integration is carried over the whole frame. A bending moment is designated negative if it causes convexity to the *inside* of the frame. The B.M.D. for the whole frame is shown in Fig. 15.19(b), Assume width of the frame as unity.

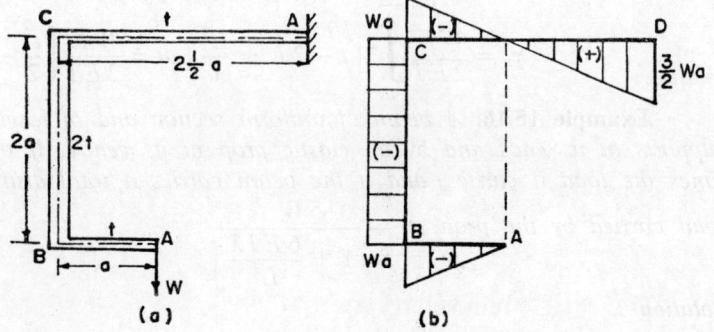

FIG. 15.19

(*i*) **For AB :** $\quad I = \frac{1}{12}\times 1\times t^3 = \frac{t^3}{12}$.

Measuring x from A, $M_x = -W.x$; $\dfrac{\partial M_x}{\partial W} = -x$

The limits of x are 0 at A to a at B.

(*ii*) **For BC :** $\quad I = \frac{1}{12}\times 1\,(2t)^3 = \frac{2t^3}{3}$; $\quad M_x = -Wa$; $\dfrac{\partial M_x}{\partial W} = -a$

The limits of x are 0 at B to $2a$ at C.

(*iii*) **For CD :** $\quad I = \frac{1}{12}\times 1\,(t)^3 = \frac{t^3}{12}$.

Measuring x from C, $\quad M_x = -W(a-x)$; $\dfrac{\partial M_x}{\partial W} = -(a-x)$

The limits of x are 0 at C to $5a/2$ at D.

Substituting the values in (1), we get

$$y_A = \frac{1}{E}\left[\int_0^a Wx\,(x)\frac{12}{t^3}\,dx + \int_0^{2a} Wa\,(a)\frac{3}{2t^3}\,dx + \int_0^{\frac{5a}{2}} W(a-x)(a-x)\frac{12}{t^3}\,dx\right]$$

$$= \frac{1}{Et^3}\left[\left(4Wx^3\right)_0^a + \left(\frac{3}{2}Wa^2x\right)_0^{2a} + 12W\left(a^2x + \frac{x^3}{3} - \frac{2ax^2}{2}\right)_0^{\frac{5a}{2}}\right]$$

$$= \frac{1}{E\,t^3}\left[4\,W\,a^3 + 3\,W\,a^3 + 12\,W\left(\frac{5}{2}\,a^3 + \frac{125}{24}\,a^3 - \frac{25}{4}\,a^3 \right) \right] = \frac{24.5\,W\,a^3}{E\,t^3}.$$

Example 15.18. *For a given cantilever of rectangular cross-section, length L, depth d and carrying a concentrated load at the free end, show that*

$$\frac{\text{Deflection due to shearing strain}}{\text{Bending deflection}} = \text{constant} \times \left(\frac{d}{L} \right)^2$$

and find the value of the constant for a steel cantilever. Hence find the least value of (L/d) if the deflection due to shearing strain is not to exceed 1% of the total deflection.

Take $E = 2 \times 10^5 \, N/mm^2$ *and* $N = 0.765 \times 10^5 \, N/mm^2$.

Solution :

At any layer distant y from the N.A., shear stress is given by

$$q = \frac{F}{2I}\left(\frac{d^2}{4} - y^2 \right), \quad \text{where } F = W \text{ and } I = \frac{1}{12}\,b\,d^3$$

$$\therefore \qquad q = \frac{6\,W}{b\,d^3}\left(\frac{d^2}{4} - y^2 \right)$$

The total strain energy stored due to shear is given by Eq. 15.10, from which

$$U = \int_0^L \int_{-\frac{d}{2}}^{+\frac{d}{2}} \frac{b}{2N}\left\{ \frac{6\,W}{b\,d^3}\left(\frac{d^2}{4} - y^2 \right) \right\}^2 dx\,dy = \frac{b}{2N} \int_0^L \int_{-\frac{d}{2}}^{+\frac{d}{2}} \frac{36\,W^2}{b^2\,d^6}\left(\frac{d^4}{16} - \frac{d^2 y^2}{2} + y^4 \right) dx\,dy$$

$$= \frac{18\,W^2}{N\,b^2\,d^6} \int_0^L \left(\frac{d^5}{16} - \frac{d^2}{6}\cdot\frac{d^3}{4} + \frac{1}{5}\frac{d^5}{16} \right) dx = \frac{18\,W^2}{N\,b\,d^6}\cdot\frac{d^5}{30}\cdot L = \frac{3}{5}\frac{W^2 L}{N\,b\,d} \qquad ...(1)$$

Also, work done $= \dfrac{1}{2}\,W\,y_s$ $\qquad ...(2)$

Equating the two, we get $\dfrac{1}{2}\,W\,y_s = \dfrac{3}{5}\dfrac{W^2 L}{N\,b\,d}$ From which $y_s = \dfrac{6\,W\,L}{5\,N\,b\,d}$ $\qquad ...(a)$

Deflection due to bending $= y_b = \dfrac{W\,L^3}{3\,E\,I} = \dfrac{4\,W\,L^3}{E\,b\,d^3}$ $\qquad ...(4)$

$$\therefore \qquad \frac{y_s}{y_b} = \frac{6\,W\,L}{5\,N\,b\,d} \times \frac{b\,d^3 E}{4\,W\,L^3} = \frac{3}{10}\frac{E}{N}\left(\frac{d}{L} \right)^2 = k\left(\frac{d}{L} \right)^2$$

Hence $\qquad k = \dfrac{3}{10}\dfrac{E}{N}$ (Ans.)

Substituting numerical values, $k = \dfrac{3}{10} \times \dfrac{2 \times 10^5}{0.765 \times 10^5} = 0.7843$

Again $\qquad y_s = 0.01\,(y_s + y_b)...$(Given) or $\dfrac{y_s}{y_b} = \dfrac{1}{99} = \left(\dfrac{d}{L} \right)^2 k$

$$\therefore \qquad \left(\frac{d}{L}\right)^2 = \frac{1}{99\,k} = \frac{1}{99 \times 0.7843}$$

From which $\qquad \dfrac{L}{d} = (99 \times 0.7843)^{1/2} = \mathbf{8.81}$

PROBLEMS

1. A cantilever AB of length L is loaded with U.D.L. w over a length L_1 from the fixed end. (Fig. 15.20). Using the method of strain energy, calculate the deflection at the free end.

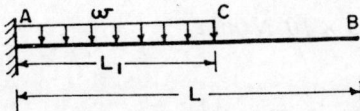

FIG. 15.20

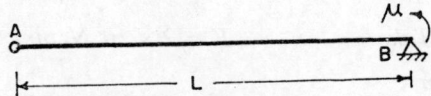

FIG. 15.21

2. A simply supported beam AB is loaded with a couple μ at the end B (Fig. 15.21). Determine the slopes at the ends, using strain energy method.

3. A beam AB of length L is loaded with U.D.L. w /unit length extending from the centre towards the left for a length a (Fig. 15.22). Calculate the central deflection.

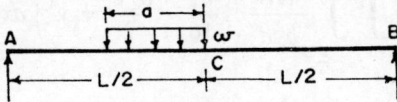

FIG. 15.22

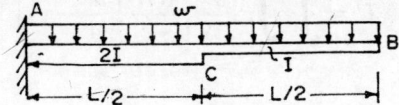

FIG. 15.23

4. A cantilever beam AB with two different moments of inertia I and $2I$ supports a uniformly distributed load w (Fig. 15.23). Determine the deflection at the free end, using strain energy method.

5. A simply beam with overhang is loaded as shown in Fig. 15.24. Find the deflection at the free end.

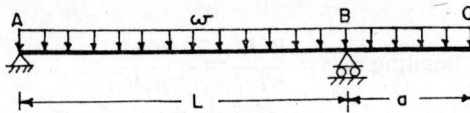

FIG. 15.24

ANSWERS

1. $\quad y_B = \dfrac{w L_1^4}{8\,E I} + \dfrac{w L_1^3}{6\,E I}(L - L_1);$ 2. $\quad i_A = \dfrac{\mu L}{6\,E I} \,; \, i_B = -\dfrac{\mu L}{3\,E I}$

3. $\quad y_C = \dfrac{w a}{24\,E I}\left\{ L^3 - 2 L a^2 + a^3 \right\};$ 4. $\quad y_B = \dfrac{17\,w L^4}{256\,E I}$

5. $\quad y_C = \dfrac{w a}{24\,E I}\left(3 a^3 + 4 a^2 L - L^3 \right)$

16

Fixed Beams

16.1. STATICALLY INDETERMINATE BEAMS

A beam is said to be statically determinate if all the reaction components can be calculated by applying the three conditions of static equilibrium, *i.e.* $\Sigma V = 0$, $\Sigma H = 0$ and $\Sigma M = 0$, where ΣV is the algebraic sum of all vertical forces, ΣH is the algebraic sum of all horizontal forces and ΣM is the algebraic sum of moment of all the forces about a point. However, when the number of unknown reaction components exceeds the static conditions of equilibrium, the beam is said to be *statically indeterminate*. To determine the reaction components at the supports of such beams we will have to consider the equations of deformations or displacements, in addition to the equations of statics. For vertical system of loading, there are two conditions of statical equilibrium available (*i.e.* $\Sigma V = 0$ and $\Sigma M = 0$). For such loading, Fig. 16.1(a), 16.1(b), 16.1(c), 16.1(d) and 16.1(e) are the examples of statically determinate beams while fig 16.1(f), 16.1(g) and 16.1(h) are the examples of statically indeterminate beams.

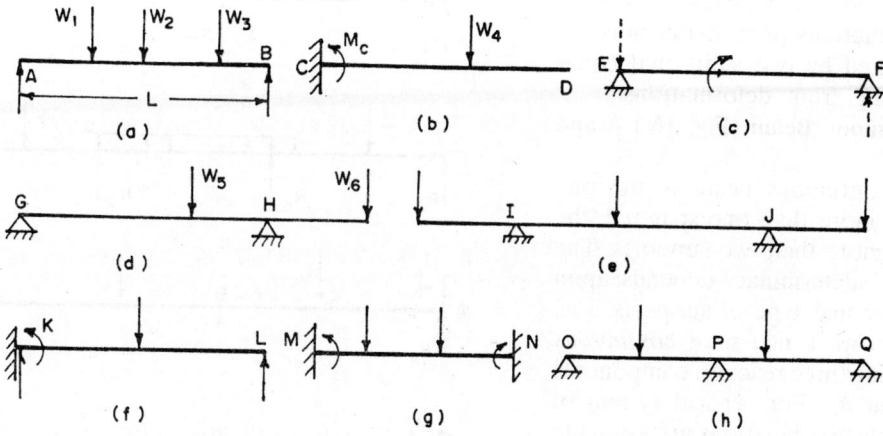

FIG. 16.1. STATICALLY DETERMINATE AND STATICALLY INDETERMINATE BEAMS.

Although there are a wide variety of statically indeterminate beams, we shall be considering here three basic types of statically indeterminate beams : (*i*) propped cantilever (*ii*) fixed beam, and (*iii*) continuous beam.

1. Propped Cantilever (Fig. 16.1f and 16.2)

A propped cantilever is a cantilever which is propped either at the free end or at some intermediate point. There are *three* reaction components : R_A, R_B and M_A. For vertical system of loading, only two equations of statics are available, *i.e.* $\Sigma V = 0$ and $\Sigma M = 0$. *Hence the beam is statically indeterminate to first degree.* The two equations of statics must be supplemented by the third equation expressing the conditions of compatibility (or continuity) of deformations. Since end B (*i.e.* the propped end) cannot yield, we have

y_B due to $W = y_B{}'$ due to R_B

Such cases have been discussed fully in the previous four chapters.

2. Fixed Beam (Fig. 16.1 g and 16.3)

In the case of a fixed beam, the ends are *constrained* or *built-in* so that the tangents there remain in horizontal position. A fixed beam is also known as a *built-in* or *encastre* beam. In order to satisfy the condition of zero slope at each end, a fixidity moment will be induced at each end. Due to this, there will be *four* reaction components at the ends : R_A, M_A, R_B, M_B. For vertical system of loading, only two equations are available from statical equilibrium (*i.e.* $\Sigma V = 0$ and $\Sigma M = 0$). *Hence a fixed beam is a statically indeterminate beam of second order.* To analyse such a beam, the two equations from statics must be supplemented by two additional equations arising from deformations.

3. Continuous Beam (Fig. 16.1 h and 16.4).

A continuous beam is the one which has more than one span, *i.e.* the beam has more than two supports. The degree of indeterminacy depends upon the number and type of supports. Fig. 16.4(*a*) shows a *two span continuous beam*, having three reaction components R_A, R_B and R_C. For vertical system of loading only two equations are available from statical equilibrium. Hence the beam is statically indeterminate to the first degree. Similarly, Fig. 16.4(*b*) shows a *three span continuous beam* having four reaction components R_A, R_B, R_C and R_D;

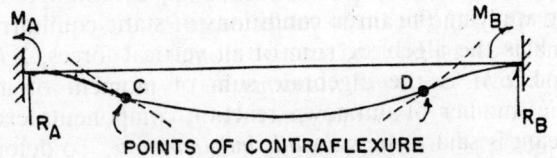

FIG. 16.2. PROPPED CANTILEVER

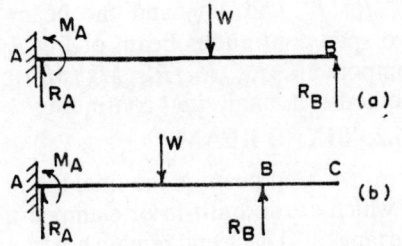

POINTS OF CONTRAFLEXURE

FIG. 16.3. FIXED BEAM

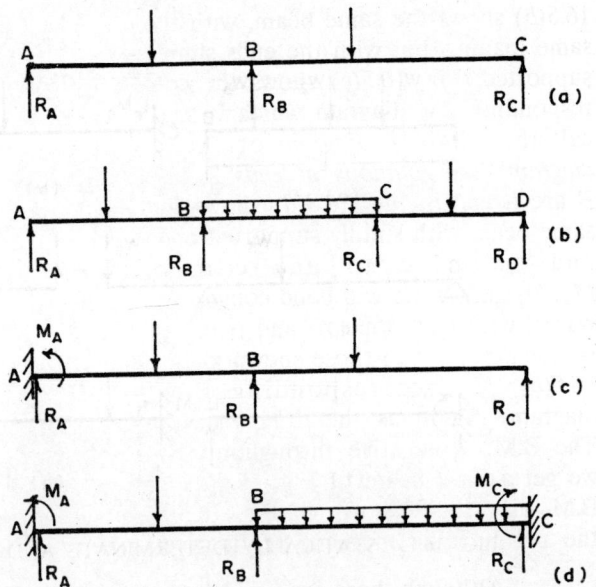

FIG. 16.4. CONTINUOUS BEAMS

the beam is therefore statically indeterminate to *second degree*. The two span continuous beam of Fig. 16.4(c) has one end *A* fixed. Hence there are four reaction components (*i.e.* R_A, R_B, R_C and M_A) and the beam is statically indeterminate to second degree. Similarly, the two span continuous beam of Fig .16.4(d) has ends *A* and *C* fixed; hence there are five reaction components (R_A, R_B, R_C, M_A, M_C) and the beam is statically indeterminate to *third degree*. The methods of analyzing continuous beams have been discussed in chapter 17.

16.2. FIXED BEAM

A fixed beam is the one, the ends of which are so built-in or clamped that the tangent at each end remain horizontal when the beam is subjected to external loading. Hence a fixed beam may be looked upon as a simply supported beam subjected to end moments of such magnitude that the slope at each end is zero when the beam is subjected to external loading. The end reactive moments are known as *fixing moments*.

Fig. 16.5 (*a*) shows a fixed beam subjected to external loading. When the beam bends under external loading, the ends will try to rotate; this is prevented by the reactive couples M_1 and M_2, induced at the two ends so as to reduce slope at each end to zero value. Fig 16.5(*b*) shows the same beam, with the same loading, but with the ends simply supported. Fig. 16.5(*c*) shows the corresponding B.M. diagram, which we shall call the *free B.M. diagram* or the *μ-diagram*. The rotations at ends *A* and *B* are i_1 and i_2. Fig .16.5(*d*) shows the same beam with simply supported ends and subjected to end couples M_1, M_2; the beam will bend convex upwards, with end slopes i_1 and i_2 in the *reverse directions* to those shown in Fig. 16.5(*b*). The corresponding B.M.

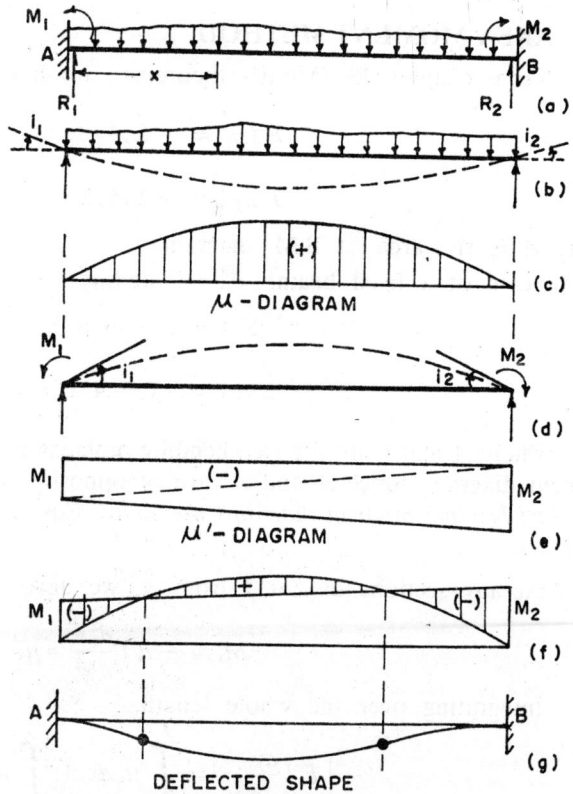

FIG. 16.5. EFFECTS OF FIXIDITY

diagram, known as the *fixing moment diagram* or the *μ'-diagram* is shown in Fig. 16.5 (*e*). The B.M. is negative throughout. By super-imposing the effects of Fig .16.5(*b*) and 16.5(*d*), we get a fixed beam of Fig. 16.5(*a*), with slopes at each end equal to zero; the corresponding B.M. diagram is shown in Fig. 16.5(*f*). Thus, at any section distant *x* from the left supports, the net bending moment M_x is given by,

$$M_x = \mu_x + \mu_x'$$ ...(16.1)

where μ_x is the free B.M. and μ_x' is the fixed B.M. at the section. Since μ_x and μ_x' are of opposite sign, there will be two points of contraflexure, as shown in Fig. 16.5(*f, g*), The bent shape of the beam is shown in Fig. 16.5(*g*). It is important and interesting to note that the bending moment in a fixed beam (Fig. 16.5 f) is much lesser that the B.M. at the corresponding point in the simply supported beam (Fig. 16.5 c). *The effect of fixidity of the beam at the ends is thus to reduce the bending moment.* However, the B.M. M_x at any point cannot be evaluated unless M_1 and M_2 are evaluated first. There are several methods of analysing a fixed beam. But we shall discuss here the following methods :

> (*i*) Area moment method.
> (*ii*) Double integration method
> (*iii*) Method of super-position (flexibility method)
> (*iv*) Method of three moment theorem.

The last method has been discussed in the next chapter.

16.3. AREA-MOMENT METHOD

From chapter 13 (Mohr's theorems), we have

$$EI\theta_A^B = -\sum_A^B A \qquad \qquad ...(1)$$

and

$$EIy_A^B = -\sum_A^B A \cdot \bar{x} \qquad \qquad ...(2)$$

where A is the area of B.M. diagram.

In the case of a fixed beam, $\theta_A^B = 0$ and $y_A^B = 0$

$$\therefore \qquad \sum_A^B A = A + A' = 0 \qquad \qquad ...(16.2)$$

and

$$\sum_A^B A\,\bar{x} = A\,\bar{x} + A'\,\bar{x}' = 0 \qquad \qquad ...(16.3)$$

where A and $\bar{x}$ are for free bending moment diagram and A' and $\bar{x}'$ are for fixed bending moment diagram. Since A and A' are of opposite sign, it is concluded that the *areas of free and fixed bending moment diagrams are equal.* Eqs. 16.2 and 16.3 can be derived independently as under.

At any sections distant x from A, we have

$$M_x = -EI\frac{d^2y}{dx^2} = \mu_x + \mu_x' \qquad \qquad ...(3)$$

Integrating over the whole length,

$$-\left[EI\frac{dy}{dx}\right]_0^L = \int_0^L \mu_x\,dx + \int_0^L \mu_x'\,dx$$

or

$$-EI\left(\theta_B - \theta_A\right) = A + A'$$

But
$$\theta_B = 0 \text{ and } \theta_A \text{ is also zero.}$$

Hence
$$A + A' = 0 \qquad \qquad ...(16.2)$$

Also, multiplying both sides of Eq. 3 by x and integrating over the whole length

$$-\int_0^L EIx\frac{d^2y}{dx^2} = \int_0^L x\,\mu_x\,dx + \int_0^L x\,\mu_x'\,dx$$

or

$$-EI\left[x\frac{dy}{dx} - y\right]_0^L = A\bar{x} + A'\bar{x}'$$

or $-EI[(L\theta_B - y_B) - (0.\theta_A - y_A)] = A\bar{x} + A'\bar{x}'$

But θ_B, y_B, θ_A and y_A are each zero.

$$\therefore \qquad A\bar{x} + A'\bar{x}' = 0 \qquad \qquad ...(16.3)$$

Values of $A, A', \bar{x}$ and $\bar{x}'$

The values of A and $\bar{x}$ will depend upon the type of external loading. However, the area of fixing B.M. diagram is given by

$$A' = -\frac{M_1 + M_2}{2}.L \qquad \qquad ...(16.4)$$

The value of $A'\bar{x}'$ of the fixing moment diagram can be found by splitting the diagram into two triangles by a dotted line a shown in Fig. 16.5(e).

Thus $$A'\bar{x}' = -\left[\left(\frac{1}{2}M_1 L . \frac{L}{3}\right) + \left(\frac{1}{2}M_2 L . \frac{2}{3}L\right)\right]$$

or $$A'\bar{x}' = -\left[\frac{M_1 L^2}{6} + \frac{M_2 L^2}{3}\right] = -\frac{L^2}{6}(M_1 + 2M_2)$$

where $\bar{x}'$ is measured from end A.

We shall now consider different cases of loading on a fixed beam.

16.4. FIXED BEAM WITH U.D.L.

Fig. 16.6(a) shows a fixed beam with U.D.L. Fig. 16.6(b) shows the μ diagram. Due to symmetry, we have $M_1 = M_2 = M$. Hence μ' diagram will be a rectangle.

Hence $A' = -M.L$

The μ-diagram will be a parabola with maximum ordinate equal to $\frac{wL^2}{8}$.

$$\therefore \qquad A = \left(\frac{2}{3}L\right)\left(\frac{wL^2}{8}\right) = \frac{wL^3}{12}$$

Now $A + A' = 0$

$$\therefore \qquad \frac{wL^3}{12} + (-ML) = 0$$

From which $$M = \frac{wL^2}{12} \qquad ...(16.6)$$

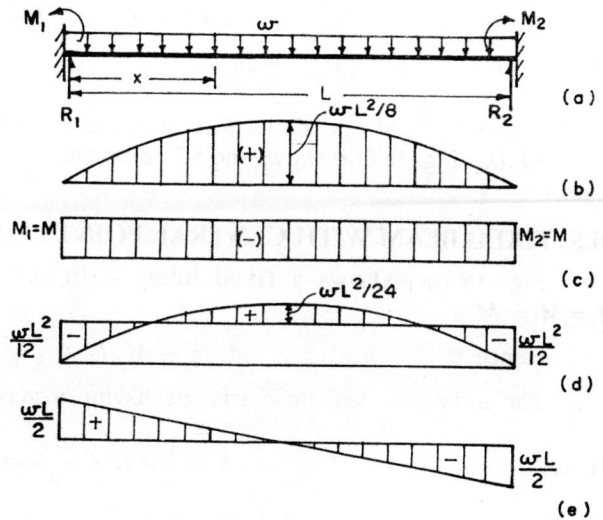

FIG. 16.6

B.M. Diagram : Fig. 16.6 (d) shows the B.M. diagram obtained by super-position of μ_x and μ_x'. The B.M. at any point distant x from the end A is given by

$$M_x = \mu_x + \mu_x' = \left(\frac{wL}{2}x - \frac{wx^2}{2}\right) - \frac{wL^2}{12} \qquad ...(1)$$

For points of contraflexure, equate M_x to zero.

Thus,
$$\frac{wL}{2}x - \frac{wx^2}{2} - \frac{wL^2}{12} = 0$$

or
$$x^2 - Lx + \frac{L^2}{6} = 0$$

or
$$\left(x - \frac{L}{2}\right)^2 = \frac{L^2}{12}$$

which gives
$$x = \frac{L}{2} \pm \frac{L}{2\sqrt{3}} = 0.5L \pm 0.289L = 0.211L \text{ or } 0.789L$$

At the centre,

$$M_C = \frac{wL}{2}\cdot\frac{L}{2} - \frac{w}{2}\left(\frac{L}{2}\right)^2 - \frac{wL^2}{12} = +\frac{wL^2}{24} \qquad ...(16.7)$$

Thus, the central B.M. is 1/3 of the B.M. for a freely supported beam. The slope and deflection at any point can be found by Mohr's theorem.

Maximum deflection : By inspection, maximum deflection occurs at the centre. Hence, we have, from Mohr's theorem :

$$EIy_C^A = -\overset{A}{\underset{C}{\Sigma}}A\bar{x} = -\left[\left(\frac{2}{3}\times\frac{L}{2}\times\frac{wL^2}{8}\right)\left(\frac{3}{8}\frac{L}{2}\right) - \left(\frac{wL^2}{12}\times\frac{L}{2}\times\frac{L}{4}\right)\right]$$

$$= -\left[\frac{wL^4}{128} - \frac{wL^4}{96}\right] = \frac{wL^4}{384}$$

$$\therefore \qquad y_C^A = \frac{wL^2}{384\,EI} \qquad ...(16.8)$$

This is 1/5 of the deflection of a freely supported beam with U.D.L.

S.F.D. : Fig. 16.6(e) shows the S.F. diagram, which is similar to that for a simply supported beam.

16.5. FIXED BEAM WITH CENTRAL POINT LOAD

Fig. 16.7(a) shows a fixed beam with central point load W. Due to symmetry, $M_1 = M_2 = M$.

Hence
$$A' = -M.L$$

The μ-diagram will be a triangle having a maximum ordinate of $+\frac{WL}{4}$ at the centre.

Hence,
$$A = \frac{1}{2}\times L\times\frac{WL}{4} = \frac{WL^2}{8}$$

Now
$$A + A' = 0$$

$$\therefore \qquad -ML + \frac{WL^2}{8} = 0$$

From which
$$M = \frac{WL}{8} \qquad ...(16.9)$$

Thus, the fixing moment is known.

(a) B.M. diagram

Fig. 16.7(d) shows the B.M. diagram obtained by super-imposing μ and μ' diagrams. At any point distant x from A,

$$M_x = \mu_x + \mu_x' = \frac{W}{2}x - \frac{WL}{8}$$

At $x = \frac{L}{2}$, $M_C = \frac{W}{2} \cdot \frac{L}{2} - \frac{WL}{8} = +\frac{WL}{8}$

...(16.9 a)

Thus, the central B.M. is half of the B.M. for a freely supported beam. For point of contraflexure,

$$M_x = 0 = \frac{W}{2}x - \frac{WL}{8}$$

This gives $x = \dfrac{L}{4}$

(b) Maximum deflection :

The slope and deflection at any point can be found using Mohr's theorems. The maximum deflection will evidently occur at C, for which

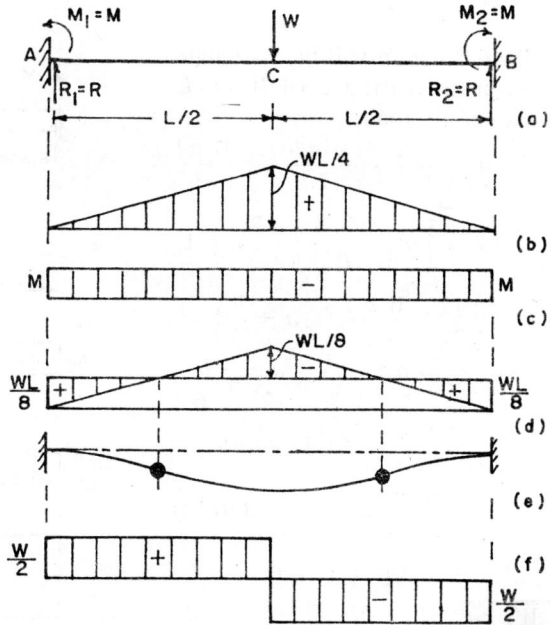

FIG. 16.7

$$E I y_C^A = -\sum_C^A A \bar{x} = -\left[\left(\frac{1}{2} \times \frac{L}{2} \times \frac{WL}{4} \times \frac{1}{3} \cdot \frac{L}{2} \right) - \left(M \cdot \frac{L}{2} \cdot \frac{L}{4} \right) \right]$$

$$= -\left[\frac{WL^3}{96} - \frac{WL^2}{64} \right] = \frac{WL^3}{192}$$

$$\therefore \qquad y_C^A = \frac{WL^3}{192 E I} \qquad\qquad ...(16.10)$$

This is 1/4 of the corresponding deflection for a simply supported beam. The deflected shape of the beam is shown in Fig. 16.7(e), in which the beam has two points of contraflexure at $L/4$ from each end.

(c) S.F.D. : The S.F.D. shows in Fig. 16.7(f) is similar to the one for the simply supported beam.

16.6. FIXED BEAM WITH ECCENTRIC POINT LOAD

Fig. 16.8(a) shows a fixed beam subjected to a point load W placed at a distance a from A and b from B. Due to eccentric loading, M_1 and M_2 will not be equal. Let $a > b$. In that case, $M_2 > M_1$ and the μ'-diagram will be a trapezium.

$$\therefore \qquad A' = -\frac{M_1 + M_2}{2}L$$

and

$$A' \bar{x} = -\left[\frac{M_1 + M_2}{2}L \left\{ \frac{L}{3} \frac{M_1 + 2M_2}{M_1 + M_2} \right\} \right] = -\frac{L^2}{6}\left(M_1 + 2M_2 \right) \qquad ...(16.11)$$

(with A as the origin)

The μ-diagram will be a triangle with maximum ordinate of Wab/L under the point load.

$$\therefore \quad A = \frac{1}{2} \cdot L \cdot \left(\frac{Wab}{L} \right) = \frac{Wab}{2}$$

$$A\bar{x} = \frac{1}{2} a \left(\frac{Wab}{L} \right) \left(\frac{2}{3} a \right) +$$

$$\frac{1}{2} b \left(\frac{Wab}{L} \right) \left(a + \frac{b}{3} \right)$$

$$= \frac{Wab}{L} \left(\frac{a^2}{3} + \frac{ab}{2} + \frac{b^2}{6} \right)$$

$$= \frac{Wab}{6L} \left(2a^2 + 3ab + b^2 \right)$$

$$= \frac{Wab}{6} \left(2a + b \right) \quad ...(16.12)$$

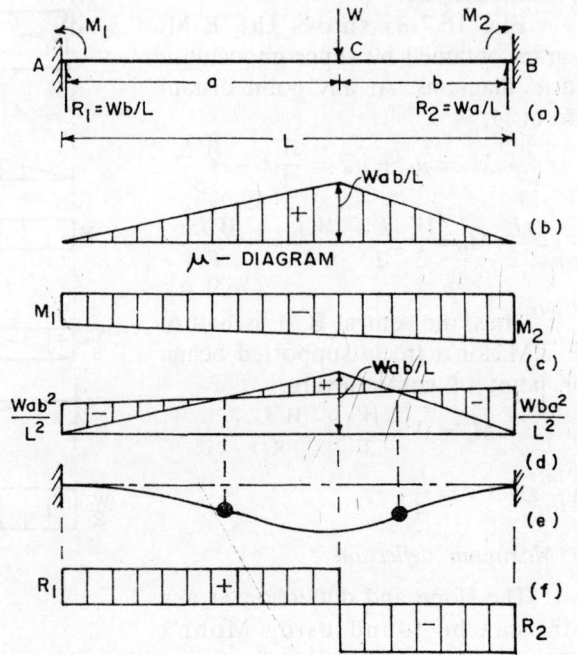

FIG. 16.8

Now $\quad\quad A + A' = 0$

or $\quad \dfrac{Wab}{2} - \dfrac{M_1 + M_2}{2} L = 0$

From which $\quad M_1 + M_2 = \dfrac{Wab}{L}$

$$...(1)$$

Also, $\quad\quad A\bar{x} + A'\bar{x}' = 0$

or $\quad \dfrac{Wab}{6} (2a + b) - \dfrac{L^2}{6} \left(M_1 + 2M_2 \right) = 0$

or $\quad\quad\quad M_1 + 2M_2 = \dfrac{Wab}{L^2} \left(2a + b \right)$ $\quad\quad\quad\quad\quad$ ...(2)

Solving Eqs. (1) and (2) we get $\quad M_1 = \dfrac{Wab^2}{L^2}$ and $\quad M_2 = \dfrac{Wba^2}{L^2}$ ...(16.13)

Thus the fixing moments M_1 and M_2 are known.

B.M. diagram : Fig. 16.8(d) shows the B.M.D. obtained by superimposing μ and μ' diagrams. The B.M. at any point in AD, distant x from A is given by

$$M_x = \mu_x + \mu_x' = \frac{Wb}{L} x - \left[M_1 + \left(M_2 - M_1 \right) \frac{x}{L} \right] = \frac{Wbx}{L} - \frac{Wab^2}{L^2} - \frac{Wab(a-b)}{L^3} x$$

For point of contraflexure in AD, equate M_x to zero.

$$\therefore \quad\quad 0 = \frac{Wbx}{L} - \frac{Wab^2}{L^2} - \frac{Wab(a-b)}{L^3} x$$

which gives $\quad\quad\quad x = \dfrac{aL}{3a + b}$ $\quad\quad\quad\quad\quad$ ...(16.14)

End reactions and S.F. diagrams : After having known the end moments, the end reactions R_1 and R_2 can be easily found by using the two equations of statics.

Taking moments about B, we get $R_1 L - M_1 - Wb + M_2 = 0$

or
$$R_1 L = M_1 - M_2 + Wb = \frac{Wab^2}{L^2} - \frac{Wba^2}{L^2} + Wb = \frac{Wb^2}{L^2}\left(a - \frac{a^2}{b} + \frac{L^2}{b}\right)$$

From which
$$R_1 = \frac{Wb^2}{L^3}\left(3a + b\right) \qquad \qquad \qquad ...(16.15\ a)$$

Similarly,
$$R_2 = \frac{Wa^2}{L^3}\left(a + 3b\right) \qquad \qquad \qquad ...(16.15\ b)$$

Example 16.1. *Find the support moments of a built-in beam loaded at third points by two point loads W each. Also, draw the B.M. and S.F. diagrams and compute the deflection at the centre.*

Solution :

Due to symmetrical loading, $M_1 = M_2 = M$ and $R_1 = R_2 = R$. The μ'-diagram will therefore be a rectangle (Fig. 16.9 c). The μ diagram is shown in Fig. 16.9 (b) in which $\mu_C = \mu_D = (WL)/3$.

Now area of μ diagram.

$$A = \left(2 \times \frac{1}{2} \times \frac{L}{3} \times \frac{WL}{3}\right) + \left[\frac{WL}{3} \times \frac{L}{3}\right]$$

$$= \frac{2WL^2}{9}$$

Area of μ' diagram $= A' = -M.L$

Now $A + A' = 0$ or $A = -A'$

$\therefore ML = \frac{2WL^2}{9}$ or $M = \frac{2}{9}WL$

Also, due to symmetry,
$$R_1 = R_2 = R = W$$

FIG. 16.9

Now, at any distance x from A, the B.M. in AD is given by
$$M_x = Wx - \frac{2}{9}WL \qquad \qquad ...(1)$$

This will be zero at $\quad x = \frac{2}{9}L$

At the mid-span, $\quad M_C = \frac{WL}{3} - \frac{2}{9}WL = \frac{WL}{9}$

The B.M. and S.F. diagrams are shown in Fig. 16.9 (d) and (e).

Again $EIy_C^A = -\overset{A}{\underset{C}{\Sigma}} A\bar{x} = \left[\frac{2}{9}WL \cdot \frac{L}{2} \cdot \frac{L}{4}\right] - \left[\left(\frac{WL}{3} \times \frac{L}{6} \times \frac{L}{12}\right) + \left(\frac{1}{2}\frac{WL}{3} \times \frac{L}{3}\right) \times \left(\frac{L}{6} + \frac{L}{9}\right)\right]$

$$= \frac{WL^3}{36} - \left[\frac{WL^3}{216} + \frac{5WL^3}{18 \times 18}\right] = \frac{5}{648}\frac{WL^3}{EI}$$

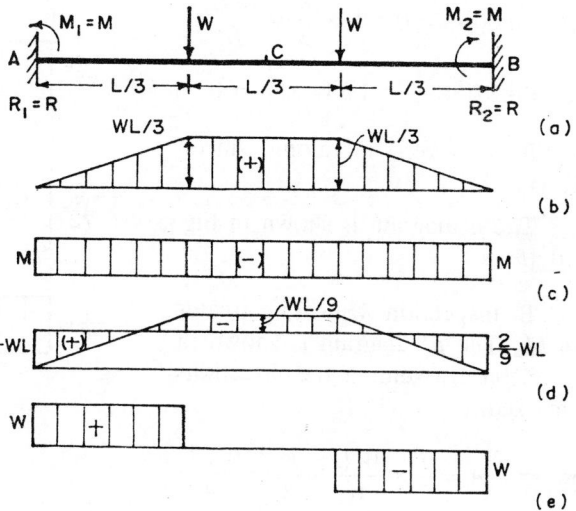

Example 16.2. *A fixed beam is loaded as shown. Determine the end reactions and fixing couples and draw the B.M. and S.F. diagrams for the beam.*

Solution :

Let us first plot the μ-diagram for which

$$R_A = \frac{1}{L}\left[1.5\,W \times \frac{2L}{3} - \frac{WL}{2}\right]$$
$$= 0.5\,W\,(\uparrow)$$

Similarly,

$$R_B = \frac{1}{L}\left[1.5\,W \times \frac{L}{3} - \frac{WL}{2}\right] = 0$$

$$\therefore \;\; \mu_A = 0 \;;\;\; \mu_D = 0.5\,W \times \frac{L}{3} = \frac{WL}{6}$$

$$\mu_C = 0.5\,W \times \frac{L}{2} - 1.5\,W \times \frac{L}{6} = 0$$

For *CB*, μ is zero all along, since $R_B = 0$

The μ diagram is shown in Fig. 16.10 (*b*).

By inspection, M_1 will be greater than M_2. The μ' diagram is shown in Fig. 16.10(*c*), assuming the directions as marked.

Now $\quad A = \dfrac{1}{2} \times \dfrac{WL}{6} \times \dfrac{L}{2} = \dfrac{WL^2}{24}$

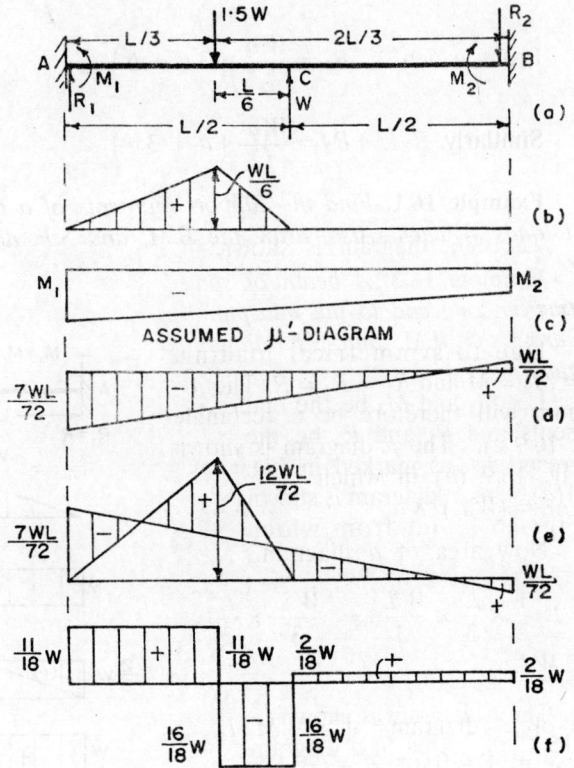

FIG. 16.10

$$A\,\bar{x} \text{ (with } A \text{ as origin)} = \left(\frac{1}{2} \times \frac{WL}{6} \times \frac{L}{3} \times \frac{2L}{9}\right) + \left(\frac{1}{2} \times \frac{WL}{6} \times \frac{L}{6}\right)\left(\frac{L}{3} + \frac{L}{18}\right) = \frac{5}{432}\,WL^3$$

Also, $\qquad\qquad A' = -\dfrac{M_1 + M_2}{2} \times L \quad$ and $\quad A'\,\bar{x}' = -\left(M_1 + 2\,M_2\right)\dfrac{L^2}{6}$

Now $\qquad\qquad A + A' = 0 \quad$ or $\quad \dfrac{WL^2}{24} - \dfrac{M_1 + M_2}{2}L = 0$

or $\qquad\qquad\qquad M_1 + M_2 = \dfrac{WL}{12} \qquad\qquad\qquad\qquad\qquad\qquad\qquad\qquad\qquad\qquad ...(1)$

and $\qquad\qquad A\,\bar{x} + A'\,\bar{x}' = 0, \quad$ or $\quad \dfrac{5}{432}\,WL^3 - \left(M_1 + 2\,M_2\right)\dfrac{L^2}{6} = 0$

or $\qquad\qquad\qquad M_1 + 2\,M_2 = \dfrac{5}{72}\,WL \qquad\qquad\qquad\qquad\qquad\qquad\qquad\qquad\qquad ...(2)$

Solving (1) and (2), we get $\quad M_1 = +\dfrac{7\,WL}{72} \quad$ and $\quad M_2 = -\dfrac{WL}{72}$

The plus sign with M_1 shows that M_1 is in the *same direction* as marked in Fig. 16.10(*a*), while the $-$ sign with M_2 shows that the direction of M_2 is reverse to the assumed one, *i.e.* M_2 is in the anticlockwise direction. The actual μ' diagram is shown in Fig. 16.10(*d*), while Fig. 16.10(*e*) shows the resultant B.M. diagram.

For reaction R_1, take moments about B. Thus.

$$R_1 L + W \frac{L}{2} - 1.5 W \times \frac{2L}{3} - M_2 - M_1 = 0$$

$$\therefore \qquad R_1 = \frac{1}{L} \left[-\frac{WL}{2} + WL + \frac{7WL}{72} + \frac{WL}{72} \right] = \frac{11}{18} W \,(\uparrow)$$

Similarly $R_2 L + M_1 + M_2 + \dfrac{WL}{2} - 1.5 W \dfrac{L}{3} = 0$

$$\therefore \qquad R_2 = \frac{1}{L} \left[-\frac{7}{72} WL - \frac{1}{72} WL - \frac{WL}{2} + 0.5 WL \right] = -\frac{1}{9} W = \frac{1}{9} W \,(\downarrow)$$

The S.F. diagram is shown in Fig. 16.10.

Example 16.3. *A beam of span L has its ends fixed and carries a U.D.L. of w per unit length from one end to the midspan. Calculate the fixing moments and reactions at the supports and draw the B.M. and S.F. diagrams.*

Solution :

Let M_1 and M_2 be the end moments and R_1 and R_2 be the end reactions, as marked in Fig. 16.11(a). The μ' diagram is shown in Fig. 16.11 (c) from which

$$A' = -\left(M_1 + M_2 \right) \frac{L}{2} \text{ and}$$

$$A' \bar{x}' = -\left(M_1 + 2 M_2 \right) \frac{L^2}{6}$$

(with A as origin)

The μ-diagram is shown in Fig. 16.11 (b). Area of μ diagram

$$= A = \int_0^{L/2} \mu_x \, dx + \int_{L/2}^L \mu_x \, dx$$

For a simply supported beam,

$$V_1 = \frac{3}{8} w L \quad \text{and} \quad V_2 = \frac{wL}{8}$$

For $AC \quad \mu_x = \frac{3}{8} w L x - \frac{w x^2}{2}$

At $x = \frac{L}{2}$,

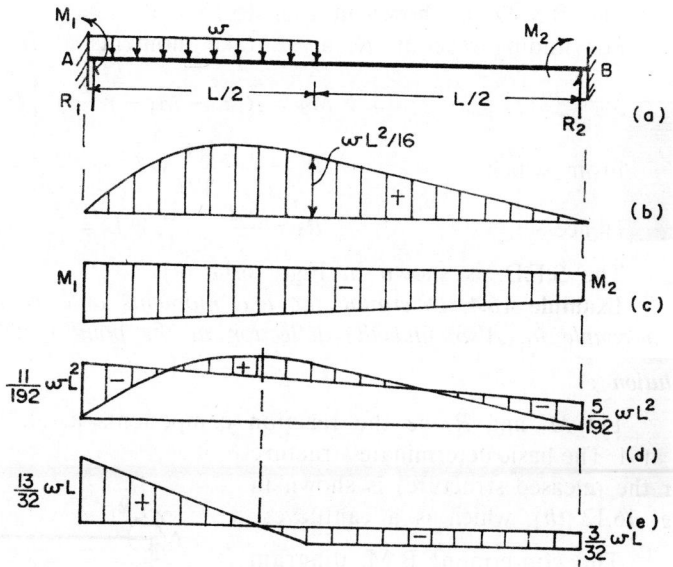

FIG. 16.11

$$\mu_C = \frac{3}{8} w L \cdot \frac{L}{2} - \frac{w}{2} \left(\frac{L}{2} \right)^2 = \frac{wL^2}{16}$$

Hence $\quad A = \left[\int_0^{\frac{L}{2}} \left(\frac{3}{8} w L x - \frac{w x^2}{2} \right) dx \right] + \left[\frac{1}{2} \times \frac{L}{2} \times \frac{wL^2}{16} \right]$

$$= \left[\frac{3}{8} w L \frac{x^2}{2} - \frac{w x^3}{6} \right]_0^{\frac{L}{2}} + \frac{wL^3}{64} = \frac{3}{8} \frac{wL}{2} \left(\frac{L}{2} \right)^2 - \frac{w}{6} \left(\frac{L}{2} \right)^3 + \frac{wL^3}{64} = \frac{wL^3}{24}$$

and $A\bar{x} = \left[\int_0^{\frac{L}{2}} \left(\frac{3}{8}wLx - \frac{wx^2}{2}\right)x\,dx\right] + \left[\frac{1}{2}\times\frac{L}{2}\times\frac{wL^2}{16}\left(\frac{L}{2}+\frac{L}{6}\right)\right]$

$= \left[\frac{3}{8}wL\frac{x^3}{3} - \frac{wx^4}{8}\right]_0^{\frac{L}{2}} + \frac{wL^3}{64}\times\frac{2L}{3} = \left[\frac{3}{24}wL\left(\frac{L}{2}\right)^3 - \frac{w}{8}\left(\frac{L}{2}\right)^4\right] + \frac{wL^4}{96} = \frac{7}{384}wL^4$

Now, from area moment equations, $A + A' = 0$

or $\qquad \frac{wL^3}{24} - \left(M_1 + M_2\right)\frac{L}{2} = 0$, from which $M_1 \quad M_2 = \frac{wL^2}{12}$ ...(a)

and $\qquad\qquad\qquad\qquad A\bar{x} + A'\bar{x}' = 0$

or $\qquad \frac{7}{384}wL^4 - \left(M_1 + 2M_2\right)\frac{L^2}{6} = 0$, from which $M_1 + 2M_2 = \frac{7}{64}wL^2$ ...(b)

From (a) and (b), we get $M_2 = \frac{5}{192}wL^2$ and $M_1 = \frac{11}{192}wL^2$

The B.M.D. is shown in Fig. 16.11 (d).

For finding reaction R_1 at A, take moments at B.

$$\Sigma M_B = R_1 L - M_1 - w\frac{L}{2}\left(\frac{3}{4}L\right) + M_2 = 0$$

From which $\qquad R_1 = \frac{1}{L}\left[\frac{11}{192}wL^2 + \frac{3wL^2}{8} - \frac{5}{192}wL^2\right] = \frac{13}{32}wL$

Hence $\qquad\qquad R_2 = \frac{wL}{2} - \frac{13}{32}wL = \frac{3}{32}wL$

The S.F.D. is shown in Fig. 16.11 (e).

Example 16.4. *Determine the end moments and reactions for a fixed end beam loaded by a couple μ_0. Also, find the deflection at the point C where the couple acts.*

Solution :

Let M_1 and R_1 be the reaction components at A. Release end A and apply M_1 and R_1 at A. The basic determinate structure (or the released structure) is shown in Fig. 16.12 (b), which is a cantilever.

The component B.M. diagram showing the effects of R_1, M_1 and μ_0 separately is shown in Fig. 16.12 (c). There are two unknowns: M_1 and R_1, and hence two condition equations are required. As a first condition, since both the ends of the beam have zero slopes, the change of slope between A and B is zero. Hence from area moment theorem

$$\sum_A^B A_M = 0$$

(Since EI is constant throughout)

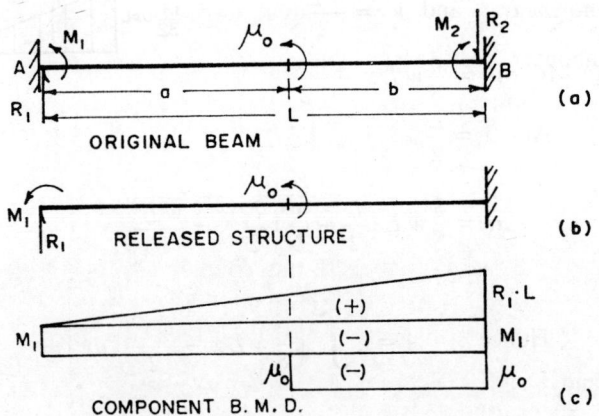

FIG. 16.12

$$\therefore \quad \frac{1}{2} R_1 L . L - M_1 . L - \mu_0 b = 0$$

or
$$R_1 - \frac{2 M_1}{L} = \frac{2 \mu_0 b}{L^2} \qquad \qquad ...(1)$$

The second condition is obtained from the fact that tangent to the deflection curve at A passes through point B. This means that the moment of the area of B.M. diagram between A and B, taken about B, is zero.

$$\therefore \qquad \qquad \sum_A^B A_M \bar{x} = 0 \quad \text{(since } EI \text{ is constant throughout)}$$

$$\therefore \quad \left(\frac{1}{2} R_1 L . L \right) \left(\frac{L}{3} \right) - M_1 L . \frac{L}{2} - b \mu_0 . \frac{b}{2} = 0$$

or
$$R_1 - \frac{3 M_1}{L} = \frac{3 \mu_0 b^2}{L^3} \qquad \qquad ...(2)$$

Solving (1) and (2), we get
$$M_1 = \frac{\mu_0 b}{L^2} (2 L - 3 b) = \frac{\mu_0 b}{L^2} (2 a - b)$$

and
$$R_1 = \frac{6 \mu_0 a b}{L^3} \ (\uparrow)$$

Since $\Sigma V = 0$ for the whole beam, we get $R_2 = - R_1 = - \dfrac{6 \mu_0 a b}{L^3}$ (*i.e.* $\downarrow$)

Taking moments about A and assuming M_2 to be clockwise, we get

$$M_2 - M_1 - \mu_0 + \frac{6 \mu_0 a b}{L^2} = 0$$

or
$$M_2 = \frac{\mu_0 b}{L^2} (2 a - b) + \mu_0 - \frac{6 \mu_0 a b}{L^2}$$

From which
$$M_2 = \frac{\mu_0 a}{L^2} (a - 2 b)$$

Thus reaction components are completely known.

Now y_C is equal to the vertical offset from the tangent at A, since tangent at A is horizontal. Hence y_C is equal to moment of the area of $\dfrac{M}{EI}$ diagram between A and C, taken about C.

$$\therefore \quad y_C = \sum_C^A \frac{A_M}{EI} \bar{x} = \left[\frac{1}{2} a . R_1 a \left(\frac{a}{3} \right) - M_1 . a . \frac{a}{2} \right] \frac{1}{EI}$$

$$= \left(\frac{R_1 a^3}{6} - \frac{M_1 a^2}{2} \right) \frac{1}{EI} = \frac{1}{EI} \left[\frac{6 \mu_0 a^4 b}{6 L^3} - \frac{\mu_0 b}{2 L^2} (2 a - b) a^2 \right] = \frac{\mu_0 a^2 b^2 (b - a)}{2 L^3 EI}$$

Special Case : If the couple acts at the mid-point (*i.e.* $a = b = \dfrac{L}{2}$)

$$M_1 = - M_2 = \frac{\mu_0}{4} \text{ and } R_1 = - R_2 = \frac{3}{2} \frac{\mu_0}{L}$$

and
$$y_C = 0$$

16.7. DOUBLE INTEGRATION METHOD

We shall now apply the double integration method (including Macaulay's method) to various standard cases of loadings on a fixed beam.

1. U.D.L. w over the whole span :

The loading is symmetrical.

Hence $M_1 = M_2 = M$ and $R_1 = R_2 = R = \dfrac{wL}{2}$.

At any distance x from end A,

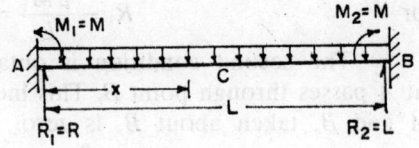

$$E I \frac{d^2 y}{d x^2} = - M_x = - \left[- M + \frac{wL}{2} x - \frac{w x^2}{2} \right]$$

$$= M - \frac{wL}{2} x + \frac{w x^2}{2}$$

FIG. 16.13

Integrating, $E I \dfrac{dy}{dx} = Mx - \dfrac{wL}{4} x^2 + \dfrac{w}{6} x^3 + 0$ (Since $\dfrac{dy}{dx} = 0$ at $x = 0$)   ...(2)

Integrating further, $E I y = \dfrac{M x^2}{2} - \dfrac{wL}{12} x^3 + \dfrac{w}{24} x^4 + 0$ (Since $y = 0$ at $x = 0$)   ...(3)

Now at $x = L$, $\dfrac{dy}{dx} = 0$. Hence from (2), we get $0 = ML - \dfrac{wL}{4} (L^2) + \dfrac{w}{6} (L)^3$

From which $M = \dfrac{wL^2}{4} - \dfrac{wL^2}{6} = \dfrac{wL^2}{12}$, which is the same as Eq. 16.6.

The maximum deflection at $x = \dfrac{L}{2}$ is given by

$$E I y_C = \frac{wL^2}{24} \left(\frac{L}{2} \right)^2 - \frac{wL}{12} \left(\frac{L}{2} \right)^3 + \frac{w}{24} \left(\frac{L}{2} \right)^4 = \frac{wL^4}{96} - \frac{wL^4}{96} + \frac{wL^4}{384}$$

$\therefore$ $y_C = \dfrac{wL^4}{384 E I}$, as before.

2. Point load at mid-span :

Here also, due to symmetry,

$M_1 = M_2 = M$ and $R_1 = R_2 = R = \dfrac{W}{2}$.

At any distance x from A,

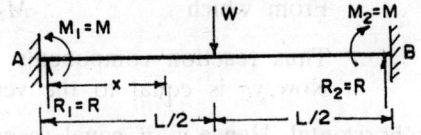

$$E I \frac{d^2 y}{d x^2} = - M_x = M - \frac{W}{2} x \; \bigg| \; + W \left(x - \frac{L}{2} \right)$$

FIG. 16.14

$\therefore$ $E I \dfrac{dy}{dx} = Mx - \dfrac{W x^2}{4} + 0 \; \bigg| \; + \dfrac{W}{2} \left(x - \dfrac{L}{2} \right)^2$ ...(1) (since $\dfrac{dy}{dx} = 0$ at $x = 0$)

and $E I y = \dfrac{M x^2}{2} - \dfrac{W x^3}{12} + 0 \; \bigg| \; + \dfrac{W}{6} \left(x - \dfrac{L}{2} \right)^3$ ...(2) (since $y = 0$ at $x = 0$)

At $x = L$, $\dfrac{dy}{dx} = 0 = ML - \dfrac{WL^2}{4} + \dfrac{W}{2} \left(L - \dfrac{L}{2} \right)^2$

From which $M = \dfrac{WL}{4} - \dfrac{WL}{8} = \dfrac{WL}{8}$ which is the same as found earlier.

The central deflection is found by substituting $x = L/2$ in (2).

$$E I y_C = \frac{M}{2} \left(\frac{L}{2} \right)^2 - \frac{W}{12} \left(\frac{L}{2} \right)^3 = \frac{WL}{8 \times 2} \times \frac{L^2}{4} - \frac{WL^3}{96} = \frac{WL^3}{192}$$

$\therefore$ $y_C = \dfrac{WL^3}{192 E I}$, which is the same as found earlier.

3. Eccentric point load : Let M_1 be the reactive moment and R_1 be the vertical reaction at A, both of which are presently unknown. At any distance x from A,

$$E I \frac{d^2 y}{d x^2} = - M_x = M_1 - R_1 x \;\bigg|\; + W (x - a) \quad ...(1)$$

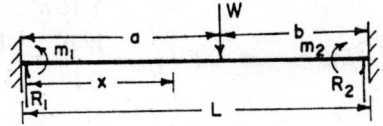

$$\therefore \quad E I \frac{dy}{dx} = M_1 x - R_1 \frac{x^2}{2} + 0 + \frac{W (x - a)^2}{2} \quad ...(2)$$

FIG. 16.15

and

$$E I y = M_1 \frac{x^2}{2} - R_1 \frac{x^3}{6} + 0 + \frac{W (x - a)^3}{6} \quad ...(3)$$

At $x = L$, $\dfrac{dy}{dx} = 0$ and $y = 0$. Hence from (2) and (3), we obtain

$$0 = M_1 L - R_1 \frac{L^2}{2} + \frac{W}{2} b^2 \quad ...(a)$$

and

$$0 = M_1 \frac{L^2}{2} - R_1 \frac{L^3}{6} + \frac{W}{6} b^3 \quad ...(b)$$

Solving (a) and (b), we get $\quad M_1 = \dfrac{W a b^2}{L^2}$ and $R_1 = \dfrac{W b^2}{L^3} \left(3 a + b \right)$

Substituting the values of M_1 and R_1 and $x = L$ in (1) we get

$$E I \frac{d^2 y}{d x^2} \text{ (at } x = L) = M_2 = \frac{W a b^2}{L^2} - \frac{W b^2}{L^3} \left(3 a + b \right) L + W b = \frac{W b a^2}{L^2}$$

For maximum deflection, $dy/dx = 0$. Assuming that this occurs in AD, we get

$$0 = \frac{W a b^2}{L^2} x - \frac{W b^2}{L^3} \left(3 a + b \right) \frac{x^2}{2}, \text{ from (2). This gives } x = \frac{2 a L}{3 a + b}$$

$$\therefore \quad E I y_{\max} = \frac{W a b^2}{2 L^2} \left[\frac{2 a L}{3 a + b} \right]^2 - \frac{W b^2}{6 L^3} \left(3 a + b \right) \left[\frac{2 a L}{3 a + b} \right]^3$$

$$= \frac{W a^3 b^2}{\left(3 a + b \right)^2} \left[2 - \frac{4}{3} \right] = \frac{2}{3} \frac{W a^3 b^2}{\left(3 a + b \right)^2} \quad ...(16.16)$$

The deflection under the load is obtained by substituting $x = a$ in (3)

$$E I y_D = \frac{W a b^2}{2 L^2} (a^2) - \frac{W b^2}{6 L^3} (3a + b) (a^3) = \frac{W a^3 b^2}{6 L^3} (3L - 3a - b)$$

$$= \frac{W a^3 b^2}{6 L^3} (3a + 3b - 3a - b) = \frac{W a^3 b^3}{3 L^3} \quad ...(16.17)$$

The deflection at the midspan is obtained by substituting at $x = L/2$ in (3)

$$E I y_C = \frac{W a b^2}{2 L^2} \left(\frac{L}{2} \right)^2 - \frac{W b^2}{6 L^3} \left(3 a + b \right) \left(\frac{L}{2} \right)^3 = \frac{W a b^2}{8} - \frac{W b^2 \left(3 a + b \right)}{48}$$

$$= \frac{W b^2}{48} [6 a - 3 a - b] = \frac{W b^2}{48} (3 a - b) = \frac{W b^2}{48} (3 L - 4 b) \quad ...(16.18)$$

Special Case : When $a = b = L/2$, we get from Eq. 16.16,

$$EIy_{max} = \frac{2}{3}\frac{Wa^5}{16\,a^2} = \frac{W}{24}a^3 = \frac{W}{24}\left(\frac{L}{2}\right)^3 = \frac{WL^3}{192}$$

Also, $$EIy_D = \frac{Wa^6}{3\,L^3} = \frac{W}{3\,L^3}\left(\frac{L}{2}\right)^6 = \frac{WL^3}{192} = EIy_{max}$$

and $$EIy_C = \frac{W}{48}\left(\frac{L}{2}\right)^2\left(3L - \frac{4L}{2}\right) = \frac{WL^3}{192} = EIy_{max}$$

Hence $y_C = y_D = y_{max}$, as expected for a central point load.

4. Moment at intermediate point : Let M_1 be the reactive moment and R_1 be the vertical reaction, in the directions marked in Fig. 16.16. At any distance x from A

$$EI\frac{d^2y}{dx^2} = -M_x = -[-M_1 + R_1 x \;|$$

$$- \mu_0(x-a)^0]$$

or $EI\dfrac{d^2y}{dx^2} = M_1 - R_1 x \;\Big| + \mu_0(x-a)^0$

...(1)

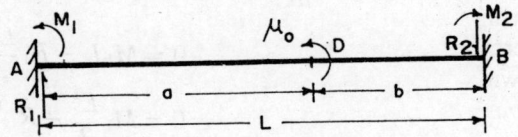

FIG. 16.16

$\therefore$ $$EI\frac{dy}{dx} = M_1 x - R_1\frac{x^2}{2} + 0 \;\Big| + \mu_0(x-a)$$ ...(2)

and $$EIy = M_1\frac{x^2}{2} - \frac{R_1 x^3}{6} + 0 \;\Big| + \frac{\mu_0(x-a)^2}{2}$$ ...(3)

At $x = L$, $\dfrac{dy}{dx} = 0$ and $y = 0$. Hence from (2) and (3), we get

$$0 = M_1 L - \frac{R_1}{2}L^2 + \mu_0 b$$ ...(a)

and $$0 = M_1\frac{L^2}{2} - \frac{R_1}{6}L^3 + \frac{\mu_0 b^2}{2}$$ ...(b)

Solving (a) and (b), we get $M_1 = \dfrac{\mu_0 b}{L^2}(2a - b)$ ...(16.19 a)

and $$R_1 = \frac{6\mu_0 a b}{L^3}$$ ...(16.20)

At $x = L, EI\dfrac{d^2y}{dx^2} = M_2 = M_1 - R_1 L + \mu_0 = \dfrac{\mu_0 b}{L^2}(2a-b) - \dfrac{6\mu_0 a b}{L^2} + \mu_0$

$$= \frac{\mu_0}{L^2}\left[b(2a-b) - 6ab + L^2\right] = \frac{\mu_0 a}{L^2}(a - 2b)$$ ...(16.19 b)

Also, $R_2 = -R_1 = \dfrac{6\mu_0 a b}{L^3}(\downarrow)$

For the deflection under the load, put $x = a$ in Eq. (3)

$\therefore$ $$EIy_D = M_1\frac{a^2}{2} - \frac{R_1}{6}a^3 = \frac{\mu_0 b}{2L^2}a^2(2a-b) - \frac{6\mu_0 a b}{6L^3}a^3$$

$$= \frac{\mu_0 b a^2}{L^2}\left[\frac{2a-b}{2} - \frac{a^2}{L}\right] = \frac{\mu_0 a^2 b^2}{2L^3}(a-b)$$ ...(16.21)

Special Case : If $a = b = \dfrac{L}{2}$: $M_1 = -M_2 = \dfrac{\mu_0}{4}$ and $R_1 = -R_2 = \dfrac{3}{2}\dfrac{\mu_0}{L}$

16.8. METHOD OF SUPER POSITION
(FLEXIBILITY METHOD OR FORCE METHOD)

The method of super-position is an important tool in analysing statically indeterminate structures. The method essentially consists of identifying the statical redundants from the indeterminate structure, and removing the redundant reactions, thus making the structure statically determinate. Such a structure is known as the *released structure* or the *basic determinate structure*. The displacements of the released structure are now found. Next, the redundant reactions themselves are visualised as loads acting on the released structure, and the corresponding displacements are calculated. The principle of super-position is then applied, according to which the *final displacements*

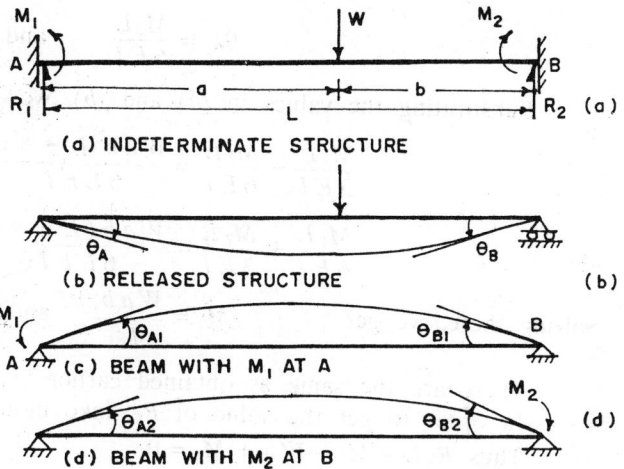

FIG. 16.17

due to both the actual loads and the redundant reactions must be equal to the sum of those displacements as calculated separately. In the case of redundant constraints, these displacements are either zero (in case of non-yielding supports) or have known magnitudes (in case of yielding supports). Thus, equations of superposition expressing these relationships are obtained, the solution of which give the redundant reactions. The method is known as the *method of consistent deformation* or the *flexibility method* or the *force method*. We shall now illustrate the method for analysing a fixed beam subjected to an eccentric point load.

Fig. 16.17(a) shows the fixed beam having four reaction components : M_1, M_2, R_1 and R_2. Since only two equations are available from statical equilibrium, the beam is statically indeterminate to second degree, *i.e.* there are two redundant reactions. Let us choose M_1 and M_2 as the redundants. Remove these redundants, thus obtaining the *basic determinate structure* or the *released structure*, as shown in Fig. 16.17(b). Let θ_A and θ_B be the slopes at the ends A and B, of the released structure, due to external load. Now remove the external load, and apply redundant moment M_1 at A, as shown in Fig. 16.17(c), the corresponding rotations at A and B being θ_{A1} and θ_{B1}. Now remove M_1, and apply redundant moment M_2 at B, as shown in Fig. 16.17(d), the corresponding rotations being θ_{A2} and θ_{B2} at A and B. Since the angles of rotation at both ends in the original beam (*i.e.* fixed beam) are zero, we have the following two equations of compatibility :

$$\Sigma\theta_A = \theta_A - \theta_{A1} - \theta_{A2} = 0 \qquad \qquad \ldots(a)$$

and
$$\Sigma\theta_B = \theta_B - \theta_{B1} - \theta_{B2} = 0 \qquad \qquad \ldots(b)$$

Now consider Fig. 16.17(b). The angles of rotations at the ends, due to load W are:

$$\theta_A = \frac{Wab(L+b)}{6LEI} \quad \text{and} \quad \theta_B = \frac{Wab(L+a)}{6LEI} \qquad \text{...(12.19)}$$

Again, consider Fig. 16.17(c), The angles of rotations at the ends, due to M_1 at A are:

$$\theta_{A_1} = \frac{M_1 L}{3EI} \quad \text{and} \quad \theta_{B_1} = \frac{M_1 L}{6EI} \qquad \text{...(12.24 } a)$$

Finally, consider Fig. 16.17(d). The angles of rotations at ends, due to M_2 at B are:

$$\theta_{A_2} = \frac{M_2 L}{6EI} \quad \text{and} \quad \theta_{B_2} = \frac{M_2 L}{3EI} \qquad \text{...(12.24 } b)$$

Substituting the values in (a) and (b), we get

$$\frac{M_1 L}{3EI} + \frac{M_2 L}{6EI} = \frac{Wab(L+b)}{6LEI} \qquad \text{...(I)}$$

and

$$\frac{M_1 L}{6EI} + \frac{M_2 L}{3EI} = \frac{Wab(L+a)}{6LEI} \qquad \text{...(II)}$$

Solving these, we get $\qquad M_1 = \dfrac{Wab^2}{L^2} \quad$ and $\quad M_2 = \dfrac{Wba^2}{L^2}$

These are the same as obtained earlier.

In order to get the value of R_1, take moments about B.

Thus $R_1 L - M_1 - Wb + M_2 = 0$

or

$$R_1 = \frac{1}{L} \left(M_1 + Wb - M_2 \right) = \frac{1}{L} \left[\frac{Wab^2}{L^2} + Wb - \frac{Wba^2}{L^2} \right]$$

From which

$$R_1 = \frac{Wb^2}{L^3} \left(L + 2a \right) = \frac{Wb^2}{L^3} \left(3a + b \right)$$

Similarly

$$R_2 = \frac{Wa^2}{L^3} \left(L + 2b \right) = \frac{Wa^2}{L^3} \left(a + 3b \right)$$

16.9. FIXED BEAM WITH UDL OVER A PART LENGTH FROM ONE END

Consider a section X distant x from A. Load acting on an elemental distance $dx = w\, dx$. Due to this elemental point load $w\, dx$, the fixed end moments at A and B are :

$$dM_1 = \frac{(w\, dx)\, x\, (L-x)^2}{L^2}$$

and $\qquad dM_2 = \dfrac{(w\, dx)\, (L-x)\, (x^2)}{L^2}$

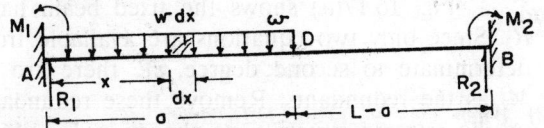

FIG. 16.18

$$\therefore \text{ Total } M_1 \text{ at } A = \int_0^a \frac{wx(L-x)^2}{L^2} = \frac{w}{L^2} \int_0^a (L^2 x + x^3 - 2Lx^2)\, dx = \frac{w}{L^2} \left(\frac{L^2 x^2}{2} + \frac{x^4}{4} - \frac{2Lx^3}{3} \right)$$

$$= \frac{w}{L^2} \left[\frac{L^2 a^2}{2} + \frac{a^4}{4} - \frac{2La^3}{3} \right] = \frac{w\, a^2}{12 L^2} \left[6L^2 + 3a^2 - 8La \right] \qquad \text{...(16.22 } a)$$

Similarly, total M_2 at $B = \displaystyle\int_0^a \dfrac{w\,dx\,(L-x)\,x^2\,dx}{L^2} = \dfrac{w}{L^2}\int_0^a \left(Lx^2 - x^3\right)dx$

$$= \dfrac{w}{L^2}\left[\dfrac{Lx^3}{3} - \dfrac{x^4}{4}\right]_0^a = \dfrac{w\,a^3}{12\,L^2}[4L - 3a] \qquad\qquad ...(16.22\ b)$$

For reaction R_1, take moments about B.

Thus $\qquad \Sigma M_B = 0 = R_1 L + M_2 - M_1 - w\,a\left(L - a + \dfrac{a}{2}\right)$

$\therefore \qquad R_1 = \dfrac{1}{L}\left[M_1 - M_2 + w\,a\left(L - \dfrac{a}{2}\right)\right]$

$$= \dfrac{1}{L}\left[\dfrac{w\,a^2}{12\,L^2}\left(6L^2 + 3a^2 - 8La\right) - \dfrac{w\,a^3}{12\,L^2}(4L - 3a) + \dfrac{w\,a\,(2L-a)}{2}\right]$$

$$= \dfrac{w\,a}{2\,L^3}\left[a^3 - 2La^2 + 2L^3\right] \qquad\qquad ...(16.23\ a)$$

Similarly, taking moments about A,

$$R_2 L + M_1 - M_2 - \dfrac{w\,a^2}{2} = 0$$

From which $\qquad R_2 = \dfrac{1}{L}\left[M_2 - M_1 + \dfrac{w\,a^2}{2}\right]$

$$= \dfrac{1}{L}\left[\dfrac{w\,a^3}{12\,L^2}(4L - 3a) - \dfrac{w\,a^2}{12\,L^2}\left(6L^2 + 3a^2 - 8La\right) + \dfrac{w\,a^2}{2}\right]$$

$$= \dfrac{w\,a^3}{2\,L^3}(2L - a) \qquad\qquad ...(16.23\ b)$$

Special Cases *(1)* : *When* $a = L$ *(i.e. U.D.L. over the whole span)*

$$M_1 = \dfrac{w}{12\,L^2}(L)^2\left[6L^2 + 3L^2 - 8L.L\right] = \dfrac{wL^2}{12}$$

$$M_2 = \dfrac{w}{12\,L^2}(L)^3[4L - 3L] = \dfrac{wL^2}{12}$$

$$R_1 = \dfrac{w}{2\,L^3}.L\left[L^3 - 2L.L^2 + 2L^3\right] = \dfrac{wL}{2}$$

and $\qquad R_2 = \dfrac{w}{2\,L^3}(L)^3(2L - L) = \dfrac{wL}{2}$

These results match with the results of the standard case.

(2) When $a = \dfrac{L}{2}$ *(i.e. U.D.L. over left half span)*

$$M_1 = \dfrac{w}{12\,L^2}\left(\dfrac{L}{2}\right)^2\left[6L^2 + 3\left(\dfrac{L}{2}\right)^2 - 8L\left(\dfrac{L}{2}\right)\right] = \dfrac{11}{192}wL^2$$

$$M_2 = \dfrac{w}{12\,L^2}\left(\dfrac{L}{2}\right)^3\left[4L - 3\dfrac{L}{2}\right] = \dfrac{5}{192}wL^2$$

$$R_1 = \dfrac{w}{2\,L^3}\left(\dfrac{L}{2}\right)\left[\left(\dfrac{L}{2}\right)^3 - 2L\left(\dfrac{L}{2}\right)^2 + 2L^3\right] = \dfrac{13}{32}wL$$

$$R_2 = \frac{w}{2L^3} \left(\frac{L}{2} \right)^3 \left(2L - \frac{L}{2} \right) = \frac{3}{32} wL$$

These results match with the results of example 16.3 solved by the area moment method.

16.10. FIXED BEAM WITH TRIANGULAR LOAD HAVING ZERO INTENSITY AT ONE END AND w AT THE OTHER END

Consider a section X, distant x from A. Intensity of loading at X $= \frac{w \cdot x}{L}$. Hence point load dW acting on an element at distance dx is $dW = \frac{w}{L} x \, dx$.

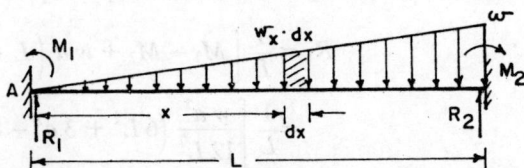

Fixed end moments due to this elemental load are given by

FIG. 16.19

$$dM_1 = \left(\frac{w}{L} x \, dx \right) \frac{x(L-x)^2}{L^2} = \frac{w x^2 (L-x)^2 \, dx}{L^3}$$

and

$$dM_2 = \left(\frac{w}{L} x \, dx \right) \frac{x^2 (L-x)}{L^2} = \frac{w x^3}{L^3} (L-x) \, dx$$

$\therefore$ Total

$$M_1 = \int_0^L \frac{w x^2}{L^3} (L-x)^2 \, dx = \frac{w}{L^3} \int_0^L \left(L^2 x^2 + x^4 - 2L x^3 \right) dx$$

$$= \frac{w}{L^3} \left[L^2 \frac{L^3}{3} + \frac{L^5}{5} - 2L \left(\frac{L}{4} \right)^4 \right] = \frac{w L^2}{30} \qquad \qquad ...(16.24 \ a)$$

and   Total

$$M_2 = \int_0^L \frac{w x^3}{L^3} (L-x) \, dx = \frac{w}{L^3} \int_0^L \left(L x^3 - x^4 \right) dx = \frac{w}{L^3} \left[L \cdot \frac{L^4}{4} - \frac{L^5}{5} \right] = \frac{w L^2}{20}$$

$$...(16.24 \ b)$$

For R_1, take moments about B.

Thus $\Sigma M_B = 0 = R_1 L + M_2 - M_1 - \frac{w L^2}{6}$

$\therefore$

$$R_1 = \frac{1}{L} \left[\frac{w L^2}{30} - \frac{w L^2}{20} + \frac{w L^2}{6} \right] = \frac{3}{20} wL \qquad \qquad ...(16.25 \ a)$$

Similarly, $\Sigma M_A = 0 = R_2 L + M_1 - M_2 - \frac{w L^2}{3}$

From which $R_2 = \frac{1}{L} \left[M_2 - M_1 + \frac{w L^2}{3} \right] = \frac{1}{L} \left[\frac{w L^2}{20} - \frac{w L^2}{30} + \frac{w L^2}{3} \right] = \frac{7}{20} wL \quad ...(16.25 \ b)$

16.11. FIXED BEAM WITH TRIANGULAR LOAD FOR A GIVEN DISTANCE FROM ONE END

Consider a section X distant x from A. The intensity of loading at X is $w_x = \frac{w}{a} x$.

Hence load dW acting on an elemental distance $dx = \frac{w}{a} \cdot x dx$.

Hence fixed end moments due to dW load are given by

$$dM_1 = \left(\frac{w}{a}x\,dx\right)\frac{x}{L^2}(L-x)^2$$

$$= \frac{w\,x^2}{a\,L^2}(L-x)^2\,dx$$

and

$$dM_2 = \left(\frac{w}{a}x\,dx\right)\frac{x^2(L-x)}{L^2}$$

$$= \frac{w\,x^3}{a\,L^2}(L-x)\,dx$$

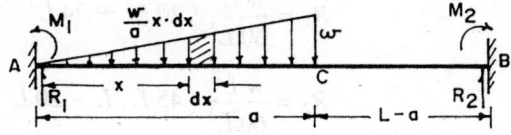

FIG. 16.20

$\therefore$ Total $M_1 = \displaystyle\int_0^a \frac{w\,x^2}{a\,L^2}(L-x)^2\,dx = \frac{w}{a\,L^2}\int_0^a \left(x^2 L^2 + x^4 - 2Lx^3\right)dx$

$$= \frac{w}{a\,L^2}\left[L^2\frac{a^3}{3} + \frac{a^5}{5} - 2L\frac{a^4}{4}\right] = \frac{w\,a^2}{30\,L^2}\left[10L^2 + 6a^2 - 15La\right] \quad ...(16.26\ a)$$

and total $M_2 = \displaystyle\int_0^a \frac{w\,x^3}{a\,L^2}(L-x)\,dx = \frac{w}{a\,L^2}\int_0^a \left(Lx^3 - x^4\right)dx$

$$= \frac{w}{a\,L^2}\left[L\frac{a^4}{4} - \frac{a^5}{5}\right] = \frac{w\,a^3}{20\,L^2}[5L - 4a] \quad ...(16.26\ b)$$

For reaction R_1, take moments about B.

Hence $R_1 L + M_2 - M_1 - \dfrac{1}{2}a\,w\left(L - \dfrac{2}{3}a\right) = 0$

$\therefore \quad R_1 = \dfrac{1}{L}\left[M_1 - M_2 + \dfrac{a\,w\,(3L - 2a)}{6}\right]$

$$= \frac{1}{L}\left[\frac{w\,a^2}{30\,L^2}\left(10L^2 + 6a^2 - 15La\right) - \frac{w\,a^3}{20\,L^2}(5L - 4a) + \frac{a\,w}{6}(3L - 2a)\right]$$

$$= \frac{w\,a^2}{60\,L^3}\left(20L^2 + 24a^2 - 45La\right) + \frac{a\,w}{6L}(3L - 2a) \quad ...(16.27\ a)$$

Similarly, $R_2 L + M_1 - M_2 - \dfrac{1}{2}a\,w\cdot\dfrac{2}{3}a = 0$

$\therefore \quad R_2 = \dfrac{1}{L}\left(M_2 - M_1 + \dfrac{w\,a^2}{3}\right)$

$$= \frac{1}{L}\left[\frac{w\,a^3}{20\,L^2}(5L - 4a) - \frac{w\,a^2}{30\,L^2}\left(10L^2 + 6a^2 - 15La\right) + \frac{w\,a^2}{3}\right]$$

$$= \frac{w\,a^2}{60\,L^3}\left(45La - 20L^2 - 24a^2\right) + \frac{w\,a^2}{3L} \quad ...(16.27\ b)$$

Special Case : When $a = L$ (i.e. triangular load over the whole span)

$$M_1 = \frac{w\,L^2}{30\,L^2}\left[10L^2 + 6L^2 - 15L.L\right] = \frac{w\,L^2}{30}$$

$$M_2 = \frac{w L^3}{20 L^2} (5 L - 4 L) = \frac{w L^2}{20}$$

$$R_1 = \frac{w L^2}{60 L^3} \left(20 L^2 + 24 L^2 - 45 L . L \right) + \frac{L w}{6 L} (3 L - 2 L) = \frac{3}{20} w L$$

and

$$R_2 = \frac{w L^2}{60 L^3} \left(45 L . L - 20 L^2 - 24 L^2 \right) + \frac{w L^2}{3 L} = \frac{7}{20} w L$$

These values are the same as found in the previous article.

16.12. FIXED BEAM WITH TRIANGULAR LOAD HAVING MAXIMUM INTENSITY AT MID-SPAN AND ZERO AT ENDS

Fig. 16.21 shows the loading. Because of symmetry,

$$M_1 = M_2 = M \qquad \text{and}$$

$$R_1 = R_2 = R = \frac{1}{2} \left(\frac{1}{2} L w \right) = \frac{w L}{4}$$

At any section X distant x from

A, $w_x = \dfrac{w}{L/2} . x = \dfrac{2 w}{L} x$

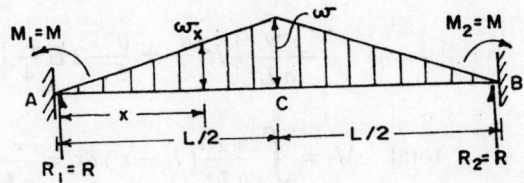

FIG. 16.21

For portion AC of the beam, we have

$$E I \frac{d^2 y}{d x^2} = - M_x = M - \frac{w L}{4} x + \frac{1}{2} \left(\frac{2 w}{L} x \right) x . \frac{x}{3} = M - \frac{w L x}{4} + \frac{w x^3}{3 L} \qquad ...(1)$$

$$\therefore \qquad E I \frac{dy}{dx} = M x - \frac{w L x^2}{8} + \frac{w x^4}{12 L} + 0 \qquad ...(2)$$

and

$$E I y = \frac{M x^2}{2} - \frac{w L x^3}{24} + \frac{w x^5}{60 L} + 0 \qquad ...(3)$$

Due to symmetry, $\dfrac{dy}{dx} = 0$ at $x = \dfrac{L}{2}$

$$\therefore \qquad 0 = M \left(\frac{L}{2} \right) - \frac{w L}{8} \left(\frac{L}{2} \right)^2 + \frac{w}{12 L} \left(\frac{L}{2} \right)^4$$

This gives $\qquad M = \dfrac{5}{96} w L^2 \qquad \qquad ...(16.28)$

Thus the reaction components at the ends are completely known. For deflection at mid-span, put $x = L/2$ in (3), alongwith the value of M.

$$\therefore \qquad E I y_C = \frac{5}{96} w L^2 . \frac{1}{2} \left(\frac{L}{2} \right)^2 - \frac{w L}{24} \left(\frac{L}{2} \right)^3 + \frac{w}{60 L} \left(\frac{L}{2} \right)^5 = \frac{7}{3840} w L^4$$

$$\therefore \qquad y_C = \frac{7}{3840} \frac{w L^4}{E I} \qquad \qquad ...(16.29)$$

Example 16.5. *Find the support moments of a fixed beam loaded at third points by two point loads of W each as shown in Fig. 16.22(a). Draw the B.M. and S.F. diagrams and calculate the deflection at the centre.*

Solution :

Let M_1 be the support moment and R_1 be the vertical reaction in the direction marked in Fig. 16.22(a). At any distance x from A, we have

$$E I \frac{d^2 y}{d x^2} = - M_x = M_1 - R_1 x \bigg|$$

$$+ W\left(x - \frac{L}{3}\right)\bigg| - W\left(x - \frac{2L}{3}\right)\dots(1)$$

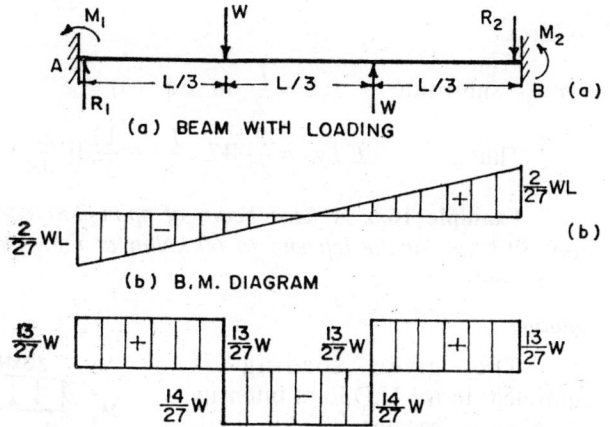

(a) BEAM WITH LOADING

(b) B.M. DIAGRAM

FIG. 16.22

Integrating successively,

$$E I \frac{dy}{dx} = M_1 x - R_1 \frac{x^2}{2} + 0 \bigg| + \frac{W}{2}\left(x - \frac{L}{3}\right)^2 \bigg| - \frac{W}{2}\left(x - \frac{2L}{3}\right)^2 \qquad \dots(2)$$

and

$$E I y = \frac{M_1 x^2}{2} - \frac{R_1 x^3}{6} + 0 \bigg| + \frac{W}{6}\left(x - \frac{L}{3}\right)^3 \bigg| - \frac{W}{6}\left(L - \frac{2L}{3}\right)^3 \qquad \dots(3)$$

At

$$x = L, \frac{dy}{dx} = 0 = M_1 L - \frac{R_1 L^2}{2} + \frac{W}{2}\left(L - \frac{L}{3}\right)^2 - \frac{W}{2}\left(L - \frac{2L}{3}\right)^2$$

or

$$18 M_1 - 9 R_1 L + 3 W L = 0 \qquad \dots(a)$$

Also, at

$$x = L, y = 0 = \frac{M_1}{2} L^2 - \frac{R_1}{6} L^3 + \frac{W}{6}\left(L - \frac{L}{3}\right)^3 - \frac{W}{6}\left(L - \frac{2L}{3}\right)^3$$

or

$$81 M_1 - 27 R_1 L + 7 W L = 0 \qquad \dots(b)$$

Solving Eqs. (a) and (b), we get $M_1 = + \frac{2}{27} W L$ and $R_1 = + \frac{13}{27} W$

The plus sign with M_1 and R_1 values shows that the *assumed directions* are correct. Again, substituting $x = L$, and values of R_1 and M_1 in Eq. (1), we get

$$E I \frac{d^2 y}{d x^2} = - M_x = M_1 - R_1 L + W\left(L - \frac{L}{3}\right) - W\left(L - \frac{2L}{3}\right)$$

But

$$M_x = M_2$$

∴

$$- M_2 = M_1 - R_1 L + \frac{1}{3} W L$$

or

$$M_2 = - M_1 + R_1 L - \frac{1}{3} W L = - \frac{2}{27} W L + \frac{13}{27} W L - \frac{1}{3} W L = \frac{2}{27} W L$$

Thus $M_2 = + \frac{2}{27} W L$; this means that M_2 is of sagging nature, and is therefore in the anticlockwise direction as marked in Fig. 16.22 (a). The B.M.D. is shown in Fig. 16.22 (b), from which we find that B.M. is zero at the midspan, *i.e.* point C is the point of contraflexure. From statics, since $\Sigma V = 0$, $R_2 = -R_1 = -\frac{13}{27} W$ (*i.e.* $\frac{13}{27} W \downarrow$). The S.F.D. is shown in Fig. 16.22(*c*).

For y_C, substitute $\qquad x = \frac{L}{2}$ in Eq. (3).

Thus $\qquad EI y_C = \frac{2}{27} WL \cdot \frac{L^2}{8} - \frac{13}{27} W \frac{L^3}{48} + \frac{W}{6} \left(\frac{L}{2} - \frac{L}{3} \right)^3 = \frac{WL^3}{108} - \frac{13 WL^3}{27 \times 48} + \frac{W}{6} \frac{L^3}{36 \times 6} = 0$

Example 16.6. *A fixed beam of span 4 m carries a distributed load whose intensity varies from 30 kN/m at the left end to 60 kN/m at the right end. Find the fixing moments and reactions at the ends.*

Solution :

The given loading is equivalent to (*a*) U.D.L. of intensity 30 kN/m throughout, plus (*b*) a triangularly varying load having zero intensity at A to 30 kN/m at B. These two effects have been shown separately in Fig. 16.23 (*b*) and (*c*) respectively.

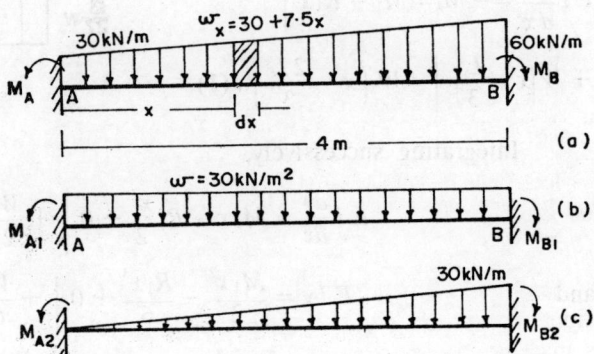

FIG. 16.23

For case (a) of loading : w throughout the length

$$M_{A1} = M_{B1} = \frac{wL^2}{12} = \frac{30 \,(4)^2}{12} = 40 \text{ kN-m}$$

For case (b) of loading : Triangularly varying load.

$$M_{A2} = \frac{wL^2}{30} = \frac{30 \,(4)^2}{30} = 16 \text{ kN-m} \quad \text{...(Eq. 16.24 } a\text{)}$$

$$M_{B2} = \frac{wL^2}{20} = \frac{30 (4)^2}{20} = 24 \text{ kN-m} \quad \text{...(Eq. 16.24 } b\text{)}$$

$\therefore$ Total $\qquad M_A = M_{A1} + M_{A2} = 40 + 16 = \textbf{56 kN-m}$

Total $\qquad M_B = M_{B1} + M_{B2} = 40 + 24 = \textbf{64 kN-m.}$

$$R_1 = \frac{w_1 L}{2} + \frac{3}{20} w_2 L = \frac{1}{2} \times 30 \times 4 + \frac{3}{20} \times 30 \times 4 = \textbf{78 kN} \quad \text{...(16.25 } a\text{)}$$

$$R_2 = \frac{w_1 L}{2} + \frac{7}{20} w_2 L = \frac{1}{2} \times 30 \times 4 + \frac{7}{20} \times 30 \times 4 = \textbf{102 kN}$$

Alternative independent solution

At any distance x from A, rate of loading $w_x = 30 + \frac{60 - 30}{4} x = 30 + 7.5 x$

$\therefore \qquad dM_A = \left\{ \left(30 + 7.5 x \right) dx \right\} \dfrac{x (4 - x)^2}{16}$

and $\qquad dM_B = \left\{ \left(30 + 7.5 x \right) dx \right\} \dfrac{x^2 (4 - x)}{16}$

$\therefore$ Total $\quad M_A = \int\limits_0^4 \dfrac{(30 + 7.5\,x)\,x\,(4-x)^2}{16}\,dx = \dfrac{1}{16} \int\limits_0^4 \left(7.5\,x^4 - 30\,x^3 - 120\,x^2 + 480\,x\right) dx$

$= \dfrac{1}{16} \left[\dfrac{7.5\,x^5}{5} - 30\left(\dfrac{x^4}{4}\right) - 120\left(\dfrac{x^3}{3}\right) + 480\left(\dfrac{x^2}{2}\right) \right]_0^4 = \mathbf{56 \ \ kN\text{-}m}$

Similarly Total $\quad M_B = \int\limits_0^4 \left(30 + 7.5\,x\right)\dfrac{x^2(4-x)}{16} = \dfrac{1}{16}\int\limits_0^4 \left(120\,x^2 - 7.5\,x^4\right) dx$

$= \dfrac{1}{16}\left[120\left(\dfrac{x^3}{3}\right) - 7.5\left(\dfrac{x^5}{5}\right)\right]_0^4 = \mathbf{64 \ \ kN\text{-}m}$

For finding R_1, take moments about B.

Thus $\qquad 4\,R_1 + M_B - M_A - 30 \times 4 \times 2 - \dfrac{1}{2} \times 30 \times 4 \times \dfrac{4}{3} = 0$

From which $\quad R_1 = \dfrac{1}{4}\left[-64 + 56 + 240 + 80 \right] = \mathbf{78 \ kN}$

$\therefore \qquad R_2 = \dfrac{1}{2}\left(30 + 60\right)4 - 78 = \mathbf{102 \ kN}$

Example 16.7. *A fixed beam AB of span 4.5 m is subjected to a concentrated couple of 400 kN-m applied at a section 3 m from end A. Find the end moments from the first principles and draw the B.M. and S.F. diagrams.*

Solution : Let M_1 and R_1 be the reaction components at A in the directions marked. At any section distant x from A.

$E I \dfrac{d^2 y}{dx^2} = -M_x = R_1 x - M_1 \Big|$

$\qquad\qquad - 400\,(x-3)^0 \quad ...(1)$

$\therefore \quad E I \dfrac{dy}{dx} = R_1\dfrac{x^2}{2} - M_1 x + 0 \Big|$

$\qquad\qquad - 400\,(x-3) \qquad ...(2)$

$E I y = R_1\dfrac{x^3}{6} - \dfrac{M_1 x^2}{2} + 0 \Big| - \dfrac{400(x-3)^2}{2}$

$\qquad\qquad\qquad ...(3)$

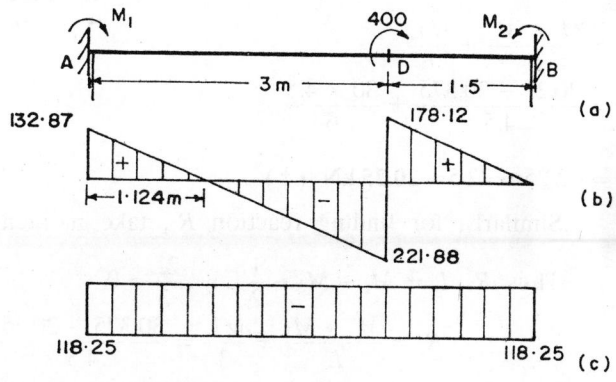

FIG. 16.24

At $\qquad\qquad x = 4.5 \text{ m}, \dfrac{dy}{dx} = 0$ Hence from (2)

$$0 = \dfrac{R_1}{2}\,(4.5)^2 - M_1\,(4.5) - 400\,(4.5 - 3)$$

or $\qquad R_1 - 0.444\,M_1 = 59.259 \qquad\qquad\qquad ...(a)$

Also, at $x = 4.5$ m, $y = 0$. Hence from (3),

$$0 = \dfrac{R_1}{6}\,(4.5)^3 - \dfrac{M_1}{2}\,(4.5)^2 - 200\,(4.5 - 3)^2$$

or $\qquad R_1 - 0.667\,M_1 = 29.63 \qquad\qquad\qquad ...(b)$

Solving (a) and (b), we get $M_1 = \mathbf{132.87}$ **kN-m** and $R_1 = \mathbf{118.25\ kN}$. *Plus signs with tł values of M_1 and R_1 show that the assumed directions of M_1 and R_1 are correct.*

From statics, $\qquad\qquad R_2 = -R_1 = -118.25$ (*i.e.* **118.25** ↑)

For the whole beam, $\Sigma M = 0$ $\quad \therefore \quad 132.87 + 400 - 118.25\,(4.5) = M_2$

From which $\qquad\qquad M_2 = \mathbf{0}$. The complete B.M.D. is shown in Fig. 16.24(b).

The B.M. is zero at $x = 132.87/118.25 = 1.125$ m from A. The S.F. diagram is shown i Fig. 16.24(c). The S.F. will be $-\mathbf{118.25\ kN}$ throughout.

Example 16.8. *A beam AB of span 4.5 m is built-in at its both ends. It carries a graduall\ varying load from zero at A to 30 kN/m at B. Determine the fixed end moments and support: reactions at both ends of the beam, and hence plot the B.M. and S.F. diagrams for the beam*

Solution : From Eq. 16.24(a),

$$M_1 = \frac{wL^2}{30} = \frac{30\,(45)^2}{30}$$

$$= \mathbf{20.25}\ \ \mathbf{kN\text{-}m}$$

$$M_2 = \frac{wL^2}{20} = \frac{30\,(4.5)^2}{20}$$

$$= \mathbf{30.375}\ \ \mathbf{kN\text{-}m}$$

For finding reaction R_1, take moments about B.

or $\quad R_1.L + M_2 - M_1$

$$-\frac{1}{2} \times L \times w \cdot \frac{L}{3} = 0$$

$$R_1 = \frac{M_1 - M_2}{L} + \frac{wL}{6}$$

$$= \frac{20.25 - 30.375}{4.5} + \frac{30 \times 4.5}{6}$$

$$= -2.25 + 22.5 = \mathbf{20.25\ kN}\ (\uparrow)$$

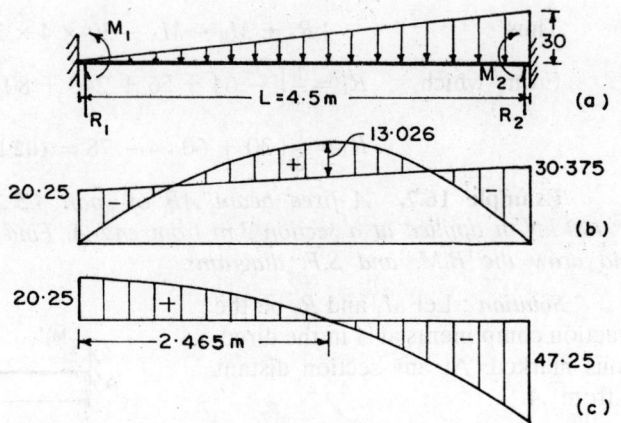

FIG. 16.25

Similarly, for finding reaction R_2, take moments about A.

Thus $R_2.L + M_1 - M_2 - \dfrac{1}{2}Lw \cdot \dfrac{2L}{3} = 0$

ır $\qquad R_2 = \dfrac{M_2 - M_1}{L} + \dfrac{wL}{3} = \dfrac{30.375 - 20.25}{4.5} + \dfrac{30 \times 4.5}{3} = 2.25 + 45 = \mathbf{47.25\ kN}\ (\uparrow)$

Check $\qquad R_1 + R_2 = 20.25 + 47.25 = 67.5$ kN

Total load $= \dfrac{1}{2} \times 4.5 \times 30 = 67.5$ kN.

At any distance x from A, $\quad w_x = \dfrac{30}{4.5}x = 6.667\,x$

$$F_x = R_1 - \frac{1}{2}\,(6.667\,x)\,x = 20.25 - 3.3333\,x^2$$

The variation is parabolic. S.F. is zero at $x = \sqrt{(20.25/3.3333)}$

$\qquad\qquad = 2.465$ m from A. The S.F.D. is shown in Fig. 16.25(c).

\gain, at any distance x from A, $\quad M_x = R_1 x - M_1 - \dfrac{1}{2}w_x \cdot x \cdot \dfrac{x}{3} = 20.25\,x - 20.25 - 1.111\,x^3$

This is a cubic variation. At $\quad x = 2.465$ m, $M_x = +13.026$ kN-m

The B.M. diagram is shown in Fig. 16.25(c).

Example 16.9. *A beam AB is fixed at A and B and carries a load which varies uniformly from w at A to 2w at B. The moment of inertia of the beam also varies uniformly having its value I at A and 2I at B. Determine (a) the fixing moments at A and B, and (b) the maximum deflection.*

Solution : At any distance x from A,

$$E\frac{d^4y}{dx^4} = \frac{w_x}{I_x} = \frac{w + w\frac{x}{L}}{I + I\frac{x}{L}} = \frac{w(L+x)}{I(L+x)} = \frac{w}{I}$$

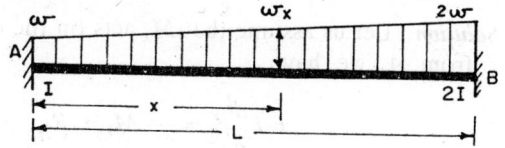

FIG. 16.26

$$\therefore \quad E\frac{d^3y}{dx^3} = \frac{w}{I}x + C_1 \qquad \ldots(1)$$

$$E\frac{d^2y}{dx^2} = \frac{w}{2I}x^2 + \frac{C_1}{2}x + C_2 \qquad \ldots(2)$$

$$E\frac{dy}{dx} = \frac{w}{6I}x^3 + \frac{C_1}{2}x^2 + C_2x + 0\ldots(3), \qquad \text{since } \frac{dy}{dx} = 0 \text{ at } x = 0$$

and

$$Ey = \frac{w}{24I}x^4 + \frac{C_1}{6}x^3 + \frac{C_2}{2}x^2 + 0\ldots(4) \qquad \text{since } y = 0 \text{ at } x = 0$$

At $\quad x = L, \frac{dy}{dx} = 0$ and $y = 0$. Hence substituting in (3) and (4), we get

$$\frac{wL^2}{I} + 3C_1L + 6C_2 = 0 \qquad \ldots(a)$$

and

$$\frac{wL^2}{I} + 4C_1L + 12C_2 = 0 \qquad \ldots(b)$$

Solving (a) and (b), we get $C_1 = -\frac{wL}{2I}$ and $C_2 = \frac{wL^2}{12I}$

Substituting the values of C_1 and C_2 in (2), we get

$$E\frac{d^2y}{dx^2} = \frac{w}{2I}x^2 - \frac{wL}{2I}x + \frac{wL^2}{12I} \qquad \ldots(I)$$

This is the equation for B.M. at any point.

At $x = 0$, $\qquad\qquad E\frac{d^2y}{dx^2} = \frac{wL^2}{12I}$

Hence $\qquad\qquad M_A = -EI_A\frac{d^2y}{dx^2} = -\frac{wL^2}{12}$ (Since $I_A = I$).

Also, at $x = L$, $\qquad \frac{Ed^2y}{dx^2} = \frac{w}{2I}(L)^2 - \frac{wL}{2I}(L) + \frac{wL^2}{12I} = \frac{wL^2}{12I}$

Hence $\qquad M_B = -EI_B\frac{d^2y}{dx^2} = \left(-E\frac{d^2y}{dx^2}\right)I_B = \left(-\frac{wL^2}{12I}\right)(2I) = -\frac{wL^2}{6}$ **(Ans.)**

For maximum deflection, equate (3) to zero

$$\therefore \quad \frac{wx^3}{6I} - \frac{wL}{4I}x^2 + \frac{wL^2}{12I}x = 0$$

or $\qquad 2x^2 - 3xL + L^2 = 0$, which gives $x = L/2$

Hence maximum deflection occurs at mid-span. Hence from (4)

$$\therefore \qquad y_{max} = \frac{wL^4}{EI}\left[\frac{1}{384} - \frac{1}{96} + \frac{1}{96}\right] = \frac{wL^4}{384\,EI} \quad \text{(Ans.)}$$

Example 16.10. *A fixed beam of length 4 m is loaded as shown in Fig. 16.27(a). Find the end moments and reactions and plot the B.M. and S.F. diagrams.*

Solution : Let us assume that M_1 acts on the clockwise direction ans R_1 acts downwards. Measuring x from A, we have

$$EI\frac{d^2y}{dx^2} = -M_1 + R_1 x \ \Big| \ + 5(x-3) - 40(x-3)^\circ \qquad \qquad ...(1)$$

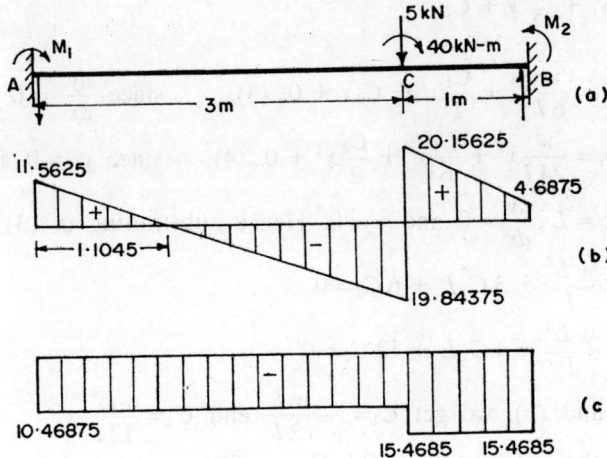

FIG. 16.27

$$\therefore \qquad EI\frac{dy}{dx} = -M_1 x + \frac{R_1 x^2}{2} + 0 \ \Big| \ \frac{5(x-3)^2}{2} - 40(x-3) \qquad ...(2)$$

and $\qquad EIy = -\frac{M_1 x^2}{2} + \frac{R_1 x^3}{6} + 0 \ \Big| \ + \frac{5(x-3)^3}{6} - \frac{40(x-3)^2}{2} \qquad ...(3)$

At $x = 4$ m, $\quad \dfrac{dy}{dx} = 0 - M_1(4) + \dfrac{R_1}{2}(4)^2 + 2.5(4-3)^2 - 40(4-3)$

From which $\quad R_1 = \dfrac{M_1}{2} + 4.6875$. Substituting in (3), we get

$$EIy = -\frac{M_1}{2}x^2 + \frac{1}{6}\left(\frac{M_1}{2} + 4.6875\right)x^3 \ \Big| \ + \frac{5}{6}(x-3)^3 - \frac{40(x-3)^2}{2} \qquad ...(4)$$

At $x = L = 4$ m, $y = 0$. Hence from (4), we get

$$0 = -\frac{M_1}{2}(4)^2 + \frac{1}{6}\left(\frac{M_1}{2} + 4.6875\right)(4)^3 + \frac{5}{6}(4-3)^3 - 20(4-3)^2$$

From which $M_1 = +\mathbf{11.5625}$ **kN-m**

The plus sign shows that the moment at A acts in the same direction as assumed.

Also, $R_1 = \dfrac{11.5625}{2} + 4.6875 = \mathbf{10.46875}$ **kN**

Here also, plus sign shows that R_1 acts in the same direction as assumed *i.e.* it acts in the downward direction.

Again, substituting $x = L$ in (1), we get

$$(-M_x)_{x=L} = -M_2 = E\,I\frac{d^2 y}{dx^2} = -11.5625 + 10.46875\,(4) + 5\,(4-3) - 40\,(4-3)$$

or $-M_2 = -4.6875$ or $M_2 = \mathbf{4.6875}$ kN-m (*i.e.* M_2 is of sagging nature, as marked.)

B.M. diagram $M_1 = +11.5625$; $M_2 = +4.6875$

For AC, $M_x = 11.5625 - 10.46875\,x$

Hence M_x is zero at $x = 11.5625/10.46875 = 1.1045$ m

M_C (left) $= 11.5625 - 10.46875 \times 3 = -19.84375$ kN-m

M_C (right) $= 11.5625 - 10.46875 \times 3 + 40 = +20.15625$

The B.M. diagram is shown in Fig. 16.27(*b*)

S.F. diagram $R_2 = \left(R_1 + 5\right)(\uparrow) = (10.46875 + 5) = 15.46875$ kN ($\uparrow$)

The S.F. diagram is shown in Fig. 16.27.

16.13. EFFECT OF SINKING OF A SUPPORT

Fig. 16.28(*a*) shows a fixed beam AB, the right hand end B of which settles downwards by an amount δ. Due to this settlement or sinking of support B, moments and vertical reactions will be induced at both the ends. In order to know their directions, consider a simply supported beam AB (Fig. 16.28 *b*), the right hand end B of which settles downwards by amount δ. Due to this settlement, the beam will rotate in the clockwise direction, and the slope at each end will change from 0 to θ in the clockwise direction. Since ends A and B are built-in, the fixity will not permit this rotation θ of the tangents, and consequently, fixing couples (M) will be induced at each end in such directions so as to make the tangents there horizontal. Hence the fixing moment M will be induced in the anticlockwise direction at each end. If however, the left hand A sinks downwards relative to the right hand one, the beam will have a tendency to rotate in the anticlockwise direction and hence the fixing moment will be induced in the clockwise direction at each end.

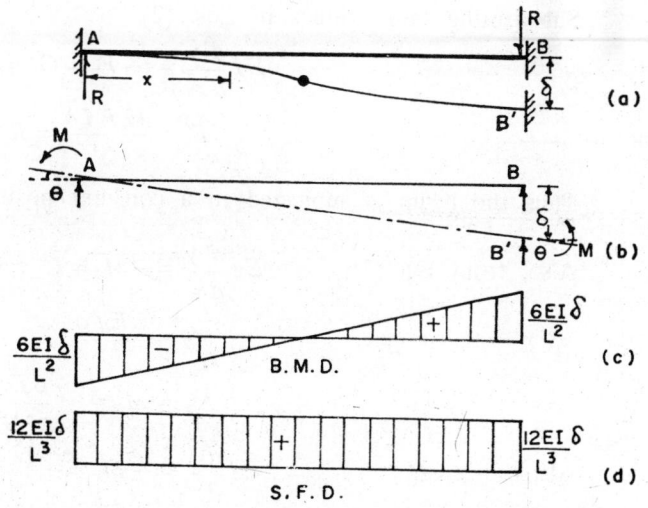

FIG. 16.28

For the present case, shown in Fig. 16.28, fixing moment at each end will be M (i.e. equal) and will be in the anticlockwise direction since the beam has the tendency to rotate in the clockwise direction due to sinking of the support B. The vertical reactions at A and B will be *equal and opposite* (since $\Sigma V = 0$) and will be of such magnitude so as to provide a total couple equal to the total moments induced, since ΣM has to be zero.

Hence we have, from statics $\qquad R \times L = 2M \qquad$ or $\qquad R = \dfrac{2M}{L}$

At any distance x from the support A,

$$EI\frac{d^4y}{dx^4} = \text{rate of loading} \quad w = 0 \qquad\qquad ...(1)$$

Integrating successively, we get $\quad EI\dfrac{d^3y}{dx^3} = C_1 = -F_x \qquad\qquad ...(2)$

$$EI\frac{d^2y}{dx^2} = C_1 x + C_2 = -M_x \qquad\qquad ...(3)$$

$$EI\frac{dy}{dx} = C_1\frac{x^2}{2} + C_2 x + 0 \qquad ...(4), \text{ since } \frac{dy}{dx} = 0 \text{ at } x = 0$$

and $\qquad\qquad EIy = \dfrac{C_1 x^3}{6} + \dfrac{C_2 x^2}{2} + 0 \qquad ...(5), \text{ since } y = 0 \text{ at } x = 0$

In the above five equations, there are only two unknowns, C_1 and C_2, which can be evaluated by using the boundary conditions that at $x = L$, $\dfrac{dy}{dx} = 0$ and $y = +\delta$.

Hence $\qquad\qquad\qquad 0 = C_1\dfrac{L^2}{2} + C_2 L \qquad\qquad ...(i)$

and $\qquad\qquad\qquad EI\delta = \dfrac{C_1 L^3}{6} + \dfrac{C_2 L^2}{2} \qquad\qquad ...(ii)$

Solving (i) and (ii), we get $\qquad C_1 = -\dfrac{12EI\delta}{L^3} \qquad$ and $\qquad C_2 = \dfrac{6EI\delta}{L^2}$

Substituting these values in Eqs. (2)

$$EI\frac{d^3y}{dx^3} = -F_x = C_1 = -\frac{12EI\delta}{L^3} \qquad\qquad ...(a)$$

or $\qquad\qquad\qquad F_x = \dfrac{12EI\delta}{L^3} = R \qquad\qquad ...(16.30)$

Thus the beam is subjected to a constant positive S.F. of magnitude $\dfrac{12EI\delta}{L^3}$

Also, from Eq. (3), $\qquad EI\dfrac{d^2y}{dx^2} = -M_x = C_1 x + C_2 = \dfrac{-12EI\delta}{L^3}x + \dfrac{6EI\delta}{L^2}$

At $x = 0$, we get $\qquad -M_x = \dfrac{6EI\delta}{L^2}$

$\therefore \qquad\qquad\qquad M_x = M_1 = -\dfrac{6EI\delta}{L^2} \qquad\qquad ...(16.31\ a)$

Also, at $x = L$, $\qquad EI\dfrac{d^2y}{dx^2} = -M_x = -\dfrac{12EI\delta}{L^3}L + \dfrac{6EI\delta}{L^2} = -\dfrac{6EI\delta}{L^2}$

$\therefore \qquad\qquad\qquad \left(M_x\right)_{x=L} = M_2 = +\dfrac{6EI\delta}{L^2} \qquad\qquad ...(16.31\ b)$

The B.M. and S.F. diagrams are shown in Fig. 12.28(c) and (d) respectively. We observe that there is a point of contraflexure at the midspan. If the beam is loaded with U.D.L., and the right hand end also sinks by δ, the fixing moment at the higher end A will be $-\left(\dfrac{wL^2}{12} + \dfrac{6EI\delta}{L^2}\right)$ and that at the lower end will be $\dfrac{6EI\delta}{L^2} - \dfrac{wL^2}{12}$.

16.14. EFFECT OF ROTATION OF A SUPPORT : PARTIALLY FIXED BEAM

Let us now take the case of a beam which is perfectly fixed at end A (so that angle of rotation is zero there) and *partially fixed* at B so that its tangent rotates through an angle θ_B in the *anticlockwise* direction.

Let M_1 and M_2 be the end moments at A and B respectively in the directions marked. Since there is no external load on the beam, the vertical reactions R_1 and R_2 will be equal and opposite such that

$$R \times L = M_1 + M_2 \quad \text{or} \quad R = \frac{M_1 + M_2}{L}$$

Now at any distance x from A,

$$EI\frac{d^4y}{dx^4} = \text{rate of loading} = 0 \quad \text{...(1)}$$

Integrating successively,

$$EI\frac{d^3y}{dx^3} = C_1 = -F_x \quad \text{...(2)}$$

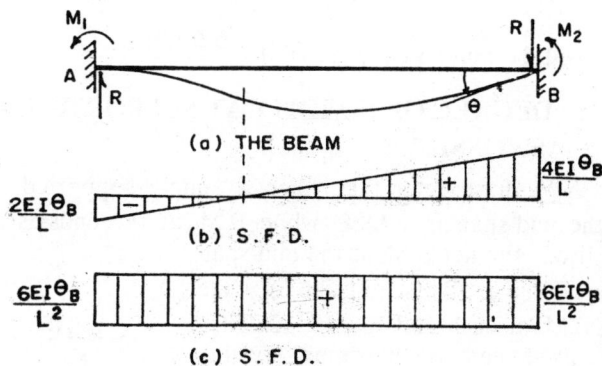

(a) THE BEAM

(b) S.F.D.

(c) S.F.D.

FIG. 16.29

$$EI\frac{d^2y}{dx^2} = C_1x + C_2 = -M_x \quad \text{...(3)}$$

$$EI\frac{dy}{dx} = \frac{C_1x^2}{2} + C_2x + 0 \quad \left(\text{since } \frac{dy}{dx} = 0 \text{ at } x = 0\right) \quad \text{...(4)}$$

and
$$EIy = \frac{C_1x^3}{6} + \frac{C_2x^2}{2} + 0 \quad (\text{since } y = 0 \text{ at } x = 0) \quad \text{...(5)}$$

In the above equations, there are only two unknowns : C_1 and C_2

At $x = L$, $\quad \dfrac{dy}{dx} = -\theta_B$. Hence from Eq. (4):

$$-EI\theta_B = \frac{C_1L^2}{6} + C_2L \quad \text{...(i)}$$

Also, at $\quad x = L, y = 0$. Hence from Eq. (5) :

$$0 = \frac{C_1L^3}{6} + \frac{C_2L^2}{2} \quad \text{...(ii)}$$

Solving (i) and (ii), we get $\quad C_1 = -\dfrac{6EI\theta_B}{L^2} + \text{ and } C_2 = \dfrac{2EI\theta_B}{L}$

Substituting in Eq. (3), we get

$$EI\frac{d^2y}{dx^2} = -M_x = C_1x + C_2 = -\frac{6EI\theta_B}{L^2}x + \frac{2EI\theta_B}{L}$$

At $x = 0$, $\qquad M_x = M_1$

$$\therefore \qquad -M_1 = \frac{2EI\theta_B}{L} \quad \text{or} \quad M_1 = -\frac{2EI\theta_B}{L} \qquad \dots(16.33\ a)$$

Also, at $\qquad\qquad x = L, M_x = M_2$

$$\therefore \qquad -M_2 = -\frac{6EI\theta_B}{L^2}\cdot L + \frac{2EI\theta_B}{L} = -\frac{4EI\theta_B}{L}$$

or $$\qquad\qquad\qquad M_2 = +\frac{4EI\theta_B}{L} \qquad \dots(16.33\ b)$$

The B.M. diagram is shown in Fig. 16.29(b).

Also, from   Eq. (2), $\qquad F_x = -C_1 = \dfrac{6EI\theta_B}{L^2} \qquad \dots(16.34)$

Hence the beam is subjected to a constant S.F. of $\dfrac{6EI\theta_B}{L^2}$. The reaction R at each

end will be numerically equal to $\dfrac{6EI\theta_B}{L^2}$.

16.15. DEGREE OF FIXITY AT SUPPORTS TO HAVE MAXIMUM B.M. AS SMALL AS POSSIBLE

We have seen that when a simply supported beam is subjected to U.D.L., the B.M. at the mid-span is $wL^2/8$ while B.M. at the ends is zero. When the ends of the same beam are fixed , the net B.M. at the mid-span is equal to $wL^2/24$ (see Fig. 16.6), while the B.M. at each end is $wL^2/12$. Thus for a fixed beam, the maximum hogging B.M. is *twice* the maximum sagging B.M. If the degree of fixity at each end is *reduced*, the hogging B.M. at each end will decrease and consequently the sagging B.M. at the mid- span will increase. Hence for the maximum B.M. to be as small as possible, the maximum sagging moment should be equal to maximum hogging moment. Let that B.M. be M_0. Now for a simply supported beam, central B.M. $= wL^2/8$.

Hence we have the condition :

$M_0 = \dfrac{wL^2}{8} - M_0$. From which M_0

$= \dfrac{wL^2}{16}$. For such a *partially fixed beam*, let θ_0 be the slope at each end (Note that $\theta = 0$ for a fixed beam).

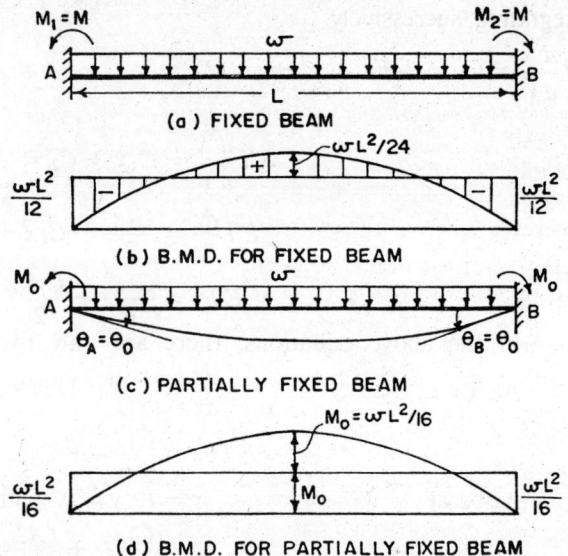

FIG. 16.30

Due to symmetry $\qquad R_1 = R_2 = R = \dfrac{wL}{2}$

Hence at any section distant x from A,

$$EI\frac{d^2y}{dx^2} = -M_x = -\left[\frac{wL}{2}x - M_0 - \frac{wx^2}{2}\right] = -\frac{wL}{2}x + \frac{wL^2}{16} + \frac{wx^2}{2}$$

Integrating, $\qquad E I \dfrac{dy}{dx} = -\dfrac{wL}{4}x^2 + \dfrac{wL^2}{16}x + \dfrac{wx^3}{6} + C_1$

Due to symmetry, $\qquad \dfrac{dy}{dx} = 0$ at $x = \dfrac{L}{2}$

$\therefore \qquad 0 = -\dfrac{wL}{4}\left(\dfrac{L}{2}\right)^2 + \dfrac{wL^2}{16}\left(\dfrac{L}{2}\right) + \dfrac{w}{6}\left(\dfrac{L}{2}\right)^3 + C_1$

From which $\qquad C_1 = \dfrac{wL^3}{96}$

Hence $\qquad E I \dfrac{dy}{dx} = -\dfrac{wL}{4}x^2 + \dfrac{wL^2}{16}x + \dfrac{wx^3}{6} + \dfrac{wL^3}{96}$

This is the equation for the slope. At $x = 0, \dfrac{dy}{dx} = \theta_A$

$\therefore \qquad E I \theta_A = \dfrac{wL^3}{96}$ or $\theta_A = +\dfrac{wL^3}{96EI}$ $\qquad ...(16.35\ a)$

Similarly, at $x = L$, $\qquad \dfrac{dy}{dx} = \theta_B$

$\therefore \qquad E I \theta_B = -\dfrac{wL}{4}\left(L^2\right) + \dfrac{wL^2}{16}\left(L\right) + \dfrac{w}{6}\left(L\right)^3 + \dfrac{wL^3}{96} = -\dfrac{wL^3}{96}$

Hence $\qquad \theta_B = -\dfrac{wL^3}{96EI}$ $\qquad ...(16.35\ b)$

Thus θ_A and θ_B are numerically equal.

16.16. ADDITIONAL ILLUSTRATIVE EXAMPLES

Example 16.11. *A encastre beam of span L carries a load wL uniformly distributed over the span. The second moment of area of the beam section is not the same throughout; for a length L/4 for each end, its value is 2 I and for a middle length L/2, it is I. Determine the B.M. at the ends and sketch the B.M. diagram.*

Solution :

Fig. 16.31 (*b*) shows the component B.M.D. for U.D.L., for half of the length of the beam. Fig. 16.31(*c*) shows the component B.M.D. for reaction R_1 for half the length of the beam while Fig. 16.31(*d*) shows the component B.M.D. for fixing moment $M_1 (= M_2 = M)$ for half the length. From Mohr's theorem,

$$E \Sigma \theta_A^C = -\sum_{A}^{C} \dfrac{A}{I \text{ or } 2I} = 0$$

since the tangent at C is horizontal due to symmetry.

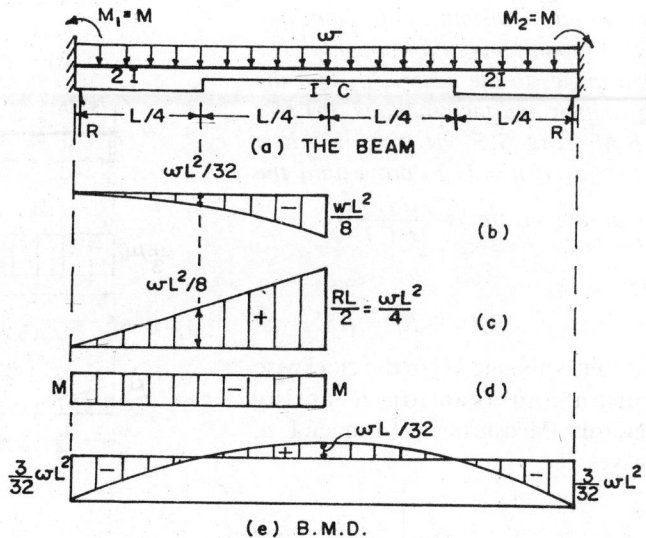

FIG. 16.31

Now for B.M.D.   of Fig. 16.31 (b)

$$\overset{C}{\underset{A}{\Sigma}} \frac{A}{I \text{ or } 2I} = -\left(\frac{1}{3} \times \frac{wL^2}{32} \times \frac{L}{4} \times \frac{1}{2I}\right) - \left\{\left(\frac{1}{3} \times \frac{wL^2}{8} \times \frac{L}{2}\right) - \left(\frac{1}{3} \times \frac{wL^2}{32} \times \frac{L}{4}\right)\right\}\frac{1}{I}$$

$$= -\frac{wL^3}{768\,I} - \frac{wL^3}{48\,I} + \frac{wL^3}{384\,I} = -\frac{15}{768}\frac{wL^3}{I} \qquad \qquad ...(i)$$

For B.M.D.   of fig. 16.31 (c)

$$\overset{C}{\underset{A}{\Sigma}} \frac{A}{I \text{ or } 2I} = \left(\frac{1}{2} \cdot \frac{wL^2}{8} \times \frac{L}{4} \times \frac{1}{2I}\right) + \left\{\frac{1}{2}\left(\frac{wL^2}{8} + \frac{wL^2}{4}\right)\frac{L}{4} \cdot \frac{1}{I}\right\}$$

$$= \frac{wL^3}{128\,I} + \frac{3\,wL^3}{64\,I} = \frac{7}{128}\frac{wL^3}{I} \qquad \qquad ...(2)$$

For B.M.D. of Fig. 16.31   (d)

$$\overset{C}{\underset{A}{\Sigma}} \frac{A}{I \text{ or } 2I} = \left(-M_1\frac{L}{4} \cdot \frac{1}{2I}\right) + \left(-M_1 \times \frac{L}{4} \times \frac{1}{I}\right) = -\frac{3\,M_1\,L}{8\,I} \qquad ...(3)$$

$$\therefore \text{ Total } \overset{C}{\underset{A}{\Sigma}} \frac{A}{I \text{ or } 2I} = -\frac{15}{768}\frac{wL^3}{I} + \frac{7}{128}\frac{wL^3}{I} - \frac{3}{8}\frac{M_1\,L}{I} = 0$$

or

$$\frac{3}{8}\frac{M_1\,L}{I} = \frac{7}{128}\frac{wL^3}{I} - \frac{15}{768}\frac{wL^3}{I} = \frac{27}{768}\frac{wL^3}{I}$$

From which $M_1 = \dfrac{3}{32}wL^2 = M_2$

Also, $M_C = $ sum of ordinates of (b), (c) and (d)$ = -\dfrac{wL^2}{8} + \dfrac{wL^2}{4} - \dfrac{3}{32}wL^2$

$$= +\frac{wL^2}{32}. \text{ The B.M.D. is shown in Fig. 16.31 (e).}$$

Example 16.12. *A beam of span L is fixed at both the ends. A couple μ is applied to the beam at a distance nL from the left hand support, about a horizontal axis at right angles to the beam. (a) find the fixing couples and the reactions, (b) plot the B.M. and S.F. diagrams when $n = 2/3$ (c) If $n = 1/2$, prove that the slope at the centre is $\dfrac{\mu L}{16EI}$.*

Solution :

$$R_A = -R_B = R$$

Let as assume M_A in the clockwise direction and reaction R acting downwards. Measuring x from end A, we have

$$EI\frac{d^2y}{dx^2} = Rx - M_A \;\Big|\; -\mu(x - nL)^0$$

$$...(1)$$

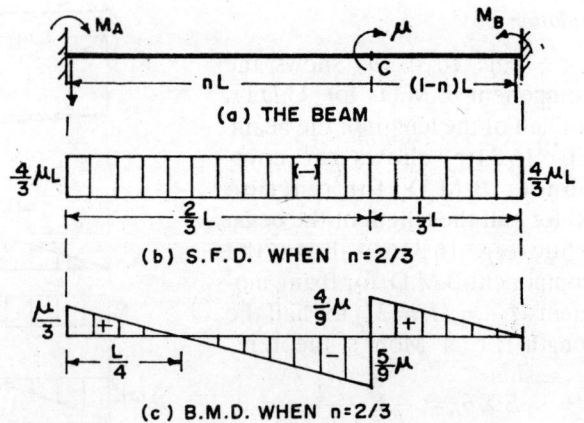

FIG. 16.32

$\therefore$ $$E I \frac{dy}{dx} = \frac{R x^2}{2} - M_A . x + 0 \left| - \mu (x - n L) \right.$$ ...(2)

$$E I y = \frac{R x^3}{6} - M_A \frac{x^2}{2} + 0 \left| - \frac{\mu (x - n L)^2}{2} \right.$$ ...(3)

At $\quad x = L, \dfrac{dy}{dx} = 0$

$\therefore$ $$0 = \frac{R}{2} L^2 - M_A . L - \mu (L - n L)$$

or $$R = \frac{1}{L} \left[2 M_A + 2 \mu (1 - n) \right] = \frac{2}{L} \left\{ M_A + \mu (1 - n) \right\}$$ ...(4)

Again, at $\quad x = L, y = 0$ and R as in (4). Hence from (3)

$$0 = \frac{2}{L} \left\{ M_A + \mu (1 - n) \right\} \frac{L^3}{6} - M_A \frac{L^2}{2} - \frac{\mu (1 - n)^2 L^2}{2}$$

or $$2 M_A + 2 \mu (1 - n) - 3 M_A - 3 \mu (1 - n)^2 = 0$$

or $$M_A = 2 \mu (1 - n) - 3 \mu (1 - n)^2 = \mu \left(2 - 2 n - 3 - 3 n^2 + 6 n \right)$$

or $$M_A = \mu (- 3 n^2 + 4 n - 1) = \mu (1 - n) (3 n - 1)$$ ...(5)

Hence $$R = \frac{2}{L} \left[\mu (1 - n) (3 n - 1) + \mu (1 - n) \right]$$

$$= \frac{2}{L} \left[\mu \left(4 n - 3 n^2 - 1 + 1 - n \right) \right] = \frac{6 \mu n (1 - n)}{L}$$

Substituting the values of M_A and L in the moment equation (i.e. Eq. 1)

$$- M_x = E I \frac{d^2 y}{d x^2} = R x - M_A \left| - \mu = \frac{6 \mu n (1 - n)}{L} x - \mu (1 - n) (3 n - 1) \right| - \mu$$

At $\quad x = L, M_x = M_B$;

$\therefore$ $\quad - M_B = 6 \mu n (1 - n) - \mu (1 - n) (3 n - 1) - \mu$

or $\quad M_B = \mu \left[- 6 n + 6 n^2 + 3 n - 3 n^2 - 1 + n + 1 \right] = \mu \left[3 n^2 - 2 n \right]$

or $\quad M_B = \mu n (3 n - 2) = - \mu n (2 - 3 n)$ ...(7)

It will be seen from Eq. (5) that $M_A = 0$ at $n = 1/3$. It will be positive for all values of n greater than 1/3 and negative for all values less than 1/3. The sign of M_B will be opposite to M_A, except at $n = 1/2$ in which case $M_A = M_B = \mu/4$, *in the same direction as* μ.

(b) **When** $n = \dfrac{2}{3}$: $M_A = \mu \left(1 - \dfrac{2}{3} \right) \left(3 \times \dfrac{2}{3} - 1 \right) = + \dfrac{\mu}{3}$. The plus sign shows that the assumed direction is correct. Also, $M_B = - \mu \times \dfrac{2}{3} \left(2 - 3 \times \dfrac{2}{3} \right) = 0$.

$$R_A = R = \frac{6 \mu}{L} \times \frac{2}{3} \left(1 - \frac{2}{3} \right) = \frac{4}{3} \frac{\mu}{L}, \text{ acting downwards}$$

$R_B = -R = \dfrac{4}{3}\dfrac{\mu}{L}$, acting upwards. The S.F. diagram will be a rectangle as shown in Fig. 16.32 (b). At any distance x from A,

$$M_x = \dfrac{\mu}{3} - \dfrac{4}{3}\dfrac{\mu}{L}x \ \bigg| + \mu.$$

At $x = 0$, $M_A = +\dfrac{\mu}{3}$; At $x = \dfrac{2}{3}L$,

$$M_{C\,(left)} = \dfrac{\mu}{3} - \dfrac{4}{3}\dfrac{\mu}{L}\times\dfrac{2}{3}L = -\dfrac{5}{9}\mu$$

$$M_{C(right)} = -\dfrac{5}{9}\mu + \mu = \dfrac{4}{9}\mu.$$

At $x = L$, $M_B = \dfrac{\mu}{3} - \dfrac{4}{3}\dfrac{\mu}{L}\cdot L + \mu = 0$

Also, M_x is zero at $x = \dfrac{L}{4}$.

(c) **When** $n = \dfrac{1}{2}$: $M_A = \mu\left(1 - \dfrac{1}{2}\right)\left(\dfrac{3}{2} - 1\right) = \dfrac{\mu}{4}$, in the same direction as μ.

Also, $R = \dfrac{6\mu}{L}\cdot\dfrac{1}{2}\left(1 - \dfrac{1}{2}\right) = \dfrac{3}{2}\dfrac{\mu}{L}\ (\downarrow)$

$\therefore$ $\dfrac{EId^2y}{dx^2} = -M_x = \dfrac{3}{2}\dfrac{\mu}{L}x - \dfrac{\mu}{4} \ \bigg| -\mu(x - nL)^\circ$

$\therefore$ $EI\dfrac{dy}{dx} = \dfrac{3}{2}\dfrac{\mu}{L}\dfrac{x^2}{2} - \dfrac{\mu}{4}x + 0 \ \bigg| -\mu(x - nL).$

At $x = \dfrac{L}{2}$, $\left(\dfrac{dy}{dx}\right)_{centre} = \dfrac{1}{EI}\left[\dfrac{3}{4}\dfrac{\mu}{L}\cdot\dfrac{L^2}{4} - \dfrac{\mu}{4}\dfrac{L}{2}\right] = \dfrac{\mu L}{16\,EI}$ (Proved)

Example 16.13. *A horizontal shaft of length L is subjected at its centre to a vertical load W. The shaft fits in bearings at its ends and when the slope of the shaft at the end is θ, the bearing exerts a bending moment on the shaft of magnitude k θ. Find (a) the B.M. at the ends and (b) deflection of the shaft at mid-span.*

Solution : The shaft is partially fixed at the ends. Let the support moment, exerted by the bearings be μ. Then $\mu = k\theta$.

or $\theta = \dfrac{\mu}{k} = \dfrac{dy}{dx}$ at the end.

Also, due to symmetry, $R_1 = R_2 = R = \dfrac{W}{2}$, at each end.

At any point distant x from the left support

$$EI\dfrac{d^2y}{dx^2} = -M_x = \mu - \dfrac{W}{2}x \ \bigg| + W\left(x - \dfrac{L}{2}\right) \qquad\qquad ...(1)$$

$\therefore$ $EI\dfrac{dy}{dx} = \mu x - \dfrac{W}{2}\dfrac{x^2}{2} + C_1 \ \bigg| + \dfrac{W}{2}\left(x - \dfrac{L}{2}\right)^2 \qquad\qquad ...(2)$

At $x = 0$, $\qquad\qquad \dfrac{dy}{dx} = \theta = \dfrac{\mu}{k}$ (given)

$\therefore \qquad\qquad\qquad C_1 = E I \left(\dfrac{dy}{dx} \right)_{x=0} = E I . \dfrac{\mu}{k}.$

Hence from (2) $\qquad E I \dfrac{dy}{dx} = \mu x - \dfrac{W}{4} x^2 + E I \dfrac{\mu}{k} \bigg| + \dfrac{W}{2} \left(x - \dfrac{L}{2} \right)^2 \qquad$ ...(3)

Also, at $x = \dfrac{L}{2}$, $\qquad\qquad \dfrac{dy}{dx} = 0$, due to symmetry.

$\therefore \qquad\qquad\qquad 0 = \dfrac{\mu L}{2} - \dfrac{W}{4} \left(\dfrac{L}{2} \right)^2 + E I \dfrac{\mu}{k}$

or $\qquad\qquad\qquad \mu \left(\dfrac{L}{2} + \dfrac{E I}{k} \right) = \dfrac{W L^2}{16}$

From which $\qquad\qquad\qquad \mu = \dfrac{W L^2 k}{8 \left(L k + 2 E I \right)}$ (Ans.)

Substituting this value of μ in (3), we get, for half the shaft,

$$E I \dfrac{dy}{dx} = \dfrac{W L^2 k}{8 \left(L k + 2 E I \right)} . x - \dfrac{W}{4} x^2 + E I \dfrac{\mu}{k}$$

Integrating, $\qquad E I y = \dfrac{W L^2 k}{8 \left(L k + 2 E I \right)} . \dfrac{x^2}{2} - \dfrac{W}{4} . \dfrac{x^3}{3} + E I \dfrac{\mu}{k} x + 0$

(Since $y = 0$ at $x = 0$)

At $x = \dfrac{L}{2}$, we get the maximum deflection.

$\therefore \qquad\qquad E I y_{max} = \dfrac{W L^2 k}{16 \left(L k + 2 E I \right)} \left(\dfrac{L}{2} \right)^2 - \dfrac{W}{12} \left(\dfrac{L}{3} \right)^3 + E I \dfrac{\mu}{k} \left(\dfrac{L}{2} \right)$

or $\qquad\qquad E I y_{max} = \dfrac{W L^4 k}{64 \left(L k + 2 E I \right)} - \dfrac{W L^3}{96} - \dfrac{E I L}{2 k} \left[\dfrac{W L^2 k}{8 \left(L k + 2 E I \right)} \right]$

or $\qquad\qquad y_{max} = \dfrac{W L^3}{192 E I} \left[\dfrac{3 k L}{k L + 2 E I} - 2 + \dfrac{12 E I}{\left(k L + 2 E I \right)} \right]$

$\qquad\qquad = \dfrac{W L^3}{192 E I} \left[\dfrac{3 k L - 2 k L - 4 E I + 12 E I}{k L + 2 E I} \right] = \dfrac{W L^3}{192 E I} \left[\dfrac{k L + 8 E I}{k L + 2 E I} \right]$ Ans.

Example 16.14. *A beam AB of constant section and span L is fixed at end A and carries a central load W. During loading, B sinks by an amount δ and rotates through an angle δ/L. Determine the fixing moment at A if the rotation at B is (a) anticlockwise, (b) clockwise.*
Solution :

Let M_A and R_A be the reaction components at end A. Measuring x from A,

$$E I \dfrac{d^2 y}{dx^2} = - M_x = M_A - R_A x \bigg| + W \left(x - \dfrac{L}{2} \right) \qquad ....(1)$$

$$\therefore \qquad EI\frac{dy}{dx} = M_A x - R_A x^2 + 0 \Big| + \frac{W}{2}\left(x - \frac{L}{2}\right)^2 \qquad \ldots(2)$$

and

$$EIy = \frac{M_A x^2}{2} - \frac{R_A x^3}{6} + 0 \Big| + \frac{W}{6}\left(x - \frac{L}{2}\right)^3 \qquad \ldots(3)$$

At $x = L$, $y = \delta$. Hence from (3)

$$EI\delta = M_A\frac{L^2}{2} - \frac{R_A L^3}{6} + \frac{W}{6}\cdot\frac{L^3}{8}$$

or

$$24 M_A - 8 R_A L + WL = \frac{48 EI\delta}{L^2} \qquad \ldots(I)$$

(a) For anticlockwise rotation

At $x = L, \dfrac{dy}{dx} = -\dfrac{\delta}{L}$ Hence from (2)

$$-EI\frac{\delta}{L} = M_A \cdot L - R_A\frac{L^2}{2} + \frac{WL^2}{8}$$

or

$$8 M_A - 4 R_A \cdot L + WL = -\frac{8 EI\delta}{L^2} \qquad \ldots(II)$$

From (I) and (II), $\qquad M_A = \dfrac{WL}{8} + \dfrac{8 EI\delta}{L^2}$

(b) For clockwise rotation

At $x = L$, $\qquad \dfrac{dy}{dx} = \dfrac{\delta}{L}$. Hence from (2)

$$EI\frac{\delta}{L} = M_A L - R_A\frac{L^2}{2} + \frac{WL^2}{8}$$

or

$$8 M_A - 4 R_A L + WL = \frac{8 EI\delta}{L^2} \qquad \ldots(III)$$

Hence from (I) and (II), $\qquad M_A = \dfrac{WL}{8} + \dfrac{4 EI\delta}{L^2}$

Example 16.15. *A beam AB of uniform section and 4 m span is built-in at the ends, and is loaded as shown in Fig. 16.33(a). Determine the fixing moments and reactions at the ends and plot the B.M. and S.F. diagrams. Also, Find magnitude and position of maximum deflection.*

Take $E = 2 \times 10^5$ N/mm^2 and $I = 5 \times 10^8$ mm^4.

Solution :

Let M_A and R_A be the reaction components at A, in the directions marked. Measuring x from A, we have

$$EI\frac{d^2 y}{dx^2} = -M_x = M_A - R_A x + \frac{8x^2}{2}\Big| - \frac{8(x-10)^2}{2}\Big| + 120(x-15) \qquad \ldots(1)$$

$$\therefore \qquad EI\frac{dy}{dx} = M_A x - R_A\frac{x^2}{2} + \frac{4x^3}{3} + 0\Big| - \frac{8(x-10)^3}{6}\Big| + \frac{120(x-15)^2}{2} \qquad \ldots(2)$$

and
$$EIy = M_A \frac{x^2}{2} - \frac{R_A x^3}{6} + \frac{4x^4}{12} + 0 \left| - \frac{8(x-10)^4}{24} \right| + \frac{120(x-15)^3}{6} \dots(3)$$

At $x = 20$ m, $\frac{dy}{dx} = 0$ Hence from (2)

$$0 = M_A(20) - \frac{R_A}{2}(20)^2 + \frac{4}{3}(20)^3 - \frac{8(20-10)^3}{6} + \frac{120}{2}(20-15)^2$$

or $\qquad M_A - 10 R_A = -541.7 \qquad\qquad\qquad\qquad\qquad \dots(I)$

Also, at $x = 20$ m, $y = 0$. Hence from (3)

$$0 = \frac{M_A}{2}(20)^2 - \frac{R_A}{6}(20)^3 + \frac{4}{12}(20)^4 - \frac{8}{24}(20-10)^4 + \frac{120}{6}(20-15)^3$$

or $\qquad M_A - 6.667 R_A = -262.5 \qquad\qquad\qquad\qquad \dots(II)$

Solving (I) and (II), we get $\quad R_A = + \textbf{83.77 kN}$ and $M_A = + \textbf{296 kN}$.

The plus signs with R_A and M_A show that the assumed directions of R_A and M_A are correct.

Again $\qquad\qquad R_B = \left[(8 \times 10) + 120 \right] - 83.77 = \textbf{116.23 kN} \ (\uparrow)$

Again putting $x = 20$ m in Eq. (1), we get

$$(-M_x)_{x=20} = 296 - 83.77(20) + 4(20)^2 - 4(20-10)^2 + 120(20-15) = 420.6$$

$(M_x)_{x=0} = M_B = -420.6$ kN-m

The B.M. and S.F. diagrams are shown in Fig. 16.33(b) and (c) respectively.

Since the concentrated load is greater than the total U.D.L. and acts at an equal distance from the nearest end, zero slope will evidently occur between $x = 10$ m to $x = 15$ m. Hence from Eq. (2), noting that $x \approx 10$ m, we get

$$EI\frac{dy}{dx} = 296x - 83.77\frac{x^2}{2} + \frac{4x^3}{3}$$
$$- \frac{8}{6}(x-10)^3 = 0$$

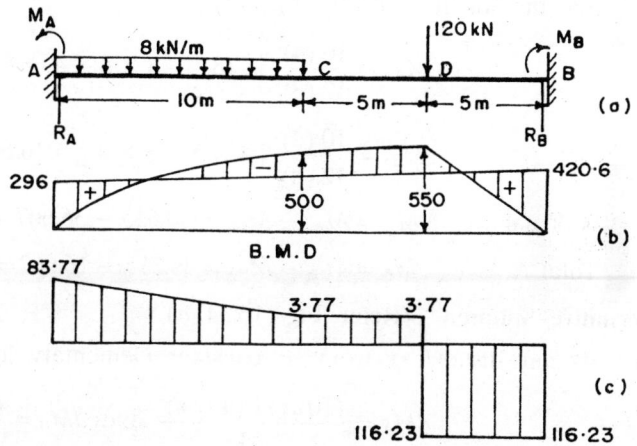

FIG. 16.33

or $\qquad x^2 - 31.41x + 222 = 0$, from which we get $x = 10.74$ m

Hence from Eq. (3)

$$EIy_{max} = \frac{296(10.74)^2}{2} - \frac{83.77(10.74)^3}{6} + \frac{4}{12}(10.74)^4 - \frac{8(10.74-10)^4}{24} = 4210 \text{ kN-m}^3$$

$\therefore \qquad y_{max} = \frac{\left(4210 \times 10^{12} \right)}{\left(2 \times 10^5 \times 5 \times 10^8 \right)} = \textbf{42.1 mm}$

Example 16.16. *Find the fixing moments and end reactions for a fixed beam shown in Fig. 16.34(a).*

Solution :

The loading shown in Fig. 16.34(a) is equivalent to the algebraic sum of the loadings shown in Fig. 16.34(b) and (c).

For loading of Fig. 16.34 (b)

$$M_{A1} = \frac{w\,a^2}{12\,L^2}(6L^2 - 8\,La + 3\,a^2)...(16.22a)$$

$$= \frac{10\,(6)^2}{12\,(8)^2}\left[6\,(8)^2 - 8 \times 8 \times 6 + 3\,(6)^2\right]$$

$$= 50.625 \quad \text{kN-m (hogging)}$$

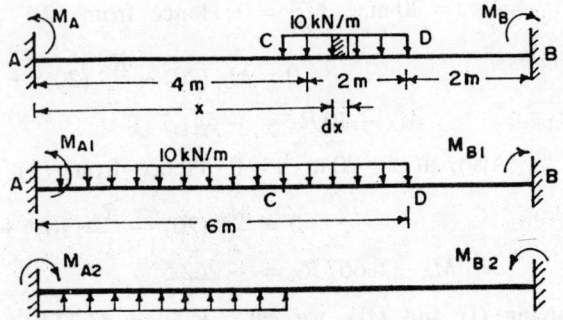

FIG. 16.34

$$M_{B1} = \frac{w\,a^3}{12\,L^2}(4L - 3\,a) \qquad\qquad ...(16.22a)$$

$$= \frac{10\,(6)^3}{12\,(8)^2}[4 \times 8 - 3 \times 6] = 39.375 \quad \text{kN-m (hogging)}$$

For the loading of Fig. 16.34(c),

$$M_{A2} = \frac{10\,(4)^2}{12\,(8)^2}\left[6\,(8)^2 - 8 \times 8 \times 4 + 3\,(4)^2\right] = 36.667 \quad \text{kN-m (sagging)}$$

$$M_{B2} = \frac{10\,(4)^3}{12\,(8)^2}[4 \times 8 - 3 \times 4] = 16.667 \quad \text{kN-m (sagging)}$$

∴ Total $M_A = M_{A1} - M_{A2} = 50.625 - 36.667 = \textbf{13.958} \quad \textbf{kN-m (hogging)}$

Total $M_B = M_{B1} - M_{B2} = 39.375 - 16.667 = \textbf{22.708} \quad \textbf{kN-m (hogging)}$

Alternative Solution   (Refer Fig. 16.34 a)

At any distance x from A, consider elementary load $w\,dx = 10\,dx$, due to which

$$dM_A = \frac{(10\,dx)\,x\,(8-x)^2}{64} \quad \text{and} \quad dM_B = \frac{(10\,dx)\,(8-x)\,x^2}{64}$$

∴

$$M_A = \int_4^6 \frac{10\,x\,(8-x)^2}{64}\,dx = \frac{5}{32}\left[\int_4^6 \left(x^3 - 16x^2 + 64x\right)dx\right] = 13.958 \quad \text{kN-m}$$

and

$$M_B = \int_4^6 \frac{10}{64}(8-x)\,x^2\,dx = \frac{5}{32}\left[\int_4^6 \left(8x^2 - x^3\right)dx\right] = 22.708 \quad \text{kN}$$

End Reactions : Taking moments about B, $\quad R_A = \frac{1}{8}\left[13.958 - 22.708 + 60\right] = \textbf{6.406 kN} \; (\uparrow)$

Similarly, $\quad R_B = \frac{1}{8}\left[22.708 - 13.958 + 20 \times 5\right] = \textbf{13.594 kN} \; (\uparrow)$

Example 16.17. *A beam AB fixed at A and B and 7 m long, carries U.D.L. of 30 kN/m over the whole span and is propped at C, distant 3 m from A. The prop at C sinks slightly such that the pressure on the prop is 98 kN. Find the support moments and reactions at A and B.*

Solution :

The above problem may be considered as the problem of a fixed beam *AB*, subjected to a downward load in the form of U.D.L. of 20 kN/m and an upward point load P = 98 kN

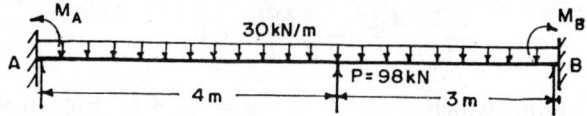

FIG. 16.35

$$\therefore \quad M_A = \frac{wL^2}{12} - \frac{Pab^2}{L^2} = \frac{30\,(7)^2}{12} - \frac{98 \times 4\,(3)^2}{(7)^2} = 50.5 \quad \text{kN-m} \quad \text{(hogging)}$$

$$M_B = \frac{wL^2}{12} - \frac{Pba^2}{L^2} = \frac{30\,(7)^2}{12} - \frac{98 \times 3\,(4)^2}{(7)^2} = 26.5 \quad \text{kN-m} \quad \text{(hogging)}$$

For finding reaction at *A*, take moments at *B*.

$$\therefore \quad R_A L + M_B - M_A - 30 \times 7 \times 3.5 + 98 \times 3 = 0$$

From which $\quad R_A = 66.429 \text{ kN}$

Similarly, $\qquad R_B L + M_A - M_B + 98 \times 4 - 30 \times 7 \times 3.5 = 0$

From which $\quad R_B = 45.571 \text{ kN}$

Example 16.18. *A fixed beam AB of length L carries a concentrated load W at the midspan. The moment of inertia of the beam from either end to a distance of L/4 is I and 2I for the remaining length, as shown in Fig. 16.36(a). Determine the end moments and plot the B.M.D.*

Solution :

From the geometrical point of view as well as loading point of view, the beam is symmetrical. Hence $M_1 = M_2 = M$ and $R_1 = R_2$ = $R = \dfrac{W}{2}$. The component B.M. diagrams due to R and M are shown in Fig. 16.36 (*b*) and (*c*) respectively. From Mohr's theorems,

$$E\,\theta_A^C = - \sum_A^C \frac{A_M}{I \text{ or } 2I} = 0$$

(since the tangent at *C* is horizontal.)

For B.M.D. of Fig. 16.36(b) :

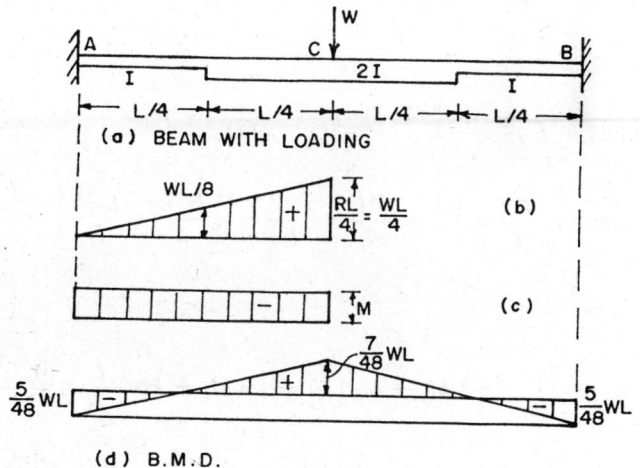

(a) BEAM WITH LOADING

(b)

(c)

(d) B.M.D.

FIG. 16.36

$$\sum_A^C \frac{A_M}{I \text{ or } 2I} = \left(\frac{1}{2} \times \frac{L}{4} \times \frac{WL}{8} \right) \frac{1}{I} + \frac{1}{2} \left(\frac{WL}{8} + \frac{WL}{4} \right) \times \frac{L}{4} \times \frac{1}{2I} = \frac{5}{128} \frac{WL^2}{I}$$

For B.M.D. of Fig. 16.36(c)

$$\sum_A^C \frac{A_M}{I \text{ or } 2I} = -\left[\left(M \times \frac{L}{4} \times \frac{1}{I}\right) + \left(M \times \frac{L}{4} \times \frac{1}{2I}\right)\right] = -\frac{3}{8}\frac{ML}{I}$$

$$\therefore \qquad \frac{5}{128}\frac{WL^2}{I} - \frac{3}{8}\frac{ML}{I} = 0$$

From which $\qquad\qquad M = \frac{5}{48}WL$. Fig 16.36(*d*) shows the B.M. diagram.

Note : If the beam were of uniform *I*, the support moment due to central point load would be $\frac{1}{8}WL\left(=\frac{6}{48}WL\right)$.

Example 16.19. *A fixed beam ACB has variable moment of inertia as shown in Fig. 16.37(a). Determine the fixed end moments at A and B due to a concentrated load W applied at C. Hence find fixed the support moments if (a) $I_2 = I_1$ and (b) $I_2 = 2I_1$.*

Solution :

The μ and μ' diagrams are shown in Fig. 16.37 (*b*) and (*c*) respectively.

From Mohr's theorems,

$$E\,\theta_B^A = -\sum_A^B \frac{A_M}{I} = 0 \qquad ...(1)$$

and $\qquad E\,y_B^A = -\sum_A^B \frac{A_M \bar{x}}{I} = 0 \qquad ...(2)$

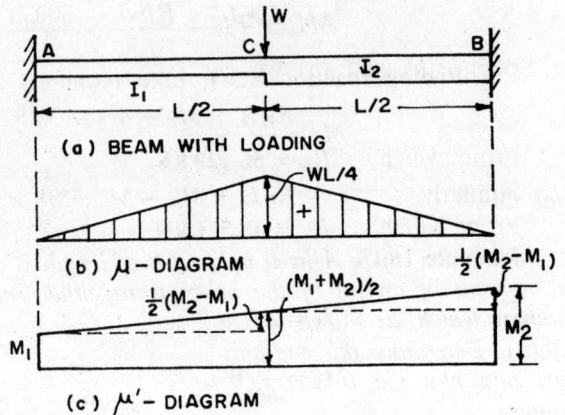

(a) BEAM WITH LOADING

(b) μ – DIAGRAM

(c) μ' – DIAGRAM

FIG. 16.37

Now $\quad \sum_B^A \frac{A_M}{I} = \left[\frac{1}{2} \times \frac{WL}{4} \times \frac{L/2}{I_1} + \frac{1}{2}\frac{WL}{4} \times \frac{L/2}{I_2}\right] - \left[\frac{1}{2}\left(M_1 + \frac{M_1 + M_2}{2}\right)\frac{L/2}{I_1}\right.$

$$\left. + \frac{1}{2}\left(\frac{M_1 + M_2}{2} + M_2\right)\frac{L/2}{I_2}\right] - 0$$

or $\qquad \left(3M_1 + M_2\right)\frac{L}{I_1} + \left(3M_2 + M_1\right)\frac{L}{I_2} = \frac{WL^2}{2I_1} + \frac{WL^2}{2I_2}$

or $\qquad M_1\left(\frac{3}{I_1} + \frac{1}{I_2}\right) + M_2\left(\frac{3}{I_2} + \frac{1}{I_1}\right) = \frac{WL}{2}\left(\frac{1}{I_1} + \frac{1}{I_2}\right)$

or $\qquad\qquad M_1 + M_2\left(\frac{3I_1 + I_2}{3I_2 + I_1}\right) = \frac{WL}{2}\left(\frac{I_1 + I_2}{I_1 + 3I_2}\right) \qquad ...(a)$

Also $\sum\limits_{B}^{A} \dfrac{A_M \bar{x}}{I} = \left[\left\{ \dfrac{1}{2} \dfrac{WL}{4} + \dfrac{L/2}{I_1} \left(\dfrac{L}{2} + \dfrac{L}{6} \right) \right\} + \left\{ \dfrac{1}{2} \times \dfrac{WL}{4} \times \dfrac{L/2}{I_2} \left(\dfrac{L}{3} \right) \right\} \right]$

$$- \left[\left\{ \dfrac{M_1 L}{I_1} \dfrac{L}{2} \left(\dfrac{L}{2} + \dfrac{L}{4} \right) \right\} + \left\{ \dfrac{1}{2} \cdot \dfrac{L}{2} \left(\dfrac{M_2 - M_1}{2 I_1} \right) \left(\dfrac{L}{2} + \dfrac{L}{6} \right) \right\} \right]$$

$$+ \left\{ \dfrac{M_1 + M_2}{2 I_2} \times \dfrac{L}{2} \times \dfrac{L}{4} \right\} + \left\{ \dfrac{1}{2} \times \dfrac{L}{2} \left(\dfrac{M_2 - M_1}{2 I_2} \right) \times \dfrac{L}{6} \right\} \right] = 0$$

or $\quad \dfrac{3}{8} \dfrac{M_1 L^2}{I_1} + \dfrac{(M_2 - M_1) L^2}{12 I_1} + \dfrac{(M_1 + M_2) L^2}{16 I_2} + \dfrac{(M_2 - M_1) L^2}{48 I_2} = \dfrac{WL^3}{24 I_1} + \dfrac{WL^3}{48 I_2}$

or $\quad M_1 \left(\dfrac{3}{8 I_1} - \dfrac{1}{12 I_1} + \dfrac{1}{16 I_2} - \dfrac{1}{48 I_2} \right) + M_2 \left(\dfrac{1}{12 I_1} + \dfrac{1}{16 I_2} + \dfrac{1}{48 I_2} \right) = \dfrac{WL}{24} \left(\dfrac{1}{I_1} + \dfrac{1}{2 I_2} \right)$

or $\quad M_1 + M_2 \dfrac{2 (I_1 + I_2)}{I_1 + 7 I_2} = \dfrac{WL}{2} \left(\dfrac{I_1 + 2 I_2}{I_1 + 7 I_2} \right)$ ...(b)

Solving (a) and (b) we get

$$M_1 = \dfrac{WL}{2} \dfrac{I_1 (I_1 + 3 I_2)}{I_1^2 + I_2^2 + 14 I_1 I_2} \quad \text{and} \quad M_2 = \dfrac{WL}{2} \dfrac{I_2 (I_2 + 3 I_1)}{I_1^2 + I_2^2 + 14 I_1 I_2}$$

Special Cases

(a) When $\quad I_2 = I_1 = I$, we get $M_1 = M_2 = \dfrac{WL}{8}$

(b) When $\quad I_2 = 2 I_1 = 2 I$, we get

$$M_1 = \dfrac{7}{66} WL \quad \text{and} \quad M_2 = \dfrac{10}{66} WL.$$

PROBLEMS

1. A beam AB, fixed at the ends is loaded with three point loads as shown in Fig. 16.38. Determine the fixing moments and plot the B.M. and S.F. diagrams.

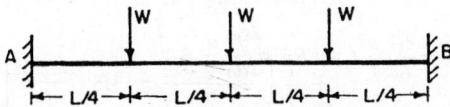

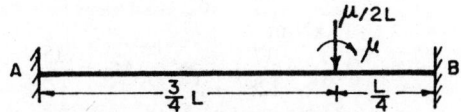

FIG. 16.38. FIG. 16.39

2. A steel beam AB of span 6 m is fixed at the ends, and is 60 mm wide and 100 mm deep. If the support B sinks by 6 mm, determine the fixing moments. Take $E = 2 \times 10^5 \, \text{N/mm}^2$.

(Based on U.L.)

3. A fixed beam of length L is loaded as shown in Fig. 16.39. Find fixing moments and end reactions and plot the B.M. and S.F. diagrams.

4. A fixed beam of variable moment of inertia is loaded as shown in Fig. 16.40. Determine the fixing moments at the ends.

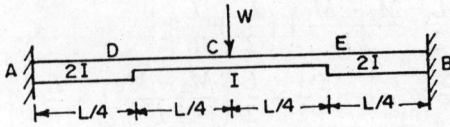

FIG. 16.40.

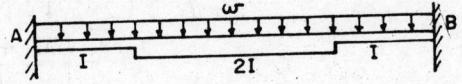

FIG. 16.41

5. A fixed beam AB of length L carries U.D.L. over the whole span. The moment of inertia of the beam from the either end to a distance of $L/4$ is I and for the middle half, it is $2I$. Determine the support moments.

6. A beam of span L is fixed at both the ends. A couple μ is applied to the beam at the middle about a horizontal axis at right angles to the beam. Prove that the fixing couple at each support is $\mu/4$ in the same direction and that the slope at the centre is $(\mu L)/(16EI)$ (Cambridge University)

7. A beam AB of flexural rigidity EI and span L carries U.D.L. of intensity w per unit length. It is encastre at A and B, but support B settled during the application of the load by an amount δ.

Show that if $\delta = \dfrac{wL^4}{72EI}$, there is no fixing moment at B.   (U.L.)

8. A beam AB, of span L and constant flexural rigidity EI is encastre at B and supported at A so that it rotates through an angle αM_A, where M_A is the moment at A. Calculate the value of the moments at both supports when it carries a load W at a distance of $L/4$ from A.

9. Find the fixed end moments and end reactions for a fixed-end beam AB loaded as shown in Fig. 16.42. Also, determine the maximum deflection.

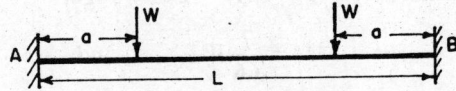

FIG. 16.42

ANSWERS

1. $M_A = M_B = \dfrac{5}{16}WL$

2. 1 kN-m

3. $M_A = \dfrac{37}{128}\mu \;(\curvearrowright); \; M_B = \dfrac{15}{128}\mu \;(\curvearrowleft) \; : R_A = \dfrac{67}{64}\dfrac{\mu}{L}(\downarrow); R_B = \dfrac{99}{64}\dfrac{\mu}{2}(\uparrow).$

4. $\dfrac{7}{48}WL$

5. $\dfrac{7}{96}wL^2$

8. $\dfrac{9WL^2}{64(L+4EI\alpha)} \; ; \; \dfrac{3WL(L+10EI\alpha)}{64(L+4EI\alpha)}$

9. $R_A = R_B = W; M_A = M_B = \dfrac{Wa}{L}(L-a)$

    $y_{max} = \dfrac{Wa^2}{24EI}(3L-4a)$

17

Continuous Beams

17.1. INTRODUCTION

A continuous beam is the one which has more than one span, and more than two supports. It is thus *statically indeterminate beam* since the number of reaction components are more than two while only two equations are available from statical equilibrium, for vertical system of loading. However, the *degree of indeterminacy* depends upon the number and type of supports.

The continuous beam, shown in Fig. 17.1 (a) has three supports, the beam being simply supported at the ends; the beam is, therefore, statically indeterminate to single degree since it has three reaction components (*i.e.* R_A, R_B and R_C). On the other hand, the same beam, with one end fixed (Fig. 17.1 b) and other simply supported has four reaction components (*i.e.* M_A, R_A, R_B and R_C); the beam is therefore statically indeterminate to *second degree*. If, however, both the ends of the two span beam are fixed (Fig. 17.1 c), there are five reaction components (*i.e.* M_A, R_A, R_B, R_C and M_C) and the beam is statically indeterminate to *third degree*. Lastly, the beam shown in Fig. 17.1 (d) has six reaction components, while *three* equations are available from statical equilibrium; the beam is therefore statically indeterminate to *third degree*.

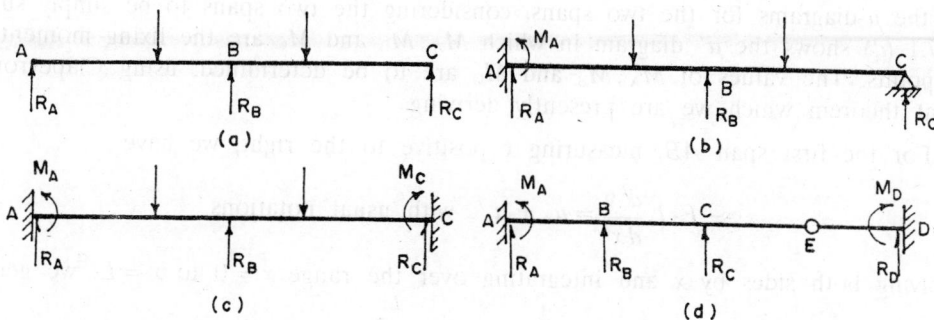

FIG. 17.1. CONTINUOUS BEAMS

Following are some of the important methods for the analysis of a continuous beam:
1. Three moment theorem method.
2. Method of consistent deformation.
3. Slope deflection method.
and 4. Moment distribution method.

However, we shall discuss in this chapter, only the first method. The remaining methods have been dealt with in Author's book 'Theory of Structures'.

17.2. CLAPEYRON'S THEOREM OF THREE MOMENTS : DERIVATION

Let us take two consecutive spans AB ($= L_1$) and BC ($= L_2$) of a continuous beam subjected to a general system of loading, as shown in Fig. 17.2 (a). We will use suffix 1 (*i.e.* L_1, E_1, I_1) for the first span AB and suffix 2 (*i.e.* L_2, E_2, I_2 etc) for the second span BC. Fig 17.2 (b) shows the deflected position of the two spans, after the supports A, B and C have settled to positions A', B' and C', by amounts δ_A, δ_B and δ_C respectively below the original centre line.

From the deflected position of two spans, we have

$$y_B^A = \delta_B - \delta_A = \delta_1 \text{ (say)}$$

where y_B^A is the deflection of B with respect to A. Similarly

$$y_B^C = \delta_B - \delta_C = \delta_2 \text{ (say)}.$$

where y_B^C is the deflection of B with respect to C.

The μ and μ' diagrams can be constructed as usual. Fig. 17.1 (c)

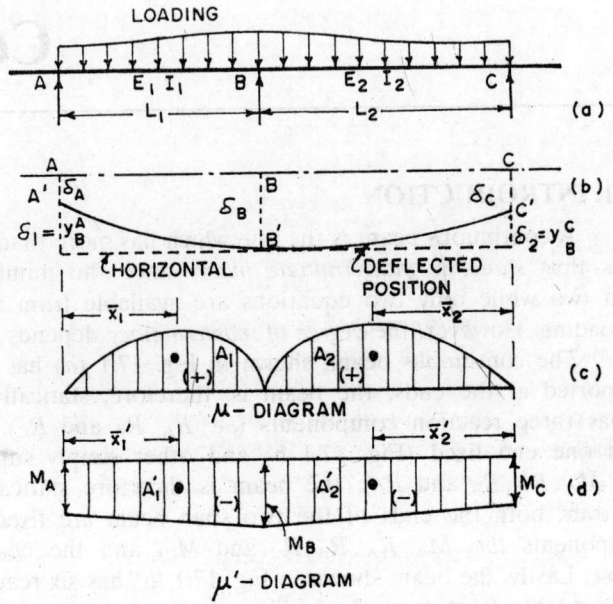

FIG. 17.2

shows the μ-diagrams for the two spans, considering the two spans to be simply supported. Fig. 17.1 (d) shows the μ' diagram in which M_A, M_B and M_C are the fixing moments at the three points. The values of M_A, M_B and M_C are to be determined, using Clapeyrons three moment theorem which we are presently deriving.

For the first span AB, measuring x positive to the right, we have

$$-E_1 I_1 \frac{d^2 y}{dx^2} = \mu_x + \mu_x', \text{ with usual notations.}$$

Multiplying both sides by x and integrating over the range $x = 0$ to $x = L$, we get

$$-E_1 I_1 \left[x \frac{dy}{dx} - y \right]_0^{L_1} = \int_0^{L_1} \mu_x \cdot x \, dx + \int_0^{L_1} \mu_x' x \, dx.$$

At $x = L_1$, $\qquad \dfrac{dy}{dx} = i_B$ and $y_B^A = \delta_1$

$\therefore \qquad -E_1 I_1 [L_1 i_B - \delta_1] = A_1 \bar{x}_1 + A_1' \bar{x}_1'$

From which $\qquad i_B = -\dfrac{1}{E_1 I_1 L_1} \left[A_1 \bar{x}_1 + A_1' \bar{x}_1' \right] + \dfrac{\delta_1}{L_1}$ $\qquad$ ...(1)

Similarly, considering span BC, taking C as the origin, and measuring x positive to the left, we can obtain :

$$i_B' = -\frac{1}{E_1 I_2 L_2}\left(A_2\bar{x}_2 + A_2'\bar{x}_2'\right) + \frac{\delta_2}{L_2} \qquad \ldots(2)$$

Due to continuity of the span, $i_B = -i_B'$ (or $i_B + i_B' = 0$). Hence from

$$\frac{1}{E_1 I_1 L_1}\left(A_1\bar{x}_1 + A_1'\bar{x}_1'\right) - \frac{\delta_1}{L_1} + \frac{1}{E_2 I_2 L_2}\left(A_2\bar{x}_2 + A_2'\bar{x}_2'\right) - \frac{\delta_2}{L_2} = 0$$

Now, for a trapezoidal μ' diagram, we know that

$$A_1'\bar{x}_1' = \left(M_A + 2M_B\right)\frac{L_1^2}{6} \text{ and } A_2'\bar{x}_2' = \left(M_C + 2M_B\right)\frac{L_2^2}{6}.$$

$$\therefore \quad \frac{A_1\bar{x}_1}{E_1 I_1 L_1} + \frac{L_1}{6E_1 I_1}\left(M_A + 2M_B\right) - \frac{\delta_1}{L_1} + \frac{A_2\bar{x}_2}{E_2 I_2 L_2} + \frac{L_2}{6E_2 I_2}\left(M_C + 2M_B\right) - \frac{\delta_2}{L_2} = 0$$

Multiplying by 6 and re-arranging, we get

$$M_A \cdot \frac{L_1}{E_1 I_1} + 2M_B\left(\frac{L_1}{E_1 I_1} + \frac{L_2}{E_2 I_2}\right) + M_C\frac{L_2}{E_2 I_2} + \left(\frac{6A_1\bar{x}_1}{E_1 I_1 L_1} + \frac{6A_2\bar{x}_2}{E_2 I_2 L_2}\right) = 6\left(\frac{\delta_1}{L_1} + \frac{\delta_2}{L_2}\right) \qquad \ldots(17.1)$$

This is the *generalised theorem of three moments*. The three moments equation was originally developed by French engineers B.P.E. Clapeyron and H. Bertot in 1857 and modified later (in 1860) by Mohr to include the effects of uneven settlements. However, the equation is commonly known as Clapeyron's equation of three moments. This equation is known as three moment equation because it relates the three consecutive bending moments in the beam. While substituting the *numerical values* of A_1 and A_2 for a given system of loading, proper care of sign must be taken. For the usual downward loading, A_1 and A_2 will be positive.

We shall now consider special cases.

17.3. CASE 1 : EI CONSTANT : GENERAL LOADING

This is a very common case. Taking $E_1 I_1 = E_2 I_2 = EI$, we get from Eq. 17.1,

$$M_A \cdot L_1 + 2M_B(L_1 + L_2) + M_C \cdot L_2 + \frac{6A_1\bar{x}_1}{L_1} + \frac{6A_2\bar{x}_2}{L_2} = 6EI\left(\frac{\delta_1}{L_1} + \frac{\delta_2}{L_2}\right) \qquad \ldots(17.2)$$

17.4. CASE II : EI CONSTANT : NO SETTLEMENT : GENERAL LOADING

Given $\qquad E_1 I_1 = E_2 I_2 = EI \qquad$ and $\qquad \delta_1 = 0 \,;\, \delta_2 = 0$
Hence from Eq. 17.2, we have

$$M_A L_1 + 2M_B(L_1 + L_2) + M_C L_2 + \frac{6A_1\bar{x}_1}{L_1} + \frac{6A_2\bar{x}_2}{L_2} = 0 \qquad \ldots(17.3)$$

17.5. CASE III : EI CONSTANT : NO SETTLEMENT : U.D.L. THROUGHOUT

Given $\qquad E_1 I_1 = E_2 I_2 = EI \,;\, \delta_1 = \delta_2 = 0$

Let U.D.L. on span AB be w_1 and U.D.L. of span BC be w_2.

Then $\qquad A_1 = \frac{2}{3}\left(\frac{w_1 L_1^2}{8}\right)L_1 = \frac{w_1 L_1^3}{12}$

$$A_1\bar{x}_1 = \frac{w_1 L_1^3}{12} \times \frac{L_1}{2} = \frac{w_1 L_1^4}{24}$$

Similarly, $A_2 \bar{x}_2 = \dfrac{w_2 L_2^4}{24}$

Hence from 17.3 : $M_A L_1 + 2 M_B (L_1 + L_2) + M_C L_2 + \dfrac{6}{L_1} \left(\dfrac{w_1 L_1^4}{24} \right) + \dfrac{6}{L_2} \left(\dfrac{w_2 L_2^4}{24} \right) = 0$

or $M_A L_1 + 2 M_B (L_1 + L_2) + M_C L_2 = -\dfrac{w_1 L_1^3}{4} - \dfrac{w_2 L_2^3}{4}$ ...(17.4)

17.6. CASE IV : EI CONSTANT : SUPPORTS SETTLE : U.D.L.

From Eqs. 17.2 and 17.4

$$M_A L_1 + 2 M_B (L_1 + L_2) + M_C L_2 = -\left(\dfrac{w_1 L_1^3}{4} + \dfrac{w_2 L_2^3}{4} \right) + 6 E I \left(\dfrac{\delta_1}{L_1} + \dfrac{\delta_2}{L_2} \right)$$ ...(17.5)

17.7. VALUES OF FACTOR $\dfrac{6 A \bar{x}}{L}$ OF μ-DIAGRAM

The usefulness of the three moment equation for finding unknowns M_A, M_B and M_C depends upon the ease with which the expressions $(6 A \bar{x})/L$ can be found. We shall now consider few cases of loading.

(a) U.D.L. (Fig. 17.3) $A = \dfrac{2}{3} \times L \times \dfrac{wL^2}{8} = \dfrac{wL^3}{12}$

$$\bar{x}_L = L/2 \; ; \bar{x}_R = L/2$$

$\therefore$ $\dfrac{6 A \bar{x}_L}{L} = \dfrac{6 A \bar{x}_R}{L} = \dfrac{wL^3}{4}$ ...(17.6)

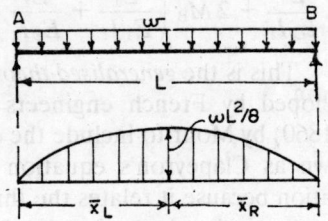

FIG. 17.3

(b) Triangularly distributed load :

Fig. 17.4 (a), (b) and (c) show three cases of triangularly distributed loads.

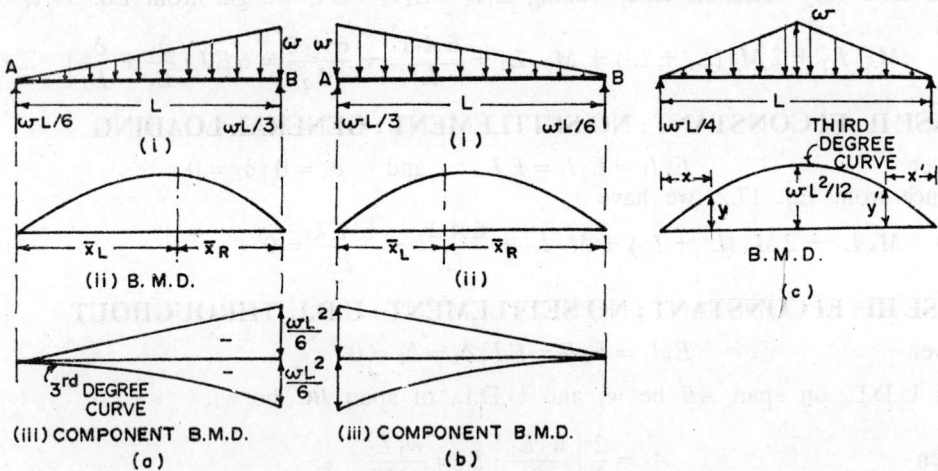

FIG. 17.4. FACTOR $\dfrac{6 A \bar{x}}{L}$ FOR TRIANGULARLY DISTRIBUTED LOADS

Triangularly distributed load of Fig. 17.4 (a).

The component B.M.D. is shown in Fig. 17.4 (*a iii*)

$$A\bar{x}_L = \frac{1}{2} \times L \times \frac{wL^2}{6} \times \frac{2}{3}L - \frac{1}{4} \times L \times \frac{wL^2}{6} \times \frac{4}{5}L = \frac{1}{45}wL^4$$

$$A\bar{x}_R = \frac{1}{2} \times L \times \frac{wL^2}{6} \times \frac{1}{3}L - \frac{1}{4}L \times \frac{wL^2}{6} \times \frac{1}{5}L = \frac{7}{360}wL^4$$

$$\therefore \quad \frac{6A\bar{x}_L}{L} = \frac{6}{L} \times \frac{1}{45}wL^4 = \frac{2}{15}wL^3 = \frac{8}{60}wL^3 \qquad ...(17.16\ a)$$

$$\frac{6A\bar{x}_R}{L} = \frac{6}{L} \times \frac{7}{360}wL^4 = \frac{7}{60}wL^3 \qquad ...(17.16\ b)$$

Triangularly distributed load of Fig. 17.4 (b)

Evidently, $\quad \dfrac{6A\bar{x}_L}{L} = \dfrac{7}{60}wL^3 \quad$ and $\quad \dfrac{6A\bar{x}_R}{L} = \dfrac{8}{60}wL^3 \qquad ...(17.17)$

Triangularly distributed load of Fig. 17.4 (c)

From Example 9.10, ordinates $y = \dfrac{wLx}{4} - \dfrac{wx^3}{3L}$ and $y' = \dfrac{wLx'}{4} - \dfrac{wx'^3}{3L}$

$$\therefore \quad A\bar{x}_L = \int_0^{L/2} \left(\frac{wLx}{4} - \frac{wx^3}{3L}\right) x\, dx + \int_0^{L/2} \left(\frac{wLx'}{4} - \frac{wx'^3}{3L}\right)(L - x')\, dx'$$

$$= \frac{wL^4}{120} + \frac{17}{960}wL^4 = \frac{5}{192}wL^4$$

$$\frac{6A\bar{x}_L}{L} = \frac{6A\bar{x}_R}{L} = \frac{6}{L} \times \frac{5}{192}wL^4 = \frac{5}{32}wL^3 \qquad ...(17.18)$$

(c) Point load : The component B.M.D. is shown in Fig. 17.5 (*c*)

$$A\bar{x}_L = \frac{1}{2} \times L \times Wb \times \frac{2L}{3}$$
$$- \frac{1}{2} \times b \times Wb \left(L - \frac{b}{3}\right)$$
$$= \frac{WbL^2}{3} - \frac{Wb^2}{6}(3L - b) = \frac{Wa}{6}(L^2 - a^2)$$

$$A\bar{x}_R = \frac{1}{2} \times L \times Wb \times \frac{L}{3} - \frac{1}{2} \times b \times Wb \times \frac{b}{3}$$
$$= \frac{WbL^2}{6} - \frac{Wb^3}{6} = \frac{Wb}{6}(L^2 - b^2)$$

$$\therefore \quad \frac{6A\bar{x}_L}{L} = \frac{Wa}{L}(L^2 - a^2) \qquad \text{and}$$

$$\frac{6A\bar{x}_R}{L} = \frac{Wb}{L}(L^2 - b^2) \qquad ...(17.19)$$

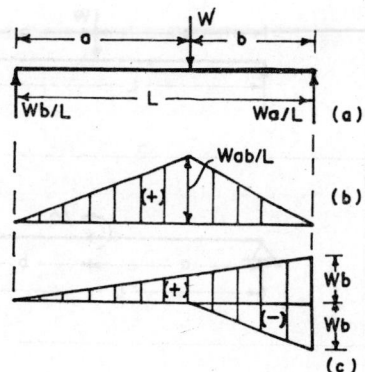

FIG. 17.5

(d) Couple at intermediate point

The component B.M.D. is shown in Fig. 17.6 (*c*).

TABLE 17.1 VALUES OF $\dfrac{6A\bar{x}_L}{L}$ **AND** $\dfrac{6A\bar{x}_R}{L}$ **FOR SOME COMMON TYPES OF LOADINGS.**

S.N.	Type of Loading	$6A\bar{x}_L/L$	$6A\bar{x}_R/L$
1.		$\dfrac{wL^3}{4}$	$\dfrac{wL^3}{4}$
2.		$\dfrac{8}{60}wL^3$	$\dfrac{7}{60}wL^3$
3.		$\dfrac{7}{60}wL^3$	$\dfrac{8}{60}wL^3$
4.		$\dfrac{5}{32}wL^3$	$\dfrac{5}{32}wL^3$
5.		$\dfrac{Wa}{L}(L^2-a^2)$	$\dfrac{Wb}{L}(L^2-b^2)$
6.		$-\dfrac{\mu}{L}(3a^2-L^2)$	$+\dfrac{\mu}{L}(3b^2-L^2)$
7.		$\dfrac{w}{4L}\left[b^2(2L^2-b^2)\right.$ $\left.-a^2(2L^2-a^2)\right]$	$\dfrac{w}{4L}\left[d^2(2L^2-d^2)\right.$ $\left.-c^2(2L^2-c^2)\right]$

$$A\,\bar{x}_{L} = \mu\,b\left(L - \frac{b}{2}\right) - \frac{1}{2}\times L\times\mu\left(\frac{2}{3}L\right)$$

$$= \frac{\mu\,b\,(2\,L - b)}{2} - \frac{\mu\,L^{2}}{3}$$

$$= -\frac{\mu}{6}\,(3\,a^{2} - L^{2})$$

$$A\,\bar{x}_{R} = \mu\,b\cdot\frac{b}{2} - \frac{1}{2}L\,\mu\times\frac{L}{3}$$

$$= \frac{\mu\,b^{2}}{2} - \frac{\mu\,L^{2}}{6} = \frac{\mu}{6}\,(3\,b^{2} - L^{2})$$

$$\therefore \qquad \frac{6\,A\,\bar{x}_{L}}{L} = -\frac{\mu}{L}\,(3\,a^{2} - L^{2})$$

and $$\frac{6\,A\,\bar{x}_{R}}{L} = +\frac{\mu}{L}\,(3\,b^{2} - L^{2}) \quad...(17.20)$$

Table 17.1 gives the values of $\dfrac{6\,A\,\bar{x}_{L}}{L}$ and $\dfrac{6\,A\,\bar{x}_{R}}{L}$ for some common types of loadings.

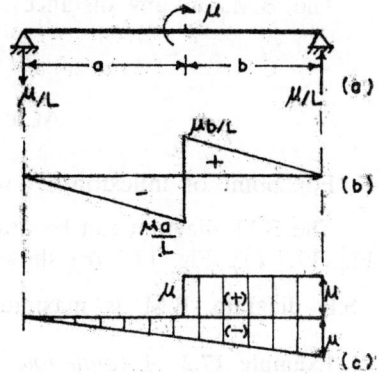

FIG. 17.6

Example 17.1. *A beam ABC of length 2L rests on three supports equally spaced and is loaded with U.D.L. w/unit length throughout the length of the beam. Draw the S.F. and B.M. diagrams for the beam.*

Solution:

Applying three moment theorem for U.D.L., we get, from Eq. 17.4

$$M_{A}\,L + 2\,M_{B}\,(L + L) + M_{C}\,L$$

$$= -\left(\frac{w\,L^{3}}{4} + \frac{w\,L^{3}}{4}\right)$$

But $M_{A} = 0$ and $M_{C} = 0$

$$\therefore \quad 4\,M_{B} = -\frac{w\,L^{2}}{2}$$

or $$M_{B} = -\frac{w\,L^{2}}{8}$$

Thus the fixing moments are known.

For R_{A}, write equation for B.M. at B. Thus,

$$R_{A}\cdot L - w\,L\cdot\frac{L}{2} = M_{B} = -\frac{w\,L^{2}}{8}$$

$$\therefore \quad R_{A} = \frac{w\,L}{2} - \frac{w\,L}{8} = \frac{3}{8}\,w\,L\,(\uparrow)$$

$$R_{C} = \frac{3}{8}\,w\,L\;(\uparrow),\text{ by symmetry.}$$

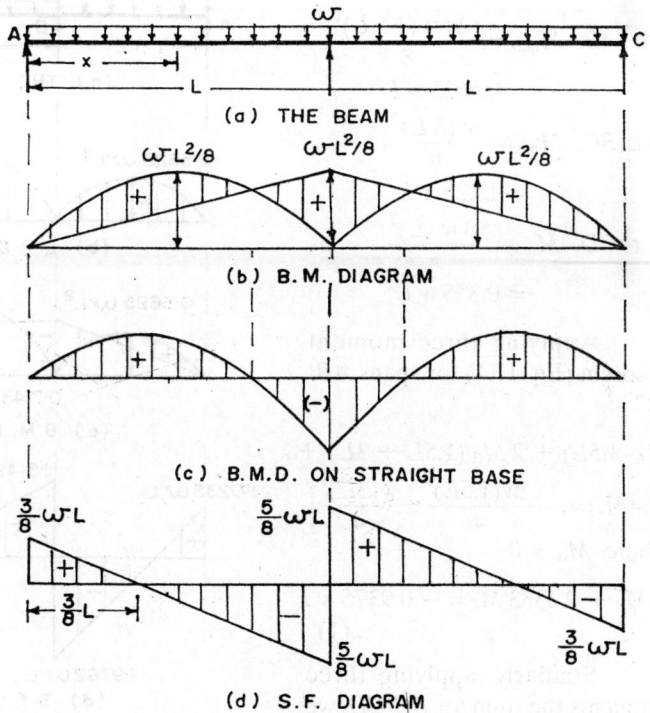

(a) THE BEAM

(b) B.M. DIAGRAM

(c) B.M.D. ON STRAIGHT BASE

(d) S.F. DIAGRAM

FIG. 17.7

$$\therefore \qquad R_B = 2\,w\,L - (R_A + R_C) = 2\,w\,L - \frac{3}{4}\,wL = \frac{5}{4}\,w\,L\,(\uparrow)$$

Thus, the reactions are completely known.

The B.M., at any distance x from A, for the span AB, is given by

$$M_x = \frac{3}{8}\,w\,L\,x - \frac{w\,x^2}{2} \quad \text{(Parabolic variation)}$$

At $x = L$, $M_{x=L} = M_B = \frac{3}{8}\,wL\,.\,L - \frac{w\,L^2}{2} = -\frac{w\,L^2}{8}$

For point of inflexion, $\frac{3}{8}\,w\,L\,x - \frac{w\,x^2}{2} = 0$, which gives $x = \frac{3}{4}\,L$.

The B.M. diagram can be drawn by super-imposing μ diagram over μ' diagram, as shown in Fig. 17.7 (b). Fig. 17.7 (c) shows the B.M. diagram on a straight base. Fig. 17.7 (d) shows the S.F. diagram. B.M. is maximum where S.F. is zero. This is obtained at $x = \frac{3}{8}\,L$.

Example 17.2. *A continuous beam ABCD covers three spans, AB=1.5 L, BC=3 L and CD=L. It carries uniformly distributed loads of 2w, w and 3w per metre run on AB, BC and CD respectively. If the girder is of the same cross-section throughout, find the bending moments at supports B and C and the pressure on each support. Also plot the B.M. and S.F. diagrams.*

Solution: Fig. 17.8 (a) shows the free B.M. diagrams (*i.e.* μ diagrams) for AB, BC and CD.

For AB, $M_{max} = \dfrac{(2\,w)\,(1.5\,L)^2}{8}$

$\qquad\qquad = 0.5625\,w\,L^2$

For BC, $M_{max} = \dfrac{w\,(3\,L)^2}{8}$

$\qquad\qquad = 1.125\,w\,L^2$

For CD, $M_{max} = \dfrac{3\,w\,(L)^2}{8}$

$\qquad\qquad = 0.375\,w\,L^2$

Applying three moment theorem (Eq. 17.4) for spans AB-BC

$M_A\,(1.5L) + 2\,M_B\,(1.5L + 3L) +$

$M_C(3L) = -\left[\dfrac{2w(1.5L)^3}{4} + \dfrac{w(3L)^3}{4}\right]$

where $M_A = 0$

$\therefore M_B + 0.3333\,M_C = -\,0.9375\,w\,L^2$

$\qquad\qquad\qquad\qquad ...(1)$

Similarly, applying three moments theorem for BC-CD, we get

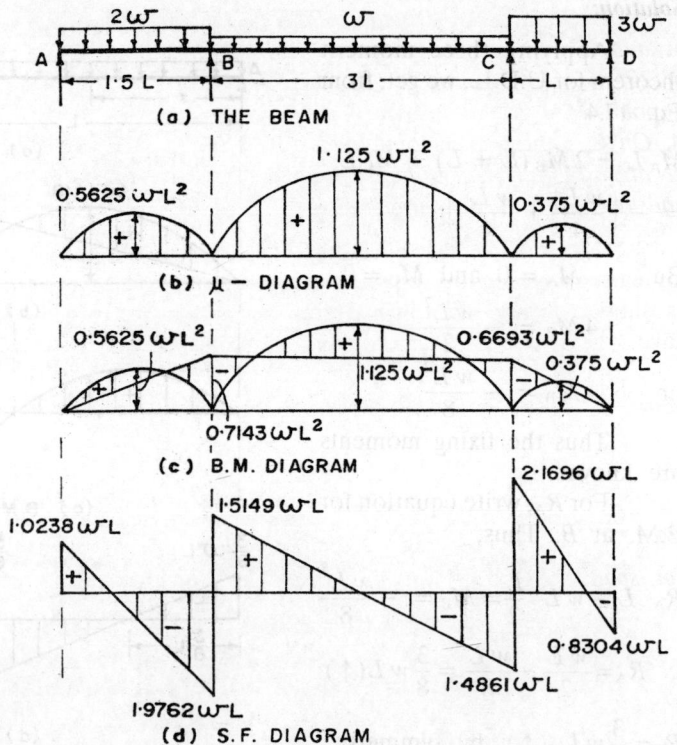

(a) THE BEAM

(b) μ – DIAGRAM

(c) B.M. DIAGRAM

(d) S.F. DIAGRAM

FIG. 17.8

$M_B (3 L) + 2 M_C (3 L + L) + M_D (L) = -\left[\dfrac{w (3 L)^3}{4} + \dfrac{3w(L)^3}{4}\right]$, where $M_D = 0$

$\therefore \quad M_B + 2.6667 M_C = -2.5 w L^2$ ...(2)

From (1) and (2), we get $M_C = -0.6696 w L^2$ and $M_B = -0.7143 w L^2$

Reactions : For reaction at A write the expression for B.M. at B.

$\therefore R_A (1.5 L) - 2 w (1.5 L) \left(\dfrac{1.5 L}{2}\right) = M_B = -0.7143 w L^2$

From which $\quad\quad\quad\quad\quad R_A = 1.0238 w L$

For R_B, write the expression for B.M. at C.

$\therefore \quad R_A (4.5 L) + R_B (3 L) - 2 w (1.5 L) (3.75 L) - w (3 L) (1.5 L) = M_C = -0.6696 w L^2$

or $\quad\quad\quad 1.0238 w L (4.5 L) + 3 R_B L - 15.75 w L^2 = -0.6696 w L^2$

From which $R_B = 3.4911 w L$

Similarly, for R_D write the equation for B.M. at C, considering right hand side.

$\therefore \quad\quad R_D (L) - 3 w \left(\dfrac{L^2}{2}\right) = M_C = -0.6696 w L^2$

$\therefore \quad\quad\quad\quad\quad R_D = 0.8304 w L$

Hence $\quad R_C = \{2 w (1.5 L) + w (3 L) + 3 w (L)\} - \{1.0238 w L + 3.4911 w L + 0.8304 w L\}$
$= 3.6547 w L$

The B.M. and S.F. diagrams are shown in Fig. 17.8 (c) and (d) respectively.

Example 17.3. *A beam ABCD, 16 m long is continuous over three spans : AB=6 m, BC=5 m and CD=5 m, the supports being at the same level. There is a uniformly distributed load of 20 kN/m over BC. On AB, there is a point load of 80 kN at 2 m from A. On CD, there is a point load of 60 kN at 3 m from D. Calculate the moments and reactions at the supports.*

Solution: The free B.M. diagrams for each span can be drawn as usual, as shown in Fig. 17.9 (b). Here, we have

$M_E = \dfrac{80 \times 2 \times 4}{6} = 106.67$ kN-m

$M_F = \dfrac{20 (5)^2}{8} = 62.5$ kN-m

$M_G = \dfrac{60 \times 2 \times 3}{5} = 72$ kN-m

For span AB

$A = \dfrac{1}{2} \times 6 \times 106.67 = 320.01$

$\bar{x} = \dfrac{1}{3}(6 + 2) = \dfrac{8}{3}$

$\therefore \quad\quad A\bar{x} = 320.01 \times \dfrac{8}{3} = 853.36$

with A as origin.

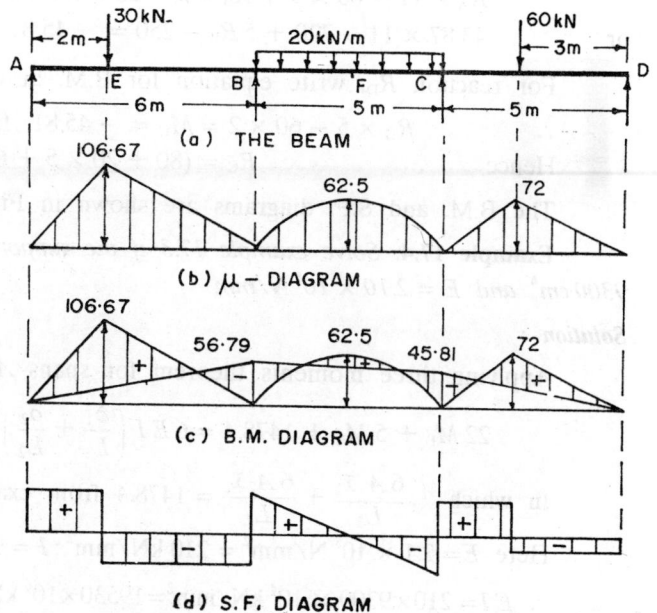

(a) THE BEAM

(b) μ – DIAGRAM

(c) B.M. DIAGRAM

(d) S.F. DIAGRAM

FIG. 17.9

For span BC $A = \frac{2}{3} \times 5 \times 62.5 = 208.33$

    With C as origin, $A\bar{x} = 208.33 \times 2.5 = 520.83$

    With B as origin, $A\bar{x} = 208.33 \times 2.5 = 520.83$

For span CD $A = \frac{1}{2} \times 5 \times 72 = 180$

$$A\bar{x} = 180 \times \frac{1}{3}(5 + 3) = 480, \text{ with } D \text{ as origin.}$$

Applying three moment theorem equation for spans $AB\text{-}BC$

$$6 M_A + 2 M_B (6 + 5) + 5 M_C + \frac{6 A_1 \bar{x}_1}{6} + \frac{6 A_2 \bar{x}_2}{5} = 0$$

or $6 \times 0 + 22 M_B + 5 M_C = -\left[\frac{6}{6} + 853.36 + \frac{6}{5} \times 520.83\right] = -1478.4$ ...(1)

Similarly, applying three moment theorem equation for spans $BC\text{-}CD$

$$5 M_B + 2 M_C (5 + 5) + 5 M_D + \frac{6 A_1 \bar{x}_1}{5} + \frac{6 A_2 \bar{x}_2}{5} = 0$$

or $5 M_B + 20 M_C + 5 \times 0 = -\left[\frac{6}{5} \times 520.83 + \frac{6}{5} \times 480\right] = -1200.1$ ...(2)

Solving (1) and (2), we get $M_B = -\mathbf{56.79}$ **kN-m** and $M_C = -\mathbf{45.81}$ **kN-m**

For finding reaction R_A, write equation for B.M. at B. Thus

$$R_A \times 6 - 80 \times 4 = M_B = -56.79, \text{ from which } R_A = \mathbf{43.87 \text{ kN}}$$

For finding reaction R_B, write equation for B.M. at C. Thus

$$R_A \times 11 - 80 \times 9 + R_B \times 5 - 20 \times 5 \times 2.5 = M_C = -45.81$$

or $43.87 \times 11 - 720 + 5 R_B - 250 = -45.81, \text{ from which } R_B = \mathbf{88.32 \text{ kN}}$

For reaction R_D, write equation for B.M. at C, considering R.H.S.

$\therefore$ $R_D \times 5 - 60 \times 2 = M_C = -45.81, \text{ from which } R_D = \mathbf{14.84 \text{ kN}}$

Hence $R_C = (80 + 20 \times 5 + 60) - (43.87 + 88.32 + 14.84) = \mathbf{92.97 \text{ kN}}$

The B.M. and S.F. diagrams are shown in Fig. 17.9 (c) and (d) respectively.

Example 17.4. *Solve example 17.3 if the support B sinks by 5 mm. I for the section is $9300 \, cm^4$ and $E = 2.10 \times 10^5 \, N/mm^2$.*

Solution :

Applying three moments theorem for spans $AB\text{-}BC$, we get

$$22 M_B + 5 M_C + 1478.4 = 6 E I \left(\frac{\delta_1}{L_1} + \frac{\delta_2}{L_2}\right)$$

In which $\frac{6 A_1 \bar{x}_1}{L_1} + \frac{6 A_2 \bar{x}_2}{L_2} = 1478.4$ from example 17.3.

Here $E = 2.1 \times 10^5 \, \text{N/mm}^2 = 210 \, \text{kN/mm}^2$; $I = 9300 \times 10^4 \, \text{mm}^4$

$\therefore \; E I = 210 \times 9300 \times 10^4 \, \text{kN/mm}^2 = 19530 \times 10^6 \, \text{kN/mm}^2 = 19530 \; \text{kN-m}^2$

$$\delta_1 = 5 \, \text{mm} = \frac{5}{1000} \, \text{m} = \frac{1}{200} \, \text{m} = \delta_2$$

Thus, substituting all the values in kN and m units, we get

$$22\,M_B + 5\,M_C + 1478.4 = 6 \times 19530 \left(\frac{1}{200 \times 6} + \frac{1}{200 \times 5} \right)$$

or $\qquad M_B + 0.2273\,M_C = -57.435 \qquad\qquad\qquad$ ...(1)

Similarly, *for span BC-CD* :

$$\delta_1 = \text{movement of } C \text{ with respect to } B = -5\,\text{mm} = -\frac{1}{200}\,\text{m}$$

(The movement of C being upwards with respect to B)

$$\delta_2 = \text{movement of } C \text{ with respect to } D = 0$$

$$\therefore 5\,M_B + 20\,M_C + 1200.1 = 6\,E\,I \left(\frac{\delta_1}{L_1} + \frac{\delta_2}{L_2} \right)$$

or $\qquad 5\,M_B + 20\,M_C + 1200.1 = 6 \times 19530 \left(-\frac{1}{200 \times 5} + 0 \right)$

or $\qquad\qquad M_B + 4\,M_C = -216.58 \qquad\qquad\qquad$ ...(2)

Solving (1) and (2), we get $M_B = -45.03$ kN-m; $M_C = -54.61$ kN-m.
For finding R_A, write equation for B.M. at B.

Thus, $\qquad R_A \times 6 - 80 \times 4 = M_B = -45.03$, from which $R_A = \mathbf{45.83\ kN}$.
For finding R_B, write equation for B.M. at C.

Thus $45.83 \times 11 + R_B \times 5 - 80 \times 9 - 20 \times 5 \times 2.5 = M_C = -54.61$

From which $R_B = 82.26$ kN
For finding R_D, write equation for B.M. at C, considering R.H.S. Thus,

$$R_D \times 5 - 60 \times 2 = M_C = -54.61, \text{ from which } R_D = \mathbf{13.08\ kN}$$

For finding R_C, write equation for B.M. at B, considering R.H.S. Thus
$13.08 \times 10 + R_C \times 5 - 60 \times 7 - 20 \times 5 \times 2.5 = M_B = -45.03$

From which $\qquad\qquad R_C = \mathbf{98.83\ kN}$

Check : $\qquad\qquad$ Total load $= 80 + 60 + 20 \times 5 = 240$ kN

$\qquad\qquad$ Total reaction $= 45.83 + 82.26 + 98.83 + 13.08 = 240$ kN

17.8. APPLICATION OF CLAPEYRON'S THEOREM FOR FIXED BEAM

A fixed beam can also be analyzed by the application of three moment theorem, by imagining a zero span to the left of A and a zero span to the right of B, as shown in Fig. 17.10 (a). Applying three moment theorem for the span $A'A - AB$, we have

$$0 + 2\,M_A\,(0 + L) + M_B\,.\,L + 0$$
$$+ \frac{6\,A\,\bar{x}_R}{L} = 0$$

or $2\,M_A\,L + M_B\,.\,L + \dfrac{6\,A\,\bar{x}_R}{L} = 0$

or $2\,M_A + M_B + \dfrac{6\,A\,\bar{x}_R}{L^2} = 0 \quad$ ...(1)

Similarly, applying the theorem for the span $AB - BB'$, we get

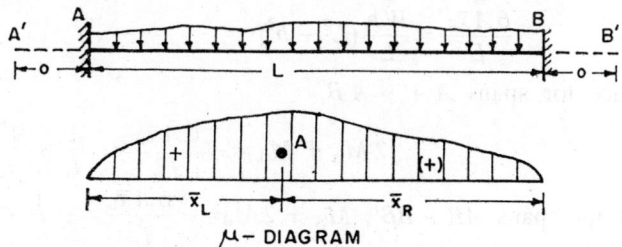

FIG. 17.10

$$M_A \cdot L + 2M_B(L+0) + 0 + \frac{6A\bar{x}_L}{L} = 0 \quad \text{or} \quad M_A + 2M_B + \frac{6A\bar{x}_L}{L^2} = 0 \qquad ...(2)$$

Solving Eqs. (1) and (2), M_A and M_B can be found.

Example 17.5 *Find the fixing moments for a fixed beam subjected to U.D.L. throughout the span.*

Solution : Imagine a zero span AA' to the left of A and zero span BB' to the right of B, as shown in Fig. 7.11 (*a*). The μ-diagram is shown in Fig. 17.11 (*b*), from which we have

$$A = \frac{2}{3} \times L \times \frac{wL^2}{8} = \frac{wL^3}{12}$$

$$\bar{x}_L = \frac{L}{2} = \bar{x}_R$$

Applying three moment equation for span $AA' - AB$, we get

$$2M_A + M_B + \frac{6A\bar{x}_R}{L^2} = 0$$

or $2M_A + M_B + \dfrac{6}{L^2}\left(\dfrac{wL^3}{12}\right)\left(\dfrac{L}{2}\right) = 0$

or $\quad 2M_A + M_B = -\dfrac{wL^2}{4} \qquad ...(1)$

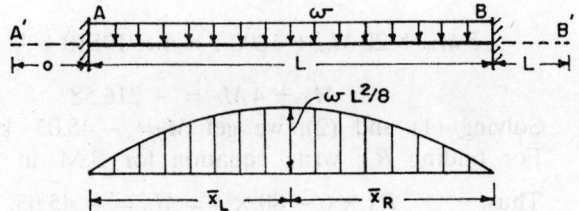

FIG. 17.11

Similarly, applying three moment equation for span $AB - BB'$, we get

$$M_A + 2M_B + \frac{6A\bar{x}_R}{L^2} = 0 \quad \text{or} \quad M_A + 2M_B = -\frac{wL^2}{4} \qquad ...(2)$$

From (1) and (2), we get $\quad M_A = -\dfrac{wL^2}{12}$ and $M_B = -\dfrac{wL^2}{12}$

Example 17.6. *Find the fixing moments for a fixed beam, subjected to an eccentric point load W.*

Solution : Imagine span AA' and BB' of zero length. The μ diagram is shown in Fig. 17.12 (*b*) from which we have

$$\frac{6A\bar{x}_L}{L} = \frac{Wa}{L}(L^2 - a^2)$$

and $\quad \dfrac{6A\bar{x}_R}{L} = \dfrac{Wb}{L}(L^2 - b^2)$

Hence for spans $AA' - AB$,

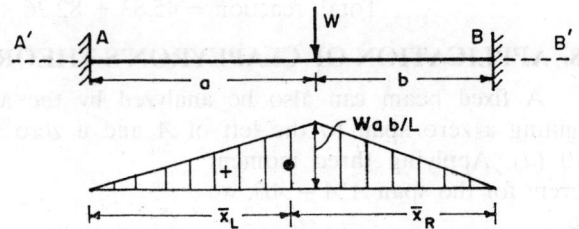

FIG. 17.12

$$2M_A + M_B = -\frac{6A\bar{x}_R}{L^2} = -\frac{1}{L} \times \frac{Wb}{L}(L^2 - b^2) = -\frac{Wb}{L^2}(L^2 - b^2) \qquad ...(1)$$

and for spans $AB - BB'$, $\quad M_A + 2M_B = -\dfrac{6A\bar{x}_L}{L^2} = -\dfrac{1}{L} \times \dfrac{Wa}{L}(L^2 - a^2) = -\dfrac{Wa}{L^2}(L^2 - a^2) \qquad ...(2)$

Solving (1) and (2), we get $\quad M_A = -\dfrac{Wab^2}{L^2}$ and $\quad M_B = -\dfrac{Wba^2}{L^2}$

Example 17.7. *Find the prop reaction and fixing moment for a propped cantilever loaded as shown in Fig. 7.13.*

Solution : Considering cantilever portion BD, we get

$$M_B = -10 \times 1 = -10 \text{ kN-m}$$

Also, for span AB,

$$\mu_C = \frac{10 \times 4}{4} = 10 \text{ kN}$$

The μ diagram for AB will be a triangle, having $A = \frac{1}{2} \times 4 \times 10 = 20$.

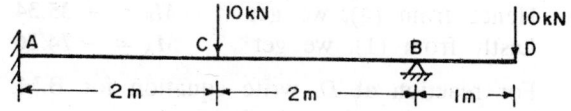

FIG. 17.13

Also $\bar{x}_L = \bar{x}_R = 2$ m

Extend A to A' such that $AA' = 0$. Then for $A'A - AC$, we have

$$0 + 2 M_A (4) + M_B (4) + \frac{6}{4}(20)(2) = 0 \text{ or } M_A + 0.5 M_B = -7.5 \quad ...(1)$$

But $M_B = -10$ kN-m. Hence $M_A = -7.5 + 0.5 \times 10 = -\textbf{2.5 kN-m}$

Now, $R_B \times 4 - 10 \times 5 - 10 \times 2 = M_A = -2.5$, from which $R_B = \textbf{16.875 kN} (\uparrow)$

Hence $R_A = 10 + 10 - 16.875 = \textbf{3.125 kN} (\uparrow)$

Example 17.8. *Solve example 17.3 if end A is fixed.*

Solution : Imagine a point A' to the left of A, such that

$AA' = 0$. Then for the spans $A'A - AB$,

$$0 + 2 M_A (0 + 6) + M_B \times 5$$
$$= -\left[0 + \frac{6}{6}\left(\frac{1}{2} \times 6 \times 106.67\right) \times \left(\frac{6 + 4}{3}\right)\right]$$

or $12 M_A + 5 M_B = -1066.7$

or $M_A + 0.4167 M_B = -88.89$
$\quad ...(1)$

For span $AB - BC$, we have

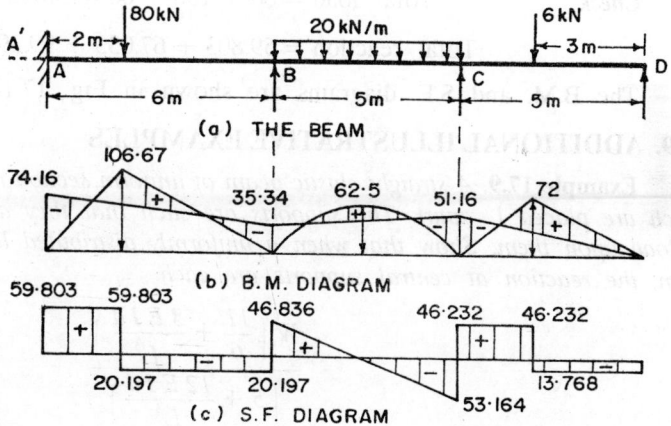

FIG. 17.14

$$6 M_A + 2 M_B (6 + 5) + 5 M_C = -1478.4 \text{ (as in example 17.3)}$$

or $M_A + 3.667 M_B + 0.833 M_C = -246.4$ $\quad ...(2)$

For span $BC - CD$, we have

$$5 M_B + 20 M_C + 5 M_D = -1200.1 \text{ (as in example 17.3)}$$

or $\qquad\qquad M_B + 4 M_C + M_D = -240$ where $M_D = 0$

$\therefore\qquad\qquad\qquad M_B + 4 M_C = -240$ ...(3)

From (1) and (2), we get $\quad M_B + 0.2564\, M_C = -48.46$ ...(4)

From (3) and (4), we get $\quad M_C = -51.16$ **kN-m**
Hence from (4), we get $\qquad M_B = -35.34$ **kN-m**
Lastly from (1), we get $\qquad M_A = -74.16$ **kN-m**

For reaction at D, write equation for B.M. at C.

$\therefore\qquad\qquad R_D \times 5 - 60 \times 2 = M_C = -51.16$, from which $R_D = 13.768$ kN

For reaction at C, write equation for B.M. at B

$\therefore\quad 13.768 \times 10 + R_C \times 5 - 60 \times 7 - 20 \times 5 \times \dfrac{5}{2} = M_B = -35.34$, from which $R_C = 99.396$ kN

For reaction at B, write equation for B.M. at A.

$\therefore\quad 13.768 \times 16 + 99.396 \times 11 + R_B \times 6 - 60 \times 13 - 100 \times 8.5 - 80 \times 2 = M_A = -74.16$

From which we get $\qquad R_B = \mathbf{67.033}$ **kN**

For reaction at A, write equation for B.M. at B, considering L.H.S.

$\qquad\qquad R_A \times 6 + M_A - 80 \times 4 = M_B$

or $\qquad\qquad 6\, R_A - 74.16 - 320 = -35.34$ from which $R_A = 59.803$ kN

Check $\qquad\qquad$ Total load $= 80 + 100 + 60 = 240$ kN

$\qquad\qquad$ Total reaction $= 59.803 + 67.033 + 99.396 + 13.768 = 240$ kN

The B.M. and S.F. diagrams are shown in Fig. 17.14 (b) and (c) respectively.

17.9. ADDITIONAL ILLUSTRATIVE EXAMPLES

Example 17.9. *A straight elastic beam of uniform section rests on four similar elastic supports which are placed L apart. The supports are such that they are compressed by d for each unit of load upon them. Show that when a uniformly distributed load of total amount W comes on them, the reaction at central supports are each*

$$\dfrac{W\left(\dfrac{11}{6} + \dfrac{3\,E\,I\,d}{L^3}\right)}{\left(5 + \dfrac{12\,E\,I\,d}{L^3}\right)}$$

(Cambridge)

Solution :

$\qquad\qquad$ Total load $= W$

$\therefore$ U.D.L., $\qquad w = W/3\,L$

Let R_A, R_B, R_C and R_D be the reactions at A, B, C and D respectively. By symmetry, $R_A = R_D$ and $R_B = R_C$.

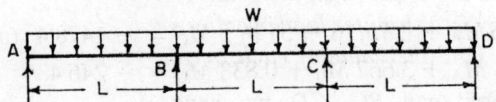

FIG. 17.15

Sinking of support at $A = R_A.d$; Sinking of support at $B = R_B.d$.
Sinking of support at $C = R_C.d$; Sinking of support at $D = R_D.d$.
Also, $M_A = M_D = 0$ and $M_B = M_C$.

$$\delta_1 = \text{deflection of } B \text{ with respect to } A = \delta_B - \delta_A = (R_B - R_A)d$$
$$\delta_2 = \text{deflection of } B \text{ with respect to } C = \delta_B - \delta_C = (R_B - R_C)d = 0.$$

Now applying three moment theorem equation for spans $AB - BC$,

$$M_A.L + 2M_B(L+L) + M_C L + \frac{6A\bar{x}_1}{L} + \frac{6A_2\bar{x}_2}{L} = 6EI\left(\frac{\delta_1}{L} + \frac{\delta_2}{L}\right)$$

or $\quad 4M_B.L + M_B L + \dfrac{wL^3}{4} + \dfrac{wL^3}{4} = \dfrac{6EId}{L}(R_B - R_A)$

or $\quad 5M_B.L + \left(\dfrac{W}{3L}\right)\dfrac{L^3}{2} = \dfrac{6EId}{L}(R_B - R_A)$

or $\qquad M_B = \dfrac{1}{5}\left[-\dfrac{WL}{6} + \dfrac{6EId}{L^2}(R_B - R_A)\right] = -\dfrac{1}{5}\left[\dfrac{WL}{6} - \dfrac{6EId}{L^2}(R_B - R_A)\right]$

Now writing equation for B.M. at M, we have

$$R_A.L - \frac{W}{3L}\left(\frac{L^2}{2}\right) = M_B = -\frac{1}{5}\left[\frac{WL}{6} - \frac{6EId}{L^2}(R_B - R_A)\right] \qquad ...(1)$$

Also, $\quad 2R_B + 2R_A = W \qquad$ or $\quad R_A = \dfrac{W}{2} - R_B \qquad ...(2)$

Substituting the value of R_A in (1), we get

$$\left(\frac{W}{2} - R_B\right)L - \frac{WL}{6} = -\frac{1}{5}\left[\frac{WL}{6} - \frac{6EId}{L^2}\left\{R_B - \left(\frac{W}{2} - R_B\right)\right\}\right]$$

or $\quad \dfrac{W}{2}L - R_B L - \dfrac{WL}{6} = -\dfrac{WL}{30} + \dfrac{6EId}{5L^2}\left(2R_B - \dfrac{W}{2}\right)$

or $\quad R_B\left[\dfrac{12EId}{5L^2} + L\right] = \dfrac{W}{2}L - \dfrac{WL}{6} + \dfrac{WL}{30} + \dfrac{3EIdW}{5L^2}$

or $\qquad R_B = \dfrac{\dfrac{11}{30}WL + \dfrac{3EIdW}{5L^2}}{\dfrac{12EId}{5L^2} + L} = \dfrac{\dfrac{WL}{5}\left[\dfrac{11}{6} + \dfrac{3EId}{L^3}\right]}{\dfrac{L}{5}\left[5 + \dfrac{12EId}{L^3}\right]} = \dfrac{W\left(\dfrac{11}{6} + \dfrac{3EId}{L^3}\right)}{\left(5 + \dfrac{12EId}{L^3}\right)}$

Hence proved.

Example 17.10. *A continuous beam ABCDE has three supports with two over hangs as shown in Fig. 17.16. The overhangs are so selected that the reaction of the three supports are equal when the beam carries a uniformly distributed load over the whole length. Find the value of each overhang.*

Solution :

Total load on the beam
$= w(2L + 2a) = 2w(L + a)$

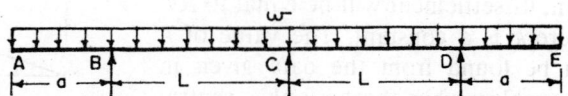

FIG. 17.16

Since all the reactions are equal, we have

$$R_B = R_C = R_D = \frac{2}{3} w (L + a)$$

Now $M_B = -\dfrac{w\,a^2}{2} = M_D$

Applying three moments theorem equation for spans $BC-CD$, we get

$$M_B . L + 2 M_C (L + L) + M_D . L = -\frac{w L^3}{4} - \frac{w L^3}{4}$$

or $-\dfrac{w\,a^2}{2} . L + 4 M_C . L - \dfrac{w\,a^2}{2} . L = -\dfrac{w L^3}{2}$

From which, we get $M_C = \dfrac{1}{4L} \left[-\dfrac{w L^3}{2} + \dfrac{w a^2 L}{2} + \dfrac{w a^2 L}{2} \right] = \dfrac{w}{4} \left(a^2 - \dfrac{L^2}{2} \right)$

or $M_C = -\dfrac{w}{8} (L^2 - 2 a^2)$ ...(1)

But $M_C = R_B . L - \dfrac{w (a + L)^2}{6} = \dfrac{2}{3} (L + a) L - \dfrac{w}{2} (L + a)^2$

$$= -\frac{w (L + a)}{6} \left[3 (L + a) - 4 L \right] = -\frac{w (L + a)}{6} (3 a - L)$$ ...(2)

Equating (1) and (2), we get

$$\frac{w}{8} (L^2 - 2 a^2) = \frac{w}{6} (L + a) (3 a - L)$$

or $18 a^2 + 8 a L - 7 L^2 = 0$

From which, we get $a = \mathbf{0.4398\,L}$

Example 17.11. *A bridge of uniform cross-section rests on rigid abutments at the ends and three equal pontoons as shown as Fig. 17.17 and has a concentrated load W at the middle. When bridge is unloaded, the pontoons just touch it without carrying any force. With the load W at the middle and the two end pontoons removed, the central deflection is one half what it would be with no pontoons. Find the reactions and draw the B.M. diagram for the bridge due to central load with three pontoons in position.*

Solution :

Due to symmetry,
    $R_A = R_E$ and $R_B = R_D$
    $M_B = M_D$
Also, $M_A = M_E = 0$

Thus, there are five unknowns :
R_A, R_B, R_C, M_B and M_C.

If R is the reaction on any pontoon, its settlement will be equal to $R.k$ where k is a constant. The value of k can be found from the data given in the problem when there is only a central pontoon. In that case, if P is the reaction on the pontoon, we have

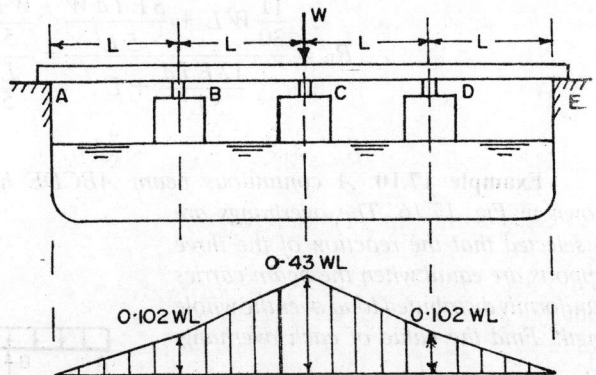

FIG. 17.17

$$\text{Central deflection} = \frac{(W - P)(4L)^3}{48 E I} = \frac{4(W - P)L^3}{3 E I}, \text{ with the pontoon.}$$

$$\text{Central deflection, with no pontoon} = \frac{W(4L)^3}{48 E I} = \frac{4 W L^3}{3 E I}$$

As per the given condition, $\dfrac{4(W-P)L^3}{3 EI} = \dfrac{1}{2}\left[\dfrac{4}{3}\dfrac{W L^3}{E I}\right]$

From which we get $\qquad P = \dfrac{W}{2}.$

$\therefore$ Central deflection with the pontoon $= P \cdot k = \dfrac{W}{2} k.$

But this is equal to $\dfrac{1}{2}\left[\dfrac{4}{3}\dfrac{W L^3}{E I}\right]$

$\therefore \qquad\qquad \dfrac{W}{2} k = \dfrac{1}{2}\left[\dfrac{4}{3}\dfrac{W L^3}{E I}\right]$

From which $\qquad\qquad k = \dfrac{4 L^3}{3 E I} \quad \text{Also, } \dfrac{6 E I k}{L^2} = 8 L$

$$\delta_1 = \delta_B - \delta_A = (R_B k - 0) = R_B \cdot k \quad (\text{Since } \delta_A = 0)$$
$$\delta_2 = \delta_B - \delta_C = (R_B - R_C) k$$

Now applying three moment theorem equation for spans $AB-BC$, we get

$$M_A \cdot L + 2 M_B (L + L) + M_C \cdot L + \frac{6 A_1 \bar{x}_1}{L} + \frac{6 A_2 \bar{x}_2}{L} = 6 E I \left(\frac{\delta_1}{L} + \frac{\delta_2}{L}\right)$$

or $\qquad 0 + 4 M_B + M_C + 0 = \dfrac{6 E I k}{L^2}(2 R_B - R_C) = 8 L (2 R_B - R_C) \qquad \dots(1)$

Similarly, for span $BC - CD$,

$M_B \cdot L + 2 M_C (L+L) + M_D \cdot L = \dfrac{6 E I k}{L}(R_C - R_B + R_C - R_D)$ where $R_B = R_D$ and $M_B = M_D$

$\therefore \qquad M_B + 2 M_C = \dfrac{6 E I k}{L^2}(R_C - R_B) = 8 L (R_C - R_B) \qquad \dots(2)$

Again $\qquad M_B = R_A \cdot L \quad \text{or } R_A = M_B/L$

Also, $\qquad M_C = R_A \cdot 2 L + R_B \cdot L, \text{ or } R_B = \dfrac{M_C}{L} - 2 R_A = \dfrac{M_C}{L} - \dfrac{2 M_B}{L} = \dfrac{M_C - 2 M_B}{L}$

Hence $\qquad R_C = W - 2 R_A - 2 R_B = W - \dfrac{2 M_B}{L} - \dfrac{2 M_C - 4 M_B}{L} = W - \dfrac{2(M_C - M_B)}{L}$

Substituting in (1) and (2), we get $52 M_B - 31 M_C = -8 W L \qquad \dots(a)$

and $\qquad\qquad\qquad\qquad 31 M_B - 26 M_C = -8 W L \qquad \dots(b)$

From (a) and (b), we get $\qquad M_B = +0.102\ W L = M_D$

and $\qquad\qquad\qquad\qquad M_C = +0.43\ W L$

Example 17.12. *A continuous beam ABC of constant moment of inertia is simply supported at A, B and C. The beam carries a central point load of 40 kN in span AB and a central* *clockwise couple of 300 kN-m in the span BC, as shown in Fig. 17.18 (a). Find the support moments and plot the shear force and bending moment diagrams.*

Solution : For simply supported span *AB*,

$$M_D = \frac{40 \times 10}{4} = 100 \quad \text{kN-m}$$

For simply supported span *BC*,

μ_E (left) $= -150$ kN-m

μ_E (right) $= +150$ kN-m.

$A_1 \bar{x}_1 = \frac{1}{2} \times 10 \times 100 \times 5 = 2500$

$A_2 = 0$. Hence $A_2 \bar{x}_2 = 0$

Applying three moment theorem for spans $AB - BC$ we get

$M_A (10) + 2 M_B (10 + 15)$

$+ M_C (15) + \frac{6 A_1 \bar{x}_1}{10} + \frac{6 A_2 \bar{x}_2}{15} = 0$

But $M_A = 0 \, ; M_C = 0$

$\therefore \; 50 M_B = - \frac{6}{10} (2500) - \frac{6}{15} (0)$

From which $M_B = -30$ **kN-m**

The B.M. diagram is shown in Fig. 17.18 (c).

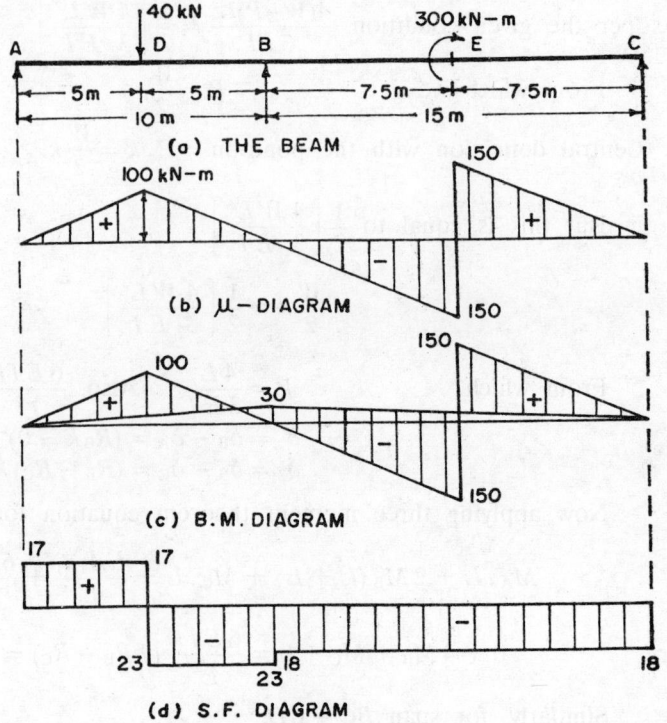

(a) THE BEAM

(b) μ−DIAGRAM

(c) B.M. DIAGRAM

(d) S.F. DIAGRAM

FIG. 17.18

Reactions :

For finding reaction R_A, write equation for B.M. at B, considering L.H.S..

Thus, $R_A \times 10 - 40 \times 5 = M_B = -30$, from which $R_A = $ **17 kN**

For finding reaction R_B, write equation for B.M. at B, considering R.H.S..

Thus $R_C \times 15 - 300 = M_B = -30$, from which $R_C = $ **18 kN**
For finding reaction R_B, write equation for B.M. at A.

Thus $18 \times 25 - 300 + 10 R_B - 40 \times 5 = M_A = 0$

From which $R_B = $ **5 kN**

Check : Total vertical load $= 40$ kN $(\downarrow)$; Total reaction $= 17 + 18 + 5 = 40$ kN$(\uparrow)$

The S.F. diagram is shown in Fig. 17.18 (d).

Example 17.13. *A continuous beam ABCD has a weight w per unit length, and rests on four knife edge supports A, B, C and D. The middle span carries a load W as shown in Fig. 17.19. Find the B.M. at B and C and reactions at A and D.*   (Cambridge)

Solution

Self weight $= w$

Point load $= W$ on BC.

For span AB or CD

$$M_{max} = \frac{w L^2}{8}$$

$$A\bar{x} = \frac{2}{3} \times \frac{w L^2}{8} \times L \times \frac{L}{2} = \frac{w L^4}{24}$$

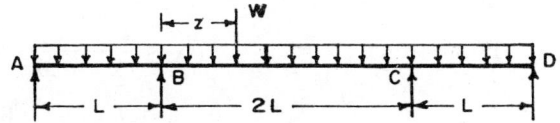

FIG. 17.19

For span BC

$$M_{max} = \frac{w(2L)^2}{8} = \frac{w L^2}{2} \text{ due to U.D.L.}$$

$$M_{max} = \frac{Wz(2L - z)}{2L} \text{ due to point load.}$$

$$A\bar{x}_L = \frac{2}{3} \times \frac{(w L^2)}{2}(2L)L + \frac{1}{2} \frac{Wz(2L - z)}{2L} \times 2L \times \frac{1}{3} \times (2L + z)$$

$$= \frac{2 w L^4}{3} + \frac{Wz}{6}(4L^2 - z^2)$$

$$A\bar{x}_R = \frac{2}{3} \times \frac{w L^2}{2}(2L)(L) + \frac{1}{2} \frac{Wz(2L - z)}{2L} \times 2L \times \frac{1}{3}(2L + 2L - z)$$

$$= \frac{2 w L^4}{3} + \frac{Wz}{6}(2L - z)(4L - z)$$

Applying three moment theorem equation for spans $AB-BC$, we get

$$M_A \cdot L + 2 M_B(L + 2L) + M_C(2L) + \frac{6}{L}\frac{w L^4}{24} + \frac{6}{2L}\left[2\frac{wL^4}{3} + \frac{Wz}{6}(2L - z)(4L - z)\right]$$

or $\quad 6 M_B + 2 M_C + \frac{9 w L^2}{4} + \frac{Wz}{2L^2}(2L - z)(4L - z)$ ...(1)

Similarly, applying three moment theorem equation for spans $BC - CD$

$$M_B(2L) + 2 M_C(2L + L) + M_D(L) + \frac{6}{2L}\left[\frac{2 w L^4}{3} + \frac{Wz}{6}(4L^2 - z^2)\right] + \frac{6}{L} \times \frac{w L^4}{24} = 0$$

or $\quad 2 M_B + 6 M_C + \frac{9}{4}w L^2 + \frac{Wz}{2L^2}(2L - z)(2L + z)$ ...(2)

Solving (1) and (2), we get

$$M_B = -\left[\frac{9}{32}w L^2 + \frac{W \cdot z}{16 L^2}(2L - z)(5L - 2z)\right] \text{ Ans.}$$

and

$$M_C = -\left[\frac{9}{32}w L^2 + \frac{Wz}{16 L^2}(2L - z)(L + 2z)\right] \text{ Ans.}$$

For reaction at A, write down equation for B.M. at B. Thus

$$R_A \cdot L - \frac{wL^2}{2} = M_B = - \left[\frac{9}{32} wL^2 + \frac{Wz}{16L^2} (2L - z)(5L - 2z) \right]$$

From which
$$R_A = \frac{wL}{2} - \frac{9}{32} wL - \frac{Wz}{16L^3} (2L - z)(5L - 2z)$$

$$= \frac{7}{32} wL - \frac{Wz}{16L^3} (2L - z)(5L - 2z) \qquad \text{...Ans.}$$

Similarly,
$$R_B = \frac{wL}{2} - \frac{1}{L} \left[\frac{9}{32} wL^2 + \frac{Wz}{16L^2} (2L - z)(L + 2z) \right]$$

$$= \frac{7}{32} wL - \frac{Wz}{16L^3} (2L - z)(L + 2z) \quad \text{Ans.}$$

Example 17.14. *A three span beam ABCD has different moments of inertia and is loaded as shown in Fig. 17.20 (a). Find the reactions and support moments and draw the S.F. and B.M. diagrams.*

Solution :

The μ-diagram is shown in Fig. 17.20 (b).

For span AB,

$$M_{max} = \frac{12 \times 3}{4} = 9 \ \text{kN-m}$$

$$A\bar{x} = \frac{1}{2} \times 9 \times 3 \times \frac{3}{2} = 20.25$$

For span BC

B.M. is zero throughout.

Hence $A\bar{x} = 0$

For span CD

$$M_{max} = \frac{4(3)^2}{8} = 4.5 \ \text{kN-m}$$

Here, $M_A = 0$ and $M_D = 0$.

Writing three moment theorem equation for spans AB–BC, we get

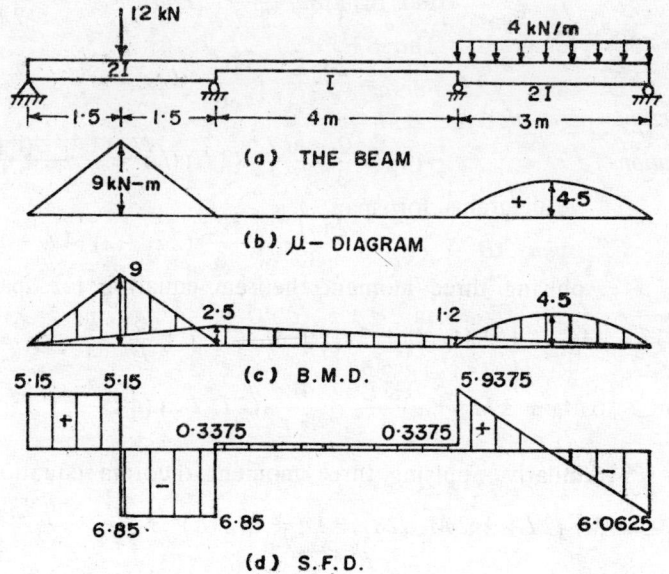

FIG. 17.20

$$M_A (3) + 2 M_B (3 + 4) + M_C (4) + \frac{6}{3} (20.25) + \frac{6}{4} (0) = 0$$

or
$$14 M_B + 4 M_C + 40.5 = 0 \qquad \text{...(1)}$$

Similarly, writing three moment theorem equation for spans BC–CD, we get

$$M_B (4) + 2 M_C (4 + 3) + M_D (3) + \frac{6}{4} (0) + \frac{6}{3} (13.5) = 0$$

or
$$4 M_B + 14 M_C + 27 = 0 \qquad \text{...(2)}$$

Solving (1) and (2), we get $M_B = -2.55$ kN-m and $M_C = -1.20$ kN-m

The B.M. diagram is shown in Fig. 17.20.

Reactions : For finding R_A, write equation for B.M. at B.

Thus $\qquad R_A \times 3 - 12 \times 1.5 = M_B = -2.55$, from which $R_A = 5.15$ kN($\uparrow$).

For finding R_B, write down equation for B.M. at C, considering L.H.S.

$\therefore \qquad 5.15\,(7) - 12\,(5.5) + R_B \times 4 = M_C = -1.20$, from which $R_B = 7.1875$ kN($\uparrow$).

For finding R_D, write equation for B.M. at C, considering R.H.S.

$R_D\,(3) - 4 \times 3 \times 1.5 = M_C = -1.20$ from which $R_D = 5.6$ kN ($\uparrow$)

Lastly, for finding R_C, write equation for B.M. at B, considering R.H.S.

$\therefore \quad 5.6 \times 7 + R_C\,(4) - 4 \times 3 \times 5.5 = M_B = -2.55$, from which $R_C = 6.0625$ kN($\uparrow$)

Check $\qquad\qquad$ Total load $= 12 + 4 \times 3 = 24$ kN

$\qquad\qquad\qquad$ Total reaction $= 5.15 + 7.1875 + 5.6 + 6.0625 = 24$ kN

S.F. diagram : The S.F. diagram is shown in Fig. 17.20 (d).

Example 17.15. *For a two span beam shown in Fig. 17.21, find the support moments and reactions, and plot the B.M. and S.F. diagrams.*

Solution :

The μ-diagrams for span AB and BC are shown in Fig. 17.21(b).

For span AB

$$M_{max} = \frac{5\,(8)^2}{8} = 40 \text{ kN-m}$$

$$A\,\bar{x}_R = \frac{2}{3} \times 8 \times 40 \times 4 = 853.33$$

$$= A\,\bar{x}_L$$

For span BC

$$A\,\bar{x}_L = -\left(\frac{1}{2} \times 3 \times 48 \times \frac{2}{3} \times 3\right)$$

$$+ \left(\frac{1}{2} \times 2 \times 32\right)\left(3 + \frac{2}{3}\right) = -26.667$$

$$A\,\bar{x}_R = \left(\frac{1}{2} \times 2 \times 32 \times \frac{2}{3}\right)$$

$$- \left(\frac{1}{2} \times 3 \times 48\right)\left(2 + \frac{3}{3}\right) = -194.667$$

Imagine a point A' to the left of A such that $AA' = 0$. Hence writing three moment theorem equation for spans $A'A - AB$, we get

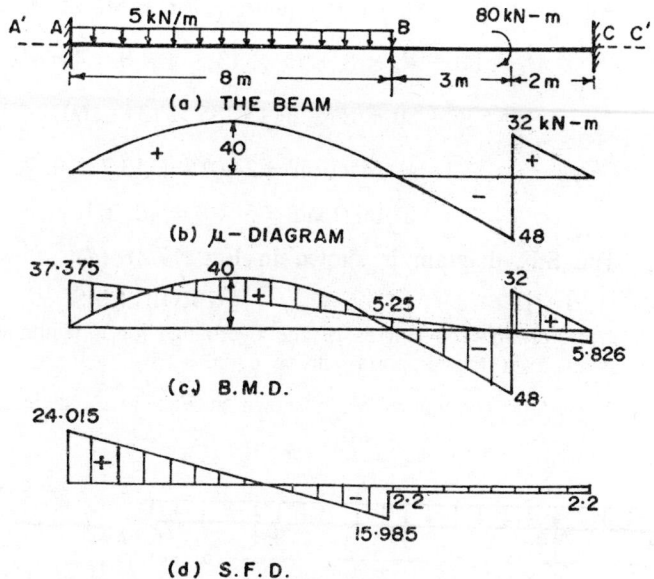

(a) THE BEAM

(b) μ - DIAGRAM

(c) B.M.D.

(d) S.F.D.

FIG. 17.21

$$0 + 2 M_A (0 + 8) + M_B (8) + 0 + \frac{6}{8} (853.33) = 0$$

or $2 M_A + M_B + 80 = 0$ ...(1)

Writing three moment theorem equation for spans $AB - BC$, we get

$$M_A (8) + 2 M_B (8 + 5) + M_C (5) + \frac{6}{8} (853.33) + \frac{6}{5} (-194.667) = 0$$

or $8 M_A + 26 M_B + 5 M_C + 406.4 = 0$ ...(2)

Imagine a point C' to the right of C such that $CC' = 0$.
Hence for spans $BC - CC'$

$$M_B (5) + 2 M_C (5 + 0) + 0 + \frac{6}{5} (-26.667) + 0 = 0$$

or $5 M_B + 10 M_C - 32 = 0$ ...(3)

Now from (1) and (2), $22 M_B + 5 M_C + 86.4 = 0$ ...(4)

From (3) and (4), we get $M_B = -5.251$ and $M_C = +5.826$ kN-m (i.e. (↰))
Hence from (1), $M_A = -37.375$. The B.M. diagram is shown in Fig. 17.21(c).

Reactions : For reaction at A, write equation for B.M. at B. Thus

$$R_A (8) + M_A - 5 \times 8 \times 4 = M_B$$

or $8 R_A - 37.375 - 160 = -5.251$ from which $R_A = 24.015$ kN (↑)

For reaction at C, write equation for B.M. at B, considering R.H.S. Thus,

$$R_C (5) + M_C - 80 = M_B$$

or $5 R_C + 5.826 - 80 = -5.251$, from which $R_C = 13.785$ kN (↑)

For reaction at B, write equation for B.M. at A, considering R.H.S. Thus

$$M_C - 80 + R_B \times 8 + R_C \times 13 - 5 \times 8 \times 4 = M_A$$

or $+ 5.826 - 80 + 8 R_B + 13.785 \times 13 - 160 = -37.375$ from which $R_B = 2.20$ (↑)

Check :   Total reaction $= 24.015 + 13.785 + 2.20 = 40.0$ kN

Total load $= 5 \times 8 = 40$ kN

The S.F. diagram is shown in Fig. 17.21 (d).

PROBLEMS

1. Determine the lengths of the overhangs for a continuous beam shown in Fig. 17.22 so that the moments over the supports will be equal.

2. For the continuous beam shown in Fig. 17.23, determine support moments at B and C.

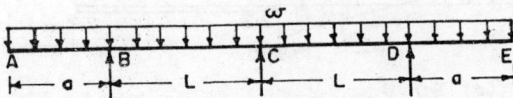

FIG. 17.22

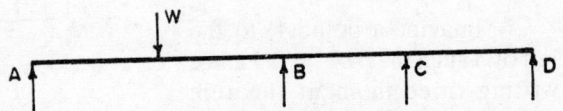

FIG. 17.23

3. For the continuous beam shown in Fig. 17.24, determine the support moments at B and C.

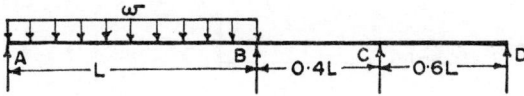

FIG. 17.24

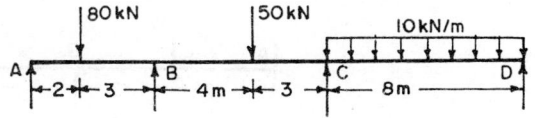

FIG. 17.25

4. A continuous beam $ABCD$ is loaded as shown in Fig. 17.25. Find the B.M. and reactions at the four supports and hence plot the B.M. and S.F. diagrams.

5. Solve problem 4 if the support B sinks by 10 mm below A and C. The moment of inertia for the whole beam $= 85 \times 10^6 \, mm^4$ and $E = 2.1 \times 10^5 \, N/mm^2$.

6. Solve problem 4 if the end A is fixed and end D is simply supported.

7. Analyse the continuous beam shown in Fig. 17.26.

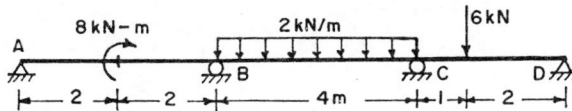

FIG. 17.26

8. $ABCD$ is a straight uniform beam of length $4L$. It is freely supported at its ends A and D, and at two intermediate supports B and C distant L from either end. The supports A and D are rigid but those at B and C are such that they deflect by an amount λ for each unit of load which is placed upon them. the beam carries a uniformly distributed load w per unit length along its entire length.

Show that the reactions at the supports are

$$\frac{wL}{8} \left[\frac{7L^3 + 48 EI\lambda}{4L^3 + 3 EI\lambda} \right] \text{ and } \frac{3wL}{8} \left[\frac{19L^3}{4L^3 + 3 EI\lambda} \right] \qquad \text{(Cambridge)}$$

9. A uniform continuous girder ABC rests upon three similar floating supports, situated at each end and at the middle point B. The buoyancy of each float is such that every additional kN of load increases its immersion by h. Initially, all floats are equally immersed. If a load W is placed on the girder at B, show that the proportion carried by the central float is

$$\frac{W \left(1 + \dfrac{3hEI}{a^3} \right)}{\left(1 + \dfrac{9hEI}{a^3} \right)}, \text{ where } 2a \text{ is the length of the girder.} \qquad \text{(Cambridge)}$$

10. For the continuous beam shown in Fig. 17.27, find the support moments.

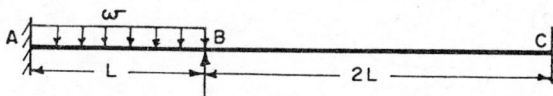

FIG. 17.27

11. For the continuous beam shown in Fig. 17.28, find the support moments

FIG. 17.28

12. Analyse the continuous beam shown in Fig. 17.29.

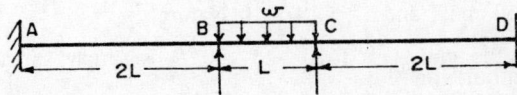

FIG. 17.29

ANSWERS

1. $a = L/\sqrt{6}$;

2. $M_B = 0.138\,W L$; $M_C = 0.028\,W L$

3. $M_B = 0.092\,w L^2$; $M_C = 0.018\,w L^2$

4. $M_B = 45.4$ kN-m ; $M_C = 63.5$ kN-m

     $R_A = 38.9$ kN ; $R_B = 60$ kN ; $R_C = 79$ kN ; $R_D = 32.1$ kN

5. $M_B = 27.4$ kN-m ; $M_C = 73$ kN-m

6. $M_A = 46.7$ kN-m ; $M_B = 34.6$ kN-m ; $M_C = 66$ kN-m

     $R_A = 50.4$ kN ; $R_B = 46.4$ kN ; $R_C = 81.4$ kN ; $R_D = 31.8$ kN

7. $M_B = 1690$ N-m; $M_C = 3230$ N-m

10. $M_A = \dfrac{w L^2}{9}$; $M_B = \dfrac{w L^2}{36}$; $M_C = \dfrac{w L^2}{72}$

11. $M_A = \dfrac{W L}{6}$; $M_B = \dfrac{W L}{24}$; $M_C = \dfrac{W L}{48}$

12. $M_A = M_D = \dfrac{w L^2}{48}$; $M_B = M_C = \dfrac{w L^2}{24}$

Combined Direct and Bending Stresses

18.1. DIRECT STRESS IN A COMPRESSION MEMBER

Any structural member loaded axially in compression is called a *compression member* in the general sense of the word. It may be horizontal, vertical and even inclined. It is variously termed as a column, stanchion, post, strut, boom etc. depending upon its use as a particular member in a structure. *Columns* are ordinarily used in buildings, as vertical members, to carry loads of beams, slabs etc. *Stanchions* are steel columns made of rolled steel sections, commonly used in buildings. The term *post* is loosely used for a column. The term *strut* is commonly used for compression member in a roof truss; it may either be in a vertical position or in inclined position. The principal compression member in a crane is called a *boom*.

A column may be either *short* or *long*. A short column is the one which fails by compression only, under increasing loads (Fig. 18.1). The average compressive stress (p_0) at any section mn is equal to P/A, where A is the area of cross-section. A *long column* is a compression member that is so slender compared to its length that under gradually increasing loads, it fails by *buckling* at loads considerably less than those required to cause failure by *crushing*. We shall consider in this chapter only *short columns*, which, even if eccentrically loaded, undergo negligible lateral deflec-tion. Such a member is sometimes called a *compression block*. The term *column* is *usually* reserved for a long compression member that fails due to buckling. Such members (*i.e.* columns) have been discussed in chapter 20.

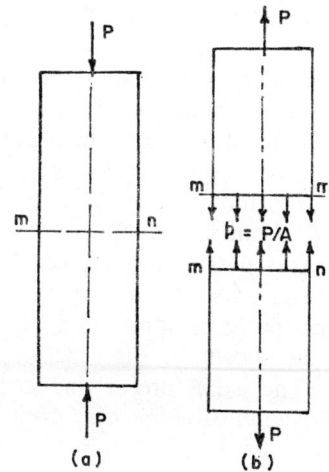

FIG. 18.1

18.2. COMBINED DIRECT AND BENDING STRESSES

There are many examples of a structural member which is simul-taneously subjected to direct stresses as well as bending stresses. For example, a beam (Fig. 18.2) may be subjected

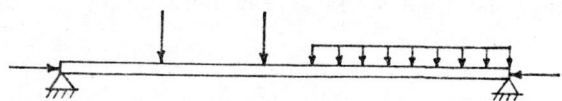

FIG. 18.2. BEAM WITH LATERAL LOAD

(633)

to some axial load in addition to transverse loads. Similarly, a compression member may be subjected to axial load which may not pass through its geometrical axis, thus causing bending as well as direct stresses (Fig. 18.3). In both such cases, a cross-section of the member is subjected to direct stresses as well as bending stresses. If the axial load is of compressive nature, compressive stresses are set up in a cross-section, while if the axial load is of tensile nature, tensile stresses are set up. Also, due to bending, *longitudinal stresses* (either tensile or compressive) are set up in the cross-section of the member subjected to bending. Hence when such a structural member is subjected to both axial force as well as bending, the resulting stresses at any layer in the cross-section will be the algebraic sum of the two.

18.3. ECCENTRIC LOADING

Fig. 18.3 (*a*) shows a prismatic bar of short length, subjected to a direct load P the line of action of which is parallel to the axis of the bar and intersects an axis of symmetry. (*i.e.* geometrical axis) at distance e from the centroid of the section (Fig. 18.3 *a ii*). The loading is therefore eccentric with respect to the axis of the bar and e is known as the *eccentricity*.

Let us now introduce equal and opposite forces P along the axis of the bar, as shown in Fig. 18.3 (*b*). The whole system thus reduces to (*i*) a *direct force P* acting along the axis of the bar, and (*ii*) a couple $M = P \cdot e$ causing bending in a vertical plane passing through the longitudinal axis of the bar and to original point of application of the load, as shown in Fig. 18.3 (*c*).

The axial force P induces a *direct compressive stress* p_0 given by

$$p_0 = \frac{P}{A} \qquad ...(18.1)$$

The bending couple $(M = P \cdot e)$ will induce *longitudinal*

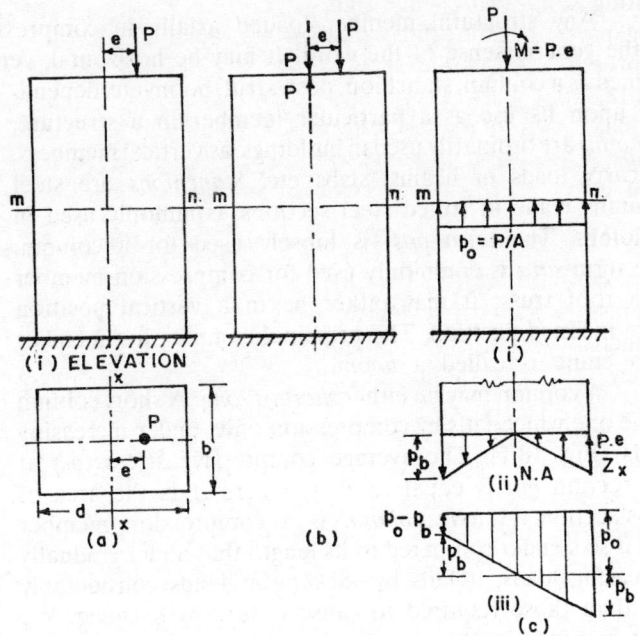

FIG. 18.3

stresses p_b (both tensile as well as compressive), the value of which depends upon the distance of the fibre from the N.A. The *bending stress* p_b at any fibre distant y from the N.A. is given by

$$p_b = \frac{M}{I_{xx}} \cdot y = \frac{P \cdot e}{I_{xx}} \cdot y \text{ (tensile or compressive)} \qquad ...(18.2)$$

Hence the total stress at any fibre distant y from the N.A. is given by :

$$p = p_0 \pm p_b = \frac{P}{A} \pm \frac{P \cdot e}{I_{xx}} \cdot y \qquad ...(18.3)$$

The extreme fibre stress $(p_{b,\max})$ due to bending is given by

$$(p_b)_{\max} = \pm \frac{M}{Z_{xx}} = \pm \frac{P \cdot e}{Z_{xx}} \qquad ...(18.4)$$

Hence the *total stresses* at the *extreme fibres* are given by

$$p_{max} = p_0 + p_b = \frac{P}{A} + \frac{M}{Z_{xx}} \qquad \qquad ...(18.5\ a)$$

and

$$p_{min} = p_0 - p_b = \frac{P}{A} - \frac{M}{Z_{xx}} \qquad \qquad ...(18.5\ b)$$

The total stress distribution, in general, is shown in Fig. 18.3 (*ciii*). However there may be three cases of variations of total stress distribution at the base, as shown in Fig. 18.4.

In case (*a*), p_0 is greater than p_b; for such a case the stress throughout the section will be of the same sign (Fig. 18.4 *a*). If, however p_0 is less than p_b, the resulting stress will change sign, being partly tensile and partly compressive across the section (Fig. 18.4 *b*). Cases (*c*) is the special case which arises when $p_0 = p_b$. This is an ideal case,

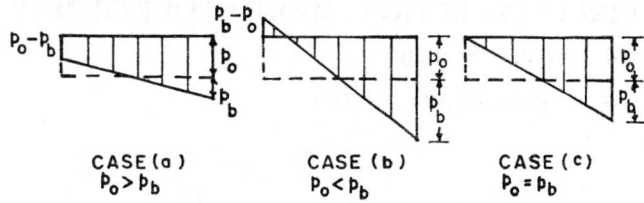

FIG. 18.4. FINAL STRESS DISTRIBUTION

which a designer tries to achieve. For such a case, $p_{min} = 0$ and $p_{max} = 2 p_0$.

18.4. RECTANGULAR SECTION : MIDDLE THIRD RULE

We have seen in case (*b*) that $p_0 < p_b$ due to which the stress changes sign, being partly compressive and partly tensile. (Fig. 18.4 *b*). In many structures such as masonry structures or concrete structures, development of tensile stress in a section is neither desirable nor permissible as they are weak in tension. In order that tension may not develop, we have the condition

$$p_0 \ge p_b \ge \frac{M}{Z}$$

or

$$\frac{P}{A} \ge \frac{P.e}{I} \cdot \frac{d}{2} \ge \frac{P.ed}{2A k^2}$$

or

$$e \le \frac{2 k^2}{d} \qquad \qquad ...(18.6)$$

where k = radius of gyration of the section with respect to the N.A.
          d = depth of the section.

Thus, for no tension in the section, the eccentricity must not exceed $\dfrac{2 k^2}{d}$. This is an important requirement.

For a rectangular section of width b and depth d.

$$I = \frac{1}{12} b\, d^3 \text{ and } A = b \cdot d. \text{ Hence } k^2 = \frac{I}{A} = \frac{d^2}{12}$$

Substituting this value of k in Eq. 18.6, we get

$$e \le \frac{2}{d} \cdot \frac{d^2}{12} \le \frac{d}{6}$$

or

$$e_{max} = \frac{d}{6} \qquad \qquad ...(18.7)$$

This limits the value of the eccentricity for no tension to develop in a rectangular section. However, this eccentricity can be on the either side of the geometrical axis. *Hence the stress will be of the same sign throughout the section if the load line is within the middle third of the section.* This requirement is commonly known as the *middle third rule*.

Extreme Stresses : For a rectangular section, $Z_{xx} = \dfrac{1}{6} b d^2$. Hence from Eq. 18.6, the maximum intensities of extreme stresses are given by

$$p_{max} = \frac{P}{A} \pm \frac{P \cdot e}{Z_{xx}} = \frac{P}{b d} \pm \frac{6 P e}{b d^2} = \frac{P}{b d}\left[1 \pm \frac{6 e}{d}\right] \qquad \ldots(18.8)$$

18.5. CIRCULAR SECTION : MIDDLE FOURTH RULE

(a) **Solid Circular Section:**

For a solid circular section,

$$I = \frac{\pi}{64} d^4 \text{ and } A = \frac{\pi}{4} d^2$$

$\therefore$
$$k^2 = \frac{I}{A} = \frac{d^2}{16}$$

For no tension to develop, $e \le \dfrac{2 k^2}{d}$, from Eq. 18.6

$\therefore$
$$e \le \frac{2}{d} \cdot \frac{d^2}{16} \le \frac{d}{8}$$

or
$$e_{max} = \frac{d}{8} \qquad \ldots(18.9)$$

Thus, in order that tension is not developed, the load line must fall within the *middle fourth* of the section.

(b) Hollow circular section

For a hollow circular section, having external diameter D and internal diameter d,

$$I = \frac{\pi}{64}(D^4 - d^4) \quad \text{and} \quad A = \frac{\pi}{4}(D^2 - d^2)$$

$\therefore$
$$k^2 = \frac{I}{A} = \frac{D^4 - d^4}{16 (D^2 - d^2)} = \frac{D^2 + d^2}{16}$$

For no tension to develop, $e \le \dfrac{2 k^2}{d}$

Hence
$$e \le \frac{2}{D}\left(\frac{D^2 + d^2}{16}\right) \le \frac{D^2 + d^2}{8 D} \qquad \ldots(18.10)$$

$\therefore$
$$e_{max} = \frac{D^2 + d^2}{8 D}$$

18.6. THE CORE OF A SECTION

We have seen in the previous articles that bending stresses are developed if the line of action of load is eccentric with respect to the axis of the section. Each section has two rectangular axes (*i.e.* $x - x$ and $y - y$ axes). If the line of action of force is on neither of the axes of the section, the *bending is unsymmetrical*. If the stress in the section is not to become tensile, the line of action of the force P must cut the cross-section within certain area. This area is known as the *core* or *kernal* of the section. The shape of the core of a section depends upon the shape of the section itself.

(a) Rectangular Section

Fig. 18.5 (*a*) shows the point of application of load P, having co-ordinates (x, y) with reference to the axes. Both x and y are positive in the first quadrant. The B.M. about x-x axis is $P.\ y$ and I_{xx} is equal to $\frac{1}{12} d b^3$. Similarly, the B.M. about $y - y$ axis is $P.x$ and I_{yy} is equal to $\frac{1}{12} b d^3$. Hence the stress at any point having coordinates (x', y') is given by

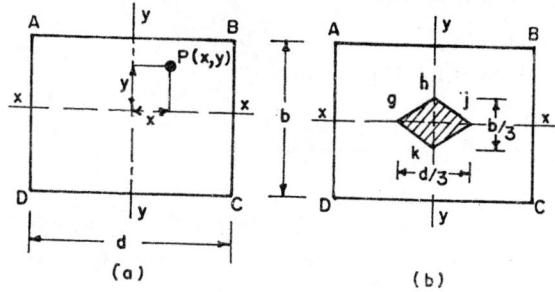

FIG. 18.5. CORE OF RECTANGULAR SECTION

$$p = \frac{P}{A} + \frac{M_{xx} y'}{I_{xx}} + \frac{M_{yy}.x'}{I_{yy}} = \frac{P}{b\,d} + \frac{P.y.y'}{\frac{1}{12} d b^3} + \frac{P.x.x'}{\frac{1}{12} b d^3} \qquad ...(18.11)$$

or

$$p = \frac{12\,P}{b\,d} \left[\frac{1}{12} + \frac{y\,y'}{b^2} + \frac{x\,x'}{d^2} \right] \qquad ...(18.11\ a)$$

At point D, $\quad x' = -\dfrac{d}{2}$ and $y' = -\dfrac{b}{2}$. Hence p will be minimum.

Thus $\qquad p_{min} = p_D = \dfrac{6\,P}{b\,d} \left[\dfrac{1}{6} - \dfrac{y}{b} - \dfrac{x}{d} \right]$

p_{min} reaches zero value when

$$\frac{y}{b} + \frac{x}{d} = \frac{1}{6}$$

or

$$\frac{6y}{b} + \frac{6x}{d} = 1 \qquad ...(18.12)$$

Hence the co-ordinates of the load line (and in other words, the *deviation* of load line from the two axes) is governed by Eq. 18.12, which is the equation for a straight line, whose intercepts on the axes are respectively $b/6$ and $d/6$.

This is true for the load line in the first quadrant. Similar limits will apply in other quadrants also. *Thus the stress will be wholly compressive throughout the section, if the line of action of P falls within the rhombus ghjk (Fig. 18.5 b), the diagonals of which are of length $d/3$ and $b/3$ respectively.* This rhombus is called the *core* or *kern* of the rectangular section.

(b) Solid circular section

We have seen in the previous articles that $e_{max} = \dfrac{d}{8}$ for a solid circular section. Hence the *core* of a solid circular section is a circle, with the same centre, and diameter $\dfrac{d}{4}$.

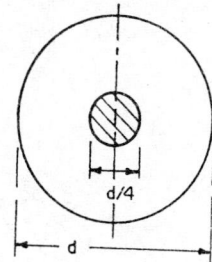

FIG. 18.6. CORE OF SOLID CIRCULAR SECTION

(c) Hollow circular section

For a hollow circular section, $e_{max} = \dfrac{D^2 + d^2}{8 D}$. Hence the core for a hollow circular section

is a concentric circle of diameter $\dfrac{D^2 + d^2}{4 D}$.

(d) I-Section

Rewriting Eq. 18.11, we get

$$p = \frac{P}{A} \left[1 + \frac{yy'}{k_x^2} + \frac{xx'}{k_y^2} \right] \qquad ...(18.13)$$

where k_x = radius of gyration of the section about X-axis.

            k_y = radius of gyration of the section about Y-axis.

For stress p to be zero at the point, we must have

$$\frac{y y'}{k_x^2} + \frac{x x'}{k_y^2} = -1 \qquad ...(18.14)$$

This is the conditional equation for a *general case*. For I-section in particular, the four corners will have limiting points having coordinates $x' = \dfrac{b}{2}$ and $y' = \dfrac{d}{2}$.

Hence, we have $\dfrac{y d}{2 k_x^2} + \dfrac{x b}{2 k_y^2} = -1$

From which $y = -\dfrac{k_x^2}{k_y^2} \cdot \dfrac{b}{d} x - \dfrac{2 k_x^2}{d} \qquad ...(18.15)$

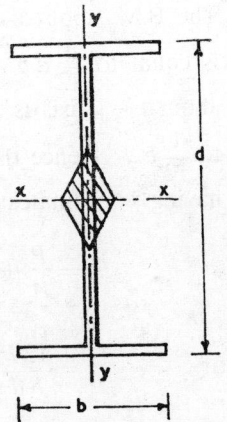

FIG. 18.7. CORE OF AN I SECTION

This gives the equation of the *bounding line* which limits the deviation of the load from the centroid, for no change in the sign of the stress, for I-section. The equations for the three other bounding lines will be similar. Thus, the *core* for a I-section will be a rhombus, having the principal axes as diagonals, as shown in Fig. 18.7.

Example 18.1. *A short C.I. column of hollow circular section is attached with a projection bracket carrying a load of 100 kN. The load line is off the axis of the column by 200 mm. Find the maximum and minimum stress intensities in the column if it has an external diameter of 200 mm and internal diameter of 150 mm.*

Solution :

$$A = \frac{\pi}{4} (200^2 - 150^2) = 13744.5 \text{ mm}^2$$

$$Z = \frac{\pi}{32} \left(\frac{D^4 - d^4}{D} \right) = \frac{\pi}{32 \times 200} (200^4 - 150^4) = 536893 \text{ mm}^3$$

$$p_0 = \frac{P}{A} = \frac{100 \times 10^3}{13744.5} = 7.28 \text{ N/mm}^3 \text{ (comp.)}$$

$$p_b = \pm \frac{M}{Z} = \pm \frac{100 \times 10^3 \times 200}{536893} = \pm 37.25 \text{ N/mm}^2$$

$$\therefore \qquad f_{max} = p_0 + p_b = 7.28 + 37.25 = \mathbf{44.53 \text{ N/mm}^2} \text{ (Comp.)}$$

$$f_{min} = p_0 - p_b = 7.28 - 37.25 = -29.97 = \mathbf{29.97 \text{ N/mm}^2} \text{ (tensile)}$$

Example 18.2. *A circular rod of 20 mm diameter carries a pull along a line which is parallel to the centroidal axis, but is displaced from it. Determine the distance of the line of pull from the centroidal axis, if the maximum stress is 20 percent greater than the mean stress on a section normal to the axis.*

Solution : $A = \dfrac{\pi}{4}(20)^2 = 314.16 \text{ mm}^2 \,; Z = \dfrac{\pi}{32}(20)^3 = 785.4 \text{ mm}^3$

Let P be the axial tension and e be its eccentricity.

$\therefore \qquad\qquad\qquad M = P.e$

Mean Stress, $p_{mean} = \dfrac{P}{A} = \dfrac{P}{314.16}$ $\qquad\qquad$ ...(1)

Max. stress $\quad p_{max} = \dfrac{P}{A} + \dfrac{M}{Z} = \dfrac{P}{314.16} + \dfrac{P.e}{785.4}$ $\qquad$ ...(2)

Now $\qquad\qquad p_{max} = p_{mean} \times \dfrac{120}{100}$

$\therefore \quad \dfrac{P}{314.16} + \dfrac{Pe}{785.4} = \dfrac{P}{314.16} \times 1.2$

or $\quad \dfrac{1}{314.16} + \dfrac{e}{785.4} = \dfrac{1.2}{314.16}$

From which $\quad e = \left(\dfrac{1.2}{314.16} - \dfrac{1}{314.16}\right) 785.4 = \textbf{0.5 mm}$

FIG. 18.8

Example 18.3. *A beam carries a uniformly distributed load of 50 kN/m over a span of 2 m, along with an axial compressive force 50 kN. The beam section is rectangular, having depth equal to 240 mm and width equal 120 mm. Compute (i) maximum fibre stress (ii) fibre stress at a point 0.5 m from the left end of the beam and 80 mm below the N.A.*
Solution :

$$Z = \frac{1}{6} \times 120\,(240)^2 = 1152 \times 10^3 \text{ mm}^3 \,; A = 240 \times 120 = 28800 \text{ mm}^2$$

$$I = Z.\frac{d}{2} = 1152 \times 10^3 \times \frac{240}{2} = 13824 \times 10^4 \text{ mm}^4$$

(i) Maximum fibre stress

B.M. $\qquad M = \dfrac{w\,L^2}{8} = \dfrac{50\,(2)^2}{8} = 25 \text{ kN-m} = 25 \times 10^6 \text{ N-mm}$

$\therefore \qquad p_b = \dfrac{M}{Z} = \dfrac{25 \times 10^6}{1152 \times 10^3} = 21.701 \text{ N/mm}^2 \text{ (comp.)}$

$\qquad\qquad p_0 = \dfrac{P}{A} = \dfrac{50 \times 10^3}{28800} = 1.736 \text{ N/mm}^2 \text{ (compressive)}$

$\therefore$ Maximum fibre stress $= 21.701 + 1.736 = \textbf{23.437 N/mm}^2$ (comp.)

(ii) Fibre stress at the given location

$$M_x = 50 \times 0.5 - \frac{50\,(0.5)^2}{2} = 18.75 \text{ kN-m} = 18.75 \times 10^6 \text{ N-mm}$$

$\therefore$ Bending stress at 80 mm below N.A.$= \dfrac{M}{I} y = \dfrac{18.75 \times 10^6}{13824 \times 10^4} \times 80 = 10.851$ (tensile)

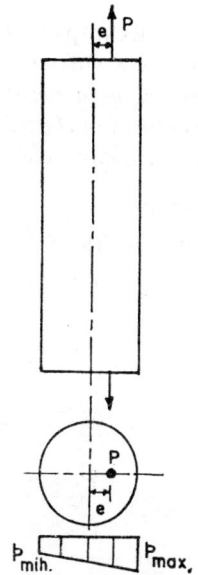

$\therefore$ Resultant fibre stress= $10.851 - 1.736 =$ **9.115 N/mm^2** (tensile)

Example 18.4. *A hollow rectangular masonry pier 600 mm × 900 mm and 150 mm thick transmits a vertical load of 500 kN in a vertical plane bisecting the 900 mm side and at an eccentricity of 100 mm from the geometrical axes of the section. Determine the maximum and minimum stress intensities in the section.*

Solution :

Outer width B= 600 mm ; Inner width b=600−2×150=300 mm

Outer depth D= 900 mm ; Inner depth d = 900−2 × 150 = 600 mm

$$\therefore \qquad A = BD - bd = 600 \times 900 - 300 \times 600 = 360000 \text{ mm}^2$$

$$Z_{yy} = \frac{DB^3 - db^3}{6B} = \frac{900\,(600)^3 - 600\,(300)^3}{6 \times 600} = 49500 \times 10^3 \text{ mm}^3$$

$$P = 500 \text{ kN} = 500 \times 10^3 \text{ N}$$

$$M = P.e = 500 \times 10^3 \times 100 = 50 \times 10^6 \text{ N-mm}$$

$$p_0 = \frac{P}{A} = \frac{500 \times 10^3}{360000} = 1.389 \text{ N/mm}^2$$

$$p_b = \pm \frac{M}{Z} = \pm \frac{50 \times 10^6}{49500 \times 10^3} = \pm 1.010 \text{ N/mm}^2$$

$$\therefore \quad f_{max} = p_0 + p_b = 1.389 + 1.010 = \textbf{2.399 N/mm}^2$$

$$f_{min} = p_0 - p_b = 1.389 - 1.010 = \textbf{0.379 N/mm}^2$$

Example 18.5. *A short hollow cylindrical column shown in Fig. 18.10 is acted on by a load of 10 kN inclined at 30° to the column axis. Calculate the maximum tensile and compressive stresses set up in the base AB of the column.*

Solution :
$$A = \frac{\pi}{4}\,(100^2 - 75^2) = 3436 \text{ mm}^2$$

$$I = \frac{\pi}{64}\,(100^4 - 75^4) = 335.6 \times 10^4 \text{ mm}^2$$

Horizontal component of the load $= P_h = P \sin 30°$
$$= 10 \sin 30° = 5 \text{ kN}$$

Vertical component of the load $= P_v = P \cos 30°$
$$= 10 \cos 30° = 8.66 \text{ kN}$$

$$M_{AB} = P_h \times L = 5 \times 10^3 \times 600 = 3 \times 10^6 \text{ N-mm}$$

$$p_0 = \frac{P_v}{A} = \frac{8.66 \times 10^3}{3436} = 2.52 \text{ N/mm}^2$$

$$p_b = \pm \frac{M}{I}\,y = \pm \frac{3 \times 10^6}{335.6 \times 10^4} \times 50 = \pm 44.700 \text{ N/mm}^2$$

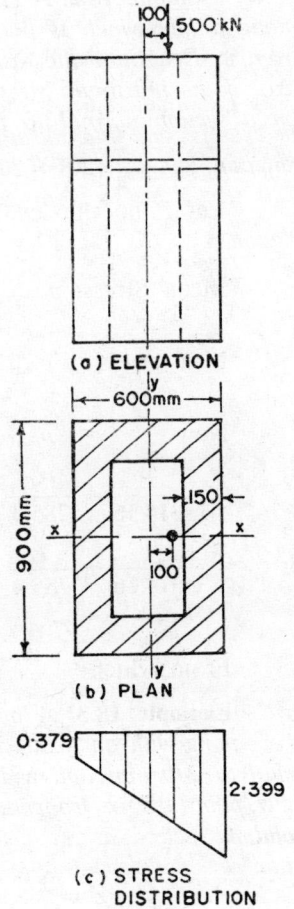

(a) ELEVATION

(b) PLAN

(c) STRESS DISTRIBUTION

FIG. 18.9

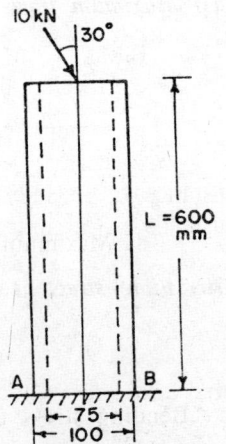

FIG. 18.10

∴   Stress at $B = p_0 + p_b = 2.52 + 44.70 = \mathbf{47.22\ N/mm^2}$ (comp.)

Stress at $A = p_0 - p_b = 2.52 - 44.70 = -42.18\ N/mm^2 = \mathbf{42.18\ N/mm^2}$ (tensile)

Example 18.6. *A short column of hollow circular section carries a compressive load W. The external and internal diameters are D and d respectively and the ratio of D/d is 7/5. Determine the maximum distance of the point of application of the load from the centre of the cross-section if no tensile stress is to exist in the material.*

Solution :   Let $e =$ eccentricity of the load

$$A = \frac{\pi}{4}(D^2 - d^2). \quad \text{But} \quad \frac{D}{d} = \frac{7}{5} \quad \text{or} \quad D = \frac{7}{5}d = 1.4\,d$$

∴ $$A = \frac{\pi}{4}\left[(1.4\,d)^2 - d^2\right] = 0.754\,d^2$$

Also
$$I = \frac{\pi}{64}(D^4 - d^4) = \frac{\pi}{64}\left[(1.4\,d)^4 - d^4\right] = 0.1395\,d^4$$

$$p_0 = \frac{W}{A} = \frac{W}{0.754\,d^2}$$

$$p_b = \pm\frac{M}{I}\,y_{max} = \pm\frac{W e}{I}\cdot\frac{d}{2} = \pm\frac{W\cdot e}{0.1395\,d^4}\times 0.7\,d$$

For no tension develop, $p_0 = p_b$

∴
$$\frac{W}{0.754\,d^2} = \frac{W e}{0.1993\,d^3}$$

From which
$$e = \frac{0.1993\,d^3}{0.754\,d^2} = \mathbf{0.2643\,d = 0.1888\,D}$$

Example 18.7. *A masonry pier of $2\,m \times 3\,m$ supports a vertical load of 50 kN as shown in Fig. 18.11. Find (a) stresses developed at each corner of the pier (b) what additional load should be placed at the centre of the pier, so that there is no tension any where in the pier section ? (c) what are the stresses at the corners with the additional load in the centre ?*

Solution : $B = 3$ m ; $D = 2$ m ; $A = B \times D = 3 \times 2 = 6$ m^2

$$I_{xx} = \frac{1}{12}\times 3\,(2)^3 = 2\ \text{m}^4 ; \quad I_{yy} = \frac{1}{12}\times 2\,(3)^3 = 4.5\ \text{m}^4$$

Eccentricity about $x-x$ axis $= e_x = 0.4$ m

Eccentricity about $y-y$ axis $= e_y = 0.8$ m

∴ Moment $M_{xx} = P\cdot e_x = 50 \times 0.4 = 20$ kN-m

Moment $M_{yy} = P\cdot e_y = 50 \times 0.8 = 40$ kN-m

Distance of A and B from y-axis $= x_A = x_B = 1.5$ m

Distance of A and D from x-axis $= y_A = y_D = 1$ m

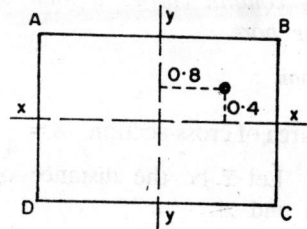

FIG. 18.11

Stress at corner A: $p_A = \dfrac{P}{A} + \dfrac{M_{xx}}{I_{xx}}\cdot y_A - \dfrac{M_{yy}}{I_{yy}}\cdot x_A = \dfrac{50}{6} + \dfrac{20}{2}\times 1 - \dfrac{40}{4.5}\times 1.5$

$$= 8.33 + 10 - 13.35 = \mathbf{5\ kN/m^2}$$

Stress at corner B: $p_B = \dfrac{P}{A} + \dfrac{M_{xx}}{I_{xx}}\,y_B + \dfrac{M_{yy}}{I_{yy}}\cdot x_B = \dfrac{50}{6} + \dfrac{20}{2}\times 1 + \dfrac{40}{4.5}\times 1.5$

$$= 8.33 + 10 + 13.33 = \mathbf{31.66\ kN/m^2}$$

Stress at corner C: $p_C = \dfrac{P}{A} - \dfrac{M_{xx}}{I_{xx}} . y_C + \dfrac{M_{yy}}{I_{yy}} . x_C = \dfrac{50}{6} - \dfrac{20}{2} \times 1 + \dfrac{40}{4.5} \times 1.5$

$$= 8.33 - 10 + 13.33 = \mathbf{11.66 \, kN/m^2}$$

Stress at corner D: $p_D = \dfrac{P}{A} - \dfrac{M_{xx}}{I_{xx}} . y_D - \dfrac{M_{yy}}{I_{yy}} . x_D = \dfrac{50}{6} - \dfrac{20}{2} \times 1 - \dfrac{40}{4.5} \times 1.5$

$$= 8.33 - 10 - 13.33 = \mathbf{-15 \, kN/m^2} \quad (i.e. \ \text{tension})$$

Additional load at the centre for no tension any where

Let W (kN) be the additional central load.

$\therefore$ Additional compressive stress $p_0 = \dfrac{W}{A} = \dfrac{W}{6} \, kN/m^2$

For no tension to develop at D, p_0 should be equal to p_D.

$\therefore \qquad \dfrac{W}{6} = 15$, from which $W = \mathbf{90 \, kN}$

Final stresses at corners due to the additional load

$$W = 90 \, kN ; \qquad \therefore \qquad p_0 = 90/6 = 15 \, kN/m^2$$

$$p_{AF} = p_A + p_0 = 5 + 15 = \mathbf{20 \, kN/m^2} \ (\text{Comp.})$$

$$p_{BF} = p_B + p_0 = 31.66 + 15 = \mathbf{46.66 \, kN/m^2} \ (\text{comp.})$$

$$p_{CF} = p_C + p_0 = 11.66 + 15 = \mathbf{26.66 \, kN/m^2} \ (\text{comp.})$$

$$p_{DF} = p_D + p_0 = -15 + 15 = \mathbf{zero}$$

Example 18.8. *A short hollow cylindrical cast iron column having outside diameter 400 mm and inside diameter 300 mm was cast in a factory. On inspection, it was found that the base is eccentric in such a way that the thickness varies from 30 mm at one end to 70 mm at the other. Calculate the extreme intensities of stress induced in the section if the column carries a load of 2000 kN along the axis of the bore.*

Solution :

Net area of cross-section, $A = \dfrac{\pi}{4}(400^2 - 300^2) = 54978 \, mm^2$

Let $\bar{x}$ be the distance of C.G. (G) of the section from end A.

Then $\qquad 54978 \bar{x} = \dfrac{\pi}{4}(400)^2 \times 200 - \dfrac{\pi}{4}(300)^2 \times 220$

$$= 25132741 - 15550884 = 9581857$$

From which $\qquad \bar{x} = 174.29 \, mm$

$\therefore$ Eccentricity $\quad e = AO - AG = 220 - 174.29$

$$= 45.71 \, mm$$

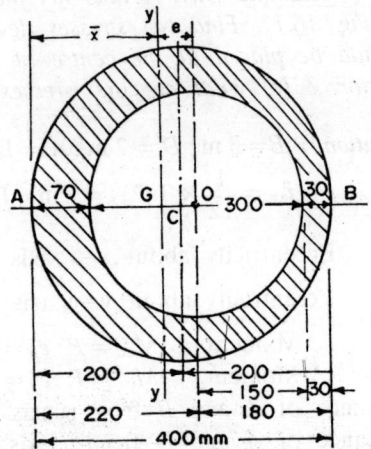

FIG. 18.12

$$I_{yy} = \left[\dfrac{\pi}{64} \times 400^4 + \dfrac{\pi}{4}(400)^2 (200 - 174.29)^2\right] - \left[\dfrac{\pi}{64} \times 300^4 + \dfrac{\pi}{4}(300)^2 (220 - 174.29)^2\right]$$

$$= 794.40 \times 10^6 \, mm^4$$

$$M = P \cdot e = 2000 \times 10^3 \times 45.71 = 91.42 \times 10^6 \text{ N-mm}$$

$$p_{bt} = \frac{M\bar{x}}{I_{yy}} = \frac{91.42 \times 10^6 \times 174.29}{794.40 \times 10^6} = 20.06 \text{ N/mm}^2$$

$$p_{bc} = \frac{M(400 - \bar{x})}{I_{yy}} = \frac{91.42 \times 10^6 (400 - 174.29)}{794.40 \times 10^6} = 25.97 \text{ N/mm}^2$$

Also,

$$p_0 = \frac{P}{A} = \frac{2000 \times 10^3}{54978} = 36.38 \text{ N/mm}^2 \text{ (comp.)}$$

∴

$$f_{max} = p_0 + p_{bc} = 36.38 + 25.97 = \mathbf{62.35 \ N/mm^2} \text{ (comp.)}$$

$$f_{min} = p_0 - p_{bt} = 36.38 - 20.06 = \mathbf{16.32 \ N/mm^2} \text{ (comp.)}$$

18.7. ADDITIONAL ILLUSTRATIVE EXAMPLES

Example 18.9. *A flat bar, 200 mm wide and 16 mm thick, carries an axial tensile load of 200 kN. A hole of 30 mm dia is punched at a distance of 60 mm from the axis of the bar. Find the maximum and minimum stress intensities at the weakest section of the flat.*

Solution :

Area of cross-section at section $x-x$ (weakest section)

$$= A = (200 - 30) \times 16 = 2720 \text{ mm}^2$$

Let the C.G. of the net section be at a distance e from the y-y axis of the bar. Taking moments of the individual areas about the y-y axis, we obtain.

$$e = \frac{(200 \times 16 \times 0) - 30 \times 16(-60)}{(200 \times 16) - (30 \times 16)} = \frac{28800}{2720} = 10.588 \text{ mm}$$

Now $I_{yy} = \dfrac{1}{12} \times 16 (200)^3 - \left[\dfrac{1}{12} \times 16 (30)^3 + 16 \times 30 (60)^2 \right]$

$$= 890.3 \times 10^4 \text{ mm}^4$$

∴ $\qquad I_{gg} = I_{yy} - (a_1 - a_2) e^2$

$$= 890.3 \times 10^4 - (200 \times 16 - 30 \times 16)(10.588)^2 = 859.8 \times 10^4 \text{ mm}^4$$

$$y_c = \frac{200}{2} - 10.588 = 89.412 \text{ mm}$$

$$y_t = \frac{200}{2} + 10.588 = 110.588 \text{ mm}$$

∴ $M = P \cdot e = 200 \times 10^3 \times 10.588 = 2.1176 \times 10^6 \text{ N-mm}$

∴

$$p_{bc} = \frac{M}{I_{gg}} \cdot y_c = \frac{2.1176 \times 10^6}{859.8 \times 10^4} \times 89.412 = 22.02 \text{ N/mm}^2 \text{ (comp.)}$$

$$p_{bt} = \frac{M}{I_{gg}} y_t = \frac{2.1176 \times 10^6}{859.8 \times 10^4} \times 110.588 = 27.24 \text{ N/mm}^2 \text{ (tensile)}$$

$$p_0 = \frac{P}{A} = \frac{200 \times 10^3}{2720} = 73.53 \text{ N/mm}^2 \text{ (tensile)}$$

∴ $f_{max} = p_0 + p_{bt} = 73.53 + 27.24 = \mathbf{100.77 \ N/mm^2}$ (tensile)

$f_{min} = p_0 - p_{bc} = 73.53 - 22.02 = \mathbf{51.51 \ N/mm^2}$ (tensile)

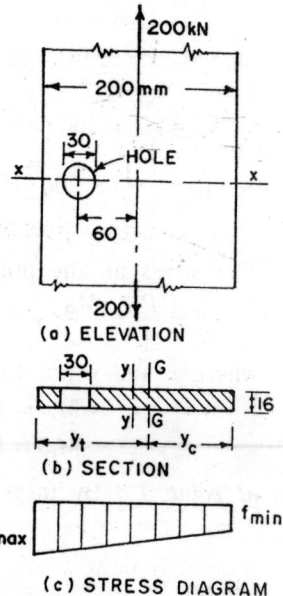

(a) ELEVATION

(b) SECTION

(c) STRESS DIAGRAM

FIG. 18.13

Example 18.10. *A short C.I. column has a rectangular section 160 mm × 200 mm with a circular hole of 80 mm diameter as shown in Fig. 18.14. It carries an eccentric load of 100 kN, located as shown in the Fig. Determine the values of the stresses at the four corners of the section.* (Based on Oxford University)

Solution :

The net section is symmetrical about X-X axis. Let the Y-Y axis be situated at a distance $\bar{x}$ from the face AD.

Let a_1 = area of solid rectangle

$\qquad = 160 \times 200 = 32000 \text{ mm}^2$

$\bar{x}_1$ = distance of c.g. of rectangle from AD

$\qquad = 80 \text{ mm}$

Let a_2 = area of the circular hole

$\qquad = \dfrac{\pi}{4}(80)^2 = 5026 \text{ mm}^2$

$\bar{x}_2$ = distance of c.g. of hole from $AD = 60 \text{ mm}$

Hence $\quad \bar{x} = \dfrac{a_1 \bar{x}_1 - a_2 \bar{x}_2}{a_1 - a_2} = \dfrac{32000 \times 80 - 5026 \times 60}{32000 - 5026}$

$\qquad = \dfrac{2258440}{26974} = 83.73 \text{ mm}$

FIG. 18.14

$I_{xx} = \dfrac{1}{12} \times 160 \, (200)^3 - \dfrac{\pi}{64}(80)^4 = 10466 \times 10^4 \text{ mm}^4$

$I_{yy} = \left[\dfrac{1}{12} \times 200 \, (160)^2 + 200 \times 160 \, (83.73 - 80)^2 \right] - \left[\dfrac{\pi}{64}(80)^4 + \dfrac{\pi}{4}(80)^2 \, (83.73 - 60)^2 \right]$

$\qquad = 6871 \times 10^4 - 484 \times 10^4 = 6387 \times 10^4 \text{ mm}^4$

The stress at any point, in general, is given by

$$p = \frac{P}{A} + \frac{M_{xx}}{I_{xx}} \cdot y + \frac{M_{yy}}{I_{yy}} \cdot x$$

where x and y are the coordinates of any point with respect to the coordinate axes,

$$M_{xx} = P \cdot e_x = 100 \times 10^3 \times 50 = 5 \times 10^6 \text{ N-mm;}$$

$$M_{yy} = P \cdot e_y = 100 \times 10^3 \times (83.73 - 60) = 2.373 \times 10^6 \text{ N-mm}$$

Stress at point A : By inspection

$$p_A = \frac{P}{A} + \frac{M_{xx}}{I_{xx}} \cdot y_A + \frac{M_{yy}}{I_{yy}} \cdot x_A$$

where $\qquad y_A = 100 \text{ mm and } x_A = 83.73 \text{ mm}$

$\therefore \qquad p_A = \dfrac{100 \times 10^3}{26974} + \dfrac{5 \times 10^6}{10466 \times 10^4} \times 100 + \dfrac{2.373 \times 10^6}{6387 \times 10^4} \times 83.73 = \mathbf{11.6 \text{ N/mm}^2}$

Stress at point B : By inspection

$$p_B = \frac{P}{A} + \frac{M_{xx}}{I_{xx}} \cdot y_B - \frac{M_{yy}}{I_{yy}} \cdot x_B$$

where $\qquad y_B = 100 \text{ mm and } x_B = 160 - 83.73 = 76.27 \text{ mm}$

$\therefore \qquad p_B = \dfrac{100 \times 10^3}{26974} + \dfrac{5 \times 10^6}{10466 \times 10^4} \times 100 - \dfrac{2.373 \times 10^6}{6387 \times 10^4} \times 76.27 = \mathbf{5.65 \text{ N/mm}^2}$

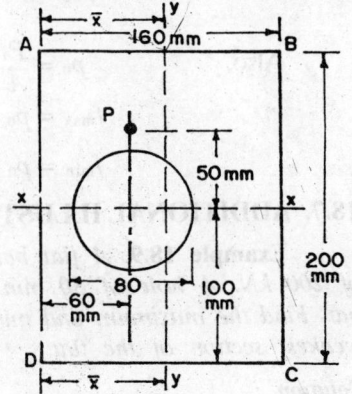

Stress at point C : By inspection

$$p_C = \frac{P}{A} - \frac{M_{xx}}{I_{xx}} y_C - \frac{M_{yy}}{I_{yy}} . x_C$$

where $\qquad y_C = 100$ mm and $x_C = 160 - 83.73 = 76.27$ mm

$\therefore \qquad p_C = \dfrac{100 \times 10^3}{26974} - \dfrac{5 \times 10^6}{10466 \times 10^4} \times 100 - \dfrac{2.373 \times 10^6}{6387 \times 10^4} \times 76.27$

$$= -3.90 \text{ N/mm}^2 = 3.90 \text{ N/mm}^2 \qquad \text{(tension)}$$

Stress at point D : By inspection :

$$p_D = \frac{P}{A} - \frac{M_{xx}}{I_{xx}} y_D + \frac{M_{yy}}{I_{yy}} . x_D$$

where $\qquad y_D = 100$ mm and $x_D = \bar{x} = 83.23$

$\therefore \qquad p_D = \dfrac{100 \times 10^3}{26974} - \dfrac{5 \times 10^6}{10466 \times 10^4} \times 100 + \dfrac{2.373 \times 10^6}{6387 \times 10^4} \times 83.23 = \mathbf{2.02 \text{ N/mm}^2}$

Example 18.11. *A bracket shown in Fig. 18.15 (a) is pulled with a force of P = 5 kN acting as shown. (a) Calculate the maximum and minimum normal stresses on the section XX; (b) Show the distribution of stress across the section by means of a diagram (c) How far from the upper edge of the XX plane is the horizontal plane of zero stress ?*

Solution :

Horizontal component of P

$= 5 \cos 45° = 3.536$ kN

Vertical component of P

$= 5 \sin 45° = 3.536$ kN

The horizontal component of P, being normal to section XX, will induce direct stress p_0, while both the horizontal and vertical components of P will induce bending moments M_1 and M_2 about the section AB both the moments M_1 and M_2 will cause tension at the upper edge (A) of the section and compression at the lower edge (B).

Now M_1 due to horizontal component $= 3.536 \times 37.5 = 132.6$ kN-mm $= 132.6 \times 10^3$ N-mm

M_2 due to vertical component $= 3.536 \times 75 = 265.2$ kN-m

$= 265.2 \times 10^3$ N-mm

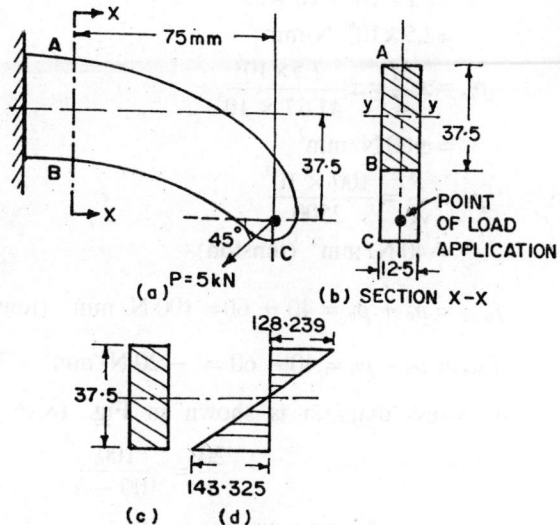

FIG 18.15

Area of cross-section at $XX = A = 12.5 \times 37.5 = 468.75 \text{ mm}^2$

$$I \text{ about } y\text{-}y \text{ axis} = \frac{b\,d^3}{12} = \frac{12.5}{12}(37.5)^3 = 54932 \text{ mm}^2$$

Direct stress $\qquad p_0 = \dfrac{P_H}{A} = \dfrac{3.536 \times 10^3}{468.75} = 7.543 \text{ N/mm}^2$

Bending stress $\qquad p_b = \pm \dfrac{M}{I}\left(\dfrac{d}{2}\right) = \pm \dfrac{(132.6 + 265.2)\,10^3}{54932} \times \dfrac{37.5}{2} = \pm 135.782 \text{ N/mm}^2$

$\therefore\ f_t$ (at the top edge) $= p_b - p_0 = 135.782 - 7.543 = \mathbf{128.239\ N/mm^2}$ (tension)

f_b (at the bottom edge) $= p_b + p_0 = 135.782 + 7.543 = \mathbf{143.325\ N/mm^2}$ (comp)

Example 18.12. *A flat steel bar 100 mm × 25 mm was subjected to an eccentric tensile load of 100 kN, under a testing machine as shown in Fig. 18.16(a). An extensometer placed in line with the load recorded extension of 0.07 mm on a gauge length of 200 mm. Calculate the maximum and minimum stresses set up in the bar and also find out Young's modulus of the material.*

Solution :

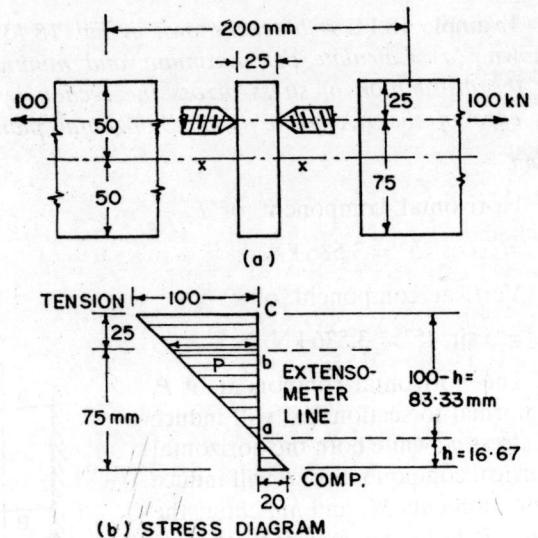

$$A = 100 \times 25 = 2500 \text{ mm}^2$$
$$I_{xx} = \frac{1}{12} \times 25\,(100)^3$$
$$= 208.3 \times 10^4 \text{ mm}^4$$
$$Z_{xx} = \frac{I_{xx}}{d/2} = \frac{208.3 \times 10^4}{50}$$
$$= 41.67 \times 10^3$$
$$e = 50 - 25 = 25 \text{ mm}$$
$$M = P.e = 100 \times 10^3 \times 25$$
$$= 2.5 \times 10^6 \text{ N-mm}$$
$\therefore \qquad p_b = \pm \dfrac{M}{Z} = \pm \dfrac{2.5 \times 10^6}{41.67 \times 10^3}$
$$\approx \pm 60 \text{ N/mm}^2$$
Also, $\qquad p_0 = \dfrac{P}{A} = \dfrac{100 \times 10^3}{2500}$
$$= 40 \text{ N/mm}^2 \text{ (tension)}$$

FIG. 18.16

$\therefore \qquad f_{max} = p_0 + p_b = 40 + 60 = 100 \text{ N/mm}^2$ (tensile)

$f_{min} = p_0 - p_b = 40 - 60 = -20 \text{ N/mm}^2 = 20 \text{ N/mm}^2$ (comp.)

The stress diagram is shown in Fig. 18.16 (*b*), from which we get

$$\frac{20}{h} = \frac{100}{100 - h}$$

or $\qquad\qquad 20\,(100 - h) = 100\,h$

From which, we get $\qquad h = \dfrac{2000}{120} = 16.67$ mm

Now measured strain, $\qquad \varepsilon = \dfrac{0.07}{200} = 3.5 \times 10^{-4}$

Let p be the stress corresponding to the measured strain of 3.5×10^{-4}.

Then from the stress\diagram, $\dfrac{p}{100} = \dfrac{ab}{ac} = \dfrac{83.33 - 25}{83.33}$

From which $\qquad p = 70 \text{ N/mm}^2$

Now $\qquad E = \dfrac{\text{stress}}{\text{strain}} = \dfrac{70}{3.5 \times 10^{-4}} = \mathbf{2 \times 10^5 \text{ N/mm}^2}$

PROBLEMS

1. Determine the maximum and minimum stress intensities set up in steel flat 150 mm wide and 20 mm thick subjected to a pull of 300 kN, which is off the geometrical axis by 4 mm in the plane which bisects the thickness.

2. A tensile test specimen has a diameter 15 mm. The line of pull is parallel to the axis of the specimen, but is displaced from it. Calculate the distance of the line of pull from the axis of the specimen when the maximum stress is 20 percent greater than the nominal mean stress on a section normal to the axis. If a load is 10 kN, plot a diagram showing how the stress distribution varies across the section. Quote the maximum and minimum values of the stress.

3. A cantilever 160 mm broad is at the wall subjected to a S.F. of 160 kN and a B.M. of 100 kN-m. Assuming uniformly varying pressure between the beam and its seating, find what length of the beam must be built into the wall in order that the pressure shall not exceed 4 N/mm^2.

4. A short C.I. column is hollow section 200 mm external dia. and of uniform thickness, 40 mm.

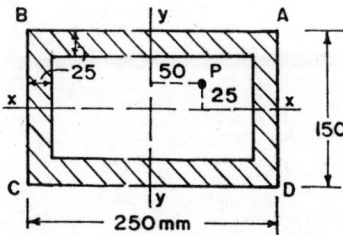

FIG. 18.17

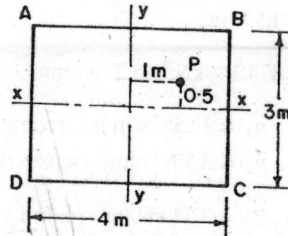

FIG. 18.18

A vertical compressive load acts at an eccentricity of 60 mm from the axis of the column. If the maximum permissible stresses are 70 N/mm^2 compression and 18 N/mm^2 tension, find the greatest allowable load. Assuming this load acting, plot a diagram of stress variation across the section.

5. The cross-section of short vertical column is as shown in Fig. 18.17. A vertical load of 125 kN is applied at the point P. Determine the stresses at corners A, B, C and D.

6. A masonry pier of $3 \text{ m} \times 4 \text{ m}$ supports a vertical load of 80 kN as shown in Fig. 18.18.

(a). Find the stresses developed at each corner of the pier. (b) What additional load should be placed at the centre of the pier so that there is no tension any where in the pier section on ? What are the stresses at the corners with the additional load at the centre ? (Based on U.L.)

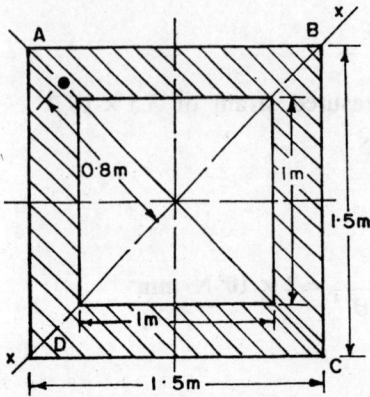

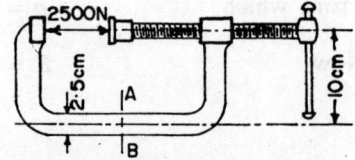

FIG. 18.19   FIG. 18.20

7. Calculate the normal stresses at the four outside corners of a horizontal section of short hollow pier 1.5 m square outside and 1 m square inside supporting a vertical point load of 500 kN on a diagonal and 0.8 m from the vertical axis of the pier. Neglect the self weight of the pier.

8. Find the maximum stress on the section AB of the cramp when a pressure of 7.5 kN is exerted by the screw. The section is rectangular, 25 mm by 10 mm
(Cambridge)

ANSWERS

1. $f_{max} = 116\ \text{N/mm}^2$ (tensile) ; $f_{min} = 84\ \text{N/mm}^2$ (tensile)

2. $e = 0.375$ mm; $f_{max} = 67.91\ \text{N/mm}^2$ (tensile), $f_{min} = 45.27\ \text{N/mm}^2$ (tension)

3.   1.59 m

4.   474.14 kN; 65.2 N/mm^2

5. $p_A = 17.58\ \text{N/mm}^2$ (comp.) ; $p_B = 5.44\ \text{N/mm}^2$ (comp.),
       $p_C = 3.3\ \text{N/mm}^2$ (tension) ; $p_D = 8.84\ \text{N/mm}^2$ (comp.)

6. (a) $p_A = 3.34\ \text{kN/m}^2$ (comp.) ; $p_B = 23.34\ \text{kN/m}^2$ (comp.),
        $p_C = 10\ \text{kN/m}^2$ (tension) ; $p_D = 10\ \text{kN/m}^2$ (tension),
   (b) $p_A = 13.34\ \text{kN/m}^2$ (comp.) ; $p_B = 33.34\ \text{kN/m}^2$ (comp.),
        $p_C = 20\ \text{kN/m}^2$ (tension) ; $p_D = 0$.

7. $(f_{max})_A = 1653.5\ \text{kN/m}^2$ (comp.)
       $(f_{max})_{B,D} = 400\ \text{kN/m}^2$ (comp.)
       $(f_{max})_C = 853.5\ \text{kN/m}^2$ (tension)

8. $f_{max} = 250\ \text{N/mm}^2$ (tensile) ; $f_{min} = 230\ \text{N/mm}^2$ (comp.)

Masonry Structures
(Retaining Walls, Dams and Chimneys)

19.1. INTRODUCTION

Masonry is one of the most common building medium used for construction. Common examples of masonry structures are : (*i*) masonry walls and masonry columns, (*ii*) masonry retaining walls, (*iii*) masonry dams, (*iv*) masonry chimneys and (*v*) masonry arches. *Masonry* may be defined as the construction of *building units* bonded together with *mortar*. The building units(commonly known as *masonry units*) may be stones, bricks or precast blocks of concrete. When stones are used as the building units or building blocks, we have *stone masonry*. Similarly, in *brick masonry*, bricks are used as the building units. A *composite masonry* is a construction in more than one type of building units. Masonry work is one of the major building crafts and one of the oldest.

Masonry walls are used almost in all the buildings. These may be either load bearing walls or partition walls. Unless otherwise specified, a *wall* may be defined as a vertical load-bearing member, the width (i.e. length) of which exceeds four times the thickness. In contrast to this, a *column* is an isolated load-bearing member, the width of which does not exceed four times the thickness. Load bearing walls carry super-imposed loads, transferred through roof etc in addition to their own weight. Load bearing walls are structurally efficient when the load is uniformly distributed and when the structure is so planned that eccentricity of loading on the wall is as small as possible. The strength of a wall is measured in terms of its resistance to the stresses set up in it by its own weight, by super-imposed loads and by lateral pressure such as wind etc, and its stability by its resistance to overturning by lateral forces and buckling caused by excessive slenderness.

An *arch* is a structure constructed of wedge-shaped units (stones or bricks) jointed together with mortar and spanning an opening to support the weight of the wall above it along with super-imposed loads. Due to wedge like form, the units support each other, the load tends to make them compact and enables them to transmit the pressure downwards to their supports. An arch transmits the super-imposed load to the side walls (or abutments) through friction between the surfaces of voussoirs and the cohesion of mortar. Every element of arch remains in compression. It has also to bear transverse shears. Masonry arches are commonly used over openings (i.e. doors, windows etc) in buildings. They are also used in bridges.

A *masonry retaining wall* is the masonry structure constructed for maintaining the ground surface(or-earthfill) at different elevations on either side of it. The material supported by the retaining wall is called *backfill*, the top surface of which may either be horizontal or inclined. Such retaining walls are also known as *gravity retaining walls* as they resist the lateral earth pressure by their own weight in contrast to the cantilever and counter-fort retaining walls in which pressure is resisted by bending action. Due to this reason, masonry retaining walls are thicker in section.

A *masonry dam* is a masonry structure which retains water on its one side, usually known as the upstream side. The upstream face of a masonry dam may be either straight and vertical or may be inclined, depending upon its height. The top width of a masonry dam depends both upon the roadway requirements as well as on economy. A masonry dam may be either a *low height dam* or a *high dam*. We shall discuss here only the low height dams. A masonry dam is subjected to a number of horizontal forces such as lateral water pressure(which is the major force), wave pressure, silt pressure and earthquake pressure, and vertical forces consisting of its own weight plus the component of weight of water supported by its upstream inclined face (if any). Due to these forces, the resultant force acts inclined on the plane lamina at any height, the point of application of which is away from the centre of lamina. The normal stress distribution is therefore not uniform. In order that no tension should develop any where on the base, the resultant should be within the middle third. Also, the dam should be safe against overturning.

Masonry chimneys are used to escape the flue gases to such a height that diffusion of gases takes place so that they do not contaminate the surroundings. The height of chimney is fixed to provide the required draft. Masonry chimneys are generally built in brick masonry, using either the common bricks or radial bricks. Though masonry chimneys may have circular, square, hexagonal or octagonal shape in plan, circular plan shape chimneys are usually preferred. Chimneys are lined from inside with fire bricks. Apart from self weight and the weight of lining, chimneys are subjected to lateral forces due to wind and/or earthquake.

19.2. GENERAL CONDITIONS OF STRENGTH AND STABILITY OF MASONRY STRUCTURES

Masonry structures, such as retaining walls, dams, chimneys etc, are subjected to net vertical force ΣV and net horizontal force ΣH, due to self weight, superimposed loads and lateral loads. The resultant R of ΣV and ΣH strikes the base at some eccentricity with respect to the c.g. of the section. Due to this, the normal stress distribution at any section, including the base section, will not be uniform. If the eccentricity *(e)* is large, there may be a possibility of development of tensile normal stress at the heel of the section. Masonry units are jointed with the help of mortar which is supposed to be weak in tension. Also, the maximum normal compressive stress at the other end may exceed the permissible compressive stress for the material. In addition to these strength criteria, the structure may be unstable because of the overturning effect of lateral force and unstable against the sliding effect. Hence we have four *safety criteria*.

(*a*) **Strength criteria**

1. The masonry structure should be safe against development of *tension* any where in the section, i.e. no tension should develop.

2. The masonry structure should be safe against *crushing*, i.e. the maximum compressive stress should be equal to or less than the safe compressive stress for the material.

(*b*) **Stability criteria**:

3. The structure should be safe against *overturning*, i.e. the restoring moment should be greater than the overturning moment.

4. The structure should be safe against *sliding*, i.e. the horizontal shear at any plane should be less than the available frictional force between the successive layers.

Strength criteria

Let us consider a plane lamina of width B, subjected to a net vertical force ΣV and a net horizontal force ΣH. Let the resultant force R strike the base at some eccentricity e, as marked in Fig. 19.1(a). This resultant R can be again resolved into two components: (i) vertical component ΣV acting at an eccentricity e and, (ii) a horizontal component, or horizontal shear ΣH acting horizontally along the section, as shown by dotted arrows in Fig. 19.1(a). If we introduce equal and opposite ΣV forces at the centre C of the lamina, we get the following system of forces:

(i) An axial force ΣV acting at C

(ii) A bending couple $M = e \, \Sigma V$

and (iii) A horizontal force ΣH along the base AB.

The axial force ΣV will cause a direct compressive stress p_0 given by

$$p_0 = \frac{\Sigma V}{A} \qquad \text{...}(a)$$

where A is the area of cross-section of the base. The distribution of p_0 is shown in Fig. 19.1(b).

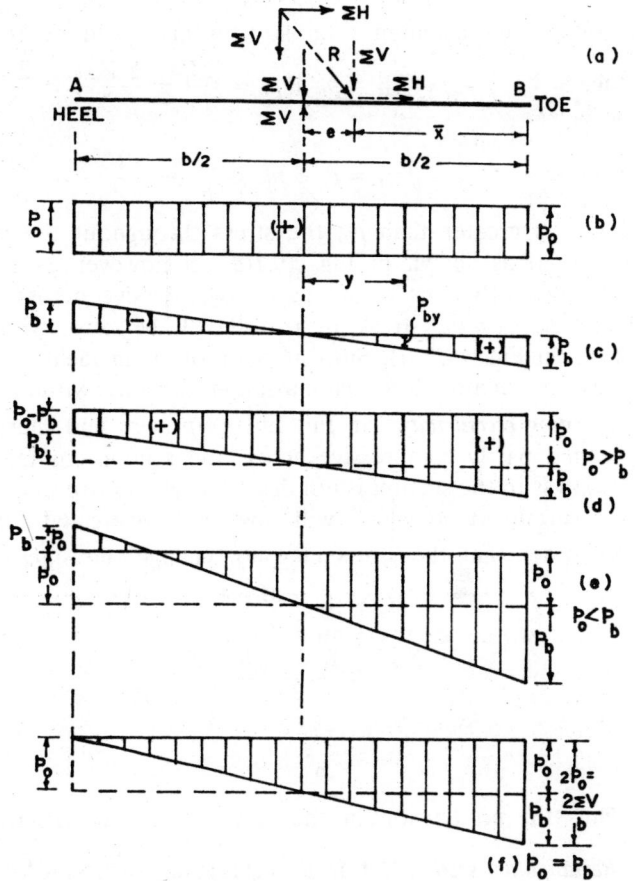

FIG. 19.1. STRENGTH CRITERIA

The bending couple (or moment) will cause longitudinal tensile and compressive stresses. The fibre stress p_b at any distance y from N.A. is given by

$$p_{by} = \frac{M}{I_x} \cdot y = \frac{\Sigma V \cdot e}{I_x} \cdot y \qquad \text{...}(b)$$

Hence the total stress at any section is given by

$$f = \frac{\Sigma V}{A} + \frac{\Sigma V \cdot e \cdot y}{I_x} \qquad \text{...}(19.1)$$

The *extreme fibre stress* p_b due to bending is given by

$$p_b = \frac{M}{Z_x} = \frac{\Sigma V \cdot e}{Z_x} = \frac{\Sigma V \cdot e}{I_x} \cdot \frac{b}{2} \qquad \text{...}(19.2 \ a)$$

where b = depth of the section and , $I_x = Ak^2$, where k is the radius of gyration of the section with regard to N.A.

$$\therefore \qquad p_b = \frac{\Sigma V \cdot e \cdot b}{2 A k^2} \qquad \qquad \ldots(19.2)$$

Again the maximum total stresses are given by the following :

At toe, $\qquad f_{max} = p_0 + p_b = \dfrac{\Sigma V}{b} + \dfrac{\Sigma V \cdot e}{Z_x} = \dfrac{\Sigma V}{b}\left(1 + \dfrac{b \cdot e}{Z_x}\right) \qquad \ldots(19.3\ a)$

At heel, $\qquad f_{min} = p_0 - p_b = \dfrac{\Sigma V}{b} - \dfrac{\Sigma V \cdot e}{Z_x} = \dfrac{\Sigma V}{b}\left(1 - \dfrac{b \cdot e}{Z_x}\right) \qquad \ldots(19.3\ b)$

If p_0 is greater than p_b, the stress throughout the section will be of the same sign (i.e. compressive) as shown in Fig. 19.1(d). If however, p_0 is less than p_b, the stress will change sign, being partly tensile and partly compressive across the section. Such a condition is not desirable. If $p_0 = p_b$, stress at the heel will be zero, while the stress at the toe will be $2p_0$, as shown in Fig. 19.1 (f). Such a condition is an ideal condition, wherein, we are in a position to stress the material to its maximum capacity without causing tension at the other end.

Limiting eccentricity : In Fig 19.1(e), $p_0 < p_b$ and therefore stress changes sign, being partly tensile and partly compressive across the section. In masonry structures, the development of tensile stress in the section is not desirable as they are weak in tension. This limits the eccentricity e to a certain value which will now be investigated for different sections.

In order that the stress may not change the sign from compressive to tensile, we have

$$p_0 \geq p_b \geq \frac{M}{Z}$$

or $\qquad \dfrac{\Sigma V}{A} \geq \dfrac{\Sigma V \cdot e \cdot b}{2 I} \geq \dfrac{\Sigma V \cdot e \cdot b}{2 A k^2}$

or $\qquad e \leq \dfrac{2 k^2}{b} \qquad \qquad \ldots(19.4)$

Thus for no tension in the section, the eccentricity must not exceed $\dfrac{2 k^2}{b}$.

Rectangular section : For a rectangular section of *unit width* and depth b,

$$I = \frac{1 \times 1}{12} b^3 = \frac{b^3}{12} \text{ and } A = b \times 1 = b$$

$\therefore \qquad k^2 = \dfrac{I}{A} = \dfrac{b^2}{12}$

Hence $\qquad e \leq \dfrac{2}{b} \cdot \dfrac{b^2}{12} \leq \dfrac{b}{6}$

or $\qquad e_{max} = \dfrac{b}{6} \qquad \qquad \ldots(19.5)$

The value of eccentricity can be on either side of the geometrical axis. Thus, the stress will be of the same sign throughout the section if the load line is within the middle third of the section. Thus, in case of rectangular section, the maximum intensities of extreme fibre stresses are given by

$$f = \frac{\Sigma V}{A} \pm \frac{\Sigma V \cdot e}{Z_x} = \frac{\Sigma V}{b \times 1} \pm \frac{\Sigma V \cdot e}{\frac{1}{6} \times 1 \times b^2} = \frac{\Sigma V}{b}\left(1 \pm \frac{6 e}{b}\right) \qquad \ldots(19.6)$$

when $\qquad$ $e = \dfrac{b}{6}$, $\qquad$ $f = \dfrac{\Sigma V}{b}(1 \pm 1)$

or $\qquad$ $f_{max} = \dfrac{2\,\Sigma V}{b}$ and $f_{min} = 0$

This condition is shown in Fig 19.1(f)

Solid circular section

For a solid circular section of diameter b, $I = \dfrac{\pi}{64}b^4$ and $A = \dfrac{\pi}{4}b^2$

$\therefore$ $\qquad$ $k^2 = \dfrac{I}{A} = \dfrac{b^2}{16}$

$\therefore$ $\qquad$ $e \leq \dfrac{2\,k^2}{b} \leq \dfrac{2}{b} \times \dfrac{b^2}{16} \leq \dfrac{b}{8}$ $\qquad$ .....(19.8)

Thus, in order that tension is not developed, the load line must fall within the *middle fourth* of the section.

Hollow circular section

For a hollow circular section, having external diameter B and internal diameter b,

$$I = \dfrac{\pi}{64}(B^4 - b^4) \text{ and } A = \dfrac{\pi}{4}(B^2 - b^2)$$

$\therefore$ $\qquad$ $k^2 = \dfrac{I}{A} = \dfrac{B^4 - b^4}{16\,(B^2 - b^2)} = \dfrac{B^2 + b^2}{16}$

$\therefore$ $\qquad$ $e \leq \dfrac{2\,k^2}{B} \leq \dfrac{2}{B}\left(\dfrac{B^2 + b^2}{16}\right) \leq \dfrac{B^2 + b^2}{8\,B}$ $\qquad$ ...(19.8 a)

Stability criteria

Safety against overturning :

The lateral forces (i.e. forces due to earth pressure in retaining walls, water pressure in dams and wind forces in chimneys and tall walls) cause overturning moments (ΣM_O) in the masonry structure endangering its stability. This must be resisted entirely or partly by the body forces (i.e. weight) of the structure, by producing the resisting moments (ΣM_R) about the toe. In fact, the resisting moments must be much more than the overturning moments. The *stability factor or factor of safety against overturning* is given by

$$\text{F.S.} = \dfrac{\Sigma M_R}{\Sigma M_O} \qquad \qquad ...(19.9\ a)$$

The minimum value of F.S. against overturning should be 1.5.

Safety against sliding : The masonry structure should be safe against sliding, under the action of lateral forces (ΣH), by the development of appropriate frictional forces. Let μ be the coefficient of friction. Mobilised frictional force $= \mu\,\Sigma V$

This should be much more than the lateral force (ΣH) acting at the base. The factor of safety against sliding is given by

$$\text{F.S.} = \dfrac{\mu\,\Sigma V}{\Sigma H} \qquad ...(19.9\ b)$$

This factor of safety should be greater than 1.5.

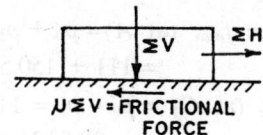

$\mu\,\Sigma V$ = FRICTIONAL FORCE

FIG. 19.2

Example 19.1. *Find the maximum and minimum stress intensities induced on the base of a masonry wall 6 m high, 4 m wide and 1.5 m thick, subjected to a horizontal wind pressure of 1.5 kN/m^2 acting on the 4 m side. The unit weight of masonry may be taken as 22.4 kN/m^3.*

Solution.

The direct stress (or axial stress) due to self weight of masonry is given by:

$$p_0 = \gamma H = 22.4 \times 6 = 134.4 \text{ kN/m}^2$$

The wind pressure $\quad P_w = p_w . L . h = 1.5 \times 4 \times 6 = 36 \text{ kN}$

Moment due to wind, $\quad M_w = P_w . \dfrac{h}{2} = 36 \times \dfrac{6}{2} = 108 \text{ kN-m}$

$$Z = \frac{1}{6} L b^2 = \frac{1}{6} \times 4 \, (1.5)^2 = 1.5 \text{ m}^3$$

$\therefore \qquad p_b = \dfrac{M_w}{Z} = \dfrac{108}{1.5} = 72 \text{ kN/m}^2$

$\therefore \qquad f_{max} = p_0 + p_b = 134.4 + 72 = 206.4 \text{ kN/m}^2 \text{ (comp.)}$

$\qquad f_{min} = p_0 - p_b = 134.4 - 72 = 62.4 \text{ kN/m}^2 \text{ (comp.)}$

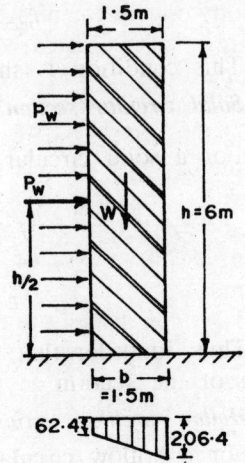

FIG. 19.3

Example 19.2. *Calculate the normal stresses at the four outside corners of a horizontal section of short hollow pier 1.5 metre square outside and 1 metre square inside supporting a vertical point load of 60 kN on a diagonal and 0.8 metre from the vertical axis of the pier. The unit weight of pier masonry may be taken as 21 kN/m^3. The height of pier is 3 m.*

Solution

Total self weight, $\quad W_s = (1.5^2 - 1^2) \times 3 \times 21 = 78.75 \text{ kN}$

$\therefore$ Uniform stress, $\quad p_0 = \dfrac{W + W_s}{A} = \dfrac{60 + 78.75}{1.5^2 - 1^2} = 111 \text{ kN/m}^2 \text{ (compressive)}$

$$I_{xx} = \frac{1}{12} \, (1.5^4 - 1^4) = 0.339 \text{ m}^4$$

$$Z_{xx} = \frac{I_{xx} \sqrt{2}}{b} = \frac{0.339 \sqrt{2}}{1.5} = 0.319 \text{ m}^3$$

Moment $\quad M = 60 \times 0.80 = 48 \text{ kN-m}$

$\therefore \; p_b$ at point $A = \dfrac{M}{Z} = \dfrac{48}{0.319}$

$\qquad = 150.5 \text{ kN/m}^2 \text{ (comp.)}$

p_b at point $C = 150.5 \text{ kN/m}^2 \text{ (tensile)}$

p_b at points B and $D = 0$

Hence f_{max} (at A) $= p_0 + p_b$

$\qquad = 111 + 150.5 = 261.5 \text{ kN/m}^2 \text{ (comp.)}$

f_{max} (at C) $= p_0 - p_b = 111 - 150.5$

$\qquad = -39.5 \text{ kN/m}^2 \text{ (i.e., tensile)}$

f_{max} (at B and D) $= p_0 = 111 \text{ kN/m}^2 \text{ (comp.)}$

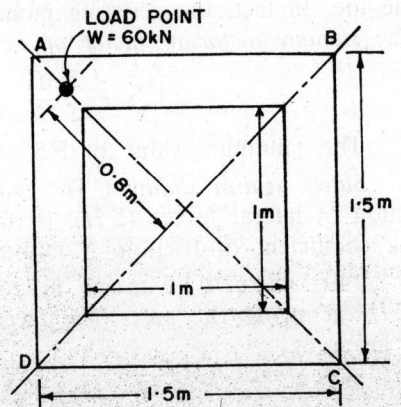

FIG. 19.4.

19.3. LATERAL EARTH PRESSURE ON RETAINING WALLS

A *retaining wall* or retaining structure is used for maintaining the ground surfaces at different elevations on either side of it. Whenever embankments are involved in construction, retaining walls are usually necessary. In the construction of buildings having basements, retaining walls are mandatory. Similarly in bridge work, the wing walls and abutments etc. are designed as retaining walls, to resist earth pressure along with superimposed loads. The material retained or supported by a retaining wall is called *backfill* which may have its top surface horizontal or inclined. The position of the backfill lying above the horizontal plane at the elevation of the top of a wall is called the *surcharge,* and its inclination to the horizontal is called the *surcharge angle* β.

In the design of retaining walls or other retaining structures, it is necessary to compute the lateral earth pressure exerted by the retaining mass of soil. The equation of finding out the lateral earth pressure against retaining wall is one of the oldest in the Civil Engineering field. The *plastic state of stress,* when the failure is imminent, was investigated by Rankine in 1860. A lot of theoretical and experimental work has been done in this field and many theories and hypothesis have been proposed.*

Retaining walls may be classified according to their mode of resisting the earth pressure, and according to their shape. Following are some of common types of retaining walls (Fig. 19.5).

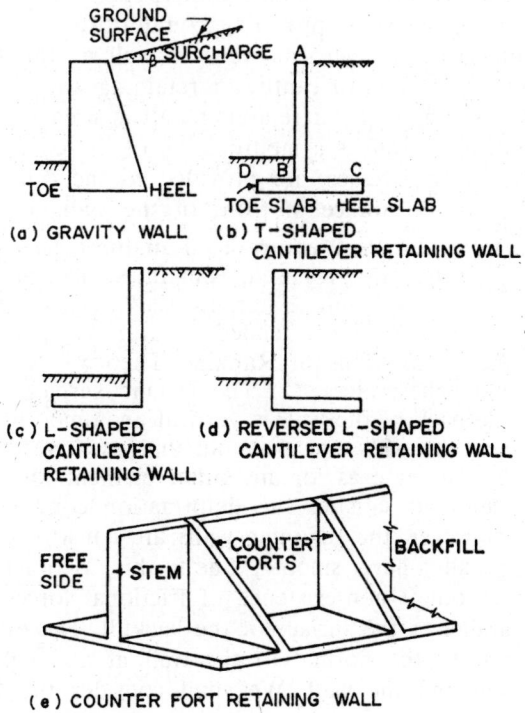

FIG. 19.5. VARIOUS TYPES OF RETAINING WALLS.

(*i*) Gravity walls
(*ii*) Cantilever retaining walls : (*a*) T-shaped (*b*) L-shaped
(*iii*) Counterfort retaining walls.
(*iv*) Buttressed walls.

A gravity retaining wall shown in Fig. 19.5(*a*) is the one in which the earth pressure exerted by the backfill is resisted by dead weight of the wall, which is either made of masonry or of mass concrete. The stress developed in the wall is very low. These walls are so proportioned that no tension is developed anywhere, and the resultant of forces remain within the middle third of the base.

* For detailed account of various earth pressure theories, the reader may refer to the Author's book 'Soil Mechanics and Foundations'

The cantilever retaining wall resists the horizontal earth pressure as well as other vertical pressures by way of bending of various components acting as cantilevers. A common form of cantilever retaining wall is the T-shaped wall shown in Fig. 19.5(b). The wall consists of stem AB, heel slab BC and toe slab DB. Each of these bend as cantilevers, about B. They are, therefore, reinforced on the tension face. Another form of cantilever retaining walls are the L-shaped walls shown in Fig. 19.5(c) and (d). They also resist the soil pressures by bending.

A counterfort retaining wall is shown in Fig. 19.5(e). The vertical stem and the heel slab are strengthened by providing counterforts at some suitable intervals. Because of provision of counterforts, the vertical stem as well as the heel slab acts as *continuous slab*, in contrast to the cantilevers of cantilever retaining wall. The toe slab however acts as cantilever bending upwards. This type of retaining wall is used when backfill of greater height is to be retained. A buttressed wall is a modification of the counterfort retaining wall in which the counterforts, called the buttresses, are provided to the other side of the backfill. However the buttresses reduce the clearance in front of the wall, and therefore these walls are commonly used.

Active Earth Pressure :   Rankine's Theory

As originally proposed, Rankine's theory of lateral earth pressure is applied to uniform cohesionless soil only. Later, it was extended to include cohesive soils, by Resal and by Bell. The theory has been extended to stratified, partially immersed and submerged soils. Following are the assumptions of Rankine Theory : (1) The soil mass is semi-infinite, homogeneous, dry and cohesionless. (2) The ground surface is plane which may be horizontal or inclined. (3) The back of the wall is vertical and smooth. In other words, there are no shearing stresses between the wall and the soil, and the stress relationship for any element adjacent to the wall is the same as for any other element for away from the wall. (4) The wall yields about the base and satisfies the deformation conditions for plastic equilibrium.

However, the retaining walls are constructed of masonry or concrete, and hence the back of the wall is never smooth. Due to this, frictional forces develop. As a consequence of Rankine's assumption of non-existence of frictional forces at the wall face, the resultant pressure must be parallel to the surface of the backfill. The existence of friction makes the resultant pressure inclined to the normal to the wall at an angle that approaches the friction angle between the soil and the wall. We shall consider the following cases of cohesionless backfill :

1.   Dry or moist backfill with no surcharge.   2.   Submerged backfill.
3.   Backfill with uniform surcharge.   4.   Backfill with sloping surfaces.

1.   Dry or moist backfill with no surcharge. Fig. 19.6 (a) shows a retaining wall of height h, having dry or moist backfill, with no surcharge. According to Rankine's theory, the intensity of *active earth pressure*, p_a, trying to move the wall away from the fill, is given by

$$p_a = K_a \gamma H \qquad \qquad \qquad ...(19.10)$$

where K_a = co-efficient of active earth pressure,

$$= \frac{1 - \sin \phi}{1 + \sin \phi} \qquad \qquad ...(19.11)$$

ϕ = angle of internal friction, for the backfill.
γ = unit weight of soil (backfill)
H = height of retaining wall.

At any height h below the horizontal ground surface, the intensity of active earth pressure is $K_a \gamma h$. Fig. 19.6(b) shows the distribution of active earth pressure p_a over the retaining wall. The total active earth pressure P_a or the resultant pressure per unit length of the wall is given by

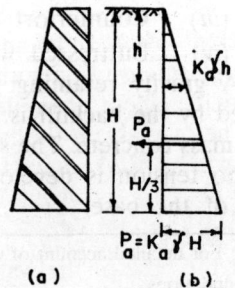

(a)   (b)

FIG. 19.6.

$$P_a = \tfrac{1}{2} K_a . \gamma . H^2$$

...(19.12)

acting at $H/3$ above the base of retaining wall. If the soil is dry, γ is the dry weight of the soil, and if wet, γ is the moist weight, to be substituted in Eq. 19.10 or 19.12.

2. Submerged backfill. In this case, the back fill behind the retaining wall is saturated with water. The lateral pressure is made up of two components.

(*i*) lateral pressure due to submerged weight γ' of soil, and

(*ii*) lateral pressure due to water.

Thus, at any depth h below the surface,

$$p_a = K_a \gamma' h + \gamma_w . h \qquad ...(19.13)$$

The pressure at the base of the retaining wall ($h = H$) is given by

$$p_a = K_a \gamma' H + \gamma_w H \qquad ...(19.14)$$

If the free water stands to both the sides of the wall[Fig 19.7(*b*)], the water pressure need not be considered, and the net lateral pressure given by

$$p_a = K_a \gamma' H \qquad ...(19.15)$$

If the backfill is partly submerged, *i.e.*, the backfill is moist to a depth H_1 below the ground level, and then it is submerged, the lateral pressure intensity at the base of the wall is given by

$$p_a = K_a . \gamma H_1 + K_a \gamma' H_2 + \gamma_w . H_2 \ ...(19.16)$$

The above expression is based on the assumption that the value of ϕ is the same for the moist as well as submerged soil. If it is different (say ϕ_1 and ϕ_2 respectively), the earth pressure coefficient K_{a1} and K_{a2} for both the portions will be different. As ϕ decreases, K_a increases. The lateral pressure intensity [Fig. 19.8(*c*)] at the base of wall is

$$p_a = K_{a2} \gamma H_1 + K_{a2} \gamma' H_2 + \gamma_w H_2 \ ...(19.17)$$

3. Backfill with uniform surcharge. If the backfill is horizontal and carries surcharge of uniform intensity q per unit area, the vertical pressure increment, at any depth h, will increase by q. The increase in the lateral pressure due to this will be $K_a q$. Hence the lateral pressure at any depth h is given by

$$p_a = K_a . \gamma . h + K_a . q \qquad ...(19.18)$$

At the base of the wall, the pressure intensity is :

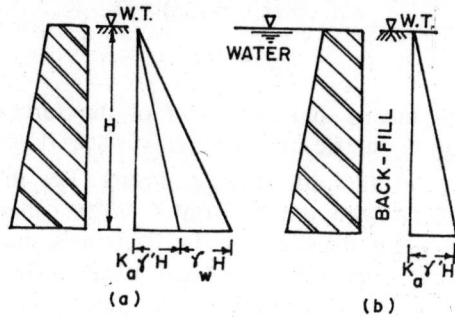

FIG. 19.7. SUBMERGED BACKFILL.

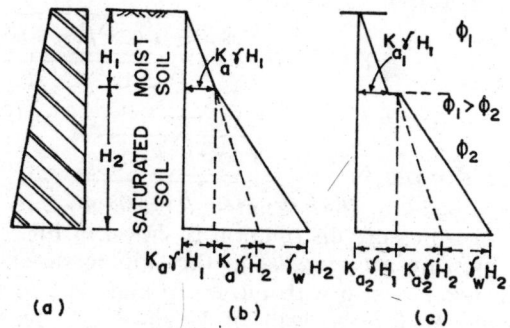

FIG. 19.8. PARTLY SUBMERGED BACKFILL

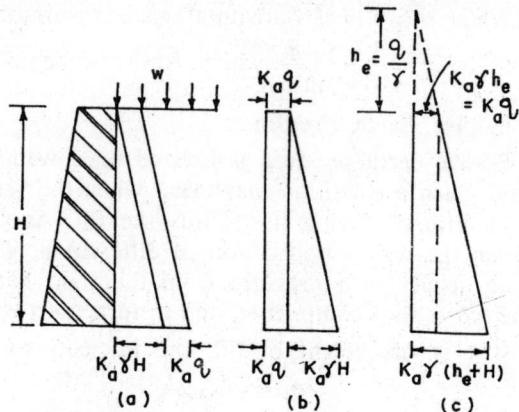

FIG. 19.9. BACK FILL WITH UNIFORM SURCHARGE

$$p_a = K_a \gamma H + K_a q \qquad \qquad \text{...[19.18 }(a)]$$

Fig. 19.9 (a) and (b) show two alternative methods of plotting the lateral pressure diagram for this case. The lateral pressure increment $K_a . q$ due to the surcharge is the same at every point of the back of the wall, and does not vary with height h. The height of fill h_e equivalent to the uniform surcharge intensity is given by the relation :

$$K_a . \gamma . h_e = K_a q$$

or

$$h_e = \frac{q}{\gamma} \qquad \qquad \text{...(19.19)}$$

This means that the effect of the surcharge of intensity q is the same as that of a fill of height h_e above the ground surface [Fig. 19.9 (c)].

4. Backfill with sloping surface. Let the sloping surface behind the wall be inclined at an angle β with the horizontal ; β is called the surcharge angle. In finding out the active earth pressure for this case by Rankine's theory, an additional assumption that the vertical and lateral stresses are *conjugate* is made. It can be shown that if the stress on a given plane at a given point is parallel to another plane, the stress on the latter plane at the same point must be parallel to the first plane.

Fig. 19.10 (a) shows the retaining wall with a sloping backfill. The intensity of lateral earth pressure at the base of wall is given by

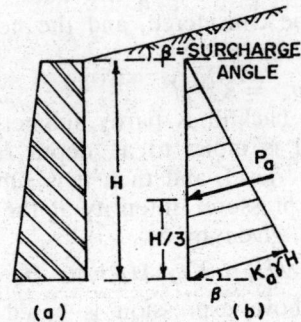

$$p_a = \gamma H . \cos\beta \frac{\cos\beta - \sqrt{\cos^2\beta - \cos^2\phi}}{\cos\beta + \sqrt{\cos^2\beta - \cos^2\phi}}$$

or

$$p_a = K_a \gamma H \qquad \text{...[19.20}(a)]$$

where $K_a = \cos\beta \dfrac{\cos\beta - \sqrt{\cos^2\beta - \cos^2\phi}}{\cos\beta + \sqrt{\cos^2\beta - \cos^2\phi}} \quad \text{...[19.20}(b)]$

The pressure distribution is shown in Fig. 19.10(b). The pressure acts *parallel* to the sloping surface of the surcharge, *i.e.*, at β with the horizontal. The total active pressure P_a for the wall of height H is given by

$$P_a = \tfrac{1}{2} K_a \gamma H^2$$

FIG. 19.10. LATERAL PRESSURE DISTRI-BUTION FOR SLOPING SURCHARGE

The resultant acts at $H/3$ above the base, in direction parallel to the surcharge. When $\beta = 0$ (*i.e.* horizontal ground surface), Eq. 19.20 (b) reduces to

$$K_a = \frac{1 - \sin\phi}{1 + \sin\phi} \text{ which is the same as Eq. 19.11.}$$

Passive Earth Pressure

Passive earth pressure is exerted on a wall when it has a tendency to move towards the backfill. Such a condition may occur when the retaining wall supports an arch, and is subjected to arch thrust, moving it towards the fill. Another condition of passive earth pressure may be when the wall supports soil of different heights on both the sides as shown in Fig. 19.11. Due to active earth pressure from the right hand side, the wall moves to the left. The soil to the left is thus compressed and in turn exert passive earth pressure, resisting such movement.

If h is the height of fill, the intensity of passive pressure at height h is given by

$$p_p = K_p . \gamma h \qquad \qquad \text{...(19.21)}$$

where K_p = coefficient of passive earth pressure $= \dfrac{1 + \sin\phi}{1 - \sin\phi} = \dfrac{1}{K_a} \qquad \text{...(19.22)}$

The passive pressure distribution will thus be a triangle. The total pressure is given by

$$P_p = K_p \cdot \frac{\gamma h^2}{2} \qquad \ldots(19.23)$$

acting at $h/3$ above base.

It should be noted that K_p is very much greater than K_a. For example when $\phi = 30°$,

$$K_a = \frac{1 - \sin\phi}{1 + \sin\phi} = \frac{1}{3} \text{ and } K_p = \frac{1 + \sin\phi}{1 - \sin\phi} = 3.$$

Thus K_p, for this case, is 9 times K_a. In making calculations for active earth pressure behind retaining walls, the passive earth pressure due to other side of walls is generally neglected, since it is possible that this soil will erode away or that shearing will occur, thus eliminating the passive pressure.

If a uniform surcharge of intensity q per unit area acts over the surface of the backfill, the increase in the passive pressures will be equal to $K_p \cdot q$. The passive pressure intensity at depth h is given by

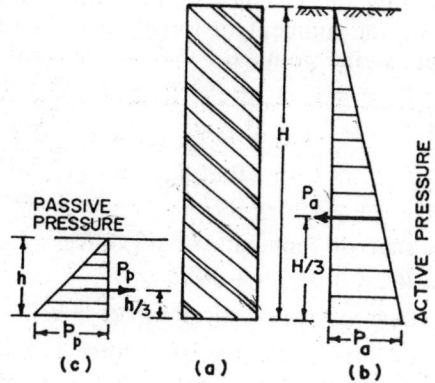

FIG. 19.11

$$p_p = K_p (\gamma h + q) \qquad \ldots(19.24)$$

If the backfill is having its top surface inclined at an angle β, the passive pressure is given by

$$p_p = \gamma h \cos\beta \frac{\cos\beta + \sqrt{\cos^2\beta - \cos^2\phi}}{\cos\beta - \sqrt{\cos^2\beta - \cos^2\phi}} \qquad \ldots(19.25)$$

or $\qquad p_p = K_p \cdot \gamma h \qquad \ldots[19.26\ (a)]$

where $\qquad K_p = \cos\beta \dfrac{\cos\beta + \sqrt{\cos^2\beta - \cos^2\phi}}{\cos\beta - \sqrt{\cos^2\beta - \cos^2\phi}} \qquad \ldots(19.26\ (b))$

19.4. DESIGN OF GRAVITY RETAINING WALL

A gravity retaining wall is the one which resists the lateral earth pressure by its own weight, in contrast to the cantilever and counterfort retaining walls in which the pressure is resisted by bending action. A gravity retaining wall is therefore thicker in section. They are constructed of mass concrete, brick or stone masonry. The criterion of design of gravity retaining walls are as follows:

(1) The base width of the wall must be such that the maximum pressure exerted on the foundation soil does not exceed the safe bearing capacity of the soil.

(2) No tension should be developed anywhere in the wall.

(3) The wall must be safe against sliding.

(4) The wall must be safe against overturning.

Let P_a be the resultant active pressure acting on the wall face. P_h and P_v are its components in horizontal and vertical directions. If W is the weight of the wall acting through its centroid, the resultant R will pass through point of intersection of W and P_a. The resultant R striking the base at some point can be resolved into vertical and horizontal components R_v and R_h.

Resolving the forces into vertical and horizontal directions, we get

$$R_v = W + P_v \qquad \qquad ...(19.27)$$

and $\qquad R_h = P_h \qquad \qquad ...(19.28)$

To find the distance of the point of application of R, equate the moment of forces to the moment of their resultant about point B.

$$R_v . \bar{x} = W . x_1 + P_v . x_2 + P_h . \bar{z}$$

or $\qquad \bar{x} = \dfrac{W x_1 + P_v x_2 + P_h . \bar{z}}{W + P_v} = \dfrac{\Sigma M}{\Sigma V} \qquad ...(19.29)$

where

ΣM = sum of moments of all forces about B

$\qquad = W . x_1 + P_v . x_2 + P_h . \bar{z}$

ΣV = sum of the vertical forces $= R_v = W + P_v$

Since the resultant vertical force R_v ($= \Sigma V$) acts eccentrically on the base, the bearing pressure on the soil beneath the base are the combination of direct and bending stress. *Assuming* a linear distribution of pressure, the pressure intensities at the ends of the base are given by :

$$f_1 = \frac{R_v}{b} \left(1 + \frac{6e}{b} \right) \qquad ...(19.30 \ a)$$

and $\qquad f_2 = \dfrac{R_v}{b} \left(1 - \dfrac{6e}{b} \right) \qquad ...(19.30 \ b)$

where $\qquad b$ = base width of the wall

$\qquad \qquad e$ = eccentricity or the distance from the mid point of the base to the point of application of $= \bar{x} - b/2$

Fig. 19.12 (b), (c), (d) shows three cases of pressure distribution below the base. When R strikes the base within the middle third (i.e. $e < b/6$), f_1 and f_2 will be compressive, as shown in Fig. 19.12 (b). Fig. 19.12 (c) shows the special case when $e = b/6$, so that

$$f_1 = \frac{2 R_v}{b} \quad \text{and} \quad f_2 = 0.$$

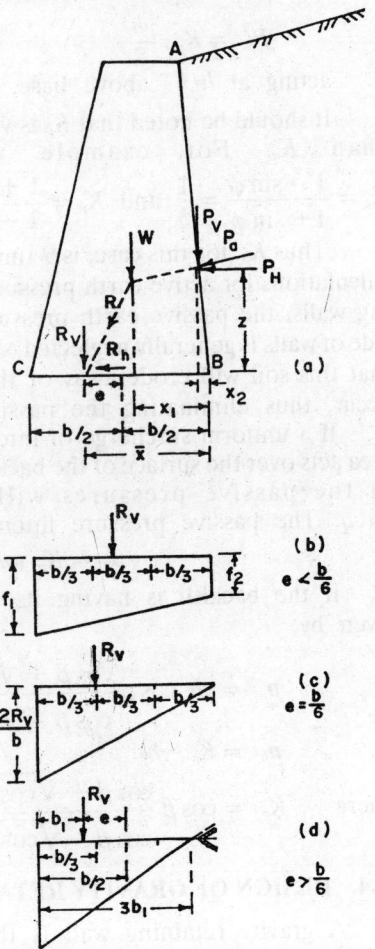

FIG. 19.12

when $e > b/6$, (Fig. 19.12 d), tension is developed at B. Since soil is generally considered incapable to resist tension, the pressure will be redistributed along the intact base, of width $3b_1$, where b_1, is the distance of the point of application of R from end C. The intensity f_1 will then be given by

$$f_1 = \frac{2 R_v}{3 b_1} \qquad ...(19.31 \ a)$$

Substituting $\qquad b_1 = \dfrac{b}{2} - e$, we get

$$f_1 = \frac{4 R_v}{3 (b - 2e)} \qquad ...(19.31 \ b)$$

The following are the criteria of design of gravity retaining walls:

1. The maximum pressure f_1 should not exceed the bearing capacity of soil.

2. For no tension to develop, $e < b/6$, or $\bar{x} \leq 2b/3$

3. For no sliding to occur, $R_h < R_v \cdot \mu$

where $\mu = \tan \delta' =$ coefficient of friction between the base of the wall and the soil. The factor of safety F against sliding is given by

$$F = \frac{R_v \cdot \mu}{R_h} \qquad \qquad ...(19.32)$$

The minimum value of F should be 1.5

4. For the wall to be stable against overturning, R must pass within the base width. However if the requirement of no tension is full-filled, complete safety against overturning is automatically assured.

Example 19.3. *Compute the intensities of active and passive earth pressure at depth of 8 metres in dry cohesionless sand with an angle of internal friction of 30° and the unit weight of 18 kN/m³. What will be the intensities of active and passive earth pressure if the water level rises to the ground level ? Take saturated unit weight of sand as 22 kN/m³.*

Solution   (a) **Dry soil** :

$$K_a = \frac{1 - \sin \phi}{1 + \sin \phi} = \frac{1 - \sin 30°}{1 + \sin 30°} = \frac{\frac{1}{2}}{\frac{2}{3}} = \frac{1}{3}.$$

$$K_p = \frac{1 + \sin \phi}{1 - \sin \phi} = \frac{1}{K_a} = 3.$$

$$p_a = K_a \gamma H = \frac{1}{3} \times 18 \times 8 = 48 \text{ kN/m}^2$$

$$p_p = K_p \cdot \gamma H = 3 \times 18 \times 8 = 432 \text{ kN/m}^2$$

(b) **Submerged backfill**

$$\gamma' = \gamma_{sat} - \gamma_w = 22 - 9.81 = 12.19 \text{ kN/m}^3$$

$$p_a = K_a \gamma' H + \gamma_w H = \frac{1}{3} \times 12.19 \times 8 + 9.81 \times 8 \approx 111 \text{ kN/m}^2$$

$$p_p = K_p \gamma' H + \gamma_w H = 3 \times 12.19 \times 8 + 9.81 \times 8 = 371 \text{ kN/m}^2$$

Example 19.4. *A retaining wall, 4 m high, has a smooth vertical back. The backfill has a horizontal surface in level with the top of the wall. There is uniformly distributed surcharged load of 36 kN/m² intensity over the backfill. The unit weight of the backfill is 18 kN/m³ its angle of shearing resistance is 30° and cohesion is zero. Determine the magnitude and the point of application of active pressure per metre length of the wall.*

Solution :

$$K_a = \frac{1 - \sin \phi}{1 + \sin \phi} = \frac{1}{3}$$

The lateral pressure intensity due to surcharge is given by

$$p_1 = K_a \cdot q = \frac{1}{3} \times 36 = 12 \text{ kN/m}^2$$

The pressure intensity due to backfill at depth $H = 4$ m is given by :

$$p_2 = K_a \gamma H = \frac{1}{3} \times 18 \times 4 = 24 \text{ kN/m}^2$$

The total pressure intensity at the base of the wall is given by

$$p_a = p_1 + p_2 = 12 + 24 = 36 \text{ kN/m}^2.$$

Fig. 19.13 shows the pressure distribution diagrams for p_1 and p_2. The resultant total pressure P_1 due to intensity p_1 is given by

$$P_1 = p_1 H = 12 \times 4 = 48 \text{ kN/m} \text{ acting at}$$

$4/2 = 2$ m from the base.

The resultant total pressure, P_2 due to intensity p_2 is given by

$$P_2 = \tfrac{1}{2} p_2 H = \tfrac{1}{2} \times 24 \times 4 = 48 \text{ kN/m}$$

acting at $\dfrac{1}{3} \times 4 = 1.33$ m from the base.

$$\therefore \ P = P_1 + P_2 = 48 + 48 = 96 \text{ kN per metre}$$

length of the wall.

The resultant P acts at a distance $\bar{z}$ above the base, given by taking the moments about the base:

$$\bar{z} = \frac{(48 \times 2) + \left(48 \times \frac{4}{3} \right)}{96} = 1.67 \text{ m}$$

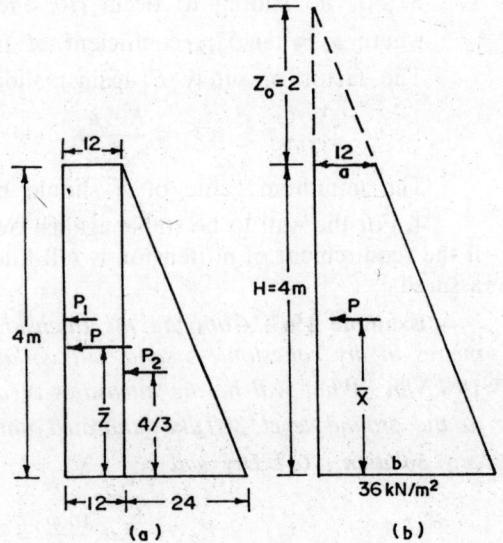

FIG. 19.13

Alternative solution : The equivalent height of surcharge is given by

$$z_e = \frac{q}{\gamma} = \frac{36}{18} = 2 \text{ m}.$$

Thus the problem reduces to the calculation of earth pressure due to height $Z_1 = H + z_e = 4 + 2 = 6$ m

The pressure intensity at the base of the wall is given by

$$p_a = k_a \cdot \gamma Z = \frac{1}{3} \times 18 \times 6 = 36 \text{ kN/m}^2$$

The pressure intensity at the top of the wall is evidently 12 kN/m^2. The pressure distribution is thus trapezoidal, having pressure intensities of 12 and 36 kN/m^2.

$$P = \tfrac{1}{2}(12 + 36) \times 4 = 96 \text{ kN/m}$$

The distance of point of application from the base is given by

$$\bar{z} = \frac{H}{3} \cdot \frac{2a + b}{a + b} = \frac{4}{3} \cdot \frac{2 \times 12 + 36}{12 + 36} = 1.67 \text{ m}$$

Example 19.5. *In example 19.4, if the water table rises behind the wall to an elevation 1.5 m below the top, determine the total active pressure and its point of application. Take submerged weight of sand as 12 kN/m^3. Assume that there is no change in the angle of shearing resistance due to submergence.*

Solution :

Let $p_1 =$ Lateral pressure intensity due to surcharge

$p_2 =$ Lateral pressure intensity due to dry soil

$p_4 =$ Lateral pressure intensity due to submerged soil

$p_5 =$ Lateral pressure intensity due to water.

$$p_1 = K_a \cdot q = \tfrac{1}{3} \times 36 = 12 \text{ kN/m}^2$$

$$p_2 = K_a \gamma H_1 = \tfrac{1}{3} \times 18 \times 1.5 = 9 \text{ kN/m}^2$$

$$p_4 \neq K_a \gamma' H_2 = \tfrac{1}{3} \times 12 \times 2.5 = 10 \text{ kN/m}^2$$

$$p_5 = \gamma_w H_2 = 9.81 \times 2.5 = 24.53 \text{ kN/m}^2$$

Fig. 19.14 shows the pressure distribution diagram with the resultant pressure P_1, P_2, P_3, P_4 and P_5

$$P_1 = p_1 H = 12 \times 4 = 48 \text{ kN/m}$$

acting @ 4/2 = 2 m from the base.

$$P_2 = \tfrac{1}{2} p_2 H_1 = \tfrac{1}{2} \times 9 \times 1.5 = 6.75 \text{ kN/m}$$

acting @ $2.5 + \dfrac{1.5}{3} = 3$ m from the base

$$P_3 = p_2 H_2 = 9 \times 2.5 = 22.5 \text{ kN/m}$$

acting @ 1.25 m from the base.

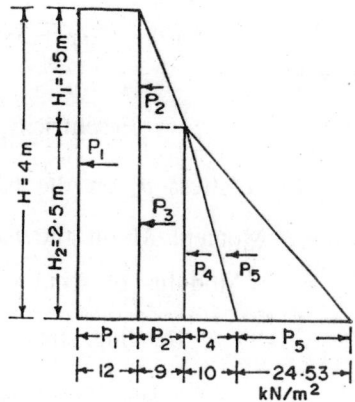

FIG. 19.14

$$P_4 = \tfrac{1}{2} p_4 H_2 = \tfrac{1}{2} \times 10 \times 2.5 = 12.5 \text{ kN/m} \text{ acting @ 0.833 m from the base.}$$

$$P_5 = \tfrac{1}{2} p_5 H_2 = \tfrac{1}{2} \times 24.53 \times 2.5 = 30.66 \text{ kN/m} \text{ acting @ 0.833 from the base.}$$

$\therefore$ Total pressure $P = P_1 + P_2 + P_3 + P_4 + P_5 = 48 + 6.75 + 22.5 + 12.5 + 30.66 = 120.41 \text{ kN/m}$

The distance $\bar{z}$ of the point of application of P above the base is obtained by taking moments about the base.

$$\bar{z} = \frac{1}{120.41} [(48 \times 2) + (6.75 \times 3) + (22.5 \times 1.25) + (12.5 \times 0.833) + (30.66 \times 0.833)]$$
$$= 1.50 \text{ m.}$$

Example 19.6. *A masonry retaining wall, trapezoidal in section, with one face vertical is 1 m wide at top and 3 m at the base and 8 m high. The material retained on the vertical face exerts a lateral pressure varying from zero at top to 25 kN/m² at the base. If the unit weight of masonry is 21 kN/m³, calculate the maximum and minimum stress intensities induced in the base.*

Solution : Consider 1 m length of the wall (Fig. 19.15)

Weight of masonry

$$W = \left(\frac{3+1}{2} \right) 8 \times 21 = 336 \text{ kN}$$

$$\bar{x} = \frac{(1 \times 8 \times 0.5) + (\tfrac{1}{2} \times 2 \times 8)(1 + \tfrac{2}{3})}{(1 \times 8) + (\tfrac{1}{2} \times 2 \times 8)} = 1.084 \text{ m.}$$

Pressure per metre run = $25 \times 1 = 25$ kN/m

Total lateral thrust $P = \tfrac{1}{2} \times 25 \times 8 = 100$ kN

Let the resultant of load W and thrust P pass through E and its magnitude be R. Let $AE = y$ m.

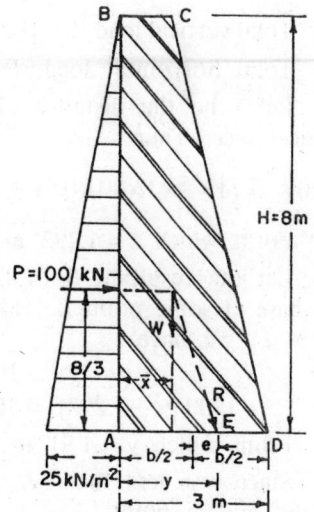

FIG. 19.15

Taking moments of all the forces about E, we have $\left(100 \times \dfrac{8}{3}\right) - 336\,(y - \bar{x}) = 0$

or $266.7 - 336\,y + 336\,\bar{x} = 0$

From which $y = 1.88$ m

$\therefore$ Eccentricity, $e = y - \dfrac{b}{2} = 1.88 - 1.5 = 0.38$ m

Direct stress p_0 on the base $= \dfrac{W}{A} = \dfrac{W}{b} = \dfrac{336}{3} = 112$ kN/m^2

Moment M on the base $= W.e = 336 \times 0.38 = 127.5$ kN-m

Modulus of section, $Z = \dfrac{1}{6} \times 1 \times 3^2 = 1.5$ m^3

Bending stress, $p_b = \dfrac{M}{Z} = \dfrac{127.5}{1.5} = 85$ kN/m^2

$\therefore$ $f_{max} = p_0 + p_b = 112 + 85 = \mathbf{197\ kN/m^2}$ (comp.) at extreme point D

and $f_{min.} = p_0 - p_b = 112 - 85 = \mathbf{27\ kN/m^2}$ (comp.) at extreme point A.

Example 19.7. *A masonry wall, trapezoidal in section with one face vertical is 3 m long, 8 m high, 1 m wide at top and 4 m wide at bottom. In the middle of the length, an inclined thrust of 141.4 kN is transmitted at the top of angle of 45° to the horizontal. Calculate the extreme stress intensities at the base, if the masonry weighs 20 kN/m³.*

Solution (Fig. 19.16)

Vertical component of inclined thrust
      $W_1 = 141.4 \sin 45° = 100$ kN

Horizontal component of inclined thrust
      $= P = 141.4 \cos 45° = 100$ kN

Weight of masonry

$$= W_2 = 3 \times \frac{1 + 4}{2} \times 8 \times 20 = 1200\ \text{kN}$$

Total vertical load $W = W_1 + W_2 = 100 + 1200 = 1300$ kN

Total horizontal load, $P = 100$ kN

Let $\bar{x}$ be the distance of the total vertical load from vertical face. Then

$$1300\,\bar{x} = (1 \times 8 \times 3 \times 20 \times 0.5) + \frac{1}{2} \times 3 \times 8 \times 3 \times 20 \left(1 + \frac{3}{3}\right)$$

Form which $\bar{x} = 1.292$ m

Let the resultant R of the two forces W and P meet the base at some point E. Taking moments of all the forces about E, we have

$$W(y - \bar{x}) = P \times h$$

or $1300\,(y - 1.292) = 100 \times 8$

From which $y = 1.91$ m

Since y is less than $b/2$, the resultant falls to the left of the middle point.

$\therefore$ $e = b/2 - y = 2 - 1.91 = 0.09$ m

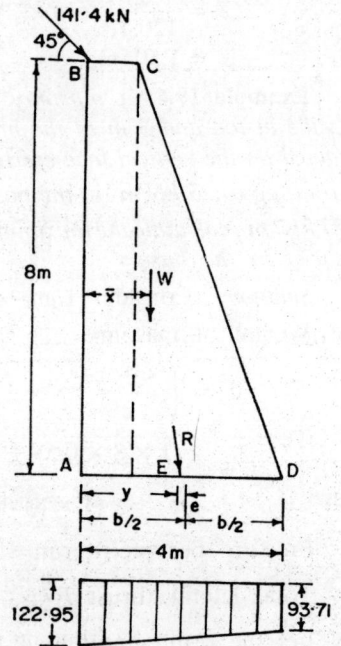

FIG. 19.16

Direct stress p_0 on the base $= \dfrac{W}{A} = \dfrac{1300}{4 \times 3} = 108.33 \text{ kN/m}^2$

Moment $M = W \times e = 1300 \times 0.09 = 117$ kN-m

$\therefore$ Bending stress, $p_b = \dfrac{M}{Z} = \dfrac{117}{\frac{1}{6} \times 3 \times 4^2} = 14.62 \text{ kN/m}^2$

$\therefore$ $f_{max.} = 108.33 + 14.62 = 122.95 \text{ kN/m}^2$ (comp.) at end A.

$f_{min.} = 108.33 - 14.62 = 93.71 \text{ kN/m}^2$ (comp.) at end D.

Example 19.8. Design of masonry retaining wall

Design a gravity retaining wall, 5 m high with vertical back to retain a dry cohesionless backfill of unit weight 18 kN/m³ and angle of shearing resistance 30°. Find also the factor of safety against sliding assuming the angle of friction between the base of the wall and the foundation soil as 30°. The wall is to be 1 m wide at the top, and to be constructed of brick masonry having unit weight 20 kN/m³. Use Rankine's theory.

Solution

$\phi = 30° \; ; \qquad \therefore K_a = \dfrac{1}{3}$

$p_a = \dfrac{1}{2} K_a \gamma H^2 = \dfrac{1}{2} \times \dfrac{1}{3} \times 18 \, (5)^2 = 75$ kN/m

It acts horizontally at a height of $\dfrac{5}{3}$ m from the base.

Let b_1 = width of wall at its top

b = width of wall at its bottom

Since p_a acts horizontally, we have

$R_v = W$ and $R_h = P_a.$

For no tension to develop, R_v must act at a distance $2b/3$ from heel B.

From statics, the moment of the forces W and P_a about B must be equal to the moment of the resultant about B. For calculating W, it is convenient to divide the trapezoidal section of the wall into rectangular and triangular portions as shown in Fig. 19.17. Let W_1 be the weight of rectangular portion and W_2 of the triangular portion.

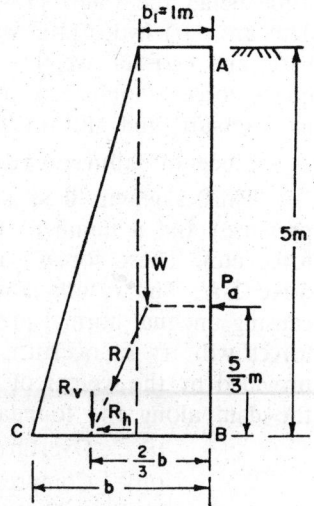

FIG. 19.17

$\therefore$ $R_v \times \dfrac{2b}{3} = W_1 \times \dfrac{b_1}{2} + W_2 \left(b_1 + \dfrac{b - b_1}{3} \right) + P_a \times \dfrac{H}{3}$ ...(19.33)

The above equation is valid only for the case when P_a acts horizontally.

Now $R_v = W = \dfrac{b + b_1}{2} H \rho = \dfrac{b + 1}{2} \times 5 \times 20 = 50 \, (b + 1)$

$W_1 = (b_1 \times H) \rho = 1 \times 5 \times 20 = 100$ kN

$W_2 = \dfrac{1}{2} (b - b_1) H \rho = \dfrac{1}{2} (b - 1) 5 \times 20 = 50 \, (b - 1)$

$P_a = 75$ kN.

Substituting these values in Eq. 19.33, we get

$$50\,(b + 1) \times \frac{2b}{3} = 100 \times \frac{1}{2} + 50\,(b - 1)\,\left(1 + \frac{b - 1}{3}\right) + \frac{75 \times 5}{3}$$

or $b^2 + b - 8.5 = 0$

From which $b = 2.45$ m. Hence adopt $b = 2.5$ m

∴ $$W = \frac{b + b_1}{2} H \rho = \frac{2.5 + 1}{2} \times 5 \times 20 = 175 \ \ \text{kN/m}$$

Factor of safety against sliding is given by

$$F = \frac{\mu\,W}{P_a} = \frac{175 \tan \delta'}{75} = \frac{175}{75} \tan 30° = 1.35$$

This is less than the recommended value of 1.5. Hence increase the base width b to 3 m. Then F comes out to be 1.54.

19.5. MASONRY DAMS

Dams are structures constructed to retain water to the required height. In other words, dams are just like retaining walls where the material retained is water. However, since the height of water retained (or stored) is very much higher, dams are much more massive than the usual retaining walls. A *gravity dam* is the one which resists the external forces (major force being the water pressure) by way of its own weight. Major forces acting on a gravity dam are : (*i*) hydrostatic water pressure (*ii*) uplift pressure exerted by water seeping below the base, and (*iii*) self weight of the dam. If the dam is located in earthquake prone zone, earth quake forces should also be considered. Other forces of minor importance are wave pressure, ice pressure and silt pressure which will not be considered here.

Mode of failure: Criteria of safe design

Thus, a gravity dam is subjected to a number of vertical forces (i.e. self weight and uplift pressure) and a number of horizontal forces (i.e hydrostatic water pressure and earth quake force etc). These forces can be resolved into a net vertical force ΣW and a net horizontal force ΣH. The resultant of these two will obviously strike the base at some eccentricity e, causing unequal normal pressure distribution below the base. In addition to this, the horizontal forces will try to overturn the dam, and this tendency is resisted by the restoring moments provided by the weight of the dam. Similarly, the net horizontal force (ΣH) will try to slide the dam along the foundation.   Hence the modes of failure of a gravity dam are :

    (*i*)   Overturning   (*ii*)   Sliding
    (*iii*)   Compression or crushing   (*iv*)   Tension

1. Overturning : The overturning of the dam section takes place when the resultant force at any section cuts the base of the dam downstream of the toe. On the other hand, if the resultant cuts the base within the body of the dam, there will be no overturning.

For stability requirements, the dam must be safe against overturning. The factor of safety against overturning is defined as the ratio of righting moment to the overturning moments:

$$\text{F.S.} = \frac{\Sigma\ \text{Righting moments}}{\Sigma\ \text{Overturning moments}} = \frac{\Sigma M_R}{\Sigma M_0} \qquad \qquad ...(19.34)$$

Since the magnitude and direction of each and every force is known, their moments about the toe can be easily found and F.S. can be computed. The factor of safety against overturning should not be less than 1.5.

2. Sliding : A dam will fail in sliding at its base, or at any other level, if the horizontal forces causing sliding are more than the resistance available to it at that level. The resistance against sliding may be due to friction alone, or due to friction and shear strength of the joint. Shear strength develops at the base if benched foundations are provided and at other joints if the joints are carefully laid so that a good bond develops. Shear strength also comes into play because of the interlocking of stones in masonry dams.

If the shear strength is not taken into account, the factor of safety is known as *factor of safety against sliding*. The factor of safety against sliding is defined as the ratio of *actual coefficient of static friction* (μ) on the horizontal joint to the *sliding friction*. The *sliding factor* (S.F.) is the minimum coefficient of friction required to prevent sliding. If ΣH is the horizontal forces causing the sliding and $\Sigma (V - U)$ is the *net vertical forces*, the sliding factor ($\tan \theta$) is given by :

$$S.F. = \tan \theta = \frac{\Sigma H}{\Sigma (V - U)} \qquad \qquad ...(19.35)$$

and the factor of safety against sliding is

$$F.S. = \frac{\mu}{\tan \theta} = \frac{\mu \, \Sigma (V - U)}{\Sigma H} \qquad \qquad ...(19.36)$$

The coefficient of friction μ varies from 0.65 to 0.75. The factor of safety against sliding should be greater than 1.

It is considered that a low gravity dam should be safe against sliding, considering friction alone. However, in large dams, shear strength of the joint should also be considered for an economical design. The factor of safety in that case is commonly known as the *shear friction factor* (S.F.F.) and is defined by the equation :

$$S.F.F. = \frac{\mu \, \Sigma (V - U) + b \, q}{\Sigma H} \qquad \qquad ...(19.37)$$

where q = shear strength of the joint (usually 1.4 N/mm^2)
            b = width of the joint or section

3. Compression or crushing : In order to calculate the normal stress distribution at the base, or at any section, let ΣH be the total horizontal force and ΣW be the total vertical force ($= \Sigma (V - U)$) and let R be the resultant force, cutting the base at an eccentricity e from the centre of base width b (Fig. 19.18).

Thus, direct stress $= \dfrac{\Sigma W}{b \times 1}$

Bending stress

$$= \pm \frac{M}{Z} = \pm \frac{\Sigma W . e}{\frac{1}{6} b^2} = \pm \frac{6 \, \Sigma W . e}{b^2}$$

Hence the *total normal stress* p_n is given by

$$p_n = \frac{\Sigma W}{b} \left(1 \pm \frac{6e}{b} \right) \quad ...(19.38)$$

Thus, at toe, $p_n = \dfrac{\Sigma W}{b} \left(1 + \dfrac{6e}{b} \right) \quad ...(19.38a)$

and, at heel, $p_n = \dfrac{\Sigma W}{b} \left(1 - \dfrac{6e}{b} \right) \quad ...(19.38b)$

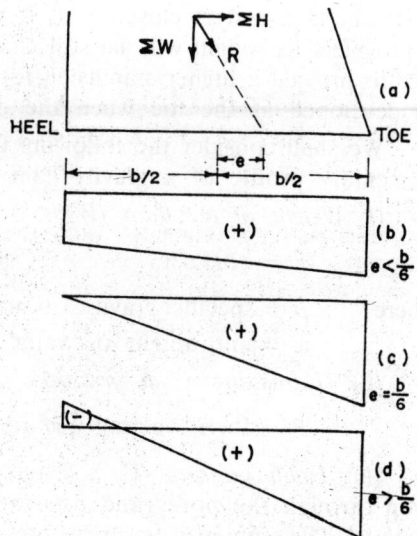

FIG. 19.18. NORMAL STRESS
DISTRIBUTION AT THE BASE

Fig. 19.18 (b) shows the normal stress distribution in general case when the pressures at both toe and heel are compressive. Evidently the maximum compressive stress occurs at the toe and for safety this should not be greater than the allowable compressive stress σ_c for the foundation material. Hence from *strength* point of view.

$$\frac{\Sigma W}{b}\left(1 + \frac{6e}{b}\right) \le \sigma_c \qquad \qquad ...(19.39)$$

When the eccentricity e is equal to $b/6$, we get

$$(p_n)_{toe} = \frac{\Sigma W}{b}\left(1 + \frac{6}{b} \times \frac{b}{6}\right) = \frac{2 \Sigma W}{b} \qquad \qquad ...(19.40)$$

The corresponding stress at the heel in that circumstance will evidently be zero. Fig. 19.18 (c) shows the pressure distribution for this case.

4. Tension : The normal stress at the heel is given by

$$(p_n)_{heel} = \frac{\Sigma W}{b}\left(1 - \frac{6e}{b}\right) \qquad \qquad ...(19.38 \ b)$$

It is evident that if $e > b/6$, the normal stress at the heel will be − ve or tensile. No tension should be permitted at any point of the dam under any circumstance. For no tension to develop, the eccentricity should be less than $b/6$. In other words, the resultant should always lie within the *middle third.*

Elementary profile of a gravity dam : Triangular profile

In the absence of any force other than the forces due to water, an elementary profile will be triangular in section, having zero width at the water level, where water pressure is zero, and a maximum base width b, where the maximum water pressure acts. Thus, the section of the elementary profile is of the same shape as the hydrostatic pressure distribution diagram. For the reservoir empty condition a right angled triangular profile as shown in Fig. 19.19 will provide the maximum possible stabilising force against overturning, without causing tension in the base. This is so because the weight of the dam acts at a distance of $b/3$ from the upstream face and is close to it. If any triangular profile, other than the right angled one, is provided, its weight will act still close to the upstream face to provide a higher stabilising force, but tension will be developed at the toe when the dam is empty.

We shall consider the following forces acting on the elementary profile of a gravity dam.

(i) *Weight of the dam (W)*:

$$W = \tfrac{1}{2} b H \rho \, w$$

where ρ = specific gravity of masonry and
             w = unit weight of water (9.81 kN/m^3)

(ii) *Hydrostatic water pressures (P)*

$$P = \tfrac{1}{2} w H^2, \text{ acting } \tfrac{1}{3} H \text{ above the base.}$$

(iii) *Uplift pressure (U)* : Water has a tendency to seep through the pores and fissures of the foundation material. The seeping water exerts pressure, known as uplift pressure, which must be accounted for in stability calculations. A portion of the weight of the dam will be supported

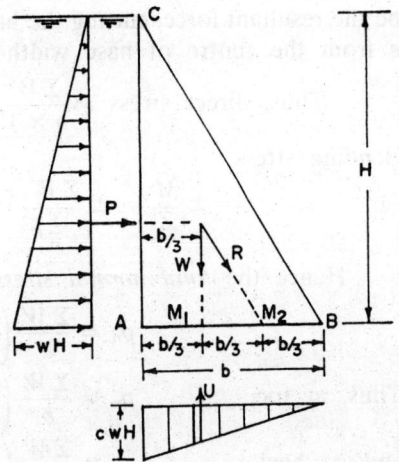

FIG. 19.19. ELEMENTARY PROFILE

on the upward pressure of water; hence net foundation reaction due to vertical force will reduce. The uplift pressure distribution, in absence of tail water, is shown in Fig. 19.19.

$$\therefore \qquad U = \frac{1}{2} \times cwbH \qquad \qquad ...(19.41)$$

where $c=$ uplift pressure intensity coefficient.

Base width of the elementary profile : The base width of the elementary profile is found under two criteria : (*i*) stress criterion and (*ii*) stability criterion.

(*i*) *Stress criterion* : When reservoir is empty the resultant should act at the inner third point (M_1) so that no tension is developed. For the reservoir full condition for no tension to develop, the resultant R must pass through the outer third point (M_2) shown in Fig. 19.19.

Taking the moment of all forces about M_2 and equating it to zero (since the moment of R about M_2 is zero), we get

$$\frac{1}{2}wH^2 \cdot \frac{H}{3} + \frac{1}{2}c\,w\,b\,H \cdot \frac{b}{3} - \frac{1}{2}bH\rho\,w \cdot \frac{b}{3} = 0$$

Multiplying all the terms by $6/wH$, we get :

$$H^2 + cb^2 - b^2\rho = 0$$

or $\qquad\qquad b^2(\rho - c) = H^2$

from which $\qquad\qquad b = \dfrac{H}{\sqrt{\rho - c}} \qquad\qquad ...(19.42)$

If uplift is not considered, $c=0$

$$\therefore \qquad\qquad b = \frac{H}{\sqrt{\rho}} \qquad\qquad ...(19.42\ a)$$

(*ii*) *Stability or sliding criterion* : For no sliding to occur, horizontal force causing sliding should be balanced by the frictional forces opposing the same.

Hence $\qquad\qquad P = \mu\,(W - U)$

$$\therefore \qquad\qquad \frac{1}{2}wH^2 = \mu\left(\frac{1}{2}bH\rho\,w - \frac{1}{2}cb\,wH\right)$$

From which $\qquad\qquad b = \dfrac{H}{\mu\,(\rho - c)} \qquad\qquad ...(19.43)$

If uplift is neglected, $\quad b = \dfrac{H}{\mu\rho} \qquad\qquad ...(19.43\ a)$

The width provided for the elementary profile should be greater of the widths given by Eq. 19.42 and 19.43.

Stresses developed in the elementary profile :

The normal stress, in general, is given by

$$p_n = \frac{\Sigma W}{b}\left(1 \pm \frac{6e}{b}\right)$$

where $\quad \Sigma W = (W - U)$ in this case and $e = b/6$

Hence for the *full reservoir case*, we have

$$(p_n)_{toe} = \frac{W - U}{b}(1 + 1) = \frac{2(W - U)}{b}$$

or
$$(p_n)_{toe} = \frac{2}{b}\left[\frac{1}{2}bH\rho w - \frac{1}{2}cbwH\right] = wH(\rho - c) \qquad ...(19.44)$$

Also,
$$(p_n)_{heel} = \frac{(W-U)}{b}(1-1) = 0$$

Reservoir empty condition : When the reservoir is empty, the only force acting on the elementary profile will be its weight, acting through the first third point M_1. Hence, the maximum compressive stress at the heel will be $= \frac{W}{b}(1+1) = \frac{2W}{b}$, and the corresponding normal stress at the toe will be $\frac{W}{b}(1-1) =$ zero.

Rectangular profile

Consider a rectangular dam of width b and height H.

$$W = bH\rho w$$
$$P = \frac{wH^2}{2}$$
$$U = \frac{1}{2}cwbH.$$

Let the resultant pass through a point M, distant $\bar{x}$ from the toe B. Taking moments about the toe, we have.

$$\Sigma M = W\cdot\frac{b}{2} - \frac{PH}{3} - U\cdot\frac{2b}{3}$$

Also $\quad \Sigma W = W - U.$

$$\therefore \qquad \bar{x} = \frac{\Sigma M}{\Sigma W} = \frac{W\dfrac{b}{2} - \dfrac{PH}{3} - \dfrac{U\cdot 2b}{3}}{W - U}$$

Substituting the values of W, P and U, we get.

$$\bar{x} = \frac{bH\rho w\cdot\dfrac{b}{2} - \dfrac{wH^3}{6} - \dfrac{2}{3}b\left(\dfrac{1}{2}cwbH\right)}{bH\rho w - \dfrac{1}{2}cwbH}$$

or
$$\bar{x} = \frac{\dfrac{b}{2}\left(bH\rho w - \dfrac{1}{2}cwbH\right) - \dfrac{wH^3}{6} - \left(\dfrac{1}{2}cwbH\right)\dfrac{b}{6}}{bH\rho w - \dfrac{1}{2}c\,wbH}$$

or
$$\bar{x} = \frac{b}{2} - \frac{\dfrac{wH^3}{6} + \dfrac{1}{2}cwbH\cdot\dfrac{b}{6}}{bH\rho w - \dfrac{1}{2}cwbH}$$

Hence
$$e = \frac{b}{2} - \bar{x} = \frac{\dfrac{wH^3}{6} + \dfrac{1}{2}cwbH\cdot\dfrac{b}{6}}{bH\rho w - \dfrac{1}{2}cwbH} = \frac{\dfrac{H^2}{6} + \dfrac{cb^2}{12}}{b\rho - \dfrac{1}{2}cb}$$

For no tension to develop

$$e = \frac{b}{6} = \frac{\dfrac{H^2}{6} + \dfrac{cb^2}{12}}{b\rho - \dfrac{1}{2}cb}$$

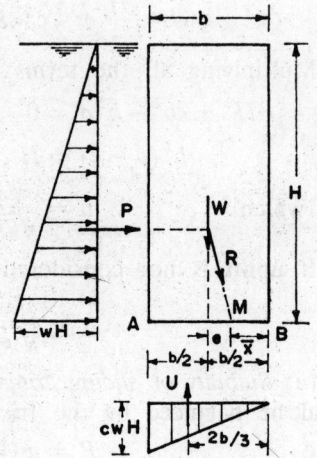

FIG. 19.20. RECTANGULAR PROFILE

or $\qquad \dfrac{b^2}{6}\left(\rho - \dfrac{c}{2}\right) = \dfrac{H^2}{6} + \dfrac{cb^2}{12}$

or $\qquad b^2\,(\rho - c) = H^2$

From which $\qquad b = \dfrac{H}{\sqrt{\rho - c}}$ $\qquad\qquad$ (19.45)

If $c = 0$ (no uplift), $\qquad b = \dfrac{H}{\sqrt{\rho}}$ $\qquad\qquad$ ...(19.45 a)

Also, the limiting height is given by, $H_{\lim} = b\,\sqrt{\rho - c}$ $\qquad$ ...(19.45 b)

From stability considerations, providing a F.S. of 1.5 against sliding, we have

$$\mu\,(W - U) = 1.5\,P$$

or $\qquad \mu\left(b\,H\rho w - \tfrac{1}{2}cwbH\right) = \dfrac{3}{2} \times \dfrac{wH^2}{2}$

or $\qquad \mu b\left(\rho - \dfrac{c}{2}\right) = \dfrac{3}{4}H$

From which $\qquad b = \dfrac{3}{4}\,\dfrac{H}{\mu\left(\rho - \dfrac{c}{2}\right)}$ $\qquad\qquad$ (19.46)

If $c = 0$ (i.e. neglecting uplift)

$$b = \dfrac{3}{4}\dfrac{H}{\mu\,\rho}$$ $\qquad\qquad$ ...(19.46 a)

Also, limiting height is, $\qquad H_{\lim} = \dfrac{4}{3}b\,\mu\left(\rho - \dfrac{c}{2}\right)$ $\qquad$ ...(19.47)

Neglecting uplift, $\qquad H_{\lim} = \dfrac{4}{3}b\mu\,\rho$ $\qquad\qquad$ ...(19.47 a)

From *crushing point of view*, when $e = b/6$, we get

$$p_n = \dfrac{2\,(W - U)}{b} = \dfrac{2}{b}\left(bH\rho w - \tfrac{1}{2}cwbH\right)$$

$\therefore \qquad \sigma_c = p_n = 2\,wH\left(\rho - \tfrac{1}{2}c\right)$

$\therefore \qquad H_{\lim} = \dfrac{\sigma_c}{2\,w\left(\rho - \tfrac{1}{2}c\right)}$ $\qquad\qquad$ ...(19.48)

If uplift is neglected,

$$H_{\lim.} = \dfrac{\sigma_c}{2\,w\,\rho}$$ $\qquad\qquad$ ...(19.48 a)

Trapezoidal profile : Consider a trapezoidal profile with top width a and bottom width b, with upstream face vertical

$$W_1 = \text{weight of rectangular portion} = aH\rho w$$

$$W_2 = \text{weight of triangular portion} = \tfrac{1}{2}bH\,.\,\rho\,w$$

$$P = \text{Water pressure} = \dfrac{wH^2}{2}$$

$$C = \text{uplift pressure} = \tfrac{1}{2}cwbH$$

Let the resultant fall at $\bar{x}$ from the toe.

If ΣM is the sum of moments of all the forces about the toe, we have

$$\Sigma M = \bar{x} . \Sigma W$$

or $\qquad \bar{x} = \dfrac{\Sigma M}{\Sigma W}$

$\therefore \ \bar{x} =$

$$\dfrac{aH\rho w\left(b - \dfrac{a}{2}\right) + \dfrac{1}{2}bH\rho w \times \dfrac{2}{3}(b - a) - \dfrac{wH^3}{6} - \dfrac{1}{2}cwbH \times \dfrac{2}{3}b}{aH\rho w + \dfrac{1}{2}bH\rho w - \dfrac{1}{2}cwbH}$$

or $\ \bar{x} = \dfrac{a\rho\left(b - \dfrac{a}{2}\right) + \dfrac{1}{3}b\rho(b - a) - \dfrac{H^2}{6} - \dfrac{1}{3}cb^2}{a\rho + \dfrac{1}{2}\rho b - \dfrac{1}{2}cb}$

$$\dots(19.49)$$

Eccentricity $e = \dfrac{b}{2} - \bar{x}$ and $p_n = \dfrac{\Sigma W}{b}\left(1 \pm \dfrac{6e}{b}\right)$

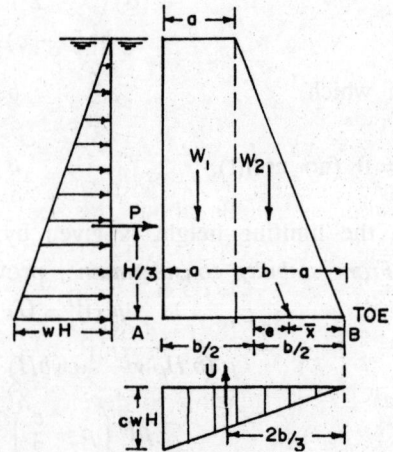

FIG. 19.21

Practical profile of a gravity dam

The elementary profile (i.e. triangular profile) of a gravity dam is only a *theoretical profile*. However, such a profile is not possible in practice because of provision of (i) roadway at top, (ii) additional loads due to roadway and (iii) free board. Free board is the margin provided between the top of the dam and the high flood level (H.F.L.) in the reservoir to prevent the splashing of the waves over the non-overflow section. Due to these provisions, the resultant forces of the weight of the dam and the water pressure falls outside the middle third of the base of the dam when the reservoir is full. To eliminate tension, some masonry is to be provided to the upstream side. Fig. 19.22 shows the dimensions of the practical profile of a gravity dam. The free board usually is kept equal to $1.5h_w$, where h_w is the height of waves. The top width equal to about 14% of h has been found to be economical.

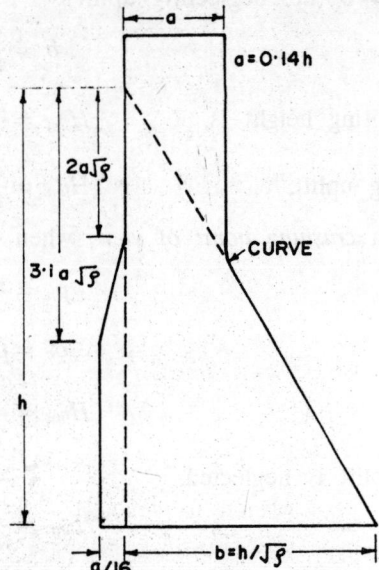

FIG. 19.22. PRACTICAL PROFILE OF A LOW GRAVITY DAM.

Example 19.9. *A rectangular masonry dam is 3 m at the base. Compute the maximum permissible height H (a) when no tension is permissible, and (b) when the factor of safety against sliding is 1.5. Given the following : (i) $\mu = 0.5$, (ii) density of masonry $= 2.4$ times the density of water, and (iii) $c = 1$.*

— *What will be the corresponding values of H if uplift is neglected ?*

Solution :

Given : $\rho = 2.4$; $w = 9.81 \text{ kN/m}^3$

(i) *Considering uplift*

$$W = bH\rho w = 3 \times 2.4 \times 9.81\, H = 70.632\, H \text{ kN}$$

$$U = \tfrac{1}{2} cwbH = \tfrac{1}{2} \times 1 \times 9.81 \times 3\, H = 14.715\, H \text{ kN}$$

$$P = \frac{wH^2}{2} = \frac{9.81\, H^2}{2} = 4.905\, H^2 \text{ kN}$$

$$\Sigma W = 70.632\, H - 14.715 = 55.917\, H$$

Taking moments about the toe,

$$\Sigma M = (70.632\, H \times 1.5) - (14.715\, H \times 2) - 4.905\, H^3/3$$
$$= 76.518\, H - 1.635\, H^3$$

$$\therefore \quad \bar{x} = \frac{\Sigma M}{\Sigma W} = \frac{76.518\, H - 1.635\, H^3}{55.917\, H} = 1.368 - 0.02924\, H^2$$

(a) For no tension to develop, $e = b/6 = 3/6 = 0.5$ m

$$\therefore \qquad e = 0.132 + 0.02924\, H^2 = 0.5$$

From which , $H_{lim.} \approx 3.55$ m

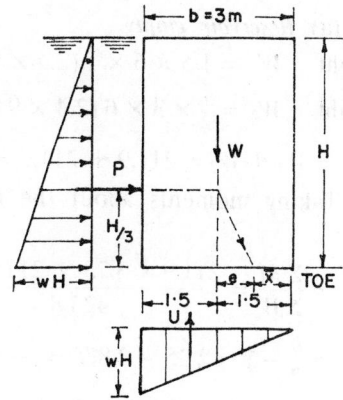

FIG. 19.23

Alternatively, from Eq. 19.45 (b), $H_{lim.} = b\sqrt{\rho - c} = 3\sqrt{2.4 - 1} = 3.55$ m

(b) From stability consideration, providing a F.S. of 1.5 against sliding, we have

$$\mu\, (W - U) = 1.5\, P$$

$$\therefore \quad 0.5\, (70.632\, H - 14.715\, H) = 1.5 \times 4.905\, H^2$$

or $\qquad\qquad 27.9585 = 7.3575\, H$

From which $\qquad\qquad H = H_{lim.} = \mathbf{3.8\ m}$

Alternatively, from Eq. 19.47, $H_{lim.} = \dfrac{4}{3} b\, \mu \left(\rho - \dfrac{c}{2} \right) = \dfrac{4}{3} \times 3 \times 0.5\, (2.4 - 0.5) = 3.8$ m.

(ii) *Neglecting uplift*

$$W = 70.632\ H \text{ and } P = 4.905\ H^2 \text{ , as before,}$$

$$\Sigma M = 70.632\ H \times 1.5 - 4.905\ H^3/3 = 105.948\ H - 1.635\ H^3.$$
$$\Sigma W = W = 70.632\ H$$

$$\therefore \qquad \bar{x} = \frac{\Sigma M}{\Sigma W} = \frac{105.948\ H - 1.635\ H^3}{70.632\ H} = 1.5 - 0.02315\ H^3$$

$$\therefore \qquad e = \frac{b}{2} - \bar{x} = 1.5 - (1.5 - 0.02315\ H^2) = 0.02315\ H^2$$

(a) For no tension to develop, $e = b/6 = 3/6 = 0.5$ m

$$\therefore \qquad 0.02315\ H^2 = 0.5$$

From which $\qquad\qquad H = H_{lim.} \approx \mathbf{4.65\ m}$

(b) From stability consideration, providing a F.S. of 1.5 against sliding,

$$\mu\, W = 1.5\ P$$

or $\qquad 0.5 \times 70.632\ H = 1.5 \times 4.905\ H^2$

From which $H = \mathbf{4.8\ m}$

Example 19.10. *A masonry dam 6 m high is 1.5 m wide at top and 4.5 m wide at the bottom, with vertical water face. Determine the normal stresses at the toe and heel for reservoir empty and reservoir full conditions. Take $\rho = 2.4$ and $c = 1$.*

Solution

Consider 1 m length of the dam.

(a) *Reservoir empty*

Weight $W_1 = 1.5 \times 6 \times 1 (2.4 \times 9.81) = 211.9$ kN

Weight $W_2 = \frac{1}{2} \times 3 \times 6 (2.4 \times 9.81) = 211.9$ kN

$\Sigma W = W_1 + W_2 = 211.9 + 211.9 = 423.8$ kN

Taking moments about the toe (B) we have

$$\bar{x} = \frac{\Sigma M}{\Sigma W} = \frac{211.9 \times 3.75 + 211.9 \times 2}{423.8} = 2.875 \text{ m}$$

$$\therefore \quad e = \frac{b}{2} - \bar{x} = 2.25 - 2.875 = -0.625 \text{ m}$$

(i.e. resultant falls to the left of middle point.)

$$\therefore \quad (p_n)_{toe} = \frac{\Sigma W}{b} \left(1 - \frac{6e}{b} \right)$$
$$= \frac{423.8}{4.5} \left(1 - \frac{6 \times 0.625}{4.5} \right)$$
$$= 15.7 \text{ kN/m}^2 \text{ (comp.)}$$

$$\therefore \quad (p_n)_{heel} = \frac{\Sigma W}{b} \left(1 + \frac{6e}{b} \right)$$
$$= \frac{423.8}{4.5} \left(1 + \frac{6 \times 0.625}{4.5} \right)$$
$$= 172.7 \text{ kN/m}^2 \text{ (comp.)}$$

The p_n distribution below the base is shown in Fig. 19.24 (c).

(b) *Reservoir full* : $W_1 = 211.9$ kN and $W_2 = 211.9$ kN, as before.

$$P = \frac{wH^2}{2} = \frac{9.81 (6)^2}{2} = 176.58 \text{ kN}$$

$$U = \frac{1}{2} cwH.b = \frac{1}{2} \times 1 \times 9.81 \times 6 \times 4.5 = 132.435 \text{ kN.}$$

$$\Sigma W = 211.9 + 211.9 - 132.435 = 291.365 \text{ kN}$$

Taking moments about the toe, we have

$$\bar{x} = \frac{\Sigma M}{\Sigma W} = \frac{211.9 \times 3.75 + 211.9 \times 2 - 132.435 \times 3 - 176.58 \times 2}{291.365} = 1.606 \text{ m}$$

$$\therefore \quad e = \frac{b}{2} - \bar{x} = 2.25 - 1.606 = 0.644 \text{ m}$$

$$\therefore \quad (p_n)_{toe} = \frac{\Sigma W}{b} \left(1 + \frac{6e}{b} \right) = \frac{291.365}{4.5} \left(1 + \frac{6 \times 0.644}{4.5} \right) = 120.3 \text{ kN/m}^2 \text{ (comp.)}$$

$$\therefore \quad (p_n)_{heel} = \frac{\Sigma W}{b} \left(1 - \frac{6e}{b} \right) = \frac{291.365}{4.5} \left(1 - \frac{6 \times 0.644}{4.5} \right) = 9.1 \text{ kN/m}^2 \text{ (comp.)}$$

The p_n distribution below the base is shown in Fig. 19.24 (d).

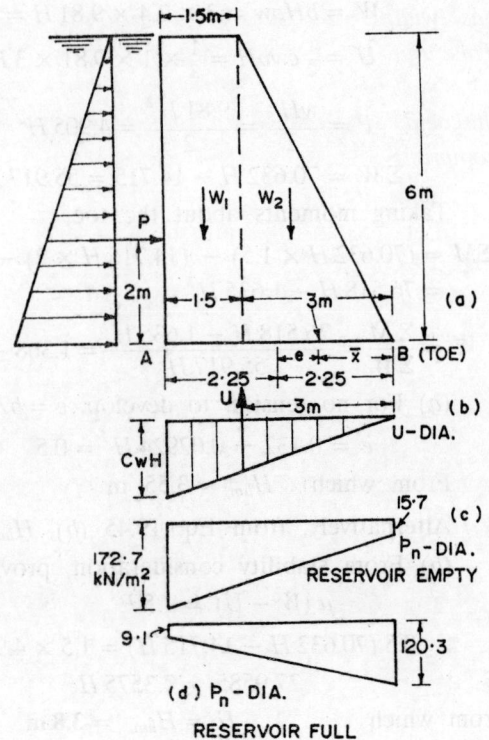

FIG. 19.24

Example 19.11. *A dam 6 m high and 1.5 m wide at the top has vertical water face. Find the base width of the dam if no tension is to develop. Take unit weight of masonry as 20 kN/m³ and c=1.*

Investigate the stability of the above dam if the coefficient of friction is 0.6 and maximum allowable compressive stress is 1800 kN/m².

Solution

Let the bottom width be b m, as shown in Fig. 19.25.

$$W_1 = 1.5 \times 6 \times 20 = 180 \ \text{kN}$$

$$W_2 = \frac{1}{2}(b - 1.5)\, 6 \times 20 = 60\,(b - 1.5)$$

$$P = \frac{wH^2}{2} = \frac{9.81\,(6)^2}{2} = 176.58 \ \text{kN}$$

$$U = \frac{1}{2}cwH.b = \frac{1}{2} \times 1 \times 9.81 \times 6\,b = 29.43 \ b.$$

$$\Sigma W = 180 + 60\,(b - 1.5) - 29.43\,b$$

$$= 90 + 30.57\,b$$

Taking moments about the toe, we get

$$\bar{x} = \frac{\Sigma M}{\Sigma W}$$

$$= \frac{180\,(b - 1.5 + 0.75) + 60\,(b - 1.5)\frac{2}{3}(b - 1.5) - 176.58 \times 2 - 29.43.b\frac{2}{3}b}{90 + 30.57\,b}$$

For no tension to develop, e should be equal to $b/6$

$$\therefore \qquad \frac{b}{2} - \bar{x} = \frac{b}{6}$$

or

$$\bar{x} = \frac{b}{3}$$

Hence,

$$\frac{b}{3} = \frac{180\,(b - 0.75) + 40\,(b - 1.5)^2 - 353.16 - 19.62\,b^2}{90 + 30.57\,b}.$$

From which, we get $b^2 - 2.944\,b - 39.074 = 0$

Hence $\qquad\qquad b \approx \mathbf{4.95 \ m}$

Check for crushing

$$\Sigma W = 90 + 30.57\,b = 90 + 30.57 \times 4.95 = 241.322 \ \text{kN}$$

$$(p_n)_{max.} = \frac{2\,\Sigma W}{b} = \frac{2(241.322)}{4.95} = 97.5 \ \text{kN/m}^2 < 1800. \ \text{OK.}$$

Check for sliding :

$$F.S. = \frac{\mu\,\Sigma W}{b} = \frac{0.6 \times 241.322}{176.58} = 0.82$$

Hence the dam is *unsafe* against sliding.

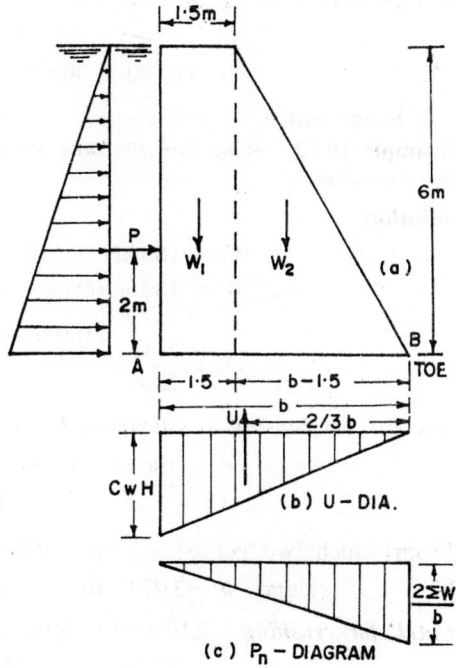

FIG. 19.25

If a minimum factor of safety of 1 is required under the conditions of uplift, we have
$$\mu \, \Sigma \, W = P$$

$$\therefore \qquad\qquad 0.6 \, (90 + 30.57 \, b) = 176.58$$

From which $\qquad\qquad b = \textbf{6.683 m}$

Example 19.12. *What will the base width if uplift is neglected ? Investigate the corresponding stability conditions.*

Solution

$$W_1 = 180 \text{ kN} \quad ; \quad W_2 = 60 \, (b - 1.5) \, ; \quad P = 176.58 \text{ kN}$$
$$\Sigma \, W = 180 + 60 \, (b - 1.5) = 90 + 60 \, b$$

$$\bar{x} = \frac{\Sigma \, M}{\Sigma \, W} = \frac{180 \, (b - 1.5 + 0.75) + 60 \, (b - 1.5) \dfrac{2}{3} (b - 1.5) - 176.58 \times 2}{90 + 60 \, b}$$

But for no tension to develop, $\bar{x} = b/3$

$$\frac{b}{3} = \frac{180 \, (b - 0.75) + 40 \, (b - 1.5)^2 - 353.16}{90 + 60 \, b}$$

From which, we get $b^2 + 1.5 \, b - 19.908 = 0$

Hence $b = \textbf{3.774 m.}$

Check for crushing : $\Sigma W = 90 + 60 \, b = 90 + 60 \times 3.774 = 316.44$ kN

$$(p_n)_{max.} = \frac{2 \, \Sigma \, W}{b} = \frac{2 \times 316.44}{3.774} = 167.7 \text{ kN/m}^2 < 1800. \text{ Hence safe.}$$

Check for sliding

$$\text{F.S.} = \frac{\mu \, \Sigma \, W}{p} = \frac{0.6 \times 316.44}{176.58} = 1.076$$

Example 19.13. *A trapezoidal dam section of 12 m height has vertical upstream face, with 3 m top width and 9 m bottom width. In order to increase the storage, it is proposed to raise the water height by erecting steel shuttering at the top of the dam, in line with the vertical face of the dam. Determine the maximum permissible height of shuttering so that no tension is developed at the upstream end of the base, under the reservoir full condition. Neglect foundation seepage. Take unit weight of masonry as 21 kN/m³.*

Solution (Fig. 19.26)

Let the height of shutters be s. In order that no tension is developed, the resultant must pass through the outer third point M_2, distant 3 m from the toe. Hence ΣM at point M_2 must be zero.

Now $\qquad W_1 = 3 \times 12 \times 21 = 756$ kN acting at
$\qquad\qquad\qquad\qquad 4.5$ m from M_2

$$W_2 = \frac{1}{2} \times 6 \times 12 \times 21 = 756 \text{ kN acting}$$
$$\text{at } 1 \text{ m from } M_2.$$

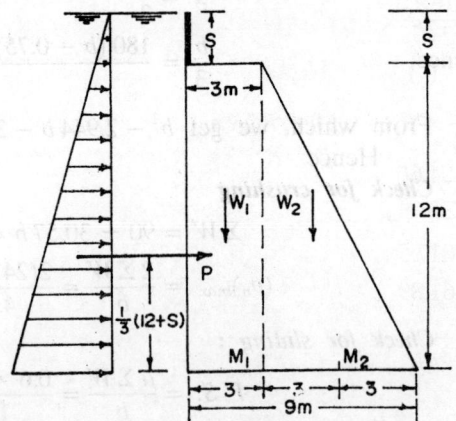

FIG. 19.26

$$P = \frac{wH^2}{2} = \frac{9.81\,(12 + s)^2}{2} = 4.905\,(12 + s)^2 \text{ kN}$$

acting at $\frac{1}{3}(12 + s)$ m above the base.

Taking moments about M_2

$$\Sigma M = 756 \times 4.5 + 756 \times 1 - 4.905\,(12 + s)^2 \times \frac{1}{3}(12 + s) = 0$$

or $(12 + s)^3 = 2543$

From which $(12 + s) = 2543^{\frac{1}{3}} = 13.65$

∴ $s = 1.65$ m

Hence height of shuttering should not exceed 1.65 m.

Example 19.14. *A masonry dam 10 m high is trapezoidal in section with a top width of 1 m and bottom width of 8.25 m. The face exposed to water has a batter of 1:10. Test the stability of the dam. Find out the normal stresses at the toe and heel of the dam. Assume unit weight of masonry as 22 kN/m³ and permissible shear stress of joint = 1200 kN/m². Take c=1 and μ = 0.75.*

Solution : Consider 1 m length of the dam. Assuming no free board, the dam is tested by considering only three forces,
(i) Weight of dam (ii) Hydrostatic water pressure and (iii) uplift pressure

(i) **Vertical forces :**

(a) Self weight of dam

$$= \frac{8.25 + 1}{2} \times 10 \times 1 \times 22$$

$$= 1017.5 \text{ kN}$$

(b) Weight of water in column $AA'B$

$$= \frac{10 \times 1}{2} \times 9.81 = 49.05 \text{ kN}$$

(c) uplift force

$$= \frac{1}{2} \times 9.81 \times 10 \times 8.25$$

$$= 404.66 \text{ kN}$$

∴ ΣW

$$= 1017.5 + 49.05 - 404.66$$

$$= 661.89 \text{ kN}$$

(ii) **Horizontal forces**

$$P = \frac{wH^2}{2} = \frac{9.81\,(10)^2}{2}$$

$$= 490.5 \text{ kN}.$$

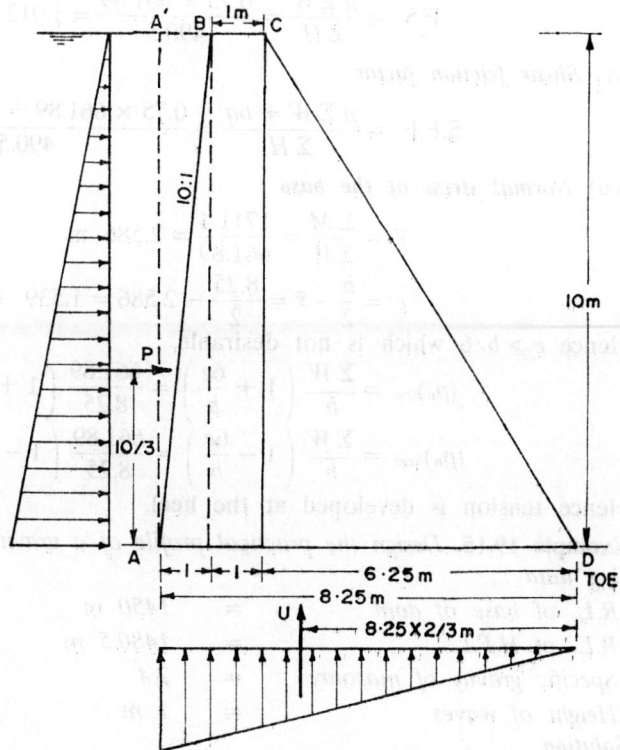

FIG. 19.27

(*iii*) *Moment of forces about toe (D)*

(*a*) Due to self weight of the dam :

$$\text{Moment} = \left\{ (\tfrac{1}{2} \times 1 \times 10 \times 22)(7.25 + \tfrac{1}{3}) \right\} + \left\{ (1 \times 10 \times 22)(6.25 + 0.5) \right\}$$
$$+ \left\{ (\tfrac{1}{2} \times 6.25 \times 10 \times 22)(\tfrac{2}{3} \times 6.25) \right\} = 5183.7 \text{ kN-m}$$

(*b*) Due to column of water in $AA'B$:

$$\text{Moment} = (\tfrac{1}{2} \times 10 \times 1 \times 9.81)(8.25 - \tfrac{1}{3}) = 388.3 \text{ kN-m}$$

(*c*) Due to uplift pressure :

$$\text{Moment} = 404.66 \times \frac{2}{3} \times 8.25 = 2225.6 \text{ kN-m}$$

(*d*) Due to horizontal water pressure :

$$\text{Moment} = 490.5 \times \frac{10}{3} = 1635 \text{ kN-m}$$

$$\therefore \quad \Sigma M = 5183.7 + 388.3 - 2225.6 - 1635 = 1711.4 \text{ kN}$$

(*iv*) *F.S. against overturning*

$$\text{F.S.} = \frac{\Sigma M_R}{\Sigma M_O} = \frac{5183.7 + 388.3}{2225.6 + 1635} = 1.44$$

(*v*) *F.S. against sliding*

$$\text{F.S.} = \frac{\mu \, \Sigma W}{\Sigma H} = \frac{0.75 \times 661.89}{490.5} = 1.012 > 1$$

(*vi*) *Shear friction factor*

$$\text{S.F.F.} = \frac{\mu \, \Sigma W + bq}{\Sigma H} = \frac{0.75 \times 661.89 + 8.25 \times 1200}{490.5} = 21.2$$

(*vii*) *Normal stress at the base*

$$\bar{x} = \frac{\Sigma M}{\Sigma W} = \frac{1711.4}{661.89} = 2.586 \text{ m}$$

$$\therefore \quad e = \frac{b}{2} - \bar{x} = \frac{8.25}{2} - 2.586 = 1.539 \text{ m}; \quad \frac{b}{6} = \frac{8.25}{6} = 1.375$$

Hence $e > b/6$ which is not desirable.

$$\therefore \quad (p_n)_{toe} = \frac{\Sigma W}{b} \left(1 + \frac{6e}{b} \right) = \frac{661.89}{8.25} \left(1 + \frac{6 \times 1.539}{8.25} \right) = 170 \text{ kN/m}^2$$

$$(p_n)_{heel} = \frac{\Sigma W}{b} \left(1 - \frac{6e}{b} \right) = \frac{661.89}{8.25} \left(1 - \frac{6 \times 1.539}{8.25} \right) = -9.6 \text{ kN/m}^2$$

Hence tension is developed at the heel.

Example 19.15. *Design the practical profile of a gravity dam of stone masonry, given the following data :*

R.L. of base of dam	=	*1450 m*
R.L. of H.F.L.	=	*1480.5 m*
Specific gravity of masonry	=	*2.4*
Height of waves	=	*1 m*

Solution

Height of waves, $h_w = 1$ m. $\therefore$ $F.B. = 1.5 \, h_w = 1.5$ m

$\therefore$ R.L. of top of dam $= 1480.5 + 1.5 = 1482$ m

Hence height of dam $= 1482 - 1450 = 32$ m

The practical profile of the dam can be designed with respect to the recommendations marked in Fig. 19.22.

Depth of water, $h = 1480.5 - 1450 = 30.5$ m

Top width a can be determined on the following criteria :

(i) $\qquad a = 14\%$ of H, for economy

$\qquad\qquad = 0.14 \times 32 \approx 4.5$ m

(ii) $\qquad a =$ width of roadway, if any.

However, keep $a = 4.5$ m

Base width of elementary profile

$$= \frac{h}{\sqrt{\rho}} = \frac{30.5}{\sqrt{2.4}} = 19.7 \text{ m}$$

Upstream offset $= \dfrac{a}{16} = \dfrac{4.5}{16} \approx 0.3$ m

$\therefore$ Total base width $= 19.7 + 0.3 = 20$ m

Distance upto which the u/s slope is vertical, from the u/s water level

$$= 2a \sqrt{\rho} = 2 \times 4.5 \sqrt{2.4} = 14 \text{ m}$$

Distance upto which the u/s slope is inclined, from the u/s water level

$$= 3.1 \, a \sqrt{\rho} = 3.1 \times 4.5 \sqrt{2.4} = 21.6 \text{ m}$$

Fig. 19.28 shows the practical profile of the masonry dam. The stability of this section can now be tested as usual.

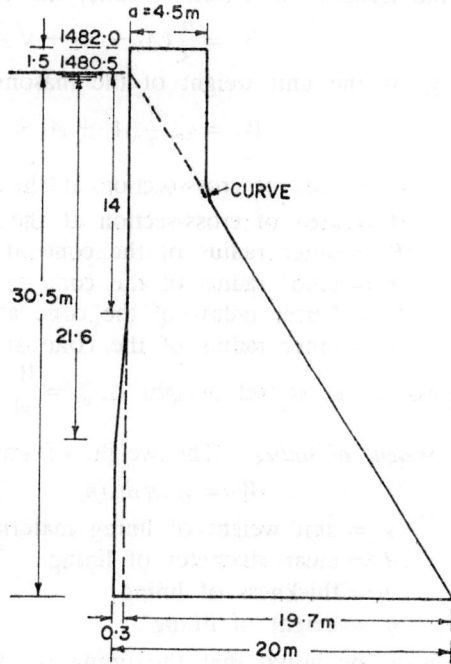

FIG. 19.28

19.6. MASONRY CHIMNEYS

Chimneys are used in almost all industries for the escape of flue gases to such a height that diffusion of gases takes place so that they do not contaminate the surroundings. The height of chimney is fixed on the basis of required draft. However, masonry chimneys are restricted to small heights only, since the section of the chimney becomes very heavy for large height, requiring heavy foundations. Masonry chimneys are generally built in bricks, with either the common bricks or radial bricks. Masonry chimneys are constructed in various shapes, such as circular, square, hexagonal or octagonal; circular shape is preferred over others. Chimney are lined from inside with fire bricks, atleast upto 20 to 25% of its height from the bottom.

Forces acting on a chimney

Various forces that act on a chimney are :

1. Self weight of masonry

2. Weight of brick lining

3. Wind pressure.

4. Seismic force.

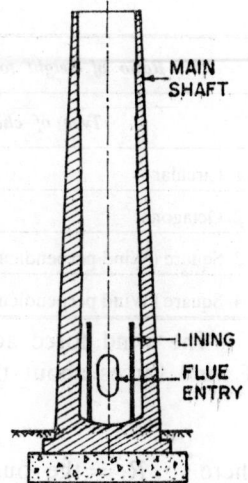

FIG. 19.29. MASONRY CHIMNEYS

(i) *Self weight of chimney* : As shown in Fig. 19.29, chimneys are tapered from top to bottom. The position of the chimney between two successive sections of height h may be considered to be the frustum of a hollow cone, the volume of which is given by.

$$V = \frac{h}{3}(A_1 + A_2 + \sqrt{A_1 A_2})$$ ...(19.50 *a*)

If γ_m is the unit weight of the masonry, the self weight of the chimney is given by

$$W_s = \gamma_m \frac{h}{3}(A_1 + A_2 + \sqrt{A_1 A_2})$$ ...(19.50)

where A_1 = area of cross-section at the bottom section = $\pi(R_1^2 - r_1^2)$

A_2 = area of cross-section at the top section = $\pi(R_2^2 - r_2^2)$

R_1 = outer radius of the cone at the bottom section

r_1 = inner radius of the cone at the bottom section

R_2 = Outer radius of the cone at the top section

r_2 = inner radius of the cone at the top section

The stress f_s due to self weight is, $f_s = \dfrac{W_s}{A} = \dfrac{W_s}{\pi(R_1^2 - r_1^2)}$ ...(19.51)

2. *Weight of lining* : The weight of lining (W_l) is given by

$$W_l = \gamma_l \cdot \pi \, d_l \, t_l \, h_l$$ ...(19.52)

where γ_l = unit weight of lining material

d_l = mean diameter of lining

t_l = thickness of lining

h_l = height of lining

It is to be noted that the lining is supported directly at the base.

3 Wind force

Wind force on the chimneys can be determined on the basis of recommendations contained in IS 875-1987, given in chapter 2. Table 19.1 gives the values of shape factors as per IS 875-1964. The wind force on chimney= shape factor × design wind pressure × projected area of the chimney.

TABLE 19.1. SHAPE FACTORS (IS : 875-1964)

Ratio of height to base width	0 to 4	4 to 8	8 and over
Type of chimney	Shape factor		
1. Circular	0.7	0.7	0.7
2. Octagonal	0.8	0.9	1.0
3. Square (Wind perpendicular to diagonal)	0.8	0.9	1.0
4. Square (Wind perpendicular to face)	1.0	1.15	1.3

The wind force acting on the chimney has an overturning effect. If M_w is the moment of wind forces about the base, the compressive and tensile stresses at the base are given by

$$f_w = \pm \frac{M_w}{I} R_1 = +\frac{M_w}{Z}$$ ...(19.53)

where R_1 = the outer radius at the base section.

I = moment of inertia of the section at base = $\dfrac{\pi}{4}(R_1^4 - r_1^4)$

Hence the total stress due to self weight and wind is given by

$$f = f_s \pm f_w = \frac{W_s}{A} \pm \frac{M_w}{I} \cdot R_1 \qquad \qquad \dots(19.54)$$

The value of *maximum stress* (using + sign) should not exceed the allowable compressive stress for masonry. Also, the minimum stress (using − sign) should be compressive in nature, i.e. no tension should develop at the base.

Example 19.16. *A circular chimney of brick masonry has uniform section throughout its height, having an inner diameter of 2 m and outer diameter of 3 m. Find the maximum permissible height of the chimney if no tension is to develop and if the allowable compressive stress in masonry is 1.5 N/mm². Take a uniform wind pressure intensity of 1.5 kN/m². Take unit weight of brick masonry as 22 kN/m³.*

Solution

Let H be the height of chimney.

$$A = \frac{\pi}{4}(3^2 - 2^2) = \frac{5}{4}\pi \ \text{m}^2$$

∴ Self weight of chimney,

$$W_s = \frac{5}{4}\pi H \times 22 = 27.5 \,\pi\, H \ \text{kN}$$

P_w = shape factor × wind pressure × projected area
    = 0.7 × 1.5 × 3H = 3.15 H kN

acting at $H/2$ from the base.

$$M_w = 3.15 H (H/2) = 1.575 H^2 \ \text{kN-m}$$

$$I = \frac{\pi}{64}(3^4 - 2^4) = \frac{65}{64}\pi \ \text{m}^4$$

$$y_{max} = 1.5 \ \text{m}$$

∴

$$f_{max.} = \frac{W_s}{A} + \frac{M_w}{I} y_{max.} = \frac{27.5\,\pi\,H}{\frac{5}{4}\pi} + \frac{1.575 H^2}{\frac{65}{64}\pi} \times 1.5$$

$$= 22 H + 2.326 \frac{H^2}{\pi}$$

$$f_{min.} = \frac{W_s}{A} - \frac{M_w}{I} y_{max} = 22 H - 2.326 \frac{H^2}{\pi}$$

For no tension to develop, $f_{min.} = 0 = 22 H - 2.326 \dfrac{H^2}{\pi}$

From which **H = 29.71 m**

∴

$$f_{max} = 22 \times 29.71 + \frac{2.326 (29.71)^2}{\pi} = 653.71 + 653.71$$

$$= 1307.4 \ \text{kN/m}^2 = 1.3074 \ \text{N/mm}^2 < 1.5 \ \text{Hence safe.}$$

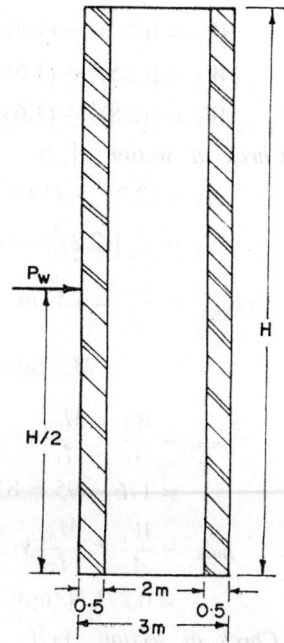

FIG. 19.30

Thus, maximum permissible height of chimney = 29.71 m

Example 19.17. *Fig. 19.31 shows a hollow square chimney having uniform inside dimension of 1.6 m × 1.6 m and varying out side dimension at different heights. Check the stability of the chimney by taking uniform wind pressure intensity of 1.5 kN/m² throughout the height. Take unit weight of masonry as 22 kN/m³ and permissible compressive stress in brick masonry as 1.8 N/mm².*

Solution

Let us test the stability of the chimney under two conditions:

(*i*) wind blowing at right angles to the face,

and (*ii*) wind blowing at right angles to the diagonal.

Case 1. Wind blowing at right angles to the face.

$\dfrac{\text{Height}}{\text{base}}$ ratio $= \dfrac{18}{2.8} = 6.43$

$\therefore$ Shape factor $= 1.15$ (Table 19.1)

Wind forces P_1 on top 8 m height :

$P_1 = 1.15 \times 1.5 \times 2.2 \times 8 = 30.36$ kN

Similarly, $P_2 = 1.15 \times 1.5 \times 2.5 \times 6 = 25.875$ kN

and $P_3 = 1.15 \times 1.5 \times 2.8 \times 4 = 19.32$ kN

The self weight of the three positions are :

$W_1 = [(2.2)^2 - (1.5)^2] \times 8 \times 22 = 401.28$ kN

$W_2 = [(2.5)^2 - (1.6)^2] \times 6 \times 22 = 487.08$ kN

and $W_3 = [(2.8)^2 - (1.6)^2] \times 4 \times 22 = 464.64$ kN

Check at section A_1B_1

$A_1 = (2.2)^2 - (1.6)^2 = 2.28$ m^2

$I_1 = \dfrac{1}{12}[(2.2)^4 - (1.6)^4] = 1.405$ m^4

$y_{1,max.} = \dfrac{2.2}{2} = 1.1$ m

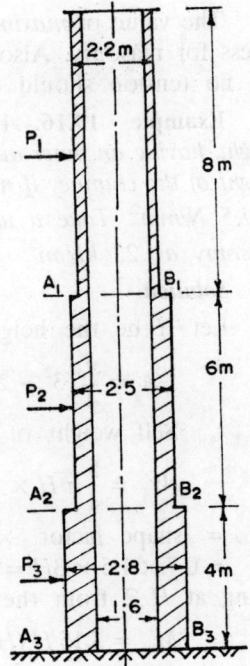

FIG. 19.31

$$M_{w1} \text{ (about } A_1B_1) = P_1 \times \frac{8}{2} = 30.36 \times 4 = 121.44 \text{ kN-m}$$

$f_{min.} = \dfrac{W_1}{A_1} - \dfrac{M_{w1}}{I_1}y_{1,max} = \dfrac{401.28}{2.28} - \dfrac{121.44}{1.405} \times 1.1$

$= 176 - 95 = 81$ kN/m^2 (safe)

$f_{max.} = \dfrac{W_1}{A_1} + \dfrac{M_{w1}}{I_1}y_{1,max} = 176 + 95 = 271$ kN/m^2

$= 0.271$ N/mm$^2 < 1.8$ (safe)

Check at section A_2B_2

$A_2 = (2.5)^2 - (1.6)^2 = 3.69$ m^2

$I_2 = \dfrac{1}{12}[(2.5)^4 - (1.6)^4] = 2.709$ m^4

$y_{2,max} = 1.25$ m

$\Sigma W = W_1 + W_2 = 401.28 + 487.08 = 888.36$ kN

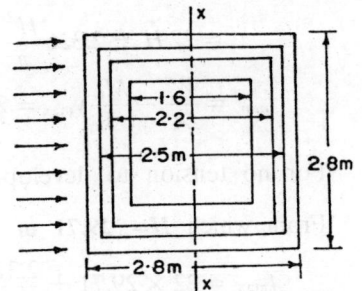

FIG. 19.32

M_{w2} (about A_2B_2) $= P_1(4 + 6) + P_2 \times \dfrac{6}{2} = 30.36 \times 10 + 25.875 \times 3 = 381.225$ kN

$\therefore$ $f_{min} = \dfrac{\Sigma W}{A_2} - \dfrac{M_{w2}}{I_2}y_{2,max} = \dfrac{888.36}{3.69} - \dfrac{381.225}{2.709} \times 1.25 = 240.7 - 175.9 = 64.8$ kN/m^2

$$f_{max} = \frac{\Sigma W}{A_2} + \frac{M_{w2}}{I_2} \cdot y_{2\,max} = 240.7 + 175.9 = 416.6 \text{ kN/m}^2 = 0.4166 \text{ N/mm}^2 < 1.8 \quad \text{(safe)}$$

Check at section $A_3 B_3$

$$A_3 = (2.8)^2 - (1.6)^2 = 5.28 \text{ m}^2 \,; I_3 = \frac{1}{12}[(2.8)^4 - (1.6)^4] = 4.576 \text{ m}^4 \,; y_{3,\,max} = 1.4 \text{ m}.$$

$$\Sigma W = W_1 + W_2 + W_3 = 401.28 + 487.08 + 464.64 = 1353 \text{ kN}$$

$$\begin{aligned} M_3 \text{ (about } A_3 B_3) &= P_1 \times 14 + P_2 \times 7 + P_3 \times 2 \\ &= 30.36 \times 14 + 25.875 \times 7 + 19.32 \times 2 = 644.805 \text{ kN-m} \end{aligned}$$

$$f_{min} = \frac{\Sigma W}{A_3} - \frac{M_{w3}}{I_3} \cdot y_{3,\,max} = \frac{1353}{5.28} - \frac{644.805}{4.576} \times 1.4 = 256.3 - 197.3 = 59 \text{ kN/m}^2$$

$$f_{max} = \frac{\Sigma W}{A_3} + \frac{M_{w3}}{I_3} \cdot y_{3,\,max} = 256.3 + 197.3 = 453.6 \text{ kN/m}^2 = 0.4536 \text{ N/mm}^2 < 1.8 \quad \text{(safe)}$$

Case 2 Wind blowing at right angles to the diagonal

The widths perpendicular to the directions of wind (i.e. length of diagonals), at various height will be $(2.2 \sqrt{2}\ (= 3.111 \text{ m}), 2.5 \sqrt{2}\ (= 3.536 \text{ m})$ and $2.8 \sqrt{2}\ (= 3.96 \text{ m})$ for the three heights.

$$\frac{\text{Height}}{\text{base width}} \text{ ratio} = \frac{18}{3.96} = 4.55.$$

Hence shape factor = 0.9

$$\therefore \quad \begin{aligned} P_1 &= 0.9 \times 1.5 \times 3.111 \times 8 = 33.6 \text{ kN} \\ P_2 &= 0.9 \times 1.5 \times 3.536 \times 6 = 28.64 \text{ kN} \\ P_3 &= 0.9 \times 1.5 \times 3.96 \times 4 = 21.384 \text{ kN} \end{aligned}$$

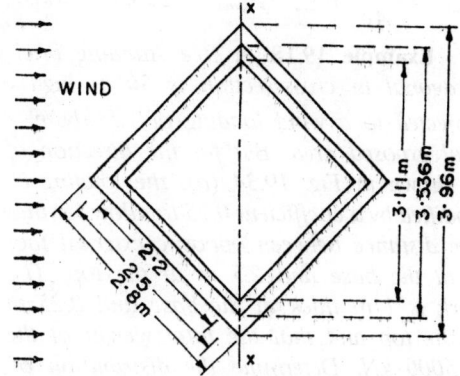

FIG. 19.33

Check at section $A_1 B_1$

$A_1 = 2.28 \text{ m}^2$ (as before);

$$\begin{aligned} I_1 &= \frac{2}{12}\left[3.111\left(\frac{3.111}{2}\right)^3 - 2.263\left(\frac{2.263}{2}\right)^3\right] \\ &= 1.405 \text{ m}^4 \end{aligned}$$

$$y_{1,\,max} = \frac{3.111}{2} = 1.556 \text{ m}$$

$$M_{w1} = P_1 \times 4 = 33.6 \times 4 = 134.4 \text{ kN-m}$$

$$\therefore \quad f_{min.} = \frac{W_1}{A_1} - \frac{M_{w1}}{I_1}y_{1,\,max} = \frac{401.28}{2.28} - \frac{134.4}{1.405} \times 1.556 = 176 - 148.8 = 27.2 \text{ kN/m}^2$$

$$f_{max.} = \frac{W_1}{A_1} + \frac{M_{w1}}{I_1} \cdot y_{1,\,max} = 176 + 148.8 = 324.8 \text{ kN/m}^2 = 0.325 \text{ N/mm}^2 < 1.8 \text{ safe.}$$

Check at section $A_2 B_2$

$$A_2 = 3.69 \text{ m}^2$$

$$I_2 = \frac{2}{12}\left[3.536\left(\frac{3.536}{2}\right)^3 - 2.263\left(\frac{2.263}{2}\right)^3\right] = 2.710 \text{ m}^4$$

$$y_{2,\,max} = \frac{3.536}{2} = 1.768 \text{ m}$$

$$M_{w_2} = P_1 \times 10 + P_2 \times 3 = 33.6 \times 10 + 28.64 \times 3 = 421.9 \text{ kN-m}$$

$$\therefore \quad f_{min} = \frac{\Sigma W}{A_2} - \frac{M_{w_2}}{I_2} \cdot y_{2\,max} = \frac{888.36}{3.69} - \frac{421.9}{2.71} \times 1.768$$

$$= 240.7 - 275.3 = -34.6 \text{ kN/m}^2. \text{ (unsafe)}$$

$$f_{max.} = \frac{\Sigma W}{A_2} + \frac{M_{w_2}}{I_2} \cdot y_{2,\,max} = 240.7 + 275.3 = 516 \text{ kN/m}^2 = 0.516 \text{ N/mm}^2 < 1.8$$

Check at section $A_3 B_3$: $\quad A_3 = 5.28 \text{ m}^2$

$$I_3 = \frac{2}{12}\left[3.96 \left(\frac{3.96}{2}\right)^3 - 2.263 \left(\frac{2.263}{2}\right)^3 \right] = 4.576 \text{ m}^4$$

$$y_{3\,max} = \frac{3.96}{2} = 1.98 \text{ m}$$

$$M_{w_3} = P_1 \times 14 + P_2 \times 7 + P_3 \times 2 = 33.6 \times 14 + 28.64 \times 7 + 21.384 \times 2 = 713.648 \text{ kN-m}$$

$$f_{min} = \frac{\Sigma W}{A_3} - \frac{M_{w_3}}{I_3} \cdot y_{3,\,max} = \frac{1353}{5.28} - \frac{713.648}{4.576} \times 1.98 = 256.3 - 308.8 = -52.5 \text{ kN/m}^2 \text{ (unsafe)}$$

$$f_{max.} = \frac{\Sigma W}{A_3} + \frac{M_{w_3}}{I_3} y_{3,\,max.} = 256.3 + 308.8 = 565.1 \text{ kN/m}^2 = 0.565 \text{ N/mm}^2 < 1.8.$$

Example 19.18. *A free standing brick shaft hexagonal in cross-section is 50 m high and is subjected to a wind loading of 1.5 kN/m² on the total exposed area. But for the direction of wind as shown in Fig. 19.34 (a), the loading is to be modified by a coefficient 0.75 to allow for the shape. The distance between opposite external faces is 4 m at the base and 2.5 m at the top. The brick work is 1 m thick at the base and 0.25 m thick at the top and that the total weight of the shaft is 5000 kN. Determine the distribution of stress across the base.*

Solution

Wind pressure at base, per m height :

$$P_B = 0.75 \times 1.5 \times 4 \times 1 = 4.5 \text{ kN/m}$$

Wind pressure at top, per m height

$$P_A = 0.75 \times 1.5 \times 2.5 \times 1 = 2.813 \text{ kN/m}$$

The wind pressure distribution is shown in Fig. 19.34

$$M_w \text{ about the base} = \left(2.813 \times 50 \times \frac{50}{2} \right)$$

$$+ \frac{1}{12}(4.5 - 2.813) \times 50 \times \frac{50}{3}$$

$$\approx 4219 \text{ kN-m}$$

For the base section (Fig. 19.34 c)

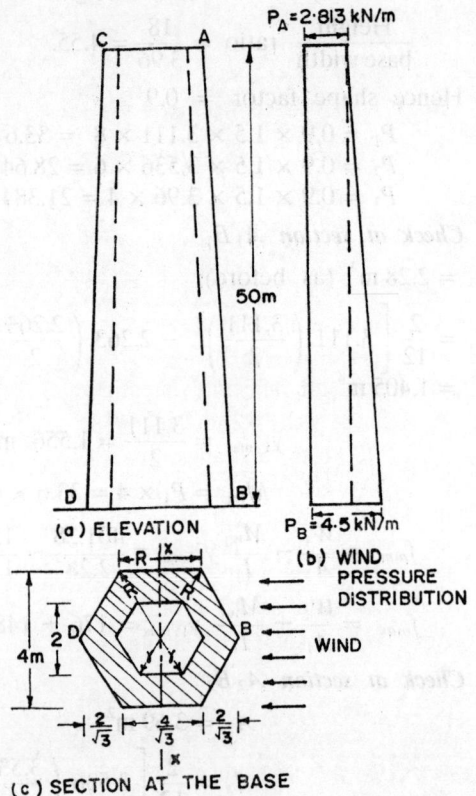

(a) ELEVATION

(b) WIND PRESSURE DISTRIBUTION

(c) SECTION AT THE BASE

FIG. 19.34

$$R = \frac{4}{\sqrt{3}} \; ; r = \frac{2}{\sqrt{3}}$$

$$I_{xx} \text{ of base} = 2\left[\left(\frac{1}{36} \times 4 \times \frac{8}{3\sqrt{3}}\right) + \left(\frac{1}{2} \times 4 \times \frac{1}{\sqrt{3}}\right) \times \left(\frac{4}{2\sqrt{3}} + \frac{2}{2\sqrt{3}}\right)^2 + \left(\frac{1}{3} \times 4 \times \frac{8}{3\sqrt{3}}\right)\right]$$

$$- 2\left[\left(\frac{1}{36} \times 2 \frac{1}{3\sqrt{3}}\right) + \left(\frac{1}{2} \times 2 \times \frac{1}{\sqrt{3}}\right) \times \left(\frac{1}{\sqrt{3}} + \frac{1}{3\sqrt{3}}\right)^2 + \left(\frac{1}{3} \times 2 \times \frac{1}{3\sqrt{3}}\right)\right]$$

$$= 2\left\{\frac{8}{27\sqrt{3}} + \frac{256}{27\sqrt{3}} + \frac{32}{9\sqrt{3}} - \frac{1}{54\sqrt{3}} - \frac{16}{27\sqrt{3}} - \frac{2}{9\sqrt{3}}\right\}$$

$$= \frac{2 \times 675}{54\sqrt{3}} \text{ m}^4 = \frac{25}{\sqrt{3}} \text{ m}^4.$$

$\therefore$ $\qquad Z_{xx}$ of base $= \dfrac{25}{\sqrt{3}} \div \dfrac{4}{\sqrt{3}} = 6.25 \text{ m}^3$

$\therefore$ $$p_b = \pm \frac{M_w}{Z_{xx}} = \pm \frac{4219}{6.25} \approx \pm 675 \text{ kN/m}^2$$

Area of base, $A = 6\left\{\dfrac{1}{2}\left(\dfrac{4}{\sqrt{3}} + \dfrac{2}{\sqrt{3}}\right) \times 1\right\} = \dfrac{6 \times 6}{2\sqrt{3}} = 6\sqrt{3} \text{ m}^2$

$\therefore$ $$p_0 = \frac{W_s}{A} = \frac{5000}{6\sqrt{3}} \approx 481 \text{ kN/m}^2$$

$\therefore$ Stress at D, $\qquad f_D = p_0 + p_b = 481 + 675 = \mathbf{1156 \text{ kN/m}^2}$ (comp.)

Stress at B, $\qquad f_B = p_0 - p_b = 481 - 675 = \mathbf{-194 \text{ kN/m}^2}$ (i.e. tension)

PROBLEMS

1. A masonry wall, 4 m high, 5 m wide and 1 m thick is subjected to a horizontal wind pressure of 1.5 kN/m² acting on the 5 m side. Taking the unit weight of masonry as 21 kN/m³, find the maximum and minimum intensities of stresses induced at the base of the wall.

2. A retaining wall, 4.2 m high, with a smooth vertical back, retains a dry sandy backfill of unit weight 18 kN/m³ and angle of shearing resistance of 30°. The backfill carries a uniformly distributed load of 10 kN/m². Find by Rankine's theory the total active pressure per metre length of wall and its point of application above the base. If the water table rises behind the back of the wall to an elevation of 2.1 m below the top of the wall, what is the change in the total active pressure per metre of the wall ? Assume no change in the angle of shearing resistance and submerged unit weight of sand as 9.5 kN/m³ .

   Ans. [(a) 67 kN ; 1.55 m above the base (b) Increase in pressure 15.72 kN]

3. Design a gravity retaining wall, 6 m high, with vertical back to retain a dry cohesionless backfill of unit weight 17 kN/m³ and angle of shearing resistance of 24°. Find also the factor of safety against sliding assuming the angle of friction between the base of the wall and the foundation soil as 30°. Keep the width of wall at the top as 1.2 m. Take the unit weight of masonry as 22 kN/m³.

4. A rectangular masonry dam is 2.4 m wide at the base. Compute the maximum permissible height H of the dam (a) when no tension is permissible and (b) when the factor of safety against sliding

is 1.5. Take $\mu = 0.5$ and unit weight of masonry equal to $2\frac{1}{2}$ times the unit weight of water. Neglect under-seepage effects.

5.   A masonry dam 8 m high and 2 m wide at the top has vertical water face. Find the base width of the dam if no tension is to develop. Take unit weight of masonry as 22 kN/m^3. Neglect uplift pressure. Also, investigate the stability of the dam section, taking $\mu = 0.7$ and maximum allowable compressive stress as 180 kN/m^2.

6.   Solve problem 5, considering the uplift pressure. Take $c=1$

7.   A hollow square chimney has inside dimensions of 1.5 m × 1.5 m at the top and 2 m × 2 m size at the bottom. It has uniform thickness of 0.5 m throughout its height of 16 m. Check the stability of the chimney at its base, for a uniform wind pressure intensity of 1.5 kN/m^2. Take unit weight of brick masonry as 20 kN/m^3 and permissible compressive stress as 2 N/mm^2.

20

Columns

20.1. INTRODUCTION

If a short length of bar or block is subjected to a compressive force P, uniform compressive stress $p = P/A$ is induced. Such a compression member fails by *crushing* on increasing the value of force P. The behavior of such a member has been discussed in chapter 2. Even if such a short compression member is subjected to eccentric load (or to a direct compressive force and a moment simultaneously), the failure is primarily by crushing. However, there remain the cases in which compression members of relatively longer length fail by *buckling* or by *lateral bending* even under a central load. Such members are commonly known as *columns*. While a *short compression member* undergoes negligible lateral deflection, *column is a compression member that is so slender compared to its length that under gradually increasing loads, it fails by buckling at loads considerably less than those required to cause failure by crushing*. Though there is no clear cut line of demarcation between a short compression member and a column, a compression member is generally considered to be a column when its unsupported length is more than 10 times its least lateral dimension.

Thus, a *compression member* is divided into three categories (*i*) *short compression members*, which fail primarily by crushing without buckling, (*ii*) *long columns* which fail by buckling or excessive lateral bending, and (*iii*) *intermediate columns* which fail by a combination of crushing and buckling. A compression member is classified by its length and least lateral dimension. Most of the practical cases of compression members fall under the second category. The *critical load*, which the member can carry before failure, depends upon (*i*) member dimensions (area, shape and length) and (*ii*) end conditions. For columns, the problem is one of determining the *critical load* which causes *elastic instability*.

Any structural member loaded axially in compression is called a *column* in the general sense of the word. It is variously termed as stanchion, post, strut, boom etc. depending upon its use as a particular member in a structure. *Columns* are ordinarily used in buildings, as vertical members, to carry loads of beams, slabs etc. *Stanchions* are steel columns made of rolled steel sections, commonly used in buildings. The term *post* is loosely used for a column; in a truss bridge girder end compression members are called *end posts*. The term *strut* is commonly used for compression member

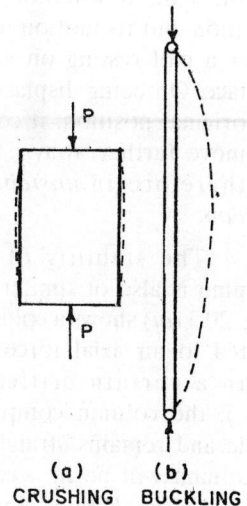

(a)   (b)
CRUSHING   BUCKLING

FIG. 20.1

in a roof truss; it may either be in vertical position or in inclined position. The principal compression member in a crane is called a *boom*.

20.2. MODES OF FAILURE OF A COLUMN : ELASTIC INSTABILITY

A column subjected to axial load, may fail under the following modes :

(*i*) crushing

(*ii*) buckling

and (*iii*) mixed mode of buckling and crushing.

If a short length of a bar or column is subjected to a compressive force P, a uniform compressive stress p is induced, p being equal to P/A. As the value of P is increased, p will increase, and ultimately, failure will occur due to *crushing* or *yielding* of the material. In the case of *long columns* subjected to axial loading, *buckling* occurs due to *elastic instability*. Every such column has a *critical load* (P_{cr}) which causes elastic instability, due to which column suddenly fails due to excessive bending stresses on the section. Columns of intermediate length fail in the mixed mode of buckling and crushing. Most of the practical columns fail due to this mixed mode of failure.

Critical Equilibrium

Equilibrium of an elastic body may be a ball resting on a concave surface (Fig. 20.2 *a*). If the ball is given a small displacement from its position, it will return to its initial position. The ball is, therefore in *stable equilibrium*. On the other hand, if the ball is resting on a horizontal surface, it will be in a *neutral equilibrum*. If a small displacement is given to the ball, it will not return to its initial position, but its motion will stop. Lastly, consider a ball resting on a convex surface. On being displaced from its original position, it continues to move further away ; the ball is therefore in *unstable equilibrium*.

(*i*) stable, (*ii*) neutral and (*iii*) unstable. Consider

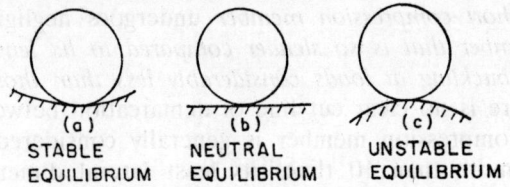

FIG. 20.2. EQUILIBRIUM CONDITIONS

The stability of a long column is also of similar nature. Fig. 20.3 (*ai*) shows a column subjected to an axial force P (less than a certain critical load P_{cr}); the column compresses a little and remains straight. Such a column will be in a condition of *stable equilibrium*. Even if it is deflected slightly by some lateral load δQ and then the lateral load is removed, the

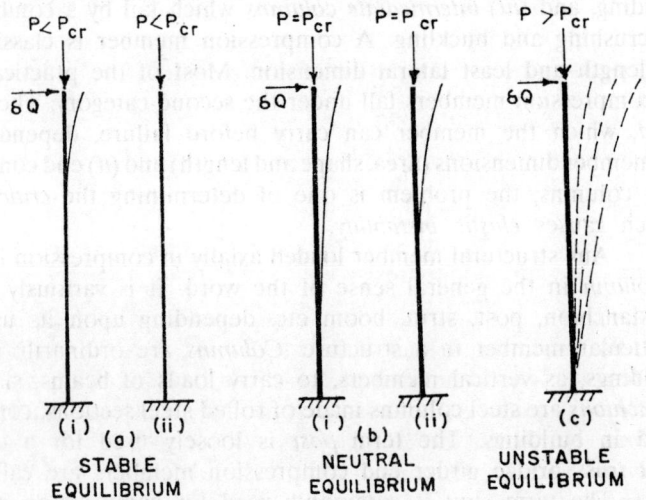

FIG. 20.3. EQUILIBRIUM CONDITIONS OF A COLUMN

column will become straight again and will assume the original configuration of equilibrium (Fig. 20.3 *aii*). The same cycle may be repeated with a force P increasing in magnitude until a critical load P_{cr} is reached at which the column remains in a slightly deformed position' after the application and removal of lateral force δQ. This instantaneous condition is the state of *neutral equilibrium* (Fig. 20.3 *b*). Finally if force P exceeds the critical one, the straight configuration of equilibrium of the column will become unstable as shown in Fig. 20.3 (*c*). At a load greater than the critical, a curvilinear configuration is stable and it can be shown by exact differential equations of elastic curve that a mere increase of 1.5 % in P_{cr} causes a maximum sideways deflection equal to 22 % of the length of the column, provided the material remains elastic. Such large deflections cannot be tolerated in engineering practice, since large stresses are induced in the column by the resulting eccentricity of the applied force and the column collapses. Therefore, *the determination of critical force P_{cr} is of utmost importance, since it represents the ultimate capacity of an ideal structure.* Investigations show that *instability* has been the cause of many accidents and structural damages.

Buckling of columns : Buckling stresses

The curved configuration of a column, under an axial load is called *buckled shape*. Due to this, the distribution of stress over the section will not be uniform, and the resulting eccentricity, however slight, will cause bending moment. This bending moment produces bending stresses which are referred as *buckling stresses* simply to prevent confusion with bending stresses produced by the eccentricity of applied loads. *Thus the buckling stresses and bending stresses are the same except that the former, by definition result from axial loads while the later from the applied eccentric load.* However, it should be clearly noted that buckling stresses are in addition to the direct compressive stress due to applied load.

In general, the buckling tendency of a column varies with the ratio of the length to least lateral dimension. The ratio is known as *slenderness ratio.* For tall slender columns, this ratio is large and if failure occurs, it will be entirely due to buckling (mode 2). When this ratio is very small, failure occurs due principally to *yielding* or crushing (mode 1). Between these extremes are the so called intermediate columns where failure will be due to combination of buckling and crushing (mode 3).

20.3. BUCKLING FAILURE : EULER'S THEORY

To investigate the *stability behavior* of columns, let us begin with a slender (i.e. very long) column with *pinned ends*. The column is loaded by a vertical load P that is applied through the centroid of the cross-section and aligned with the longitudinal axis of the column. The column is assumed to be perfectly straight and is made of a linear elastic material that follows Hooke's law, and is homogeneous in quality. We shall term such a column as an *ideal column*. The strength to resist buckling is greatly affected by conditions of the ends, whether free or fixed. To start with, we will take the *standard case* of a column hinged at both ends.

When the axial load P is small, the column remains straight and undergoes only axial compression. The compressive stress $p = P/A$, and is *uniform*. The column thus remains in *stable equilibrium*. As the axial load P is gradually increased, we reach a condition of *neutral equilibrium* in which the column may have *bent shape* (Fig. 20.4 (*b*)). The load causing *neutral equilibrium* is called the *critical load* (P_{cr}). At this load, the column may buckle in any direction, if its moment of inertia I is the same about both the axes. Generally, a compression member does not possess equal flexural rigidly in all directions. The *significant flexural rigidity EI* of a column depends on the minimum I and at the critical load; a column buckles either to one side or to the other, in that plane about which I is minimum.

The buckled shape shown in Fig. 20.4 (b) is possible only at a *critical load* called *buckling load, crippling load* or *Euler load* as prior to this load, the column remains straight. *The smallest load at which a buckled shape is possible is called critical load.* A theoretical analysis of the *critical load* for long columns was made by the great Swiss mathematician Leonhard Euler in 1757. His analysis is commonly known as *Euler's theory.*

Fig. 20.4(b) shows the centre line of a column in critical equilibrium under the action of *critical load P*. The maximum deflection δ is so small that there is no appreciable difference between the original length of the column and its projection on a vertical plane. Under these conditions, the slope dy/dx is so small that we may apply the approximate differential equation of the elastic curve of a beam :

$$E I \frac{d^2 y}{d x^2} = -M_x = -P \cdot y$$

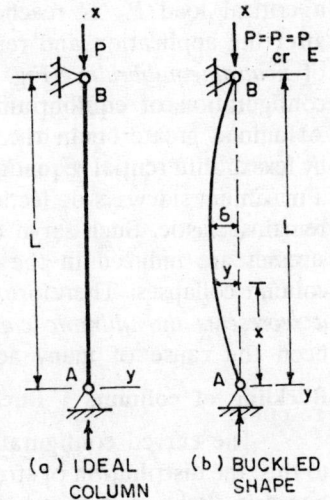

FIG. 20.4. COLUMN WITH PINNED ENDS

Rearranging the above equation, we get

$$\frac{d^2 y}{d x^2} + \frac{P}{E I} y = 0 \qquad \qquad ...(20.1)$$

In the above equation, the quantity EI is the flexural rigidity for bending in in the xy plane which is the plane of buckling.

Eq. 20.1 is the standard differential equation, the solution of which is :

$$y = C_1 \cos x \sqrt{\frac{P}{E I}} + C_2 \sin x \sqrt{\frac{P}{E I}} \qquad \qquad ...(20.1\ a)$$

In the above equation, C_1 and C_2 are constants of integration, the values of which can be found by applying end conditions.

At A, where $\qquad\qquad x = 0$, we have $y = 0$. Hence $C_1 = 0$

At B, where $\qquad\qquad x = L$, we have $y = 0$. Hence $0 = C_2 \sin L \sqrt{\frac{P}{E I}}$.

This is possible if C_2 is zero, in which case, the column has not bent at all or

$$\sin L \sqrt{\frac{P}{E I}} = 0$$

which gives $\qquad\qquad L \sqrt{\frac{P}{E I}} = 0, \pi, 2\pi...$

Since $L \sqrt{\frac{P}{E I}} = 0$ means that $P = 0$, this solution is not of interest. Hence the solutions of interest are

$$L \sqrt{\frac{P}{EI}} = n\,\pi, \text{ where } n = 1,2,3\dots$$

or
$$P = \frac{n^2 \pi^2 EI}{L^2}, \text{ (where } n = 1,2,3\dots) \qquad \dots(20.2)$$

It is theoretically possible for the column to have a bent shape only when P has one of values given by Eq. 20.2. For all other values of P, the column is in equilibrium only if it remains straight. *Therefore the values of P given by Eq. 20.2 are the critical loads for the column*

The *smaller critical load* for the column is obtained when $n = 1$, corresponding to which we get

$$P_{cr} = P_E = \frac{\pi^2 EI}{L^2} \qquad \dots(20.3)$$

The critical load (P_{cr}) for an ideal column is also known as the *Euler load* (P_E). The corresponding buckled shape, also called the *mode shape* is given by

$$y = C_2 \sin \frac{\pi x}{L} \qquad \dots(20.4)$$

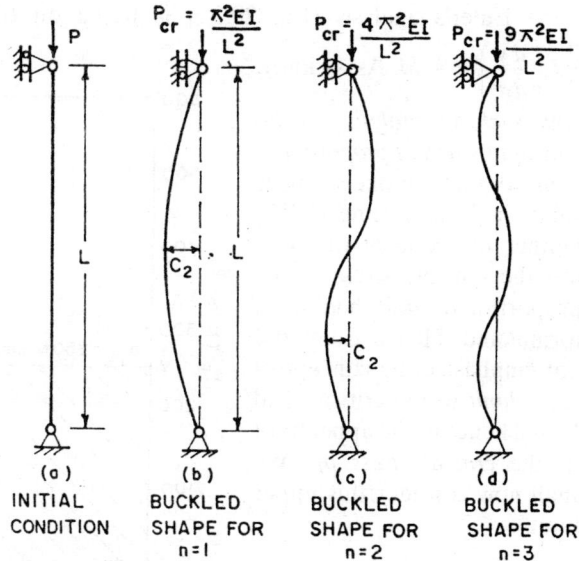

FIG. 20.5. CRITICAL LOAD

This shape is shown in Fig. 20.5(b), where the constant C_2 represents the deflection at the midpoint of the column. The buckling of a pinned-end column in the first mode ($n = 1$) is called the *fundamental case* of column buckling.

Other values of n, such as $n = 2$ and $n = 3$, occur with larger loads and are possible only if the column is braced at middle and third points respectively.

Assumptions of Euler's theory

The Euler's theory is based on the following *assumptions* :

(*i*) Axis of the column is perfectly straight when unloaded.
(*ii*) The line of thrust coincides exactly with the unstrained axis of the column.
(*iii*) Flexural rigidity EI is uniform.
(*vi*) Material is isotropic and homogeneous.
(*v*) The buckling value of $P = P_E$ is assumed to obtain for all degrees of flexure.

Usually, the first two assumptions are not fully realised in practice. The column may have initial curvature, distortion or crookedness. The theory, therefore, refers to an ideal column and not to a real one.

Limitations of Euler's Formula

A close inspection of Euler's formula (Eq. 20.3) shows that the critical load that causes buckling depends not on the strength of the material, but only on its dimensions and modulus of elasticity. Thus, two dimensionally identical slender columns, one of high strength steel and the other of ordinary structural steel, will buckle under the same critical load because, although their strengths are different, they have the same modulus of elasticity. The only material property involved in Euler's formula is the elastic modulus E, which physically represents the stiffness characteristics of the material. *The effect of imperfection is to convert the strut problem from the problem of instability to a problem of stress, of which Euler's theory takes no account.*

Euler's analysis (Eq. 20.3) is based on the differential equation of the elastic curve $E I \left(\dfrac{d^2y}{dx^2} \right) = - M.$ As we know now, *such an analysis is valid only upto stress at proportional limit* so that Hooke's law is valid. In Euler's time (1757) neither the concept of stress nor the limiting stress at the proportional limit had been formulated. Hence Euler did not emphasize the concept of *upper limit* to the critical load P_E and hence to the upper limit to the *critical stress* p_E. We shall now consider this upper limit.

The critical stress p_E, which is defined as the average stress over the cross-section is given by

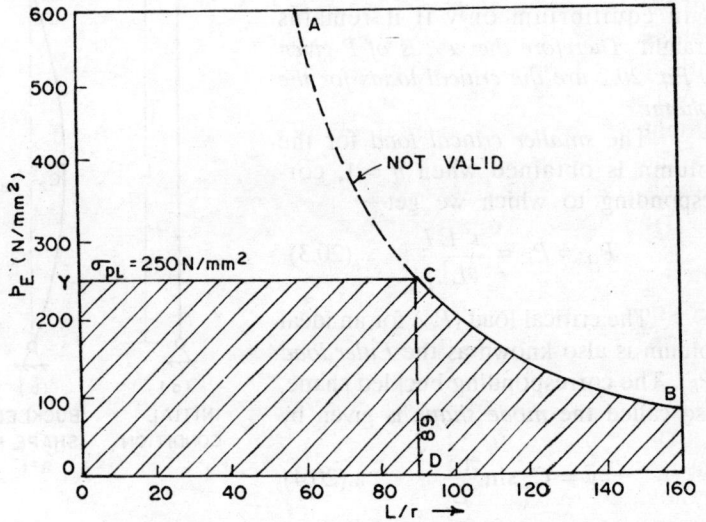

FIG. 20.6. VALIDITY LIMITS OF EULER'S FORMULA

$$p_E = \frac{P_E}{A} = \frac{\pi^2 E I}{L^2 (A)} = \frac{\pi^2 E}{\left(\dfrac{L}{r} \right)^2} \qquad \qquad ...(20.5)$$

where L/r is known as the *slenderness ratio*. The graphical representation of Eq. 20.5 is shown by the curve ACB in Fig. 20.6 where the critical stress p_E is plotted versus the slenderness ratio (L/r), for mild steel having $E = 2 \times 10^5 \, \text{N/mm}^2$. It is interesting to note that the curve is defined entirely by the magnitude of E and is independent of the ultimate strength of the material.

In order for Euler's formula to be applicable, the critical stress p_E must not exceed the proportional limit. In Fig. 20.6, OY represents the proportional limit (σ_{PL}) of the material. Euler's formula cannot apply if the corresponding slenderness ratio (l/r) is *less than OD*. If L/r is less than OD, the corresponding stress becomes greater than OY, the material becomes plastic and Hooke's law no longer remains valid. Taking the proportional limit (σ_{PL}) equal to $250 \, \text{N/mm}^2$, we have

$$\text{Limiting} \qquad \frac{L}{r} = OD = \sqrt{\frac{\pi^2 E}{p_E}} = \sqrt{\frac{\pi^2 (2.0 \times 10^5)}{250}} = 89$$

This shows that Euler's formula is applicable only if L/r is greater than 89 for mild steel of the above grade, for the column hinged at both ends. Hence the critical stress is given by the solid line YCB of Fig. 20.6. *The dotted portion of Euler's curve is not valid.* Similarly, for mild steel having proportionality limit $\sigma_{PL} = 200$, we get

Limiting $\dfrac{L}{r} = \sqrt{\dfrac{\pi^2 (2 \times 10^5)}{200}} \approx 99.$

Conventionally, *we define long columns as those for which Euler's formula applies.* The corresponding lower limit of $L/r\,(\,= OD)$ is shown in Fig. 20.6. For $\dfrac{L}{r}$ less than the governing value, the column is termed as *short* column for which Euler's formula is not valid, and *the proportional limit is taken as the critical stress.* A close study of Euler's curve (Fig. 20.6) shows that the critical stress (or allowable stress) decreases rapidly as the slenderness ratio increases. Hence a good design is the one in which L/r ratio is kept as small as possible. It is very important to note that Euler's formula determines only the critical load and not the working load. The working load (called the allowable load) is obtained by dividing the formula by a suitable factor of safety — usually between 1.7 to 2.5, depending on the material.

20.4. IDEAL END CONDITIONS AND EFFECTIVE LENGTH

A column may have two types of end conditions

(*i*) Position restraint, and (*ii*) Direction restraint.

An end has a *position restraint* when it is not free to change its position (or is not free to translate), but is free to rotate. The *hinged end* of a column is a typical example of position restraint. In the *direction restraint*, the end of the column is not free to change its direction. It may be free to change its position, or it may not be free to change its position. However, an end of a column may have both the position restraint as well as direction restraint.

Depending upon various *combinations of restraints*, there may be the following four cases of end conditions (Fig. 20.7) :

Case 1: Both ends of column hinged (Fig. 20.7 *a*) : *standard case.*

Case 2 : One end of column fixed and the other end free (Fig. 20.7 *b*).

Case 3 : Both ends of column fixed (Fig. 20.7 *c*).

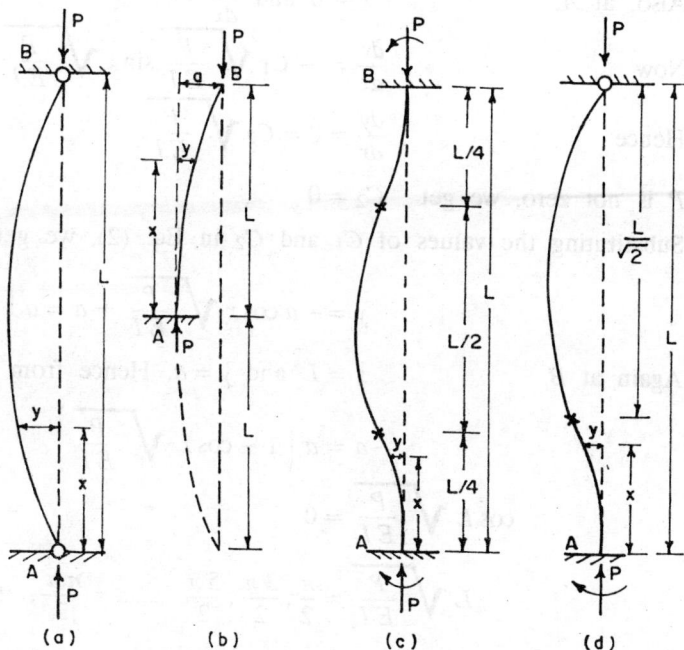

FIG. 20.7. IDEAL END CONDITIONS

Case 4 : One end of column fixed and the other end hinged (Fig. 20.7 *d*).

Case 1 : Standard Case : Both ends hinged

We have already considered this standard case in the previous article and found that the critical load, or Euler's load is given by

$$P_E = \frac{\pi^2 E I}{L^2} \qquad\qquad\qquad ...(20.3)$$

Case 2 : One end fixed, other end free (Fig. 20.7 *b*)

In Fig. 20.7 (*b*) let end A be direction fixed as well as position fixed and the end B be *free*. Let a be the deflection at the free end B. At any distance x from the base,

$$M = -P(a - y)$$

Hence the differential equation for the elastic curve is

$$E I \frac{d^2 y}{d x^2} = -M = P(a - y)$$

or

$$\frac{d^2 y}{d x^2} + \frac{P}{E I} y = \frac{P a}{E I} \qquad\qquad\qquad ...(1)$$

The solution of the above differential equation is

$$y = C_1 \cos x \sqrt{\frac{P}{E I}} + C_2 \sin x \sqrt{\frac{P}{E I}} + a \qquad\qquad ...(2)$$

At A, \qquad $x = 0$ and $y = 0$ Hence $C_1 = -a$

Also, at A, \qquad $x = 0$ and $\dfrac{dy}{dx} = 0$

Now \qquad $\dfrac{dy}{dx} = -C_1 \sqrt{\dfrac{P}{E I}} \sin x \sqrt{\dfrac{P}{E I}} + C_2 \sqrt{\dfrac{P}{E I}} \cos x \sqrt{\dfrac{P}{E I}}$

Hence \qquad $\dfrac{dy}{dx} = 0 = C_2 \sqrt{\dfrac{P}{E I}}$

Since P is not zero, we get \quad $C_2 = 0$

Substituting the values of C_1 and C_2 in Eq. (2), we get

$$y = -a \cos x \sqrt{\frac{P}{E I}} + a = a \left(1 - \cos x \sqrt{\frac{P}{E I}} \right) \qquad ...(3)$$

Again at B, \qquad $x = L$ and $y = a$. Hence from (3), we get

$$a = a \left(1 - \cos L \sqrt{\frac{P}{E I}} \right)$$

or \qquad $\cos L \sqrt{\dfrac{P}{E I}} = 0$

or \qquad $L \sqrt{\dfrac{P}{E I}} = \dfrac{\pi}{2}, \dfrac{3\pi}{2}, \dfrac{5\pi}{2}, ... = \dfrac{n\pi}{2}, \quad (n = 1, 3, , 5 ...)$

Hence \qquad $P_{cr} = P_E = \dfrac{n^2 \pi^2 E I}{4 L^2} \qquad (n = 1, 3, 5 ...) \qquad ...(20.6\ a)$

The corresponding buckled shape is $\quad y = a\left(1 - \cos\dfrac{n\pi x}{2L}\right), \quad n = 1, 3, 5\ldots \qquad \ldots(20.7\ a)$

The smallest critical load ($n = 1$), is the only load of practical interest.

Hence $\qquad\qquad\qquad P_E = \dfrac{\pi^2 E I}{4 L^2} \qquad\qquad\qquad\qquad\qquad \ldots(20.6)$

The corresponding buckled shape is

$$y = a\left(1 - \cos\dfrac{\pi x}{2 L}\right) \qquad\qquad\qquad \ldots(20.7)$$

Case 3 : Both ends fixed (Fig. 20.7 c)

Fig. 20.7 (c) shows a column with both the ends A and B direction fixed as well as position fixed. The column will deflect under the critical load, as shown in Fig. 20.7 (c), with points C and D as points of contraflexure situated at $L/4$ from either end. The column is thus concave for the middle half and convex for a length of $L/4$ from either end. If M is the fixing moment, the differential equation of the elastic curve is given by

$$E I \dfrac{d^2 y}{dx^2} = M - P.y$$

Rearranging the above equation, we get

$$\dfrac{d^2 y}{dx^2} + \dfrac{P}{E.I}.y = \dfrac{M}{E I} \qquad\qquad\qquad\qquad \ldots(i)$$

The solution of the above differential equation is

$$y = C_1 \cos x \sqrt{\dfrac{P}{E I}} + C_2 \sin x \sqrt{\dfrac{P}{E I}} + \dfrac{M}{P} \qquad\qquad \ldots(ii)$$

Differentiating it, we get

$$\dfrac{dy}{dx} = - C_1 \sqrt{\dfrac{P}{E I}} \sin x \sqrt{\dfrac{P}{E I}} + C_2 \sqrt{\dfrac{P}{E I}} \cos x \sqrt{\dfrac{P}{E I}} \qquad \ldots(iii)$$

At A, $\qquad\qquad x = 0$ and $y = 0$ Hence $C_1 = -\dfrac{M}{P}$, From (ii)

At A, $\qquad\qquad x = 0 \quad$ and $\dfrac{dy}{dx} = 0.\quad$ Hence $C_2 = 0$.

Substituting the value of $\dfrac{M}{P}$ and C_2 in (ii), we get

$$y = C_1 \cos x \sqrt{\dfrac{P}{E I}} - C_1 = C_1\left(\cos x \sqrt{\dfrac{P}{E I}} - 1\right) \qquad \ldots(iv)$$

Again at B, $\qquad x = L$ and $y = 0 = C_1\left(\cos L \sqrt{\dfrac{P}{E I}} - 1\right)$

This is possible when either $C_1 = 0$ in which case the column has not bent at all, or

$$\cos L \sqrt{\dfrac{P}{E I}} - 1 = 0 \qquad \text{or} \qquad \cos L \sqrt{\dfrac{P}{E I}} = 1$$

This gives $\qquad\qquad L \sqrt{\dfrac{P}{E I}} = 0, 2\pi, 4\pi \qquad\qquad\qquad\qquad \ldots(v)$

Also, at B, $\qquad\qquad x = L$ and $\dfrac{dy}{dx} = 0$. Hence from (iii)

$$0 = - C_1 \sqrt{\dfrac{P}{EI}} \sin L \sqrt{\dfrac{P}{EI}}$$

or $\qquad\qquad \sin L \sqrt{\dfrac{P}{EI}} = 0$

This gives $\qquad\qquad L \sqrt{\dfrac{P}{EI}} = 0, \pi, 2\pi, 3\pi$ $\qquad\qquad\qquad$ ...(vi)

The minimum significant value of $L \sqrt{\dfrac{P}{EI}}$, consistent with both (v) and (vi) is 2π.

Hence $\qquad\qquad L \sqrt{\dfrac{P}{EI}} = 2\pi$

which gives $\qquad\qquad P_{cr} = P_E = \dfrac{4\pi^2 EI}{L^2}$ $\qquad\qquad\qquad$ ...(20.8)

Case 4. One end fixed, the other end hinged

Fig. 20.7 (d) shows a column which is position and direction fixed at end A and hinged at end B. Since end A is fixed, a bending moment M is induced there; this involves the presence of a force R at right angles to AB to maintain equilibrium. The deflected shape is such that there is a point of contra-flexure at point C, distant $L/\sqrt{2}$ from the hinged end B. The differential equation for the elastic curve is

$$E I \dfrac{d^2 y}{dx^2} = - P \cdot y + R(L - x)$$

or $\qquad\qquad \dfrac{d^2 y}{dx^2} + \dfrac{P}{EI} y = \dfrac{R}{EI}(L - x)$ $\qquad\qquad\qquad$ ...(a)

Solution of the above differential equation is

$$y = C_1 \cos x \sqrt{\dfrac{P}{EI}} + C_2 \sin x \sqrt{\dfrac{P}{EI}} + \dfrac{R}{P}(L - x) \qquad\qquad ...(b)$$

$\therefore \qquad \dfrac{dy}{dx} = - C_1 \sqrt{\dfrac{P}{EI}} \sin x \sqrt{\dfrac{P}{EI}} + C_2 \sqrt{\dfrac{P}{EI}} \cos x \sqrt{\dfrac{P}{EI}} - \dfrac{R}{P}$ ...(c)

At A, $\qquad\qquad x = 0$ and $\qquad y = 0$ $\qquad$ Hence $C_1 = - \dfrac{RL}{P}$

Also, at A, $\qquad\qquad x = 0$ and $\dfrac{dy}{dx} = 0 = C_2 \sqrt{\dfrac{P}{EI}} - \dfrac{R}{P}$

Hence $\qquad\qquad C_2 = \dfrac{R}{P} \sqrt{\dfrac{EI}{P}}$

Substituting the values of C_1 and C_2 in (b), we get

$$y = - \dfrac{RL}{P} \cos x \sqrt{\dfrac{P}{EI}} + \dfrac{R}{P} \sqrt{\dfrac{EI}{P}} \sin x \sqrt{\dfrac{P}{EI}} + \dfrac{R}{P}(L - x)$$

Again, at end B, $\qquad\qquad x = L$ and $y = 0$

$$\therefore \qquad 0 = -\frac{RL}{P}\cos L\sqrt{\frac{P}{EI}} + \frac{R}{P}\sqrt{\frac{EI}{P}}\sin L\sqrt{\frac{P}{EI}}$$

or $\qquad \tan L\sqrt{\dfrac{P}{EI}} = L\sqrt{\dfrac{P}{EI}}$ $\qquad\qquad\qquad\qquad\qquad$ ...(d)

Hence the value of $L\sqrt{\dfrac{P}{EI}}$ has to be such that its tangent is equal to the angle itself. The smallest non-zero value of this angle that satisfies Eq. (d) is

$$L\sqrt{\frac{P}{EI}} = 4.4934 \text{ radians} \qquad \text{or} \qquad \frac{L^2 P}{EI} = 20.19 \approx 2\pi^2$$

Hence $\qquad\qquad P_{cr} = P_E = \dfrac{20.19\,EI}{L^2} \approx \dfrac{2\pi^2 EI}{L^2}$ $\qquad\qquad\qquad$ ...(20.9)

Equivalent (or Effective) length

To summarise, Euler's load (critical load) for each one of the above four cases are as under :

Case 1 : $\qquad\qquad P_E = \dfrac{\pi^2 EI}{L^2}$

Case 2 : $\qquad\qquad P_E = \dfrac{\pi^2 EI}{4L^2}$

Case 3 : $\qquad\qquad P_E = \dfrac{4\pi^2 EI}{L^2}.$

Case 4 : $\qquad\qquad P_E \approx \dfrac{2\pi^2 EI}{L^2}$

In general, Euler's crippling load can be expressed in the form $P_E = \dfrac{\pi^2 EI}{CL^2}$, in which C is a constant which takes into account the method of fixing the ends (*i.e.* whether the ends are fixed or hinged or free). For a column hinged at both the ends $C = 1$; hence this case is called the *standard case*. For *case 2*, $C = 4$; for *case 3*, $C = \dfrac{1}{4}$ and for *case 4*, $C = \dfrac{1}{2}$. In place of using actual length L of the column we can use length of column which is *equivalent* to that of a pin jointed column. Thus,

$$P_E = \frac{\pi^2 EI}{L_E^2} = \frac{\pi^2 EI}{l^2} \qquad\qquad\qquad ...(20.10)$$

where L_E (or l) is the *equivalent length* or *effective length*, which is equal to $L\sqrt{C}$, the values of which are given in Table 20.1.

TABLE 20.1. EQUIVALENT LENGTH FOR COLUMNS WITH IDEAL END CONDITIONS

End conditions	Both end hinged	One end fixed and other free	Both ends fixed	One end fixed and other hinged
Equivalent length l or L_E = $L\sqrt{C}$	L	2L	$\dfrac{L}{2}$	$\dfrac{L}{\sqrt{2}}$

20.5. PRACTICAL END CONDITIONS AND EFFECTIVE LENGTH FACTORS

The ideal end conditions discussed in the previous article are only of the theoretical importance, since in actual practice, none of these can be achieved. However, the concept of *equivalent length* or *effective length* developed above is useful.

Table 20.2 gives Indian Standard recommendations (IS : 800–1984) for finding effective length in the given plane. The values of these tables may also be adopted where columns form part of framed structure. Refer Fig. 20.8 also, along with Table 20.2.

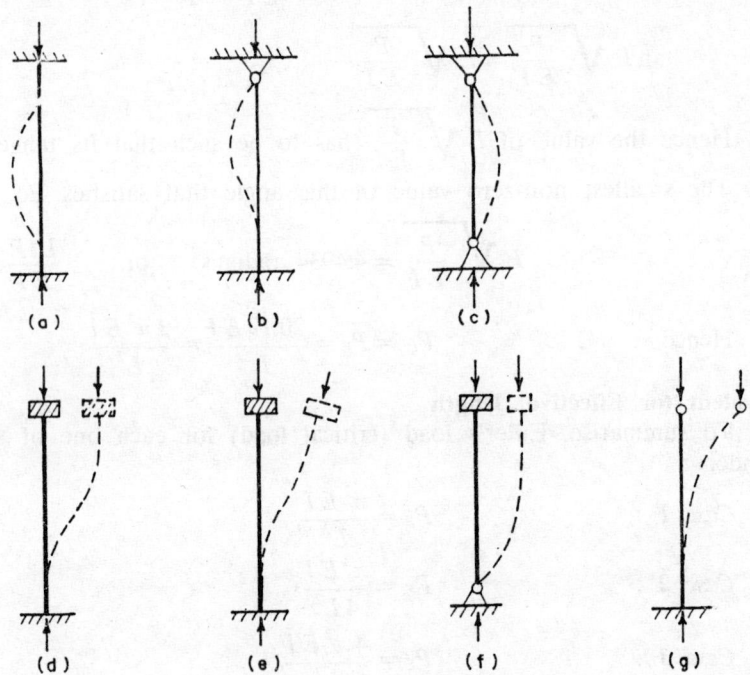

FIG. 20.8. END CONDITIONS

TABLE 20.2.   EFFECTIVE LENGTH OF COMPRESSION MEMBERS

Degree of end restraint of compression member	Recommended value of effective length
(a) Effectively held in position and restrained against rotation at both ends (Fig 20.8 a)	0.65L
(b) Effectively held in position at both ends and restrained against rotation at one end (Fig 20.8 b)	0.80L
(c) Effectively held in position at both ends, but not restrained against rotation (Fig. 20.8 c)	1.00L
(d) Effectively held in position and restrained against rotation at one end, and at the other end restrained against rotation but not held in position (Fig. 20.8 d)	1.20L
(e) Effectively held in position and restrained against rotation at one end, and at the other end partially restrained against rotation but not held in position (Fig. 20.8 e)	1.50L
(f) Effectively held in position at one end but not restrained against rotation, and at the other end restrained against rotation but not held in position (Fig 20.8 f)	2.00L
(g) Effectively held in position and restrained against rotation at one end but not held in position nor restrained against rotation at the other end (Fig 20.8 g)	2.00L

Note 1 : L is the unsupported length of compression member.

Note 2 : For battened struts, the effective length shall be increased by 10%.

Effective length of columns in framed structures : In the absence of more exact analysis, the effective length of columns in framed structures may be obtained from the ratio l/L of effective length l to unsupported length L given in Fig. 20.9(a) when relative displacement of the ends of the column is prevented and in Fig. 20.9 (b) when relative lateral displacement of the ends is not prevented. In the later case, it is recommended that the effective length ratio l/L may not be taken less than 1.2.

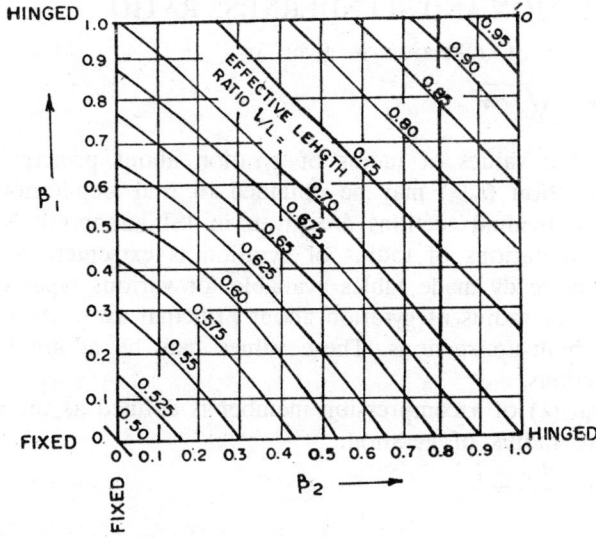

FIG. 20.9 (a). EFFECTIVE LENGTH RATIOS FOR A COLUMN IN A FRAME
WITH NO SWAY (IS : 800-1984)

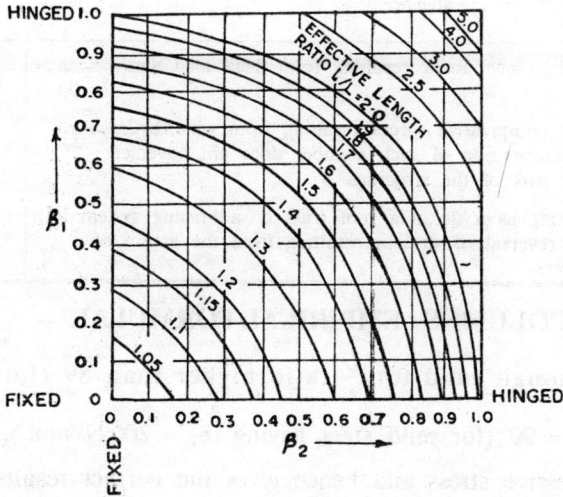

FIG 20.9 (b). EFFECTIVE LENGTH RATIOS FOR A COLUMN IN A FRAME
WITHOUT RESTRAINT AGAINST SWAY (IS : 800-1984)

In Figs. 20.9(a) and 20.9(b), β_1 and $\beta_2 = \dfrac{\Sigma K_c}{\Sigma K_c + \Sigma K_b}$ ...(20.11)

where the summation is to be done for members framing into a joint at top (for β_1) and bottom (for β_2) respectively, and K_c and K_b are the flexural stiffnesses for the column and beam respectively.

20.6. RADIUS OF GYRATION AND SLENDERNESS RATIO

The *radius of gyration* of a section is given by

$$r = \sqrt{I/A}$$

For every section, the values of radius of gyration about principal axes are required so that least radius of gyration (r_{min}) may be obtained to find slenderness ratio. The values of radius of gyration of individual sections are given in ISI handbook No. 1. However, for built-up sections, the computations of radius of gyration is extremely tedious. These values are therefore selected from ready made tables available for various types of built-up sections. Fig. 20.10 gives the values of radius of gyration about principal axes, for some common forms of individual as well as built-up sections. These values may be adopted in the preliminary design involving trial sections.

The *slenderness ratio* (λ) of a compression member is defined as the ratio of its effective length to the appropriate radius of gyration:

$$\lambda = \frac{L_E}{r} = \frac{l}{r}$$

For finding the maximum value of slenderness ratio of given member, the least value of its radius of gyration should be selected. As per Indian Standard IS : 800–1984, the maximum slenderness ratio should not exceed the values given in Table 20.3.

TABLE 20.3. MAXIMUM SLENDERNESS RATIOS

	Member	*Maximum slenderness ratio λ*
1.	A member carrying compressive loads resulting from dead load and imposed loads.	180
2.	A member subjected to compressive forces resulting from wind/earthquake forces, provided the deformation of such member does not adversely affect the stress in any part of the structure.	250
3.	A member normally acting as a tie in a roof truss or a bracing system but subject to possible reversal of stresses resulting from the action of wind or earthquake forces	350

20.7. INTERMEDIATE COLUMNS : EMPIRICAL FORMULAE

Euler's formula though valid for $\dfrac{L}{r}$ ratio higher than 89 (for mild steel having $\sigma_{PL} = 250\,\text{N/mm}^2$) and $\dfrac{L}{r} = 99$ (for mild steel having $\sigma_{PL} = 200\,\text{N/mm}^2$), does not take into account the direct compressive stress and hence gives the correct results only for very long columns. Euler's formula is not valid for smaller slenderness ratio. For short column, defined as the one whose length does not exceed 10 times its least lateral dimension, the upper limit

SECTION	r_x/h	r_y/b	SECTION	r_x/h	r_y/b	SECTION	r_x/h	r_y/b
 [section]	0.250	0.250	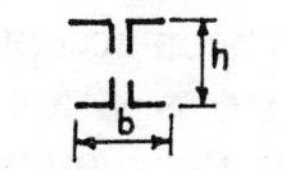 [section]	0.40 0.45	0.19 0.22	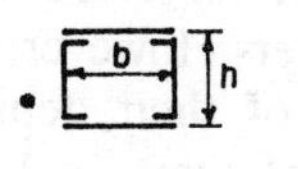 [section]	0.40 0.44	0.38 0.42
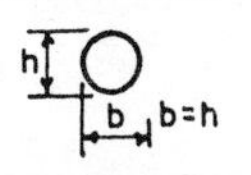 [section]	0.350	0.350	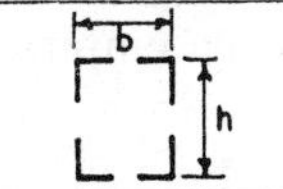 [section]	0.40 0.45	0.40 0.45	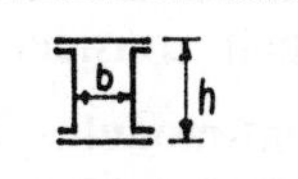 [section]	0.40 0.44	0.50 0.54
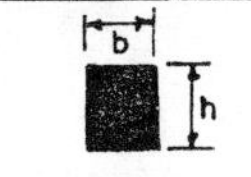 [section]	0.294	0.294	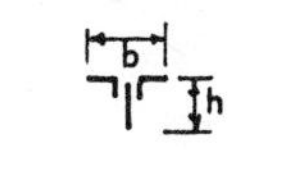 [section]	0.25 0.30	0.19 0.22	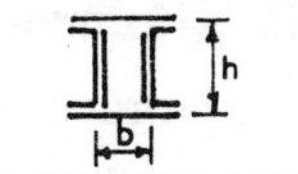 [section]	0.37 0.40	0.48 0.52
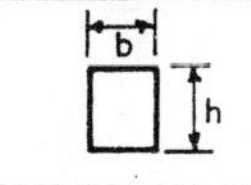 [section]	$0.5\sqrt{\dfrac{3b+h}{3(b+h)}}$	$0.5\sqrt{\dfrac{3h+b}{3(h+b)}}$	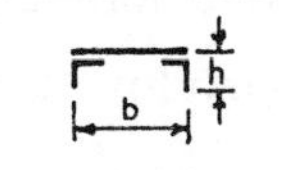 [section]	0.27 0.30	0.35 0.38	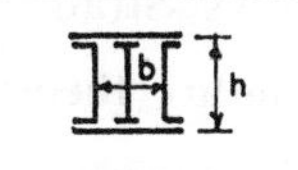 [section]	0.40 0.44	0.25 0.30
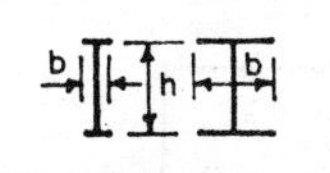 [section]	0.38 0.42	0.22 0.25	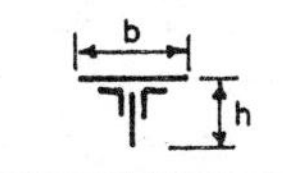 [section]	0.20 0.25	0.20 0.25	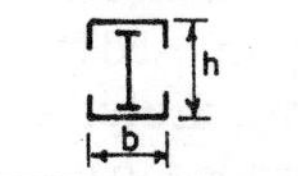 [section]	0.39 0.44	0.30 0.33
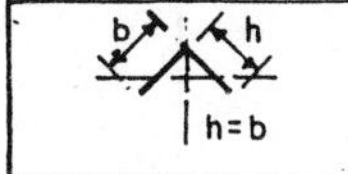 [section]	0.20	0.40	 [section]	0.38 0.40	0.19 0.23	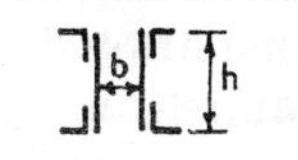 [section]	0.33 0.36	0.52 0.54

SECTION	r_x/h	r_y/b	SECTION	r_x/h	r_y/b	SECTION	r_x/h	r_y/b
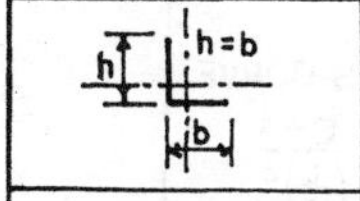 [section]	0.30 0.32	0.30 0.32	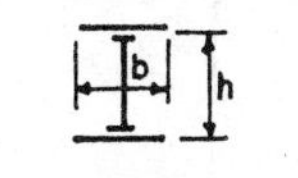 [section]	0.38 0.43	0.19 0.22	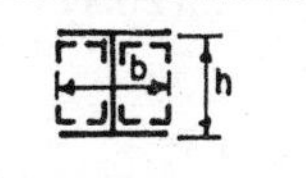 [section]	0.42 0.46	0.27 0.29
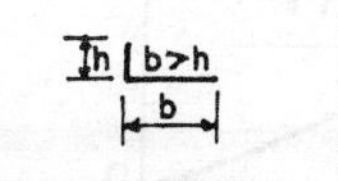 [section]	0.28 0.31	0.31 0.33	 [section]	0.40 0.45	0.20 0.25	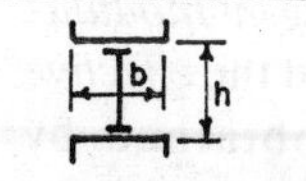 [section]	0.49 0.52	0.30 0.33
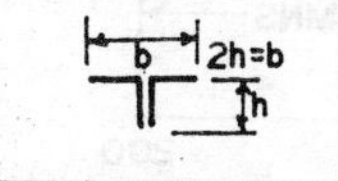 [section]	0.30 0.32	0.21 0.22	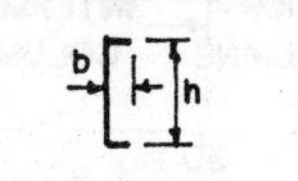 [section]	0.35 0.35	0.20 0.25	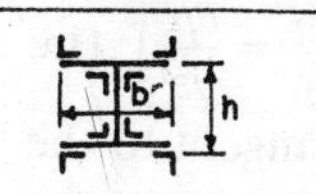 [section]	0.49 0.52	0.27 0.29
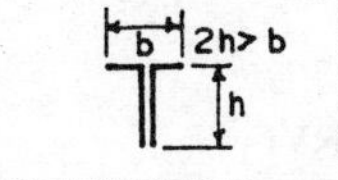 [section]	0.31 0.33	0.19 0.21	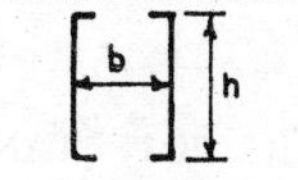 [section]	0.35 0.37	0.42 0.46	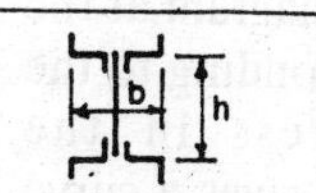 [section]	0.46 0.49	0.27 0.30
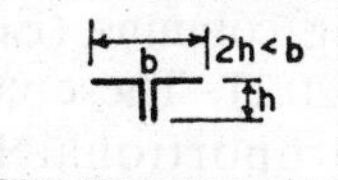 [section]	0.28 0.30	0.22 0.25	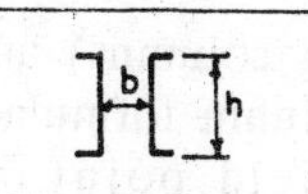 [section]	0.35 0.37	0.54 0.56	 [section]	0.36 0.40	0.52 0.56
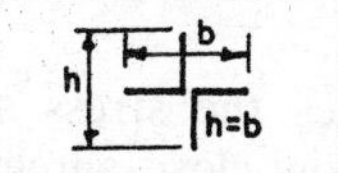 [section]	0.21 0.22	0.21 0.22	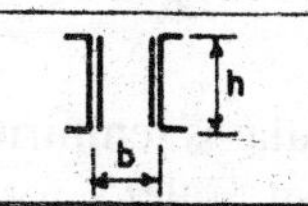 [section]	0.33 0.36	0.52 0.54	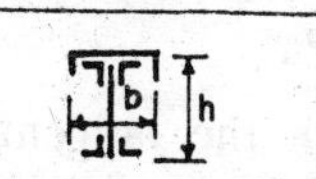 [section]	0.36 0.40	0.23 0.26

FIG. 20.10. APPROXIMATE VALUES OF RADII OF GYRATION FOR COMPRESSION MEMBERS

of slenderness ratio is 30 for rectangular section. For such short columns, the limiting stress is found to be the stress at the yield point. For intermediate columns having $\dfrac{L}{r}$ ratio between 30 and 99 (say, for steel having, $\sigma_{PL} = 200 \, \text{N/mm}^2$), empirical formulae have been proposed by various workers However, none of these has been accepted universally for intermediate columns, partly because of their departure from the stress strain relationship when the stresses exceed the proportional limit, and partly because of their intermediate mixture of direct and flexural stresses. We shall consider here the following empirical formulae.

1. Tangent-modulus formula

2. Rankine's formula

3. Rankine-Gorden formula

4. Johnson's Straight line and parabolic formulae

1. Tangent modulus theory and reduced modulus theory

In the *tangent-modulus theory* proposed by Engesser (1895), Euler's formula was extended to intermediate column stressed above the proportional limit by replacing the constant modulus E by a tangent modulus E_t :

$$p_t = \frac{P_t}{A} = \frac{\pi^2 E_t}{\left(\dfrac{L}{r}\right)^2} \qquad ...(20.12)$$

The *tangent modulus* (E_t), also called the *effective modulus*, is obtained by using for $E_t \left(= \dfrac{\partial p}{\partial \varepsilon} \right)$ the slope of the tangent to the stress strain diagram at the point corresponding to the average stress in the column. This gives a curve

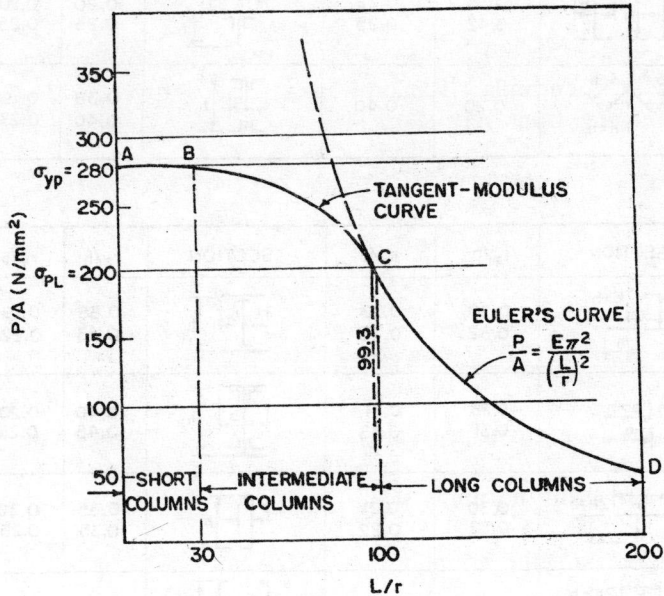

FIG. 20.11. TANGENT MODULUS CURVE

BC that connects the curve *AB* (for short columns) and curve *CD* for long columns (Euler's curve) representing the short and long column formulae, as shown in Fig. 20.11. These curves have been drawn for steel having yield point $\sigma_{YP} = 280$ MPa and proportional limit $\sigma_{PL} = 200$ MPa.

Though the tangent modulus formula is empirical because it violates the stress strain proportionality assumed in the derivation of Euler's formula, actual tests show close agreement with the theoretical curve.

Experiments conducted by French Engineer A. Considere (1889) showed that Euler's formula was not applicable to *inelastic buckling* and he stated that the *effective modulus* was between E and E_t. After studying Engesser's tangent modulus theory and Considere's work, Jasinky presented a *reduced modulus theory*; he also stated that the reduced modulus (E_r) could not be calculated theoretically. Only a month later Engesser proposed the method to obtain the *reduced modulus* (E_r) for any cross-section. Thus the tangent modulus theory is sometimes called the *Engesser theory* and the reduced modulus theory is called the *Considere-Engesser theory*. The *reduced modulus theory* was also presented by famous scientist Theodore Von Karman (1908-1910), apparently independent of earlier investigations. The *reduced modulus* (E_r) depends not only on the magnitude of the stress but also on the shape of the cross-section. For a column of *rectangular section*, the equation for reduced modulus is

$$E_r = \frac{4\,E\,E_t}{\left(\sqrt{E} + \sqrt{E_t}\right)^2} \qquad \qquad ...(20.13)$$

The equation for the critical stress by the reduced modulus theory is

$$p_r = \frac{P_r}{A} = \frac{\pi^2 E_r}{\left(\dfrac{L}{r}\right)^2} \qquad \qquad ...(20.13\ a)$$

2. Rankine's Formula : Rankine proposed an empirical formula for columns which covers all cases ranging from very short to very long struts. He proposed the relation

$$\frac{1}{P} = \frac{1}{P_C} + \frac{1}{P_E} \qquad \qquad ...(20.14)$$

where $P_C = f_c \,.\, A =$ ultimate load for a strut.

$P_E = \dfrac{\pi^2 EI}{L^2} =$ Eulerian crippling load for the standard case.

In the above relation, $\dfrac{1}{P_C}$ is constant for a material. For short column, P_E is very large and hence $\dfrac{1}{P_E}$ is small in comparison to $\dfrac{1}{P_C}$, thus making crippling load P approximately equal to P_C. For long columns, P_E is extremely small and hence $\dfrac{1}{P_E}$ is large as compared to $\dfrac{1}{P_C}$, thus making the crippling load approximately equal to P_E. Thus the value of P obtained from the above relation covers all cases ranging from short to long columns or struts.

The above relation can be re-arranged as :

$$P = \frac{P_C \,.\, P_E}{P_E + P_C} = \frac{P_C}{1 + P_C/P_E} = \frac{f_c \,.\, A}{1 + \dfrac{f_c A L^2}{\pi^2 EI}}$$

or

$$P = \frac{f_c \,.\, A}{1 + \left(\dfrac{f_c}{\pi^2 E}\right)\left(\dfrac{L}{r}\right)^2} = \frac{f_c \,.\, A}{1 + a\left(\dfrac{L}{r}\right)^2} \qquad \qquad ...(20.15)$$

In the above equation, f_c is the crushing stress for the material and a is the Rankine's constant for the material. Though the formula is empirical, the values of constant a is not calculated from the values of f_c, π^2 and E, but is determined experimentally. Table 20.4 gives the values of f_c, and a for the materials commonly used for columns and struts.

TABLE 20.4. RANKINE'S CONSTANTS.

Material	f_c		a
	kg/cm^2	N/mm^2	*(For hinged ends)*
1. Wrought Iron.	2550	255	1 / 9000
2. Cast Iron.	5670	567	1 / 1600
3. Mild Steel	3300	330	1 / 7500
4. Strong Timber	500	50	1 / 750

Eq. 20.15 is the Rankine's formula for the standard case of column hinged at ends. For columns of other end conditions, the values of constants will be changed accordingly. However,. since a is a constant for a particular material used as a hinged column, it is not convenient to remember the values of a for other end conditions. It is therefore better to modify the Rankine's formula and remember in the form :

$$P = \frac{f_c . A}{1 + a\left(\dfrac{L_E}{r}\right)^2} = \frac{f_c . A}{1 + a\left(\dfrac{l}{r}\right)^2} \qquad \qquad ...(20.16)$$

in which a is the Rankine's constant for a particular material and for the standard case of column, and L_E or l is the equivalent length of the column. Since equivalent length is generally known, it can be substituted in the above formula to get the Rankine's formula for a particular case of end conditions. *It should be noted that Eqs. 20.15 and 20.16 do not include the factor of safety.*

3. Rankine-Gorden formula: It is expressed in the form :

$$\frac{P}{A} = \frac{C_1}{1 + C_2\left(\dfrac{l}{r}\right)^2} \qquad \qquad ...(20.17)$$

A.I.S.C. adopted this formula in 1949 for design of secondary members having l/r ranging between 120 to 200, taking a value of $C_1 = 1260 \ kg/cm^2$ and $C_2 = 1/18000$. Similarly, Building Code of New York adopted this formula for main members having l/r between 60 to 120, and for secondary members having L/r ratio ranging between 60 to 200.

4. Johnson's straight line and parabolic formula : Johnson proposed the following two formulae:

$$P = A\left(f - n\frac{l}{r}\right) \qquad ...(20.18) \qquad \text{and} \qquad P = A\left(f - n'\frac{l^2}{r^2}\right) \qquad ...(20.19)$$

Eq. 20.18 is known as *straight line formula*, sometimes written in the form

$$\frac{P}{A} = C_1 - C_2\frac{l}{r} \qquad \qquad ...(20.18 \ a)$$

For mild steel, C_1 is $1125 \ kg/cm^2$ and $C_2 = 5.625 \ kg/cm^2$. The Chicago Building Code adopted this formula, taking $C_1 = 1120 \ kg/cm^2$ and $C_2 = 4.8 \ kg/cm^2$, for member having l/r ratio ranging between 30 and 120. Similarly, American Bridge Co. adopted this formula with a maximum value of permissible stress as 915 kg/cm², taking $C_1 = 1335$ kg/cm² and $C_2 = 7.03$ kg/cm².

Eq. 7.11 is known as *parabolic formula*, sometimes written in the form

$$\frac{P}{A} = C_3 - C_4 \left(\frac{l}{r}\right)^2 \qquad \qquad ...(20.19\ a)$$

AISC adopted this formula for members having $l/r < 120$, taking $C_3 = 1190$ kg/cm² and $C_4 = 0.0334$ kg/cm². A.R.E.A. and A.A.S.H.O. adopted this formula for members having $l/r < 140$, taking the following values :

$C_3 = 1090$ kg/cm² and $C_4 = 0.0175$ kg/cm², for riveted structures.

and $C_3 = 1050$ kg/cm² and $C_4 = 0.0233$ kg/cm², for welded structures.

5. AISC formula : The American Institute of Steel Construction (AISC) defines the limit between the intermediate and long columns to be the value of slenderness ratio λ_c given by

$$\lambda_c = \sqrt{\frac{2\pi^2 E}{\sigma_{YP}}} \qquad \qquad ...(20.20)$$

where σ_{YP} is the yield point stress for the particular steel under consideration. Taking $\sigma_{YP} = 280$ N/m m² and $E = 2 \times 10^5$ N/mm², we get

$$\lambda_c = \sqrt{\frac{2\pi^2 (2 \times 10^5)}{280}} \approx 119$$

The working stress σ_w, for $\frac{L_E}{r}$ (or $\frac{l}{r}$) greater than λ_c is given by

$$\sigma_w = \frac{12\pi^2 E}{23 \left(\frac{L_E}{r}\right)^2} \qquad ...(20.21)$$

It is interesting to note that this is Euler's formula with factor of safety (FS) equal to 23/12 (= 1.92).

For $\frac{L_E}{r} < \lambda_c$, AISC specifies the following *parabolic formula*

$$\sigma_w = \left[1 - \frac{\left(\frac{L_E}{r}\right)^2}{2\lambda_c^2}\right] \frac{\sigma_{yp}}{FS} \qquad ...(20.22)$$

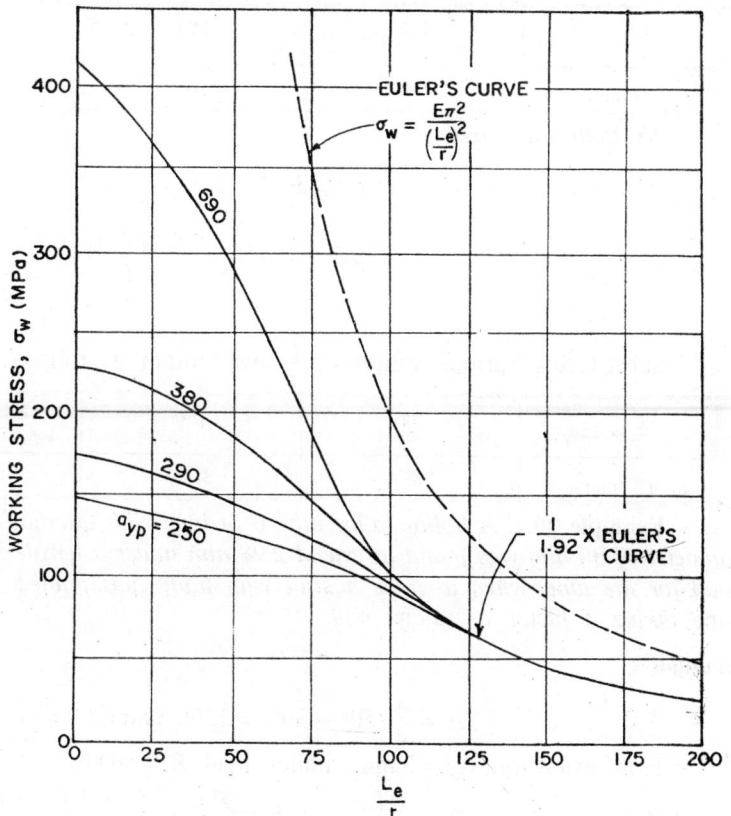

FIG. 20.12. AISC SPECIFICATION FOR σ_w

where the factor of safety (FS) is given by

$$FS = \frac{5}{3} + \frac{3\left(\dfrac{L_E}{r}\right)}{8\lambda_c} - \frac{\left(\dfrac{L_E}{r}\right)^3}{8\lambda_c^3} \qquad ...(20.23)$$

FS comes out to be 1.92 at $\dfrac{L_E}{r} = \lambda_c$, and it becomes smaller for larger values of slenderness

ratio. Fig. 20.12 shows the variation of σ_w with $\dfrac{L_E}{r}$ for several grades of steel, based on the AISC formula.

Example 20.1. *Calculate Euler's critical stresses for a series of columns having slenderness ratio of 50, 100, 150, 200 and 250 under the following conditions : (a) both ends hinged, and (b) both ends fixed. Take $E = 2 \times 10^5 \, N/mm^2$.*

Solution :

(a) Both ends hinged : $\quad p_E = \dfrac{\pi^2 E r^2}{L^2} = \dfrac{\pi^2 E}{\left(\dfrac{L}{r}\right)^2} = \dfrac{19.739 \times 10^5}{\left(\dfrac{L}{r}\right)^2}$

Substituting the values of $\dfrac{L}{r}$ in the above formula, we obtain following values.

$\dfrac{L}{r} \rightarrow$	100	150	200	250
p_E (N/mm²)	197.4	87.7	49.3	31.6

(b) Both ends fixed

$$L_E = \frac{L}{2}$$

$$\therefore \qquad p_E = \frac{4\pi^2 E}{\left(\dfrac{L}{r}\right)^2} = \frac{78.9568 \times 10^5}{\left(\dfrac{L}{r}\right)^2}$$

Substituting various values of $\dfrac{L}{r}$, we obtain as follows.

$\dfrac{L}{r} \rightarrow$	100	150	200	250
p_E (N/mm²)	789.6	350.9	197.4	126.3

Example 20.2. *A hollow alloy tube 6 m long with external diameter of 50 mm and internal diameter of 30 mm was found to extend 2.98 mm under a tensile load of 50 kN. Find the buckling load for the tube, when used as a strut with both ends pinned. Also, find the safe load on the tube taking a factor of safety of 4.*

Solution :

$$A = \frac{\pi}{4}(50^2 - 30^2) = 1256.6 \text{ mm}^2 \,; I = \frac{\pi}{64}(50^4 - 30^4) = 267035 \text{ mm}^4$$

Now extension $\Delta = 3$ mm, under load $P = 50$ kN

But $\qquad \Delta = \dfrac{PL}{AE} \quad$ or $\quad E = \dfrac{PL}{A\Delta} = \dfrac{50 \times 10^3 \times 6000}{1256.6 \times 2.98} = 0.8 \times 10^5 \text{ N/mm}^2$

Now buckling load $P_E = \dfrac{\pi^2 E I}{L^2}$, for strut with both ends pinned

$$= \frac{\pi^2 \times 0.8 \times 10^5 \times 267035}{(6000)^2} = 5865 \text{ N.}$$

$\therefore$ Safe load $= \dfrac{P_E}{F.S.} = \dfrac{5865}{3} = 1955 \text{ N} = \textbf{1.955 kN}$

Example 20.3. *An I-section joist ISWB 400 and 8 m long is used as a strut with both ends fixed. Taking $E = 2 \times 10^5 \, N/mm^2$, determine Euler's crippling load.*

Given for the section $I_{xx} = 23426.7 \, cm^4$, $I_{yy} = 1388.0 \, cm^4$

Solution :

$$I_{min} = I_{yy} = 1388 \times 10^4 \text{ mm}^4$$

For a strut fixed at both ends, $L_E = \dfrac{L}{2} = \dfrac{8}{2} = 4 \text{ m}$

$$P_E = \frac{\pi^2 E I}{L_c^2} = \frac{\pi^2 \times 2 \times 10^5 \times 1388 \times 10^4}{(4000)^2}$$

$$= 1712 \times 10^3 \text{ N} = \textbf{1712 kN}$$

Example 20.4. *A straight bar of mild steel, 1 m long and 12 mm×6 mm in section is mounted in strut testing machine and loaded axially till it buckles. Assuming Euler's formula for pinned ends to apply, estimate the maximum central deflection before the material attains its yield point of 300 N/mm². Take $E = 2 \times 10^5 \, N/mm^2$.*

Solution :

$$I_{min} = \frac{1}{12} (12) (6)^3 = 216 \text{ mm}^4$$

$\therefore$

$$P_E = \frac{\pi^2 E I}{L^2} = \frac{9.8696 \, (2 \times 10^5) \, (216)}{(1000)^2} = 426.4 \text{ N}$$

Maximum deflection (δ) occurs at half the height, where

$$M_{max} = P . \delta = p_b . Z = p_b \left(\frac{216}{3} \right) = 72 \, p_b$$

$\therefore$

$$p_b = \frac{P . \delta}{72} = \frac{426.4 \, \delta}{72} = 5.922 \, \delta$$

Also,

$$p_0 = \frac{P}{A} = \frac{426.4}{12 \times 6} = 5.922 \text{ N/mm}^2$$

Now

$$p_{max} = p_b + p_0 = 300 \quad \text{(given)}$$

$\therefore$

$$5.922 \, \delta + 5.922 = 300$$

From which

$$\delta = \frac{300 - 5.922}{5.922} = \textbf{49.66 mm}$$

20.8. LONG COLUMN UNDER ECCENTRIC LOADING : SECANT FORMULA

(a) Empirical approach : Modified Rankine's formula

When a short column is subjected to a compressive load P applied at an eccentricity e, we have

$$p = p_0 + p_b = \frac{P}{A} + \frac{P \cdot e}{Z} = \frac{P}{A} + \frac{P \cdot e \cdot y_c}{A r^2} = \frac{P}{A} \left(1 + \frac{e y_c}{r^2} \right)$$

where r = radius of gyration

and y_c = distance of extreme compressive fibre from the N.A.

Taking f_c as the permissible stress in the material, the corresponding load is given by

$$P = \frac{f_c A}{\left(1 + \frac{e y_c}{r^2} \right)} \qquad \qquad \qquad ...(20.24)$$

In the above expression, $\left(1 + \frac{e y}{r^2} \right)$ is the *reduction factor* which takes into account the *eccentricity of loading*.

Rankine's formula for a long column with axial loading is

$$P = \frac{f_c A}{1 + a \left(\frac{L}{r} \right)^2} \qquad \qquad \qquad ...(20.15)$$

In the above expression, $\left[1 + a \left(\frac{L}{r} \right)^2 \right]$ is a *reduction factor* which takes into account the *buckling of the column*.

Combining Eqs. 20.24 and 20.15, the *modified Rankine's formula* for a long column loaded with eccentric loading can be stated as follows :

$$P = \frac{f_c A}{\left(1 + e \frac{y_c}{r^2} \right) \left(1 + a \frac{L^2}{r^2} \right)} \qquad \qquad ...(20.25)$$

The above formula is applicable for the standard case. For other cases, the factor a can be changed accordingly.

(b) Theoretical approach : Secant formula

Fig. 20.13 shows the column of length L, hinged at both the ends, subjected to a load P applied at an eccentricity e. At any section distant x from A, y is the deflection of the column with reference to the line of action of P; the B.M. at that section is $P \cdot y$

$\therefore$ $$E I \frac{d^2 y}{d x^2} = -M - -P \cdot y$$

or $$\frac{d^2 y}{d x^2} + \frac{P}{E I} y = 0$$

Solving the above differential equation, we obtain

$$y = C_1 \sin x \sqrt{\frac{P}{E I}} + c_2 \cos x \sqrt{\frac{P}{E I}} \qquad ...(1)$$

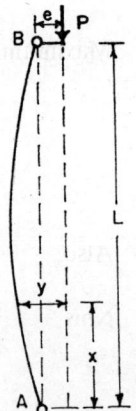

FIG. 20.13

At A, $\qquad\qquad x = 0$ and $y = e$. Hence we get $C_2 = e$

Also, $\qquad\qquad \dfrac{dy}{dx} = C_1 \sqrt{\dfrac{P}{EI}} \cos x \sqrt{\dfrac{P}{EI}} - e \sqrt{\dfrac{P}{EI}} \sin x \sqrt{\dfrac{P}{EI}}$

At the mid height, where $\qquad x = \dfrac{L}{2}$, we have $\dfrac{dy}{dx} = 0$

$\therefore \qquad\qquad 0 = C_1 \sqrt{\dfrac{P}{EI}} \cos \dfrac{L}{2} \sqrt{\dfrac{P}{EI}} - e \sqrt{\dfrac{P}{EI}} \sin \dfrac{L}{2} \sqrt{\dfrac{P}{EI}}$

From which we get $\qquad C_1 = e \dfrac{\sin \dfrac{L}{2} \sqrt{\dfrac{P}{EI}}}{\cos \dfrac{L}{2} \sqrt{\dfrac{P}{EI}}}$

Substituting the value of C_1 and C_2 in (1), we get

$$y = e \left[\frac{\sin \dfrac{L}{2} \sqrt{\dfrac{P}{EI}}}{\cos \dfrac{L}{2} \sqrt{\dfrac{P}{EI}}} \sin x \sqrt{\dfrac{P}{EI}} + \cos x \sqrt{\dfrac{P}{EI}} \right] \qquad ...(2)$$

At $\qquad\qquad x = \dfrac{L}{2}, y = y_{max}$

$\therefore \qquad\qquad y_{max} = e \left[\dfrac{\sin^2 \dfrac{L}{2} \sqrt{\dfrac{P}{EI}}}{\cos \dfrac{L}{2} \sqrt{\dfrac{P}{EI}}} + \cos \dfrac{L}{2} \sqrt{\dfrac{P}{EI}} \right] = e \sec \dfrac{L}{2} \sqrt{\dfrac{P}{EI}} \qquad ...(3)$

The largest B.M. $\left(M_{max} \right)$ occurs at $x = \dfrac{L}{2}$, where y is maximum.

$\therefore \qquad M_{max} = P \cdot y_{max} = P \cdot e \sec \dfrac{L}{2} \sqrt{\dfrac{P}{EI}} \qquad\qquad ...(20.26)$

Now, the maximum compressive stress in the column is given by

$$p = \frac{P}{A} + \frac{M}{Z} = \frac{P}{A} + \frac{P \cdot e \sec \dfrac{L}{2} \sqrt{\dfrac{P}{EI}}}{Z} \qquad ...(20.27\ a)$$

or $\qquad\qquad p = \dfrac{P}{A} \left(1 + \dfrac{e\, y_c}{r^2} \sec \dfrac{L}{2} \sqrt{\dfrac{P}{EI}} \right) \qquad ...(20.27)$

This is the well known *secant formula*

For secant formula for all end conditions may be written as

$$p = \frac{P}{A} + \frac{P \cdot e \sec \dfrac{L_E}{2} \sqrt{\dfrac{P}{EI}}}{Z} = \frac{P}{A} \left(1 + \frac{e\, y_c}{r^2} \sec \frac{L_E}{2} \sqrt{\frac{P}{EI}} \right) \qquad ...(20.28)$$

It is pertinent to note that the value of r in Eqs. 20.27 and 20.28 need not be minimum, since it is obtained from the value of I associated with the axis around which bending occurs. It should also be noted that while in the case of short column, the B.M. *at all the sections* is $P.e$, in the case of long columns, the max. B.M. is increased by a factor $\sec \dfrac{L_E}{2} \sqrt{\dfrac{P}{EI}}$

20.9. LONG COLUMN UNDER ECCENTRIC LOADING : PERRY'S FORMULA

For a long column with eccentric loading, the maximum stress can be *conveniently* computed Eq. 20.27, if P and e are given. If however, it is required to find the value of P for a given value of e, Eq. 20.27 is not convenient since the secant term contains P itself. Hence it is required to find a more workable expression from which P can be directly computed.

Now
$$\sec \frac{L}{2} \sqrt{\frac{P}{EI}} = \sec \sqrt{\frac{PL^2}{4EI}} = \sec \frac{\pi}{2} \sqrt{\frac{P}{P_E}}$$

where
$$P_E = \text{Eulerian load} = \frac{\pi^2 EI}{L^2}$$

Prof. Perry observed that $\sec \dfrac{\pi}{2} \sqrt{\dfrac{P}{P_E}} \approx \dfrac{1.2 P_E}{P_E - P}.$

$$\therefore \qquad \sec \frac{L}{2} \sqrt{\frac{P}{EI}} \approx \frac{1.2 P_E}{P_E - P} \qquad \qquad ...(20.29a)$$

Substituting this in Eq. 20.27, we have
$$p = \frac{P}{A} \left(1 + \frac{e\, y_c}{r^2} \frac{1.2 P_E}{P_E - P} \right)$$

But
$$\frac{P}{A} = p_0 \text{ and } \frac{P_E}{A} = p_E$$

Hence
$$p = p_0 \left(1 + \frac{e\, y_c}{r^2} \frac{1.2\, p_E}{p_E - p_0} \right)$$

or
$$\left(\frac{p}{p_0} - 1 \right) \left(1 - \frac{p_0}{p_E} \right) = \frac{1.2\, e\, y_c}{r^2} \qquad \qquad ...(20.29)$$

The above equation is known as Perry's approximate formula from which p_0 and hence $P\,(= p_0 . A)$ can be easily computed

20.10. DESIGN FORMULA : IS CODE FORMULA

(a) IS Code formula as per IS : 800-1962

Putting $p = p_{max}$ in secant formula (Eq. 20.27), we get
$$p_{max} = \frac{P}{A} \left(1 + \frac{e\, y_c}{r^2} \sec \frac{l}{2} \sqrt{\frac{P}{EI}} \right)$$

or
$$\frac{P}{A} = p_c = \frac{p_{max}}{1 + \dfrac{e\, y_c}{r^2} \sec \dfrac{l}{2r} \sqrt{\dfrac{p_c}{E}}}$$

Taking m = factor of safety, we get $p_c = m \cdot \sigma_{ac}$

where σ_{ac} = allowable stress. Similarly, taking $p_{max} = f_y$ = yield stress,

we get

$$\sigma_{ac} = \frac{\dfrac{f_y}{m}}{1 + \dfrac{e\,y_c}{r^2} \sec \dfrac{l}{2r} \sqrt{\dfrac{m\,\sigma_{ac}}{E}}}$$

...(20.30 a)

Indian Standard Code (IS : 800-1962) adopted the above formula for determining the permissible stress in the material by taking factor of safety $m = 1.68$ and $\dfrac{e\,y_c}{r^2} = 0.2$

Thus

$$\sigma_{ac} = \frac{\dfrac{f_y}{m}}{1 + 0.2 \sec \dfrac{l}{2r} \sqrt{\dfrac{m\,\sigma_{ac}}{E}}}$$

...(20.30)

The above formula is valid for $\dfrac{l}{r} \le 160$. However, for $\dfrac{l}{r} > 160$, the allowable stress can be found from the expression

$$\sigma_{ac}' = \sigma_{ac} \left(1.2 - \frac{l}{800\,r} \right)$$

...(20.31)

where σ_{ac} is the value found from Eq. 20.30 for the value of $\dfrac{l}{r}$.

The above formula, suggested by IS : 800-1962 was later dropped in its 1984 version.

(b) **IS Code formula as per IS : 800 - 1984 : Merchant Rankine Formula**

IS : 800-1984 has recommended the following *Merchant Rankine formula* for determining the permissible stress :

$$\sigma_{ac} = \frac{f_{cc} \cdot f_y}{m \left[\left(f_{cc} \right)^n + \left(f_y \right)^n \right]^{1/n}}$$

...(20.32 a)

where σ_{ac} = permissible stress in axial compression, N/mm^2 or MPa

f_{cc} = elastic critical stress in compression $= \dfrac{\pi^2 E}{\lambda^2}$ ...(20.33)

f_y = yield stress in steel, = N/mm^2 or MPa

E = modulus of elasticity of steel = 2×10^5 N/mm^2

$\lambda = \dfrac{l}{r}$ = slenderness ratio

m = factor of safety = $\dfrac{10}{6}$

n = a factor, assumed as 0.4

Hence

$$\sigma_{ac} = 0.6 \frac{f_{cc} \cdot f_y}{\left[\left(f_{cc} \right)^n + \left(f_y \right)^n \right]^{1/n}}$$

...(20.32)

According to IS:800-1984, the direct stress in compression on the gross cross-sectional area of axially loaded compression member shall not exceed $0.6 f_y$, nor the permissible value

σ_{ac} calculated using the above formula. The value of σ_{ac} for some of the Indian Standard structural steels are given its Table 20.5.

TABLE 20.5. PERMISSIBLE STRESS σ_{ac} (N/mm^2) IN AXIAL COMPRESSION.

$f_y \rightarrow$ $\lambda \downarrow$	220	230	240	250	260	280	300	320	340	360	380	400	420	450	480	510	540
10	132	138	144	150	156	168	180	192	204	215	227	239	251	269	287	305	323
20	131	137	142	148	154	166	177	189	201	212	224	235	246	263	280	297	314
30	128	134	140	145	151	162	172	183	194	204	215	225	236	251	266	280	295
40	124	129	134	139	145	154	164	174	183	192	201	210	218	231	243	255	267
50	118	123	127	132	136	145	153	161	168	176	183	190	197	207	216	225	233
60	111	115	118	122	126	133	139	146	152	158	163	168	173	180	187	193	199
70	102	106	109	112	115	120	125	130	135	139	142	147	150	155	160	164	168
80	93	96	98	101	103	107	111	115	118	121	124	127	129	133	136	139	141
90	85	87	88	90	92	95	98	101	103	105	108	109	111	114	116	118	119
100	76	78	79	80	82	84	86	88	90	92	93	94	96	97	99	100	101
110	68	69	71	72	73	74	76	77	79	80	81	82	83	84	85	86	87
120	61	62	63	64	64	66	67	67	69	70	71	71	72	73	73	74	75
130	55	55	56	57	57	58	59	60	61	61	62	62	63	63	64	64	65
140	49	50	50	51	51	52	53	53	54	54	54	55	55	56	56	56	57
150	44	45	45	45	46	46	47	47	48	48	48	49	49	49	49	50	50
160	40	40	41	41	41	42	42	42	43	43	43	43	43	44	44	44	44
170	36	36	37	37	37	37	38	38	38	38	39	39	39	39	39	39	39
180	33	33	33	33	33	34	34	34	34	35	35	35	35	35	35	35	35
190	30	30	30	30	30	30	31	31	31	31	31	31	32	32	32	32	32
200	27	27	28	28	28	28	28	28	28	28	28	28	28	28	28	28	28
210	25	25	25	25	25	25	26	26	26	26	26	26	26	26	26	26	26
220	23	23	23	23	23	23	23	24	24	24	24	24	24	24	24	24	24
230	21	21	21	21	21	21	21	21	22	22	22	22	22	22	22	22	22
240	20	20	20	20	20	20	20	20	20	20	20	20	20	20	20	20	20
250	18	18	18	18	18	18	18	18	18	19	19	19	19	19	19	19	19

20.11. COMPARISON OF VARIOUS FORMULAE

The graphical comparison of various column formulae is shown in Fig. 20.14.

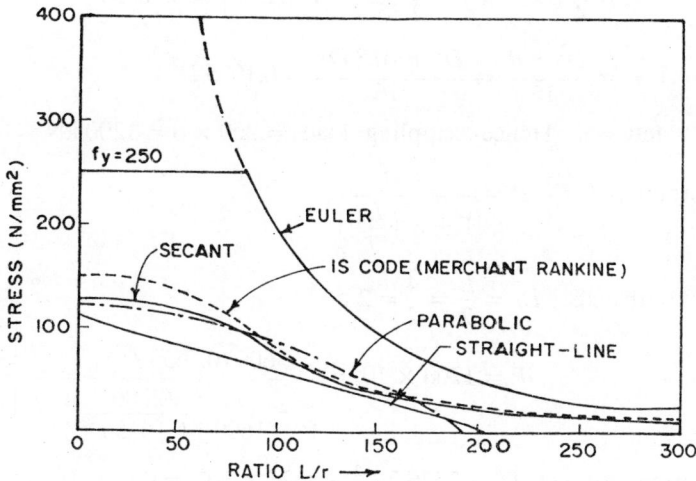

FIG. 20.14. COMPARISON OF VARIOUS COLUMN FORMULAE

Example 20.5. *A cast iron hollow column, having 100 mm external diameter and 80 mm internal diameter, is used as a column of 2.4 m length. Using Rankine's formula, determine the cripling load, when both the ends are fixed. Take* $f_c = 600 \, N/mm^2$ *and* $a = \dfrac{1}{1600}$.

Solution :

$$A = \frac{\pi}{4}(100^2 - 80^2) = 2827.4 \text{ mm}^2$$

$$I = \frac{\pi}{64}(100^4 - 80^4) = 289.8 \times 10^4 \text{ mm}^4 \, ; r^2 = \frac{I}{A} = \frac{289.8 \times 10^4}{2827.4} = 1025 \text{ mm}$$

For a column with fixed ends, $L_E = \dfrac{L}{2} = \dfrac{2.4}{2} = 1.2 \text{ m} = 1200 \text{ mm}$

Now Rankine's $P = \dfrac{f_c \cdot A}{1 + a \left(\dfrac{L_E}{r}\right)^2}$

$$= \frac{600 \times 2827.4}{1 + \dfrac{1}{1600}\dfrac{(1200)^2}{1025}} = 903300 \text{ N} = \textbf{903.3 kN}$$

Example 20.6. *A hollow cast iron cylindrical column, 4 m long with both ends firmly fixed carries an axial load of 200 kN. The internal diameter of the column is equal to 0.8 times the external diameter. Determine the section of the column, taking* $f_c = 600 \, N/mm^2$, *Rankine's constant* $a = \dfrac{1}{1600}$, *and a factor of safety of 6.*

Solution :

Let D = external diameter and d = internal dia. $= 0.8 \, D$

$$\therefore \qquad A = \frac{\pi}{4}(D^2 - d^2) = \frac{\pi}{2}\left[D^2 - (0.8\,D)^2\right] = 0.5655\,D^2$$

$$r^2 = \frac{D^2 + d^2}{16} = \frac{D^2 + (0.8\,D)^2}{16} = 0.1025\,D^2$$

Factor of safety = 6. Hence crippling load $= 200 \times 6 = 1200$ kN

From Rankine's formula, $\qquad P = \dfrac{f_c A}{1 + a\left(\dfrac{L_E}{r}\right)^2}$

For column fixed at both ends, $L_E = \dfrac{L}{2} = \dfrac{4}{2} = 2$ m

$$\therefore \qquad P = 1200 \times 10^3 = \frac{600\,(0.5655\,D^2)}{1 + \dfrac{1}{1600}\left(\dfrac{(2000)^2}{0.1025\,D^2}\right)} = \frac{339.3\,D^2}{1 + \dfrac{24390}{D^2}}$$

On simplification, we get $D^4 - 3536.7\,D^2 - 8626 \times 10^4 = 0$

From which, $\qquad\qquad D^2 = 11222.8$ and hence $D = \mathbf{106\ mm}$

$\therefore \qquad\qquad\qquad d = 0.8\,D = \mathbf{84.8\ mm}$

Example 20.7. *Compare the crippling loads given by Euler's and Rankine's formulae, for a tubular steel strut 2.5 m long, having outer and inner diameters as 40 mm and 30 mm respectively, loaded through pin joints at the ends. Take yield stress as 320 N/mm², the Rankine's constant $= \dfrac{1}{7500}$ and $E = 2 \times 10^5$ N/mm². for what length of the strut of this cross-section does the Euler's formula cease to apply ?*

Solution :

$$I = \frac{\pi}{64}(40^4 - 30^4) = 85903 \text{ mm}^4 \,;\, A = \frac{\pi}{4}(40^2 - 30^2) = 549.8 \text{ mm}^2$$

$$r = \sqrt{\frac{I}{A}} = \sqrt{\frac{85903}{549.8}} = 12.5 \text{ mm}\,;\, L = 2.5 \text{ m} = 2500 \text{ mm}$$

$$P_E = \frac{\pi^2 E I}{L^2} = \frac{\pi^2 \times 2 \times 10^5 \times 85903}{(2500)^2} = 27131 \text{ N} = \mathbf{27.131\ kN}$$

$$P_R = \frac{f_c \cdot A}{1 + a\left(\dfrac{L}{r}\right)^2} = \frac{320 \times 549.8}{1 + \dfrac{1}{7500}\left(\dfrac{2500}{12.5}\right)^2} = 27779 \text{ N} = \mathbf{27.779\ kN}$$

$$\therefore \qquad \frac{P_E}{P_R} = \frac{27.131}{27.779} = \mathbf{0.977}$$

Now $\qquad\qquad p_E = \dfrac{P_E}{A} = 320 = \dfrac{\pi^2 E}{\left(\dfrac{L}{r}\right)^2}$

$\therefore$ Validity limit of $\quad \dfrac{L}{r} = \sqrt{\dfrac{\pi^2 E}{320}} = \sqrt{\dfrac{\pi^2 (2 \times 10^5)}{320}} = \mathbf{78.54}$

Example 20.8. *A hollow cast iron column with fixed ends supports an axial load of 800 kN. If the column is 3 m long and has an external diameter of 200 mm, find the thickness of metal required. Use Rankine's formula, taking a constant of $\dfrac{1}{6400}$ and assume a working stress of 90 N/mm².*

Solution :

The value of Rankine's constant a for cast iron is $\dfrac{1}{1600}$, for the standard case. Since the given value of a is $\dfrac{1}{4}$ of this value, it includes the effect of end conditions.

$$\therefore \qquad P = \frac{f_c \cdot A}{1 + \dfrac{1}{6400}\left(\dfrac{L}{r}\right)^2}$$

Here, $\qquad A = \dfrac{\pi}{4}(D^2 - d^2)$ and $r^2 = \dfrac{D^2 + d^2}{16}$

where $\qquad D$ = external diameter = 200 mm and d = internal diameter, is mm.

$$\therefore \qquad P = 800 \times 10^3 = \frac{90 \times \dfrac{\pi}{4}(D^2 - d^2)}{1 + \dfrac{1}{6400} \times \dfrac{16\,(3000)^2}{D^2 + d^2}} = \frac{70.686\,(D^2 - d^2)}{1 + \dfrac{22500}{D^2 + d^2}}$$

or $\qquad 800 \times 10^3\,(D^2 + d^2) + 800 \times 10^3\,(22500) = 70.686\,(D^4 - d^4)$

or $\ 800 \times 10^3\,(200^2 + d^2) + 800 \times 10^3\,(22500) = 70.686\,(200^4 - d^4)$

On simplification, we get $d^4 + 11318\,d^2 - 8.927 \times 10^8 = 0$

From which $\qquad d^2 = 24750$ mm² or $d = 157.32$ mm

$$\therefore \qquad \text{Metal thickness} = \frac{D - d}{2} = \frac{200 - 157.32}{2} = \textbf{21.34 mm}$$

Example 20.9. *A mild steel column is of hollow circular section with 100 mm as external diameter and 80 mm as internal diameter. The column is 2.4 m long, hinged at both the ends and has to carry a load of 60 kN at an eccentricity of 16 mm from the geometrical axis. Calculate the maximum and minimum intensities of stresses. Also, calculate the maximum possible eccentricity so that no tension is induced any where in the section. Take $E = 2 \times 10^5$ N/mm².*

Solution :

$$A = \frac{\pi}{4}(100^2 - 80^2) = 2827.4 \text{ mm}^2 ; I = \frac{\pi}{64}(100^4 - 80^4) = 2898119 \text{ mm}^4$$

$$\therefore \qquad r^2 = \frac{I}{A} = \frac{2898119}{2827.4} = 1025 \text{ mm}^4$$

$$Z = \frac{2898119}{50} = 57962 \text{ mm}^3$$

Now, $M_{max} = P \cdot e \sec \dfrac{L}{2} \sqrt{\dfrac{P}{EI}}$ $= 60 \times 10^3 \times 16 \left[\sec \dfrac{2400}{2} \sqrt{\dfrac{60 \times 10^3}{2 \times 10^5 \times 2898119}} \right]$

$$= 60 \times 10^3 \times 16 \, (1.0795)$$

$$= 1.036 \times 10^6 \text{ N-mm}$$

Now $f_b = \dfrac{M_{max}}{Z} = \dfrac{1.036 \times 10^6}{57962} = 17.88 \text{ N/mm}^2$

Also, $f_0 = \dfrac{P}{A} = \dfrac{60000}{2827.4} = 21.22 \text{ N/mm}^2$

$\therefore$ $f_{max} = f_0 + f_b = 21.22 + 17.88 = \mathbf{39.1 \text{ N/m}^2}$ (comp.)

$f_{min} = f_0 - f_b = 21.22 - 17.88 = \mathbf{3.34 \text{ N/mm}^2}$ (comp.)

For no tension to develop, we get $f_b = f_0$

$$17.88 \times \dfrac{e}{16} = 21.22$$

or $e = \dfrac{21.22 \times 16}{17.88} = \mathbf{18.99 \text{ mm}}$

Example 20.10. *A mild steel column is of hollow circular section 100 mm as external diameter and 80 mm as internal diameter. The column is 2.4 m long and is hinged at both the ends. Calculate the maximum permissible load with an eccentricity of 16 mm if the maximum compressive stress is limited to 80 N/mm². Take $E = 2 \times 10^5$ N/mm².*

Solution :

From the previous example, we have

$$A = 2827.4 \text{ mm}^4 ; I = 2898119 \text{ mm}^4$$

$$r^2 = 1025 \text{ mm}^2 ; Z = 57962 \text{ mm}^3$$

$$P_E = \dfrac{\pi^2 EI}{L^2} = \dfrac{\pi^2 \, (2 \times 10^5) \, (2898119)}{(2400)^2} = 993170 \text{ N}$$

$\therefore$ $p_E = \dfrac{P_E}{A} = \dfrac{993170}{2827.4} = 351.3 \text{ N/mm}^2$

$$f = 90 \text{ N/mm}^2 \text{ (given)}$$

Substituting in Perry's approximate formula, we have

$$\left(\dfrac{f}{f_0} - 1 \right) \left(1 - \dfrac{f_0}{p_E} \right) = \dfrac{1.2 \, e \, y_c}{r^2}$$

or $\left(\dfrac{80}{f_0} - 1 \right) \left(1 - \dfrac{f_0}{351.3} \right) = \dfrac{1.2 \times 16 \times 40}{1025} = 0.7493$

or $(80 - f_0) \, (351.3 - f_0) = 0.7493 \times 351.3 \, f_0 = 263.2 \, f_0$

or $208104 - 351.3 \, f_0 - 80 f_o + f_0^2 = 263.2 \, f_0$

or $\qquad f_0^2 - 694.5 f_0 + 28104 = 0$

From which we get $\qquad f_0 = 43.147 \text{ N/mm}^2$

$\therefore$ Safe load $\qquad P = f_0 A = 43.147 \times 2827.4 = 121994 \text{ N} \approx \textbf{122 kN}$

Example 20.11. *A rolled steel beam section ISWB 200 @ 28.8 kg/m is used as a stanchion and has an unsupported length of 5 m. It is hinged at both the ends. Determine the axial load this stanchion can carry, if the yield stress for steel is 250 N/mm^2 and $E = 2 \times 10^5 \text{ N/mm}^2$. Use IS Code formula. For ISWB 200@28.8 kg/m, $r_{xx} = 8.46 \text{ cm}$, $r_{yy} = 2.99 \text{ cm}$ and $A = 36.71 \text{ cm}^2$.*

Solution :

Given $\qquad f_y = 250 \text{ N/mm}^2 ; L = 5 \text{ m}$

For a column with hinged ends, $L_E = L = 5 \text{ m}$

$$r_{min} = r_{yy} = 29.9 \text{ mm}$$

$$\lambda_{max.} = \frac{L_E}{r_{min}} = \frac{5000}{29.9} = 167.2$$

$\therefore \qquad f_{cc} = \dfrac{\pi^2 E}{\lambda^2} = \dfrac{\pi^2 (2 \times 10^5)}{(167.2)^2} = 70.61 \text{ N/mm}^2$

Hence $\qquad \sigma_{ac} = 0.6 \dfrac{f_{cc} \cdot f_y}{\left[(f_{cc})^n + (f_y)^n \right]^{1/n}} = \dfrac{0.6 \times 70.61 \times 250}{\left[(70.61)^{1.4} + (250)^{1.4} \right]^{1/1.4}}$

$$= 37.86 \text{ N/mm}^2$$

Alternatively, from Table 20.5, for $f_y = 250 \text{ N/mm}^2$ and $\lambda = 167.2$

we get $\qquad \sigma_{ac} = 41 - (41 - 37) \times \dfrac{7.2}{10} = 38.12 \text{ N/mm}^2$

$\therefore \qquad P = A \cdot \sigma_{ac} = 3671 \times 37.86 = 138984 \text{ N} = \textbf{138.984 kN}$

Example 20.12. *A hollow steel shaft, outside diameter 150 mm and inside diameter 100 mm is to be used as a column. Determine the maximum allowable length of this column for a maximum allowable load of 800 kN. Take $f_y = 250 \text{ N/mm}^2$. Use I.S. Code formula.*

Solution :

$$I_{xx} = \frac{\pi}{64} (D^4 - d^4) = \frac{\pi}{64} (150^4 - 100^4) = 19.9418 \times 10^6 \text{ mm}^4$$

$$A = \frac{\pi}{4} (D^2 - d^2) = \frac{\pi}{4} (150^2 - 100^2) = 9817.477 \text{ mm}^2$$

$$r = \sqrt{\frac{I}{A}} = \sqrt{\frac{9.9418 \times 10^6}{9817.477}} = 45.069 \text{ mm}$$

$$\sigma_{ac} = \frac{P}{A} = \frac{800 \times 100}{9817.477} = 81.49 \text{ N/mm}^2$$

Corresponding to this value of $\sigma_{ac} = 81.49$ and $f_y = 250 \text{ N/mm}^2$, we get from Table 20.5,

$$\lambda = 100 - (100 - 90) \frac{81.49 - 80}{90 - 80} = 98.51$$

$\therefore \qquad L = \lambda r = 98.51 \times 45.069 \approx 4440 \text{ mm} = \textbf{4.44 m}$

Example 20.13. *A solid member has the cross-section as shown in Fig. 20.15. It is to be used as a column having 3.5 m effective length. Determine the value of d if the maximum allowable load is to be 400 kN. Take $f_y = 250 \, N/mm^2$ and $E = 2 \times 10^5 \, N/mm^2$.*

Solution

$$A = 2 \times \frac{1}{2} (2d) \left(\frac{d}{2} \right) = d^2$$

$$I_X = 2 \times \frac{1}{12} (2d) \left(\frac{d}{2} \right)^3 = \frac{d^4}{24}$$

$$I_Y = 2 \times \frac{1}{12} (d) (d)^3 = \frac{d^4}{6}$$

$$\therefore \quad I_{min} = I_X = \frac{d^4}{24}.$$

$$r_{min} = \sqrt{\frac{I_{min}}{A}} = \sqrt{\frac{d^4/24}{d^2}} = \frac{d}{\sqrt{24}}$$

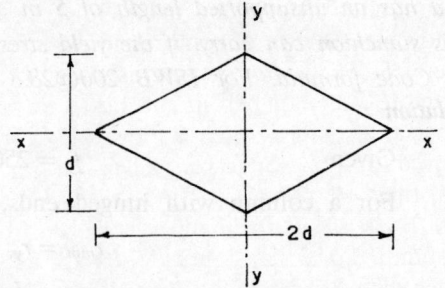

FIG. 20.15.

$$\lambda_{max} = \frac{l}{r_{min}} = \frac{3500}{d/\sqrt{24}} = \frac{17146.4}{d};$$

$$f_{cc} = \frac{\pi^2 E}{\lambda^2} = \frac{\pi^2 \times 2.0 \times 10^5}{(17146.4/d)^2} = 6.714 \times 10^{-3} d^2$$

Now

$$P = 400 \times 10^3 = \sigma_{ac} \times A$$

$$\therefore \quad \sigma_{ac} = \frac{P}{A} = \frac{400 \times 10^3}{d^2}$$

But

$$\sigma_{ac} = \frac{0.6 f_{cc} \cdot f_y}{\left[(f_{cc})^n + (f_y)^n \right]^{\frac{1}{n}}}$$

or

$$\sigma_{ac}^n \left[(f_{cc})^n + (f_y)^n \right] = \left(0.6 \cdot f_y \cdot f_{cc} \right)^n$$

or

$$\left(\frac{400 \times 10^3}{d^2} \right)^{1.4} \left[(6.714 \times 10^{-3} d^2)^{1.4} + (250)^{1.4} \right] = \left[0.6 \times 250 \times 6.714 \times 10^{-3} d^2 \right]^{1.4}$$

or

$$9.0736 \times 10^{-4} d^{2.8} + 2275.7 = 1.45 \times 10^{-8} d^{5.6}$$

or

$$d^{5.6} - 62569.4 \, d^{2.8} - 1.5693 \times 10^{11} = 0.$$

or

$$x^2 - 62569.4 \, x - 1.5693 \times 10^{11} = 0 \quad \text{(where } x = d^{2.8})$$

From which

$$x = 428658$$

$$\therefore \quad d = x^{1/2.8} = (428658)^{1/2.8} = 102.7$$

Keep

$$d = \mathbf{103 \, mm}.$$

$$\therefore \quad r_{min} = \frac{103}{\sqrt{24}} = 21.02 \; ; \; \lambda = \frac{17146.4}{103} = 166.5$$

$$\therefore \quad \sigma_{ac} = 41 - (41 - 37) \frac{6.5}{10} = 38.4 \, N/mm^2$$

$$A = (103)^2$$

$$\therefore \quad P = (103)^2 \times 38.4 \times 10^{-3} = 407.4 \, kN. \text{ Hence O.K.}$$

20.12. COMMON SHAPES OF COMPRESSION MEMBERS

We have seen in the IS Code column formula as well as in other formulae that the *permissible stress* in a compression member decreases with increase in slenderness ratio. Hence the section must be so proportioned that it has largest possible moment of inertia for the same cross-sectional area. Also, the section should have approximately the same radius of gyration about both the principal axes. Fig. 20.16 show various type of compression members. *Solid circular section* is used as compression member in machines and special structures such as legs of tall, guyed transmission towers. The cylindrical tube or *hollow circular section* (Fig. 20.16 *a*) is the optimum section for a column with equal unbraced lengths in each direction. Such sections are extensively used in *tubular trusses*. However, there are connection problems in such a section. In *square* or *rectangular tube* (Fig. 20.16 *c*), the efficiency of circular tube may be approached and at the same

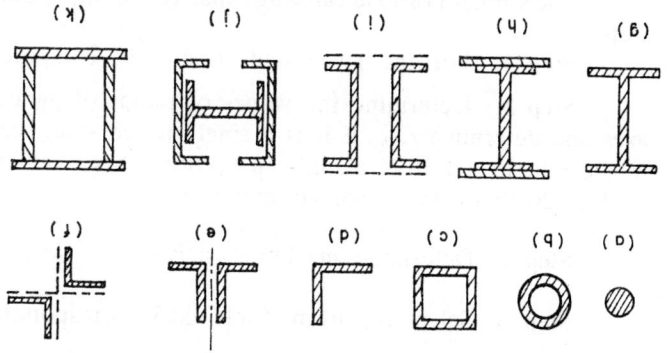

FIG. 20.16. TYPICAL COMPRESSION MEMBERS

time the connection problem can be made simple. The *single angle section* shown in Fig. 20.16 *d* are useful only for truss members and compression legs of towers. *Tee sections* are often used in welded trusses. The *double angle sections* (Fig. 20.16 *e*) are commonly used in trusses, while the *cruciform arrangement* of double angles (Fig. 20.16 *f*) gives approximately equal radii of gyration in two directions. The wide flange section shown in Fig 20.16 (*g*) is commonly used in buildings because of its easy availability in different sizes and ease with which it can be spliced and connected. If the requirement of area is in excess of available section, additional plates can be attached to the flanges as shown in Fig. 20.16 *(h)*.

The choice of arrangement of multiple rolled sections or *built-up sections* depends upon (*i*) functional aspect of the structure (*ii*) functional aspect of the member, (*iii*) inter-connection requirements, and (*iv*) high radius of gyration. Fig. 20.16 shows a large variety of built-up sections. The elements of built-up sections are placed at the farthest possible distance from the centroid of the section. A section consisting of two channel sections, suitably spaced (Fig. 20.16 *i*) is used as web compression member in lattice-girder bridges. If suitable channel sections are not available, built-up sections using four angles and plates can be conveniently used. A combination of two channels and an I-section (Fig 20.16 *j*) can be used as web member in a truss bridge. Fig 20.16 (*i*), (*j*), (*k*) show built-up column sections, to carry heavy loads.

20.13. STRENGTH OF COMPRESSION MEMBERS

The *strength* of a compression member is the load carrying capacity of a member at a safe (allowable) compressive stress corresponding to the slenderness ratio of the column. It depends upon several factors, most important amongst these being radius of gyration, effective length and area of cross-section. Thus :

$$P = \sigma_{ac} . A \qquad \qquad ...(20.34)$$

In compression members, full gross-sectional area is effective in resisting compression, and no deduction is made for rivet holes since the rivets are assumed to fill the holes. The axial compression has a tendency to further tighten the rivets in the holes aff the rivets tend to bear against the adjoining material.

It is seen in the design formula that the allowable stress σ_{ac} varies parabolically with slenderness ratio. Hence it can be easily shown that *efficiency of a shape*, which is defined as the ratio of allowable load for a given slenderness ratio to that for slenderness ratio equal to zero, is related to A/r^2.

The strength or load carrying capacity of compression member is determined in the following steps.

Step 1. For the given end conditions, compute ctive length l of the member.

Step 2. Determine the values of radius of gyration of the member about the principal axes and determine r_{min}. If it is a single rolled steel section, these values are already available in steel tables. If it is a built-up section these values are determined either with the help of Fig. 20.10 or by actual computations.

Step 3. Determine maximum slenderness ratio $\lambda = \dfrac{l}{r_{min}}$

Step 4. Select σ_{ac} from Table 20.5 corresponding to this maximum value of λ.

Step 5. Find gross cross-sectional area of the section, from steel tables.

Step 6. Finally, compute the strength of the compression member, using Eq. 20.34.

Example 20.14. *An I-joist ISMB 250 @ 37.3 kg/m has an effective length of 5 m. It is used as a stanchion with two plates 250 mm × 10 mm welded to its sides, as shown in Fig. 20.17. Compute the load carrying capacity. What will be its load capacity if one plate is attached to each flange?*

Solution : From steel tables, for ISMB 250@ 37.3 kg/m, we have :
$a = 47.55$ cm^2; $I_{xx} = 5131.6 \times 10^4$ mm^4; $I_{yy} = 334.5 \times 10^4$ mm^4.

(a) **Plates attached to sides** (Fig 20.17)

$$I_{xx} = 5131.6 \times 10^4 + 2\left[\frac{1}{12} \times 10 \times 250^3\right] = 77.35 \times 10^6 \text{ mm}^4$$

$$I_{yy} = 334.5 \times 10^4 + 2\left[\frac{1}{12} \times 250 \,(10)^3 + 2500\,(62.5+5)^2\right]$$

$$= 26.17 \times 10^6 \text{ mm}^4$$

$$A = 4755 + 2\,(250 \times 10) = 9755 \text{ mm}^2$$

$$r_{min} = r_{yy} = \sqrt{\frac{26.17 \times 10^6}{9755}} \approx 51.8 \text{ mm}$$

$$\lambda_{max} = \frac{l}{r_{min}} = \frac{5000}{51.8} = 96.53.$$

$$\therefore \quad \sigma_{ac} = 90 - 6.53\left(\frac{10}{10}\right) = 83.47 \text{ N/mm}^2$$

$$\therefore \quad P = A\,\sigma_{ac} = 9755 \times 83.47 \times 10^{-3} = \mathbf{814.25 \text{ kN}}$$

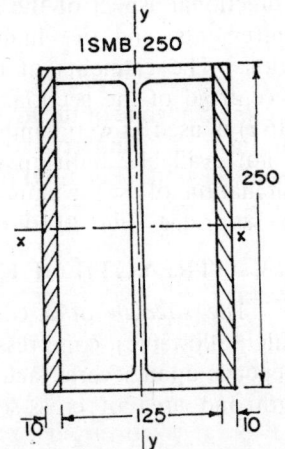

FIG. 20.17.

(b) **Plates attached to the flange** (Fig. 20.18)

$$I_{xx} = 5131.6 \times 10^4 + 2$$

$$\left[\frac{1}{12} \times 250 \,(10)^3 + 2500 \,(125 + 5)^2 \right]$$

$$= 135.86 \times 10^6 \text{ mm}^4$$

$$I_{yy} = 334.5 \times 10^4 + 2 \times \frac{1}{12} \times 10 \,(250)^3$$

$$= 29.387 \times 10^6 \text{ mm}^4$$

$$A = 4755 + 2 \,(250 \times 10) = 9755 \text{ mm}^2$$

$$\therefore \quad r_{min} = r_y = \sqrt{\frac{29.387 \times 10^6}{9755}} = 54.89$$

$$\lambda_{max} = \frac{5000}{54.89} = 91.1$$

$$\therefore \quad \sigma_{ac} = 90 - 1.1 \left(\frac{10}{10} \right) = 88.9 \text{ N/mm}^2$$

Hence $\quad P = 88.9 \times 9755 \times 10^{-3} = \textbf{876.22 kN}$

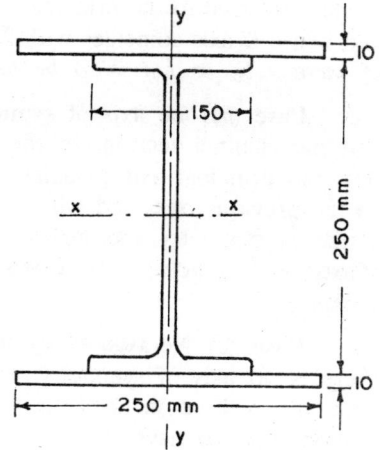

FIG. 20.18.

20.14. UNSYMMETRICAL SECTIONS AS STRUT

Structural steel section, such as T-section, channel section and angle section are normally used as struts in framed structures. In such a section, both x-axis and y-axis may not be symmetrical about the section.

In general, the following three cases may arise

(a) Both x-axis and y-axis are symmetrical such as in I-section (Fig. 20.19 a)

(b) Only one of the axes (either y-axis or x-axis) is the axis of symmetry, such as in T-section and channel section (Fig. 20.19 b, c)

and (c) None of the axes are symmetrical, such as in an angle section (Fig. 20.19 d)

Case (a) Both axes symmetrical :

In case of I-section (Fig. 20.19 a) both the axes are the axes of symmetry. Hence the *principal axes* (i.e. U-axis and V-axis) will coincide with X-axis and Y-axis respectively. The *principal axes* are defined as a pair of rectangular axes through the centre of gravity of the plane area such that the *product of inertia (i.e. $\Sigma u \cdot v \cdot \delta a$) is zero. See chapter 8. If a

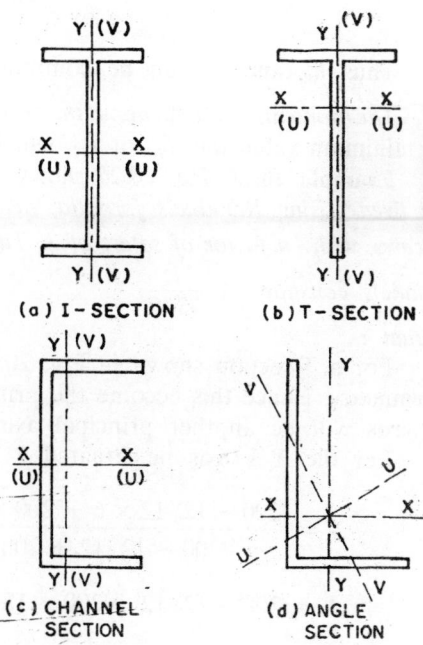

(a) I - SECTION

(b) T - SECTION

(c) CHANNEL SECTION

(d) ANGLE SECTION

FIG. 20.19. STRUCTURAL STEEL SECTIONS

plane area has an axis of symmetry, it is obviously the principal axis since the axis of symmetry has to satisfy the condition $\Sigma u \cdot v \, \delta a = 0$ about it, where δa is the elementary area with coordinates u and v referred to the principal axes U, V. In case of I-section both X and Y axes are symmetrical and hence U-axis coincides with X-axis while V-axis coincides with Y-axis. *The minimum moment of inertia (I_{xx} or I_{yy}) is to be used in various column formulae.*

Case (b) one axis of symmetry : The common examples of this case are the T-section and the channel section. In the case of T-section, y-axis is the axis of symmetry, and hence it is the principal axis (V-axis). The other principal axis (*i.e.* U-axis) has to be perpendicular to the previous one, and will thus coincide with X-axis. In the case of channel section, X-axis is the of symmetry and hence it is the principal axis (U-axis). The other principal axis (*i.e.* V-axis) will coincide with Y-axis. *The minimum of I_{xx} or I_{yy} is to be used in various column formulae.*

Case (c) No-axis of symmetry : In the case of an angle section (equal or unequal), there is no axis of symmetry. Hence the principal axis (U-axis and V-axis) will not coincide with and will be inclined to the X-axis and Y-axis, as shown in Fig. 20.19(d). For such a section, the we have

$$I_{xx} = \Sigma y^2 \, \delta a, \; I_{xy} = \Sigma x^2 \cdot \delta a \; \text{ and } \; I_{xy} = \Sigma x \cdot y \, \delta a.$$

The moments of inertia I_{uu} and I_{vv} about the principal axes are determined from the following equations :

$$I_{uu} = \frac{I_{xx} + I_{yy}}{2} + \sqrt{\left(\frac{I_{xx} - I_{yy}}{2}\right)^2 + I_{xy}^2} \qquad ...(20.35 \; a)$$

and

$$I_{vv} = \frac{I_{xx} + I_{yy}}{2} - \sqrt{\left(\frac{I_{xx} - I_{yy}}{2}\right)^2 + I_{xy}^2} \qquad ...(20.35 \; b)$$

Thus I_{uu} and I_{vv} can be computed from the given values of I_{xx}, I_{yy} and I_{xy}.

The moments of inertia about the principal axes have maximum and minimum values respectively. The minimum value (*i.e.* I_{uu} or I_{vv}, whichever is less) should be used in the column formulae.

Example 20.15. *Fig. 20.20 shows a T-section. It is used as a strut, 3 m long, with both ends fixed. Using Rankine's formula, determine the safe load it can carry, with a factor of safety of 3. Take $f_c = 320 \, N/mm^2$ and Rankine's constant as $\dfrac{1}{7500}$.*

Solution :

For a T-section shown in Fig. 20.20, Y-Y axis is the axis of symmetry. Hence this become the principal axis ($V - V$). The X-X axis will be another principal axis.

Let the X-X axis be situated $\bar{y}$ below the face AB.

$$\therefore \quad \bar{y} = \frac{(200 - 12)\, 12 \times 6 + 200 \times 12 \times 100}{(200 - 12)\, 12 + 200 \times 12} = 54.45 \text{ mm}$$

$$A = (200 - 12)\, 12 + 200 \times 12 = 4656 \text{ mm}^2$$

$$I_{AB} = \frac{1}{3} \times 188 \, (12)^3 + \frac{1}{3} \times 12 \times 200^3 = 32108288 \text{ mm}^4$$

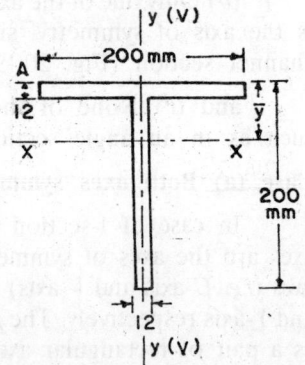

FIG. 20.20

$$I_{xx} = I_{AB} - A\bar{y}^2 = 32108288 - 4656 (54.45)^2 = 18302338 \text{ mm}^4$$

Also,

$$I_{yy} = \frac{1}{12} \times 12 (200)^3 + \frac{1}{12} \times 188 (12)^3 = 8027072 \text{ mm}^4$$

$\therefore$

$$I_{min} = I_{yy} = 8027072 \; ; r = \sqrt{\frac{I}{A}} = \sqrt{\frac{8027072}{4656}} = 41.52 \text{ mm}$$

$$L = 4 \text{ m; for column fixed at both ends, } L_E = \frac{L}{2} = \frac{3}{2} = 1.5 \text{ m} = 1500 \text{ mm}$$

Now, Rankine's $P = \dfrac{f_c A}{1 + a \left(\dfrac{L_E}{r} \right)^2} = \dfrac{320 \times 4656}{1 + \dfrac{1}{7500} \left(\dfrac{1500}{41.52} \right)^2} = 1269085 \text{ N}$

$\therefore$

$$P_{safe} = \frac{P}{F.S} = \frac{1269085}{3} = 423028 \text{ N} = \textbf{423.028 kN.}$$

Example 20.16. *An unequal angle, 100 mm × 60 mm × 10 mm is used as a strut for a length of 4 m. The strut may be considered as hinged at top and fixed at bottom. Using Euler's formula, calculate the safe load the column can carry at a factor of safety of 3. Take $E = 2 \times 10^5$ N/mm².*

Solution :

Both the X-X axis as well as Y-Y axis are not symmetrically placed. hence none of these are principal axes. Since the moment of inertia is minimum about any one of the principal axes, we have to compute I_{uu} and I_{vv} from I_{xx} and I_{yy}, using Eqs. 20.35. Let us first locate X-X and Y-Y axes with respect to faces AB and AC of the angle.

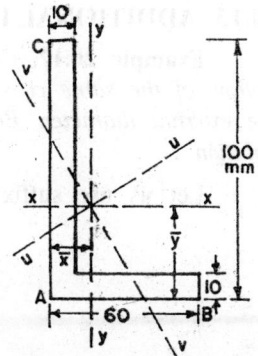

FIG. 20.21

$$A = A_1 + A_2 = 60 \times 10 + 90 \times 10 = 1500 \text{ mm}^2$$

$$\bar{y} = \frac{60 \times 10 \times 5 + 90 \times 10 \times 55}{1500} = 35 \text{ mm}$$

$$\bar{x} = \frac{60 \times 10 \times 30 + 90 \times 10 \times 5}{1500} = 15 \text{ mm}$$

$$I_{AB} = \frac{1}{3} \times 10 (100)^3 + \frac{1}{3} \times 50 (10)^3 = 335 \times 10^4 \text{ mm}^4$$

$\therefore$

$$I_{xx} = I_{AB} - A\bar{y}^2 = 335 \times 10^4 - 1500 (35)^2 = 151.25 \times 10^4 \text{ mm}^4$$

$$I_{AC} = \frac{1}{3} \times 10 (60)^3 + \frac{1}{3} \times 90 (10)^3 = 75 \times 10^4 \text{ mm}^4$$

$\therefore$

$$I_{yy} = I_{AC} - A\bar{y}^2 = 75 \times 10^4 - 1500 (15)^2 = 41.25 \times 10^4 \text{ mm}^4$$

Also,

$$I_{xy} = A_1 x_1 y_1 + A_2 x_2 y_2$$

where (x_1, y_1) are the co-ordinates of C.G. of area A_1 and (x_2, y_2) are the coordinates of the C.G. of area A_2.

$\therefore$

$$I_{xy} = 600 (30 - 15) (5 - 35) + 900 (55 - 35) (5 - 15)$$

$$= -27 \times 10^4 - 18 \times 10^4 = -45 \times 10^4 \text{ mm}^4$$

Now $\qquad \dfrac{I_{xx} + I_{yy}}{2} = \dfrac{151.25 \times 10^4 + 41.25 \times 10^4}{2} = 96.25 \times 10^4$

$$\dfrac{I_{xx} - I_{yy}}{2} = \dfrac{151.25 \times 10^4 - 41.25 \times 10^4}{2} = 55 \times 10^4$$

$\therefore \quad I_{uu} = 96.25 \times 10^4 + \sqrt{(55 \times 10^4)^2 + (-45 \times 10^4)^2} = 96.25 \times 10^4 + 71.06 \times 10^4 = 167.31 \times 10^4$

$I_{vv} = 96.25 \times 10^4 - \sqrt{(55 \times 10^4)^2 + (-45 \times 10^4)^2} = 96.25 \times 10^4 - 71.06 \times 10^4 = 25.19 \times 10^4$

Check : $\qquad\qquad I_{xx} + I_{yy} = I_{uu} + I_{vv}$

or $\qquad\qquad (151.25 + 41.25)\,10^4 = (167.31 + 25.19)\,10^4$

or $\qquad\qquad 192.5 \times 10^4 = 192.5 \times 10^4$ Hence OK.

Now $\qquad\qquad I_{min} = I_{vv} = 25.19 \times 10^4\ \text{mm}^4.$

Now, for a column hinged at top and fixed at bottom.

$$P_E = \dfrac{2\,\pi^2\,E\,I_{min}}{L^2} = \dfrac{2\,\pi^2 \times 2 \times 10^5 \times 25.19 \times 10^4}{(4000)^2} = 31.08 \times 10^3\ \text{N}$$

$\therefore \qquad\qquad P_{safe} = \dfrac{31.08 \times 10^3}{3} = 10.36 \times 10^3\ \text{N} = \textbf{10.36 kN}$

20.15. ADDITIONAL ILLUSTRATIVE EXAMPLES

Example 20.17. *Compare the ratio of the strength of a solid steel column to that of a hollow of the same cross-sectional area. The internal diameter of the hollow column is 3/4 of the external diameter. Both the columns have the same length and are pinned at the ends.*
Solution :

Let us use suffix s for solid column and h for hollow column.

$\therefore \qquad\qquad P_s = \dfrac{\pi^2\,E\,(A\,r_s^2)}{L^2} \quad$ and $\quad P_h = \dfrac{\pi^2\,E\,(A\,r_h^2)}{L^2}$

$\therefore \qquad\qquad \dfrac{P_h}{P_s} = \left(\dfrac{r_h}{r_s}\right)^2 \qquad\qquad\qquad\qquad\qquad\qquad\qquad \ldots(1)$

For a solid column, $\qquad r_s^2 = \dfrac{\pi}{64}\,d^4 \times \dfrac{4}{\pi\,d^2} = \dfrac{d^2}{16}$

and For a hollow column, $\qquad r_h^2 = \dfrac{\dfrac{\pi}{64}(D^4 - D'^4)}{\dfrac{\pi}{4}(D^2 - D'^2)} = \dfrac{D^2 + D'^2}{16}$

where $d=$ diameter of solid column and D and D' are the outer and inner dia. of hollow column, where $D' = \dfrac{3}{4}\,D.$

$\therefore \qquad\qquad \dfrac{P_h}{P_s} = \dfrac{r_h^2}{r_s^2} = \dfrac{D^2 + D'^2}{d^2} = \dfrac{D^2 + \dfrac{9}{16}D^2}{d^2} = \dfrac{25}{16}\dfrac{D^2}{d^2} \qquad\qquad \ldots(2)$

Since the area of cross-section of both the hollow and solid columns are equal,

$$A = \frac{\pi}{4} d^2 = \frac{\pi}{4} \left[D^2 - \left(\frac{3}{4} D \right)^2 \right] = \frac{7}{64} \pi D^2.$$

$$\therefore \qquad \frac{D^2}{d^2} = \frac{16}{7} \qquad\qquad\qquad\qquad\qquad ...(3)$$

Hence from (2) and (3), we get

$$\frac{P_h}{P_s} = \frac{25}{16} \left(\frac{16}{7} \right) = \frac{25}{7}$$

Example 20.18. *A cast iron hollow column of 200 mm external diameter and 160 mm internal diameter is 4 m long. It is fixed at its both ends and subjected to an eccentric load of 150 kN. Determine the maximum eccentricity, in order that there is no tension any where is the section. Take $E = 0.94 \times 10^5 \, N/mm^2$.*

Solution :

$$A = \frac{\pi}{4} (200^2 - 160^2) = 11309.7 \, \text{mm}^2$$

$$I = \frac{\pi}{64} (200^4 - 160^4) = 4637 \times 10^4 \, \text{mm}^4 \, ; \, Z = \frac{4637 \times 10^4}{100} = 463700 \, \text{mm}^3$$

For column with fixed ends, $L_E = \dfrac{L}{2} = \dfrac{4}{2} = 2 \, \text{m}$

$$\frac{L_E}{2} \sqrt{\frac{P}{EI}} = \frac{2000}{2} \sqrt{\frac{150 \times 10^3}{0.94 \times 10^5 \times 4637 \times 10^4}} = 0.1856 \, \text{radian} = 10.629°$$

Total stress at any location $= p_0 \pm p_b$.

In order that there is no tension anywhere in the section, the direct stress (p_0) should be equal to the bending stress (p_b)

$$\therefore \qquad \frac{P}{A} = \frac{P \cdot e \sec \dfrac{L_E}{2} \sqrt{\dfrac{P}{EI}}}{Z}.$$

or

$$\frac{150 \times 10^3}{11309.7} = \frac{150 \times 10^3 \, e \sec 10.629°}{463700} = \frac{150 \times 10^3 \times 1.01746 \, e}{463700}$$

$$\therefore \qquad e = \frac{463700}{11309.7 \times 1.01746} = \mathbf{40.3 \, mm}$$

Example 20.19. *A straight cylindrical bar is 20 mm diameter and 2 m long. It is freely supported at its two ends in a horizontal position and loaded at the centre with a concentrated load of 120 N. The central deflection is found to be 4 mm.*

If placed vertical and loaded along its axis, what load would cause it to buckle ? What is the ratio of the maximum stress in the two cases ?

Solution :

Now

$$y_c = 4 = \frac{W L^3}{48 \, E I} = \frac{120 \, (2000)}{48} \times \frac{L^2}{E I}$$

(where L, E and I are in mm units)

$$\therefore \qquad \frac{E\,I}{L^2} = \frac{120\,(2000)}{48 \times 4} = 1250 \qquad\qquad\qquad ...(1)$$

As a strut :

$$P_E = \frac{\pi^2 \cdot E \cdot I}{L^2} = \pi^2 \times 1250 = \textbf{12337 N} \qquad\qquad ...(2)$$

$$\therefore \qquad f_E = \frac{P_E}{A} = \frac{12337}{\frac{\pi}{4}\,(20)^2} = 39.27\ \text{N/mm}^2$$

As a beam, $\qquad M_{max} = \frac{WL}{4} = \frac{120\,(2000)}{4} = 60000\ \text{N-mm}$

$$\therefore \qquad f_b = \frac{M}{Z} = \frac{60000}{\frac{\pi}{32}\,(20)^3} = 76.39\ \text{N/mm}^2$$

$$\therefore \qquad \frac{f_b}{f_E} = \frac{76.39}{39.27} = \textbf{1.945}$$

Example 20.20. *Select the lightest wide flange joist that can be used as a column 5 m long to support an axial load of 500 kN, with a factor of safety of 3. Assume (a) both ends hinged and (b) one end fixed and the other end hinged.*

Use $\sigma_{PL} = 200\,N/mm^2$ *and* $E = 2 \times 10^5\,N/mm^2$.

Solution :

(a) Both ends hinged

For steel with proportional limit $\sigma_{PL} = 200\ \text{N/mm}^2$, the limiting value of $\frac{L}{r}$ is given by:

$$p_E = \sigma_{PL} = \frac{\pi^2 E I}{A L^2} = \frac{\pi^2 E r^2}{L^2} = \frac{\pi^2 E}{\left(\dfrac{L}{r}\right)^2}$$

$$\therefore \qquad \left(\frac{L}{r}\right)_{lim.} = \sqrt{\frac{\pi^2 E}{\sigma_{PL}}} = \sqrt{\frac{\pi^2 \times 2 \times 10^5}{200}} = 99.35$$

Hence if $\frac{L}{r} \geq 99.35$, Euler's formula applies. *If* $\frac{L}{r} < 99.35$, *the limiting stress is the proportional limit.*

The specified working load $(= 500\ \text{kN})$, when multiplied by the F.S. $(=3)$, gives the Euler's load. Hence $P_E = 500 \times 3 = 1500\ \text{kN}$.

$$\therefore \qquad I_{min} = \frac{P_E L^2}{E\,\pi^2} = \frac{(1500 \times 10^3)\,(5000)^2}{2 \times 10^5\,(\pi^2)} = 1899.8 \times 10^4\ \text{mm}^4$$

Also, for slenderness ratio $\frac{L}{r} \geq 99.35$, we have

$$r_{min} \leq \frac{L}{99.35} = \frac{5000}{99.35} = 50.33\ \text{mm.}$$

This criteria requires that the section must have a least $I \geq 1899.8 \times 10^4 \, mm^4$ and a least $r \leq 50.33$ mm. This is satisfied by choosing a section ISWB 500 having $I_{min} = I_{yy} = 2987.8 \times 10^4 \, mm^4$ and $r_{min} = 49.6$ mm.

However, if the selection were based on the proportional limit, the section must have a minimum area $A_{min} = \dfrac{P_E}{\sigma_{PL}} = \dfrac{1500 \times 10^3}{200} = 7500 \, mm^2$ and r_{min} greater 50.33 mm (so that $\dfrac{L}{r}$ is less than 99.35). These conditions are satisfied by a section ISWB 550 having $A = 14334 \, mm^2$ and $r_{min} = 51.1$ mm.

The lightest section is therefore ISWB 500.

(b) One end fixed and other end hinged

$$P_E = 1500 \text{ kN as before. } L_E = \frac{L}{\sqrt{2}} = 0.707 \, L = 0.707 \times 5 = 3.536 \text{ m}$$

$$\therefore \qquad I \geq \frac{P \, L_E^2}{E \, \pi^2} = \frac{(1500 \times 10^3) \, (3536)^2}{2 \times 10^5 \, (\pi^2)} \geq 950.1 \times 10^4 \, mm^4$$

and

$$r \leq \frac{L_E}{99.35} = \frac{3536}{99.35} = 35.59 \text{ mm}$$

No available ISWB satisfies this condition. However, the lightest ISMB section that satisfies this condition is ISMB 500 @ 86.9 kg/m, having $I_{yy} = 1369.8 \times 10^4$ and $r_{min} = 35.2$ mm.

The other set of conditions, based on proportional limit are :

$$A \geq \frac{1500 \times 10^3}{200} = 7500 \, mm^2 \text{ and } r_{min.} \text{ greater than } 35.59 \text{ mm.}$$

The lightest available section is ISWB 400 @ 66.7 kg/m, having $A = 8501 \, mm^2$ and $r_{min.} = 40.4$ mm.

The lightest section is therefore ISWB 400 @ 66.7 kg/m.

Unwary students might be tempted to select a section based on I without checking r and thereby choose a section ISWB 300 @ 48 kg/m having $I_{min} = 990.1 \times 10^4 \, mm^4$. However, this section has least $r = 40.2$ mm and area $A = 6133 \, mm^2$, which results in a stress which exceeds the proportionality limit of 200 N/mm². Such a section is not acceptable since it violates the stress-strain proportionality on which Euler's formula is based.

The above example demonstrates the importance of slenderness ratio in the column analysis and design. While in part (*a*), the design is governed by *elastic stability* (*i.e.* Euler's analysis), in part (*b*), the design is governed by the proportional limit.

Example 20.21. *A built-up column shown in Fig. 20.22 (a) consists of two ISMC 250 @ 30.4 kg/m. Determine the maximum allowable load for the column if the channels are so placed as to give the column equal resistance to bending about either axis. Take effective length of column as 4.5 m. What will be the load capacity of the column if the channels are arranged as shown in Fig. 20.22 (b)? Comment on this arrangement. Take $f_y = 250 \, N/mm^2$. The channels are braced appropriately in either case.*

Solution :

For ISMC 250 @ 30.4 kg/m, we have:

$$I_{xx} = 3816.8 \times 10^4;$$
$$I_{yy} = 219.1 \times 10^4 \;;$$
$$C_{yy} = 23.0 \text{ mm} \;;$$
$$a = 3867 \text{ mm}^2;$$
$$b = 80 \text{ mm}$$

Case (a) : Channels arranged as shown in Fig. 20.22 (a).

Let the back-to-back distance between the channels be x mm. For equal resistance, $I_X = I_Y$.

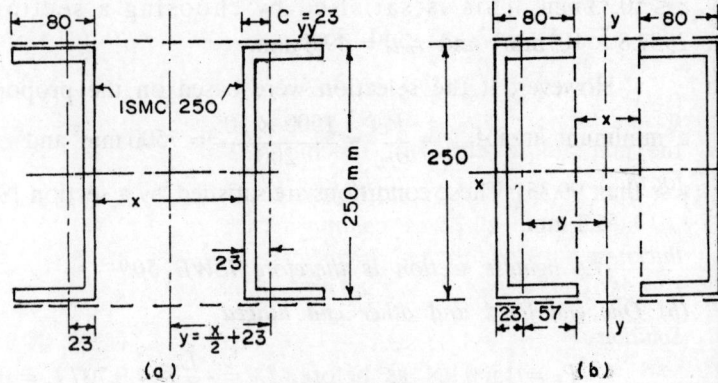

FIG. 20.22.

Now, $I_X = 2I_{xx} = 2 \times 3816.8 \times 10^4$

$$= 7633.6 \times 10^4 \text{ mm}^4$$

$$I_Y = 2[I_{yy} + ay^2] = 2\left[219.1 \times 10^4 + 3867\left(\frac{x}{2} + 23\right)^2\right] = 438.2 \times 10^4 + 7734\,(0.5x + 23)^2$$

Now $I_X = I_Y$, for equal strength.

$\therefore$ $7633.6 \times 10^4 = 438.2 \times 10^4 + 7734\,(0.5x + 23)^2$

From which $x = 146.91$ mm.

Hence keep the distance between the channels = 146.91 mm. In that case,

$$I_X = I_Y = I = 7633.6 \times 10^4 \text{ mm}^4.$$

$$r = \sqrt{I/A} = \sqrt{(7633.6 \times 10^4)/2 \times 3867} = 99.34 \text{ mm.}$$

$$\lambda = \frac{l}{r} = \frac{4.5 \times 1000}{99.34} = 45.29$$

$\therefore$ $\sigma_{ac} = 139 - (139 - 132)\dfrac{5.29}{10} = 135.3 \text{ N/mm}^2$

$\therefore$ $P_{safe} = A \cdot \sigma_{ac} = 2 \times 3867 \times 135.3 \times 10^{-3} \approx \mathbf{1046.4 \text{ kN}}$

(b) When the channels are arranged as shown in Fig. 20.22 (b).

Let the distance between the inner tips of the two channels be x mm.

$$y = 0.5x + 57$$
$$I_Y = 2[I_{yy} + ay^2] = 2[219.1 \times 10^4 + 3867\,(0.5x + 57)^2]$$
$$= 438.2 \times 10^4 + 7734\,(0.5x + 57)^2$$

For equal strength, $I_Y = I_X.$

$\therefore$ $438.2 \times 10^4 + 7734\,(0.5x + 57)^2 = 7633.6 \times 10^4$

From which $\qquad x = 78.91$ mm

In that case, $\qquad I_X = I_Y = 7633.6 \times 10^4$ mm^2

Hence, r, λ, σ_{ac} and P will be the same as before.

Comments: In this arrangement, the distance between the outer faces of channels will be $= 2 \times 80 + 78.91 = 238.91$ mm, as against a distance of $(2 \times 80 + 146.91 = 306.91$ mm). Hence the material required for bracing in the second case will be less. *However, the arrangement for the second case is unsatisfactory from the point of view of fabrication, inspection and maintenance.*

Example 20.22. *A column section, shown in Fig. 20.23, consists of three plates, each of thickness t welded together. It carries an axial load of 1000 kN over an effective length of 3.6 m. Taking* $f_y = 250 \, N/mm^2$ *and* $E = 2 \times 10^5 \, N/mm^2$, *determine the thickness t.*

Solution

$$I_X = \frac{1}{12} t (20 t)^3 + 2 \left[\frac{1}{12} \times (10 t) t^3 + 10 t^2 (10 t + \frac{t}{2})^2 \right] = 2273.33 t^4$$

$$I_Y = 2 \times \frac{1}{12} \times t (10 t)^3 + \frac{1}{12} (20 t) t^3 = 168.33 t^4$$

$$A = 2 [t (10 t)] + 20 t \times t = 40 t^2$$

$$r_{min} = \sqrt{\frac{I_{min}}{A}} = \sqrt{\frac{168.33 t^4}{40 t^2}} = 2.0514 t$$

$$\lambda = \frac{l}{r_{min}} = \frac{3600}{2.0514 t} = \frac{1754.9}{t}$$

$$\sigma_{ac} = \frac{P}{A} = \frac{1000 \times 10^3}{40 t^2} = \frac{25000}{t^2}$$

$$f_{cc} = \frac{\pi^2 E}{\lambda^2} = \frac{\pi^2 \times 2 \times 10^5 \times t^2}{(1754.9)^2} = 0.64095 t^2$$

Now $\qquad \sigma_{ac} = \dfrac{0.6 f_{cc} \cdot f_y}{[f_{cc}^n + f_y^n]^{\frac{1}{n}}}$ where $n = 1.4$.

$\therefore \qquad \dfrac{25000}{t^2} = \dfrac{0.6 (0.64095 t^2) 250}{[(0.64096 t^2)^{1.4} + (250)^{1.4}]^{\frac{1}{1.4}}}$

or $\qquad \dfrac{260.03}{t^4} = \dfrac{1}{[0.5365 t^{2.8} + 2275.7]^{\frac{1}{1.4}}}$

or $\qquad 2404.54 [0.5365 t^{2.8} + 2275.7] = t^{5.6}$

or $\qquad t^{5.6} - 1290 t^{2.8} - 5.47 \times 10^6 = 0$

or $\qquad x^2 - 1290 x - 5.47 \times 10^6 = 0$ (where $x = t^{2.8}$)

From which $\qquad x = 3071.5 = t^{2.8}$

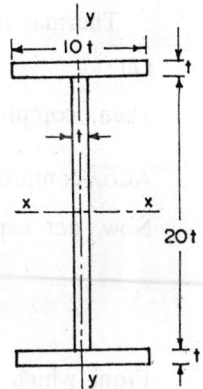

FIG. 20.23

$\therefore$ $t = (3071.5)^{\frac{1}{2.8}} = (3071.5)^{0.3571} \approx 17.6$ mm

Keep $t = 18$ mm

Check $\therefore$ $r_{min} = 2.0514\, t = 36.925$; $\lambda = \dfrac{3600}{36.925} = 97.50$

$\therefore$ $\sigma_{ac} = 90 - (90 - 80)\dfrac{7.50}{10} = 82.5$ N/mm^2

$A = 40\, t^2 = 40(18)^2 = 12960$ mm^2

$\therefore$ $P = A \cdot \sigma_{ac} = 12960 \times 82.5 \times 10^{-3} = 1069.2$ kN. Hence O.K.

Example 20.23. *A uniform bar of cross-section area A and flexural stiffness EI is heated so that its temperature varies linearly from 1/2 t at one end to t at the other end. One end is pin jointed to a rigid foundation. The other end is pin jointed so that it can slide in the direction of the length of the bar, the thermal expansion of which is resisted by a compression spring of stiffness k. If there is no load in the spring when t = 0, obtain an expression for the stress in the bar when it is heated and show that it buckles in flexure when*

$$t = \frac{4\pi^2 I}{3\alpha L^2 A}\left(1 + \frac{EA}{rL}\right)$$

where $\alpha = $ *coefficient of linear thermal expansion.*

Solution :

Average temperature along the bar $= \dfrac{1}{2}\left(\dfrac{1}{2}t + t\right) = \dfrac{3}{4}t$

$\therefore$ Thermal expansion of bar $= \Delta_t = \dfrac{3}{4}\alpha L t$ ...(1)

Let $P = $ force exerted by the spring on the bar.

Then, compression produced in the bar $= \dfrac{PL}{AE}$ ...(2)

Also, compression of the spring $= \dfrac{P}{k}$ ...(3)

Now, net expansion of the bar = compression of spring

$\therefore$ $\dfrac{3}{4}\alpha L t - \dfrac{PL}{AE} = \dfrac{P}{k}$

From which $P = \dfrac{\dfrac{3}{4}\alpha L t}{\dfrac{L}{AE} + \dfrac{1}{k}}$ ...(a)

and   stress in the bar $= p = \dfrac{P}{A} = \dfrac{\dfrac{3}{4}\alpha L t}{\dfrac{L}{E} + \dfrac{A}{k}}$,   (Ans.)   ...(b)

Now, the bar will buckle when buckling load $P = \dfrac{\pi^2 EI}{L^2}$ ...(c)

Equating (a) and (c), we get $\dfrac{\pi^2 EI}{L^2} = \dfrac{\dfrac{3}{4}L\alpha t}{\dfrac{L}{AE} + \dfrac{1}{k}}$

Rearranging, we get $t = \dfrac{4\pi^2 I}{3\alpha L^2 A}\left(1 + \dfrac{AE}{kL}\right)$

Example 20.24. *Partial fixing of ends:* *A strut of length 2a has each end fixed in an elastic material which exerts a restraint μ per unit angular displacement. Prove that the critical load P is given by the equation.*

$$\mu\, n \tan na + P = 0 \quad \text{where} \quad n^2 = \dfrac{P}{EI}$$

Such a strut, 2.5 m in length, has a theoretical critical load of 15 kN on the assumption of pinned ends. Determine the percentage increase in the critical load if the constraint offered at the ends is 170 N-m per degree of rotation. (U.L.)

Solution :

Let $M =$ restraining moment at each end

Then, as in the case of strut with fixed ends (Fig. 20.7 c),

$$EI\dfrac{d^2 y}{dx^2} = -P.y + M$$

or $$\dfrac{d^2 y}{dx^2} + \dfrac{P}{EI}y = \dfrac{M}{EI} \qquad \qquad ...(1)$$

Putting $\dfrac{P}{EI} = n^2$, we get

$$\dfrac{d^2 y}{dx^2} + n^2 y = \dfrac{M}{EI} \qquad \qquad ...(1\ a)$$

The general solution of the above equation is

$$y = A \sin nx + B \cos nx + \dfrac{M}{P} \qquad \qquad ...(2)$$

when $x = 0, y = 0$. Hence $B = -\dfrac{M}{P}$ $\qquad \qquad ...(a)$

Also, from (2) $\quad \dfrac{dy}{dx} = A n \cos nx - B n \sin nx \qquad \qquad ...(3)$

At $\quad x = 0, \dfrac{dy}{dx} = \left(\dfrac{dy}{dx}\right)_0$

$\therefore \qquad \left(\dfrac{dy}{dx}\right)_0 = A n$

$\therefore \qquad M = \mu\left(\dfrac{dy}{dx}\right)_0 = \mu A n \quad \text{or} \quad A = \dfrac{M}{\mu N} \qquad \qquad ...(b)$

Substituting the values of A and B, we get from (2)

$$y = \dfrac{M}{\mu N}\sin nx + \dfrac{M}{P}(1 - \cos nx) \qquad \qquad ...(4)$$

At the centre, $x = \dfrac{L}{2} = a$ and $\dfrac{dy}{dx} = 0$

Hence from (3) $0 = \dfrac{M}{\mu} \cos n a + \dfrac{M n}{P} \sin n a$

or $\mu n \tan n a + P = 0$ (Proved)   ...(c)

For pinned ends $\dfrac{\pi^2 E I}{(2 a)^2} = 15000$

From which $E I = \dfrac{15000 \, (2500)^2}{\pi^2} = 9499 \times 10^6$ N-mm^2

$\therefore$ $n = \sqrt{\dfrac{P}{E I}} = \dfrac{\sqrt{P}}{\sqrt{9499 \times 10^6}} = \dfrac{\sqrt{P}}{97462}$

and $n a = \dfrac{\sqrt{P}}{97462} \left(\dfrac{2500}{2} \right) = 0.0128 \sqrt{P}$

Also, $\mu = 170$ N-m/degree of rotation $= \dfrac{170 \times 10^3}{\dfrac{\pi}{180}}$ N-mm/rad $= 9740 \times 10^3$ N-mm/rad

Hence equation (c) can be written as $\tan (0.0128 \sqrt{P}) = -\dfrac{P}{9740 \times 10^3 \dfrac{\sqrt{P}}{97462}} = -0.01 \sqrt{P}$

The least solution of the above equation is for $\sqrt{P} = 166$. Hence $P = (166)^2 = $ **27500 N**

$\therefore$ % increase over the value for pinned ends $= \dfrac{27500 - 15000}{1500} = $ **83.3**.

Example 20.25. *Partial Restraint against lateral deflection : A strut of length L is encastered at its lower ends ; its upper end is elastically supported against lateral deflection so that the resisting force is k times the end deflection. Show that the crippling load P is given by*

$$\dfrac{\tan \alpha L}{\alpha L} = 1 - \dfrac{P}{k L} \text{ where } \alpha^2 = \dfrac{P}{E I}$$

Solution :

Let us choose the origin at O, and the axes as shown in Fig. 20.24.

Hence $E I \dfrac{d^2 y}{d x^2} = P (y_0 - y) - k y_0 x$

Taking $\dfrac{P}{E I} = \alpha^2$, we get

$$\dfrac{d^2 y}{d x^2} + \alpha^2 y = \alpha^2 y_0 - k y_0 \dfrac{x}{E I} \qquad \text{...(1)}$$

The solution of the above equation is

$$y = A \sin \alpha x + B \cos \alpha x + y_0 - \dfrac{k y_0 x}{P} \qquad \text{...(2)}$$

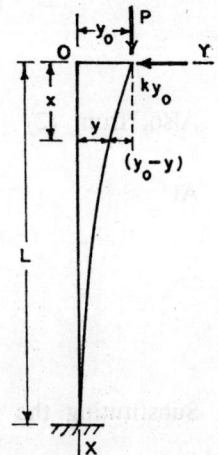

FIG. 20.24

At $\qquad\qquad x = 0, y = y_0$ Hence $B = 0$

Also, at $\qquad\qquad x = L, y = 0 \;\therefore\; A \sin \alpha L + y_0 - \dfrac{k y_0 L}{P} = 0 \qquad\qquad …(a)$

Also, at $\qquad\qquad x = L, \dfrac{dy}{dx} = 0 \quad\therefore\quad A \alpha \cos \alpha L - \dfrac{k y_0}{P} = 0 \qquad\qquad …(b)$

From (b), we get $\qquad A = \dfrac{k y_0}{P \alpha \cos \alpha L}$

Substituting in (a), we get

$$\frac{k y_0 \tan \alpha L}{P \alpha} + y_0 - \frac{k y_0 L}{P} = 0$$

Multiplying by $\dfrac{P}{k y_0 L}$ and rearranging, we get

$$\frac{\tan \alpha L}{\alpha L} = 1 - \frac{P}{k L}$$

PROBLEMS

1. Determine the section of a C.I. hollow cylindrical column, 5 m long with ends firmly built-in if it carries an axial load of 300 kN. The ratio of the internal to external diameter is 3/4. Use a factor of safety of 8. Take $f_c = 567 \text{ N/mm}^2$ and Rankine's constant $a = 1/1000$.

2. A hollow C.I. column with fixed ends supports an axial load of 1000 kN. If the column is 5 m long and has an external diameter of 250 mm, find the thickness of metal required. Use the Rankine's formula, taking a constant $1/6400$ and assume a working stresses of 80 N/mm^2.

3. A rolled steel beam section ISWB 200 @ 28.8 kg/m is used as a stanchion and has unsupported length of 5 m. It is effectively fixed at both the ends. Determine the axial load this stanchion can carry, if the yield stress for steel is 250 N/mm^2 and $E = 2 \times 10^5 \text{ N/mm}^2$. Use IS code method. For the ISWB 200 @ 28.8 kg/m, take $r_{xx} = 8.46$ cm ; $r_{yy} = 2.99$ cm and $a = 36.71 \text{ cm}^2$.

4. A steel column made of 3 m long channel section 200 mm $\times$ 80 mm, is fixed at both the ends. The thickness of flange is 10 mm while the thickness of the web is 6 mm. Using Rankine's formula, calculate the load it can carry with a factor of safety of 3. Take $f_c = 320 \text{ N/mm}^2$ and Rankine's constant $= \dfrac{1}{7500}$.

5. A hollow alloy tube 5 m with diameter 40 and 25 mm respectively was found to extend 6.4 mm under a tensile load of 60 kN. find the buckling load for the tube, when used as strut with both ends pinned. Also find the safe load on the tube taking factor of safety of 4.

6. Find the Euler's crippling load for a hollow cylindrical steel column of 38 mm external diameter and 2.5 mm thick. Take length of the column as 2.3 m and hinged at its both ends. Take $E = 205$ kN/mm^2

7. A straight bar of alloy, 1 m long and 12.5 mm $\times$ 4.8 mm is section is mounted in a strut testing machine and loaded axially until it buckles. Assuming the Euler's formula to apply, estimate the maximum central deflection before the material attains its yield point of 280 N/mm^2. Take $E = 72000 \text{ N/mm}^2$.

8. A tubular steel strut is 60 mm external diameter and 48 mm internal diameter. It is 2.2 m long and has hinged ends. The load is parallel to the axis but eccentric. Find the maximum eccentricity for a crippling load of 0.75 of the Euler value, the yield stress being $310 \text{ N/mm}^2. E = 207000 \text{ N/mm}^2$.

9(a). A column 3 m long, hinged at both ends is made up of two channels ISJC 200 and 250 mm × 10 mm flange plates as shown in Fig. 20.25. Determine the maximum eccentricity for a load of 400 kN from the Y-Y axis if the maximum permissible stress is 80 N/mm^2. Take $E = 2 \times 10^5$ N/mm^2. The properties of the channel section are $a = 1777$ mm^2, $I_{yy} = 84.2 \times 10^4$ mm^4, distance of centroid from back of web = 1.97 cm.

(b) Find the maximum deflection at the middle of the column length.   (U.L.)

(c) Also find the maximum eccentricity is order that there may be no tension anywhere on the section.

(Based on U.I.

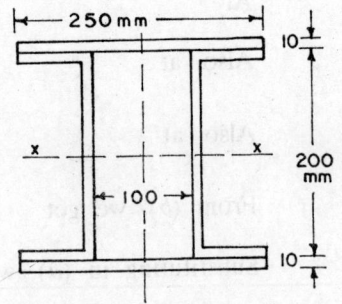

FIG. 20.25

ANSWERS

1. $D = 171.1$ mm; $d = 128.3$ mm
2. 17.19 mm
3. 235.4 kN
4. 586.5 kN
5. 643.4 N
6. 16.882 kN; 17.121 kN
7. 163 mm
8. 4.28 mm
9. (a) 28.7 mm (b) 1.2 mm (c) 40.4 mm

Torsion of Shafts

21.1. INTRODUCTION

Shafts are used for transmitting power and in that process, they are subjected to the following *torques:*

(*i*) A *driving torque* at the *input end* due to power transmitted

and (*ii*) A *resisting torque* at the output end, exerted by the driven machinery.

Torsion refers to the twisting of a structural member when it is loaded by *couples* that produce rotation about its longitudinal axis. We have seen earlier that when a moment is applied in a vertical plane containing the longitudinal axis of a structural member (*i.e.* beam or shaft) it will set bending stresses in the member. If on the contrary, the moment or couple is applied in a vertical plane perpendicular to the longitudinal axis of a member, it will be subjected to a *torque* causing *twist* or torsion in the member. Members may be subjected simultaneously to torque and bending and such cases have also been discussed in this chapter. The shaft shown in Fig. 21.1 is loaded with couples that produce torsion $T_1 = P_1 d_1$ while the second couple produces torsion $T_2 = P_2 . d_2$. However, torque T_2 is in the clockwise direction while torque T_1 is in anticlockwise direction. The couples that produce twisting of a structural member are called *torques, twisting couples* or *twisting moments.*

The couples inducing torque are represented by two alternative methods. In the first method, we use the curved arrow acting in the direction of twist as shown in Fig. 21.1 (*b*). In the second alternative, moment to the couple is represented by means of a vector in the form of *double headed arrow* using the *right hand rule* for moment vectors. By this rule, if the thumb of the closed right hand is pointed in the direction of the double headed vector, the fingers will indicate the direction of the couple. This is illustrated in Fig. 21.1 (*c*).

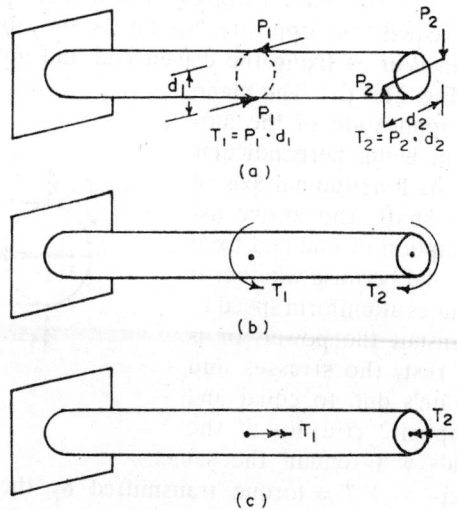

FIG. 21.1. BAR IN TORSION

A shaft may be sub-
jected to variable torques
along its length. Fig. 21.2
shows a line shaft transmitting
torque or power. To determine internal torque at any
plane, in a statically determinate member, only one
equation of statics, *i.e.*
$\Sigma M_z = 0$ is required, where the
z-axis is directed along the axis
of the member. To know the
torque at any point, pass a
section perpendicular to the
longitudinal axis of the mem-
ber and consider the forces to the one side of it.

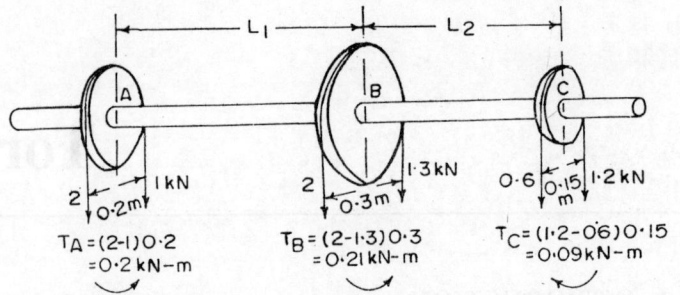

FIG. 21.2 LINE SHAFT

Thus the internal or resisting torque between A and B = 0.2 kN-m(↺) and between
B and C = 0.2 + 0.21 = 0.41 kN-m (↺).

21.2. TORSION OF CIRCULAR BARS OR SHAFTS

If the shaft revolves at constant speed, torques at the input end and the output ends
are equal and opposite. So far as the effect upon the shaft is concerned, the conditions are
equivalent to fixing the driven end and applying the driving torque at the other end, as shown
in Fig. 21.3 (*a*). The plane
of application of the mo-
ment being perpendicular
to the longitudinal axis of
the shaft, the above as-
sumption of one end fixed
is valid because whether it
rotates at uniform speed to
transmit the power, or is
at rest, the stresses and
strain's due to equal and
opposite couples at the
ends will remain the same.

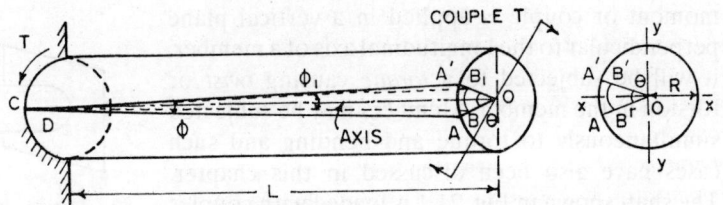

FIG. 21.3

Let T = torque transmitted by the shaft
            f_s = maximum shear stress at shaft surface
            q = shear stress at any radial distance r
            R = external radius of shaft.
            θ = angle of twist
            N = modulus of rigidity of the shaft material.
            L = length of the shaft

Fig. 21.3 shows a bar or shaft of circular section, subjected to torque T. Such a case
is a case of *pure torsion*. Due to symmetry, we assume that cross-section of the circular bar
rotates as a *rigid body* about the longitudinal axis, with radius remaining straight and cross-section
remaining plane and circular.

Under the action of the torque, a line CA drawn on the surface of the shaft is displaced to a position CA_1, through an angle φ. Hence the point A on the external surface in the end section is displaced to a position A_1, and since the driven end of the shaft is fixed, angle $A\hat{O}A_1$ is the *angle of twist* (θ). If f_s is the maximum shear stress induced at the surface of the shaft, the strain φ is given by

$$\varphi = \frac{f_s}{N} \qquad \text{...(1)}$$

Also, from Fig. 21.3 (a), $\varphi = \dfrac{A A_1}{L} = \dfrac{OA \cdot \theta}{L} = \dfrac{R\theta}{L}$ \qquad ...(2)

From (1) and (2), we get $\dfrac{f_s}{N} = \dfrac{R\theta}{L}$ \qquad ...(3)

or $\qquad\qquad\qquad \dfrac{f_s}{R} = \dfrac{N\theta}{L}$ \qquad ...(4)

Let us now take a layer DB, distant r from the axis of the shaft. The layer will be distorted to a new position DB_1, through an angle φ_1, though the angle of twist (θ) remains the same.

Now if q is the shear stress induced at a radial plane distant r from the axis of the shaft, we have

$$\frac{q}{N} = \varphi_1 = \frac{B B_1}{D B} = \frac{r\theta}{L}$$

or $\qquad \dfrac{q}{r} = \dfrac{N\theta}{L}$ \qquad ...(5)

Combining (4) and (5), we get the important relationship known as *torsion formula*

$$\frac{f_s}{R} = \frac{q}{r} = \frac{N\theta}{L} \qquad \text{...(21.1)}$$

The above relation states that *the intensity of shear stress at any point in the cross-section of a shaft subjected to pure torsion is proportional to its distance from the centre*. The variation is *linear*, as shown in Fig. 21.4. Similarly, strain varies linearly from the centre.

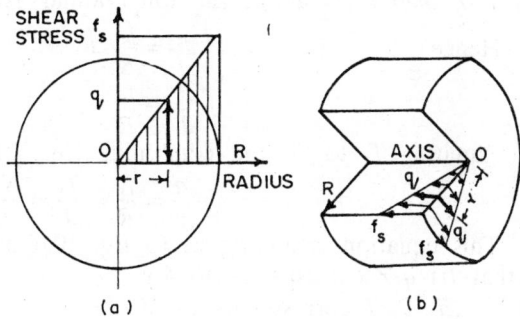

FIG. 21.4. VARIATION OF TORSIONAL SHEAR STRESS

21.3. ASSUMPTIONS :

The following assumptions have been made in developing the equations for stresses and deformations in a bar subjected to pure torsion (*i.e.* Eq. 21.1). These assumptions may be proved mathematically and some may be demonstrated experimentally.

1. Shaft is loaded with twisting couples in planes that are perpendicular to the axis of the shaft.

2. Torsion is uniform along the length *i.e.* all normal cross-section which are at the same axial distance suffer equal relative rotations.

3. Circular sections remain circular. Thus radii remain straight after torsion.

4. Plane normal sections of shaft remain plane after twisting, *i.e.* no warping or distortion of parallel planes normal to the axis of the shaft takes place.

5. Stress is proportional to strain, *i.e.* stresses do not exceed proportional limit.

6. Material is homogeneous and isotropic.

21.4. RESISTING TORQUE

From the point of view of equilibrium, the external torque T must be balanced by the resisting torque (T_r). The resisting torque is the sum of the moments of tangential shearing stress acting on any transverse section. Fig. 21.5 shows a circular shaft subjected to an external torque T. Consider a ring at radial distance r from the centre of the shaft and of thickness δr. The intensity of shear stress q is equal to $f_s.r/R$, from Eq. 21.1.

The elementary resisting couple set up by this thin ring is given by

$$\delta T_r = (q.\delta a).r$$

where δa = area of the elementary ring $= 2\pi r.\delta r$.

Hence the resisting couple T_r set up by the whole cross-section of the shaft is

$$T_r = \sum_{r=0}^{r=R} \delta T_r = \int_0^R \frac{f_s}{R}.\delta a.r^2 = \frac{f_s}{R}\int_0^R \delta a.r^2$$

In the above expression, the term $\int_0^R \delta a.r^2$ represents the *polar moment of inertia* (J) about the longitudinal axis of the shaft.

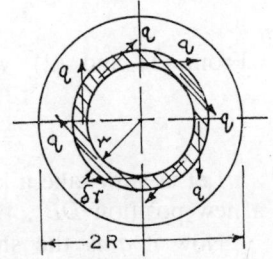

FIG. 21.5

Hence
$$T_r = \frac{f_s}{R}.J \qquad ...(21.2\ a)$$

or
$$\frac{T_r}{J} = \frac{f_s}{R} \qquad ...(21.2)$$

Equating T_r to T, and combining Eqs. 21.1 and 21.2, we obtain
$$\frac{q}{r} = \frac{f_s}{R} = \frac{T_r}{J} = \frac{N\theta}{L} \qquad ...(21.3)$$

This equation is analogous to Eq. 10.6 obtained for bending. Comparing the two, we find that (*i*) q/r corresponds to f/y

(*ii*) T_r/J corresponds to M_r/I

(*iii*) $N\theta/L$ corresponds to E/R

(*v*) J/R corresponds to $I/(d/2)$

and (*vi*) NJ corresponds to EI

J/R is known as *torsional section modulus*. Similarly, expression $N J$ is known as *torsional rigidity* of the bar or the shaft. *It is important to note that the relative stiffness of two shafts is measured by the inverse ratio of the angles of twist in equal lengths of shafts when subjected to equal torques.*

Polar moment of inertia

From Eq. 8.20, we have
$$I_{zz} = J = I_{xx} + I_{yy} \qquad ...(21.4)$$
For a *solid shaft of circular section*, $I_{xx} = I_{yy}$

$$\therefore \qquad I_{zz} = J = 2\,I_{xx} = 2 \times \frac{\pi}{64}D^4 = \frac{\pi}{32}D^4 \quad ...(21.5)$$

(where D is the external diameter of the shaft)

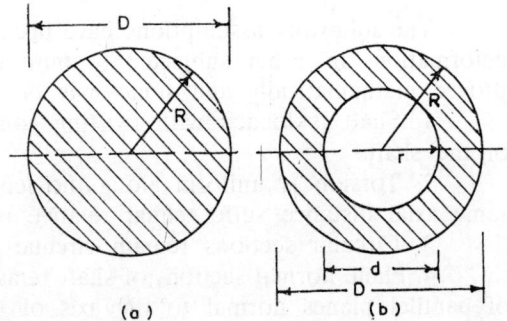

(a)   (b)

FIG. 21.6

Hence torsional section modulus $= \dfrac{J}{R} = \dfrac{J}{D/2} = \dfrac{\pi}{16} D^3$ ...(21.6)

For a *hollow circular shaft* for external diameter D and internal diameter d,

$$J = \frac{\pi}{2}(R^4 - r^4) = \frac{\pi}{32}(D^4 - d^4) \qquad ...(21.7)$$

21.5. POWER TRANSMITTED :

Let $\qquad\qquad P$ = Power transmitted in kW

Now $\qquad\qquad 1\,W = 1$ Joule/sec $= 1$ N-m/sec.

$\therefore$ Work done in transmitting P kW of power

$$= 1 \times (P \times 10^3) \text{ N-m/sec.}$$

$$= P \times 60 \times 10^6 \text{ N-m/min.}$$

$$= 60\,P \text{ kN-m/min} \qquad ....(1)$$

Let the torque supplied $= T$ kN-m.

$\therefore$ Work supplied $=$ (average couple) $\times$ angle turned through in one minute

$$= T\,(2\,\pi\,n) \text{ kN-m/min} \qquad ...(2)$$

where $n=$ revolutions of the shaft per minute (r.p.m)

Equating (1) and (2), we get

$$60\,P = 2\,\pi\,n\,T$$

or $\qquad\qquad P = \dfrac{2\,\pi\,n\,T}{60} \text{ kW} \qquad ...(21.8\ a)$

or $\qquad\qquad T = \dfrac{60\,P}{2\,\pi\,n} \text{ kN-m} \qquad ...(21.8\ b)$

Note that 1 metric H.P. $= 0.75$ kW

21.6. DESIGN OF SHAFT

The resisting couple should be equal to the applied torque. Hence

$$T_r = T = f_s \frac{J}{R}$$

or $\qquad\qquad \dfrac{J}{R} = \dfrac{T}{f_s} \qquad ...(21.9)$

In the above expression, T is known from Eq. 21.8 b (*i.e.* $T = \dfrac{60\,P}{2\,\pi\,n}$). Setting f_s equal to the allowable stress (f_{sa}) we have

$$\frac{J}{R} = \frac{T}{f_{sa}} = \frac{60\,P}{2\,\pi\,n \cdot f_{sa}} \qquad ...(21.10)$$

Thus, the torsional section modulus is known, from which the diameter D of the shaft can be computed. Thus, for a solid circular shaft,

$$T = f_{sa} \cdot \frac{J}{R} = f_{sa} \cdot \frac{\pi}{16} D^3 \qquad ...(21.11)$$

In the above expression, the value of T, computed from Eq. 21.8 (b), should be substituted in N-mm units, if f_{sa} is in N/mm^2 units.

Maximum and Mean torque : If the torque fluctuates, the greatest value of the torque must be used in evaluating the maximum shear stress due to torsion. On the other hand, for calculating power P, using Eq. 21.8 (a), mean torque should be used.

Example 21.1. *A solid shaft of 80 mm diameter is transmitting 100 kW power at 200 r.p.m. Calculate the maximum shear stress induced in the shaft and the angle of twist in degrees for a length of 6 m. Take $N = 8 \times 10^4 N/mm^2$.*

Solution :

Given $P = 100$ kW ; $n = 200$ r.p.m ; $d = 80$ mm ; $L = 6$ m.

Now $T = \dfrac{60 P}{2 \pi n} = \dfrac{60 \times 100}{2 \pi (200)} = 4.775$ kN-m $= 4.775 \times 10^6$ N-mm

Also, $T = f_s \dfrac{J}{R} = f_s \cdot \dfrac{\pi}{16} d^3$

or $f_s = \dfrac{16 T}{\pi d^3} = \dfrac{16 \times 4.775 \times 10^6}{\pi (80)^3} = \mathbf{47.49\ N/mm^2}$

Also, $\theta = \dfrac{f_s}{R} \cdot \dfrac{L}{N} = \dfrac{47.49}{40} \times \dfrac{6000}{8 \times 10^4} = \mathbf{0.089\ radian}$

Example 21.2. *Find the torque which a shaft of 200 mm diameter can safely transmit, if the shear stress is not to exceed 50 N/mm^2.*

Solution :

Given : $D = 200$ mm and $f_s = 50$ N/mm^2

Now $T = \dfrac{\pi}{16} f_s D^3 = \dfrac{\pi}{16} \times 50 (200)^3 = 78.54 \times 10^6$ N-mm

               $= \mathbf{78.54\ kN\text{-}m}$

Example 21.3. *A solid shaft is required to transmit 120 kW power at 200 r.p.m. Find the suitable diameter of the shaft if the maximum torque transmitted in each revolution exceeds the mean by 20%. Take allowable shear stress as 70 N/mm^2 for the material of the shaft.*

Solution :

Given : $P = 120$ kW; $n = 200$ r.p.m. ; $f_{sa} = 70$ N/mm^2

Average torque $T_{av} = \dfrac{60 P}{2 \pi n} = \dfrac{60 \times 120}{2 \pi (200)} = 5.7296$ kN-m

          $T_{max} = 1.2\, T_{av} = 1.2 \times 5.7296 = 6.8755$ kN-m $= 6.8755 \times 10^6$ N-mm

But $T = f_s \dfrac{\pi}{16} d^3$

$\therefore$ $d^3 = \dfrac{16 T}{f_s \pi} = \dfrac{16 \times 6.8755 \times 10^6}{70 \times \pi} = 500237$ mm^3

From which $d = 79.38$ mm $\approx \mathbf{80\ mm}$

Example 21.4. *A solid shaft is subjected to a torque of 12000 metre-N. Find the necessary diameter of the shaft if the allowable shear stress in 60 N/mm^2, and the allowable twist is 1° for every 20 diameters length of the shaft. Take $N = 0.8 \times 10^5 N/mm^2$.*

Solution :

Given : $\qquad T = 12000$ m-N ; $f_s = 60$ N/mm^2 and $\theta = 1° = \dfrac{1 \times \pi}{180}$ radian for $L = 20 D$

For strength : $\quad T = \dfrac{\pi}{16} f_s D^3$

or $\qquad D^3 = \dfrac{16\,T}{\pi f_s} = \dfrac{16 \times 12000 \times 10^3}{\pi \times 60} = 1018592$

From which $\quad D = 100.62$ mm $\qquad\qquad\qquad\qquad\qquad$ ...(1)

For stiffness : $\quad \dfrac{T}{J} = \dfrac{N\theta}{L}$, where $J = \dfrac{\pi}{32} D^4$

$\therefore \qquad \dfrac{12000 \times 10^3}{\dfrac{\pi}{32} D^4} = \dfrac{0.8 \times 10^5\,\dfrac{\pi}{180}}{20\,D}$

or $\qquad D^3 = 1750830$

From which $\quad D = 120.53$ mm $\qquad\qquad\qquad\qquad\qquad$ ...(2)

The necessary diameter of the shaft will be the greater of the two.

$\therefore \qquad D = 120.53$ mm $\approx$ **121 mm**

Example 21.5. *A shaft transmits 300 kW power at 120 r.p.m. Determine (a) the necessary diameter of solid circular shaft (b) the necessary diameter of hollow circular section, the inside diameter being 2/3 of the external diameter. The allowable shear stress is 70 N/mm^2. Taking the density of material is 77 kN/m^3, calculate the % saving in the material if hollow shaft is used.*

Solution :

Given $\qquad P = 300$ kN, $n = 120$ r.p.m. ; $f_s = 70$ N/mm^2

Now $\qquad T = \dfrac{60\,P}{2\,\pi\,n} = \dfrac{60 \times 300}{2\,\pi\,(120)} = 23.87$ kN-m $= 23.87 \times 10^6$ N-mm

For solid section $\quad T = f_s \dfrac{\pi}{16} d^3$

$\therefore \qquad d^3 = \dfrac{16\,T}{f_s\,\pi} = \dfrac{16 \times 23.87 \times 10^6}{70\,(\pi)} = 1736935$

From which $\quad d = 120.21$ mm $\approx$ **121 mm**

For hollow circular section : $d = \dfrac{2}{3} D$

$$T = f_s \dfrac{\pi}{16}\left(\dfrac{D^4 - d^4}{D}\right) = \dfrac{f_s}{16}\pi D^3 \left(1 + \dfrac{4}{9}\right)\left(1 - \dfrac{4}{9}\right) = 0.1576 f_s D^3$$

$\therefore \qquad D^3 = \dfrac{T}{0.1576 f_s} = \dfrac{23.87 \times 10^6}{0.1576\,(70)} = 2.1642 \times 10^6$

$\therefore \qquad D = 129.35$ mm $\approx$ **130 mm**

$$d = \frac{2}{3}D = \frac{2}{3} \times 129.35 = 86.2 \text{ mm} \approx \textbf{86.5 mm}$$

Percentage saving of material

Weight of solid shaft per mm length is

$$W_s = \frac{\pi}{4}(121)^2 \times 1 \times \rho = \frac{\pi}{4}\rho \,(14641)$$

Weight of hollow shaft per mm length is

$$W_h = \frac{\pi}{4}\left[(130)^2 - (86.5)^2\right] \times 1 \times \rho = \frac{\pi}{4}\rho \,[9417.8]$$

$$\therefore \ \% \text{ Saving} = \frac{W_s - W_h}{W_s} \times 100 = \frac{14641 - 9417.8}{14641} \times 100 = \textbf{35.7 \%}$$

Example 21.6. *Find the maximum torque that can be safely applied to a shaft of 200 mm diameter if the permissible angle of twist is 1° in a length of 5 m and the permissible shear stress is 45 N/mm². Take N = 0.8 × 10⁵ N/mm².*

Solution :

Given : $D = 200$ mm ; $\theta = 1°$ for $L = 5$ m ; $f_s = 45 \text{ N/mm}^2$

(a) Torque based on permissible shear stress

$$T = \frac{\pi}{16}f_s D^3 = \frac{\pi}{16} \times 45 \,(200)^3 = 70.686 \times 10^6 \text{ N-mm} \qquad \text{...(1)}$$

(b) Torque based an angle of twist

$$J = \frac{\pi}{32}D^4 = \frac{\pi}{32}(200)^4 = 15708 \times 10^4$$

or

$$T = \frac{N\theta}{L} \times J = \frac{0.8 \times 10^5}{5000}\left(\frac{1 \times \pi}{180}\right) \times 15708 \times 10^4 = 43.865 \times 10^6 \text{ N-mm} \qquad \text{...(2)}$$

The permissible torque will be the lesser of the two.

$\therefore$ Permissible $T = 43.865 \times 10^6$ N-mm $= \textbf{43.865 kN-m}$

Example 21.7. *A hollow steel shaft 5 m long is to transmit 160 kW of power at 120 r.p.m. The total angle of twist is not to exceed 2° in this length and the allowable shear stress is 50 N/mm².*

Determine the inside and outside diameters of the shaft, taking N = 0.8 × 10⁵ N/mm².

Solution : Given · $P = 160$ kW ; $n = 120$ r.p.m. ; $f_s = 50 \text{ N/mm}^2$; $L = 5$ m; $\theta = 2°$

For stiffness : $\theta = 2° = \dfrac{2\pi}{180}$ radians

$$\theta = \frac{TL}{NJ} = \frac{TL \times 32}{N\pi(D^4 - d^4)}$$

or $$D^4 - d^4 = \frac{32\,TL}{N\pi\theta} \qquad \text{...(1)}$$

For strength : $f_s = 50 \text{ N/mm}^2$

$$T = f_s \frac{J}{R} = f_s \frac{\pi}{16}\left(\frac{D^4 - d^4}{D}\right)$$

or $$D^4 - d^4 = \frac{16\,T\,D}{f_s\,\pi}$$ ...(2)

Equating (1) and (2), we get

$$\frac{32\,T\,L}{N\,\pi\,\theta} = \frac{16\,T\,D}{f_s\,\pi}$$

From which $$D = \frac{2\,L\,f_s}{N\,\theta} = \frac{2 \times 5000 \times 50}{0.8 \times 10^5 \left(\dfrac{2\,\pi}{180}\right)} = 179.05 \approx \mathbf{180\ mm}$$

Again, $$T = \frac{60\,P}{2\,\pi\,n} = \frac{60 \times 160}{2\,\pi\,(120)} = 12.732\ \text{kN-m} = 12.732 \times 10^6\ \text{N-mm}$$

Hence from (2), $$D^4 - d^4 = \frac{16\,T\,D}{f_s\,\pi} = \frac{16 \times 12.732 \times 10^6 \times D}{50\,\pi} = 1.2961 \times 10^6\,D$$

$\therefore$ $$(179.05)^4 - d^4 = 1.2961 \times 10^6\,(179.05)$$

or $$d^4 = 795561288$$

From which $$d = 167.95\ \text{mm} \approx \mathbf{168\ mm}$$

Hence keep $$D = 180\ \text{mm and } d = 168\ \text{mm}$$

Example 21.8. *A solid shaft of aluminium of length 1.5 m and of 60 mm diameter is to be replaced by a tubular steel shaft of the same length and the same outside diameter, such that each of two shafts have the same angle of twist per unit torsional moment over the total length. Determine the inner diameter of the tubular steel shaft, if the modulus of rigidity of steel is three times that of aluminium.*

Solution :

Given $$L_s = L_A = 1.5\ \text{m}\ ;\ D = 60\ \text{mm}\ ;\ N_s = 3\,N_A\ ;\ \theta s = \theta_A\ ;\ T_s = T_A$$

Let $$d = \text{inner diameter of steel shaft.}$$

Polar moment of inertia of solid aluminium shaft $= J_A = \dfrac{\pi}{32}D^4 = \dfrac{\pi}{32}(64)^4$

Polar moment of inertia of hollow steel shaft $= J_s = \dfrac{\pi}{32}(D^4 - d^4) = \dfrac{\pi}{32}[(60)^4 - d^4]$

Now, in general, $$\frac{T}{J} = \frac{N\theta}{L}$$

or $$\frac{TL}{\theta} = NJ$$

Since T, θ and L are the same for both the shafts, we have

$$N_A\,J_A = N_s\,J_s$$

or $$N_A \times \frac{\pi}{32}(60)^4 = N_s\,\frac{\pi}{32}[(60)^4 - d^4]$$

or $$(60)^4 = \frac{N_s}{N_A}[(60)^4 - d^4] = 3\,[(60)^4 - d^4]$$

or $\qquad\qquad \dfrac{12960000}{3} = 12960000 - d^4$

or $\qquad\qquad d^4 = \dfrac{12960000 \times 3 - 12960000}{3} = 8640000$

From which $\qquad\qquad d = \textbf{54.22 mm}$

Example 21.9. *A solid shaft of 250 mm diameter has the same cross-sectional area as the hollow shaft of the same material with inside diameter of 200 mm. (a) Find the ratio of power transmitted by the two shafts for the same angular velocity, and (b) compare the angles of twist in equal lengths of these shafts, when stressed to the same intensity.*

Solution :

Let the outside diameter of hollow shaft $= D$ mm

Area of cross-section of solid shaft $= A_S = \dfrac{\pi}{4}(250)^2$

Area of cross-section of hollow shaft $= A_H = \dfrac{\pi}{4}[D^2 - (200)^2]$

Since $\quad A_S = A_H$, we have $\dfrac{\pi}{4}[D^2 - (200)^2] = \dfrac{\pi}{4}(250)^2$.

From which we get $D = [(250)^2 + (200)^2]^{\frac{1}{2}} = 320.16$ mm

(a) Ratio of power transmitted

We know that $\qquad\qquad P = \dfrac{2\pi n T}{60}$

Shafts having same angular velocity will have same r.p.m. Hence ratio of H.P. transmitted will be equal to the ratio of torques transmitted. Hence if $f_{sa} =$ allowable shear stress for the material, we have

$\therefore \qquad\qquad \dfrac{P_S}{P_H} = \dfrac{T_S}{T_H} = \dfrac{\dfrac{\pi}{16} f_{sa} . D_S^3}{\dfrac{\pi}{16} f_{sa}\left[\dfrac{D^4 - d^4}{D}\right]} = \dfrac{(250)^3}{\dfrac{(320.16)^4 - (200)^4}{320.16}}$

or $\qquad\qquad \dfrac{P_S}{P_H} = 0.56165$

or $\qquad\qquad \dfrac{P_H}{P_S} = \textbf{1.78}$

(b) Angles of twists : Let $\theta_s =$ angles of twist for the solid shaft and θ_H be the angle of twist for the hollow shaft, for the same length.

In general, we have $\qquad\qquad \dfrac{f_s}{R} = \dfrac{N\theta}{L}$

or $\qquad\qquad \theta = \dfrac{f_s L}{R N}$, where $R =$ outside diameter.

Now, for both the shafts, f_s, N and L are the same.

$\therefore \qquad\qquad \dfrac{\theta_S}{\theta_H} = \dfrac{R_H}{R_S} = \dfrac{D_H}{D_S} = \dfrac{320.16}{250} = 1.2806$

or $$\frac{\theta_H}{\theta_S} = 0.7809$$

Example 21.10. *A solid shaft of mild steel 240 mm dia. is to be replaced by a hollow shaft of alloy steel for which allowable shear stress is 22 percent greater. The power to be transmitted is to be increased by 20 percent and the speed of rotation increased by 5 percent. Determine the maximum internal diameter of the hollow shaft.*

Solution :

Let us use suffix S for solid shaft and suffix H hollow shaft

Given $D_S = 240$ mm ; $f_{sH} = 1.22 f_{ss}$; $P_H = 1.2 P_S$ and $N_H = 1.05 N_S$

Since $T \propto \dfrac{P}{N}$, we have $\dfrac{T_H}{T_S} = \dfrac{P_H}{P_S} \cdot \dfrac{N_S}{N_H} = \dfrac{1.2}{1.05} = \mathbf{1.1429}$ ...(1)

Now $f_{sH} = 1.22 f_{ss}$ (But $f_s = \dfrac{T \cdot R}{J}$, in general)

$\therefore$ $\dfrac{T_H R_H}{J_H} = 1.22 \dfrac{T_S R_S}{J_S}$

or $\dfrac{T_H}{T_S} = 1.22 \cdot \dfrac{J_H}{R_H} \cdot \dfrac{R_S}{J_S}$ (where $\dfrac{J}{R} = \dfrac{\pi}{16} D^3$, in general)

$\therefore$ $\dfrac{T_H}{T_S} = 1.22 \left[\dfrac{D_H^4 - d_H^4}{D_H} \times \dfrac{\pi}{16} \right] \times \dfrac{16}{\pi D_S^3}$ ....(2)

Equating (1) and (2), we get

$$1.1429 = 1.22 \frac{D_H^4 - d_H^4}{D_H \cdot D_S^3} \quad \text{...(3)}$$

Now for maximum value of internal diameter of the hollow shaft, its external diameter (D_H) will be equal to the diameter D_S of the solid shaft.

$\therefore$ $1.1429 = 1.22 \dfrac{D_S^4 - d_H^4}{D_S^4} = 1.22 \dfrac{(240)^4 - d_H^4}{(240)^4}$

From which $d_H^4 = 209671554$ or $d_H \approx \mathbf{120\ mm}$

21.7. STRAIN ENERGY IN TORSION

Consider a solid shaft of length L, under the action of torque T. The torsional strain energy of a shaft is equal to the work done in twisting.

Hence $$U = \frac{1}{2} T \theta \quad \text{...(21.12)}$$

The above form of torsional strain energy is useful only if T and θ have been previously found. Let us now express the torsional strain energy in terms of maximum stress f_s. We already know that the elastic energy in a material subjected to uniform shear stress q is equal to $q^2/2N$ per unit volume. Now consider an elementary ring of thickness δr, at a radius r. The torsional strain energy of this ring, for a length L, is given by

$$\delta U = \frac{q^2}{2N} (2 \pi r \, \delta r) L$$

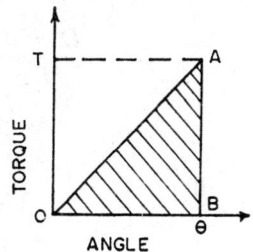

FIG. 21.7

But
$$\frac{q}{r} = \frac{f_s}{R} \qquad \text{or} \qquad q = \frac{f_s}{R} \cdot r$$

$\therefore$
$$\delta U = \frac{f_s^2 r^2}{2 R^2 N}(2\pi r \, \delta r . L) = \frac{f_s^2 r^3}{2 R^2 N} 2\pi L \, \delta r$$

Hence total
$$U = \frac{f_s^2 \, 2\pi L}{2 R^2 N} \int_0^R r^3 \, dr = \frac{f_s^2 \pi L}{R^2 N} \cdot \frac{R^4}{4} = \frac{f_s^2}{4 N}(\pi R^2 L)$$

or
$$U = \frac{f_s^2}{4 N} \times \text{volume of the shaft} \qquad\qquad ...(21.13)$$

Similarly, for a hollow shaft of internal diameter d and external diameter D,

Total
$$U = \frac{f_s^2 \pi L}{R^2 N} \int_{\frac{d}{2}}^{\frac{D}{2}} r^3 \, dr = \frac{f_s^2 \pi L}{64 N R^2}(D^4 - d^4)$$

or
$$U = \frac{f_s^2}{4 N}\left(\frac{D^2 + d^2}{D^2}\right) \times \text{volume of the shaft} \qquad\qquad ...(21.14)$$

For the *thin* tube, D approach d.

Hence
$$U \approx \frac{f_s^2}{2 N} \times \text{volume of the shaft}$$

Example 21.11. *A hollow shaft, subjected to pure torque, attains a maximum shear stress of f_s. Given that the strain energy per unit volume is $f_s^2/3 N$, calculate the ratio of shaft diameters.*

Determine the actual diameters of such a shaft to transmit 5 MW at 120 r.p.m. when energy stored is 25000 Nm/m^3 and $N = 80000$ N/mm^2.

Solution :

From Eq. 21.14, We have
$$\frac{U}{\text{Volume}} = \frac{f_s^2}{4 N}\left(\frac{D^2 + d^2}{D^2}\right) \quad \text{for a hollow shaft}$$

But
$$\frac{U}{\text{volume}} = \frac{f_s^2}{3 N} \quad \text{(Given)}$$

$\therefore$
$$\frac{f_s^2}{4 N}\left(\frac{D^2 + d^2}{D^2}\right) = \frac{f_s^2}{3 N}$$

or
$$\frac{D^2 + d^2}{D^2} = \frac{4}{3}, \text{ from which } \frac{d}{D} = \sqrt{\frac{1}{3}} \qquad\qquad ...(1)$$

or
$$\frac{D}{d} = \sqrt{3} = 1.732$$

If
$$\frac{f_s^2}{3 N} = 25000 \text{ N-m/m}^3 = 25000 \times 10^{-6} \text{ N-mm/mm}^3 \quad \text{(Given)}$$
$$f_s = (25000 \times 10^{-6} \times 3 \times 80000)^{1/2} = 77.46 \text{ N/mm}^2$$

Also
$$T = \frac{60 P}{2\pi n} = \frac{60 \times 5 \times 10^3}{2\pi (120)} = 397.89 \text{ kN-m} = 397.89 \times 10^6 \text{ N-mm}$$

Now
$$f_s = T \cdot \frac{R}{J} = T \frac{D/2}{\frac{\pi}{32}(D^4 - d^4)} = \frac{16\, D\, T}{\pi\,(D^4 - d^4)} \qquad \ldots(2)$$

Substituting the values of f_s and T and noting that $\dfrac{d}{D} = \left(\dfrac{1}{3}\right)^{\frac{1}{2}}$, we get

$$77.46 = \frac{16\, D\, (397.89 \times 10^6)}{\pi\, D^4 \left(1 - \dfrac{1}{9}\right)} = \frac{2280 \times 10^6}{D^3}$$

From which $\quad D^3 = 29.43 \times 10^6 \text{ or } D \approx \mathbf{309\ mm}$

and
$$d = \frac{309}{\sqrt{3}} \approx \mathbf{178\ mm}$$

21.8. SHAFTS OF VARYING DIAMETER

Fig. 21.8 shows a shaft AB of length L, having diameter d_1 (or radius r_1) at one end A and diameter d_2 (or radius r_2) at the other end B, and is subjected to *uniform torque* T. Consider a strip of thickness dx at a distance x from the end A. The radius r_x at this section is given by

$$r_x = r_1 + \frac{(r_2 - r_1)\, x}{L}$$

The polar moment of inertia of the elemental section is given by

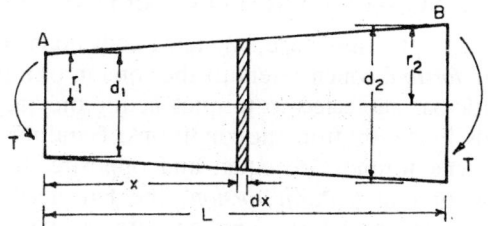

FIG. 21.8

$$J = \frac{\pi}{2} r_x^4 = \frac{\pi}{2}\left[r_1 + \left(\frac{r_2 - r_1}{L}\right) x\right]^4$$

If $\delta\theta$ is the angle through which the shaded element of length δx is twisted, then

$$\delta\theta = \frac{T\, L}{N\, J} = \frac{T\, \delta x}{N\, \dfrac{\pi}{2}\left[r_1 + \left(\dfrac{r_2 - r_1}{L}\right) x\right]^4}$$

Hence the total angle of twist for the whole shaft is

$$\theta = \overset{L}{\underset{0}{\Sigma}}\, \delta\theta = \frac{2\,T}{N\pi} \int_0^L \frac{dx}{\left[r_1 + (r_2 - r_1)\dfrac{x}{L}\right]^4} = \frac{2\,T}{N\pi}\left(-\frac{1}{3}\right)\left(\frac{L}{r_2 - r_1}\right)\left[\frac{1}{\left\{r_1 + \left(\dfrac{r_2 - r_1}{L}\right) x\right\}^3}\right]_0^L$$

or
$$\theta = \frac{2}{3}\frac{T\,L}{N\pi\,(r_2 - r_1)}\left[\frac{1}{r_1^3} - \frac{1}{r_2^3}\right] \qquad \ldots(21.15\ a)$$

or
$$\theta = \frac{32\,T\,L}{3\,N\pi\,(d_2 - d_1)}\left[\frac{1}{d_1^3} - \frac{1}{d_2^3}\right] \qquad \ldots(21.15\ b)$$

Another convenient form of expression for θ is as under.

$$\theta = \frac{T\,L}{N\,J_1}\left(\frac{\beta^2 + \beta + 1}{3\,\beta^3}\right) \qquad \ldots(21.15\ c)$$

where $$J_1 = \frac{\pi d_1^4}{32} \quad \text{and} \quad \beta = \frac{d_2}{d_1}$$

If $\beta = 1$ (*i.e.* $d_2 = d_1 = d$) the above expression reduces to

$$\theta = \frac{TL}{NJ} = \frac{TL}{N\left(\frac{\pi d^4}{32}\right)} = \frac{32\,TL}{N\pi d^4} \qquad \ldots(21.15\ d)$$

which is the same expression as obtained for a shaft of uniform section.

If $\beta = 2$ (*i.e.* $d_2 = 2d_1$), we get

$$\theta = \frac{7}{24}\frac{TL}{NJ_1} = \frac{7}{24}\frac{TL}{N\left(\frac{\pi d_1^4}{32}\right)} = \frac{28}{3}\frac{TL}{N\pi d_1^4} \qquad ..(21.15\ e)$$

This is much less than for the case of $\beta = 1$ because of increased stiffness due to the larger diameter at end B.

21.9. NON-UNIFORM OR VARYING TORSION

Upto this stage, we have considered only *pure torsion*, which refers to the torsion of a prismatic bar subjected to torques acting only at the ends. Evidently, from the conditions of equilibrium, the end torques are equal and opposite. In the case of non *uniform torsion*, the bar need not be prismatic and the applied torques may vary along the length of the bar or shaft. Fig. 21.9

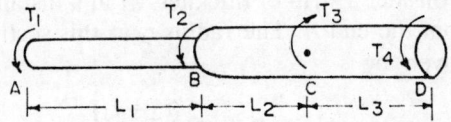

FIG. 21.9. NON-UNIFORM TORSION

shows one such case of non-uniform torsion. To analyse such cases, the total length of the bar or shaft is subdivided into different sections or segments or regions. Each region of the bar between applied torques or between changes in cross-section is in pure torsion. Hence formulae derived earlier for pure torsion can be used. For that purpose, it is necessary to determine the magnitude and direction of internal torque for each region. The torque T_i for any region i in a cross-section of the rod is equal to the algebraic sum of the moments of all the external couples acting about the line geometric axis of the rod and to one side of the cross-section being considered.

Knowing the internal torque, the maximum stress and angle of rotation for each region can be calculated. The *total angle of twist* of one end of the bar with respect to the other is obtained by summation, using the general formula :

$$\theta = \sum_{i=1}^{n} \frac{T_i L_i}{N_i J_i} \qquad \ldots(21.16)$$

The external couples can be concentrated couples T or can be distributed, uniformly or non-uniformly, along the length of the bars as shown in Fig. 21.10. In that case, we can use the following general formula for the torque in any arbitrary cross-section of the rod :

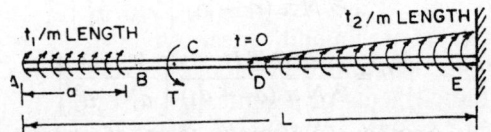

FIG. 21.10. NON-UNIFORM TORSION

$$T_i = \Sigma\,T + \Sigma\int t\,dx \qquad ...(21.17)$$

Integration is carried out along the length of each part which is subjected to distributed couple, and summation is carried out over all the parts located to one side of the cross-section under consideration. It is preferred to plot the torque diagram, indicating the variation of torque along the length.

Another interesting case of non-uniform torsion arises when a bar of *varying cross-section* is subjected to varying torque. This is illustrated in Fig. 21.11 (a). The differential angle of twist for an element of length dx [Fig. 21.11 (b)] is given by

$$d\theta = \frac{T_x \cdot dx}{N\,J_x}$$

where T_x is the torque at distance x

FIG. 21.11. BAR WITH VARYING CROSS-SECTION AND VARYING TORQUE

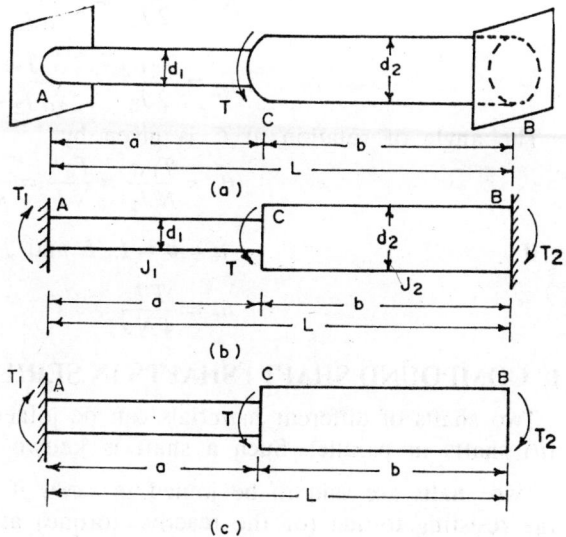

from one end and J_x is the polar moment of inertia at that location.

The total angle of twist between the ends is found from the expression

$$\theta = \int_0^L d\theta = \int_0^L \frac{T_x\,dx}{N\,J_x} \qquad ...(21.18)$$

21.10. STATICALLY INDETERMINATE TORSIONAL MEMBERS

The reactions of a torsionally loaded member which is *restrained at both ends* are dependent not only on the conditions of equilibrium but also on the relative stiffness of the various shaft segments. In solving such problems, simultaneous use is made of the equations of combined displacements and pertinent equations of statics. The former are based on non-separability of the elements of the system and represent the geometric dependences between the displacements of elements making up the system. If the redundant constraints are *absolutely rigid*, their deformation equals zero, while if they are elastic, their displacement are found by means of deformations determined by Hooke's law. If all the elements of a statically indeterminate system are subject to torsion, the elastic displacements are expressed by angles of twist.

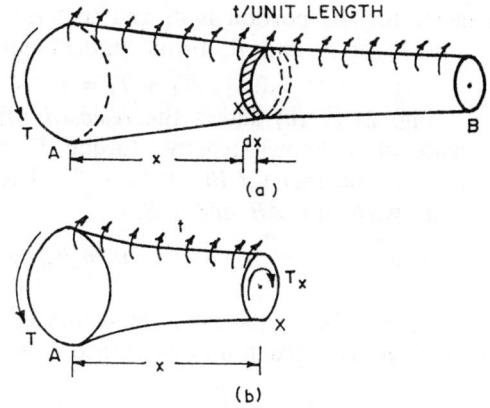

FIG. 21.12. STATICALLY INDETERMINATE SHAFT

Fig. 21.12 (a) shows a statically indeterminate shaft ACB fixed at ends A and B, and subjected to a torque T at an intermediate point C, distant a from A and b from B. The diameter for AC portion is d_1 and that for CB is d_2. Fig. 21.12 (b) shows the reactive torques T_1 and T_2 at A and B. From statical equilibrium we have

$$T_1 + T_2 = T \qquad\qquad\qquad ...(1)$$

Fig. 21.12 (c) shows the *released structure*, in which end B has been released, and in its place an unknown reactive torque T_2 has been introduced. Naturally, the torque for AC is $(T - T_2)$ and that for BC, it is $-T_2$. The total angles of twist at B is equal to the algebraic sum of twists for AB and CB.

Thus
$$\theta_B = \theta_{AC} + \theta_{CB} = \frac{(T - T_2)\,a}{N J_1} - \frac{T_2 \cdot b}{N J_2}$$

where J_1 and J_2 are the polar moments of inertia for AB and BC respectively. However, since end B is actually fixed, $\theta_B = 0$. Hence from the equation of compatibility (*i.e.* $\theta_B = 0$), we have

$$\frac{T \cdot a}{N J_1} - \frac{T_2 a}{N J_1} - \frac{T_2 b}{N J_2} = 0 \qquad\qquad ...(2)$$

Solving Eqs. (1) and (2) for T_1 and T_2, we get

$$T_1 = T\left(\frac{b J_1}{a J_2 + b J_1}\right) \quad \text{and} \quad T_2 = T\left(\frac{a J_2}{a J_2 + b J_1}\right) \qquad ...(21.19)$$

If
$$d_1 = d_2 = d \ (\textit{i.e. bar of uniform section}), \text{ we get}$$

$$T_1 = \frac{T b}{L} \quad \text{and} \quad T_2 = \frac{T a}{L} \qquad\qquad ...(21.20)$$

These equations are analogous to those of fixed beam subjected to a point load. The maximum shear stresses for each part are given by

$$f_{s_1} = \frac{T_1 d_1}{2 J_1} = \frac{T b d_1}{2\,(a J_2 + b J_1)} \qquad\qquad ...(21.12\ a)$$

and
$$f_{s_2} = \frac{T_2 d_2}{2 J_2} = \frac{T a d_2}{2\,(a J_2 + b J_1)} \qquad\qquad ...(21.12\ b)$$

The angle of rotation at C is given by

$$\theta_c = \frac{T_1 a}{N J_1} = \frac{T_2 b}{N J_2} = \frac{T a b}{N\,(a J_2 + b J_1)} \qquad\qquad ...(21.22)$$

If
$$a = b = L/2 \text{ and } J_1 = J_2 = J, \text{ we get}$$

$$\theta_c = \frac{T L}{4 N J} \qquad\qquad ...(21.22\ a)$$

21.11. COMPOUND SHAFT : SHAFTS IN SERIES AND PARALLEL

Two shafts of different materials can be joined together in two ways (*i*) shafts in series and (*ii*) shafts in parallel. Such a shaft is known as a *compound shaft*.

Two shafts are said to be joined in *series* if the driving torque is applied at one end and the resisting torque (or the reactive torque) at the other end (Fig. 21.13 *a*). For shafts in series, both the shafts carry the same torque T and the total angle of twist at the resisting end is the sum of separate angles of twist of two shafts.

Thus $\theta = \theta_1 + \theta_2 = \dfrac{T L_1}{N_1 J_1} + \dfrac{T L_2}{N_2 J_2}$

$$\qquad \ldots(21.23)$$

If both the shafts are of the same material, $N_1 = N_2 = N$

Then $\theta = \dfrac{T}{N}\left(\dfrac{L_1}{J_1} + \dfrac{L_2}{J_2}\right) \quad \ldots(21.23\ a)$

Two shafts are said to be connected in *parallel* if the torque is applied at the junction of two shafts and the reactive torques T_1 and T_2 are at the remote ends. Such an arrangement is shown in Fig. 21.13 (b). Naturally the angle of twist for both the shafts is the same

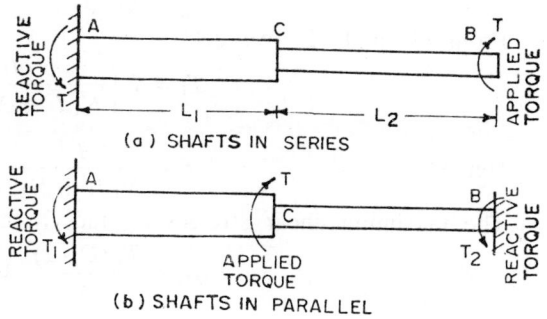

(a) SHAFTS IN SERIES

(b) SHAFTS IN PARALLEL

FIG. 21.13

$\therefore \qquad\qquad \theta_1 = \theta_2$

or $\qquad\qquad \dfrac{T_1 L_1}{N_1 J_1} = \dfrac{T_2 L_2}{N_2 J_2}$

or $\qquad\qquad \dfrac{T_1}{T_2} = \dfrac{L_2}{L_1}\cdot\dfrac{N_1}{N_2}\cdot\dfrac{J_1}{J_2} \qquad\qquad \ldots(1)\ldots(21.24)$

If both the shafts are of the same material,

$$\dfrac{T_1}{T_2} = \dfrac{L_2}{L_1}\cdot\dfrac{J_1}{J_2} \qquad\qquad \ldots(21.24\ a)$$

Also, $\qquad\qquad T_1 + T_2 = T \qquad\qquad \ldots(2)$

Thus, the value of T_1 and T_2 can be found from Eqs. (1) and (2)

21.12. SHAFT OF TWO MATERIALS : COMPOSITE SHAFT

A composite shaft is made of concentric circular torsional bars that are firmly bonded together to act as a single member. Fig. 21.14 shows such a composite shaft where a hollow tube and a core are securely bonded to act as a solid shaft. Such a shaft is statically indeterminate, since both the hollow tube and the solid core have different properties.

Let us use suffix 1 for the core and 2 for the hollow tube.

Let the composite shaft be acted upon by a total torque T. This is evidently resisted by the torque T_1 and T_2 developed in the core and the tube respectively.

Hence from the condition of statical equilibrium,

$$T = T_1 + T_2 \qquad\qquad \ldots(1)$$

Since both the parts are rigidly bonded together, they must rotate by the same amounts, *i.e.* the angle of twist must be the same. Hence from the compatibility of rotations, we have

$$\theta = \dfrac{T_1 L}{N_1 J_1} = \dfrac{T_2 L}{N_2 J_2}$$

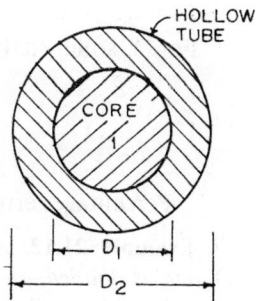

FIG. 21.14. COMPOSITE SHAFT

or $$\frac{T_1}{T_2} = \frac{N_1}{N_2} \cdot \frac{J_1}{J_2} \qquad \qquad \qquad ...(2)$$

From (1) and (2), we get

$$T_1 = T\left(\frac{N_1 J_1}{N_1 J_1 + N_2 J_2}\right) \text{ and } T_2 = T\left(\frac{N_2 J_2}{N_1 J_1 + N_2 J_2}\right) \quad ...(21.25)$$

Hence $$\theta = \frac{TL}{N_1 J_1 + N_2 J_2} \qquad \qquad \qquad ...(21.26)$$

The maximum shear stresses f_{s_1} and f_{s_2} in the core and tube are given by

$$f_{s_1} = \frac{T_1 (D_1/2)}{J_1} \text{ and } f_{s_2} = \frac{T_2 (D_2/2)}{J_2} \qquad \qquad ...(21.27)$$

Hence $$\frac{f_{s_1}}{f_{s_2}} = \frac{T_1 D_1}{T_2 D_2} \cdot \frac{J_2}{J_1} = \frac{N_1}{N_2} \cdot \frac{D_1}{D_2} \qquad \qquad ...(21.28)$$

Example 21.12. *A solid circular shaft has a radius of 100 mm at one end and 115 mm at the other end, the length of the shaft being 2 m. Calculate the percentage error committed if θ is calculated on the basis of a mean radius of 120 mm.*

Solution :

Given : $\quad r_1 = 100$ mm $(d_1 = 200$ mm$)$ and $r_2 = 115$ mm $(d_2 = 230$ mm$)$

$$L = 2 \text{ m} = 2000 \text{ mm}$$

From Eq. 21.15 (b),

$$\theta = \frac{32\,TL}{3\,N\pi\,(d_2 - d_1)} \left[\frac{1}{d_1^3} - \frac{1}{d_2^3}\right] = \frac{32}{3} \cdot \frac{T}{N} \cdot \frac{2000}{\pi\,(230 - 200)} \left[\frac{1}{(200)^3} - \frac{1}{(230)^3}\right]$$

$$= 9.69 \times 10^{-6} \frac{T}{N} \text{ radian}$$

Alternatively, from Eq. 21.15(c), $\theta = \dfrac{TL}{NJ_1}\left(\dfrac{\beta^2 + \beta + 1}{3\,\beta^3}\right)$

Here $\quad \beta = \dfrac{d_2}{d_1} = \dfrac{230}{200} = 1.15 \; ; \; J_1 = \dfrac{\pi\,d_1^4}{32} = \dfrac{\pi}{32}\,(200)^4 = 157.08 \times 10^6 \text{ mm}^4$

$\therefore \quad \theta = \dfrac{T}{N} \times \dfrac{2000}{157.08 \times 10^6}\left[\dfrac{(1.15)^2 + 1.15 + 1}{3\,(1.15)^3}\right] = 9.69 \times 10^{-6} \dfrac{T}{N} \text{ radian}$

For a solid shaft of average dia. $d = \dfrac{1}{2}\,(d_1 + d_2) = \dfrac{1}{2}\,(200 + 230) = 215$ mm

$$\theta = \frac{32\,TL}{N\pi\,d^4} = \frac{32\,T}{N} \times \frac{2000}{\pi\,(215)^4} = 9.534 \times 10^{-6} \frac{T}{N} \text{ radian}$$

$\therefore$ Percentage error $= \dfrac{9.69 - 9.534}{9.69} \times 100 = \textbf{1.61 \%}$

Example 21.13. *A solid steel shaft ABCD, shown in Fig. 21.15 turns freely in a bearing at D and is loaded at B and C by torques $T_1 = 2500$ N-m and $T_2 = 1500$ N-m. The shaft is connected in the gear box at A to gears that are temporarily locked in position. Determine (a) maximum shear stress in each part and (b) the angle of twist at end D. Take $N = 0.8 \times 10^5$ N/mm² and diameter of shaft as 80 mm.*

Solution :

$T_{ab} = T_1 + T_2 = 2500 + 1500$

$= 4000$ N-m $= 4 \times 10^6$ N-mm

$T_{bc} = T_2 = 1500$ N-m

$= 1.5 \times 10^6$ N-mm

$T_{cd} = 0$. The torque diagram is shown in Fig. 21.15 (c)

(a) Maximum shear stress in each part

$f_{sab} = \dfrac{16\, T_{ab}}{\pi\, d^3} = \dfrac{16 \times 4 \times 10^6}{\pi\,(80)^3}$

$= \mathbf{39.79\ N/mm^2}$

$f_{sbc} = \dfrac{16\, T_{bc}}{\pi\, d^3} = \dfrac{16 \times 1.5 \times 10^6}{\pi\,(80)^3}$

$= \mathbf{14.92\ N/mm^2}$

$f_{scd} = \dfrac{16\, T_{cd}}{\pi\, d^3} = 0$

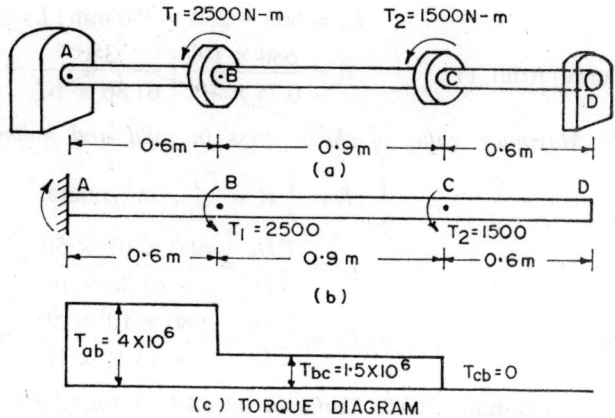

(c) TORQUE DIAGRAM

FIG. 21.15

(b) Angle of twist at end D

The angle of twist at the end D is given by

$$\theta_D = \sum_{i=1}^{n} \frac{T_i\, L_i}{N_i\, J_i}, \ \text{where } J_i = J = \frac{\pi}{32} d^4 = \frac{\pi}{32}(80)^4 = 402.1 \times 10^4\, mm^4$$

or

$$\theta_D = \frac{1}{NJ}\left[T_{ab}.L_{ab} + T_{bc}.L_{bc} + T_{cd}.L_{cd} \right]$$

$$= \frac{1}{0.8 \times 10^5 \times 402.1 \times 10^4}\left[4 \times 10^6 \times 600 + 1.5 \times 10^6 \times 900 + 0 \right]$$

$$= 0.01165 \text{ radian} = \mathbf{0.668°}$$

Example 21.14. *A 50 mm diameter steel bar, 60 cm long has a 30 mm hole bored axially through it for a distance of 25 cm from one end. The bar is then subjected to a torque of 680 N-m. Find (a) the total angle of twist in degrees (b) the maximum value of shear stress in the hollow and solid parts respectively. Take* $N = 0.75 \times 10^5\, N/mm^2$.

Solution : The single shaft is now converted into two shafts :

(i) solid shaft of 50 mm diameter and of 350 mm length, and (ii) hollow shaft of 30 mm internal dia and 50 mm external dia. and of 250 mm length. Both the shafts are evidently *series connected*. Let us use suffix *s* for solid shaft and *h* for hollow shaft.

(a) Total angle of twist

$$\theta = \theta_s + \theta_h = \frac{T L_s}{N J_s} + \frac{T L_h}{N J_h} = \frac{T}{N}\left(\frac{L_s}{J_s} + \frac{L_h}{J_h} \right) \qquad ...(1)$$

Now

$$J_s = \frac{\pi}{32} D^4 = \frac{\pi}{32}(50)^4 = 61.36 \times 10^4\, mm^4$$

$$J_h = \frac{\pi}{32}(D^4 - d^4) = \frac{\pi}{32}\left[(50)^4 - (30)^4\right] = 53.41 \times 10^4 \text{ mm}^4$$

$$L_s = 600 - 250 = 350 \text{ mm}; L_h = 250 \text{ mm}$$

Hence from (1), $\theta = \frac{680 \times 10^3}{0.75 \times 10^5}\left[\frac{350}{61.36 \times 10^4} + \frac{250}{53.41 \times 10^4}\right] = 0.009416 \text{ radian} = \mathbf{0.54°}$

(b) Maximum value of shear stress in solid and hollow parts

$$f_s = \frac{T}{J}R = \frac{TD}{2J}, \text{ in general}$$

$$\therefore \qquad f_{ss} = \frac{TD_s}{2J_s} = \frac{680 \times 10^3 \times 50}{2 \times 61.36 \times 10^4} = \mathbf{27.71 \text{ N/mm}^2}$$

and $f_{sh} = \frac{TD_h}{2J_h} = \frac{680 \times 10^3 \times 50}{2 \times 53.41 \times 10^4} = \mathbf{31.83 \text{ N/mm}^2}$

Example 21.15. *Shafts in parallel. A round steel rod ACB, 1.8 m long, is firmly held at its ends A and B. AC is 1.2 m and 50 mm dia; BC is 0.6 m and 40 mm dia. At C, a twisting couple of moment 580 N-m is applied. Find the moment of resisting couples at A and B and the maximum shear stresses in parts AC and BC of the rod.*

Solution :

Refer Fig. 21.16. Since torque is being applied at the junction, both the shafts are being arranged in parallel. Let us use suffix 1 for section *AC* and suffix 2 for the section *CB*.

(a) Resisting couples at end A and B

Now, $\theta_1 = \theta_2$

$$\therefore \qquad \frac{T_1 L_1}{N J_1} = \frac{T_2 L_2}{N J_2}$$

FIG. 21.16

or $T_1 = \frac{J_1}{J_2}\cdot\frac{L_2}{L_1}T_2 = \left(\frac{50}{37.5}\right)^4 \times \frac{0.6}{1.2}T_2 = 1.5802\,T_2$ ...(1)

Also, for equilibrium, $T_1 + T_2 = T = 580$

$$\therefore \qquad 1.5802\,T_2 + T_2 = 580$$

From which $T_2 = \mathbf{224.78}$ N-m and $T_1 = 224.78 \times 1.5802 = \mathbf{355.22}$ N-m

(b) Maximum shear stress in parts CA and CB

In general, $f_s = \frac{TR}{J} = \frac{TD}{2J}$

$$\therefore \qquad f_{s1} = \frac{T_1 D_1}{2 J_1} = \frac{355.22 \times 10^3 \times 50}{2 \times \frac{\pi}{32}(50)^4} = \mathbf{14.47 \text{ N/mm}^2}$$

$$f_{s2} = \frac{T_2 D_2}{2 J_2} = \frac{224.78 \times 10^3 \times 37.5}{2 \times \frac{\pi}{32}(37.5)^4} = \mathbf{21.71 \text{ N/mm}^2}$$

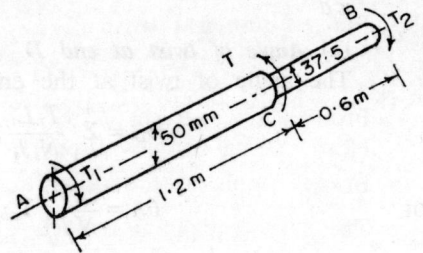

Example 21.16. *A horizontal shaft, securely fixed at each end, has a free length of 8 m. Viewed from one end of the shaft, axial couples of 40 kN-m clockwise and 50 kN-m counter clockwise act on the shaft at distance of 3.2 m and 5.5 m from the viewed end. Determine the end fixing couples in magnitude and direction and find the diameter of solid shaft for a maximum shearing stress of 65 N/mm². Also, find the position where the shaft suffers no angular twist.*

Solution :

Let $\quad T =$ fixing torque at the viewed end.

$\therefore$ Torque in the middle portion
$= (T - 40)$ kN-m

and torque at the far end
$= T - 40 + 50 = (T + 10)$ kN-m

In general, twist $\theta = \dfrac{TL}{NJ}$

Here NJ is constant throughout.

Total twist $= \Sigma\theta = \dfrac{1}{NJ}\Sigma TL$

For no resultant twist

$$\Sigma\theta = 0 = \Sigma TL = (T \times 3.2) + (T - 40) \times 2.3 + (T + 10) \times 2.5$$

From which, we get $T = 8.375$ kN-m

Hence fixing couple at one end $= T = 8.375$ kN-m

Fixing couple at the other end $= T + 10 = 8.375 + 10 = 18.375$ kN-m

The torque diagram is shown in Fig. 21.17 (*a*).

Maximum torque $= T - 40 = 8.375 - 40 = 31.625$ kN-m (numerically)

Maximum shear stress $\quad f_s = \dfrac{16\,T_{max}}{\pi D^3} = \dfrac{16 \times 31.625 \times 10^6}{\pi D^3} = \dfrac{161.06 \times 10^6}{D^3}$ N/mm²

But this is equal to 65 N/mm² (given). $\therefore \quad \dfrac{161.06 \times 10^6}{D^3} = 65$

From which, we obtain $\quad D = 135.3$ mm $\approx$ **136 mm**

The twists at ends are zero. The twist diagram is shown in Fig. 21.17 (*b*) in which, twist $ab \infty TL = 8.375 \times 3.2 = 26.8$

Also, twist $\quad cd \infty TL = 18.375 \times 2.5 = 45.94$

Let the point of zero twist be at a distance of x m from the viewed end.

$$\therefore \qquad x = 3.2 + \left(\frac{ab}{ab + cd}\right) 2.3 = 3.2 + \left(\frac{26.8}{26.8 + 45.94}\right) 2.3 = \textbf{4.047 m}$$

Example 21.17. *A circular bar AB, fixed at one end and free at the other is loaded by a uniformly distributed torque of intensity t per unit distance, along the axis of the bar, as shown*

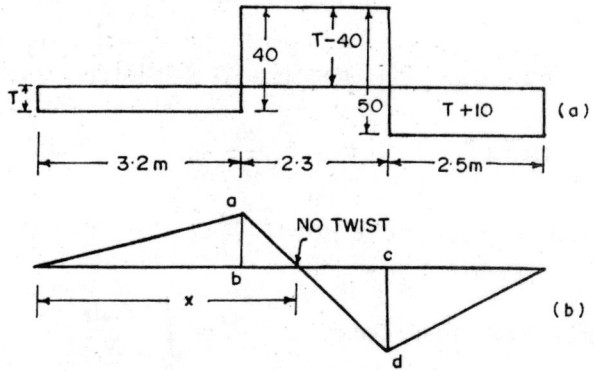

FIG. 21.17

in Fig. 21.18. Determine the strain energy stored in the bar. Taking L = 6 m, diameter of bar = 200 mm, t = 6 kN-m/m and N = 0.8 × 10⁵ N/mm², find the value of the strain energy.

Solution :

Consider a section at a distance x from the free end B. The torque T_x at that section $= t \cdot x$. Consider a length dx, where the angle of rotation is θ_x.

$\therefore$
$$dU = \frac{1}{2} T_x \cdot \theta_x \qquad ...(1)$$

But
$$\theta = \frac{TL}{NJ}, \text{ in general.}$$

Hence
$$\theta_x = \frac{T_x \cdot dx}{NJ_x} \qquad ...(2)$$

Substituting in (1), we get $dU = \dfrac{T_x^2 \, dx}{2NJ_x}$

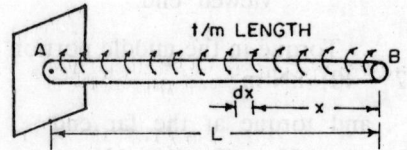

FIG. 21.18

Hence total strain energy
$$U = \int_0^L \frac{T_x^2 \, dx}{2NJ_x} \qquad ...(21.29)$$

or
$$U = \frac{1}{2NJ} \int_0^L (tx)^2 \, dx = \frac{t^2 L^3}{6NJ} \qquad ...(21.30)$$

This is the standard expression for strain energy stored in the bar subjected to uniformly distributed torque t.

Here
$$t = 6 \text{ kN-m/m} \; ; \; L = 6 \text{ m} ; N = 0.8 \times 10^5 \text{ N/mm}^2 = 80 \times 10^6 \text{ kN/m}^2$$

$$J = \frac{\pi}{32} d^4 = \frac{\pi}{32} (0.2)^4 = 1.57 \times 10^{-4} \text{ m}^4$$

$\therefore$
$$U = \frac{(6)^2 (6)^3}{6 (80 \times 10^6) (1.57 \times 10^{-4})} = 10.3 \times 10^{-2} \text{ kN-m} = \mathbf{103 \text{ N-m}} = \mathbf{103 \text{ J}}$$

(Note that $1 \text{ J} = 1$ N-m)

Example 21.18. *A shaft is subjected to torques as shown in Fig. 21.19 (a). Plot the diagram showing the variation of torque along the length of the shaft.*

Solution :

The shaft is subjected to variable torques along its length.

(i) For portion AB

This portion is subjected to uniformly distributed torque $t = 1$ kN-m/m.

$\therefore$
$$T_x = t \cdot x = 1 \cdot x \; (\curvearrowright) \qquad \text{(The variation being linear)}$$

At A,
$$x = 0. \text{ Hence } T_A = 0$$

At B,
$$x = 2 \text{ m. Hence } T_B = 1 \times 2 = 2 \text{ kN-m} \; (\curvearrowright)$$

(ii) For portion BC

This portion is subjected to a constant torsion $= 1 \times 2 = 2$ kN-m

(iii) For portion CD

At C, the shaft is subjected to a concentrated torque of 4 kN-m in the anticlockwise direction.

Now T_c (left) $= 2$ kN-m($\circlearrowright$); T_c (right) $= 2 - 4 = -2$, *i.e.* 2 kN-m ($\circlearrowleft$).

Thus, the torque changes sign at C.

The torque is constant from C to D.

(iv) For portion DE

This portion is subjected to a uniformly variable torque, having intensity $t = 0$ at D to $t = 2$ kN-m/m at E. Consider a section X at a distance x metres from D. The intensity of torque at that section is

$$t_x = \frac{2}{4}x = \frac{x}{2} \text{ kN-m/m}$$

Hence total torque at X is

$$T_x = (1 \times 2) - 4 + \frac{1}{2}x\left(\frac{x}{2}\right) = -2 + \frac{x^2}{4} \ (\circlearrowright)$$

The variation is parabolic.

At D, $x = 0$. Hence $T_D = -2$ kN-m (as earlier)

At E, $x = 4$ m. Hence $T_E = -2 + \frac{1}{4}(4)^2 = 2$ kN-m ($\circlearrowright$)

Thus, the torque changes sign in the portion DE; the torque is zero at $x = \sqrt{8}$ $= 2.828$ m from D or at 1.172 m from E.

Fig. 21.19 (b) shows the variation of torque along the length of the shaft.

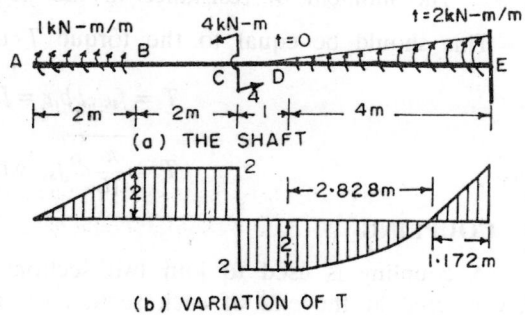

(a) THE SHAFT

(b) VARIATION OF T

FIG. 21.19

21.13. KEYS AND COUPLINGS

(A) KEYS : Power is transmitted from the rotating shaft through pulley which is keyed to the shaft. In this process, the key is also subjected to the twisting moment, and consequently, shearing stress is developed in the key.

In order to house the key between the pulley (or flange) and the shaft, a rectangular notch is cut on the circumference of the shaft, and a similar notch is cut on the inner side of the pulley (or flange), as shown in Fig. 21.20. The pulley is placed on the shaft in such a way that the two notches form a rectangular slot into which a rectangular key is inserted.

Let l_k = length of the key

           b_k = width of the key

           f_{sk} = shear stress in the key

            r = distance of the centre of the key from the centre of the shaft $= \dfrac{d}{2}$

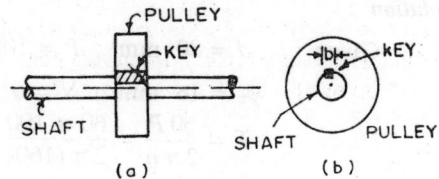

FIG. 21.20

where d is the diameter of the shaft

$\therefore$ The moment of resistance of the key $= f_{sk} . l . b . r$

This should be equal to the torque T transmitted.

$$\therefore \qquad T = f_{sk} . l b r = f_{sk} . l b \frac{d}{2} \qquad \qquad ...(21.31)$$

where $\qquad T = \dfrac{\pi}{16} d^3 f_s$, where d is the diameter of the shaft.

(B) COUPLING

A coupling is used to join two sections of a shaft. For such a connection, either a pulley is used at the end of each section of the shaft or else, the ends of each section of the shaft has flanges. The pulleys are keyed to the shaft, and are inter-connected through a number of bolts, as shown in Fig. 21.21. Such a coupling is usually called a *flanged coupling*. Torque is transferred from one section of the shaft to the other section through a number of bolts ; hence the bolts are subjected to shear stress.

Let $\qquad N =$ number of bolts in the coupling

$\qquad R_b =$ radius of the circle on which bolts are arranged

$\qquad \varphi_b =$ diameter of each bolt

$\qquad f_{sb} =$ shear stress in each bolt

$\therefore$ Total torque transmitted by N bolts

$$= N \left(f_{sb} \frac{\pi}{4} \varphi_b^2 \right) R_b$$

This should be equal to the external torque be T

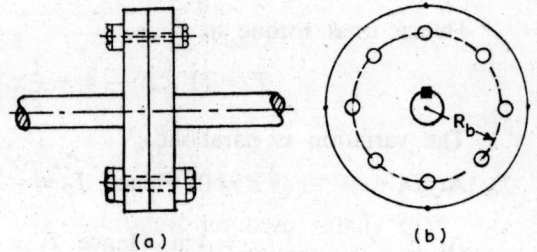

(a)   (b)

FIG. 21.21. COUPLING

$$\therefore \qquad T = f_{sb} . N R_b \frac{\pi}{4} \varphi_b^2 \qquad \qquad ...(21.32)$$

In the above expression, $T = \dfrac{\pi}{16} d^3 f_s$, where d is the diameter of the shaft.

Example 21.19. *A shaft of 80 mm diameter transmits 100 kW power at 160 r.p.m. A flanged coupling is keyed to the shaft by means of a key 75 mm long and 25 mm wide. The coupling has 6 bolts of 16 mm diameter, symmetrically arranged along a bolt circle of 250 mm diameter. Determine the shearing stresses in the shaft, the key and the bolts of the coupling.*

Solution :

Given $\qquad d = 80$ mm ; $P = 100$ kW ; $n = 160 ; b = 25$ mm, $l = 75$ mm

$\qquad \qquad \varphi_b = 16$ mm ; $N = 6 ; R_b = 250/2 = 125$ mm

$\qquad \qquad T = \dfrac{60 P}{2 \pi n} = \dfrac{60 \times 100}{2 \pi (160)} = 5.9683$ kN-m $= 5.9683 \times 10^6$ N-mm

$\qquad \qquad f_s = \dfrac{16 T}{\pi d^3} = \dfrac{16 \times 5.9683 \times 10^6}{\pi (80)^3} = \mathbf{59.37 \, N/mm^2}$

$$f_{sk} = \frac{T}{l b r} = \frac{T}{l b \frac{d}{2}} = \frac{5.9683 \times 10^6}{75 \times 25 \times 40} = \mathbf{79.48 \ N/mm^2}$$

and
$$f_{sb} = \frac{T}{N R_b \frac{\pi}{4} \varphi_b^2} = \frac{5.9683 \times 10^6}{6 \times 125 \times \frac{\pi}{4} (16)^2} = \mathbf{39.58 \ N/mm^2}$$

Example 21.20. *A 100 mm dia. shaft transmits power at maximum shear stress of 70 N/mm², while the stress in key and coupling bolts is 60 N/mm² and 50 N/mm² respectively. The coupling has 4 bolts arranged symmetrically along a circle of 300 mm diameter. Determine (a) diameter of the bolts, and (b) length of the key if its width is 30 mm.*

Solution :

Given
$$d = 100 \ \text{mm}; \ f_s = 70 \ \text{N/mm}^2 \ ; \ f_{sk} = 60 \ \text{N/mm}^2 ; f_{sb} = 50 \ \text{N/mm}^2$$
$$N = 4 ; R_b = 300/2 = 150 \ \text{mm} ; b = 30 \ \text{mm}$$
$$T = f_s . \frac{\pi}{16} D^3 = 70 \times \frac{\pi}{16} (100)^3 = 13.744 \times 10^6 \ \text{N-mm}$$

Now
$$l = \frac{T}{f_{sk} . b . r} = \frac{T}{f_{sk} . b . \frac{d}{2}} = \frac{13.744 \times 10^6}{60 \times 30 \times 50} = \mathbf{152.7 \ mm}$$

Also,
$$T = f_{sb} N . R_b \frac{\pi}{4} \varphi_b^2$$

From which
$$\varphi_b = \left(\frac{4 T}{f_{sb} N . R_b \pi} \right)^{\frac{1}{2}} = \left(\frac{4 \times 13.744 \times 10^6}{50 \times 4 \times 150 \times \pi} \right)^{\frac{1}{2}} = \mathbf{24.15 \ mm}$$

21.14. COMBINED BENDING AND TORSION

The shafts, used for transmitting power are also subjected to bending moment M, in addition to the torsion. The bending moment may be induced due to the following (*i*) self weight of the shaft, acting as U.D.L. (*ii*) weights of pulleys and couplings, acting as concentrated loads and (*iii*) lateral pulls exerted by belts and rope drives. Let us study the combined effect of twisting moments T and bending moment M, acting at a section of the shaft.

Consider point P, in the shaft, at a radial distance r from the centre and at a distance y from the N.A.

The shear stress (q) due to torsion is given by

$$q = \frac{T}{J} r \qquad \ldots(1)$$

The bending stress
$$f = \frac{M}{I} y \qquad \ldots(2)$$

The shear stress resulting from bending forces at the plane is given by

$$q' = \frac{F}{I z} (A \bar{y}) \qquad \ldots(3)$$

where F is the S.F. at the section.

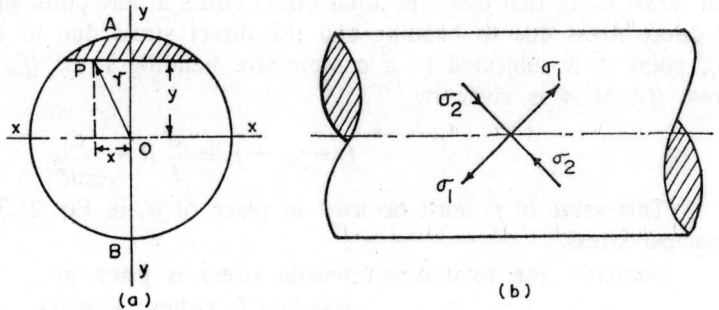

(a)

(b)

FIG. 21.22

Thus, the component stresses at any point in the shaft are given by

(i) Shear stress q due to torsion

(ii) Bending stress f (tensile or compressive)

and   (iii) Shear stress q' due to bending forces.

Out of these three component stresses, q and f are maximum at the surface points A or B, and the shear stress q' there is zero. Hence at surface points A and B, the stresses will be

(i) *Shear stress*   (f_s) due to torsion, the magnitude of which is given by

$$f_s = \frac{T}{J}R = \frac{16\,T}{\pi\,d^3} \qquad \qquad ...(4)$$

and   (ii) the bending stress (f_b), the magnitude of which is given by

$$f_b = \frac{M}{I}R = \frac{32\,M}{\pi\,d^3} \qquad \qquad ...(5)$$

Hence the principal stresses are

$$\sigma = \frac{f_b}{2} \pm \sqrt{\frac{f_b^2}{4} + f_s^2} = \frac{16}{\pi\,d^3}\left[M \pm \sqrt{M^2 + T^2}\right] \qquad ...(21.33)$$

The position of the principal planes are given by

$$\tan 2\theta = \frac{2f_s}{f_b} = \frac{T}{M} \qquad \qquad ...(21.34)$$

The principal stresses σ_1 and σ_2 will be of opposite sign, as shown in Fig. 21.22 (b).

Note : In the case of very short shaft, B.M. is very small. Hence the bending stress f_b is quite small in comparison to the component shear stress q' caused due to S.F. For such cases the maximum principal stresses may occur within the shaft. Usually, however, the maximum principal stress is at the circumference, given by Eq. 21.33.

21.15. EFFECT OF END THRUST

Sometimes, a shaft may also be subjected to end thrust acting axially along the shaft. In that case, the shaft will also be subjected to constant compressive stress (f_o) due to the end thrust C. In that case, the total direct stress at any point in the shaft will be the resultant of direct stress due to bending and the direct stress due to the thrust. Thus, in Fig. 21.22 (a), point A is subjected to a compressive bending stress ($f_{bc} = f_b$); hence total compressive stress (f_c) at A is given by

$$f_c = f_{bc} + f_o = \frac{M}{I}R + \frac{C}{\pi R^2} \qquad \qquad ...(21.35)$$

This value of f_c must be used in place of f_b, in Eq. 21.33 to calculate the compressive principal stress.

Similarly, the total direct tensile stress is given by

$$f_t = f_{bt} - f_o \quad (\text{where } f_{bt} = f_b) \qquad \qquad ...(21.36)$$

If f_t is positive, it must be used in place of f_b in Eq. 21.33 to calculate the tensile principal stress.

21.16. HYPOTHESES OF ELASTIC FAILURE

The following hypotheses are used for the design of shaft

1. Maximum principal stress hypothesis
2. Maximum principal strain hypothesis
3. Maximum shear stress hypothesis
4. Maximum elastic strain energy hypothesis

and 5. Maximum elastic shear strain energy hypothesis

1. Maximum principal stress hypothesis

Let f = stress at elastic failure in simple direct stress.

Then
$$f = \sigma_1 = \frac{16}{\pi d^3}\left[M + \sqrt{M^2 + T^2}\right] = \frac{32}{\pi d^3}\sqrt{M_e} \qquad ...(21.37)$$

where
$$M_e = \frac{1}{2}\left[M + \sqrt{M^2 + T^2}\right] = \text{equivalent B.M.}$$

2. Maximum principal strain hypothesis

$$f = \sigma_1 - \frac{\sigma_2}{m} = \frac{1}{2}f_b\left(1 - \frac{1}{m}\right) + \left(1 + \frac{1}{m}\right)\sqrt{\frac{f_b^2}{4} + f_s^2} \qquad ...(21.37\ a)$$

or
$$f = \frac{16}{\pi d^3}\left[M\left(1 - \frac{1}{m}\right) + \left(1 + \frac{1}{m}\right)\sqrt{M^2 + T^2}\right] \qquad ...(21.37\ b)$$

3. Maximum shear stress hypothesis

$$q_{max} = \frac{f}{2} = \frac{\sigma_1 - \sigma_2}{2} = \sqrt{\frac{f_b^2}{4} - f_s^2} = \frac{16}{\pi d^3}\sqrt{M^2 + T^2} = \frac{16}{\pi d^3}T_e \qquad ...(21.38)$$

where
$$T_e = \sqrt{M^2 + T^2} = \text{equivalent twisting moment}$$

4. Maximum elastic strain energy hypothesis

$$f^2 = \sigma_1^2 + \sigma_2^2 - \frac{2\sigma_1\sigma_2}{m}$$

or
$$f^2 = f_b^2 + 2f_s^2\left(1 + \frac{1}{m}\right)$$

or
$$f^2 = \left(\frac{32M}{\pi d^3}\right)^2 + 2\left(\frac{16T}{\pi d^3}\right)^2\left(1 + \frac{1}{m}\right)$$

or
$$f = \frac{16}{\pi d^3}\sqrt{4M^2 + \frac{2(m+1)}{m}T^2} \qquad ...(21.39)$$

5. Maximum elastic shear strain energy hypothesis

$$f^2 = \sigma_1^2 + \sigma_2^2 - \sigma_1\sigma_2 = f_b^2 + 3f_s^2$$

or
$$f^2 = \left(\frac{32M}{\pi d^3}\right)^2 + 3\left(\frac{16T}{\pi d^3}\right)^2$$

or
$$f = \frac{16}{\pi d^3}\sqrt{4M^2 + 3T^2} \qquad ...(21.40)$$

Example 21.21. *At a certain cross-section, a shaft of 80 mm diameter is subjected to (i) a bending moment of 6 kN-m, and (b) a twisting moment of 9 kN-m. Compute the maximum direct stress induced in the section, indicating the position of the plane on which it acts. Taking 1/m = 0.3, find the stress, which acting alone, will produce the same maximum (i) strain (ii) strain energy*

Solution :

Given : $d = 80$ mm ; $M = 6$ kN-m $= 6 \times 10^6$ N-mm ; $T = 9$ kN-m $= 9 \times 10^6$ N-mm

∴ Shear stress $f_s = \dfrac{16\,T}{\pi\,d^3} = \dfrac{16 \times 9 \times 10^6}{\pi\,(80)^3} = 89.52 \text{ N/mm}^2$

Bending stress $f_b = \dfrac{32\,M}{\pi\,d^3} = \dfrac{32 \times 6 \times 10^6}{\pi\,(80)^3} = 119.34 \text{ N/mm}^2$

$$\tan 2\theta = \frac{2 f_s}{f_b} = \frac{T}{M} = \frac{9}{6} = 1.5$$

∴ $2\theta = 56°31'$; $\theta_1 = \textbf{28°9'}$ or $61°51'$ with the axis of the shaft

$\theta_2 = \textbf{118°9'}$ or $28°9'$ with the axis of the shaft

$$\sigma_1 = \frac{f_b}{2} + \sqrt{\frac{f_b^2}{4} + f_s^2} = \frac{119.34}{2} + \sqrt{\frac{(119.34)^2}{4} + (89.52)^2} = \textbf{167.2 N/mm}^2$$

$$\sigma_2 = \frac{f_b}{2} - \sqrt{\frac{f_b^2}{4} + f_s^2} = \frac{119.34}{2} - \sqrt{\frac{(119.34)^2}{4} + (89.52)^2} = -\,\textbf{47.98 N/mm}^2$$

(i) For maximum strain, we have

$$f = Ee = \sigma_1 - \frac{1}{m}\,\sigma_2 = 167.2 + 47.98 \times 0.3 = \textbf{181.6 N/mm}^2$$

(ii) For maximum strain energy, we have

$$f^2 = \sigma_1^2 + \sigma_2^2 - \frac{2\,\sigma_1\,\sigma_2}{m}$$

$$= (167.2)^2 + (-47.98)^2 + (2 \times 167.2 \times 47.98 \times 0.3) = 35071$$

∴ $f = \textbf{187.3 N/mm}^2$

Example 21.22. *A circular shaft, transmitting 50 kW of power at 120 r.p.m, is supported in bearings that are 4 metres apart. At 1.5 m from one bearing, it carries a pulley which exerts a transverse load of 16 kN on the shaft. Determine the suitable diameter of the shaft if (a) the maximum direct stress is not to exceed 120 N/mm², (b) the maximum intensity of shear stress is not to exceed 60 N/mm², (c) the stress which acting alone would produce the same maximum strain, is not to exceed 120 N/mm², and (d) the direct stress which acting alone would produce the same maximum strain energy is not to exceed 120 N/mm². Take 1/m = 0.3.*

Solution :

$$T = \frac{60\,P}{2\,\pi\,n} = \frac{60 \times 50}{2\,\pi\,(120)} = 3.9789 \text{ kN-m} = 3.9789 \times 10^6 \text{ N-mm}$$

$$M = \frac{W\,a\,b}{L} = \frac{16 \times 1.5 \times 2.5}{4} = 15 \text{ kN-m} = 15 \times 10^6 \text{ N-mm}$$

(i) Maximum principal stress criterion

$$f = \frac{16}{\pi d^3} \left[M + \sqrt{M^2 + T^2} \right]$$

$\therefore \qquad d^3 = \frac{16}{\pi \times 120} \left[15 + \sqrt{(15)^2 + (3.9789)^2} \right] 10^6 = 1.2953 \times 10^6$

$\therefore \qquad d = \textbf{109}$ mm

(ii) Maximum shear stress criterion

$$q_{max} = \frac{16}{\pi d^3} \sqrt{M^2 + T^2}$$

or $\qquad d^3 = \frac{16}{\pi \times 60} \left[\sqrt{(15)^2 + (3.9789)^2} \right] \times 10^6 = 1.3173 \times 10^6$

$\therefore \qquad d = \textbf{109.6 mm}$

(iii) Maximum strain criterion

$$f = \frac{16}{\pi d^3} \left[M \left(1 - \frac{1}{m} \right) + \left(1 + \frac{1}{m} \right) \sqrt{M^2 + T^2} \right]$$

or $\qquad d^3 = \frac{16}{\pi (120)} \left[(1 - 0.3) \, 15 + (1 + 0.3) \sqrt{(15)^2 + (3.9789)^2} \right] \times 10^6$

$$= 1.3019 \times 10^6$$

$\therefore \qquad d = \textbf{109.2 mm}$

(iv) Maximum strain energy criterion

$$f = \frac{16}{\pi d^3} \sqrt{4 M^2 + \frac{2 (m + 1)}{m} T^2}$$

or $\qquad d^3 = \frac{16}{\pi (120)} \left[\sqrt{4 (15)^2 + 2 (1 + 0.3) (3.9789)^2} \right] \times 10^6 = 1.3020 \times 10^6$

$\therefore \qquad d = \textbf{109.2 mm}$

Hence adopt the diameter of shaft as **110 mm**

Example 21.23. *A propeller shaft 160 mm external diameter and 80 mm internal diameter transmits 1000 kW of power at 100 r.p.m. In addition, it subjected to a B.M. of 8 kN-m and an end thrust of 120 kN. Find (i) the principal stresses and their planes (ii) the maximum shear stress and its plane, (iii) the stress which acting alone would produce the same maximum strain. Take 1/m = 0.3.*

Solution :

Given $\qquad D = 160$ mm ; $d = 80$ mm; $P = 1000$ kW ; $n = 100$ r.p.m.

$M = 8$ kN-M $= 8 \times 10^6$ N-mm ; $C = 120$ kN $= 120 \times 10^3$ N

$A = \frac{\pi}{4} (160^2 - 80^2) = 15080$ mm^2

$$Z = \frac{\pi}{32}\left(\frac{D^4 - d^4}{D}\right) = \frac{\pi}{32}\frac{(160)^4 - (80)^4}{160} = 376991 \text{ mm}^4$$

$$\text{Torsional section modulus} = \frac{\pi}{16}\frac{D^4 - d^4}{d} = \frac{\pi}{16}\frac{(160)^4 - (80)^4}{160} = 753982 \text{ mm}^4$$

$$f_o = \frac{C}{A} = \frac{120 \times 10^3}{15080} = 7.96 \text{ N/mm}^2$$

$$f_b = \frac{M}{Z} = \frac{8 \times 10^6}{376991} = 21.22 \text{ N/mm}^2$$

$\therefore$ Max. compressive direct stress $= f_c = 7.96 + 21.22 = 29.18 \text{ N/mm}^2$

$$T = \frac{60\,P}{2\,\pi\,n} = \frac{60 \times 1000}{2\,\pi\,(100)} = 95.493 \text{ kN-m} = 95.493 \times 10^6 \text{ N-mm}$$

$\therefore$ \qquad Max. shear stress, $f_s = \dfrac{95.493 \times 10^6}{753982} = 126.65 \text{ N/mm}^2$

(i) Principal stresses

$$\sigma_1 = \frac{f_c}{2} + \sqrt{\left(\frac{f_c}{2}\right)^2 + f_s^2} = \frac{29.18}{2} + \sqrt{\left(\frac{29.18}{2}\right)^2 + (126.65)^2}$$

$$= 14.59 + 127.49 = \mathbf{142.08 \text{ N/mm}^2} \text{ (comp.)}$$

$$\sigma_2 = 14.59 - 127.49 = -112.9 \text{ } i.e. \text{ } \mathbf{112.9 \text{ N/mm}^2} \text{ (tensile)}$$

(ii) Maximum shear stress intensity

$$= \sqrt{\left(\frac{29.18}{2}\right)^2 + (126.25)^2} = \mathbf{127.49 \text{ N/mm}^2}$$

(iii) Stress to give maximum strain

$$f = \sigma_1 - \frac{1}{m}\sigma_2 = 142.08 + 0.3 \times 112.9 = \mathbf{175.95 \text{ N/mm}^2}$$

21.17. ADDITIONAL ILLUSTRATIVE EXAMPLES

Example 21.24. *Derive an expression for the allowable twisting moment for a thin walled tube. Also, derive an approximate expression for the strength weight ratio for such a tube. Take f_s as the allowable shear stress. It is assumed that the tube does not buckle.*

Solution :

Thickness of the wall of the tube $= t = \dfrac{D - d}{2}$; outer radius of tube $= R$

where \qquad $D =$ outer diameter $= 2\,R$ and $d =$ inner diameter $= 2\,(R - t)$

$\therefore$ \qquad $J = \dfrac{\pi}{32}(D^4 - d^4) = \dfrac{\pi}{32}\left[(2\,R)^4 - 2^4\,(R - t)^4\right] = \dfrac{\pi}{2}\left[R^4 - (R - t)^4\right]$

$$= \frac{\pi}{2}\left[4\,R^3\,t - 6\,R^2\,t^2 + 6\,R\,t^3 - t^4\right] = \frac{\pi}{2}\,R^4\left[4\,\frac{t}{R} - 6\left(\frac{t}{R}\right)^2 + 6\left(\frac{t}{R}\right)^3 - \left(\frac{t}{R}\right)^4\right]$$

For a thin tube, $\dfrac{t}{R}$ is quite small and hence higher power of $\dfrac{t}{R}$ can be neglected

$$\therefore \qquad J \approx 2\pi R^3 t \qquad\qquad ...(21.31)$$

Again, $\qquad\qquad T = \dfrac{J}{R}\cdot f_s = 2\pi R^2 t f_s \qquad\qquad ...(21.32)$

Also, area of cross-section, $A = \pi\left[R^2 - (R-t)^2\right] = \pi\left[2Rt - t^2\right]$

$$= \pi R^2\left[\dfrac{2t}{R} - \left(\dfrac{t}{R}\right)^2\right]$$

Neglecting higher powers of $\dfrac{t}{R}$, we get $A \approx 2\pi r t$

Let γ be the unit weight of the material.

$\therefore$ Weight of tube of length $L = W = A L \cdot \gamma = 2\pi R t L \gamma$

$$\therefore \quad \textit{Strength-weight ratio} \ = \dfrac{T}{W} = \dfrac{2\pi R^2 t f_s}{2\pi R t L \gamma} = \dfrac{R f_s}{L\gamma} \qquad\qquad ...(21.41)$$

which is the required expression.

Example 21.25. *A 40 mm diameter circular shaft is provided with enlarged portions A and B as shown in Fig. 21.23. On to the enlarged portion, a steel tube of 2 mm thickness is shrunk. While the shrinking process is going on, the 40 mm shaft is held twisted by a couple of magnitude of 400 N-m. When the tube is firmly set on the shaft, this twisting couple is removed. Calculate what twisting couple is left on the shaft, the shaft and tube being made of the same material.*

Solution :

Let us use suffix 1 for the shaft and 2 for the tube.

For the shaft, $\quad J_1 = \dfrac{\pi}{32}(40)^4 = 251327 \text{ mm}^4$

For the tube, $\quad J_2 = \dfrac{\pi}{32}\left\{(74)^4 - (70)^4\right\}$

$$= 586749 \text{ mm}^4$$

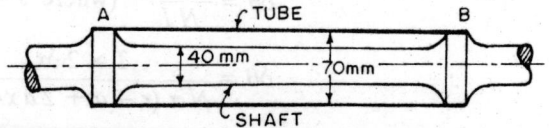

FIG. 21.23

Let $\qquad \theta_1 =$ initial angle of twist in the shaft

$$\therefore \qquad \dfrac{N\theta_1}{L} = \dfrac{T_1}{J_1} = \dfrac{400\times 10^3}{251327}$$

or $\qquad\qquad \theta_1 = 1.592 \dfrac{L}{N} \qquad\qquad ...(1)$

Final condition Let $\theta_1' =$ residual angle of twist in the shaft

$\qquad\qquad \theta_2' =$ residual angle of twist in the tube

$\qquad\qquad T =$ residual twisting couple on the shaft

$$\therefore \qquad T = \dfrac{N\theta_1' J_1}{L} = \dfrac{N\theta_2' J_2}{L}$$

$$\therefore \qquad \theta_1' = \theta_2' \cdot \frac{J_2}{J_1} = \theta_2' \frac{586749}{251327} = 2.335\,\theta_2' \qquad\qquad \ldots(2)$$

But from compatibility, $\theta_1' + \theta_2' = \theta_1$

or $\qquad\qquad 2.335\,\theta_2' + \theta_2' = 1.592\,\dfrac{L}{N} \quad$ (where $\theta_2' = \dfrac{TL}{NJ_2}$)

or $\qquad\qquad 3.335 \left[\dfrac{TL}{NJ_2} \right] = 1.592\,\dfrac{L}{N}$

From which, $\qquad T = \dfrac{1.592}{3.335} J_2 = \dfrac{1.592}{3.335} \times 586749 = 280091 \ \text{N-mm}$

$$\approx \textbf{280.1 \ N-m}$$

Example 21.26. *A shaft tapers uniformly from a radius* $(r + a)$ *at one end to* $(r - a)$ *at the other. If it is under the action of an axial torque* T *and* $a = 0.1\,r$, *find the percentage error in the angle of twist for a given length when calculated on the assumption of a constant radius* r. *(U.L.)*

Solution :

Let $\qquad L =$ length of the shaft

Change in radius $= (r + a) - (r - a) = 2\,a$, in a length L.

Consider a section at a distance x from the small end.

Radius at this section is, $r_x = r - a + \dfrac{2\,a\,x}{L}$

Angle of twist of a length δx is given by

$$\delta\theta = \frac{T \cdot \delta x}{NJ} \quad \left(\text{where } J = \frac{\pi}{32} d^4 = \frac{\pi}{32}(2\,r)^4 = \frac{\pi}{2} r^4, \text{ in general }\right)$$

$$\therefore \qquad \delta\theta = \frac{T \times 2\,\delta x}{N\pi\,(r - a + 2\,a\,x/L)^4}$$

$\therefore$ Total angle, $\qquad \theta = \dfrac{2\,T}{N\pi} \displaystyle\int_0^L \dfrac{dx}{(r - a + 2\,a\,x/L)^4} = \dfrac{2\,T}{3\,N\pi}\,\dfrac{L}{2\,a}\left[\dfrac{1}{(r-a)^3} - \dfrac{1}{(r+a)^3}\right]$

Substituting $a = 0.1\,r = \dfrac{r}{10}$, we get

$$\theta = \frac{10\,TL}{3\,N\pi\,r^4}\left[\frac{1000}{729} - \frac{1000}{1331}\right] = 2.065\,\frac{TL}{N\pi\,r^4} \qquad\qquad \ldots(1)$$

For a shaft of uniform radius r,

$$\theta = \frac{TL}{NJ} = \frac{TL}{N\left(\dfrac{\pi}{2} r^4\right)} = \frac{2\,TL}{N\pi\,r^4} \qquad\qquad \ldots(2)$$

$\therefore$ Percentage error $= \dfrac{2.065 - 2}{2.065} \times 100 = \textbf{3.15\,\%}$

Example 21.27. *A solid alloy shaft 60 mm diameter is to be coupled in series with a hollow steel shaft of the same external diameter. Find the internal diameter of the steel shaft if the angle of twist per unit length is to be 75% of that of the alloy shaft. Determine the speed at which the shafts are to be driven to transmit 400 kW, if the limits of shearing stress are to 60 N/mm² and 80 N/mm² in alloy and steel respectively. Take $N_{steel} = 2.2\, N_{alloy}$.*

Solution :

Let us use suffix *s* for steel shaft and *a* for alloy shaft.

Angle of twist per unit length $= \dfrac{\theta}{L} = \dfrac{T}{NJ}$

$\therefore$ $$\left(\frac{T}{NJ}\right)_s = 0.75 \left(\frac{T}{NJ}\right)_a$$

or $$\frac{32\,T}{\pi\,(60^4 - d^4)} = \frac{0.75 \times 2.2 \times 32\,T}{\pi\,(60)^4}$$

or $$12960000 - d^4 = \frac{12960000}{0.75 \times 2.2} = 7854545$$

From which $\quad\quad d = \mathbf{47.53\ mm}$

Again, $\quad\quad \dfrac{f_s}{D/2} = \dfrac{N\theta}{L}$

$\therefore$ $$\frac{f_{ss}}{f_{sa}} = \left(\frac{N_s}{N_s}\right)\left(\frac{D_s}{D_a}\right)\frac{(\theta/L)_s}{(\theta/L)_a}$$

But $\quad\quad D_s = D_a,\ \left(\dfrac{\theta}{L}\right)_s = 0.7 \left(\dfrac{\theta}{L}\right)_a \quad$ and $\ N_s = 2.2\,N_a$

$\therefore$ $$\frac{f_{ss}}{f_{sa}} = 2.2 \times 1 \times 0.7 = 1.54$$

The limits of shearing stresses are 80 N/mm² in steel and 60 N/mm² in alloy, but the actual maximum stresses must be 80 N/mm² in steel and $80/1.54 = 51.95$ N/mm² in alloy.

Now, for the solid shaft, $T = f_s \cdot \dfrac{\pi D^3}{16} = \dfrac{51.95 \times \pi\,(60)^3}{16} = 2203277$ N-mm $= 2.203$ kN-m

Now $$P = \frac{2\pi N T}{60}$$

or $$n = \frac{60\,P}{2\pi\,T} = \frac{60 \times 400}{2\pi\,(2.203)} = \mathbf{1734}\ \text{r.p.m.}$$

Example 21.28. *A gun-metal sleeve is fixed securely to a steel shaft and the compound shaft is subjected to a torque. If the torque on the sleeve is twice that on the shaft, find the ratio of external diameter of sleeve to diameter of the shaft.*

If the limits of shearing stress in the gun-metal and steel are 45 and 80 N/mm² respectively, find the torque that may be transmitted by the compound shaft when the steel shaft diameter is 50 mm . Take $N_{steel} = 2.5\, N_{gm}$.

(U.L.)

Solution :

Let us use suffix s for steel shaft and suffix g for the gun metal sleeve. Also, let d be the external diameter of the steel shaft and D be the external diameter of the gunmetal sleeve. The internal diameter of the gun metal sleeve is evidently equal to d.

Now
$$\frac{\theta}{L} = \frac{T}{JN}, \text{ in general}$$

Since both the steel shaft and gun metal sleeve are securely fixed, θ/L is the same for both.

$$\therefore \qquad \frac{T_s}{J_s N_s} = \frac{T_g}{J_g N_g}$$

or
$$\frac{J_g}{J_s} = \frac{T_g}{T_s} \cdot \frac{N_s}{N_g} = 2 \times 2.5 = 5$$

or
$$\frac{\dfrac{\pi}{32}(D^4 - d^4)}{\dfrac{\pi}{32} d^4} = 5$$

or
$$D^4 - d^4 = 5 \, d^4$$

Giving
$$\frac{D}{d} = (6)^{\frac{1}{4}} = 1.5651$$

Again
$$\frac{f_{sg}}{f_{ss}} = \frac{\left(\dfrac{TR}{J}\right)_g}{\left(\dfrac{TR}{J}\right)_s} = \frac{\left(\dfrac{TD}{2J}\right)_g}{\left(\dfrac{JD}{2J}\right)_s} = \left(\frac{T_s}{T_s}\right)\left(\frac{D}{d}\right)\left(\frac{J_s}{J_g}\right)$$

or
$$\frac{f_{sg}}{f_{ss}} = \left(\frac{T_g}{T_s}\right)\left(\frac{D}{d}\right)\left(\frac{d^4}{D^4 - d^4}\right) = (2)(1.5651)\left(\frac{1}{5}\right) = 0.62604$$

or
$$\frac{f_{ss}}{f_{sg}} \approx 1.6$$

If the maximum stress in gun metal = 45, corresponding maximum steel in steel will be = $1.6 \times 45 = 72 \text{ N/mm}^2$, which is less than permissible value of 80 N/mm^2.

Now torque carried by steel shaft $= \frac{J}{R} f_{ss} = \frac{\pi}{16}(50)^3 \times 72 \times 10^{-3} = 1767$ N-m.

Hence total torque of composite shaft = $(2 + 1) \times 1767 = $ **5301** N-m.

Example 21.29. *A solid circular shaft which transmits 300 metric H.P. at 150 r.p.m. is to be replaced by a hollow shaft of equal weight and of the same material, having the bore equal to half the external diameter. If the horse power transmitted is to remain unaltered, find the percentage change in the speed of the shaft. The maximum shear stress in the shaft is not to exceed 66.5 N/mm².*

Solution :

Let D_s = diameter of solid shaft

D_H = outer diameter of hollow shaft

and d_H = inner dia. of hollow shaft = $\dfrac{D_H}{2}$

(a) Diameter of solid shaft

$$T = \frac{J}{R} f_s = \frac{\pi D_s^4}{32} \times \frac{2}{D_s} \times 66.5 = 13.057 \, D_s^3 \text{ (N-mm)} \qquad ...(1)$$

Now
$$T = \frac{60 \, P}{2 \pi n} = \frac{60 \, (300 \times 0.75)}{2 \pi \, (150)} \text{ kN-m (where } P = 300 \times 0.75 \text{ kW)}$$

$$= 14.324 \text{ kN-m} = 14.324 \times 10^6 \text{ N-mm} \qquad ...(2)$$

Equating (1) and (2), we get $13.057 \, D_s^3 = 14.324 \times 10^6$

From which $D_s = 103.2$ mm

(b) Dimensions of hollow shaft

Since the weights are the same, we have

$$\frac{\pi}{4} D_s^2 L = \frac{\pi}{4} L \, (D_H^2 - d_H^2) = \frac{\pi}{4} L \left[D_H^2 - (0.5 \, D_H)^2 \right]$$

or
$$0.75 \, D_H^2 = (103.2)^2$$

From which $D_H = 119.2$ mm and $d_H = \dfrac{119.2}{2} = 59.6$ mm

(c) Change in speed

$$T = \frac{J}{R} f_s = \frac{\pi}{32} \frac{D_H^4 - d_H^4}{D_H} \times 2 \times 66.5 = \frac{\pi}{32} \frac{(119.2)^4 - (59.6)^4}{119.2} \times 2 \times 66.5$$

$$= 20.73 \times 10^6 \text{ N-mm} = 20.73 \text{ kN-m}$$

Now
$$P = \frac{2 \pi n \, T}{60} \quad \text{or} \quad n = \frac{60 \, P}{2 \pi \, T} = \frac{60 \, (300 \times 0.75)}{2 \pi \, (20.73)} = 103.56 \text{ r.p.m.}$$

$\therefore$ Change in speed $= \dfrac{150 - 103.56}{150} \times 100 = 30.9 \%$

Example 21.30. *A composite shaft consists of a steel rod of 80 mm diameter surrounded by a closely fitting tube of brass. Find the outside diameter of the brass tube when a torque of 2000 N-m is applied on the composite shaft and shared equally by the two materials. Take N for steel as $= 0.84 \times 10^5 \, N/mm^2$ and N for brass as $0.42 \times 10^5 \, N/mm^2$. Also, determine the common angles of twist in a length of 5 metres.*

Solution :

Given : outer diameter of steel rod $= D_s = 80$ mm

Let us use suffix s for steel rod and suffix b for the brass tube

D_b = outer diameter of brass tube (to be determined)

d_b = inner diameter of brass tube $= D_s = 80$ mm

Torque $\quad T = 2000$ N-m; $T_s = T_b = \dfrac{2000}{2} = 1000$ N-m

(a) Outside diameter of brass tube

In general, $\quad \dfrac{T}{J} = \dfrac{N \theta}{L} \quad \text{or} \quad \theta = \dfrac{T L}{N J}$

$$\therefore \qquad \frac{T_b L_b}{N_b J_b} = \frac{T_s L_s}{N_s J_s} \ (\text{But } T_b = T_s \text{ and } L_b = L_s)$$

$$\therefore \qquad N_b J_b = N_s J_s$$

or $$\qquad J_b = \frac{N_s}{N_b} . J_s$$

or $$\qquad \frac{\pi}{32}(D_b^4 - 80^4) = \frac{0.84 \times 10^5}{0.42 \times 10^5} \times \frac{\pi}{32}(80)^4$$

or $$\qquad D_b^4 - 40.96 \times 10^6 = 2 \times 40.96 \times 10^6$$

or $$\qquad D_b^4 = 3 \times 40.96 \times 10^6, \text{ from which } D_b = \textbf{105.3 mm}$$

(b) Common angle of twist

$$\theta = \theta_s = \frac{T_s L_s}{N_s J_s} = \frac{(1000 \times 10^3)(5000)}{0.84 \times 10^5 \times \frac{\pi}{32}(80)^4} = \textbf{0.0148 radian}$$

Check : $$\qquad \theta_b = \frac{T_b L_b}{N_b J_b} = \frac{(1000 \times 10^3)(5000)}{0.42 \times 10^5 \times \frac{\pi}{32}\left[(105.3)^4 - (80)^4\right]} = \textbf{0.0148 radian}$$

Hence $$\qquad \theta = \theta_b = \theta_s = \textbf{0.0148 radian} = \textbf{0.847}°$$

Example 21.31. *A shaft ACB of 1 m length and 100 mm external diameter is bored, for a part of its length AC to 50 mm diameter and for the remaining length CB to 75 mm diameter bore. If the shear stress is not to exceed 76 N/mm², find the maximum power the shaft can transmit at a speed of 240 r.p.m.*

If the angle of twist in the length of 50 mm diameter bore is equal to that in the 75 mm diameter bore, find the length of the shaft that has been bored to 50 mm and 75 mm diameters.

Solution :

Let us use suffix 1 for length *AC* and 2 for *CB*.

(a) Maximum power

$$T = \frac{\pi}{16} f_s \left(\frac{D^4 - d^4}{D}\right), \text{ in general. Since } D \text{ is}$$

the same for both the portions, safe torque will be governed by the greater value of *d*.

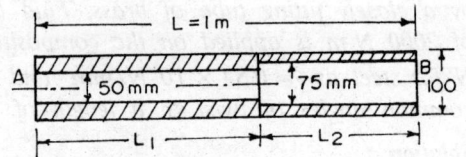

FIG. 21.24

$$\therefore \qquad T_{safe} = T_2 = \frac{\pi}{16} \times 76 \left[\frac{100^4 - 75^4}{100}\right]$$

$$= 10.2 \times 10^6 \text{ N-mm} = 10.2 \text{ kN-m}$$

Now $$\qquad P_{safe} = \frac{2\pi n T_{safe}}{60} = \frac{2\pi(240)(10.2)}{60} = \textbf{256.4 kW}$$

(b) Individual lengths

In general, $$\qquad \theta = \frac{TL}{NJ}$$

Since θ is the same for both the portions, and since T and N are also the same, we have

$$\frac{L_1}{J_1} = \frac{L_2}{J_2} \quad \therefore \quad \frac{L_1}{L_2} = \frac{J_1}{J_2} = \frac{\frac{\pi}{32}\left[100^4 - 50^4\right]}{\frac{\pi}{32}\left[100^4 - 75^4\right]} = 1.371$$

or $$L_1 = 1.371\, L_2 \qquad \qquad \qquad \text{...(1)}$$

Also, $$L_1 + L_2 = L = 1000$$

$\therefore \qquad 1.371\, L_2 + L_2 = 1000,$ from which $L_2 = \mathbf{421.8\ mm}$

$\therefore \qquad L_1 = 1.371 \times 421.8 = \mathbf{578.2\ mm}$

Example 21.32. *A steel shaft ABCD having a total length of 3 m consists of the following different sections : AB is hollow having outside and inside diameters of 100 mm and 60 mm respectively, and BC and CD are solid, BC having a diameter of 100 mm and CD a diameter of 85 mm. If the angle of twist is the same for each section, determine the length of each section. Find the values of the applied torque and the total angles of twist, if maximum shear stress in the hollow portion is 50 N/mm^2 and N = 0.82 × 10^5 N/mm^2.* (Based on U.L.)

Solution :

Given $$L = 3\ \text{m}$$

(a) Length of individual portions

Total length $$L = L_{ab} + L_{bc} + L_{cd} = 3000\ \text{mm} \qquad \qquad \text{...(1)}$$

Now $$\theta = \frac{TL}{NJ}, \text{ in general}$$

Since the angle of twist for each portion is the same, we have

$$\frac{TL_{ab}}{NJ_{ab}} = \frac{TL_{bc}}{NJ_{bc}} = \frac{TL_{cd}}{NJ_{cd}}$$

or $$\frac{L_{ab}}{J_{ab}} = \frac{L_{bc}}{J_{bc}} = \frac{L_{cd}}{J_{cd}}$$

or $$\frac{L_{ab}}{\frac{\pi}{32}(100^4 - 60^4)} = \frac{L_{bc}}{\frac{\pi}{32}(100)^4} = \frac{L_{cd}}{\frac{\pi}{32}(85)^4}$$

or $$\frac{L_{ab}}{87040000} = \frac{L_{bc}}{100000000} = \frac{L_{cd}}{52200625}$$

$\therefore \qquad L_{bc} = \dfrac{100000000}{87040000}\, L_{ab} = 1.1489\, L_{ab} \qquad \qquad \text{...(2)}$

and $$L_{cd} = \frac{52200625}{87040000}\, L_{ab} = 0.5997\, L_{ab} \qquad \qquad \text{...(3)}$$

Substituting the values of L_{bc} and L_{cd} in (1), we get

$$L_{ab} + 1.1489\, L_{ab} + 0.5997\, L_{ab} = 3000$$

From which $$L_{ab} = \mathbf{1091.5\ mm}$$

Hence $$L_{bc} = 1.1489 \times 1091.5 = \mathbf{1254\ mm}$$

and $$L_{cd} = 0.5997 \times 1091.5 = \mathbf{654.5\ mm}$$

(b) Applied torque on the shaft

$$T_{ab} = \frac{\pi}{16} \frac{(100^4 - 60^4)}{100} \times 50 = 8.545 \times 10^6 \text{ N-mm} = 8.545 \text{ kN-m}$$

$$T_{bc} = \frac{\pi}{16} (100)^3 \times 50 = 9.817 \times 10^6 \text{ N-mm} = 9.817 \text{ kN-m}$$

$$T_{cd} = \frac{\pi}{16} (85)^3 \times 50 = 6.029 \times 10^6 \text{ N-mm} = 6.029 \text{ kN-m}$$

Hence applied torque will be the maximum of the three.

(c) Total angle of twist

$$\theta_{cd} = \frac{T L_{cd}}{J_{cd} . N} = \frac{6.029 \times 10^6 (654.4)}{\frac{\pi}{32} (85)^4 \times 0.82 \times 10^5} = 9.39 \times 10^{-3} \text{ radian}$$

∴ Total $\theta = \theta_{ab} + \theta_{bc} + \theta_{cd} = 3\,\theta_{cd} = 3 \times 9.39 \times 10^{-3} =$ **0.0282 radian**

Example 21.33. *A solid circular shaft of diameter d = 100 mm is loaded with torques as shown in Fig. 21.25(a). Plot the diagrams showing variation of T and* θ.

Solution :

(a) T-diagram

For *CB*, measuring *x* from *C*,

$$T_x = 4 - 8 + 4 (4 - x) = 12 - 4x \quad ...(1)$$

The variation is linear.

At *C*, *x* = 0. Hence $T_c = 12$ kN-m (↷)

At *B*, *x* = 4 m. Hence
$T_B(left) = 12 - 4 \times 4 = -4$ kN-m (i.e. ↶)

The torsion changes sign from *C* to *B*

and is zero at $x = \frac{12}{4} = 3$ m from *C*.

For *BA*: $T = 4$ kN-m (↷)

This is constant from *B* to *A*.

The complete torque diagram is shown in Fig. 21.25 (*b*).

(b) θ **- diagram:** The left hand section is fixed and cannot turn; hence the angle of twist should be calculated from the left hand end of the rod,

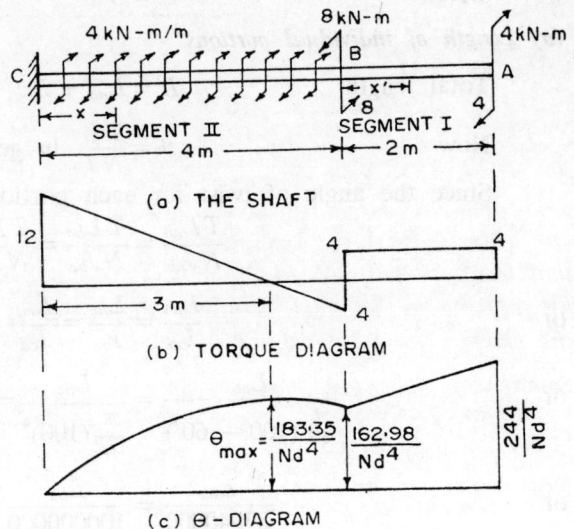

(a) THE SHAFT

(b) TORQUE DIAGRAM

(c) θ - DIAGRAM

FIG. 21.25

In general $\theta = \frac{T L}{N J} = \frac{T L}{N \frac{\pi}{32} d^4} = 10.186 \frac{T L}{N d^4}.$

For segment CB

Consider a section of length *dx*, distant *x* from *C*, where torsion is T_x.

∴ $$\theta_x = \int_0^x \frac{10.186 \, T_x \, dx}{N d^4} = \frac{10.186}{N d^4} \int_0^x (12 - 4x) \, dx$$

or
$$\theta_x = \frac{10.186}{N d^4} \left[12x - \frac{4x^2}{2} \right] \qquad \qquad ...(2)$$

At C, $x = 0$. Hence $\theta_c = 0$

At B, $x = 4$ m, $\qquad \theta_B = \frac{10.186}{N d^4} \left[12 \times 4 - \frac{4}{2}(4)^2 \right] = \frac{162.98}{N d^4}$

For max. value of θ_x, we have $\dfrac{d\theta_x}{dx} = 0 = 12 - 4x$, giving $x = 3$ m.

Hence θ is maximum where T is zero.

Hence $\qquad \theta_{max} = \frac{10.186}{N d^4} \left[12 \times 3 - \frac{4}{2}(3)^2 \right] = \frac{183.35}{N d^4}$

For segment BA

Measuring x' from B,

$$\theta_x = \theta_B + \int_0^{x'} 10.186 \frac{T_x\, dx'}{N d^4} = \frac{162.98}{N d^4} + \frac{10.186}{N d^4} \int_0^{x'} 4\, dx'$$

or
$$\theta_x = \frac{162.98}{N d^4} + \frac{10.186}{N d^4}(4x')$$

At B, $x' = 0$. Hence $\theta_B = \frac{162.98}{N d^4}$, as before

At A, $x' = 2$ m. Hence $\theta_A = \frac{162.98}{N d^4} + \frac{10.186}{N d^4}(4 \times 2) = \frac{244.47}{N d^4}$

The θ-diagram is shown in Fig. 21.25 (c).

Example 21.34. *A shaft ABC (Fig. 21.26 a) of 60 mm diameter is driven at A by a motor that transmits 100 kW to the shaft at 20 Hz. The gears at B and C remove 60 kW and 40 kW respectively. Compute the maximum shear stress f_s in the shaft and the angle of twist (θ) between the ends A and C. Take $N = 0.8 \times 10^5$ N/mm².*

Solution :

Given $\qquad f = 20$ Hz

Now 1 Hz = 1 r.p.s. = 60 r.p.m.

$\therefore \qquad n = 20 \times 60 = 1200$ r.p.m.

Now $\qquad P = \dfrac{2\pi n T}{60}$ kW

or $\qquad T = \dfrac{60 P}{2\pi n}$ kN-m

$\qquad = \dfrac{60 \times 100}{2\pi (1200)} = 0.7958$ kN-m

$\qquad = 795.8$ N-m

$\therefore \qquad T_B = 795.8 \times 0.6 = 477.5$ N-m

and $\qquad T_C = 795.8 \times 0.4 = 318.3$ N-m

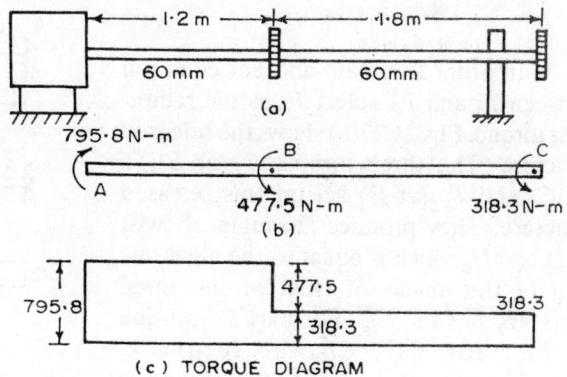

(a)

795.8 N-m

(b)

477.5 N-m

318.3 N-m

(c) TORQUE DIAGRAM

FIG. 21.26

(a) Shear stress

In general $\qquad f_s = \dfrac{16\,T}{\pi\,d^3}$

$\therefore \qquad\qquad f_{sab} = \dfrac{16\,(795.8 \times 10^3)}{\pi\,(60)^3} = 18.76 \text{ N/mm}^2$

For CB, $\qquad f_{scb} = \dfrac{16 \times 318.3 \times 10^3}{\pi\,(60)^3} = 7.51 \text{ N/mm}^2$

$\therefore \qquad\qquad f_{s,\,\max} = 18.76 \text{ N/mm}^2$, which occurs in part AB.

(b) Angles of twist

$$\theta = \dfrac{T\,L}{N\,J}, \text{ in general}$$

$\therefore \qquad \theta_{ab} = \dfrac{(795.8 \times 10^3)\,(1200)}{(0.8 \times 10^5)\,\dfrac{\pi}{32}\,(60)^4} = 0.00938 \text{ radian}$

and $\qquad \theta_{bc} = \dfrac{(318.3 \times 10^3)\,(1800)}{(0.8 \times 10^5)\,\dfrac{\pi}{32}\,(60)^4} = 0.00563 \text{ radian}$

$\therefore$ Total angle of twist $\quad \theta = \theta_{ab} + \theta_{bc} = 0.00938 + 0.00563$

$$= \mathbf{0.01501 \text{ radian} = 0.86°}$$

Example 21.35. *A solid circular bar with fixed ends is acted upon by two oppositely directed torques T as shown in Fig. 21.27(a). Find (a) the reactive torques at ends A and D, (b) the angle of twist at B, and (c) the angle of twist at the mid section M of the bar.*

Solution :

Let T_A and T_D be the reactive torques, acting is the directions as marked in Fig. 21.27. From statics we have

$$T_A - T + T - T_D = 0$$

or $\qquad\qquad T_A = T_D \qquad ...(1)$

In order to obtain another equation between T_A and T_D, select T_D as the redundant torque. Fig. 21.27(b) shows the released structure. The three torques T (at B), T (at C) and T_D (at D) act on this released structure. They produce an angle of twist θ_D at end D, which is equal to the algebraic sum of the angles of twist of the three parts AB, BC and CD. For part DC torque is T_D ; for part CB, the torque is $(T_D - T)$, while for part A, the torque is equal to $T_D - T + T = T_D$.

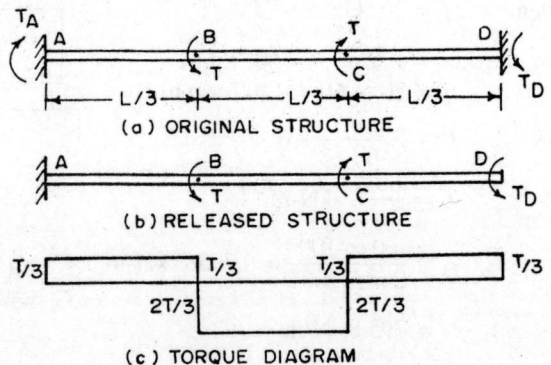

(a) ORIGINAL STRUCTURE

(b) RELEASED STRUCTURE

(c) TORQUE DIAGRAM

FIG. 21.27

Now, in general $\qquad \theta = \dfrac{TL}{NJ}$

$\therefore \qquad \theta_D = \dfrac{T_{AB} \cdot L_{AB}}{NJ} + \dfrac{T_{BC} \cdot L_{BC}}{NJ} + \dfrac{T_{CD} L_{CD}}{NJ}$

Since the angle of rotation at end D, in the original bar is equal to zero, we have $\theta_D = 0$.

$\therefore \quad T_D \left(\dfrac{L}{3}\right) + (T_D - T) \left(\dfrac{L}{3}\right) + T_D \left(\dfrac{L}{3}\right) = 0$

or $\qquad\qquad T_D + (T_D - T) + T_D = 0$

or $\qquad\qquad\qquad 3 \times T_D = T$ from which $T_D = \dfrac{T}{3}$ (Ans)

Also, $\qquad\qquad\qquad T_A = T_D = \dfrac{T}{3}$ (Ans)

(b) Angle of twist at B

$$\theta_B = \dfrac{T_{AB} \cdot L_{AB}}{NJ} = \dfrac{\left(\dfrac{T}{3}\right)\left(\dfrac{L}{3}\right)}{NJ} = \dfrac{TL}{9NJ} \text{ (Ans)}$$

(c) Angle of twist at mid-point M

$$\theta_M = \dfrac{T_{AB} \cdot L_{AB}}{NJ} + \dfrac{T_{BM} \cdot L_{BM}}{NJ} = \dfrac{\left(\dfrac{T}{3}\right)\left(\dfrac{L}{3}\right)}{NJ} + \dfrac{\left(\dfrac{-2T}{3}\right)\left(\dfrac{L}{6}\right)}{NJ} = \dfrac{TL}{9NJ} - \dfrac{TL}{9NJ} = 0$$

Example 21.36. *A solid circular shaft AB of total L is fixed against rotation at both ends, as shown in Fig. 21.28. The shaft has diameters d_a and d_b in parts AC and CB respectively. A torque T acts at section C. What should be the length a and b for the most economical design of the shaft ?*

Solution :

Let T_A and T_B be two reactive torques at A and B, in the directions marked. Choosing T_B as the redundant structure, the released structure is shown in Fig. 21.28 (b).

From statics,

$$T_A + T_B - T = 0$$

or $\qquad\qquad T_A + T_B = T \qquad ...(1)$

For the most economical design, T_A must be equal to T_B. Hence from (1) $T_B = \dfrac{T}{2}$.

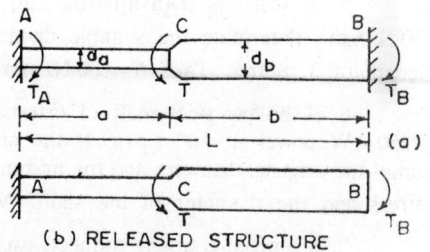

(b) RELEASED STRUCTURE

FIG. 21.28

Portion CB is subjected to a torque T_B, while portion BA is subjected to a torque $T_B - T$.

$\therefore \qquad\qquad \theta_C = 0 = \dfrac{T_{AB} \cdot L_{AB}}{NJ_{AB}} + \dfrac{T_{BC} \cdot L_{BC}}{NJ_{BC}}$

$\therefore \qquad \dfrac{(T_B - T) \cdot a}{N\dfrac{\pi}{32}(d_a)^4} + \dfrac{T_B(L - a)}{N\dfrac{\pi}{32}(d_b)^4} = 0$

or
$$\frac{\left(\dfrac{T}{2}\right)a}{(d_a)^4} + \frac{(-T/2)(L-a)}{(d_b)^4} = 0$$

or
$$a\,(d_b)^4 - L\,(d_a)^4 + a\,(d_a)^4 = 0$$

or
$$a\,(d_b^4 + d_a^4) = L\,(d_a^4)$$

From which
$$a = \frac{d_a^4 \cdot L}{d_a^4 + d_b^4} \quad \text{(Ans.)}$$

PROBLEMS

1. 450 kW of power has to be transmitted at 100 r.p.m. Find (a) the necessary diameter of a solid circular shaft (b) the necessary diameter of hollow circular section, the inside diameter being 3/4 of the external diameter. Take allowable shear stress $= 75 \text{ N/mm}^2$.

2. Select a suitable diameter of solid shaft of circular section to transmit 100 kW of power at 200 r.p.m., if the allowable shear stress is 76 N/mm^2 and the allowable twist is 1° in a length of 3.2 metres. Take $N = 0.8 \times 10^5 \text{ N/mm}^2$.

3. A bar of magnesium alloy 30 mm in diameter was tested on a gauge length of 250 mm in tension and in torsion. A tensile load of 60 kN produced an extension of 0.52 mm and a torque of 100 N-m produced a twist of 1.21°. Determine (i) Young's modulus (ii) the modulus of rigidity (iii) the bulk modulus, and (iv) the Poisson's ratio for the material.

4. A solid aluminium shaft 1 m long and 40 mm diameter is to be replaced by a tubular steel shaft of the same length and same outside diameter, so that either shaft could carry the same torque and have the same angle of twist over the total length. Determine the inner diameter of the tabular steel shaft. Take $N_s = 3 N_a$.

5. A shaft is transmitting 100 kW at 180 r.p.m. If the allowable stress in the material is 60 N/mm^2, determine the suitable diameter for the shaft. The shaft is not to twist more than 1° in a length of 3 metres. Take $N = 80 \text{ N/mm}^2$.   (Cambridge University)

6. A hollow steel shaft of external diameter equal to twice the internal diameter has to transmit 2250 kW power at 400 r.p.m. If the angle of twist has not to exceed 1° in a length equivalent to 16 times the external diameter and the maximum turning moment is 1/4 times the mean, calculate the maximum stress and the diameter of the shaft. Assume the modulus of rigidity to be $0.8 \times 10^5 \text{ N/mm}^2$.

7. A flanged coupling connects two length of 100 mm dia shafting. The pitch circle of the six coupling bolts is 250 mm and the shaft transmit 90 kW of power at 240 r.p.m. Determine (a) the maximum shear stress in the shaft (b) the angle of twist in degrees of the shaft over a length of 3 m, and (c) the dia. of the bolts if the average shear stress of the material of the bolts is to be the same as the maximum shear stress in the shaft. Assume the modulus of rigidity as $0.8 \times 10^5 \text{ N/mm}^2$.

8. A solid shaft 75 mm dia. transmits 60 kW of power and rotates at a speed of 140 r.p.m. The modulus of rigidity of the material is $0.8 \times 10^5 \text{ N/mm}^2$. Determine (a) the angle of twist of the shaft, in degrees, over a length of 1.8 m (b) the maximum shear stress in the material due to torsion. (c) If a 37.5 mm dia. hole is bored down the centre of the shaft, find the power that can be transmitted at the same speed and with the same maximum shear stress.

9. Find the power that can be safely transmitted by a solid steel shaft 100 mm dia. running at 250 r.p.m. without exceeding a shearing stress of 60 N/mm². If this shaft is to be replaced by a hollow shaft of the same external dia. but with a permissible shearing stress of 72 N/mm², determine the internal dia. to transmit the same power at the same speed as the solid shaft.

10. Compare the weights of equal lengths of hollow and solid shafts to transmit a given torque for the same maximum shear stress if the inside diameter is 2/3 of the outside.

11. A compound shaft, shown in Fig. 21.29, consists of a 1 m long aluminium bar securely jointed to a 1 m length of brass bar, the diameter of each being 50 mm. Calculate the maximum torque that can be applied at the lower end if the allowable angle of twist is 1° and the allowable shear stress in aluminium is 75 N/mm² and that in brass is 50 N/mm².

Take N for brass = 0.34 × 10⁵ N/mm² and that for aluminium as 0.27 × 10⁵ N/mm².

12. A shaft of 80 mm diameter transmits 150 kW power at 180 r.p.m. A flanged coupling is keyed to the shaft by means of a key 100 mm long and 30 mm wide. The coupling has 6 bolts of 20 mm dia. symmetrically arranged along a bolt circle of 200 mm dia. Calculate the shear stress in the shaft, the key and the bolts of the coupling.

13. Calculate the angle of twist for a shaft having diameter of 60 mm at one end and 70 mm at the other end in a length of 2 m. Also, find the % error committed in calculating θ, if it is calculated on the basis if an average diameter of 65 mm.

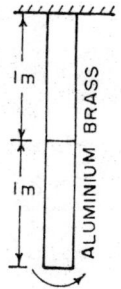

FIG. 21.29

14. A stepped steel shaft shown in Fig. 21.30 is subjected to a torque (T) at the free end and a torque ($2T$) in the opposite direction at the junction of the two sizes.

What is the total angle of twist at the free end, if the maximum shear stress in the shaft is limited to 70 N/mm². Assume modulus of rigidity as 0.84 × 10⁵ N/mm².

(U.L)

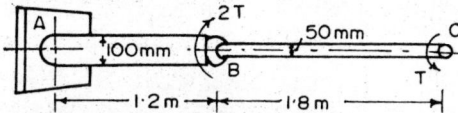

FIG. 21.30

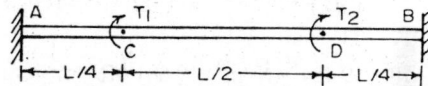

FIG. 21.31

15. A solid circular shaft with fixed ends is acted upon by torques T_1 and T_2 at location shown in Fig. 21.31. Determine the reactive torques T_a and T_b.

16. A bar ABC that is fixed at bolts the ends is subjected to torque T at section B, as shown in Fig. 21.32. The bar has a solid, circular cross-section, having a diameter d_1 from A to B and a hollow, circular section, having outside dia. d_2 and inside dia. d_1 from B to C. Find the ratio a/L so as to make the reactive torques at A and C to be equal.

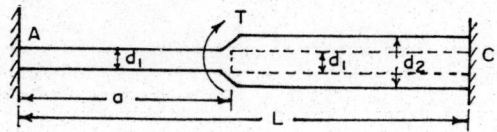

FIG. 21.32

17. A ship's propeller shaft transmits 7.5 × 10⁶ W at 240 r.p.m. The shaft has an internal diameter of 15 cm. Calculate the minimum permissible external diameter if the shearing stress in the shaft is limited to 150 N/mm².

(Cambridge).

18. A steel shaft, 20 cm external diameter and 7.5 cm internal, is subjected to a twisting moment of 30 kN-m, and a thrust of 150 kN. Find the shearing stress due to torque alone and the resultant shearing stress when the thrust is taken into account.

ANSWERS

1. (a) 143 mm (b) 162.2 mm ; 121.6 mm
2. 103 mm
3. $E = 0.408 \times 10^5 \, \text{N/mm}^2 ; N = 0.156 \times 10^5 \, \text{N/mm}^2 ; K = 0.349 \times 10^5 \, \text{N/mm}^2 ; \frac{1}{m} = 0.3052$
4. 36.14 mm
5. 103.8 mm
6. $D = 203$ mm ; $d = 101.5$ mm ; $f_s = 43.63 \, \text{N/mm}^2$
7. (a) 18.24 N/mm^2 (b) 0.783° (c) 18.26 mm
8. (a) 1.699° (b) 49.4 N/mm^2 (c) 56.24 kW
9. 308.43 kW ; 63.9 mm
10. 0.643
11. 161.2 N-m
12. 79.16 N/mm^2 ; 66.32 N/mm^2 ; 42.22 N/mm^2
13. $1.164 \times 10^{-3} \dfrac{T}{N}$; 1.98 %
14. 3° 17.7'
15. $T_a = \dfrac{3T_1 + T_2}{4} ; T_b = \dfrac{T_1 + 3T_2}{4}$
16. $\left(\dfrac{d_1}{d_2}\right)^4$
17. 231 mm
18. 19.484 MN/m^2 ; 19.681 MN/m^2

Springs

22.1. INTRODUCTION

Springs are used to absorb energy and restore it slowly or rapidly, according to the function of a particular spring under consideration. Spring may be regarded as a device for storing up energy in the form of *resilience*. The most common use of springs is for absorbing shocks, such as the springs of buffers of railway rolling stock and the springs of wheels on all types of vehicles. In such cases, some of the kinetic energy of the moving body, the vehicle, or that due to the vertical motion of the wheels and axis, is converted into strain energy in the spring, the effects of the blow on the vehicle as a whole being thereby reduced. The springs, in returning to their original shape, give back this energy, tending to reverse the relative motion of the colliding bodies. On the other hand, the spring in the clockwork is used to store work in the form of strain energy which is regained when the spring takes its original shape.

The best form of spring is that which absorbs greatest amount of energy for a given stress. The properties of a spring which are usually of most interest to an engineer are as follows:

(i) The *capacity* of the spring for absorbing the energy.

(ii) The *deformation* produced by a given load, without exceeding the safe working stress for the material.

and (iii) The *natural frequency* of vibration, in some cases.

The *stiffness* of the spring is the load required to produce unit deflection.

The *resilience* of the spring is its *capacity* for storing energy without exceeding a certain stress limit. Springs usually belong to one of the two *families*.

(a) Springs in which a length of rod or wire is made into a coil of some kind. Under this category fall (i) close-coiled springs (ii) open-coiled springs, (iii) plane spiral springs, and (iv) close-coiled conical spiral springs.

(b) Springs consisting of one or more approximately-flat plates. Under this category fall the *leaf springs* commonly used for carriages.

Depending upon the load to be carried, springs may be divided into two *categories* :

(i) Torsion springs, and (ii) Bending springs.

A *torsion spring* is the one which is subjected to a twisting moment. The resilience of such a spring is mainly due to torsion. The common example of a torsion spring is the closely-coiled helical spring subjected to axial pull. Such a spring is made of a rod or wire in the form of a helix described on a right circular cylinder. The coils of a helical springs are so close together that they can be regarded as practically lying in planes at right angles to the axis of the helix.

A *bending spring* is the one which is subjected to bending only. The resilience of such a spring is mainly due to bending. The leaf or plate springs fall under this category.

An *open coiled helical spring* falls under both the categories. In such a spring, the coils are not so close, and the angle of inclination of the coils with the axis of the spring cannot be neglected. It is subjected to both the torsional couple as well as to the flexural couple, and the resilience is due to both.

22.2. CLOSE-COILED HELICAL SPRING : AXIAL PULL

A helical or coiled spring is frequently used as a resistance to an axial load which lengthens or shortens the spring, the latter acting as an energy reservoir. For a close coiled helical spring, the helix angle (α) is very small, and it may be assumed that each coil is situated in a plane perpendicular to the axis of the spring.

Generally, springs having helix angle less than 10° are named as close coiled springs and those with helix angle greater than 10° as open coiled springs. In practice, helical springs are subjected to axial load and/or twisting moment. Generally the close-coiled springs are used to carry axial tension, whereas open coiled helical springs are used to carry axial compression.

Fig. 22.1 (*a*) shows such a spring. The helix angle α is very small. When an axial load is applied to the spring, stresses are setup due to (*i*) torsion, (*ii*) direct shear and (*iii*) bending. The stresses due to direct shear and bending are very small and may be neglected in comparison to torsion. It is, therefore, a *torsion spring.*

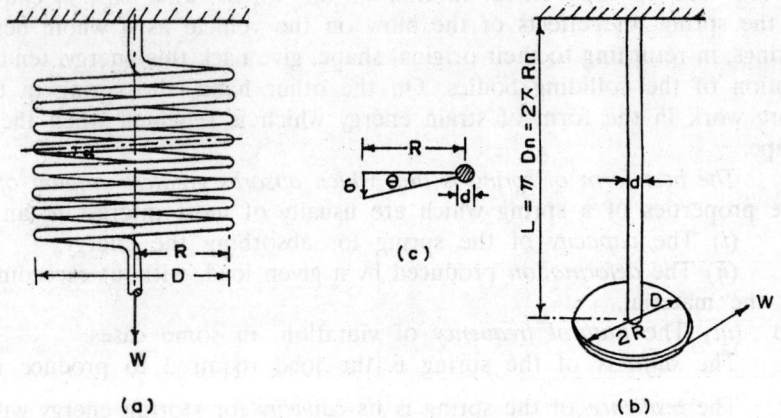

FIG. 22.1. CLOSE-COILED HELICAL SPRING

Let R = mean radius of the coil ; n = number of turns (*i.e.* numbers of coils)

d = diameter of wire or rod ; L = length of the spring

W = axial pull

It is assumed that the angle of helix (α) is quite small. Hence the action on any cross-section is approximately of a pure torque (T) given by

$$T = W.R \qquad \qquad ...(22.1)$$

The length of the spring, L may be taken equal to $2\pi R n$ (Fig. 22.1 *b*).

The wire is therefore being twisted like a shaft, and if θ is the *total* angle of twist along the wire, and δ is the deflection of W along the axis of the coils (Fig. 22.1 *c*) we have

$$\delta = R\,\theta \ \text{(approx.)} \qquad\qquad\qquad ...(22.2)$$

The equivalent shaft of L has been shown in Fig. 22.1 (b).

Angle of twist and axial deflection : Applying the formulae for torsion of shafts, and making the above substitutions, we have

$$\theta = \frac{TL}{NJ} = \frac{WRL}{N\dfrac{\pi}{32}d^4} = \frac{32\,WRL}{\pi\,d^4\,N} \ \text{radians} \qquad\qquad ...(22.3\ a)$$

or
$$\theta = \frac{32\,WR\,(2\,\pi\,n\,R)}{N\,\pi\,d^4} = \frac{64\,WR^2\,n}{N\,d^4} \ \text{radians} \qquad\qquad ...(22.3)$$

Axial movement $\quad\delta = \dfrac{32\,WR^2\,L}{N\,\pi\,d^4} = \dfrac{64\,WR^3\,n}{N\,d^4} \qquad\qquad\qquad ...(22.4)$

The axial movement or the deflection δ can also be found by equating the torsional strain energy to the work done by axial force in deflecting by δ. Thus

$$\frac{1}{2}\,W\delta = \frac{1}{2}\,T\theta = \frac{1}{2}\,(WR)\left(\frac{32\,WRL}{N\,\pi\,d^4}\right)$$

or
$$\delta = \frac{32\,WR^2\,L}{N\,\pi\,d^4} = \frac{64\,WR^3\,n}{N\,d^4} \qquad\qquad\qquad ...(22.4)$$

Stiffness of spring : The Stiffness S of the spring is given by

$$S = \frac{W}{\delta} = \frac{Nd^4}{64\,nR^3} \qquad\qquad\qquad ...(22.5)$$

Rewriting Eq 22.4, we have $\quad W = \dfrac{Nd^4}{64\,R^3\,n}\cdot\delta$

Fig. 22.2 shows three types of curves between W and δ, corresponding to the three types of springs, i.e. (i) linear spring, (ii) hard spring and (iii) soft spring.

A *linear spring* is the one in which the deflection is proportional to the applied load. A *hard spring* is the one in which the rate of deflection decreases with the increase in the load, while a *soft spring* is the one in which the rate of deflection increases with the increase in the load. Ordinary helical springs are linear springs. Hard springs and soft springs are the two categories of non-linear springs.

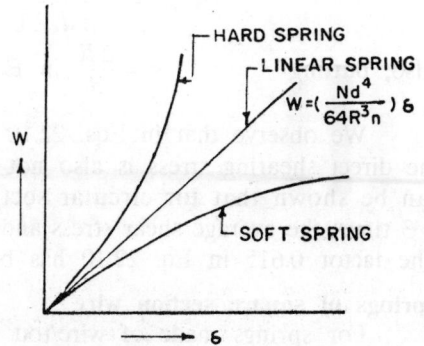

FIG. 22.2

Shear stress in spring

Consider a section distant R from the axis of the spring. The section is subjected to (i) shear stress due to torsion $T = WR$ and (ii) shear stress due to shear force W.

(a) *Shear stress due to torsion* : Maximum intensity of shear stress $\left(f_{s_1}\right)$ due to torsion is given by

$$f_{s_1} = \frac{T}{J}\left(\frac{d}{2}\right) = \frac{16\,T}{\pi\,d^3} = \frac{16\,WR}{\pi\,d^3} \qquad\qquad\qquad ...(22.6)$$

(b) Shear stress due to axial load W

$$f_{s_2} = \frac{W}{area} = \frac{W}{\frac{\pi}{4}d^2} = \frac{4W}{\pi d^2} \qquad \qquad ...(22.7)$$

(c) Total shear stress alone to T and W

$$f_{s,max} = \frac{16WR}{\pi d^3} + \frac{4W}{\pi d^2} = \frac{16WR}{\pi d^3}\left(1 + \frac{d}{4R}\right) \qquad ...(22.8)$$

The factor $d/4R$ is generally quite small for *light springs*. However, for heavy springs, such as those used in railway cars, the effect of the factor $d/4R$ is quite substantial.

Maximum deflection under compressive load

Under a compressive axial load W, the maximum deflection will be there when the spring 'shuts', *i.e.* when the coils touch each other. Hence $\delta_{max} = L - nd$.

Effect of curvature of coils

Eq. 22.6 for torsional shear stress is based on the assumption that the bar is straight, while in fact it is curved. Hence Eq. 22.6 contains an error which is quite significant in heavy springs. Due to the effect of curvature, the stresses at the inner side of the coil are higher than those computed from Eq. 22.6. A.M. Wahl* (1929) developed the following formula for calculating the maximum shearing stress :

$$f_{s,max} = \frac{16WR}{\pi d^3}\left[\frac{4k-1}{4k-4} + \frac{0.615}{k}\right] \qquad ...(22.9)$$

where $$k = \frac{2R}{d} = \frac{D}{d}$$

In *light springs*, the ratio k is quite large and hence the first term in parentheses approaches unity. Hence the equation for light spring reduces to

$$f_{s,max} = \frac{16WR}{\pi d^3}\left[1 + \frac{0.615}{k}\right] \qquad ...(22.10)$$

Also, putting $$k = \frac{2R}{d} \text{ in Eq. 22.8, we get } f_{s,max} = \frac{16WR}{\pi d^3}\left[1 + \frac{0.5}{k}\right] \qquad ...(22.10\ a)$$

We observe that in Eqs. 22.10 and 22.10 (a), the factors 0.615 and 0.5 differ because the direct shearing stress is also not actually uniformly distributed over the cross-section. It can be shown that for circular section the maximum shearing stress produced is nearly 4/3 times the average shear stress and varies from 1.23 at the outer edge to 1.38 at the centre. The factor 0.615 in Eq. 22.10 has been obtained by multiplying 0.5 by 1.23.

Springs of square section wire

For springs made of wire/rod of square section of side b

$$\theta = \frac{410\,TL}{Nb^4} \text{ degrees } = \frac{7.11\,TL}{Nb^4} \text{ radians } = \frac{7.11\,WRL}{Nb^4} \text{ radians } \qquad ...(22.11)$$

$$\delta = R.\theta = \frac{7.11\,WR^2L}{Nb^4} = \frac{44.7\,WR^3\,n}{Nb^4} \qquad ...(22.12)$$

Stiffness $$S = \frac{W}{\delta} = \frac{Nb^4}{44.7\,n\,R^3} \qquad ...(22.13)$$

---

*A.M. Wahl : Trans. A.S.M.E., 1928

Note that for bar of square section, $T = f_s \cdot \dfrac{\pi}{16} d^3 = 0.1963 f_s d^3$, while for the bar of square section, $T = 0.208 f_s b^3$.

22.3. CLOSED - COILED HELICAL SPRINGS : AXIAL COUPLE OR TORQUE

When a close-coiled spring, fixed at one end is subjected at the other end to a twisting couple M about the central axis of the spring, bending moment of magnitude M will be produced at all the cross-sections. The twisting couple will tend to unwind or wind up the spring.

Now, bending moment, $M = E I \times (\text{change in curvature}) = E I \left(\dfrac{1}{R'} - \dfrac{1}{R} \right)$ \qquad ...(1)

where \qquad R = original radius of curvature
\qquad\qquad R' = new radius of curvature

Let \qquad n = original number of coils in the spring
\qquad\qquad n' = resulting number of coils, due to winding/unwinding effect

$\therefore$ \qquad\qquad $L = 2 \pi R n = 2 \pi R' n'$

or \qquad\qquad $\dfrac{1}{R} = \dfrac{2 \pi n}{L}$ \quad and \quad $\dfrac{1}{R'} = \dfrac{2 \pi n'}{L}$ \qquad ...(2)

Substituting for R and R' in (1), we get

$$M = E I \left[\dfrac{2 \pi n'}{L} - \dfrac{2 \pi n}{L} \right] = \dfrac{E I . 2 \pi}{L} (n' - n) \qquad ...(22.14)$$

In the above analysis, it is assumed that the *sense* of the B.M. M is such that it increases the curvature, i.e. $R' < R$ and $n' > n$.

If φ is the total angle of twist at the free end, in radians, we have :

$$\varphi = 2 \pi (n' - n) = \dfrac{M L}{E I} \qquad ...(22.15)$$

The above result can also be obtained from the consideration of strain energy. Thus,

$$\dfrac{1}{2} M \varphi = \dfrac{1}{2 E I} \int_0^L M^2 dx = \dfrac{1}{2} \dfrac{M^2 L}{E I}$$

or \qquad\qquad $\varphi = \dfrac{M L}{E I}$ \qquad ...(22.15)

The change in curvature or angle of bend per unit length

$$\dfrac{d \varphi}{d L} = \dfrac{1}{R'} - \dfrac{1}{R} = \dfrac{M}{E I} \qquad ...(22.16)$$

For solid circular section, $I = \dfrac{\pi}{64} d^4$. Hence from Eq. 22.15,

$$\varphi = \dfrac{64 M L}{\pi E d^4} = \dfrac{128 M R n}{E d^4} \text{ radians} \qquad ...(22.17)$$

For a square section of side b, $I = \dfrac{1}{12} b^4$. Hence from Eq. 22.15

$$\varphi = \dfrac{12 M L}{E b^4} = \dfrac{24 \pi M R n}{E b^4} \text{ radians} \qquad ...(22.18)$$

For solid circular section, the maximum bending stress is given by

$$f_b = \frac{M}{I} y = \frac{M}{Z} = \frac{32 M}{\pi d^3} \qquad \qquad ...(22.19)$$

For a square section, $\qquad f_b = \frac{M}{Z} = \frac{M}{\frac{1}{6} b^3} = \frac{6 M}{b^3} \qquad \qquad ...(22.20)$

Strain Energy Stored : Strain energy stored in the spring $= \frac{1}{2} M \varphi$

(a) Bar of circular cross-section

$$f_{max} = f_b = \frac{32 M}{\pi d^3}, \text{ (from Eq. 22.19) or } M = \frac{f_{max} \cdot \pi d^3}{32}$$

Also $\qquad \varphi = \frac{128 M R n}{E d^4}, \text{ from Eq. 22.17}$

$\therefore \qquad U = \frac{1}{2} M \varphi = \frac{1}{2} \left[f_{max} \cdot \frac{\pi d^3}{32} \right] \left[\frac{128 M R n}{E d^4} \right] = \frac{1}{2} \left[f_{max} \frac{\pi d^3}{32} \right] \left[\frac{128 R N}{E d^4} \times f_{max} \frac{\pi d^3}{32} \right]$

or $\qquad U = \frac{f_{max}^2}{8 E} \cdot \frac{1}{2} \left(\pi d^3 \right)^2 \cdot \frac{R n}{d^4} = \frac{f_{max}^2}{8 E} \frac{\pi^2 d^2 R n}{2}$

Now volume of spring, $V = \frac{\pi}{4} d^2 L = \frac{\pi}{4} d^2 (2 \pi R n) = \frac{\pi^2 d^2 R n}{2}$

Hence $\qquad U = \frac{f_{max}^2}{8 E} \times V \qquad \qquad ...(22.21)$

(b) Bar of square section

$$f_{max} = f_b = \frac{6 M}{b^3} \quad \text{ or } M = f_{max} \cdot \frac{b^3}{6}$$

$$\varphi = \frac{24 \pi M R n}{E b^4} = \frac{24 \pi}{E b^4} \left(f_{max} \cdot \frac{b^3}{6} \right) R n$$

$\therefore \qquad U = \frac{1}{2} M \varphi = \frac{1}{2} \left(f_{max} \cdot \frac{b^3}{6} \right) \left[\frac{24 \pi}{E b^4} \cdot f_{max} \cdot \frac{b^3}{6} R n \right] = \frac{f_{max}^2}{6 E} \times 2 \pi b^2 R n$

Now, volume of spring, $V = b^2 \cdot L = b^2 (2 \pi R n)$

$\therefore \qquad U = \frac{f_{max}^2}{6 E} \times V \qquad \qquad ...(22.22)$

Torsional stiffness : Torsional stiffness (S_T) of spring is given by

$$S_T = \frac{M}{\varphi} = \frac{E I}{L} = \frac{E I}{2 \pi n R} \text{ (N-m/radian)} \qquad \qquad ...(22.23)$$

Example 22.1. *A close-coiled helical spring is subjected to an axial pull of 600 N. The spring is made out of a 16 mm diameter rod, and has 12 complete coils, each of mean diameter 120 mm. Compute (a) shear stress induced in the rod, (b) deflection under the pull, and (c) energy stored in spring during the extension. Take $N = 0.85 \times 10^5 \, N/mm^2$.*

Solution : Given $d = 16$ mm ; $n = 12$; $R = \frac{120}{2} = 60$ mm ; $W = 600$ N

$$T = WR = 600 \times 60 = 36000 \text{ N-mm}$$

(a) **Shear stress**

$$f_{s_1} = \frac{16\,T}{\pi\,d^3} = \frac{16 \times 36000}{\pi\,(16)^3} = 44.76 \text{ N/mm}^2$$

$$f_{s_2} = \frac{4\,W}{\pi\,d^2} = \frac{4 \times 600}{\pi\,(16)^2} = 2.98 \text{ N/mm}^2$$

$$\therefore \quad f_{s,max} = f_{s_1} + f_{s_2} = 44.76 + 2.98 = \mathbf{47.74 \text{ N/mm}^2}$$

Alternatively : $f_{s,max} = \dfrac{16\,W R}{\pi\,d^3}\left(1 + \dfrac{d}{4R}\right) = \dfrac{16 \times 36000}{\pi\,(16)^2}\left(1 + \dfrac{16}{4 \times 60}\right)$

$$= \frac{16 \times 36000}{\pi\,(16)^3}\left(1 + 0.0667\right) = 44.76\,(1 + 0.0667) = 47.74 \text{ N/mm}^2$$

(b) f_s **by Wahl's formula** :

$$k = \frac{2\,R}{d} = \frac{D}{d} = \frac{120}{16} = 7.5$$

Hence from Eq. 22.9, $f_{s,max} = \dfrac{16\,W R}{\pi\,d^3}\left[\dfrac{4k-1}{4k-4} + \dfrac{0.615}{k}\right] = 44.76\left[\dfrac{4 \times 7.5 - 1}{4 \times 7.5 - 4} + \dfrac{0.615}{7.5}\right]$

$$= 44.76\,[\,1.115 + 0.082\,] = \mathbf{53.59 \text{ N/mm}^2}$$

which is much larger than the one obtained above neglecting the effect of initial curvature of the spring rod.

(b) **Deflection** $\delta = R\,.\,\theta = \dfrac{64\,W R^3 n}{N\,d^4} = \dfrac{64\,(600)\,(60)^3\,(12)}{0.85 \times 10^5\,(16)^4} = \mathbf{17.87 \text{ mm}}$

(c) **Energy stored** $U = \frac{1}{2}\,W\,.\,\delta = \frac{1}{2} \times 600 \times 17.87 = 5360 \quad \text{mm-N} = 5.360 \text{ m-N} = \mathbf{5.36 \text{ J}}$

Example 22.2. *A close-coiled helical spring is to carry a load of 120 N. The mean coil diameter has to be 10 times that of the wire diameter. If the maximum shear stress is not to exceed 100 N/mm², calculate (a) the diameter of the wire, and (b) diameter of the coil.*

Solution :   Given $W = 120 \text{ N}\,;\,D = 10\,d\,;\,R = 5\,d\,;\,f_s = 100$

$$f_s = \frac{16\,W R}{\pi\,d^3}\left(1 + \frac{d}{4R}\right) = \frac{16\,W\,(5\,d)}{\pi\,d^3}\left(1 + \frac{d}{4\,(5d)}\right) = \frac{80\,W}{\pi\,d^2}\,(1 + 0.05)$$

$$\therefore \qquad d^2 = \frac{1.05 \times 80\,W}{\pi\,f_s} = \frac{1.05 \times 80 \times 120}{\pi\,(100)} = 32.08$$

$$\therefore \qquad d = 5.66 \text{ mm} \approx \mathbf{5.7 \text{ mm}}$$

and $D = 10\,d = \mathbf{57 \text{ mm}}$

Example 22.3. *A wagon weighing 25 kN and moving at 4 km/hour is to be stopped at the bufferstop. Compute the number of close-coiled springs that would be required in the buffer stop to absorb the energy of motion during a compression of 250 mm.*

Each spring has 20 coils, made of 20 mm wire, the mean diameter of the coils being 200 mm. Take $N = 0.84 \times 10^5 \text{ N/mm}^2$.

Solution : $W_w = 25 \text{ kN} = 25 \times 10^3 \text{ N}\,; V = 4 \text{ km/h}\,; \delta = 250 \text{ mm}\,; n = 20\,; d = 20 \text{ mm},$

$$R = \frac{200}{2} = 100 \text{ mm}$$

$$V = 4 \text{ km/h} = \frac{4 \times 1000 \times 100}{60 \times 60} = 111.11 \text{ cm/sec}$$

$\therefore$ K.E. absorbed by the buffer springs $= \dfrac{W_w V^2}{2g} = \dfrac{25 \times 10^3 (111.11)^2}{2 \times 981}$

$\qquad\qquad = 157.31 \times 10^3$ cm-N $= 157.31 \times 10^4$ mm-N

If W is the axial load for each spring, for a compression of δ, we have

$$\delta = \dfrac{64\, W R^3 n}{N d^4}$$

or $\qquad\qquad W = \dfrac{N d^4 \delta}{64 R^3 n} = \dfrac{0.84 \times 10^5 (20)^4 \, 250}{64 (100)^3 (20)} = 2625$ N

Energy stored by one spring $= \dfrac{1}{2} W \delta = \dfrac{1}{2} \times 2625 \times 250 = 32.81 \times 10^4$ mm-N

$\therefore$ No. of springs required $= \dfrac{157.31 \times 10^4}{32.81 \times 10^4} = 4.79 \approx \mathbf{5}$ (say).

Example 22.4. *A close-coiled helical spring has to absorb 60 N-m of energy when compressed 60 mm. The coil diameter is eight times the wire diameter. If there are ten coils, determine (a) diameter of the coil, (b) diameter of the wire, and (c) the maximum shear stress. Take $N = 0.86 \times 10^5 \, N/mm^2$.*

Solution : $\qquad U = 60$ N-m $= 60 \times 10^3$ N-mm; $\;\; \delta = 60$ mm ; $\;\; D = 8\,d \,; n = 10$

Now $\qquad U = \dfrac{1}{2} W \delta$

or $\qquad 60 \times 10^3 = \dfrac{1}{2} W (60)$, from which $\;\; W = 2000$ N

Also, $\qquad \delta = \dfrac{64\, W R^3 n}{N d^4} = \dfrac{64\, W (4\,d)^3 n}{N d^4} = \dfrac{64 \times 64\, W n}{N d}$

or $\qquad d = \dfrac{64 \times 64\, W n}{N \delta} = \dfrac{64 \times 64 \times 2000 \times 10}{0.86 \times 10^5 \times 60} = \mathbf{16\ mm}$

$\therefore \qquad D = 8\,d = 8 \times 16 = \mathbf{128\ mm}$

$f_s = \dfrac{16\, W R}{\pi d^3} \left(1 + \dfrac{d}{4R} \right) = \dfrac{16 \times 2000\,(64)}{\pi (16)^3} \left(1 + \dfrac{16}{4 \times 64} \right)$

$\qquad = \dfrac{16 \times 2000\,(64)}{\pi (16)^3} (1 + 0.0625) = \mathbf{169.1\ N/mm^2}$

Example 22.5. *A close-coiled helical compression spring is made of 10 mm steel wire closely coiled to a mean diameter of 100 mm with 20 coils. A weight of 100 N is dropped on to the spring. If the maximum instantaneous compression is 60 mm, calculate the height of the drop. Take $N = 0.85 \times 10^5 \, N/mm^2$.*

Solution : Given $d = 100$ mm ; $D = 100$ mm; $R = 50$ mm; $n = 20 \,; P = 100$ N; $\delta = 60$ mm

Let $\qquad W =$ equivalent gradually applied load to produce the same compression

$\qquad\quad h =$ height of drop, in mm.

From Eq. 22.4, we have $\delta = \dfrac{64\, W R^3 n}{N d^4}$

$\therefore \qquad W = \dfrac{N d^4 \delta}{64 R^3 n} = \dfrac{0.85 \times 10^5 (10)^4 (60)}{64 (50)^3 \times 20} = 318.75$ N

Equating the energy supplied by the impact load to the energy stored,

we get
$$P(h + \delta) = \frac{1}{2}W\delta$$

or
$$100(h + 60) = \frac{1}{2} \times 318.75 \times 60 = 9562.5$$

From which we get
$$h = \frac{9562.5}{100} - 60 = \mathbf{35.625\ mm}$$

Example 22.6. *A close-coiled helical spring, made of 12 mm diameter steel rod, has 12 complete turns over a mean diameter of 100 mm. Determine (a) increase in the number of turns, and (b) bending stress induced, if it is subjected to an axial twist of 16 N-m. Take $E = 2 \times 10^5 N/mm^2$. Also, compute the torsional stiffness of the spring.*

Solution :

Given :
$$d = 12\ \text{mm}\ ;\ n = 12\ ;\ D = 100\ \text{mm}\ ;\ R = 50\ \text{mm}$$
$$M = 16\ \text{N-m} = 16 \times 10^3\ \text{N-mm}$$
$$I = \frac{\pi}{64}d^4 = \frac{\pi}{64}(12)^4 = 1017.9\ \text{mm}^4$$
$$Z = \frac{I}{d/2} = \frac{1017.9}{6} = 169.65\ \text{mm}^3$$
$$f_b = \frac{M}{Z} = \frac{16 \times 10^3}{169.65} = \mathbf{94.31\ N/mm^2}$$
$$\varphi = \frac{ML}{EI} = \frac{M(2\pi nR)}{EI} = \frac{16 \times 10^3 \times 2\pi(12)(50)}{2 \times 10^5 \times 1017.9} = 0.2963\ \text{radians}$$

But
$$\varphi = 2\pi(n' - n)$$

$\therefore$
$$n' - n = \frac{\varphi}{2\pi} = \frac{0.2963}{2\pi} = \mathbf{0.04716}$$

$\therefore$
$$n' = 0.04716 + 12 = 12.04716$$

Torsional stiffness of the spring$= \dfrac{M}{\varphi} = \dfrac{EI}{2\pi nR}$

$$= \frac{2 \times 10^5 \times 1017.9}{2\pi(12)(50)} = 54 \times 10^3\ \text{N-mm/radians} = \mathbf{54\ N\text{-}m/radian}$$

22.4. OPEN-COILED HELICAL SPRING : AXIAL FORCE

In an open-coiled helical spring, shown in Fig. 22.3(a), the coils are not close together and hence angle α cannot be considered as small. Hence the *bending couple* is also substantial in comparison with the *torsional couple*. Due to this reason, an open-coiled helical spring falls under both the categories of spring, *i.e.* it is both a torsion spring as well as a bending spring.

Let the centre line of the each coil be inclined at an angle α with the horizontal

Let $R =$ mean radius of each coil; $d =$ diameter of the wire of coils
$\quad\quad n =$ total number of turns ; $L =$ total length of the spring

Then, $\quad L = 2\pi Rn\sec\alpha$ ...(22.24)

If an axial force W is applied, it will have a moment WR about the $U - U$ axis (*i.e.* horizontal axis). This moment WR will have two resolved components :

(1) A moment T in the XX plane, causing twisting action :

$$T = WR \cos \alpha \qquad\qquad\qquad ...(22.25\ a)$$

and   (2) A moment M normal to X-X plane, causing bending action :

$$M = WR \sin \alpha \qquad ...(22.25\ b)$$

The torsional angle due to $T = \theta_t = \dfrac{TL}{NJ}$

Angular rotation due to M : $\theta_b = \dfrac{ML}{EI}$

$\therefore$ Work done against torsional stress

$$= \frac{1}{2} T \cdot \theta_t = \frac{T^2 L}{2NJ} = \frac{W^2 R^2 L \cos^2 \alpha}{2NJ} \qquad ...(1)$$

Work done against bending stress

$$= \frac{1}{2} M \cdot \theta_b = \frac{M^2 L}{2EI} = \frac{W^2 R^2 L \sin^2 \alpha}{2EI} \qquad ...(2)$$

$\therefore$ Total work done

$$= \frac{W^2 R^2 L \cos^2 \alpha}{2NJ} + \frac{W^2 R^2 L \sin^2 \alpha}{2EI} \qquad ...(3)$$

If δ is the axial extension due to W, work done $= \dfrac{1}{2} W \delta \qquad ...(4)$

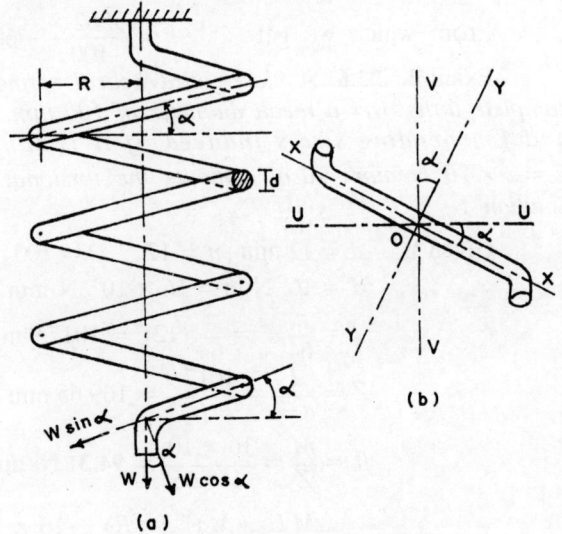

FIG. 22.3. OPEN COILED HELICAL SPRING

Equating (1) and (2), $\dfrac{1}{2} W \delta = \dfrac{W^2 R^2 L \cos^2 \alpha}{2NJ} + \dfrac{W^2 R^2 L \sin^2 \alpha}{2EI}$

$\therefore$
$$\delta = WR^2 L \left[\frac{\cos^2 \alpha}{NJ} + \frac{\sin^2 \alpha}{EI} \right] \qquad ...(22.26)$$

or
$$\delta = WR^2\, 2 \pi n R \sec \alpha \left[\frac{\cos^2 \alpha}{NJ} + \frac{\sin^2 \alpha}{EI} \right]$$

or
$$\delta = 2 \pi n\, WR^3 \sec \alpha \left[\frac{\cos^2 \alpha}{NJ} + \frac{\sin^2 \alpha}{EI} \right] \qquad ...(22.26\ a)$$

For a *circular section*, $J = 2I = \dfrac{\pi}{32} d^4$

$\therefore$
$$\delta = \frac{64\, WR^3 n \sec \alpha}{d^4} \left[\frac{\cos^2 \alpha}{N} + \frac{2 \sin^2 \alpha}{E} \right] \qquad ...(22.26\ b)$$

Taking $\dfrac{E}{N} = 2.5$ for steel, $\delta = \dfrac{64\, WR^3 n \sec \alpha}{d^4 E} \left[2.5 \cos^2 \sin \alpha + 2 \sin^2 \alpha \right] \qquad ...(22.27\ a)$

or
$$\delta = \frac{64\, WR^3 n \sec \alpha}{N d^4} \left[\cos^2 \alpha + 0.8 \sin^2 \alpha \right] \qquad ...(22.27\ b)$$

or
$$\delta = \frac{64\,W R^3 n \sec \alpha}{N d^4} \left[1 - 0.2 \sin^2 \alpha \right] \qquad \qquad ...(22.28)$$

When $\alpha = 0$, we get $\delta = \dfrac{64\,W R^3 n}{N d^4}$, which is the same as Eq. 22.4, obtained for a close-coiled helical spring.

When $\qquad \alpha = 10°$, we get $\delta = 1.0093 \left[\dfrac{64\,W R^3 n \sec \alpha}{N d^4} \right]$, from Eq. 22.28

When $\qquad \alpha = 30°$, we get $\delta = 1.097 \left[\dfrac{64\,W R^3 n \sec \alpha}{N d^4} \right]$, from Eq. 22.28

Hence we observe that the effect of obliquity on the deflection for all values of α below $10°$ is less than 1% and for $\alpha = 30°$, this effect is about 10%, as compared to the case of a close coiled helical spring of circular section, where $\alpha = 0$. However, for other sections, the effect is slightly larger.

Alternative solution

Let us obtain an alternative solution for δ, by considering component deflections in XX and YY directions (Fig. 22.4)

(a) Twisting effect

Fig. 22.4(a) shows the effects of twisting moment, where in ab represents the movement due to twisting per unit length of the coil, in the plane XX. If θ_t is the torsional angle, we have $ab = R\,\theta_t$

The movement ab can be resolved into (i) a vertical movement ac and (ii) horizontal movement cb.

$\therefore \quad ac = \delta_t = ab \cos \alpha = R\,\theta_t \cos \alpha \quad ...(1a)$

and $\quad cb = ab \sin \alpha = R\,\theta_t \sin \alpha \quad ...(1b)$

The movement cb will have a winding action tending to *increase* the number of turns.

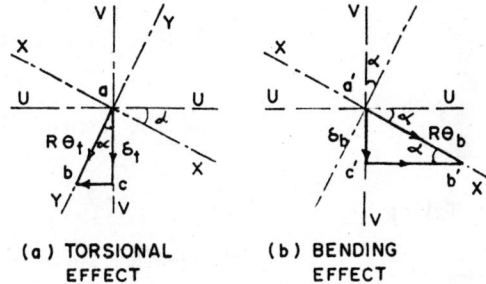

(a) TORSIONAL EFFECT (b) BENDING EFFECT

FIG. 22.4

(b) Bending effect : Fig. 22.4(b) shows the bending effect, where $a'b'$ represents the movement due to bending, per unit lengths of the coil, in plane YY. If θ_b is the angular change in the centre line of the spring, due to bending, we have $a'b' = R\,\theta_b$.

The movement $a'b'$ can be resolved into (i) a vertical movement $a'c'$ and (ii) horizontal movement $c'b'$.

$\therefore \qquad a'c' = \delta_b = a'b' \sin \alpha = R\,\theta_b \sin \alpha$

and $\qquad c'b' = a'b' \cos \alpha = R\,\theta_b \cos \alpha \qquad \qquad ...(2)$

The movement $c'b'$ will have *unwinding action*, tending to decrease the number of turns.

Now : $\qquad \theta_t = \dfrac{T}{NJ} ; \theta_b = \dfrac{M}{EI} ; T = W R \cos \alpha$ and $M = W R \sin \alpha$

Total vertical deflection, per unit length $= \delta_v = \delta_t + \delta_b$

or
$$\delta_v = R\,\theta_t \cos \alpha + R\,\theta_b \sin \alpha = \frac{R\,T \cos \alpha}{NJ} + \frac{R\,M \sin \alpha}{EI}$$

or
$$\delta_v = \frac{WR^2\cos^2\alpha}{NJ} + \frac{WR^2\sin^2\alpha}{EI} = WR^2\left(\frac{\cos^2\alpha}{NJ} + \frac{\sin^2\alpha}{EI}\right)$$

Total deflection δ for length $L = L . \delta_v$

$\therefore$
$$\delta = WR^2 L\left[\frac{\cos^2\alpha}{NJ} + \frac{\sin^2\alpha}{EI}\right] \qquad \qquad ...(22.26)$$

The above expression is the same as Eq. 22.26 obtained from the consideration of strain energy.

Also, angular winding up movement (φ_h) per unit length $= \dfrac{cb - c'b'}{R} = \theta_t\sin\alpha - \theta_b\cos\alpha$

$\therefore$ Total winding up movement, φ for length $(L) = L\,\varphi_h$

$\therefore$
$$\varphi = L\,(\theta_t\sin\alpha - \theta_b\cos\alpha) = L\left[\frac{WR\cos\alpha}{NJ}\sin\alpha - \frac{WR\sin\alpha}{EI}\cos\alpha\right]$$

or
$$\varphi = WRL\left[\frac{\sin\alpha\cos\alpha}{NJ} - \frac{\sin\alpha\cos\alpha}{EI}\right] = WRL\sin\alpha\cos\alpha\left[\frac{1}{NJ} - \frac{1}{EI}\right]$$

For a solid circular section, $J = 2I = \dfrac{\pi}{32}d^4$

$\therefore$
$$\varphi = \frac{32\,WRL\sin\alpha\cos\alpha}{\pi\,d^4\,N}\left[1 - \frac{2N}{E}\right] \qquad \qquad ...(22.29\ a)$$

or
$$\varphi = \frac{32\,WR\,(2\,\pi\,n\,R\sec\alpha)\sin\alpha\cos\alpha}{\pi\,d^4}\left[\frac{1}{N} - \frac{2}{E}\right]$$

or
$$\varphi = \frac{64\,WR^2\,n\sin\alpha}{d^4}\left[\frac{1}{N} - \frac{2}{E}\right] = \frac{64\,WR^2\,n\sin\alpha}{d^4\,N}\left[1 - \frac{2N}{E}\right] \qquad ...(22.29)$$

Taking $\dfrac{N}{E} = \dfrac{2}{5}$, we get

$$\varphi = \frac{32\,WRL\sin\alpha\cos\alpha}{5\,\pi\,d^4\,N} = \frac{64\,WR^2\,n\sin\alpha}{5\,d^4\,N} \qquad \qquad ...(22.29\ b)$$

Evidently, φ is maximum when $\alpha = 45°$.

Stresses in spring made of wire of circular section

(i) Bending stress :
$$f_b = \frac{M}{Z} = \frac{32\,WR\sin\alpha}{\pi\,d^3} \qquad \qquad ...(22.30)$$

(ii) Shear stress :
$$f_s = \frac{16\,T}{\pi\,d^3} + \frac{W\sin\alpha}{\frac{\pi}{4}d^2} = \frac{16\,WR\cos\alpha}{\pi\,d^3} + \frac{4\,W\sin\alpha}{\pi\,d^2}$$

or
$$f_s = \frac{16\,WR\cos\alpha}{\pi\,d^3}\left[1 + \frac{d\tan\alpha}{4R}\right] \qquad \qquad ...(22.31)$$

In the above expression, the value of $\dfrac{d\tan\alpha}{4R}$ ranges from 0.01 to 0.02. Hence neglecting this factor, we get

$$f_s \approx \frac{16\,W\,R\cos\alpha}{\pi\,d^3} \qquad\qquad\qquad ...(22.31\ a)$$

(iii) Principal stresses (σ_1 and σ_2)

$$\sigma = \frac{f_b}{2} \pm \sqrt{\left(\frac{f_b}{2}\right)^2 + f_s^2} = \frac{16\,W\,R}{\pi\,d^3}\left[\sin\alpha \pm \sqrt{\sin^2\alpha + \cos^2\alpha}\right]$$

or $$\sigma = \frac{16\,W\,R}{\pi\,d^3}[\sin\alpha \pm 1], \quad \left(\text{taking } f_s \approx \frac{16\,W\,R\cos\alpha}{\pi\,d^3}\right)$$

$$\therefore \qquad \sigma_1 = \frac{16\,W\,R}{\pi\,d^3}\left[1 + \sin\alpha\right] \text{ and } \sigma_2 = -\frac{16\,W\,R}{\pi\,d^3}[1 - \sin\alpha] \qquad ...(22.32)$$

(iv) Maximum shear stress ($f_{s,max}$)

$$f_{s,max} = \frac{\sigma_1 - \sigma_2}{2} = \frac{16\,W\,R}{\pi\,d^3} \qquad\qquad ...(22.32)$$

22.5. OPEN-COILED HELICAL SPRING : AXIAL TORQUE

Now let us take the case when the spring is subjected to an axial torque M. The torque M will be taken as positive it it tends to increase φ or to increase the curvature of the coils. The resolved components of M about XX will be equal to $M\cos\alpha$, which will cause bending. Similarly, the resolved component of M about YY will be equal to $M\sin\alpha$, which will cause torsion.

Work done against bending stress $= \frac{1}{2}(M\cos\alpha)(M\cos\alpha)\dfrac{L}{E\,I} = \dfrac{1}{2}\cdot\dfrac{M^2\,L\cos^2\alpha}{E\,I}$

Work done against torsional stress $= \frac{1}{2}(M\sin\alpha)(M\sin\alpha)\dfrac{L}{N\,J} = \dfrac{1}{2}\dfrac{M^2\,L\sin^2\alpha}{N\,J}$

$$\therefore \text{ Total work done} = \frac{1}{2}\frac{M^2\,L\cos^2\alpha}{E\,I} + \frac{1}{2}\frac{M^2\,L\sin^2\alpha}{N\,J}$$

If φ is the total twist of the free end due to M, work done $= \dfrac{1}{2}M\varphi$

$$\therefore \qquad \frac{1}{2}M\varphi = \frac{1}{2}\frac{M^2\,L\cos^2\alpha}{E\,I} + \frac{1}{2}\frac{M^2\,L\sin^2\alpha}{N\,J}$$

or $$\varphi = M\,L\left[\frac{\cos^2\alpha}{E\,I} + \frac{\sin^2\alpha}{N\,J}\right] \qquad\qquad ...(22.34)$$

or $$\varphi = 2\pi\,R\,n\,M\sec\alpha\left[\frac{\cos^2\alpha}{E\,I} + \frac{\sin^2\alpha}{N\,J}\right] = \frac{64\,M\,R}{d^4}n\sec\alpha\left[\frac{2\cos^2\alpha}{E} + \frac{\sin^2\alpha}{N}\right] \ ...(22.35)$$

When $\alpha = 0$, we get $\varphi = \dfrac{128\,M\,R\,n}{E\,d^4}$ radians $\qquad\qquad ...(22.35\ a)$

which is the same as Eq. 22.15 obtained for a close-coiled helical spring.

The axial extension δ caused by couple M may be found by resolving the rotations as before.

$$\therefore \qquad \delta = M.R\sin\alpha\cos\alpha.L\left[\frac{1}{NJ}-\frac{1}{EI}\right] \qquad\qquad ...(22.36\ a)$$

for a circular section of diameter d, $J = 2I = \dfrac{\pi}{32}d^4$

$$\therefore \qquad \delta = \frac{32\,MRL}{\pi\,d^4}\sin\alpha\cos\alpha\left[\frac{1}{N}-\frac{2}{E}\right]=\frac{64\,MR^2}{d^4}n\sin\alpha\left[\frac{1}{N}-\frac{2}{E}\right] ...(22.36)$$

Example 22.7. *A open coiled helical spring, made out of 20 mm diameter steel rod, has 10 complete turns at a mean diameter of 150 mm, the angle of helix being 15°. An axial load of 400 N is applied. Compute (a) deflection under the load and (b) maximum intensities of direct and shear stresses, induced in the section of the wire.*

Take $N=0.84\times10^5\,N/mm^2$ and $E=2\times10^5\,N/mm^2$.

Solution :

Given : $\qquad n = 10$; $D = 150$ mm ; $R = 75$ mm ; $\alpha = 15°$; $W = 400$ N

$\qquad\qquad T = WR\cos\alpha = 400\times75\cos15° = 28978$ N-mm

$\qquad\qquad M = WR\sin\alpha = 400\times75\sin15° = 7764.6$ N-mm

(a) Deflection

Deflection, $\qquad \delta = \dfrac{64\,WR^3\,n\sec\alpha}{d^4}\left[\dfrac{\cos^2\alpha}{N}+\dfrac{2\sin^2\alpha}{E}\right]$

$$= \frac{64\times400\,(75)^3\times10\sec15°}{(20)^4}\left[\frac{\cos^2 15°}{0.84\times10^5}+\frac{2\sin^2 15°}{2\times10^5}\right] = \mathbf{8.23\ mm}$$

(b) Direct and shearing stresses

$$f_b = \frac{M}{Z} = \frac{7764.6}{\dfrac{\pi}{32}(20)^3} = \mathbf{9.89\ N/mm^2}$$

$$f_s = \frac{T}{J}\cdot\frac{d}{2} = \frac{28978}{\dfrac{\pi}{16}(20)^3} = \mathbf{18.45\ N/mm^2}\qquad\text{(Neglecting the term }\frac{d\tan\alpha}{4R}\text{)}$$

However, $\qquad \dfrac{d\tan\alpha}{4R} = \dfrac{20\tan15°}{4\times75} = 0.0179$

$\therefore \qquad\qquad f_s = 18.45\,(1+0.0179) = \mathbf{18.78\ N/mm^2}$

Thus, the effect of the term $\dfrac{d\tan\alpha}{4R}$ is 1.8% only, and therefore, this term may be neglected.

Principal stresses, $\qquad \sigma = \dfrac{f_b}{2}\pm\sqrt{\dfrac{f_b^2}{4}+f_s^2} = \dfrac{9.89}{2}\pm\sqrt{\left(\dfrac{9.89}{2}\right)^2+(18.45)^2} = 4.945\pm19.101$

$\therefore \qquad\qquad \sigma_1 = \mathbf{24.05\ N/mm^2}$ and $\sigma_2 = \mathbf{-14.16\ N/mm^2}$

Maximum shear stress, $f_s' = \sqrt{\left(\dfrac{f_b}{2}\right)^2+(f_s)^2} = \mathbf{19.101\ N/mm^2}$

Example 22.8. *In the previous example, if the axial load of 400 N is replaced by an axial torque of 96 N-m, calculate the angle of rotation about the axis of the coil and the axial deflection.*

Solution : Axial torque $M = 96$ N-m $= 96 \times 10^3$ N-mm

Angle of rotation, $\varphi = \dfrac{64\,M\,R\,n \sec \alpha}{d^4}\left[\dfrac{2\cos^2 \alpha}{E} + \dfrac{\sin^2 \alpha}{N}\right]$

$$= \dfrac{64 \times 96 \times 10^3 \times 75 \times 10 \sec 15°}{d^4}\left[\dfrac{2\cos^2 15°}{2 \times 10^5} + \dfrac{\sin^2 15°}{0.84 \times 10^5}\right]$$

$$= 0.3023 \text{ radians} = \mathbf{17° 18'}$$

Deflection, $\delta = \dfrac{64\,M\,R^2\,n \sin \alpha}{d^4}\left[\dfrac{1}{N} - \dfrac{2}{E}\right]$

$$= \dfrac{64 \times 96 \times 10^3\,(75)^2 \times 10 \sin 15°}{(20)^4}\left[\dfrac{1}{0.84 \times 10^5} - \dfrac{2}{2 \times 10^5}\right] = \mathbf{1.06\ mm}$$

22.6. SERIES AND PARALLEL ARRANGEMENT OF SPRINGS

(a) Springs in series

Fig. 22.5 shows two springs of stiffness S_1 and S_2 respectively, arranged in series. For such an arrangement, the same load (W) is transmitted through each spring. Hence the total extension produced will be the sum of individual extensions (δ_1 and δ_2) of each spring. Hence

$$\delta = \delta_1 + \delta_2$$

or $\qquad \dfrac{W}{S} = \dfrac{W}{S_1} + \dfrac{W}{S_2},\qquad$ where

$S = $ stiffness of the composite springs.

$\therefore \qquad \dfrac{1}{S} = \dfrac{1}{S_1} + \dfrac{1}{S_2} \qquad\qquad ...(22.37)$

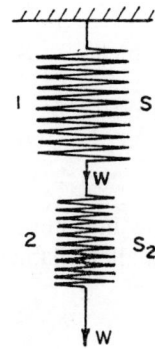

FIG. 22.5. SPRINGS IN SERIES

(b) Springs in parallel

When the springs are connected in parallel the total load (W) is divided between the two springs, while the extension of each spring is the same (Fig. 22.6)

Let $\qquad W_1 = $ load carried by one spring

$\qquad\qquad W_2 = $ load carried by the second spring

$\qquad\qquad \delta = $ common extension of each spring

$\therefore \qquad W = W_1 + W_2$

or $\qquad \delta . S = \delta S_1 + \delta S_2,$

where $\qquad S = $ stiffness of the composite spring

$\therefore \qquad S = S_1 + S_2 \qquad\qquad ...(22.38)$

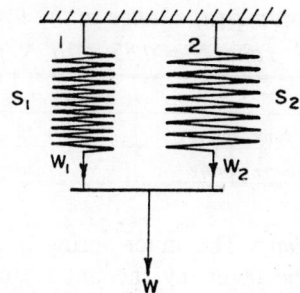

FIG. 22.6 SPRINGS IN PARALLEL

Example 22.9. *A composite spring has two close coiled springs in series. Each spring has a mean coil diameter eight times the wire diameter. One spring has 20 coils of wire diameter 2.5 mm. Find the diameter of the wire in the other spring if it has 15 coils and the stiffness of the composite spring is 1.3 N/mm. Find the greatest axial load that can be applied and the corresponding extension for a maximum shearing stress of 300 N/mm². Take N = 0.8 × 10⁵ N/mm².*

Solution : Given : $D = 8d$ or $R = 4d$; $d_1 = 2.5$ mm ; $n_2 = 15$; $S = 1.3$ N/mm

In general, $S = \dfrac{N d^4}{64 n R^3}$ or $\dfrac{1}{S} = \dfrac{64 n R^3}{N d^4}$

$\therefore$ $\dfrac{1}{S_1} = \dfrac{64 n_1 R_1^3}{N d_1^4} = \dfrac{64 \times 20 (4 d_1)^3}{N d_1^4} = \dfrac{64 \times 20 \times 64}{0.8 \times 10^5 \times 2.5} = 0.4076$

$\dfrac{1}{S_2} = \dfrac{64 n_1 R_2^3}{N d_2^4} = \dfrac{64 \times 20 (4 d_2)^3}{N d_2^4} = \dfrac{64 \times 15 \times 64}{0.8 \times 10^5 \times d_2} = \dfrac{0.768}{d_2}$

$S = 1.3$ N/mm or $\dfrac{1}{S} = \dfrac{1}{1.3} = 0.7692$

Now $\dfrac{1}{S} = \dfrac{1}{S_1} + \dfrac{1}{S_2}$ $\therefore$ $0.7692 = 0.4096 + \dfrac{0.768}{d_2}$

From which $d_2 = \dfrac{0.768}{0.7692 - 0.4096} = 2.14$ mm

Again $f_s = \dfrac{16 W R}{\pi d^3} \left(1 + \dfrac{d}{4R} \right)$ or $W = f_s \dfrac{\pi d^3}{16 R \left(1 + \dfrac{d}{4R} \right)}$

Now the maximum load the composite spring may carry will be limited by the spring having the smaller diameter (*i.e.* spring 2). For spring 2, $d_2 = 2.14$ mm.

Hence $R_2 = 4 d_2 = 4 \times 2.14 = 8.56$ mm.

$\therefore$ $W = \dfrac{300 \times \pi (2.14)^3}{16 \times 8.56 \left(1 + \dfrac{2.14}{4 \times 8.56} \right)} = \dfrac{67.44}{(1 + 0.0625)} = \textbf{63.47 N}$

Deflection caused by the composite spring $= \delta = \dfrac{W}{S} = \dfrac{63.47}{1.3} = \textbf{48.82 mm}$

Example 22.10. *The table below gives particulars of a compound spring consisting of two co-axial close-coiled springs. If the spring is subjected to an axial load of 400 N, determine for each spring (a) change in the length (b) the amount of load carried, and (c) the maximum shearing stress. Take N = 0.85 × 10⁵ N/mm².*

	Mean coil dia. (mm)	Dia. of wire (mm)	No. of turns	Free length (mm)
Outer spring	45	5	10	100
Inner spring	30	4	8	85

(Based on U.L)

Solution : The inner spring is shorter than the outer spring by 15 mm. Hence the initial load will be taken by the outer spring till it deflects by 15 mm. Thereafter, both the springs will be compressed together. Let us use suffix 1 for outer spring and 2 for the inner spring. Let W be the *initial load* taken by the outer spring to deflect by $\delta_1 = 15$ mm.

Now $\qquad \delta = \dfrac{64\,W R^3 n}{N d^4}$, in general.

Hence $\qquad W_1 = \dfrac{N d_1^4 \delta_1}{64\, R_1^3 n_1} = \dfrac{0.85 \times 10^5\,(5)^4\,(15)}{64\,(22.5)^3\,(10)} = 109.31$ N

$\therefore$ Load W shared by both the springs for further deflection$= 400 - 109.31 = 290.69$ N

Let $\qquad W_1' =$ additional load taken by the outer spring and

$\qquad W_2 =$ load taken by the inner spring.

$\therefore \qquad\qquad\qquad\qquad W = W_1' + W_2$ $\qquad\qquad\qquad\qquad$ ...(1)

If δ is the common deflection on the two springs, we get

$W_1' = \dfrac{N d_1^4 \delta}{64\, R_1^3 n_1} = \dfrac{0.85 \times 10^5\,(5)^4\,\delta}{64\,(22.5)^3\,(10)} = 7.2874\,\delta$; $W_2 = \dfrac{N d_2^4 \delta}{64\, R_2^3 n_2} = \dfrac{0.85 \times 10^5\,(4)^4\,\delta}{64\,(15)^3\,(8)} = 12.5926\,\delta$

Hence from (1), $\qquad 290.69 = 7.2874\,\delta + 12.5926\,\delta$; from which $\delta = 14.62$ mm

$\therefore$ Change in the length of outer spring $= 15 + 14.62 = $ **29.62 mm**

Change in the length of inner spring $= \delta = $ **14.62 mm**

Load taken by outer spring $= 109.31 + 7.2874 \times 14.62 = $ **215.87 N**

Load taken by inner spring $= 12.5926 \times 14.62 = $ **184.13 N**

Check : $\qquad\qquad$ Total load $= 215.87 + 184.13 = 400$ N

Shear stress in the outer spring $= \dfrac{16 \times 215.87 \times 22.5}{\pi\,(5)^3} \left[1 + \dfrac{5}{4 \times 22.5} \right] = 208.9$ N/mm^2

Shear stress in the inner spring $= \dfrac{16 \times 184.13 \times 15}{\pi\,(4)^3} \left[1 + \dfrac{4}{4 \times 15} \right] = 234.4$ N/mm^2

Hence max. shear stress $= $ **234.4 N/mm^2** in the inner spring.

22.7. LEAF OR CARRIAGE SPRINGS : SEMI - ELLIPTIC SPRING

A leaf or carriage spring, shown in Fig. 22.7 is made up of a number of parallel plates (or strips) of varying length, but having the same width and thickness, strapped together. The plates are bent to the same radius so that they contact only at their edges. The function of such a spring is to provide large deflections at low loads without inducing high bending stresses at any point in the material. Leaf springs are of two types.

(a) Semi-elliptic type $\qquad$ and $\qquad$ (b) Quarter-elliptic type

The most common form of leaf spring is the *semi-elliptic* type, which is supported at the ends, the load being applied centrally (Fig. 22.7). It is normally assumed for a leaf spring that the plates taper uniformly to a point, and that for a semi-elliptic type, the smallest plate is a *diamond shape* (Fig. 22.7 b). Neglecting friction, each plate is free to slide relative to the next one. Hence each plate acts as a separate beam, and the entire spring consists of a number of separate beams. Each such beam (*i.e.* plate) is regarded as supported at its points of contact with one below it, the load transmitted at its-over hanging end being $W/2$, where W is the total load transmitted.

If L is the total length of the spring (*i.e.* the length of the longest plate), and n is the total number of plates, the *overhang a* will be equal to $L/2n$. With such an arrangement, in which the plates are of varying length, each differing in length by $2a$ from the next plate, the second moment of inertia I will vary uniformly from a maximum at the mid span to zero at the point of contact. The bending moment M also varies in the same manner as I, and consequently *the ratio M/I, and therefore the stress intensity, are constant for all sections of spring. For this reason, the spring bends to the form of a circular arc.*

Let us cut all the plates, except the one at the top, longitudinally through the centre and place as shown in Fig. 22.7(c). In doing so, we would obtain what is commonly known as *equivalent plate* of diamond shape. The width B of the equivalent plate at the centre would be equal to nb where b is the width of each plate, and thickness of the equivalent plate will be equal to t, the thickness of the individual plate.

Determination of shape of the plate

Let us consider a plate of length L, width b and thickness t, bent into a circular arc, as shown in Fig. 22.8. The plate is supported at points C and D, the points of contact of the plate with the one immediately below it. The distance AC (or BD) is equal to overhang a, and the plate is loaded with loads $W/2$ at each end.

The B.M. at A and B will be zero. The B.M. at C and D will be equal to $\dfrac{Wa}{2}$.

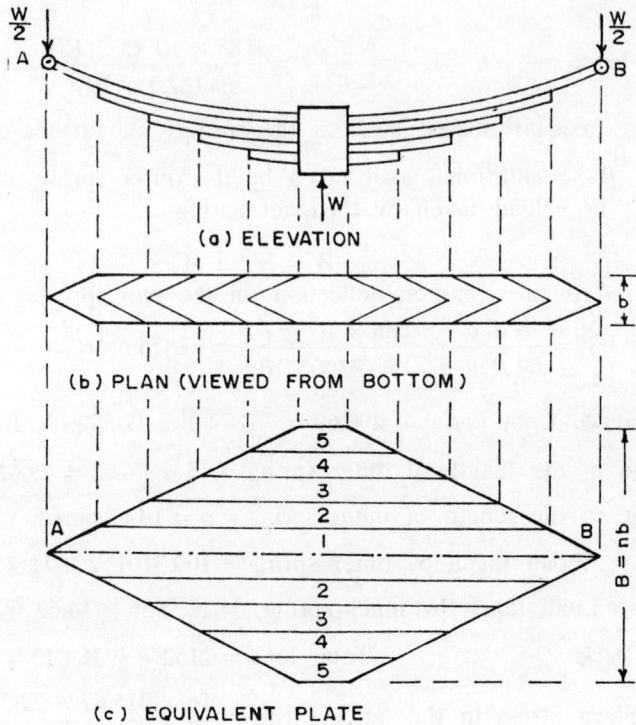

(a) ELEVATION

(b) PLAN (VIEWED FROM BOTTOM)

(c) EQUIVALENT PLATE

FIG. 22.7. SEMI-ELLIPTIC SPRING

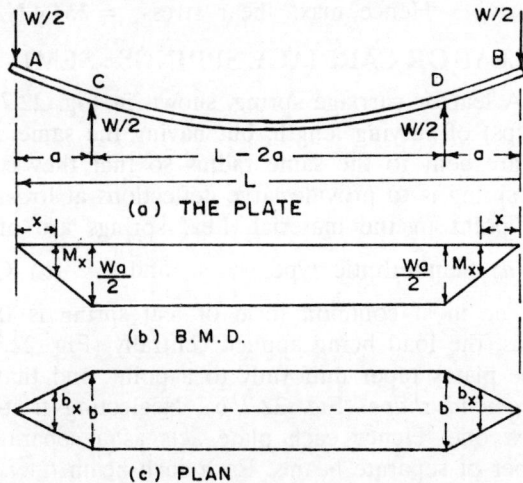

(a) THE PLATE

(b) B.M.D.

(c) PLAN

FIG. 22.8. SHAPE OF EACH PLATE

The B.M. between C to D will have a constant value of $Wa/2$.

Consider a section distant x from either A or B. The B.M. will be $M_x = \dfrac{W}{2} \cdot x$

Now, we have $\qquad \dfrac{1}{R} = \dfrac{M}{EI}$

In order that the plate bends into a circular arc of radius R, M/I must be constant. The B.M. is constant from C to D, but it is not constant from A to C, and from D to B. In order to make M/I constant, I must vary from A to C, and also from D to B. This is achieved by making the ends triangular in plan, as shown in Fig. 22.8 (c), maintaining constant thickness. Now, at any section distant x from A (or B),

$$I_x = \frac{b_x t^3}{12}, \text{ (where } b_x \text{ is the width there) and } M_x = \frac{Wx}{2}$$

Hence $\qquad \dfrac{M_x}{I_x} = \dfrac{Wx/2}{b_x t^3/12} = \dfrac{6W}{t^3} \cdot \dfrac{x}{b_x} = \dfrac{6W}{t^3} \cdot \dfrac{a}{b} = $ constant

Thus, we get M_x/I_x constant, by making the ends triangular in plan, for the over hanging portion. The complete shape of the top plate is shown in Fig. 22.8(c). Each subsequent plate will be of similar shape, but of length shorter by $2a$ from the plate immediately above it.

Deflection of the spring:

For a beam of span L, simply supported at the ends and loaded with central point load W,

$$\text{B.M.} = \frac{WL}{4}$$

This is the total B.M. at the centre, which is shared by n number of plates.

$\therefore \qquad$ B.M. per plate $= \dfrac{WL}{4n}$

Moment of inertia of each plate, $I = \dfrac{1}{12} b t^3$

Now $\qquad \dfrac{M}{I} = \dfrac{E}{R} \quad$ or $\quad R = \dfrac{EI}{M} = \dfrac{E\left(\dfrac{bt^3}{12}\right)}{\dfrac{WL}{4n}}$

or $\qquad R = \dfrac{b t^3 n E}{3 WL}$

By the geometry of a circle $(2R - \delta)\,\delta = \dfrac{1}{2}L \cdot \dfrac{1}{2}L$

Hence neglecting the higher powers of small quantities,

We get $\qquad 2R\delta = \dfrac{1}{4}L^2$

or $\qquad \delta = \dfrac{L^2}{8R} = \dfrac{L^2}{8\left(\dfrac{b t^3 n E}{3 WL}\right)} = \dfrac{3 WL^3}{8 b t^3 n E} \qquad \dots(22.39)$

The above expression for central deflection can also be obtained from the consideration of strain energy. If f is the bending stress, resilience due to bending $= f^2/6E$.

$\therefore$ Total work done in stressing $= \dfrac{f^2}{6E} \times V = \dfrac{f^2}{6E}\left(L\,t\,\dfrac{n\,b}{2}\right)$

$\therefore$ $\dfrac{1}{2}\,W\delta = \dfrac{f^2\,L\,n\,t\,b}{12\,E}$ ...1)

But $f = \dfrac{M}{I}\cdot\dfrac{t}{2} = \dfrac{\dfrac{WL}{4}}{\dfrac{n\,b\,t^3}{12}} \times \dfrac{t}{2} = \dfrac{3}{2}\,\dfrac{WL}{n\,b\,t^2}$ ...(22.40)

Substituting the value of f in (1), we get

$$\dfrac{1}{2}\,W\cdot\delta = \left(\dfrac{3}{2}\,\dfrac{WL}{n\,b\,t^2}\right)^2 \dfrac{L\,n\,t\,b}{12\,E} = \dfrac{3}{16}\,\dfrac{W^2\,L^3}{n\,b\,t^3\,E}$$

or $\delta = \dfrac{3}{8}\,\dfrac{WL^3}{n\,b\,t^3\,E}$, as before

Proof Load

Let δ_o be the central deflection, so as to make the plate flat. This is evidently the maximum deflection. The corresponding load W_o is known as the *proof load*, which makes the plate flat.

Now $\delta_o = \dfrac{3\,W_o\,L^3}{8\,E\,n\,b\,t^3}$

or $W_o = \dfrac{8\,E\,n\,b\,t^3}{3\,L^3}\cdot\delta_o$ ...(22.41)

At the proof, load the maximum bending stress $f_o\ (=f_{max})$ induced in the plate will be

$$f_o = \dfrac{3\,W_o\,L}{2\,n\,b\,t^2} = \dfrac{3\,L}{2\,n\,b\,t^2} \times \dfrac{8\,E\,n\,b\,t^3}{3\,L^3}\,\delta_o$$

or $f_o = \dfrac{4\,E\,t}{L^2}\cdot\delta_o$ ...(22.42)

For a given material of the spring, E and f_o *are prescribed. Hence Eq. 22.42 gives the relationship between thickness t and the initial radius to which the plate should be bent.

Example 22.11. *A leaf spring of semi-elliptic type consists of 8 plates, each of 40 mm width and 6 mm thickness, the length of the longest plate being 500 mm. If the greatest bending stress is not to exceed 180 N/mm² and the central deflection is limited to 12 mm, determine the magnitude of the greatest load that can be applied to it. Take $E = 2 \times 10^5\,N/mm^2$.*

Solution :

Given : $n = 8$; $b = 40$ mm ; $t = 6$ mm $L = 500$ mm; $f_s = 180\,\text{N/mm}^2$; $\delta = 12$ mm

(i) From deflections consideration

We have $\delta = \dfrac{3\,WL^3}{8\,E\,n\,b\,t^3}$, from Eq. 22.39

$$\therefore \qquad W = \frac{8\,E\,n\,b\,t^3 . \delta}{3\,L^3} = \frac{8 \times 2 \times 10^5\,(8)\,(40)\,(6)^3\,(12)}{3\,(500)^3} = 3539 \text{ N}$$

(ii) From stress consideration

We have $\qquad F = \dfrac{3}{2}\dfrac{WL}{n\,b\,t^2}$, from Eq. 22.40

or $\qquad W = \dfrac{2\,n\,b\,t^2}{3\,L}f = \dfrac{2 \times 8\,(40)\,(6)^2}{3 \times 500} \times 180 = 2765 \text{ N}$

$\therefore$ Allowable load will be the lesser of the two = **2765 N**

Example 22.12. *Design a laminated steel spring, simply supported at the ends, and centrally loaded with a span of 800 mm, given the following*

(i) Proof load : 8.5 kN
(ii) Maximum central deflection : 50 mm
(iii) Ratio of width to thickness : 10
(iv) $E = 2 \times 10^5\,N/mm^2$
(v) Permissible bending stress $= 370\,N/mm^2$

The plate are available in the multiple of 1 mm for thickness and in the multiple of 3 mm for width.

Solution :

Given : $W_o = 8.5$ kN $= 8500$ N ; $\delta_o = 50$ mm ; $\dfrac{b}{t} = 10$; $L = 800$ mm

From Eq. 22.42, $f_o = \dfrac{4\,E\,t}{L^2} . \delta_o$

or $\qquad t = \dfrac{L^2 f_o}{4\,E\,\delta_o} = \dfrac{(800)^2\,(370)}{4 \times 2 \times 10^5\,(50)} = 5.92$ mm

Since the thickness is available in the multiple of 1 mm, keep $t =$ **6 mm**

$\therefore \qquad b = 10\,t = 10 \times 6 = 60$ mm, which is in the multiple of 3 mm.

Now, from Eq. 22.40, $n = \dfrac{3\,WL}{2fb\,t^2} = \dfrac{3 \times 8500 \times 800}{2 \times 370\,(60)\,(6)^2} = 12.76$

$\therefore$ Provide **13** plates.

Modified value of stress $f = \dfrac{3\,WL}{2\,n\,b\,t^2} = \dfrac{3 \times 8500\,(800)}{2 \times 13\,(60)\,(6)^2} = 363.24 \text{ N/mm}^2$

But $\qquad \dfrac{f}{y} = \dfrac{E}{R}$

$\therefore \qquad R = \dfrac{E}{f}y = \dfrac{2 \times 10^5}{363.24} \times 3 \approx$ **1652 mm**

22.8. QUARTER ELLIPTIC SPRINGS

The second type of leaf spring is the quarter elliptic spring, which is fixed at one end and the load *(W)* is applied at the free end, as shown in Fig. 22.9(*a*). Such a spring has maximum I at the fixed end and zero I at the free end. The bending moment (M) also varies in the same manner, and hence ratio M/I, and therefore the stress intensity, are constant for all sections of the spring. For this reason, this spring also bends to the form of a circular arc.

Let L = unloaded length of the spring

        b = width of each plate

        n = number of plates

        t = thickness of each plate

    M = B.M. at the fixed end $= W . L$

    I = moment of inertia at the fixed end

$$= n \times \frac{b\,t^3}{12}$$

Now $\dfrac{1}{R} = \dfrac{M}{E\,I} = \dfrac{W\,L}{E\left(\dfrac{n\,b\,t^3}{12}\right)} = \dfrac{12\,W\,L}{n\,b\,t^3\,E}$ ...(1)

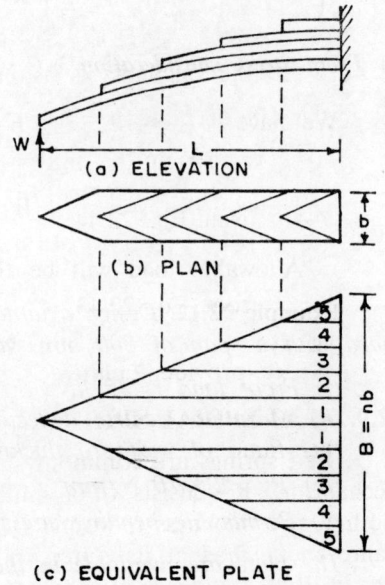

(a) ELEVATION

(b) PLAN

(c) EQUIVALENT PLATE

FIG. 22.9. QUARTER ELLIPTIC SPRING

Also, from the property of a circle, if δ is the central deflection,

$$(2\,R - \delta)\,\delta = L . L$$

Neglecting the product of small quantities,

$$2\,R\,\delta \approx L^2$$

or

$$\delta = \frac{L^2}{2\,R} = \frac{6\,W\,L^3}{n\,b\,t^3\,E} \qquad \qquad ...(2)$$

Maximum bending stress (f_b) is given by

$$f_b = \frac{M}{I}\,y = \frac{W\,L \cdot \left(\dfrac{t}{2}\right)}{\left(\dfrac{n\,b\,t^3}{12}\right)} = \frac{6\,W\,L}{n\,b\,t^2} \qquad \qquad ...(22.44)$$

If W_o is the proof load and δ_o is the *free height* of the spring, we get

$$W_o = \frac{n\,b\,t^3\,E}{6\,L^3}\,\delta_o \qquad \qquad ...(4) \qquad\qquad\qquad ...(22.45)$$

The proof stress f_{bo} is given by

$$f_{bo} = \frac{6\,L}{n\,b\,t^2} . W_o = \frac{t\,E}{L^2}\,\delta_o \qquad ...(5) \qquad\qquad\qquad ...(22.46)$$

Example 22.13. *Design a quarter elliptic type laminated spring for carrying a load of 12 kN, over a span of 900 mm. The bending stress is not to exceed 310 N/mm^2 and the maximum deflection is limited to 80 mm. Take width of the plate equal to eight times the thickness. The steel plates are available in the multiples of 4 mm in width and 1 mm is thickness.*

Take $E = 2 \times 10^5\,N/mm^2$.

Solution :

Given : $W_o = 12$ kN ; $L = 900$ mm ; $f_{bo} = 310\,N/mm^2$; $\delta_o = 80$ mm; $b = 8\,t$

From Eq. 22.40, $t = \dfrac{f_{bo} \cdot L^2}{E \, \delta_o} = \dfrac{310 \, (900)^2}{2 \times 10^5 \times 80} = 15.7 \text{ mm}$

Since the thickness is available in the multiple of 1 mm thickness, adopt $t = 16$ mm.

∴ Width of plate $b = 8 \, t = 8 \times 16 = \mathbf{128 \text{ mm}}$.

This is also in the multiple of 4 mm.

Also, from Eq. 22.44, $\quad n = \dfrac{6 \, WL}{f_b \cdot b \, t^2} = \dfrac{6 \times 12000 \, (900)}{310 \, (128) \, (16)^2} = 6.38$

Also, from Eq. 22.43, $\quad n = \dfrac{6 \, WL^3}{\delta \, b \, t^3 \, E} = \dfrac{6 \times 12000 \, (900)^3}{80 \, (128) \, (16)^3 \times 2 \times 10^5} = 6.26$

Hence provide **7 plates**, **128 mm** wide and **16 mm** thick.

22.9. FLAT SPIRAL SPRINGS

Flat springs are commonly used in clock work mechanisms. It consists of a uniform thin strip of width b and thickness t, wound into a spiral in one plane, and *pinned* at its outer end O, as shown in Fig. 22.10. A spindle is attached to the centre of the spiral which is wound up by applying a torque (T) to the spindle. When the spring in wound up under the action of torque T, reactions R_x and R_y are induced at the pinned end O, in the horizontal and vertical directions, as marked in Fig. 22.10.

Now consider an element A of length ds of the spring having co-ordinates x and y, with respect to point O. The bending moment at the point is given by

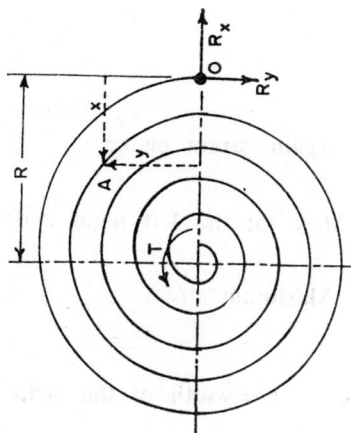

FIG. 22.10. FLAT SPIRAL SPRING

$$M = R_y \cdot x - R_x \cdot y \qquad \ldots(1)$$

Also, by taking moments about the axis of the spindle, we have

$$T = R_y \cdot R \quad \text{or} \quad R_y = \frac{T}{R} \cdot \qquad \ldots(2)$$

where $\qquad R = $ maximum radius of the spring

∴ Strain energy of the element, $dU = \dfrac{M^2 \cdot ds}{2 \, E \, I} \qquad \ldots(3)$

∴ Total strain energy $U = \displaystyle\int \dfrac{(R_y \, x - R_x y)^2}{2 \, E \, I} \, ds$

or $\qquad U = \displaystyle\int \left[\dfrac{T}{R} x - R_x \cdot y \right]^2 \dfrac{ds}{2 \, E \, I} \qquad \ldots(4)$

Since O is a fixed point, $\quad \dfrac{\partial U}{\partial R_x} = 0$. Hence we get from (4)

$$R_x = \frac{\left(\dfrac{T}{R}\right) x\, y\, ds}{y^2\, ds} = 0, \text{ since } y^2\, ds \text{ is zero by symmetry.}$$

Hence from (4), $$U = \int \frac{T^2}{R^2} x^2 \frac{ds}{2\,E\,I} \qquad \qquad ...(5)$$

$$\therefore \qquad \theta = \frac{\partial U}{\partial T} = \frac{\left(\dfrac{2\,T}{R^2}\right) \displaystyle\int x^2\, ds}{2\,E\,I} \qquad \qquad ...(6)$$

Treating the spiral as a uniform disc, $\displaystyle\int x^2\, ds \approx \left(\dfrac{R^2}{4} + R^2\right) L \approx 1.25\, R^2 L$, where L is the total length of the spiral.

$$\therefore \qquad \theta = \frac{\left(\dfrac{2\,T}{R^2}\right)(1.25\, R^2 L)}{2\,E\,I} = 1.25\, \frac{T\,L}{E\,I} \qquad ...(22.47)$$

Again, strain energy $$U = \frac{1}{2} T \theta = \frac{1.25\, T^2 L}{2\,E\,I} \qquad ...(7) \qquad ...(22.48)$$

$$M_{max} \text{ (at the left hand end)} = R_y \cdot 2 R = \left(\frac{T}{R}\right) 2 R = 2\, T. \qquad ..(22.49)$$

Maximum stress $$f_s = \frac{M_{max}}{Z} = \frac{2\,T}{Z} = \frac{2\,T}{\left(\dfrac{b\,t^2}{6}\right)} = \frac{12\,T}{b\,t^2} \qquad ...(22.50)$$

where b = width of the strip and t = thickness of the strip of the spring.

Example 22.14. *A flat spiral spring is 5 mm wide, 0.2 mm thick and 2 m long. If the maximum stress is induced at the point of maximum B.M. is 600 N/mm², determine (a) torque (b) work stored, and (c) the number of turns to wind up the spring.*

Take $E = 2 \times 10^5 \, N/mm^2$.

Solution :

Given : $b = 5$ mm ; $t = 0.2$ mm ; $L = 2000$ mm ; $f_s = 600 \, \text{N/mm}^2$

From Eq. 22.50, $f_s = \dfrac{12\,T}{b\,t^2}$

$$\therefore \qquad T = \frac{b\,t^2}{12} \cdot f_s = \frac{5\,(0.2)^2}{12} \times 600 = \textbf{10 \ N-mm}$$

From Eq. 22.47, $\theta = 1.25 \dfrac{T\,L}{E\,I} = \dfrac{1.25 \times 10\,(2000)}{2 \times 10^5 \left(\dfrac{1}{12} \times 5 \times 0.2^3\right)} = 37.5$ radians

$$= \frac{37.5}{2\,\pi} \text{ turns} = \textbf{5.97} \text{ turns of the spindle}$$

Work stored in the spring $= \frac{1}{2}T\theta = \frac{1}{2} \times 10 \times 37.5 = $ **187.5 N-mm**

22.10. ADDITIONAL ILLUSTRATIVE EXAMPLES

Example 22.15. *A safety valve is 100 mm in dia. to blow off at a pressure of 1.2 N/mm² gauge. It is held by a close coiled compression spring of circular steel bar. The mean diameter of the spring is 200 mm and the initial compression is 25 mm. Find the diameter of the steel bar and the number of convolutions necessary if the allowable shear stress is 50 N/mm². Take N = 0.84 × 10⁵ N/mm².*

Solution :

Given : $p = 1.2 \text{ N/mm}^2$; $D = 200$ mm ; $R = 100$ mm; $\delta = 25$ mm; $f_s = 90 \text{ N/mm}^2$

$W = $ total force $=$ Area of valve $\times$ pressure $= \frac{\pi}{4}(100)^2 \times 1.2 = 9424.8$ N

Now $f_s = \frac{16\,WR}{\pi d^3}\left(1 + \frac{d}{4R}\right)$

or $\dfrac{d^3}{1 + \dfrac{d}{4R}} = \dfrac{16\,WR}{f_s\,\pi} = \dfrac{16 \times 9424.8\,(100)}{90 \times \pi} = 53333$

To solve the above equation, by trial and error, let us first neglect $\dfrac{d}{4R}$.

Then we get $d = (53333)^{\frac{1}{3}} \approx 37.64$ mm

Then $\dfrac{d}{4R} = \dfrac{37.64}{4\,(100)} = 0.094$

$\dfrac{d^3}{1 + 0.094} = 53333$, from which we get $d = 38.8$ or say **39 mm**

Again, from Eq. 22.4, $n = \dfrac{N d^4 \delta}{64\,W R^3} = \dfrac{0.84 \times 10^5\,(39)^4\,(25)}{64\,(9424.8)\,(100)^3} = 8.1$

Hence keep $n = 9$

Example 22.16. *Compare the resilience of a closely coiled helical spring of square section wire with that of a circular section if the volume of both the springs is the same. Prove that for equal weight a closely coiled circular section helical spring of given diameter is 1.36 times as strong and will absorb 1.62 times as much energy as square section.*

Solution :

Let $b = $ length of each side of square and $d = $ dia. of circular section.

(a) For square section :

$$T = 0.208\,f_s\,b^3 \; ; \; \theta = \frac{7.11\,TL}{N b^4}$$

$\therefore$ Work absorbed, $U_s = \frac{1}{2}T\theta = \frac{1}{2}(0.208\,f_s\,b^3)\left[\frac{7.11\,L}{N b^4}(0.208\,f_s\,b^3)\right]$

$$= \frac{0.1538\,f_s^2}{N}(b^2 L) = \frac{0.1538\,f_s^2}{N}(V)$$

Hence resilience $u_s = \dfrac{0.1538 f_s^2}{N}$ ...(1)

(b) For circular section

$$T = f_s \frac{\pi}{16} d^3 \; ; \; \theta = \frac{TL}{NJ} = \frac{TL}{N \dfrac{\pi}{32} d^4} = \frac{32\,T}{\pi N d^4}$$

∴ Work absorbed, $U_c = \dfrac{1}{2} T \theta$

$$= \frac{1}{2}\left(f_s \frac{\pi}{16} d^3\right)\left[\frac{2L}{N \dfrac{\pi}{16} d^4} \times f_s \frac{\pi}{16} d^3\right] = \frac{1}{4}\frac{f_s^2}{N}\left(\frac{\pi}{4} d^2 L\right) = \frac{1}{4}\frac{f_s^2}{N}(V)$$

∴ Resilience, $u_c = \dfrac{1}{4}\dfrac{f_s^2}{N} = 0.25 \dfrac{f_s^2}{N}$ ...(2)

∴ $\dfrac{\text{Resilience of circular section}}{\text{Resilience of square section}} = \dfrac{u_c}{u_s} = \dfrac{0.25}{0.1538} = \mathbf{1.625}$

Hence for equal weight, the circular section will absorb 1.625 times more energy than the square section.

Also, for circular section, $T_c = f_s \dfrac{\pi d^3}{16} = f_s \cdot \dfrac{d}{4} \times \text{Area}$

For square section, $T_s = 0.208 f_s b^3 = 0.208 f_s b \times \text{Area}$

∴ $\dfrac{T_c}{T_s} = \dfrac{d}{4 \times 0.208 b}$

But, for equal weight $\dfrac{\pi}{4} d^2 L = b^2 L$

or $d = b \sqrt{\dfrac{4}{\pi}} = 1.1284\, b$

Hence $\dfrac{T_c}{T_s} = \dfrac{1.1284\, b}{4 \times 0.208 b} = \mathbf{1.356}$

Hence for equal weight, a circular section is 1.356 times as strong as the square section.

Example 22.17. *A close-coiled helical spring is to have a stiffness of 900 N/m in compression with a maximum load of 45 N and a maximum shearing stress of 120 N/mm². The "solid" length of the spring (i.e. coils touching) is 45 mm. Find the wire diameter, mean coil radius, and number of coils. Take* $N = 40000 \, N/mm^2$. (U.L.)

Solution :

Given : $S = 900 \, \text{N/m} \; ; W = 45 \, \text{N} \; ; \; f_s = 120 \, \text{N/mm}^2;$

From Eq. 22.5 $S = \dfrac{N d^4}{64 R^3 n}$; Given $S = 900 \, \text{N/m} = 0.9 \, \text{N/mm}$

or $\qquad d^4 = \dfrac{64 R^3 n}{N} S = \dfrac{64 R^3 n}{40000} \times 0.9 = 1.44 \times 10^{-3} R^3 n \qquad$ ...(1)

From Eq. 22.6, $\qquad f_s = \dfrac{16 WR}{\pi d^3}$

or $\qquad R = \dfrac{\pi d^3 f_s}{16 W} = \dfrac{\pi (120) d^3}{16 \times 45} = 0.5236 \, d^3 \qquad$ ...(2)

Also, solid length $= n \, d$

∴ $\qquad n = \dfrac{\text{solid length}}{d} = \dfrac{45}{d} \qquad$ ...(3)

Substituting the value of R and n in (1), we get

$$d^4 = 1.44 \times 10^{-3} (0.5236 \, d^3)^3 \left(\dfrac{45}{d}\right) = 0.0093 \, d^8$$

∴ $\qquad d^4 = \dfrac{1}{0.0093} = 107.5$

From which $\qquad d = 3.22 \text{ mm}$

Hence from (2), $\qquad R = 0.5236 (3.22)^3 = 17.48 \text{ mm}$

and, from (3), $\qquad n = \dfrac{45}{3.22} = 13.975 \approx 14$

Example 22.18. *The mean diameter of a close-coiled helical spring is 10 times the diameter of the wire and when 3000 N-m of work is done upon the spring, a compression of 300 mm is produced. Given that the maximum torsional shear stress under these conditions is not to exceed 500 N/mm³ and N = 0.84 × 10⁵ N/mm², determine (a) the diameter of wire (b) the mean diameter of coils (c) number of free coils.*

Solution :

Given $\quad D = 10 \, d$; $U = 3000$ N-mm$= 3 \times 10^6$ N-mm ; $\delta = 300$ mm ; $f_s = 500$ N/mm^2

$$U = \dfrac{1}{2} W . \delta$$

∴ $\qquad W = \dfrac{2U}{\delta} = \dfrac{2 \times 3 \times 10^6}{300} = 20 \times 10^3 \text{ N}$

Now $\qquad f_s = \dfrac{16 WR}{\pi d^3} = \dfrac{8 WD}{\pi d^3} = \dfrac{8 W (10 \, d)}{\pi d^3} = \dfrac{80 W}{\pi d^2}$

∴ $\qquad d^2 = \dfrac{80 W}{\pi f_s} = \dfrac{80 \times 20 \times 10^3}{\pi (500)} = 1018.6$

From which $\qquad d = 31.92 \text{ mm}$

Mean diameter of coils, $\quad D = 10 \, d = 319.2 \text{ mm}$; $R = 159.6$ mm

Also, from Eq. 22.4, $\qquad n = \dfrac{N d^4 \delta}{64 W R^3} = \dfrac{0.84 \times 10^5 (31.92)^4 (300)}{64 \times 20 \times 10^3 (159.6)^3} = \mathbf{5.03}$

Example 22.19. *In a compound helical spring, the inner spring is arranged within and concentric with the outer one, but is 9 mm shorter. The outer spring has ten coils of mean diameter 24 mm, and the wire diameter is 3 mm. Find the stiffness of the inner spring if an axial load of 150 N causes the outer one to compress 18 mm.*

If the radial clearance between the springs is 1.5 mm, find the wire diameter of the inner spring when it has eight coils. $N = 77000 \, N/mm^2$.   *(U.L.)*

Solution :

Since the inner spring is shorter than the outer spring by 9 mm, the outer spring compresses first, before both the springs start taking the load.

∴ Load taken by the outer spring to compress 18 mm is given by (Eq. 22.4)

$$W_1 = \frac{N d_1^4 \delta_1}{64 R_1^3 n_1} = \frac{77000 \, (3)^4 \, (18)}{64 \, (12)^3 \, (10)} = 101.5 \text{ N}$$

∴   Load taken by the inner spring $W_2 = 150 - 101.5 = 48.5$ N

Compression of inner spring $\delta_2 = 18 - 9 = 9 \text{ mm}$

∴   Stiffness of inner spring $S_2 = \dfrac{W_2}{\delta_2} = \mathbf{5.39 \ N/mm}$

Mean diameter of outer spring, $D_1 = 24$ mm

∴   Mean diameter of inner spring, $D_2 = 24 - 3 - 2 \times 1.5 - d = 18 - d$

Also, number of coils for inner spring, $n_2 = 8$

For inner spring, $S_2 = \dfrac{N d_2^4}{64 \, n_2 R_2^3} = \dfrac{N d_2^4}{8 \, n_2 D_2^3} = \dfrac{N d_2^4}{8 \, n_2 \, (18 - d_2)^3}$

or $\dfrac{d_2^4}{(18 - d_2)^3} = \dfrac{8 \, n_2 \, S_2}{N} = \dfrac{8 \times 8 \, (5.39)}{77000} = \dfrac{1}{223.2}$

The above equation is solved by trial and error. In the first trial, neglecting d_2 in comparison to 18, we get

$$d_2^4 = \frac{(18)^3}{223.3} \text{ , from which we get } d_2 = 2.26$$

Second trial : $\dfrac{d_2^4}{(18 - 2.26)^3} = \dfrac{1}{223.2}$, from which $d_2 = 2.04$ mm

Final trial : $\dfrac{d_2^4}{(18 - 2.04)^3} = \dfrac{1}{223.2}$, from which $d_2 = \mathbf{2.06 \ mm}$

Example 22.20. *A close-coiled helical spring whose free length when not compressed is 150 mm, is required to absorb strain energy equal to 50 N-m when fully compressed with the coils in contact. The maximum torsional shear stress is limited to 140 N/mm². Assuming a mean coil diameter of 100 mm, find the diameter of steel wire required and the number of coils. Take $N = 0.8 \times 10^5 \, N/mm^2$.*

Solution :

Given : Uncompressed length = 150 mm ; solid length = nd

$$U = 50 \text{ N-m} = 50 \times 10^3 \text{ N-mm} \; ; \; f_s = 140 \text{ N/mm}^2;$$
$$D = 100 \text{ mm} ; R = 50 \text{ mm}$$

$$\delta = \text{uncompressed length} - \text{solid length} = 150 - nd$$

Now
$$U = \frac{f_s^2}{4N} \times V = \frac{f_s^2}{4N} \times \frac{\pi}{4} d^2 (2 \pi R n)$$

$\therefore$
$$50 \times 10^3 = \frac{(140)^2}{4 \times 0.8 \times 10^5} \times \frac{\pi}{4} d^2 (2 \pi \times 50) n$$

From which, we get $\quad n d^2 = 3308.4$ ...(1)

Also,
$$f_s = \frac{16 W R}{\pi d^3}$$

$\therefore$
$$\frac{W}{d^3} = \frac{f_s \pi}{16 R} = \frac{140 \pi}{16 \times 50} = 0.5498$$ ...(2)

Again
$$\delta = \frac{64 W R^3 n}{N d^4}$$

or
$$(150 - nd) = \frac{64 R^3 n}{N d} \left(\frac{W}{d^3} \right) = \frac{64 (50)^3 n}{0.8 \times 10^5 d} \times 0.5498$$

Substituting the value of $\quad n d = \dfrac{3308.4}{d}$ and $n = \dfrac{3308.4}{d^2}$, we get

$$\left(150 - \frac{3308.4}{d} \right) = \frac{54.98}{d} \left(\frac{3308.4}{d^2} \right)$$

or $\quad 150 d^3 - 3308.4 d^2 - 181896 = 0$

or $\quad d^3 - 22.06 d^2 - 1212.6 = 0$

Solving this equation by trial and error, we get $d = \textbf{24.1 mm}$

Hence from (1), $n = \dfrac{3308.4}{(24.1)^2} \approx \textbf{5.7}$

Example 22.21. *A stiff bar of negligible weight transmits a load W to a combination of 3 springs, as shown in Fig. 22.11. The three springs are made of the same material and out of rods of equal diameters. They are of the same length before loading. The number of coils in the three springs are 10, 12 and 15 respectively while the mean radii of the coils are in the proportion 1 : 1.2 : 1.4 respectively. Find the distance x such that the stiff bar remains horizontal after applying the load.*   *(AMIE Nov. 1961).*

Solution :

Since the bar is rigid, and remains horizontal after the load P is applied, the deflection of each spring will be the same.

$\therefore$
$$\delta_1 = \delta_2 = \delta_3 = \delta \text{ (say)}$$

Also, the springs are made of the same material and out of the rods of equal diameter, we have

$$N_1 = N_2 = N_3 = N \text{ and } d_1 = d_2 = d_3 = d$$

Also : Given $n_1 = 10$; $n_2 = 12$ and $n_3 = 15$ and $R_1 : R_2 ; R_3 = 1 : 1.2 : 1.4$. Hence $R_2 = 1.2 R_1$ and $R_3 = 1.4 R_1$.

Now $W_1 = \dfrac{N d^4 \delta}{64 R_1^3 n_1} = \dfrac{N d^4 \delta}{64 R_1^3 (10)} = \dfrac{N d^4 \delta}{640 R_1^3}$ ...(1)

$W_2 = \dfrac{N d^4 \delta}{64 R_2^3 n_2} = \dfrac{N d^4 \delta}{64 (1.2 R_1)^3 (12)} = \dfrac{N d^4 \delta}{1327.1 R_1^3}$ ...(2)

and $W_3 = \dfrac{N d^4 \delta}{64 R_3^3 n_3} = \dfrac{N d^4 \delta}{64 (1.4 R_1)^3 15} = \dfrac{N d^4 \delta}{2634.2 R_1^3}$

...(3)

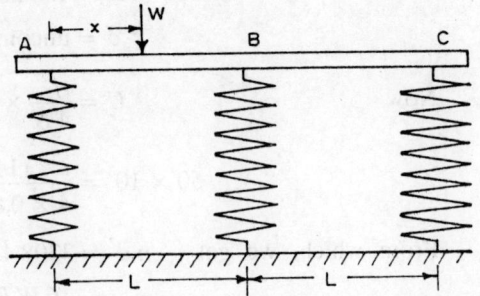

FIG. 22.11

From (1) and (2), we get $\quad W_2 = \dfrac{640}{1327.1} W_1 = 0.4823 W_1$

From (1) and (3), we get $\quad W_3 = \dfrac{640}{2634.2} W_1 = 0.2430 W_1$

Now, taking moments about the line of action of W_1, we get

$$W_2 L + W_3 (2 L) = W x$$

or $\quad 0.4823 W_1 L + 0.2430 W_1 (2 L) = W x$

$\therefore \qquad\qquad\qquad\qquad x = \dfrac{(0.4823 W_1 + 0.4860 W_1) L}{W}$ ...(a)

But $\qquad\qquad W = W_1 + W_2 + W_3 = W_1 + 0.4823 W_1 + 0.2430 W_1 = 1.7253 W_1$ ...(b)

Hence from (a), we get $\quad x = \dfrac{0.4823 W_1 + 0.4860 W_1}{1.7253 W_1} L = \mathbf{0.5612 L}$

Example 22.22. *A close-coiled helical spring of circular section extends 1 cm when subjected to an axial load W, and there is an angular rotation of 1 radian when a torque T is independently applied about the axis. If D is the mean coil diameter, show that*

$$\frac{T}{W} = \frac{D^2 (1 + \mu)}{4} \qquad \text{where } \mu \text{ is the Poisson's ratio.}$$

Determine Poisson's ratio if D = 3 cm, a load of 55 N extends the spring 5.45 cm, and a torque of 300 N-mm produces an angular rotation of 60°. *(Based on U.L.)*

Solution :

From Eq. 22.4, we know that $W = \dfrac{N d^4 \delta}{8 D^3 n}$ ...(1)

Also, from Eq. 22.15, we have $\varphi = \dfrac{T L}{E I} = \dfrac{T (\pi D n)}{E \dfrac{\pi}{64} d^4} = \dfrac{64 T D n}{E d^4}$

or $\qquad\qquad\qquad\qquad T = \dfrac{E d^4 \varphi}{64 D n}$ ...(2)

Here, $\qquad\qquad\qquad \delta = \varphi = 1$. Hence

$$\frac{T}{W} = \left(\frac{E \, d^4}{64 \, D \, n} \right) \left(\frac{8 \, D^3 \, n}{N \, d^4} \right) = \frac{E}{N} \cdot \frac{D^2}{8}$$

But

$$\frac{E}{N} = 2 \, (1 + \mu)$$

∴

$$\frac{T}{W} = \frac{D^2 \, (1 + \mu)}{4} \quad \text{(Proved)} \qquad \qquad ...(3)$$

For the given data : $D = 3$ cm ; $W = 55$ N / 5.45 = 10.092 N/cm

$$T = \frac{300}{600 \times \dfrac{\pi}{180}} = \frac{300 \times 3}{\pi} \text{ N-mm/radian } = \frac{90}{\pi} \text{ N-cm/radian}$$

Hence from (3), we get $(1 + \mu) = \dfrac{4 \, T}{W \, D^2} = \dfrac{4 \times 90 / \pi}{10.092 \, (3)^2} = 1.262$

∴ $\mu = \mathbf{0.262}$

Example 22.23. *An open coiled helical spring and a close-coiled helical spring are similar in every respect, except that the elongation of the open coiled spring is 2.5% greater than that of the close-coiled spring, under the same load. Determine the angle of inclination of the coils of the open coil springs. Take E/N = 2.5.*

Solution :

Using suffix 1 for open coiled spring and 2 for close-coiled spring,

We have $\delta_1 = 1.025 \, \delta_2$

∴ $\dfrac{64 \, W R^3 \cdot n}{d^4 \cos \alpha} \left[\dfrac{\cos^2 \alpha}{N} + \dfrac{2 \sin^2 \alpha}{E} \right] = 1.025 \times \dfrac{64 \, W R^3 \, n}{N \, d^4}$

or $\dfrac{1}{N \cos \alpha} \left[\cos^2 \alpha + \dfrac{2 N}{E} \sin^2 \alpha \right] = \dfrac{1.025}{N}$

or $\cos^2 \alpha + \dfrac{2}{2.5} \, (1 - \cos^2 \alpha) = 1.025 \cos \alpha$

or $\cos^2 \alpha + 0.8 \, (1 - \cos^2 \alpha) = 1.025 \cos \alpha$

or $0.2 \cos^2 \alpha - 1.025 \cos \alpha + 0.8 = 0$

or $\cos^2 \alpha - 5.125 \cos \alpha + 4 = 0$

∴ $\cos \alpha = \dfrac{5.125 \pm \sqrt{(5.125)^2 - 4 \times 4 \times 1}}{2 \times 1} = 4.102 \text{ and } 0.9604$

∴ $\cos \alpha = 0.9604$

From which $\alpha = \mathbf{16.16°}$

Example 22.24. *An open coiled helical spring of a given length of wire, 5 mm is diameter is coiled to a mean diameter of 40 mm, and is loaded with an axial load. If the spring is assumed to be a closely coiled, it would cause an error of 2.5 % in axial deflection. Determine the pitch of the open-coiled spring. Take μ = 0.3.*

Solution : Given : $d = 5$ mm ; $D = 40$ mm ; $R = 20$ mm ; $\mu = 0.3$

Now $E = 2N(1 + \mu)$

$\therefore$ $\dfrac{2N}{E} = \dfrac{1}{1 + \mu} = \dfrac{1}{1 + 0.3} = 0.7692$ ...(1)

Let us use suffix 1 for open coiled spring and 2 for closed coiled spring. We have $L_1 = 2 \pi R n \sec \alpha$ and $L_2 = 2 \pi R n$

$\therefore$ $L_1 > L_2$ and hence $\delta_1 > \delta_2$

$\therefore$ $\dfrac{\delta_1 - \delta_2}{\delta_1} = 0.025$

or $1 - \dfrac{\delta_2}{\delta_1} = 0.025$

$\therefore$ $\delta_2 = 0.975 \, \delta_1$ ...(2)

or $\dfrac{64 \, W R^3 n}{N d^4} = 0.975 \times \dfrac{64 \, W R^3 n}{d^4 \cos \alpha} \left[\dfrac{\cos^2 \alpha}{N} + \dfrac{2 \sin^2 \alpha}{E} \right]$

or $1 = \dfrac{0.975}{\cos \alpha} \left[\cos^2 \alpha + \dfrac{2N}{E} \sin^2 \alpha \right]$

or $1 = \dfrac{0.9575}{\cos \alpha} \left[\cos^2 \alpha + 0.7692 \, (1 - \cos^2 \alpha) \right]$, from (1)

$1.0256 \cos \alpha = \cos^2 \alpha + 0.7692 - 0.7692 \cos^2 \alpha$

or $0.2308 \cos^2 \alpha - 1.0256 \cos \alpha + 0.7692 = 0$

or $\cos^2 \alpha - 4.4437 \cos \alpha + 3.3328 = 0$

$\therefore$ $\cos \alpha = \dfrac{4.4437 \pm \sqrt{(4.4437)^2 - 4 \times 3.3328}}{2} = 3.4883 \, , 0.9554$

$\therefore$ $\cos \alpha = 0.9554$

From which $\alpha = 17.17°$

Now, if p is the pitch, we have $\dfrac{p}{\pi D} = \tan \alpha$

$\therefore$ $p = \pi D \tan \alpha = \pi \, (40) \tan 17.17° = \textbf{38.84 mm}$

Example 22.25. *An open coiled helical spring made of 4 mm dia. steel wire, has 8 coils of 40 mm diameter and 30 mm pitch. The spring is subjected to a winding torque about the axis of the spring, resulting in an increase in the number of coils by 0.8, the length remaining the same (i.e. 240 mm). Determine (a) the torque required, and (b) minimum elastic limit strength of steel to permit this amount of winding. Take $E = 2 \times 10^5 \, N/mm^2$ and $N = 0.83 \times 10^5 \, N/mm^2$.*

Solution :

Given : $d = 4$ mm ; $n = 8$; $D = 40$ mm ;
$R = 20$ mm ; $p = 30$ mm ; $n' - n = 0.8$

Vertical length of spring $= p \cdot n = 30 \times 8 = 240$ mm.

The spring is subjected to a winding torque T. Due to this torque, the vertical length of the spring is bound to increase, *i.e.* δ has to be a finite positive value. However, since the length does not increase (*i.e.* since $\delta = 0$), a restraining force W exists there, due to which the resulting deflection is zero. In other words, the spring is subjected to (*a*) a winding torque T and (*b*) a restraining force W of opposite nature. Under the combined action of T and W, we have

$$\delta = \frac{64\,T R^2 n \sin\alpha}{d^4}\left[\frac{1}{N} - \frac{2}{E}\right] - \frac{64\,W R^3 n \sec\alpha}{d^4}\left[\frac{\cos^2\alpha}{N} + \frac{2\sin^2\alpha}{E}\right] \qquad ...(1)$$

and $$\varphi = \frac{64\,T R n \sec\alpha}{d^4}\left[\frac{2\cos^2\alpha}{E} + \frac{\sin^2\alpha}{N}\right] - \frac{64\,W R^2 n \sin\alpha}{d^4}\left[\frac{1}{N} - \frac{2}{E}\right] \qquad ...(2)$$

Now $\tan\alpha = \dfrac{p}{\pi D} = \dfrac{30}{\pi\,(D)}$, from which $\alpha = 13.427°$

∴ $\sin\alpha = 0.2322;\qquad \cos\alpha = 0.9727;\qquad \sec\alpha = 1.0281$

$\sin^2\alpha = 0.0539;\qquad \cos^2\alpha = 0.9461$

Substituting the values in (1) and putting $\delta = 0$, we get

$$\frac{64\,T\,(20)^2\,8\,(0.2322)}{(4)^4}\left[\frac{1}{0.8\times10^5} - \frac{2}{2\times10^5}\right] - \frac{64\,W\,(20)^3\,8\,(1.0281)}{(4)^4}\left[\frac{0.9461}{0.83\times10^5} + \frac{2\times0.0539}{2\times10^5}\right] = 0$$

or $4.644 \times 10^{-4}\,T - 0.1964\,W = 0$

From which $\qquad\qquad W = 2.3648 \times 10^{-3}\,T \qquad\qquad\qquad\qquad ...(3)$

Now angle of rotation $\quad \varphi = 0.8$ coils $= 0.8\,(2\pi)$ radians $= 5.0265$ radians

Substituting $\qquad\qquad \varphi = 5.0265$ radians

and $\qquad\qquad\qquad W = 2.5012 \times 10^{-3}\,T$ in Eq. (2), we get

$$5.0265 = \frac{64\,T\,(20)\,8\,(1.0281)}{(4)^4}\left[\frac{2\times0.9461}{2\times10^5} + \frac{0.0539}{0.83\times10^5}\right] - \frac{64\,(2.3648\times10^{-3}\,T)\,(20)^2\,8\,(0.2322)}{(4)^4}$$
$$\times\left[\frac{1}{0.83\times10^5} - \frac{2}{2\times10^5}\right]$$

or $\qquad\qquad 5.0265 = 4.1578 \times 10^{-4}\,T - 8.9974 \times 10^{-7}\,T$

From which, we get $\qquad T = 12116$ **N-mm** $= 12.116$ **N-mm**

Now $$\frac{M}{I} = \frac{f_b}{y} = \frac{f_b}{d/2}$$

∴ $$f_b = \frac{M}{I}\frac{d}{2} = \frac{T}{\dfrac{\pi}{64}d^4}\cdot\frac{d}{2} = \frac{32\,T}{\pi\,d^3}$$

(since the spring is subjected to a winding torque T only)

∴ $$f_b = \frac{32 \times 12116}{\pi\,(4)^3} = 1928.2\ \textbf{N/mm}^2$$

PROBLEMS

1. A close-coiled helical spring, made out of a 10 mm diameter steel rod, has 10 complete coils each of mean diameter of 80 mm. Calculate (a) the stress induced in the section of the rod, (b) the deflection under the pull and (c) the amount of energy stored in the spring during the extension if it is subjected to an axial pull of 200 N. Take $N = 0.84 \times 10^5$ N/mm^2.

2. A weight of 200 N is dropped on to a helical compression spring made of 15 mm steel wire closely coiled to a mean diameter of 150 mm with 24 coils. If the instantaneous compression is 100 mm, calculate the height of drop. Take $N = 0.9 \times 10^5$ N/mm^2.

3. A close coiled helical spring is made of 10 mm diameter steel rod, the coils having 10 complete turns and a mean diameter of 80 mm. Calculate the increase in the number of turns and the bending stress induced in the section, if it is subjected to an axial twist of 10 N-m. Take $E = 2.1 \times 10^5$ N/mm^2. Also, calculate the torsional stiffness of the spring.

4. A composite spring has two close-coiled helical springs connected in series : each spring has 12 coils at a mean diameter of 25 mm. Find the wire diameter for one if the other is of 2.5 mm diameter and the stiffness of the composite spring is 700 N/m.

Estimate the greatest load that can be carried by the composite spring, and the corresponding extension, for a maximum shear stress of 180 N/mm^2. Take $N = 80000$ N/mm^2. (U.L.)

5. In an open coiled helical spring having $\alpha = 25°$, calculate the error in the value obtained for the stiffness if the inclination of the coil is neglected. Take $E/N = 2.5$.

6. An open coiled helical spring is made having ten turns around to a mean diameter of 120 mm. The wire diameter is 10 mm and the coils make an angle of 30° with the plane perpendicular to the axis of the coil. Find (a) the axial extension with a load of 100 N and (b) the angle the free end will turn through with this load if free to rotate. Take $E = 208000$ N/mm^2 and $N = 83000$ N/mm^2.

7. A laminated spring of the quarter-elliptic type, 0.6 m long, is to provide a static deflection of 75 mm under an end load of 1962 N. If the leaf material is 60 mm wide and 6 mm thick, Find the number of leaves required and the maximum stress.

From what height can the load be dropped on the undeflected spring to cause a maximum stress of 750 N/mm^2 ? $E = 208000$ N/mm^2. (Based on U.L.)

8. A flat spiral spring is 6 mm wide, 0.25 mm thick, and 2.5 m long. Assuming the maximum stress of 800 N/mm^2 to occur at the point of greatest B.M., calculate the torque, the work stored, and the number of the turns to wind up the spring. $E = 20800$ N/mm^2. (U.L.)

ANSWERS

1.   (a) 43.29 N/mm^2 (b) 9.75 mm (c) 0.975 J
2.   75.8 mm
3.   0.0388 ; 101.86 N/mm^2; 41 N-m/rad.
4.   2.11 mm ; 25.45 N ; 36.36 mm
5.   6.4 %
6.   18.26 mm ; 1.61°
7.   13 ; 251.54 N/mm^2 ; 106.2 mm
8.   25 mm ; 600 N-mm ; 7.65 turns.

Thin Cylinders and Spheres

23.1. INTRODUCTION

Cylindrical and spherical shells are frequently used in Engineering works, common examples being steam boilers, reservoirs, tanks, working chambers of engines, gas cylinders etc. The walls of the shells are subjected to pressure from fluids, dry materials or gases. These shells may be basically of two types. (*i*) thin shells, and (*ii*) thick shells, depending upon the ratio of the thickness of the wall to the diameter of the shell. If the thickness of the wall of the shell is less than 1/10 to 1/15 of its diameter, the shell may be treated as a thin shell. For such a shell, it is assumed, with sufficient accuracy that the normal stresses, which may be either tensile or compressive, are uniformly distributed through the thickness of the wall. If, on the other hand, the thickness of the wall of the shell is more than the above limit, the shell is treated as a thick shell, the analysis of which is more complex, and the normal stresses vary along the thickness of the wall of the shell. This chapter deals with thin shells only, while the thick shells have been discussed in the next chapter.

23.2. PROJECTED AREA THEOREM

Fig. 23.1(*a*) shows a hemispherical vessel subjected to internal pressure *p*. Let us find the resultant upward force *P*, usually known as *bursting force*, acting at *C*. Consider an element of surface area δA ($= r\,\delta\theta$), the normal of which makes an angle θ with the vertical centre line, the element itself subtending an angle $\delta\theta$ at the centre. Normal force on the element

$$= \delta P_n = p \cdot \delta A = p \cdot r\,\delta\theta \cdot L \quad ...(i)$$

(where *L* is the length of the elementary ring)

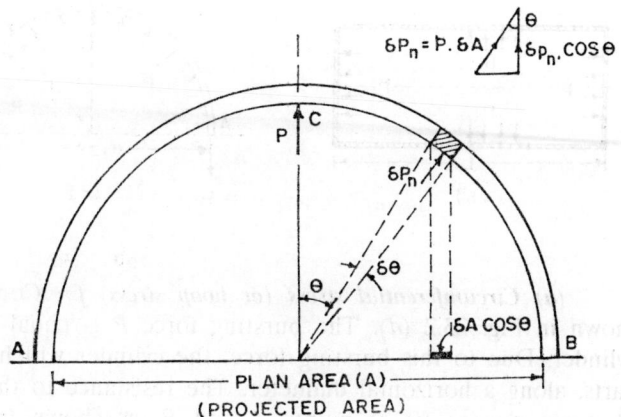

FIG. 23.1

Vertical component of this force $= \delta P_n \cos\theta = p \cdot \delta A \cos\theta = p \cdot r\,\delta\theta \cdot L \cos\theta$ ...(*ii*)

$$\therefore \text{ Total vertical force } \quad P = \Sigma \, \delta P_n = 2 \int_0^{\pi/2} p \cdot \delta A \cdot \cos \theta = 2 \int_0^{\pi/2} p \, (r \, \delta\theta \, L) \cos \theta$$

or $$P = 2 \, p \, r \, L = p \, d \, L = p \times \text{projected area}$$

Hence Bursting force (vertical force) = $p \times$ projected area of the surface on an horizontal plane.

23.3. THIN CYLINDRICAL SHELL SUBJECT TO INTERNAL PRESSURE

Consider a thin cylinder of internal diameter d and wall thickness t, subject to internal gauge pressure p (Fig.23.2 a,b). The following stresses are induced in the cylinder (Fig. 23.2 c)

(i) Circumferential tensile stress (or hoop stress) f

(ii) Longitudinal (or axial) tensile stress f_0

(iii) Radial compressive stress f which varies from a value at the inner surface equal to the pressure p to the atmospheric pressure at the outside surface.

Since the internal pressure in thin cylinders must, of necessity, be low, the radial stress is negligible compared with the axial stress and hoop tension. Hence the third stress is neglected.

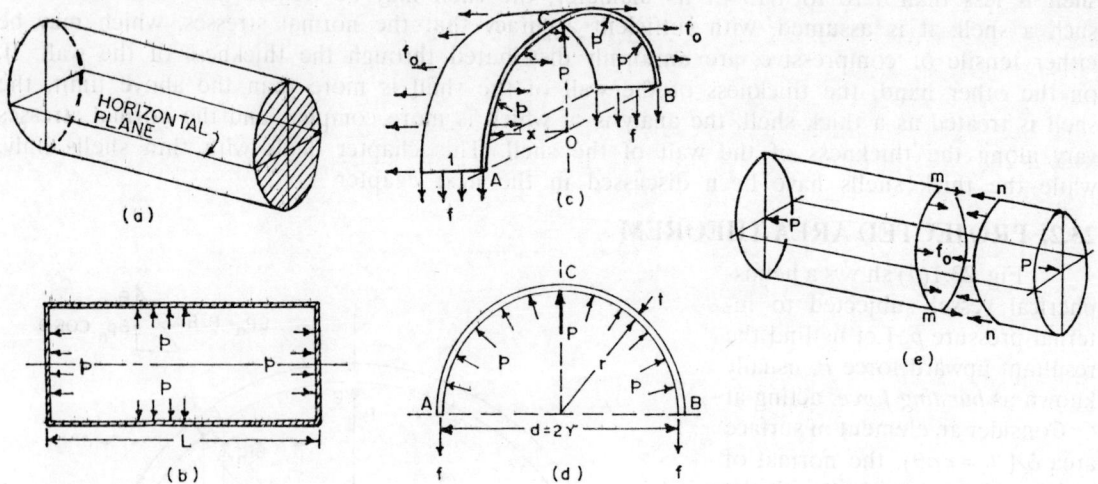

FIG. 23.2

(a) Circumferential stress (or hoop stress) f : Consider the cross-section of the cylinder, shown in Fig. 23.2 (d). The bursting force P is equal to $p.d.L$, where L is the length of the cylinder. Due to this bursting force, the cylinder will have a tendency to get splitted into two parts, along a horizontal diameter. The resistance to this action is offered by the development of hoop stresses (f) at points A and B, as shown in Fig. 23.2 (d).

For equilibrium, we have : $f(2tL) = P = p \cdot d \cdot L$

or $$f = \frac{pd}{2t} \qquad\qquad ...(23.1)$$

However, if η is the efficiency of the longitudinal riveted joint, $f_j = \dfrac{pd}{2t\eta}$ $\qquad$ ...(23.1 a)

(b) Longitudinal stress (or axial stress) f_0 : Since the cylinder is closed at the ends, the internal pressure on each end will give rise to a *bursting force* $P = p \cdot \frac{\pi}{4} d^2$. Due to the bursting force P on each end, the cylinder will have the tendency to get splitted at two transverse planes mm and nn (say), and this is resisted by the development of longitudinal stress f_0, as shown in Fig. 23.2(e).

For equilibrium, we have $f_0 (\pi d t) = p \cdot \frac{\pi}{4} d^2$, from which $f_0 = \frac{p d}{4 t}$ ...(23.2)

Thus we find that the magnitude of the longitudinal stress is one half of the circumferential stress, both the stresses being of tensile nature.

If η is the efficiency of the circumferential riveted joint, $f_{oj} = \frac{p d}{4 t \eta}$ ...(23.2 a)

23.4. MAXIMUM SHEAR STRESS IN CYLINDRICAL SHELL

We have seen in the previous article that a thin cylindrical shell is subjected to three stresses on an element (Fig. 23.3 a, b): (i) the circumferential tensile stress f (ii) the longitudinal tensile stress f_0 and (iii) the radial compressive stress p on the internal face of the element. If p is neglected, the state of stress in the wall of the cylinder approximates to a simple two dimensional system with principal stresses f and f_0. The maximum shearing stress in *the plane of f and f_0* is therefore :

$$\left(\tau_{max}\right) = \frac{1}{2}\left(f - f_0\right) = \frac{p d}{8 t} \quad ...(i)$$

Similarly, maximum shearing stress in *the plane of f and p* (Fig. 23.3 c) is given by

$$\left(\tau_{max}\right) \approx \frac{1}{2}(f) = \frac{p d}{4 t} \quad ...(ii)$$

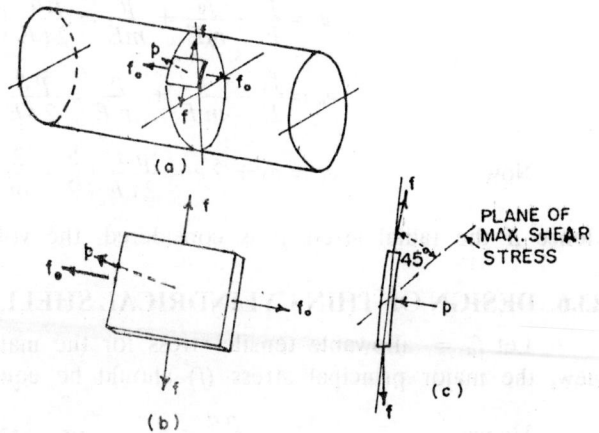

Lastly, the maximum shearing stress in the plane of f_0 and p is given by

$$\tau_{max} \approx \frac{1}{2} f_0 = \frac{p d}{8 t} \quad ...(iii)$$

The greatest of these maximum shearing stresses is given by Eq. (ii)

i.e. $\tau_{max} \approx \frac{1}{2} f = \frac{p d}{4 t}$ ...(23.3)

FIG. 23.3

This occurs on a plane at 45° to the tangent and parallel to the longitudinal axis of the cylinder, as shown in Fig. 23.3(c).

23.5. VOLUMETRIC STRAIN OF THIN CYLINDRICAL SHELL

Let e = circumferential strain (= major principal strain) and e_0 = longitudinal strain

(a) Neglecting the effect of internal pressure p

$$e = \frac{f}{E} - \frac{f_0}{m E} = \frac{f}{E} - \frac{f}{2 m E} \quad \text{(since } f_0 = \frac{f}{2}\text{)}$$

or $e = \frac{f}{E}\left(1 - \frac{1}{2 m}\right) = \frac{p d}{2 t E}\left(1 - \frac{1}{2 m}\right)$ ...(23.4)

Also, $e_0 = \dfrac{f_0}{E} - \dfrac{f}{mE} = \dfrac{f}{2E} - \dfrac{f}{mE} = \dfrac{f}{E}\left(\dfrac{1}{2} - \dfrac{1}{m}\right) = \dfrac{pd}{2tE}\left(\dfrac{1}{2} - \dfrac{1}{m}\right)$ ..(23.5)

Now $e = \dfrac{\text{Change in circumference}}{\text{Original circumference}} = \dfrac{\pi\,\delta d}{\pi d} = \dfrac{\delta d}{d}$

$\therefore$ $\delta d = e \cdot d$; similarly, $\delta L = e_0 \cdot L$ ...(23.6)

From the above relations, the change in the dimensions of the cylinder (i.e. change in the diameter and the change in the length) can be found.

For a cylinder, volume $V = \dfrac{\pi}{4}d^2 \cdot L$

$\therefore$ Change in the volume, $\delta V = \dfrac{\pi}{4}d^2\,\delta L + 2\dfrac{\pi}{4}L\,d \cdot \delta d$

$\therefore$ $\dfrac{\delta V}{V} = e_v = \dfrac{\delta L}{L} + \dfrac{2\,\delta d}{d}$

or $e_v = e_0 + 2\,e$

Substituting the values of e and e_0 from Eq. 23.4 and 23.5, we get

$$e_v = \dfrac{pd}{2tE}\left(\dfrac{1}{2} - \dfrac{1}{m}\right) + 2 \cdot \dfrac{pd}{2tE}\left(1 - \dfrac{1}{2m}\right) = \dfrac{pd}{2tE}\left(\dfrac{5}{2} - \dfrac{2}{m}\right)   ...(23.7)$$

(b) Considering the internal pressure p

$$e = \dfrac{f}{E} - \dfrac{f_0}{mE} + \dfrac{p}{mE} = \dfrac{pd}{2tE}\left(1 - \dfrac{1}{2m}\right) + \dfrac{p}{mE}   ...(23.4\ a)$$

$$e_0 = \dfrac{f_0}{E} - \dfrac{f}{mE} + \dfrac{p}{mE} = \dfrac{pd}{2tE}\left(\dfrac{1}{2} - \dfrac{1}{m}\right) + \dfrac{p}{mE}   ...(23.5\ a)$$

Now $e_v = e_0 + 2\,e = \dfrac{pd}{2tE}\left(\dfrac{5}{2} - \dfrac{2}{m}\right) + \dfrac{3p}{mE}$ ...(23.7\ a)

Hence if the radial stress p is considered, the volumetric strain e_v is increased by $\dfrac{3p}{mE}$.

23.6. DESIGN OF THIN CYLINDRICAL SHELL

Let f_a = allowable tensile stress for the material of the shell. From strength point of view, the major principal stress (f) should be equal to or less than the above value.

Hence $\dfrac{pd}{2t} \le f_a$ or $t \ge \dfrac{pd}{2f_a}$ ...(23.8)

The thickness t of the cylindrical shell of a given diameter d can be found from Eq. 23.8.

Example 23.1 *(a). A thin cylindrical shell has an internal diameter of 250 mm and is 6 mm thick. It is subjected to an internal pressure of 3 MN/m². Estimate the circumferential and longitudinal stresses if the ends of the cylinder are closed. (b) If the ends of the cylinder are closed by pistons sliding in the cylinder, estimate the circumferential and longitudinal stresses.*

Solution :   Given : $d = 250$ mm ; $t = 6$ mm ; $p = 3$ MN/m² $= 3$ N/mm²

(a) *Ends of cylinder closed* : $f = \dfrac{pd}{2t} = \dfrac{3 \times 250}{2 \times 6} = \textbf{62.5}\ \text{N/mm}^2 = \textbf{62.5 MN/m}^2$

$f_0 = \dfrac{pd}{4t} = \dfrac{3 \times 250}{4 \times 6} = \textbf{31.25}\ \text{N/mm}^2 = \textbf{31.25 MN/m}^2$

(b) *Ends closed by sliding pistons* : The effect of taking the end pressure on sliding pistons is to remove the force on the cylinder causing longitudinal stress.

$$\therefore \qquad f = \textbf{62.5 N/mm}^2, \text{ as before} \qquad \text{and } f_0 = \textbf{0}$$

Example 23.2. *A steam boiler, 3 m in diameter, is made of 25 mm thick mild steel plates. The efficiency of longitudinal riveted joint is 88% and that of circumferential riveted joint is 70 %. Determine the permissible steam pressure if the maximum tensile stress in the plate section through the rivets is not to exceed 120 N/mm². Also calculate (a) circumferential stress in the solid plate section, and (b) longitudinal stress in the plate section through the rivets.*

Solution :   Given: $d = 3\,m$; $t = 25$ mm ; $\eta_1 = 88\%$; $\eta_2 = 70\%$; $f_j = 120\,N/mm^2$

$$f_j = \frac{p\,d}{2\,t\,\eta} \qquad \text{or} \qquad p = \frac{2\,f_j\,t\,\eta}{d} = \frac{2 \times 120 \times 25 \times 0.88}{3000} = 1.76\,N/mm^2$$

$$f = \frac{p\,d}{2\,t} = \frac{1.76 \times 3000}{2 \times 25} = 105.6\,N/mm^2 \; ; \quad \text{Also, } f_{oj} = \frac{p\,d}{4\,t\,\eta} = \frac{1.75 \times 3000}{4 \times 25 \times 0.7} = 75\,N/mm^2$$

Example 23.3. *A cylindrical shell 2 m long and 90 cm internal diameter and 12 mm metal thickness is subjected to an internal pressure of 1.6 N/mm². Determine (a) maximum intensity of shear stress, and (b) changes in the dimensions of the shell. Take $E = 2 \times 10^5 \, N/mm^2$ and $1/m = 0.3$.*

Solution :   Given $L = 2$ m ; $d = 900$ mm ; $t = 12$ mm ; $p = 1.6\,N/mm^2$

(a) Maximum shear stress

$$f = \frac{p\,d}{2\,t} = \frac{1.6 \times 900}{2 \times 12} = \textbf{60 N/mm}^2 \text{ (tensile)} \; ; \; f_0 = \frac{p\,d}{4\,t} = \frac{f}{2} = \textbf{30 N/mm}^2 \text{ (tensile)}$$

$$\tau_{max} = \frac{f + p}{2} = \frac{60 + 1.6}{2} = \textbf{30.8 N/mm}^2$$

or $$\tau_{max} = \frac{f}{2} = \frac{60}{2} = 30\,N/mm^2, \text{ if } p \text{ is neglected}$$

(b) Changes in the dimensions of the shell

$$e = \frac{f}{E} - \frac{f_0}{m\,E} = \frac{1}{E}(60 - 30 \times 0.3) = \frac{51}{E} \text{ (increase)}$$

$$e_0 = \frac{f_0}{E} - \frac{f}{m\,E} = \frac{1}{E}(30 - 60 \times 0.3) = \frac{12}{E} \text{ (increase)}$$

$$\therefore \text{ Change in the dia.} = \delta d = e\,.\,d = \frac{51 \times 900}{2 \times 10^5} = \textbf{0.2295 mm} \text{ (increase)}$$

Change in the length $= \delta L = e_0\,.\,L = \dfrac{12 \times 2000}{2 \times 10^5} = \textbf{0.12 mm}$ (increase)

$$\frac{\delta V}{V} = e_v = e_0 + 2\,e = \frac{12}{E} + 2 \times \frac{51}{E} = \frac{114}{E}$$

$$\therefore \qquad \delta V = \frac{114}{2 \times 10^5} \left[\frac{\pi}{4}(900)^2 \times 2000 \right] = \textbf{725.2} \times \textbf{10}^3\,\textbf{mm}^3 \text{ (increase)}$$

Example 23.4. *A seamless pipe of 1.2 m diameter is to carry fluid under a pressure of 1.6 N/mm². Taking the permissible stress in the metal as 100 N/mm², determine the thickness of the metal required.*

Solution : Given : $p = 1.6 \, \text{N/mm}^2$; $d = 1.2 \, \text{m}$; $f_a = 100 \, \text{N/mm}^2$

$$i \geq \frac{p\,d}{2\,f_a} \geq \frac{1.6 \times 1200}{2 \times 100} \geq 9.6 \text{ mm. Hence keep } t = \textbf{10 mm.}$$

Example 23.5. *A pipe of internal diameter 150 mm and 4 mm thick is made of mild steel having a tensile yield stress of 380 N/mm². Determine the maximum permissible internal pressure if the stress factor on the maximum shear stress is to be 4.*

Solution : Given $d = 150$ mm ; $t = 4$ mm ; $f_y = 380 \, \text{N/mm}^2$; F.S. = 4

$$\left(\tau_{\max} \right)_{allowable} = \frac{\tau_{\max}}{\text{F.S}} = \frac{1}{4} \left[\frac{1}{2} f_y \right] = \frac{1}{4} \times \frac{1}{2} \times 380 = 47.5 \, \text{N/mm}^2$$

Now $\tau_{\max} = \dfrac{p\,d}{4\,t}$ (Eq. 23.3)

$$\therefore \quad p = \frac{4\,t}{d} (\tau_{\max}) = \frac{4 \times 4}{150} \times 47.5 = \textbf{5.07 N/mm}^2$$

Example 23.6. *A copper cylinder 900 mm long, 400 mm internal diameter and 6 mm thick, with flat ends, is initially full of oil at atmospheric pressure. Calculate the volume of oil which must be pumped into the cylinder in order to raise the pressure to 5 N/mm² above atmospheric pressure. For copper, take E = 1 × 10⁵ N/mm² and Poisson's ratio = 1/3. Take bulk modulus of oil as 2500 N/mm². Neglect the deformation of the end plates.*

Solution : Given $L = 900$ mm ; $d = 400$ mm ; $t = 6$ mm ; $p = 5 \, \text{N/mm}^2$

Under the action of internal pressure, the cylinder expands and the oil is compressed.

Internal volume, $V = \dfrac{\pi}{4} d^2 L = \dfrac{\pi}{4} (400^2) \times 900 = 113.1 \times 10^6 \, \text{mm}^3$

Now volume pumped in = (δV) = Expansion of cylinder (δV_1) + compression of oil (δV_2)

Expansion of cylinder = $\delta V_1 = \dfrac{p \cdot d \cdot V}{2\,t\,E} \left(\dfrac{5}{2} - \dfrac{2}{m} \right) = \dfrac{5 \times 400 \times 113.1 \times 10^6}{2 \times 6 \times 1 \times 10^5} \left(\dfrac{5}{2} - \dfrac{2}{3} \right)$

$$= 345583 \, \text{mm}^3$$

Compression of oil = $\delta V_2 = \dfrac{p\,V}{K} = \dfrac{5 \times 113.1 \times 10^6}{2500} = 226200 \, \text{mm}^3$

$\therefore$ Volume of oil pumped in $= \delta V = \delta V_1 + \delta V_2 = 345583 + 226200 = 571783 \, \text{mm}^3 = \textbf{571.8 cm}^3$

Example 23.7. *A non-ferrous metal tube having a bore of 32 mm and a wall thickness of 1.6 mm has plugged ends. The effective length of the tube between the plugs is 500 mm and an internal fluid pressure of 2 N/mm² is applied. An axial pull of 2000 N is also applied externally to the plugs. Determine when the forces are acting (a) the change in the internal diameter of the tube (b) change in the length. Take E = 104500 N/mm² and Poisson's ratio = 0.35.*

Solution : Given: $d = 32$ mm; $t = 1.6$ mm; $L = 500$ mm; $p = 2 \, \text{N/mm}^2$; $P = 2000 \, \text{N}$

Method 1 : Method of super-position : *Both the effects are evaluated separately.*

(a) *Strains due to internal pressure*

$$f = \frac{p\,d}{2\,t} = \frac{2 \times 32}{2 \times 1.6} = 20 \, \text{N/mm}^2 \text{ (tensile)} \; ; \; f_0 = \frac{p\,d}{4\,t} = \frac{f}{2} = 10 \, \text{N/mm}^2 \text{ (tensile)}$$

$$e = \frac{1}{E}\left(f - \frac{f_0}{m}\right) = \frac{1}{104500}(20 - 10 \times 0.35) = \mathbf{1.579 \times 10^{-4}} \text{ (tensile)}$$

$$e_0 = \frac{1}{E}\left(f_0 - \frac{f}{m}\right) = \frac{1}{104500}(10 - 20 \times 0.35) = \mathbf{0.287 \times 10^{-4}} \text{ (tensile)}$$

(b) Strains due to external load

$$f_0' = \frac{P}{A} = \frac{2000}{\pi \, d \, t} = \frac{2000}{\pi \, (32) \, (1.6)} = 12.43 \text{ N/mm}^2$$

$$\therefore \quad e_0' = \frac{f_0'}{E} = \frac{12.43}{104500} = 1.189 \times 10^{-4} \text{ (tensile)}$$

$$e' = -\frac{f_0'}{m \, E} = -0.35 \times \frac{12.43}{104500} = -0.416 \times 10^{-4} \text{ (i.e. compressive)}$$

(c) By super-position

$$e_f = e + e' = (1.579 - 0.416)\,10^{-4} = 1.163 \times 10^{-4} \text{ (tensile)}$$

$$\therefore \quad \delta d = e_f . d = 1.163 \times 10^{-4} \times 32 = \mathbf{0.00372 \text{ mm}} \text{ (increase)}$$

$$e_{of} = e_0 + e_0' = (0.287 + 1.189)\,10^{-4} = 1.476 \times 10^{-4} \text{ (tensile)}$$

$$\therefore \quad \delta L = e_{of} . L = 1.476 \times 10^{-4} \times 500 = \mathbf{0.0738 \text{ mm}} \text{ (increase)}$$

Method 2 : Direct Method

Since the hoop stress is not affected by the presence of axial load, $f = \frac{pd}{2t} = \frac{2 \times 32}{2 \times 1.6} = 20$ N/mm^2 (tension). The axial stress is affected by the presence of axial load, and is not one half of the hoop stress. Consider the equilibrium of one of the plugs.

$$f_0 \, (\pi \, d \, t) = p \frac{\pi}{4} d^2 + 2000 \; ; \; \text{ or } f_0 \, (\pi \times 32 \times 1.6) = 2 \times \frac{\pi}{4}(32)^2 + 2000$$

From which
$$f_0 = 22.43 \text{ N/mm}^2 \text{ (tension)}$$

$$\therefore \quad e = \frac{1}{E}\left(f - \frac{f_0}{m}\right) = \frac{1}{104500}(20 - 0.35 \times 22.43) = 1.163 \times 10^{-4}$$

and
$$\delta d = e . d = 1.163 \times 10^{-4} \times 32 = \mathbf{0.00372 \text{ mm}} \text{ (increase)}$$

Also,
$$e_0 = \frac{1}{E}\left(f_0 - \frac{f}{m}\right) = \frac{1}{104500}(22.43 - 0.35 \times 20) = 1.476 \times 10^{-4}$$

and
$$\delta L = e_0 . L = 1.476 \times 10^{-4} \times 500 = \mathbf{0.0738 \text{ mm}} \text{ (increase)}$$

Example 23.8. *A steel tube 1.27 mm thick and 100 mm internal diameter is plugged at each end to form a closed cylinder with internal length of 250 mm. The tube is completely filled with oil and subjected to a compressive load of 45 kN. Find (a) pressure in N/mm^2 produced in the oil, (b) the resulting circumferential stress in N/mm^2 in the tube wall. Take $E = 2 \times 10^5$ N/mm^2 and $1/m = 0.28$ for steel and $K = 2667$ N/mm^2 for oil.*

Solution : Given : $d = 100$ mm ; $t = 1.27$ mm; $L = 250$ mm; $P = 45$ kN.

Let
p = internal pressure, in N/mm^2
f = circumferential stress, in N/mm^2
f_0 = longitudinal stress, in N/mm^2 (compressive)

Consider the equilibrium of the plugs

$$f_0 (\pi d t) + p \frac{\pi}{4} d^2 = P = 45000$$

or $\quad f_0 (\pi \times 100 \times 1.27) + p \frac{\pi}{4} (100)^2 = 45000$

or $\qquad f_0 = 112.787 - 19.685 p \quad \text{(compression)...(1)}$

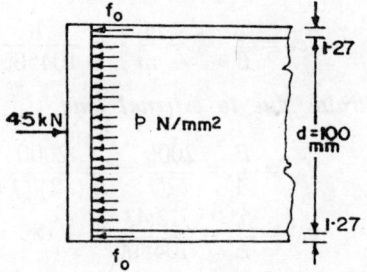

Also, $\quad f = \frac{p d}{2 t} = p \left(\frac{100}{2 \times 1.27} \right)$

$\qquad\qquad = 39.37 p \quad \text{(tension)} \qquad\qquad ...(2)$

Now $\quad \dfrac{\delta V}{V} = 2 e + e_0$

The volumetric strain is negative, i.e. compressive.

FIG. 23.4

$$\therefore \qquad - \frac{p}{K} = \frac{2}{E} \left[f - \frac{f_0}{m} \right] + \frac{1}{E} \left(f_0 - \frac{f}{m} \right) \quad \text{or} \quad - \frac{p E}{K} = 2 \left(f - \frac{f_0}{m} \right) + \left(f_0 - \frac{f}{m} \right)$$

or $- p \times \dfrac{2 \times 10^5}{2667} = 2 (f - 0.28 f_0) + (f_0 - 0.28 f) = 1.72 f + 0.44 f_0 \qquad\qquad ...(3)$

Substituting the values of f and f_0 from (2) and (1), we get

$$- 74.99 p = 1.72 (39.37 p) - 0.44 (112.787 - 19.685 p) = 76.378 p - 49.626$$

From which $\qquad p = \mathbf{0.328 \, N/mm^2} \; ; \; \therefore \; f = 39.37 p = \mathbf{12.91 \, N/mm^2} \; \text{(tension)}$

23.7. THIN SPHERICAL SHELLS SUBJECT TO INTERNAL PRESSURE

Let us now take the case of thin spherical shell of internal diameter d and thickness t subjected to an internal pressure p. Consider a diametral plane through the shell (Fig. 23.5 a). The internal fluid pressure (p) gives rise to a bursting force P given by

$$P = p \times \text{projected area} = p \left(\frac{\pi}{4} d^2 \right) \; ...(i)$$

This is resisted by tensile stress p (known as hoop stress or tangential stress) in the walls of the shell. By symmetry, f is the same at all points of the shell.

For the equilibrium of the shell,

$$f (\pi d t) = P = p \left(\frac{\pi}{4} d^2 \right)$$

From which $\qquad f = \dfrac{p d}{4 t} \qquad ...(23.9)$

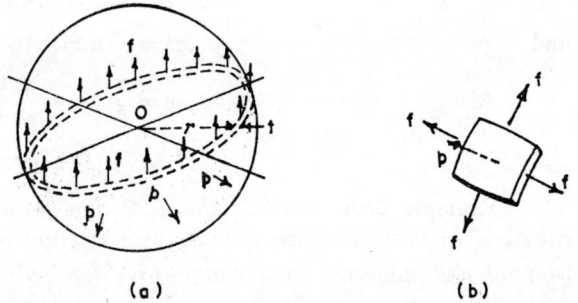

(a)   (b)

If, however, η is the efficiency of the riveted joint, $f_j = \dfrac{p d}{4 \eta t} \qquad ...(23.9 \, a)$

FIG. 23.5

At any point of the shell, the direct stress f has the same magnitude in all directions in the plane of the surface of the shell. Fig. 23.5 (b) shows the membrane stresses in the thin spherical shell under internal pressure. Thus, at any point, the three principal stresses are :

(i) $f_1 = f = \dfrac{pd}{4t}$ (tensile) (ii) $f_2 = f = \dfrac{pd}{4t}$ (tensile) and (iii) p (compressive)

Since p is small compared to f, the maximum shearing stress occurs on planes at $45°$ to the tangent plane at that point, and its magnitude is given by

$$\therefore \qquad \tau_{max} = \frac{f}{2} = \frac{pd}{8t} \text{ (if } p \text{ is neglected)} \qquad ...(23.10)$$

or

$$\tau_{max} = \frac{1}{2}\left(\frac{pd}{4t} + p\right) \text{ (if } p \text{ is considered)} \qquad ...(23.10\ a)$$

23.8. VOLUMETRIC STRAIN IN A THIN SPHERICAL SHELL

The state of stress in a thin spherical shell, subjected to internal pressure p is shown in Fig. 23.5 (c).

(a) Neglecting internal radial pressure p

Hoop strain $e = \dfrac{f}{E} - \dfrac{f}{mE} = \dfrac{f}{E}\left(1 - \dfrac{1}{m}\right) = \dfrac{pd}{4tE}\left(1 - \dfrac{1}{m}\right)$ ...(23.11)

Now $\delta d = e.d$;   Also, $V = \dfrac{\pi}{6}d^3$

$\therefore$ $\delta V = 3\dfrac{\pi}{6}d^2.\delta d$; $\therefore$ $e_v = \dfrac{\delta V}{V} = 3\dfrac{\delta d}{d} = 3e = \dfrac{3pd}{4tE}\left(1 - \dfrac{1}{m}\right)$ ...(23.12)

(b) Considering radial stress p

$$e = \frac{pd}{4tE}\left(1 - \frac{1}{m}\right) + \frac{p}{mE} \qquad ...(23.11\ a)$$

$$\therefore \qquad e_v = \frac{\delta V}{V} = \frac{3pd}{4tE}\left(1 - \frac{1}{m}\right) + \frac{3p}{mE} \qquad ...(23.12\ a)$$

Example 23.9. *A seamless spherical shell is of 0.8 m internal diameter and 4 mm thickness. It is filled with fluid under pressure until its volume increases by 50 cubic centimetres. Determine the fluid pressure, taking $E = 2 \times 10^5\ N/mm^2$ and Poisson's ratio = 0.3.*

Solution :   Given : $d = 0.8$ m $= 800$ mm ; $t = 4$ mm ; $\delta V = 50\ \text{cm}^3$

Volume of the shell, $V = \dfrac{\pi}{6}d^3 = \dfrac{\pi}{6}(800)^3 = 0.268 \times 10^9\ \text{mm}^3$

$\therefore$ $e_v = \dfrac{\delta V}{V} = \dfrac{50 \times 1000}{0.268 \times 10^9} = 1.866 \times 10^{-4}$

But $\dfrac{\delta V}{V} = 3e$, from which $e = \dfrac{1}{3}e_v = \dfrac{1}{3} \times 1.866 \times 10^{-4} = 0.622 \times 10^{-4}$

Hence $e = \dfrac{f}{E}\left(1 - \dfrac{1}{m}\right) = 0.622 \times 10^{-4}$

From which $f = \dfrac{0.622 \times 10^{-4}E}{\left(1 - \dfrac{1}{m}\right)} = \dfrac{0.622 \times 10^{-4} \times 2 \times 10^5}{(1 - 0.3)} = 17.77\ \text{N/mm}^2$

But $f = \dfrac{pd}{4t}$,   or $p = \dfrac{4tf}{d} = \dfrac{4 \times 4 \times 17.77}{800} = 0.355\ \text{N/mm}^2$

23.9. CYLINDRICAL SHELL WITH HEMISPHERICAL ENDS

Many times, hemispherical ends are used in cylindrical shells, to minimise the bending stresses in the cylinder when the ends are flat. Let t_1 be the thickness of the cylindrical shell and t_2 be the thickness of the hemispherical ends. *The thicknesses t_1 and t_2 are proportioned so that the radial expansion is the same in both cylinder and the hemisphere.* By doing so, the bending stresses are eliminated at the junction of the two parts.

Let p be the internal pressure.

Hoop stress in cylindrical portion

$$f = \frac{p\,d}{2\,t_1}$$

Longitudinal stress in cylindrical portion,

$$f_0 = \frac{p\,d}{4\,t_1}$$

∴ Hoop strain,

$$e_c = \frac{1}{E}\left[f - \mu f_0\right] = \frac{p\,d}{4\,t_1 E}(2 - \mu)$$

...(1)

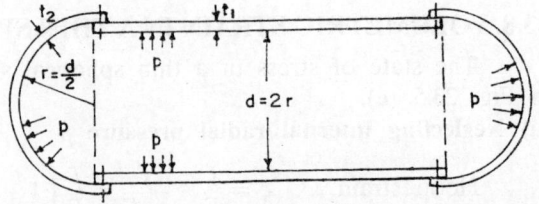

FIG. 23.6

Hoop stress in spherical ends, $f = \dfrac{p\,d}{4\,t_2}$

∴ Hoop strain $e_s = \dfrac{1}{E}(f - \mu f) = \dfrac{p\,d}{4\,t_2 E}(1 - \mu)$ ...(2)

For no distortion of the junction under pressure, $e_c = e_s$

∴ $\qquad \dfrac{2 - \mu}{t_1} = \dfrac{1 - \mu}{t_2}$ or $\dfrac{t_1}{t_2} = \dfrac{2 - \mu}{1 - \mu}$ ...(23.13)

For most metals, μ is approximately 0.3.

∴ $\qquad \dfrac{t_1}{t_2} = \dfrac{2 - 0.3}{1 - 0.3} = \dfrac{1.7}{0.7} = \dfrac{17}{7}$ ...(23.13 *a*)

23.10. WIRE WINDING OF THIN CYLINDERS OR TUBES

We have seen earlier that the thickness t of a thin cylindrical shell depends upon the internal pressure p. If the internal pressure is large, such as in the case of a gun tube etc, the thickness required comes out to be large, with the result that the design becomes very heavy and un-economical. In that case, we may adopt two methods of resisting high internal pressure : (1) providing wire winding around the cylinder/tube, thereby reinforcing it, or (*ii*) providing a *compound tube*. The theory of the compound tube has been discussed in the next chapter. The first method, consisting of reinforcing the cylinder or tube, by winding the wire around it is very commonly used. The wire is wound under tension, thus putting the walls of the cylinder or tube under compression. This way, the cylinder or tube is *prestressed*. When internal pressure is applied, this pressure is resisted jointly by the cylinder/tube and the wire. The final hoop stress produced in the cylinder/tube

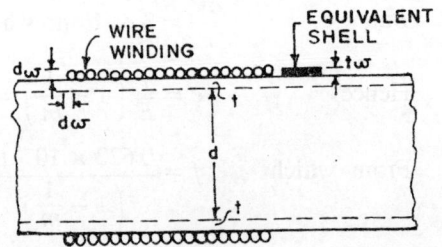

FIG. 23.7

walls is much lesser than it would be without wire reinforcement. The maximum hoop stress will be in the wire; hence the wire must be made of high tensile material. Fig. 23.7 shows a tube of internal diameter d and thickness t, wound with wire of diameter d_w. The analysis is made in the following steps :

Step 1: Replace the wire by an equivalent cylindrical shell of thickness t_w, which has the same area of cross-section in a longitudinal plane as the original wire. Thus, if a length of d_w is considered, original area of cross-section is $\frac{\pi}{4} d_w^2$, while the equivalent area is $d_w . t_w$.

Hence
$$d_w t_w = \frac{\pi}{4} d_w^2 \quad \text{or} \quad t_w = \frac{\pi d_w}{4} \qquad \qquad ...(23.13)$$

Step 2: Let T be the initial tension in the wire. The initial tensile stress f_w in the wire is
$$f_w = \frac{T}{A} = \frac{4 T}{\pi d_w^2} \qquad \qquad ...(23.14)$$

Step 3: Let f_c be the *initial compressive hoop stress* in the cylinder/tube. Then for equilibrium (Fig. 23.8a)
$f_c . t = f_w . t_w$

or $f_c = f_w . \dfrac{t_w}{t}$ ...(23.15)

Step 4: Let us now apply internal pressure p and let f_w' be the additional tensile stress in

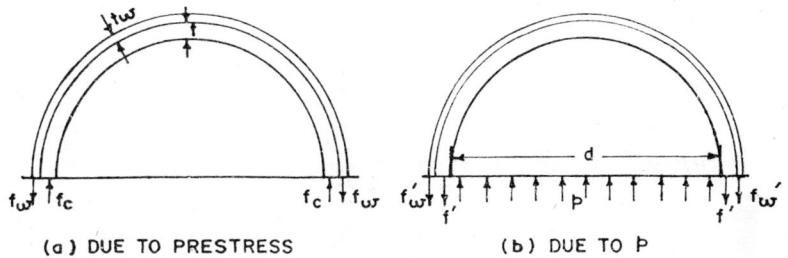

(a) DUE TO PRESTRESS   (b) DUE TO P

FIG. 23.8

wire and f' be the additional tensile hoop stress in the cylinder/tube due to p. For the equilibrium (Fig. 23.8 b)
$$f' . 2 t + f_w' . 2 t_w = p d \qquad \qquad ...(a)$$

Step 5: The longitudinal stress in the cylinder due to p is $f_0 = \dfrac{p d}{4 t}$

Step 6: Since, the wire and cylinder remain in contact, the changes in hoop strain due to the application of pressure must be the same for the, both. Hence
$$\frac{1}{E} \left[f' - \mu f_0 \right] = \frac{1}{E_w} f_w' \qquad \qquad ...(b)$$

where E is the modulus of elasticity for the tube material and E_w is the modulus of elasticity for the wire material.

From Eqs (a) and (b), the stresses f' and f_w' can be found.

Step 7: Final stresses in the cylinder/wire are :

Circumferential stress $= f = f' - f_c$ (tensile)

Longitudinal stress $= f_0$ (tensile)

Final stress in wire $= f_w + f_w'$

Example 23.10. *A cast iron pipe, having 250 mm internal diameter and 15 mm metal thickness, is closely wound with a layer of 6 mm diameter steel wire under a tensile stress of 40 N/mm². Water is admitted under a pressure of 2.5 N/mm² in the pipe. Determine the final stresses set up in the pipe and the wire.*

Take E for $C.I. = 1.02 \times 10^5 \, N/mm^2$, E for steel $= 2.04 \times 10^5 \, N/mm^2$ and $\mu = 0.3$.

Solution :

Given : $d = 250$ mm; $t = 15$ mm; $d_w = 6$ mm; $f_w = 40 \, N/mm^2$; $p = 2.5 \, N/mm^2$.

Step 1: Equivalent thickness of wire, $t_w = \dfrac{\pi \, d_w}{4} = \dfrac{\pi \times 6}{4} = 4.712$ mm

Step 2: $f_w = 40 \, N/mm^2$ (given)

Step 3: Initial compressive hoop stress in pipe $= f_c = f_w \dfrac{t_w}{t} = 40 \times \dfrac{4.712}{15} = 12.566 \, N/mm^2$

Step 4: $f' \cdot 2t + f_w' \cdot 2t_w = p \, d$ or $f' \, (2 \times 15) + f_w' \, (2 \times 4.712) = 2.5 \times 250$

or $f' + 0.314 f_w' = 20.833$ ...(a)

Step 5: $f_0 = \dfrac{p \, d}{4 \, t} = \dfrac{2.5 \times 250}{4 \times 15} = 10.417 \, N/mm^2$

Step 6: $\dfrac{1}{E} \left[f' - \mu f_0 \right] = \dfrac{f_w'}{E_w}$

or $f' - 0.3 \times 10.417 = f_w' \times \dfrac{1.02 \times 10^5}{2.04 \times 10^5}$ or $f' - 0.5 f_w' = 3.125$ ...(b)

From (a) and (b), we get $f_w' = 21.754 \, N/mm^2$ and $f' = 14.002 \, N/mm^2$

Step 7: Final stress in wire $= f_w + f_w' = 40 + 21.754 = \mathbf{61.754 \, N/mm^2}$

Circumferential stress in pipe $= f = f' - f_c = 14.002 - 12.566 = \mathbf{1.436 \, N/mm^2}$

Longitudinal stress in pipe $= f_0 = \mathbf{10.417 \, N/mm^2}$

Alternative solution : In 1 mm length of pipe, there are $\left(\dfrac{1}{6} \times 2 \right) = \dfrac{1}{3}$ sections of wire, and total area of cross-section of wire per 1 mm length $= \dfrac{1}{3} \times \dfrac{\pi}{4} (6)^2 = 9.425$ mm². Hence total compressive force in wire $= 9.425 \times 40 \approx 377$ N. Hence intensity of compressive stress in pipe $= f_c = \dfrac{377}{2 \times 15 \times 1} = 12.566 \, N/mm^2$, which is the same as obtained in step 3.

After water is admitted, let the additional stress in pipe and wire be f' and f_w' respectively.

Bursting force per mm length of pipe $= p \cdot d \cdot L = 2.5 \times 250 \times 1 = 625$ N
Resisting force by pipe, per mm length $= f' L \cdot 2t = f' \times 1 \, (2 \times 15) = 30 f'$
Resisting force of wire, per mm length $= f_w' \times 9.425$

Hence we have from equilibrium, $30 f' + 9.425 f_w' = 625$

or $f' + 0.314 f_w' = 20.833$ ...(a)

Also, from compatibility, $(e)_{pipe} = (e)_{wire}$

where
$$(e)_{pipe} = \frac{f'}{E} - \frac{1}{m E}\frac{p d}{4 t} = \frac{1}{E}\left[f' - \frac{0.3 \times 2.5 \times 250}{4 \times 15}\right] = \frac{1}{E}(f' - 3.125)$$

$$\therefore \quad \frac{1}{E}(f' - 3.125) = \frac{f_w'}{E_w}$$

or
$$f' - 3.125 = f_w' \cdot \frac{E}{E_w} = f_w' \times \frac{1.02 \times 10^5}{2.04 \times 10^5} = 0.5 f_w' \qquad \qquad ...(b)$$

Solving (a) and (b), we get $f_w' = 21.754$ N/mm² and $f' = 14.002$ N/mm²

Hence final stress in wire = 21.754 + 40 = **61.754** N/mm² (tensile)

and Final hoop stress in pipe = 14.002 − 12.566 = **1.436** N/mm² (tensile)

23.11. ADDITIONAL ILLUSTRATIVE EXAMPLES

Example 23.11 *A copper tube 1.2 m long, has 80 mm internal diameter and 2 mm wall thickness. It has closed ends, and is filled with water under pressure. What will be the alteration of pressure if an additional 10 cubic centimeter of water is pumped into the tube. Neglect the distortion of end plates. Take E for copper = 1.02 × 10⁵ N/mm² and μ = 0.3 and bulk modulus for water = 2.1 × 10³ N/mm².*

Solution : Given $L = 1.2$ m ; $d = 80$ mm ; $t = 2$ mm ; $\delta V = 10$ cm³

$V = \frac{\pi}{4}(80)^2 \times 1200 = 6031.9 \times 10^3$ mm³. Let p be the alteration in pressure.

For the tube : Hoop stress $\qquad f = \frac{p d}{2 t} = \frac{p (80)}{2 \times 2} = 20 p$ (tensile)

Longitudinal stress $\qquad f_0 = \frac{p d}{4 t} = \frac{f}{2} = 10 p$ (tensile)

$$e_v = e_0 + 2 e = \frac{1}{E}(10 p - 0.3 \times 20 p) + \frac{2}{E}(20 p - 0.3 \times 10 p)$$

$$= \frac{p}{E}(10 - 6 + 40 - 6) = \frac{38 p}{E} \text{ (increase)}$$

$\therefore$ Change in the volume of the tube $= \frac{38 p}{E} \times V \qquad \qquad ...(i)$

For water : Water will be compressed.

Volumetric strain $= \frac{p}{K}$ $\qquad \therefore$ Change in volume of water $= \frac{p}{K} V \qquad \qquad ...(ii)$

Now total space created = volumetric change in tube + volumetric change in water

or
$$10 (10)^3 = \frac{38 p}{E} V + \frac{p}{K} V = p V\left(\frac{38}{E} + \frac{1}{K}\right)$$

or
$$10000 = 6031.9 \times 10^3 p\left(\frac{38}{1.02 \times 10^5} + \frac{1}{2.1 \times 10^3}\right) = 5119.5 p$$

From which $\qquad p = \mathbf{1.953}$ **N/mm²**

Example 23.12. *A thin cylinder, 150 mm internal diameter and 2.5 mm thick, has its ends closed by rigid plates and is then filled with water. When an external axial pull of 37 kN is applied to the ends, the water pressure is observed to fall by 0.1 N/mm². Determine the value of Poisson's ratio. E = 140000 N/mm² and K = 2200 N/mm².*

(U.L)

Solution : Given: $d = 150$ mm ; $t = 2.5$ mm ; $P = 37$ kN ; $\delta p = -0.1 \, \text{N/mm}^2$

Let us assume that water is under pressure so that cylinder remains full of water when the external pull is applied. Hence the increase in the volume of water is equal to increase in the capacity of cylinder. Since the volumetric strain is determined by *changes* of stresses, only stresses due to drop in pressure need be considered.

$$\text{Reduction in hoop stress} = f = \frac{\delta p \, d}{2 \, t} = \frac{0.1 \times 150}{2 \times 2.5} = 3 \, \text{N/mm}^2$$
$$\text{(compressive)}$$

For increase in the longitudinal stress f_0, refer Fig 23.9. From considerations of equilibrium,

$$f_0 \, (\pi \, d \, t) + \delta p \left(\frac{\pi}{4} d^2 \right) = P$$

or $f_0 \, (\pi \times 150 \times 2.5) + 0.1 \times \frac{\pi}{4} (150)^2 = 37000$

From which $f_0 = 29.907 \, \text{N/mm}^2$ (tensile)   FIG. 23.9

$$e = \frac{1}{E} \left(f + \frac{f_0}{m} \right) = \frac{1}{E} (3 + 29.907 \, \mu) \; \dots \; \text{(decrease)}$$

$$e_0 = \frac{1}{E} \left(f_0 + \frac{f}{m} \right) = \frac{1}{E} (29.907 + 3 \, \mu) \; \dots \; \text{(increase)}$$

$\therefore$ Volumetric strain of cylinder $= e_0 + 2 e = \dfrac{1}{E} \left[(29.907 + 3 \, \mu) - 2 (3 + 29.907 \, \mu) \right]$

$$= \frac{1}{E} [23.907 - 56.814 \, \mu]$$

Volumetric strain of water $= \dfrac{p}{K} = \dfrac{0.1}{K}$. Equating the two strains, we get

$$\frac{0.1}{2200} = \frac{23.907 - 56.814 \, \mu}{140000}. \quad \text{From which } \mu = \textbf{0.309}$$

Example 23.13. *A steel tube having outside and inside diameters of 40 mm and 35 mm is firmly plugged at both the ends, leaving an internal length of 200 mm between the flat ends of the plugs. The plugs are designed so that water can be admitted to the inner space and also so that an axial pull can be applied to the tube. If the tube is subjected to an axial pull of 20 kN and in addition is filled with water at a gauge pressure of $2 \, \text{N/mm}^2$, find the volume of water which will escape from the tube if the axial load is removed and the inner space is open to the atmosphere.*
For steel, take $E = 2.1 \times 10^5 \, \text{N/mm}^2$ and $\mu = 0.286$. For water, take $K = 2.1 \times 10^3 \, \text{N/mm}^2$.

Solution :   Given $d = 35$ mm ; $D = 40$ mm ; $L = 200$ mm ; $P = 20$ kN ; $p = 2 \, \text{N/mm}^2$

$$V = \frac{\pi}{4} d^2 L = \frac{\pi}{4} (35)^2 \times 200 = 19.24 \times 10^4 \, \text{mm}^3$$

Initial conditions :

$$\text{Longitudinal stress } f_0 = \frac{1}{A} \left(\frac{\pi}{4} d^2 p + P \right) = \frac{\frac{\pi}{4} (35)^2 \times 2 + 20000}{\frac{\pi}{4} (40^2 - 35^2)} = 74.44 \, \text{N/mm}^2$$

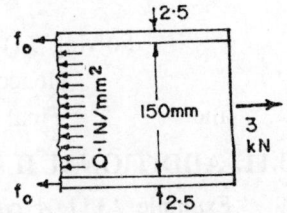

Hoop stress $\qquad f = \dfrac{p\,d}{2\,t} = \dfrac{2 \times 35}{2\,(20 - 17.5)} = 14\ \text{N/mm}^2$ (tensile)

Transverse compressive stress $=$ water pressure, $p = 2\ \text{N/mm}^2$

$\therefore \qquad e = \dfrac{1}{E}\Big[\,14 - 0.286 \times 74.44 + 0.286 \times 2\,\Big] = -\dfrac{6.72}{E}$

$\qquad\qquad e_0 = \dfrac{1}{E}\Big[\,74.44 - 0.286 \times 14 + 0.286 \times 2\,\Big] = +\dfrac{71.01}{E}$

$\therefore$ Volumetric strain $\qquad e_v = e_0 + 2\,e = \dfrac{71.01}{E} - \dfrac{2 \times 6.72}{E} = \dfrac{57.57}{E}$ (increase)

Now $\qquad\qquad \delta V =$ expansion of tube caused by water pressure and external force

$\qquad\qquad\quad = \dfrac{57.57}{2.1 \times 10^5} \times 19.24 \times 10^4 = 52.745\ \text{mm}^3$

$\qquad\qquad \delta V' =$ compression of water under compressive stress p

$\qquad\qquad\quad = \dfrac{p\,V}{K} = \dfrac{2 \times 19.24 \times 10^4}{2.1 \times 10^3} = 183.238\ \text{mm}^3$

$\therefore$ Volume of water escaping when both external load and internal pressure is removed
$= \delta V + \delta V' = 52.745 + 183.238 \approx \mathbf{236\ mm^3}.$

Example 23.14. *A cylindrical tank is 1.6 m diameter, 2 m long and 10 mm thick. Its ends are flat and are joined by nine tie bars, each 30 mm diameter equally spaced. If the tie bars are initially stressed to 40 N/mm² and the tank is filled with water, find (a) the increase in capacity when the pressure is raised to 1.5 N/mm², and (b) the final stress in the tie bars. Take $E = 2 \times 10^5\ N/mm^2$ and $\mu = 0.29$.*

Solution : Given : $\qquad d = 1.6$ m; $L = 2$ m ; $t = 10$ mm ; $p = 1.5\ \text{N/mm}^2$; $\varphi = 30$ mm

Initial Condition: The tie bars are under tensile stress (f_t) of 40 N/mm². Hence let f_0 be the longitudinal *compressive* stress in the cylinder walls (Fig. 23.10 *a*).

From equilibrium conditions,

$f_0\,(\pi\,d\,t) = f_t\,n\,\dfrac{\pi}{4}\,\varphi^2$

or $f_0\,(\pi \times 1600 \times 10) = 40 \times 9 \times \dfrac{\pi}{4}\,(30)^2$

From which $f_0 = 5.063\ \text{N/mm}^2$

There is no hoop stress initially.

Final condition (Fig. 23.10 *b*)

Let f_t' be the final tensile stress in tie bars and f_0' be the final *tensile* longitudinal stress in the cylinder. From equilibrium conditions

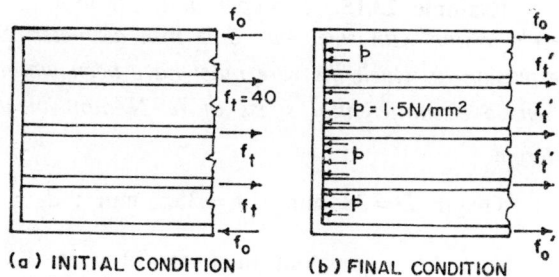

(a) INITIAL CONDITION   (b) FINAL CONDITION

FIG. 23.10

$$f_0' \, \pi \, d \, t + f_t' \, n \frac{\pi}{4} \varphi^2 = p \left(\frac{\pi}{4} d^2 - n \frac{\pi}{4} \varphi^2 \right)$$

or $\quad f_0' \, \pi \times 1600 \times 10 + f_t' \times 9 \times \frac{\pi}{4}(30)^2 = 1.5 \left[\frac{\pi}{4}(1600)^2 - 9 \times \frac{\pi}{4}(30)^2 \right]$

or $\qquad\qquad f_0' + 0.1265 f_t' = 59.81$ ...(a)

Hoop stress in the cylinder $= \frac{p \, d}{2 \, t} = \frac{1.5 \times 1600}{2 \times 10} = 120 \, \text{N/mm}^2$

(This hoop stress is not affected by the tie bars)

One relation between f_t' and f_0' is given by Eq. (a). Another relation is obtained by considering the following *compatibility equation*:

THE INCREASE IN LONGITUDINAL STRAIN FOR THE BARS= INCREASE IN LONGITUDINAL STRAIN FOR CYLINDER

or $\qquad\qquad e_t = e_{oc}$

where $\quad e_t =$ increase in longitudinal strain of tie bars $= \dfrac{f_t' - 40}{E}$

$e_{oc} =$ increase in longitudinal strain of cylinder= final strain $-$ initial strain

$$= \frac{1}{E} (f_0' - 0.29 \times 120) - \frac{1}{E} (-5.063)$$

$\therefore \qquad\qquad \dfrac{f_t' - 40}{E} = \dfrac{1}{E} (f_0' - 34.8 + 5.063)$

or $\qquad\qquad f_t' = f_0' + 10.263$ ...(b)

From Eqs (a) and (b), we get $f_0' = 51.94 \, \text{N/mm}^2$ and $f_t' = \mathbf{62.20 \, N/mm^2}$

INCREASE IN CAPACITY= (2 × INCREASE IN HOOP STRAIN+INCREASE IN LONGITUDINAL STRAIN) × VOLUME

$$= (2 \, e + e_0) V = \frac{1}{2 \times 10^5} \left[2 (120 - 0.29 \times 51.94 - 0.29 \times 5.063) + 62.20 - 40 \right]$$

$$\times \frac{\pi}{4} (1600)^2 \times 2000 = \mathbf{4.61 \times 10^6 \, mm^3}$$

Example 23.15. *A copper tube, 38 mm external diameter, 35.5 mm internal diameter, is closely wound with steel wire 0.75 mm diameter. Stating clearly the assumptions made, estimate the tension at which the wire must have been wound if an internal pressure of 2 N/mm² produces a tensile circumferential stress of 6.5 N/mm² in the tube. Take $E_s = 1.6 \, E_c$.* (U.L.)

Solution :

Given: $D = 38$ mm ; $d = 35.5$ mm ; $d_w = 0.75$ mm ; $p = 2 \, \text{N/mm}^2$; $f = 6.5 \, \text{N/mm}^2$

Step 1: Equivalent thickness of wire, $t_w = \dfrac{\pi \, d_w}{4} = \dfrac{\pi \times 0.75}{4} = 0.589$ mm

Step 2: Winding stress in wire $= f_w$, which is to be found.

Step 3: Initial compressive hoop stress in tube,

$$f_c = \frac{t_w}{t} \times f_w = \frac{0.589}{\frac{1}{2}(38 - 35.5)} f_w = 0.4712 f_w \qquad ...(1)$$

Step 4: If f' and f_w' are the hoop stress in tube and tensile stress in wire due to p, we have, from equilibrium, $f'.2t + f_w'.2t_w = pd$.

or $\qquad 2.5 f' + 2 \times 0.589 f_w' = 2 \times 35.5 \qquad ...(a)$

But final hoop stress $= f' - f_c = 6.5 \text{ N/mm}^2$ (given)

or $\qquad f' = 6.5 + f_c = 6.5 + 0.4712 f_w \qquad ...(2)$

Hence from (a), $2.5 (6.5 + 0.4712 f_w) + 1.178 f_w' = 71$

From which $\qquad f_w' = \frac{71 - 16.25 - 1.178 f_w}{1.178} = 46.477 - f_w \qquad ...(3)$

Step 5: Since Poisson's ratio has not been given, neglect longitudinal stress f_0.

Step 6: Equate the change of hoop strain in wire and tube, due to pressure p

$\therefore \qquad\qquad \frac{f'}{E_c} = \frac{f_w'}{E_s} \quad \text{or} \quad f_w' = \frac{E_s}{E_c} f' = 1.6 f' \qquad ...(b)$

Substituting the values of f and f_w' we get

$$(46.477 - f_w) = 1.6 (6.5 + 0.4712 f_w) = 10.4 + 0.7539 f_w$$

From the above, we get $f_w = 20.569 \text{ N/mm}^2$

Hence winding tension $\quad T = f_w \frac{\pi}{4} d_w^2 = 20.569 \times \frac{\pi}{4} (0.75)^2 = \textbf{9.09 N}$

Example 23.16. *A spherical vessel having an inside diameter of 760 mm and a wall thickness of 11 mm is filled with water at gauge pressure of 5.6 N/mm². The pressure is lowered by allowing some water to escape and, to reduce the pressure to atmospheric, the volume of water released is 885 cm³. Find the bulk modulus of water. Take E for steel= 2 × 10⁵ N/mm² and μ = 0.286.*

Solution :

Given : $\qquad\qquad d = 760$ mm; $t = 11$ mm; $p = 5.6 \text{ N/mm}^2$

$$V = \frac{4}{3}\pi r^3 = \frac{4}{3}\pi \left(\frac{760}{2}\right)^3 = 229.85 \times 10^6 \text{ mm}^3$$

Contraction of vessel $= \delta V_1 = \frac{3pd}{4tE}\left(1 - \frac{1}{m}\right)V = \frac{3 \times 5.6 \times 760}{4 \times 11 \times 2 \times 10^5}(1 - 0.286) \times 229.85 \times 10^6$

$$= 238110 \text{ mm}^3$$

Expansion of water $= \delta V_2 = \frac{pV}{K} = \frac{5.6 \times 229.85 \times 10^6}{K} = \frac{1287.2 \times 10^6}{K}$

$\therefore$ Total $\qquad \delta V = 885 \times 10^3 = \delta V_1 + \delta V_2 = 238110 + \frac{1287.2 \times 10^6}{K}$

From which $\qquad \textbf{K = 1990 N/mm}^2$

PROBLEMS

1. A long steel tube, 80 mm internal diameter and 1.5 mm thick has closed ends and is subjected to an internal fluid pressure of 2.5 N/mm^2. Taking $E = 2 \times 10^5$ N/mm^2 and $\mu = 0.29$, estimate the percentage increase in the internal volume of the tube.

2. A thin cylindrical shell is subjected to internal fluid pressure, the ends being closed by
    (a) two water tight pistons attached to a common piston rod (b) flanged ends
Find the increase in internal diameter in each case, given that the internal diameter is 20 cm, thickness is 0.5 cm. Poisson's ratio is 0.3. Young's modulus is 200 GN/m^2, and internal pressure is 3.5 MN/m^2.

3. A thin cylinder of 100 mm internal diameter and wall thickness 2 mm has its ends closed by rigid plates and is then filled with water. When an external pull of 20 kN is applied to the ends, the water pressure read by the gauge, is observed to fall by 0.075 N/mm^2. Neglecting any end effect due to plates, determine the value of Poisson's ratio for the metal. Take E for metal $= 2.1 \times 10^5$ N/mm^2 and bulk modulus of water $= 2.17 \times 10^3$ N/mm^2.

4. Compare (a) the maximum tensile stresses and (b) the proportional increase in volume of a thin cylinder and a thin spherical shell having the same internal pressure and the diameter/thickness ratio. Take $\mu = 0.3$.

5. A boiler drum consists of a cylindrical portion 2.4 m long, 1.2 m diameter and 30 mm thick, closed by hemispherical ends. In a hydraulic test at 9 N/mm^2, how much additional water will be pumped in, after initial filling at atmospheric pressure ? Assume the circumferential strain at the junction of cylinder and hemisphere is the same for both. For the drum material, $E = 2 \times 10^5$ N/mm^2, $\mu = 0.3$. For water, $K = 2100$ N/mm^2.

6. An air vessel of a torpedo is 500 mm diameter and 10 mm thick, the length being 2 m. From fundamentals, find the change in diameter and length, when charged to 10 N/mm^2 internal pressure. Take $E = 200$ kN/mm^2 and $\mu = 0.3$.   (U.L.)

7. A cast iron pipe of 300 mm internal diameter and 12 mm thick is wound closely with a single layer of circular steel wire of 5 mm diameter, under a tension of 60 N/mm^2. Find the initial compressive stress in the pipe section. Also, find the stresses set up in the pipe and steel wire, when water under a pressure of 4 N/mm^2 is admitted into the pipe. Take E for cast iron and steel as 1×10^5 N/mm^2 and 2×10^5 N/mm^2 respectively, and $\mu = 0.3$.   (U.L.)

ANSWERS

1. 0.064 %
2. (a) 0.07 mm   (b) 0.0595 mm
3. $\mu = 0.332$
4. 1.81
5. 22.23×10^6 mm^3.
6. $\delta d = 0.55$ mm ; $\delta l = 0.5$ mm
7. $f_c = 19.63$ N/mm^2 ; $f = 13.55$ N/mm^2 ; $f_w = 111.36$ N/mm^2

Thick Cylinders and Spheres

24.1. INTRODUCTION

In the previous chapter, we have analysed thin cylinders, which are basically used for low internal pressure p. Due to this, p was considered negligible in comparison to the circumferential stress and longitudinal stress. In contrast to this, thick cylinders are invariably designed to resist very high internal pressure, the magnitude of which may be of the order of $40\,\text{N/mm}^2$ to $60\,\text{N/mm}^2$. Due to this reason, the radial compressive stress p on the internal face cannot be neglected. In addition to this, the circumferential stress (or hoop stress), which was assumed to be constant along the thickness of the thin cylinder, is no longer constant, but varies along the thickness of the shell. The problem of thick cylinder is some what of complex nature. The problem of determining the tangential stress and the radial stress at any point on a thick walled cylinder, in terms of applied pressure and the dimensions, was first solved by the French elastician Gabriel Lame in 1833. His analysis is commonly known as Lame's theory which is given below.

24.2. THICK CYLINDRICAL SHELLS : LAME'S THEORY

Fig. 24.1 (a) shows a thick cylinder of internal radius r and external radius R, subjected to an internal pressure p_r and external pressure p_R. Evidently, these pressures are compressive and act *radially*. The radial pressure varies along the thickness of the shell. Consider an annular

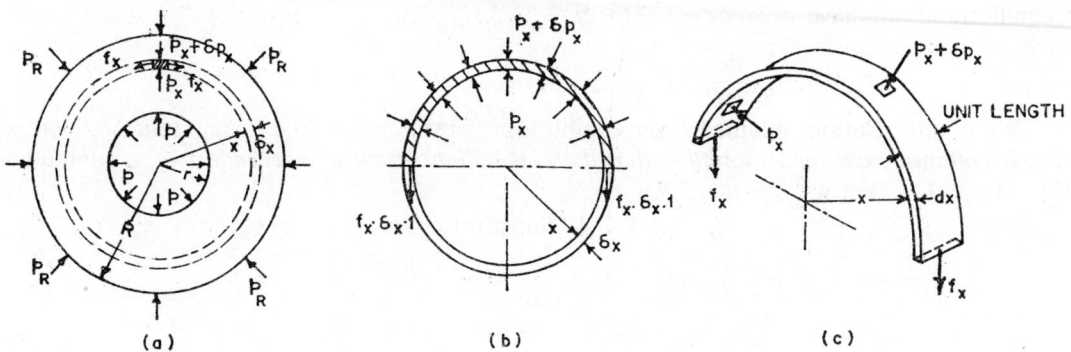

FIG. 24.1. THICK CYLINDRICAL SHELL

ring of the cylinder of internal radius x and thickness δx. Let the internal radial pressure on this ring be p_x and external pressure be $(p_x + \delta p_x)$. On any small element of this ring, let f_x be the *circumferential stress* (or tangential stress).

Lame's Assumptions : Lame analysed the problem of stress distribution in thick shells, making the following assumptions :

1. The material of the shell is homogeneous and isotropic.
2. Plane sections of the cylinder, perpendicular to the longitudinal axis, remain plane under the pressure.

The implication of the assumption no. 2 is that the *longitudinal strain* is the same at all points in the cylindrical wall, i.e. it is independent of the radius. This assumption is nearly true at a considerable distance from the ends.

Let p_x = radial pressure at any radius x (compressive)
   f_x = circumferential stress (assumed tensile)
   f_0 = longitudinal tensile stress   and e_0 = longitudinal strain

Hence the requirement of *uniform longitudinal strain* is satisfied by :

$$e_0 = \frac{1}{E}\left(f_0 - \frac{f_x}{m} + \frac{p_x}{m}\right) = \text{ constant} \qquad \qquad ...(24.1)$$

or $\qquad\qquad\qquad\qquad f_x - p_x = \text{ constant} = 2A \text{ (say)} \qquad\qquad\qquad ...(24.1\ a)$

$$\text{(since } p_0, m \text{ and } E \text{ are all constants)}$$

Thus, Lame's theory is based on the important assumption expressed by Eq. 24.1.

Fig. 24.1 (*b*) shows a *thin ring* of the thick cylinder, taken at radius x. Fig. 24.1 (*c*) shows the pictorial view of half ring. The conditions for equilibrium of one half of this ring are similar to those in the case of thin cylinder. Considering unit length of the cylinder:

Bursting force $\qquad\qquad P_x = (p_x . 2x . 1) - (p_x + \delta p_x) 2 (x + \delta x) 1$

$$= 2\left[-p_x \delta x - x . \delta p_x - \delta x . \delta p_x\right] \approx -2(p_x . \delta x + x \delta p_x)$$

$$\text{(neglecting the product of small quantities)}$$

Resisting force $= 2 f_x . \delta x . 1$

For equilibrium, we have $\quad 2 f_x \delta x = -2(p_x \delta x + x . \delta p_x) \quad$ or $\quad f_x = -p_x - x\dfrac{\delta p_x}{\delta x}$

or $\qquad\qquad\qquad f_x + p_x + x\dfrac{dp_x}{dx} = 0 \qquad\qquad\qquad\qquad\qquad ...(1)$

This is one relation obtained from equilibrium considerations (i.e. from statics). *Another relation is obtained from the assumption that the longitudinal strain is independent of x,* contained in Eq. 24.1 (*a*). Hence $\quad f_x - p_x = 2A \qquad\qquad\qquad\qquad\qquad\qquad ...(2)$

From (2), $\qquad\qquad\qquad f_x = p_x + 2A$. Substituting in (1), we get

$$p_x + 2A + p_x + x\frac{dp_x}{dx} = 0 \quad \text{ or } \quad \frac{dp_x}{dx} = -\frac{2(p_x + A)}{x}$$

or $\qquad\qquad\qquad\qquad \dfrac{dp_x}{p_x + A} = -\dfrac{2\,dx}{x} \qquad\qquad\qquad\qquad\qquad ...(3).$

Integrating, we get $\quad \log_e (p_x + A) = -\log_e x^2 + \log_e B = \log_e \dfrac{B}{x^2}$

$$\text{(where } \log_e B = \text{constant of integration)}$$

or $\qquad\qquad\qquad p_x + A = \dfrac{B}{x^2}$, from which $p_x = \dfrac{B}{x^2} - A$

Also, from (2), $\qquad\qquad f_x = p_x + 2A = \dfrac{B}{x^2} - A + 2A = \dfrac{B}{x^2} + A$

Hence we have Lame's equations

$$p_x = \dfrac{B}{x^2} - A \qquad ...(24.2\ a) \qquad \text{and} \qquad f_x = \dfrac{B}{x^2} + A \qquad\qquad\qquad ...(24.2\ b)$$

The above expressions for radial stress and circumferential stress contain two unknowns A and B, which can be evaluated from the known internal and external pressures at radii r and R respectively. *Note carefully* that p_x is *compressive* while f_x is *tensile*.

Longitudinal stress : The longitudinal stress (f_0) can be found in the same manner, as found for the thin cylinder, in the previous chapter.

Thus bursting force $= p_r . \pi r^2$ while the resisting force $= f_0 \pi (R^2 - r^2)$

Equating the two, we get $f_0 \pi (R^2 - r^2) = p_r . \pi r^2$

From which $\qquad\qquad\qquad f_0 = p_r . \dfrac{r^2}{R^2 - r^2} \qquad\qquad\qquad\qquad ...(24.3)$

We shall now consider various cases of internal and external pressures.

24.3. CASE 1: INTERNAL PRESSURE p_r AND EXTERNAL PRESSURE ZERO

This is the common case of cylindrical shells containing fluids under high pressure.

Boundary conditions : At $x = r , p = p_r$ and at $x = R , p = 0$

Hence from Eq. 24.2 (a), $p_r = \dfrac{B}{r^2} - A \quad ...(a) \qquad\qquad p_R = \dfrac{B}{R^2} - A = 0 \qquad\qquad ...(b)$

Solving (a) and (b), we get $\quad A = p_r . \dfrac{r^2}{R^2 - r^2}$

and $\qquad\qquad\qquad\qquad\qquad\qquad B = p_r \dfrac{r^2 R^2}{R^2 - r^2}$

$\therefore\ p_x = \dfrac{p_r}{x^2} \times \dfrac{r^2 R^2}{R^2 - r^2} - p_r \dfrac{r^2}{R^2 - r^2} = p_r \dfrac{R^2 - x^2}{R^2 - r^2} . \dfrac{r^2}{x^2} \ ...(24.4\ a)$

and $\quad f_x = \dfrac{p_r}{x^2} . \dfrac{r^2 R^2}{R^2 - r^2} + p_r \dfrac{r^2}{R^2 - r^2} = p_r \dfrac{R^2 + x^2}{R^2 - r^2} . \dfrac{r^2}{x^2} ...(24.4\ b)$

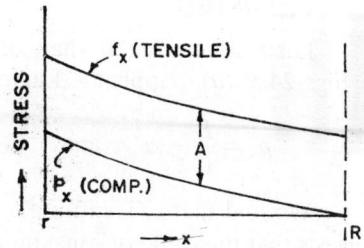

FIG. 24.2

The variation of p_x and f_x across the diameter is shown in Fig. 24.2, the *curves being parallel* since $f_x - p_x = 2A$.

$\therefore \qquad\qquad f_{x,\max} = f_{x=r} = f_r = p_r \dfrac{r^2 R^2}{(R^2 - r^2) r^2} + p_r \dfrac{r^2}{R^2 - r^2} = p_r \dfrac{R^2 + r^2}{R^2 - r^2} \ ...(24.5)$

Max. shear stress, $\qquad f_{s,\max} = \dfrac{1}{2}(f_r + p_r) = p_r \dfrac{R^2}{R^2 - r^2} \qquad\qquad ...(24.5\ a)$

24.4 . CASE 2 : INTERNAL PRESSURE ZERO AND EXTERNAL PRESSURE p_R

Boundary Conditions : At $x = r, p = p_r = 0$ and at $x = R, p = p_R$

Hence from Eq. 24.2 (a), $p_r = 0 = \dfrac{B}{r^2} - A$ and $p_R = \dfrac{B}{R^2} - A$

Solving these, we get $B = -p_R \dfrac{R^2 r^2}{R^2 - r^2}$ and $A = -p_R \cdot \dfrac{R^2}{R^2 - r^2}$ ...(24.6)

Hence the maximum hoop stress at $x = r$ is given by Eq. 24.2

$$(f_x)_{max} = f_{x=r} = f_r = -p_R \left(\frac{2 R^2}{R^2 - r^2} \right) \qquad ...(24.7)$$

The minus sign denotes that f_r will be compressive.

24.5. CASE 3 : INTERNAL PRESSURE p_r AND EXTERNAL PRESSURE p_R

Boundary conditions : At $x = r, p = p_r$ and at $x = R, p = p_R$

Hence from Eq. 24.2 (a), $p_r = \dfrac{B}{r^2} - A$ and $p_R = \dfrac{B}{R^2} - A$

Solving these, we get $B = (p_r - p_R) \dfrac{r^2 R^2}{R^2 - r^2}$ and $A = \dfrac{p_r r^2 - p_R \cdot R^2}{R^2 - r^2}$ ...(24.8)

The maximum hoop stress evidently occurs at $x = r$ and its value is given by

$$(f_x)_{max} = f_{x=r} = f_r = \frac{(p_r - p_R) R^2}{R^2 - r^2} + \frac{P_r r^2 - p_R \cdot R^2}{R^2 - r^2}$$

or $\qquad f_r = \dfrac{p_r \cdot R^2 - p_R \cdot R^2 + p_r \cdot r^2 - p_R \cdot R^2}{R^2 - r^2} = \dfrac{p_r (R^2 - r^2) - 2 p_R \cdot r^2}{R^2 - r^2}$ ...(24.9)

24.6. CASE 4 : SOLID CIRCULAR SHAFT SUBJECTED TO EXTERNAL RADIAL PRESSURE

Let a solid circular shaft of radius R be subjected to external radial pressure p, as shown in Fig. 24.3 (a). Applying Lame's equations,

$$p_x = \frac{B}{x^2} - A \quad \text{and} \quad f_x = \frac{B}{x^2} + A$$

We find that p_x is infinite at $x = 0$. This suggests that the value of constant B in Lame's equations is zero. Hence we have

$$p_x = -A = p \qquad ...(24.10\,a)$$

Thus the intensity of radial pressure is constant every where and its value is equal to the external pressure p.

Also, $\qquad f_x = 0 + A$ where $A = -p$

Hence $\quad f_x = -p \qquad ...(24.10\ b).$

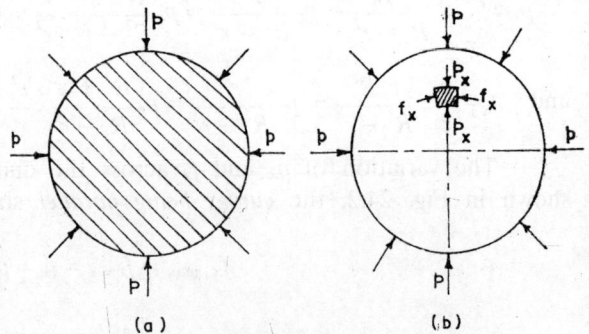

(a)   (b)

FIG. 24.3. SOLID CIRCULAR SHAFT

The minus sign suggests that f_x is compressive. *Hence the intensity of hoop pressure is constant every where, and is compressive, its value being equal to the external pressure p.* The values and sign of both p_x and f_x on an element are shown in Fig. 24.3 (b).

24.7. GRAPHICAL SOLUTION : LAME'S LINES

In the previous few articles, we have seen that the constants A and B can be found if the radial pressures at the inner and outer radii are given. This involves the solution of two simultaneous equations. This procedure is slightly tedious. The solution can be easily obtained by a graphical procedure detailed below, involving the construction of *Lame's Lines.*

Graphical Procedure : Let us construct Lame's line for the first case when $p_R = 0$ (Fig. 24.4).

FIG. 24.4. GRAPHICAL SOLUTION :
LAME'S LINES FOR CASE 1

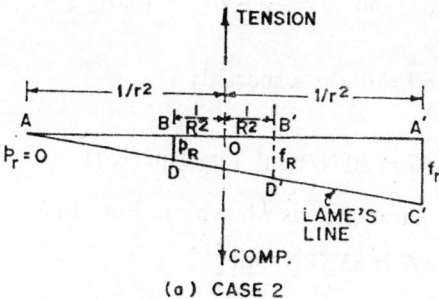

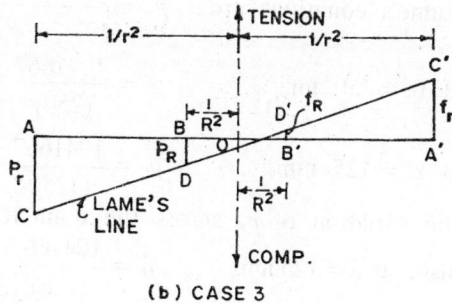

1. Select an origin O on a horizontal line. Plot points A and A' at distances $1/r^2$ on either side of O. Similarly, plot points B and B' at distances $1/R^2$ on either side of O.

2. Radial pressures are plotted to the left side of O. Similarly, tensile stresses/pressures are plotted above the horizontal line while the compressive stresses/pressures are plotted below the horizontal line.

3. At point A, corresponding to distance $1/r^2$, erect perpendicular AC equal to p_r (given), below the horizontal line, since p_r is compressive. Similarly, at B, corresponding to distance $1/R^2$, erect a perpendicular of zero value, since p_R is zero.

4. Join C and B, and prolong it to the other side of O. Thus the slope of the Lame's line CB is known.

5. At point A' representing distance $1/r^2$, erect a perpendicular $A'C'$ to meet the Lame's line in C'. The ordinate $A'C'$ gives the hoop stress f_r at a radius r. For this case, it comes out to be tensile. Similarly, the ordinate $B'D'$ gives the value of hoop stress f_R at radius R, which is also tensile.

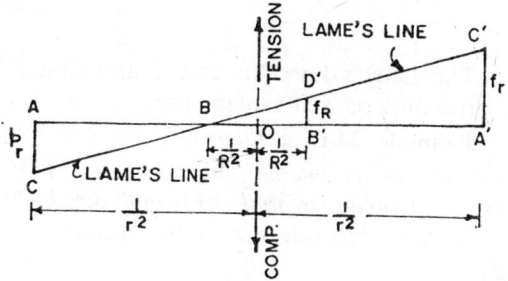

(a) CASE 2

(b) CASE 3

FIG. 24.5. LAME'S LINES

Proof : By inspection of similar triangles, we have

$$\frac{AC}{AB} = \frac{A'C'}{A'B} \quad \text{or} \quad \frac{p_r}{\dfrac{1}{r^2} - \dfrac{1}{R^2}} = \frac{f_r}{\dfrac{1}{r^2} + \dfrac{1}{R^2}}$$

From which $\qquad f_r = p_r \dfrac{\dfrac{1}{r^2} + \dfrac{1}{R^2}}{\dfrac{1}{r^2} - \dfrac{1}{R^2}} = p_r \dfrac{R^2 + r^2}{R^2 - r^2}$ which is the same as Eq. 24.5.

The Lame's lines for case 2 and case 3 are shown in Fig. 24.5 (*a*) and (*b*) respectively. The procedure is self-explanatory.

Example 24.1. *A thick cylinder 125 mm inside diameter and 250 mm outside diameter is subjected to an internal fluid pressure of 50 N/mm². Calculate the maximum and minimum intensities of circumferential stress and sketch the distribution of circumferential stress intensity and radial pressure intensity across the section.*

Solution :

Given $\qquad r = 125$ mm; $R = 250$ mm. $\quad p = 50$ N/mm²

At $\quad r = 125$ mm, $p = 50$ N/mm²;

At $\quad R = 250$ mm, $p = 0$

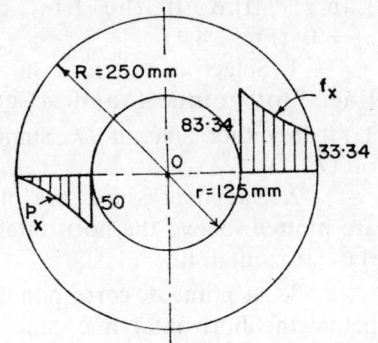

FIG. 24.6

Hence from Eq. 24.2(*a*)

$$50 = \frac{B}{(125)^2} - A \qquad \qquad ...(i)$$

and $\qquad 0 = \dfrac{B}{(250)^2} - A \qquad \qquad ...(ii)$

From (*ii*), $\qquad A = \dfrac{B}{(250)^2}$

Hence from (*i*), $50 = \dfrac{B}{(125)^2} - \dfrac{B}{(250)^2} = \dfrac{B\left[(250)^2 - (125)^2\right]}{(125 \times 250)^2}$

From which $\qquad B = \dfrac{50 \times (125 \times 250)^2}{(250)^2 - (125)^2} = 1041667$; hence $A = \dfrac{B}{(250)^2} = \dfrac{1041667}{(250)^2} = 16.67$

Hence Lame's equations are : $\quad p_x = \dfrac{1041667}{x^2} - 16.67$ and $f_x = \dfrac{1041667}{x^2} + 16.67$

At $x = 250$ mm , $\qquad p_x = \dfrac{1041667}{(250)^2} - 16.67 = 0$ (as expected)

At $x = 125$ mm, $\qquad p_r = \dfrac{1041667}{(125)^2} - 16.67 = 50$ N/mm² (as expected)

The variation of p_x across the diameter is parabolic, as shown in Fig. 24.6.

Also, at $x = 125$ mm, $\qquad f_r = \dfrac{1041667}{(125)^2} + 16.67 = 83.34$ N/mm²

At $x = 250$ mm, $\qquad f_R = \dfrac{1041667}{(250)^2} + 16.67 = 33.34$ N/mm²

The variation of f_x across the diameter is shown in Fig. 24.6.

Example 24.2. *A thick cylindrical shell of 100 mm internal diameter is to withstand an internal pressure of 20 N/mm². Taking the maximum permissible tensile stress as 60 N/mm² and maximum permissible shear stress as 50 N/mm², determine the metal thickness necessary for the shell.*

Solution : Given : $r = \dfrac{100}{2} = 50$ mm; $p_r = 20$ N/mm²; $f_{max} = 60$ N/mm²; $f_{s,\,max} = 50$ N/mm².

From Eq. 24.5, $\qquad f_{max} = f_r = p_r \dfrac{R^2 + r^2}{R^2 - r^2}$, where $f_{max} = 60$ N/mm² (given)

$\therefore \qquad\qquad\qquad 60 = 20 \dfrac{R^2 + 50^2}{R^2 - 50^2},$

or $\qquad\qquad\qquad 3\,(R^2 - 2500) = R^2 + 2500$

or $\qquad\qquad\qquad 2\,R^2 = 10000$, from which $R = 70.71$ mm $\qquad\qquad ...(i)$

Also, from Eq. 24.5 (*a*), $\qquad f_{s,\,max} = p_r \dfrac{R^2}{R^2 - r^2}$, where $f_{s,\,max} = 50$ N/mm²

$\therefore \qquad\qquad\qquad 50 = 20 \dfrac{R^2}{R^2 - 50^2}$

or $\qquad\qquad\qquad 2.5\,(R^2 - 2500) = R^2$

or $\qquad\qquad\qquad 1.5\,R^2 = 2.5 \times 2500$, from which $R = 64.55$ mm $\qquad\qquad ...(ii)$

Required R will be the greater of the two. Hence $R = 70.71$ mm

$\therefore \qquad\qquad$ Metal thickness $= R - r = 70.71 - 50 = \mathbf{20.71\ mm}$

24.8. STRAIN COMPONENTS AND RADIAL DISPLACEMENTS

Fig. 24.7 shows an element *abcd* at radius x. This element deforms to the position *a'b'c'd'*, when the cylinder is subjected to an internal pressure p. Let u be the *radial displacement* at radius x and $u + \delta u$ be the radial displacement at radius $x + \delta x$.

$\therefore \qquad$ Change is displacement $= (u + \delta u) - u = \delta u$

Hence radial strain $\qquad \varepsilon_x = \underset{\delta x \to 0}{\text{Lt}} \cdot \dfrac{\delta u}{\delta x} = \dfrac{du}{dr} \qquad ...(24.11)$

Change in the circumferential length of the element

$\qquad\qquad = a'd' - ad = (x + u)\,\delta\theta - x\,\delta\theta = u\,\delta\theta$

$\therefore \qquad$ Circumferential strain $= \varepsilon_y = \dfrac{u\,\delta\theta}{x\,\delta\theta} = \dfrac{u}{x} \qquad ...(24.12)$

$\therefore \qquad$ Radial displacement $u = x\,\varepsilon_y = \dfrac{x}{E}\left(f_x + \mu\,p_x\right) \qquad ...(24.13)$

(Ignoring longitudinal stress)

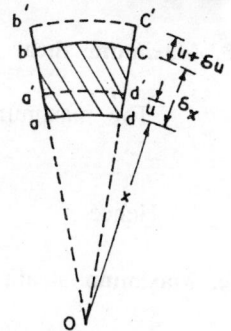

FIG. 24.7

24.9. DESIGN OF THICK CYLINDRICAL SHELL

At any element of a thick cylinder, the three principal stresses are (*i*) radial stress p_x, (*ii*) circumferential stress f_x and (*iii*) longitudinal stress f_0. We have seen earlier that the maximum values of p_x and f_x occur at radius $x = r$ (*i.e.* at the inner radius). Hence, *at any point* at radius r, the three principal stresses are as follows:

(*i*) The radial stress p_r (compressive)

(*ii*) The circumferential stress f_r (tensile), given by

$$f_r = p_r \frac{R^2 + r^2}{R^2 - r^2} = p_r \frac{K^2 + 1}{K^2 - 1}, \text{ where } K = \frac{R}{r}$$

(*iii*) The longitudinal stress f_0 (tensile), given by :

$$f_0 = p_r \cdot \frac{r^2}{R^2 - r^2} = \frac{p_r}{K^2 - 1}$$

Out of these three principal stresses, the circumferential stress (f_r) is the largest.

The design of a thick cylinder consists of finding the safe ratio of thickness of the wall (*i.e.* $R - r$) to the bore of the tube (*i.e.* r), on the basis of any of the five theories of failure.

1. **Maximum principal stress theory :** If f is the simple stress for elastic failure, we have

$$f_r \leq f, \quad \text{or} \quad p_r \left(\frac{K^2 + 1}{K^2 - 1} \right) \leq f \qquad \qquad ...(24.14)$$

2. **Maximum principal strain theory :** Maximum strain, $e_r = \dfrac{f_r}{E} + \dfrac{p_r}{mE} - \dfrac{f_0}{mE}$

$$\therefore \qquad f = e_r E \geq f_r + \frac{p_r}{m} - \frac{f_0}{m}$$

or

$$f \geq p_r \left(\frac{K^2 + 1}{K^2 - 1} + \frac{1}{m} - \frac{1}{m} \frac{1}{K^2 - 1} \right) \geq p_r \left[\frac{K^2 + 1}{K^2 - 1} + \frac{1}{m} \frac{K^2 - 2}{K^2 - 1} \right] ...(24.15)$$

However, if there is no longitudinal stress,

$$f \geq p_r \left[\frac{K^2 + 1}{K^2 - 1} + \frac{1}{m} \right] \qquad \qquad ...(24.15\ a)$$

3. **Maximum shear stress theory :**

The maximum shear stress $= \dfrac{f_r - (-p_r)}{2} = \dfrac{f_r + p_r}{2} = \dfrac{p_r}{2} \left[\dfrac{K^2 + 1}{K^2 - 1} + 1 \right] = \dfrac{p_r}{2} \cdot \dfrac{2K^2}{K^2 - 1}$

Hence

$$\frac{f}{2} \geq \frac{p_r}{2} \frac{2K^2}{K^2 - 1} \quad \text{or} \quad f \geq p_r \cdot \frac{2K^2}{K^2 - 1} \qquad \qquad ...(24.16)$$

4. **Maximum strain energy theory :** Strain energy u per unit volume is given by

$$u = \frac{1}{2E} \left[\sigma_1^2 + \sigma_2^2 + \sigma_3^2 - \frac{2}{m} (\sigma_1 \sigma_2 + \sigma_2 \sigma_3 + \sigma_3 \sigma_1) \right]$$

Here

$$\sigma_1 = f_r = p_r \frac{K^2 + 1}{K^2 - 1}; \sigma_2 = p_r \text{ (comp.)} \text{ and } \sigma_3 = f_0 = p_r \frac{1}{K^2 - 1}$$

Hence $\quad u = \dfrac{p_r^2}{2E}\left[\left(\dfrac{K^2+1}{K^2-1}\right)^2 + (-1)^2 + \left(\dfrac{1}{K^2-1}\right)^2 - \dfrac{2}{m}\left\{-\dfrac{K^2+1}{K^2-1}\cdot 1 - 1\cdot\dfrac{1}{K^2-1} + \dfrac{1}{K^2-1}\cdot\dfrac{K^2+1}{K^2-1}\right\}\right]$

or $\quad u = \dfrac{p_r^2}{2E}\dfrac{(K^2+1)^2 + (K^2-1)^2 + 1 - \dfrac{2}{m}\left\{-(K^2+1)(K^2-1) - (K^2-1) + (K^2+1)\right\}}{(K^2-1)^2}$

or $\quad u = \dfrac{p_r^2}{2E}\dfrac{\left[2\left(1+\dfrac{1}{m}\right)K^4 + 3\left(1-\dfrac{2}{m}\right)\right]}{\left(K^2-1\right)^2}$

Strain energy per unit volume for single tensile stress $= \dfrac{f^2}{2E}$

Hence we have, $\quad f \geq p_r\dfrac{\sqrt{2\left(1+\dfrac{1}{m}\right)K^4 + 3\left(1-\dfrac{2}{m}\right)}}{(K^2-1)}$ ...(24.17)

If, however, there is no longitudinal stress, it can be shown that

$$f \geq \dfrac{p_r\sqrt{2\left(1+\dfrac{1}{m}\right)K^4 + 2\left(1-\dfrac{1}{m}\right)}}{(K^2-1)}$$ ...(24.17 a)

5. **Maximum shear strain energy theory** : We have the following criterion :

$$f^2 \geq \dfrac{1}{2}(\sigma_1-\sigma_2)^2 + \dfrac{1}{2}(\sigma_2-\sigma_3)^2 + \dfrac{1}{2}(\sigma_3-\sigma_1)^2$$

Here $\quad \sigma_1 = f_r = p_r\dfrac{K^2+1}{K^2-1}$; $\sigma_2 = -p_r$ (i.e. comp.) and $\sigma_3 = \sigma_0 = p_r\dfrac{1}{K^2-1}$

Hence we have $\quad f^2 \geq p_r^2\cdot\dfrac{3K^4}{(K^2-1)^2}$ or $f \geq p_r\cdot\dfrac{\sqrt{3.K^4}}{K^2-1}$ ...(24.18)

If, however, f_0 is neglected, we have $f \geq p_r\dfrac{\sqrt{3K^4+1}}{K^2-1}$ ...(24.18 a)

Example 24.3. *In example 24.1, determine the increase in inside and outside radii of the thick cylinder when it is subjected to internal pressure. Take $E = 2\times 10^5\,N/mm^2$ and $\mu = 0.3$ for the material of the cylinder.*

Solution : Given $\quad r = 125$ mm, $R = 250$ mm ; $p_r = 50\,N/mm^2$

From Eq. 24.13, we have $u = x\,\varepsilon_y = \dfrac{x}{E}(f_x + \mu\,p_x)$

At radius $x = r$, we get $\quad u_r = \dfrac{r}{E}(f_r + \mu\,p_r) = \dfrac{125}{2\times 10^5}(83.34 + 0.3\times 50)$

$\qquad\qquad = \mathbf{0.0615\,mm}$ (increase in inside radius)

Also, at $x = R$, we get $u_R = \dfrac{R}{E}(f_R + \mu\,p_R) = \dfrac{250}{2\times 10^5}(33.34 + 0)$

$\qquad\qquad = \mathbf{0.0417\,mm}$ (increase in outside radius)

Hence inside radius r becomes equal to **125.0615 mm** and the outside radius R becomes equal to **250.0417 mm**.

Example 24.4. *A thick cylindrical shell 150 mm internal diameter has to withstand an internal pressure of 30 N/mm². Calculate the thickness of the metal necessary for the cylinder on the basis of (i) maximum principal stress (ii) maximum principal strain, (iii) maximum shear, and (iv) maximum stain energy. Neglect the longitudinal direct stress. The permissible tensile stress for the shell material is 120 N/mm² and 1/m = 0.3.*

Solution :   Given : $r = 75$ mm ; $p_r = 30$ N/mm² ; $f = 120$ N/mm²

(1) Maximum principal stress hypothesis

From Eq. 24.14, $p_r \left(\dfrac{K^2 + 1}{K^2 - 1} \right) \le f$ or $\dfrac{K^2 + 1}{K^2 - 1} = \dfrac{f}{p_r} \le \dfrac{120}{130} \le 4$

From which $K^2 \ge 5/3$, or $K = 1.291$

Hence $R = K \cdot r = 1.291 \times 75 = 96.82$ mm

$\therefore$ Metal thickness $= R - r = 96.82 - 75 = \textbf{21.82 mm}$

(2) Maximum principal strain hypothesis

From Eq. 24.15 (a): $p_r \left[\dfrac{K^2 + 1}{K^2 - 1} + \dfrac{1}{m} \right] \le f$

or $\left(\dfrac{K^2 + 1}{K^2 - 1} + \dfrac{1}{m} \right) \le \dfrac{f}{p_r} \le \dfrac{120}{30} \le 4$ or $\dfrac{K^2 + 1}{K^2 - 1} \le (4 - 0.3) \le 3.7$

From which $K^2 = 4.7/2.7 = 1.7407$ or $K = 1.3194$

Hence $R = K \cdot r = 1.3194 \times 75 = 98.95$ mm

$\therefore$ Hence thickness $= R - r = 98.95 - 75 = \textbf{23.95 mm}$

3. Maximum shear stress hypothesis

From Eq. 24.16, $p_r \dfrac{2 K^2}{K^2 - 1} \le f$ or $\dfrac{K^2}{K^2 - 1} < \dfrac{f}{2 p_r} \le \dfrac{120}{2 \times 30} \le 2$

From which $K^2 = 2$ or $K = 1.4142$

$\therefore$ $R = K \cdot r = 1.4142 \times 75 = 106.07$ mm

$\therefore$ Metal thickness $= R - r = 106.07 - 75 = \textbf{31.07 mm}$

4. Maximum strain energy hypothesis

From Eq. 24.17, $\dfrac{p_r^2 \left[2 \left(1 + \dfrac{1}{m} \right) K^4 + 2 \left(1 - \dfrac{1}{m} \right) \right]}{(K^2 - 1)^2} \le f^2$

or $\dfrac{2 (1 + 0.3) K^4 + 2 (1 - 0.3)}{(K^2 - 1)^2} \le \left(\dfrac{f}{p_r} \right)^2 \le \left(\dfrac{120}{30} \right)^2 \le 16$

or $2.6 K^4 + 1.4 = 16 (K^4 + 1 - 2 K^2)$ or $K^4 - 2.388 K^2 + 1.0896 = 0$

or $(K^2 - 1.194)^2 = 0.336$ or $K^2 - 1.194 = \pm 0.5797$

$$K^2 = 1.194 + 0.5797 = 1.3318 \quad \text{(The minus sign being inadmissible)}$$

From which $K = 1.3318$ $\therefore$ $R = K \cdot r = 1.3318 \times 75 = 99.89$ mm

$\therefore$ Metal thickness $= R - r = 99.89 - 75 =$ **24.89 mm**

Example 24.5. *Determine the maximum allowable internal pressure to which a cylinder with an internal diameter of 200 mm and external diameter of 300 mm may be subjected if the cylinder is to have a factor of safety of 3. Use maximum shear stress theory of failure. Yield point stress determined by actual test for the material is 300 N/mm^2. What will be the internal pressure if the maximum stress theory of failure is used ?*

Solution : Given $r = 100$ mm ; $R = 150$ mm ; F.S = 3 ; $f_y = 300$ N/mm^2

$$f_{s,\,max} \text{ (allowable)} = \frac{f_y}{2 \times \text{F. S.}} = \frac{300}{2 \times 3} = 50 \text{ N/mm}^2$$

Lame's equations are : $p_x = \dfrac{B}{x^2} - A$ and $f_x = \dfrac{B}{x^2} + A$

At $x = r = 100$ mm, $p_x = p = \dfrac{B}{(100)^2} - A$ ...(i) At $x = R = 150$ mm, $p_x = 0 = \dfrac{B}{150^2} - A$ ...(ii)

From (ii), $A = \dfrac{B}{22500}$. Substituting in (i), we get $B = 18000\,p$. Hence $A = \dfrac{18000\,p}{22500} = 0.8\,p$

Hence $$f_x = \frac{18000\,p}{x^2} + 0.8\,p \qquad\qquad ...(iii)$$

. At $x = r$, $$f_x = f_{x,\,max} = f_r = \frac{18000\,p}{(100)^2} + 0.8\,p = 2.6\,p \quad \text{(tensile)}$$

Also $$p_r = p \text{ (compressive)} \quad\therefore\quad f_{s,\,max} = \frac{2.6\,p - (-p)}{2} = 1.8\,p \qquad ...(iv)$$

Hence we have $1.8\,p = 50$; from which $p = 50/1.8 =$ **27.78 N/mm^2**

If maximum principal stress theory is used, $\dfrac{f_y}{\text{F. S.}} = f_r$

or $$300/3 = 2.6\,p, \quad \text{from which } p = \textbf{38.46 N/mm}^2$$

Comparing the results obtained by the two theories of failure, we observe that the safe pressure is **27.78 N/mm^2**, obtained by the shear stress theory of failure.

24.10. COMPOUND CYLINDERS

We have seen that the maximum stress in a thick-walled cylinder, subjected to internal pressure, occurs at the inside surface (*i.e.* at $x = r$). It is interesting to note that no matter how thick a cylinder resisting internal pressure is made, the maximum tangential stress (i.e. circumferential stress) will not be smaller than p_r. In practice, this necessitates *special techniques* to reduce the maximum stress. If the cylinder is designed for the maximum stress, which occurs at the inner surface, the material in the rest of the wall will not be used so effectively as it would be if the stresses were distributed uniformly throughout the wall. A direct method of reducing the maximum stress at the inside surface, and thereby achieving a more nearly uniform distribution of stress is to subject the material near the inside wall to an *initial compressive stress* when the fluid pressure is not there. Consequently, when the fluid pressure is applied at the inside surface, the initial compressive stresses existing inside will first be relieved before tensile stresses are developed. This will result in lower values of maximum stress at the inside surface. Following techniques are used for developing initial compressive stress :

(*i*) *Winding* the cylinder with wire under tension (as is done for thin cylinders)

(*ii*) *Shrinking* an external cylinder on the original cylinder, giving rise to a *compound cylinder*

and   (*iii*) *Applying* temporary internal pressure sufficiently high to produce *plastic flow*, resulting in a residual compressive stress upon the removal of the initial high pressure. This technique is known as *Auto Frettage*, and has to be applied under perfectly controlled conditions.

Compound cylinders : A more common method of producing initial compressive stress at the inside surface of a thick cylinder is to shrink a tube or thin cylinder on the outer surface of the thick cylinder (Fig. 24.8 *a*). This technique is invariably used in the manufacture of a gun tube. By keeping proper initial difference in the common radii, the required shrinkage pressure at the junction can be achieved. The inside diameter of the outer cylinder is kept slightly less than the outside diameter of the main cylinder (i.e. inner cylinder). The outside cylinder is heated and slipped over the inner cylinder. As it cools, it shrinks, producing an *external pressure* around the outside of the inner cylinder. As a result, *initial compressive stresses* are induced in the entire inner cylinder, and *initial tensile hoop stresses* are induced in the outer cylinder (Fig. 24.8 *b*). When fluid is admitted in the inner cylinder, the internal pressure is jointly resisted by both the internal and external cylinders. Due to the fluid pressure applied in the inner cylinder, *tensile hoop stresses* will be set up in both the inner as well as outer cylinders (Fig. 24.8 *c*). The final stresses, shown in Fig. 24.8 (*d*) will be the algebraic sum of (*b*) and

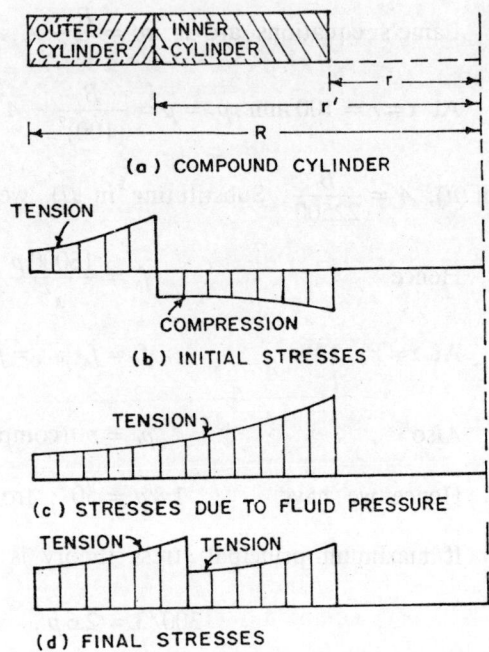

(a) COMPOUND CYLINDER

(b) INITIAL STRESSES

(c) STRESSES DUE TO FLUID PRESSURE

(d) FINAL STRESSES

FIG. 24.8. DEVELOPMENT OF STRESSES IN COMPOUND CYLINDER

(*c*). Thus, the final hoop stress (tensile) will be more or less uniform, and its maximum magnitude will be very much reduced by this technique.

Let r' be the radius at the common surface of the inner and outer cylinders, and let p' be the shrinkage pressure induced. Lame's equations for the two cylinders are as follows:

For inner cylinder : $p_x = \dfrac{B}{x^2} - A$ ...(1)   and $f_x = \dfrac{B}{x^2} + A$ ...(2)

For outer cylinder: $p_x = \dfrac{B'}{x^2} - A'$ ...(3)   and $f_x = \dfrac{B'}{x^2} + A'$ ...(4)

Here, A, B, A' and B' are Lame's constants which can be evaluated by applying the following *initial conditions* :

For inner tube : Inner radius $= r$; outer radius $= r'$

At $x = r$, $p = 0$ and at $x = r'$, $p = p'$

Hence $\dfrac{B}{r^2} - A = 0$ ...(a) and $\dfrac{B}{r'^2} - A = p'$ ...(b)

For outer tube : Inner radius $= r'$; outer radius $= R$

At $x = r'$, $p = p'$ and at $x = R$, $p = 0$

$\therefore$ $\dfrac{B'}{r'^2} - A' = p'$ ...(c) and $\dfrac{B'}{R^2} - A' = 0$ ...(d)

Initial stresses : Using Eqs. (a), (b), (c) and (d), the four constant A, B, A' and B' can be determined. The *initial hoop stresses* (compressive) can be found from Eqs. (2) and (4), for the two cylinders.

Stresses due to internal pressure : When fluid pressure is applied at the inside of the inner tube, the resulting stresses can be found from the following Lame's equations

$$p_x = \frac{b}{x^2} - a \quad ...(5) \qquad \text{and} \qquad f_x = \frac{b}{x^2} + a \quad ...(6)$$

where the constants a and b can be evaluated from the following boundary conditions:

At $x = r$, $p_x = p_r$ and at $x = R$, $p_x = 0$

Final stresses : The final stress in the *compound cylinder* will be the *algebraic sum* of (a) initial stresses and (b) stresses due to internal pressure.

24.11. SHRINK FIT ALLOWANCE

As stated earlier, the initial difference in radii of the common junction of the shrink fit assembly is necessary to induce the required shrinkage pressure p' at the junction due to which the inner tube will be in the state of initial compression and the outer tube will be in the state of initial tension. Let us now calculate the necessary difference of radii at the junction to create the required shrinkage pressure p'.

Let r' = common radius at the junction after shrinking

δr_1 = difference between outer radius of the inner tube and r'

δr_2 = difference between inner radius of the outer tube and r'

$\delta r'$ = difference in the radii of the two tubes, before shrinking.

Hence $\delta r' = \delta r_1 + \delta r_2$ (Fig. 24.9) ...(1)

Circumferential strain for the inner tube, at the common radius r' is

$$\varepsilon_{yi} = \frac{\delta r_1}{r'} = \frac{1}{E}\left[\left(\frac{B}{r'^2} + A\right) + \frac{p'}{m}\right], \text{ compressive.}$$

...(2)

Similarly, circumferential strain for the outer tube, at the common radius r' is

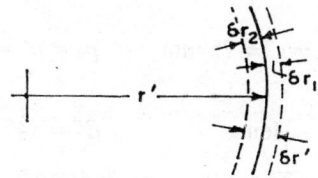

FIG. 24.9. SHRINK FIT ALLOWANCE

$$\varepsilon_{y0} = \frac{\delta r_2}{r'} = \frac{1}{E}\left[\left(\frac{B'}{r'^2} + A'\right) + \frac{p'}{m}\right] \text{ tensile} \qquad ...(3)$$

From (2) and (3), we get $\qquad \dfrac{\delta r'}{r'} = \dfrac{\delta r_1 + \delta r_2}{r'} = \dfrac{1}{E}\left[\left(\dfrac{B'}{r'^2} + A'\right) - \left(\dfrac{B}{r'^2} + A\right)\right]$

Hence the original difference of the radii at the junction, before shrinking-on, divided by the radius r' at the junction, is equal to the algebraic difference (or numerical sum) of the hoop stresses for the two tubes at the common surface divided by E.

Example 24.6. *A compound cylinder, formed by shrinking one tube on to another, is subjected to an internal pressure of 50 N/mm². Before the fluid is admitted, the internal and external diameters of the compound cylinder are 100 mm and 180 mm, and the diameter at the junction is 150 mm. If, after shrinking on, the radial pressure at the common surface is 8 N/mm², calculate the final stresses set up by the section.*

Solution : Given : $\qquad p_r = 50 \text{ N/mm}^2 ; R = 90 \text{ mm} ; r = 50 \text{ mm} ; r' = 75 \text{ mm}; p' = 8 \text{ N/mm}^2$

For the inner tube, $\qquad p_x = \dfrac{B}{x^2} - A \quad ...(1) \text{ and } f_x = \dfrac{B}{x^2} + A \qquad\qquad ...(2)$

For the outer tube, $\qquad p_x = \dfrac{B'}{x^2} - A' \quad ...(3) \text{ and } f_x = \dfrac{B'}{x^2} + A' \qquad\qquad ...(4)$

(a) Before the fluid is admitted : Inner tube

At $\qquad\qquad x = 50 \text{ mm}, p_x = 0 \quad \therefore \quad \dfrac{B}{2500} - A = 0 \quad \text{or} \quad A = \dfrac{B}{2500}$

At $\qquad\qquad x = r' = 75 \text{ mm}; p_x = p' = 8 = \dfrac{B}{(75)^2} - A = \dfrac{B}{5625} - \dfrac{B}{2500} = -2.222 \times 10^{-4} B$

Hence $\qquad\qquad B = -36000 \text{ and } A = -14.4$

Hence $\qquad\qquad f_x = \dfrac{B}{x^2} + A = -\dfrac{36000}{x^2} - 14.4$

The minus sign indicates that f_x will be compressive throughout.

At $x = r = 50 \text{ mm}, \qquad f_{50} = -\dfrac{36000}{(50)^2} - 14.4 = -14.4 - 14.4 = 28.8 \text{ N/mm}^2 \text{ (comp.)}$

At $x = r' = 75 \text{ mm}, \qquad f_{75} = -\dfrac{36000}{(75)^2} - 14.4 = -6.4 - 14.4 = 20.8 \text{ N/mm}^2 \text{ (comp.)}$

(b) Before the fluid is admitted : Outer tube

At $x = R = 90 \text{ mm}, \qquad p_x = 0 \therefore \dfrac{B'}{(90)^2} - A' = 0 \text{ or } A' = \dfrac{B'}{8100}$

At $x = r' = 75 \text{ mm}, \qquad p_x = p' = 8 = \dfrac{B'}{(75)^2} - A' = \dfrac{B'}{56.25} - \dfrac{B'}{8100} = 5.432 \times 10^{-4} B'$

Hence $\qquad\qquad B' = 147273 \text{ and } A' = 18.18. \quad \text{Hence } f_x = \dfrac{147273}{x^2} + 18.18$

The plus sign indicates that f_x will be tensile throughout.

At $x = r' = 75 \text{ mm}, \qquad f_{75} = \dfrac{147273}{(75)^2} + 18.18 = 26.18 + 18.18 = 44.36 \text{ N/mm}^2 \text{ (tensile)}$

At $x = R = 90$ mm, $\qquad f_{90} = \dfrac{147273}{(90)^2} + 18.18 = 18.18 + 18.18 = 36.36$ N/mm^2 (tensile)

(c) After the fluid is admitted: compound tube

Lame's equations are $p_x = \dfrac{b}{x^2} - a$ ...(5) $\qquad$ and $\qquad f_x = \dfrac{b}{x^2} + a$ $\hfill$ ...(6)

At $\qquad x = R = 90$ mm, $p_x = 0$ $\qquad \therefore \quad \dfrac{b}{8100} - a = 0$ or $a = \dfrac{b}{8100}$

At $\qquad x = r = 50$ mm, $p_x = 50 = \dfrac{b}{2500} - a = \dfrac{b}{2500} - \dfrac{b}{8100} = 2.7654 \times 10^{-4} b$

$\therefore \qquad b = 180804$ and $a = 180804/8100 = 22.32$

Hence $\quad f_x = \dfrac{180804}{x^2} + 22.32$

At $x = r = 50$ mm, $\qquad f_{50} = 180804/2500 + 22.32 = 72.32 + 22.32 = 94.64$ N/mm^2 (tensile)

At $x = r' = 75$ mm, $\qquad f_{75} = 180804/(75)^2 + 22.32 = 32.14 + 22.32 = 54.46$ N/mm^2 (tensile)

At $x = R = 90$ mm, $\qquad f_{90} = 180804/(90)^2 + 22.32 = 22.32 + 22.32 = 44.64$ N/mm^2 (tensile)

The *final circumferential stresses* at various points are shown in the table below.

STRESSES AT VARIOUS POINTS OF COMPOUND TUBE
(+ FOR TENSION ; – FOR COMPRESSION)

Hoop stress (N/mm^2)	Inner tube		Outer tube	
	$x = r = 50$ mm	$x = r' = 75$ mm	$x = r' = 75$ mm	$x = R = 100$ mm
(i) Initial	– 28.8	– 20.8	+ 44.36	+ 36.36
(ii) Due to fluid pressure	+ 94.64	+ 54.46	+ 54.46	+ 44.64
(iii) Final	+ 65.84	+ 33.66	+ 98.82	+ 81.00

Example 24.7. *In example 24.6, calculate the necessary difference in the diameters of the two tubes at the common surface before shrinking on, so as to produce a radial pressure of 8 N/mm^2. Also, calculate the minimum temperature to which the outer tube should be heated before it can be slipped on. Take $E = 2 \times 10^5$ N/mm^2, $1/m = 0.3$ and $\alpha = 6 \times 10^{-6}$ per °F.*

Solution : From Eq. 24.19, we have

$$\frac{\delta r'}{r'} = \frac{1}{E}\left[\left(\frac{B'}{r'^2} + A' \right) - \left(\frac{B}{r'^2} + A \right) \right] = \frac{1}{E}\left[\left\{ \frac{147273}{(75)^2} + 18.18 \right\} - \left\{ -\frac{36000}{(75)^2} - 14.4 \right\} \right]$$

$$= \frac{1}{2 \times 10^5}\left[\left\{ 26.18 + 18.18 \right\} - \left\{ -6.4 - 14.4 \right\} \right] = 3.258 \times 10^{-4}$$

$\therefore \qquad\qquad \delta r' = 3.258 \times 10^{-4} \times 7.5 = 0.024475$ mm

$\therefore \qquad\qquad \delta d' = 2 \times 0.024435 = \mathbf{0.04887\ mm}$

Now $\qquad (\pi d') \alpha t = \pi \delta d'$

$\therefore \qquad\qquad t = \dfrac{\delta d'}{\alpha . d'} = \dfrac{0.04887}{6 \times 10^{-6}(150)} = \mathbf{54.3° F}$

Example 24.8. *A compound thick cylinder is formed by shrinking a tube of external diameter 300 mm over another tube of internal diameter 150 mm. After shrinking, the diameter at the junction of the tube is found to be 250 mm and radial compression as 28 N/mm². Find the original difference in radii at the junction. Take $E = 2 \times 10^5 \, N/mm^2$.*

Solution :

Given $\qquad\qquad\qquad R = 150 \text{ mm} ; r = 75 \text{ mm} ; r' = 125 \text{ mm} ; p' = 28 \text{ N/mm}^2$

(a) For the inner tube : before fluid is admitted

$$p_x = \frac{B}{x^2} - A$$

At $x = r = 75$ mm, $\qquad p_x = 0 = \dfrac{B}{(75)^2} - 4$, from which $A = \dfrac{B}{5625}$

At $x = r' = 125$ mm, $\qquad p_x = p' = 28 = \dfrac{B}{(125)^2} - A = \dfrac{B}{15625} - \dfrac{B}{5625} = -1.1378 \times 10^{-4} B$

From which $B = -246094$. Hence $A = -\dfrac{246094}{5625} = -43.75$

(b) For the outer tube : before fluid is admitted

$$p_x = \frac{B'}{x^2} - A'$$

At $\qquad x = R = 150$ mm, $p_x = 0 = \dfrac{B'}{(150)^2} - A'$, from which $A' = \dfrac{B'}{22500}$

At $\qquad x = r' = 75, p_x = p' = 28 = \dfrac{B'}{(125)^2} - A' = \dfrac{B'}{15625} - \dfrac{B'}{22500} = 1.956 \times 10^{-5} B'$

From which $B' = 1431818$. Hence $A' = 1431818/22500 = 63.64$

(c) Original difference in radii

From eq. 24.19, $\qquad \dfrac{\delta r'}{r'} = \dfrac{1}{E}\left[\left(\dfrac{B'}{r'^2} + A' \right) - \left(\dfrac{B}{r'^2} + A \right) \right]$

$$= \frac{1}{2 \times 10^5}\left[\left\{ \frac{1431818}{(125)^2} + 63.45 \right\} - \left\{ -\frac{246094}{(125)^2} - 43.75 \right\} \right]$$

$$= \frac{1}{2 \times 10^5}[(155.28) - (-59.50)] = \frac{214.78}{2 \times 10^5} = 107.39 \times 10^{-5}$$

$\therefore \qquad\qquad\qquad \delta r' = 107.39 \times 10^{-5} \times 125 = \mathbf{0.134 \ mm}$

Example 24.9. *The external diameter of a steel collar is 240 mm. When shrunk on a solid of 150 mm diameter, the internal diameter of the collar decreases by 0.15 mm. Find (a) the reduction in the diameter of the shaft (b) the radial pressure between the collar and the shaft, and (c) hoop stress at the inner surface of the tube. Take $E = 2 \times 10^5 \, N/mm^2$ and $1/m = 0.304$.*

Solution : Let us use suffix 1 for the shaft and 2 for the collar. Due to radial pressure (p) at the junction, the shaft will have compressive stress throughout. Let f be the hoof stress at the junction.

$$\therefore \qquad f = p\left(\frac{R^2 + r^2}{R^2 - r^2}\right) = p\,\frac{(240)^2 + (150)^2}{(240)^2 - (150)^2} = 2.282\,p \qquad \qquad ...(1)$$

Now $\qquad e_2 = \dfrac{1}{E}\left(f + \dfrac{p}{m}\right)$ But $e_2 = \dfrac{0.15}{150}$ $\quad \therefore \quad \dfrac{0.15}{150} = \dfrac{1}{E}\left(2.282\,p + \dfrac{p}{m}\right).$

or $\qquad p\,(2.282 + 0.304) = 2 \times 10^5 \times \dfrac{0.15}{150} = 200.$ From which $p = \mathbf{77.34\,N/mm^2}$ (compressive)

$$\therefore \qquad f = 2.282 \times 77.34 = \mathbf{176.49\,N/mm^2} \text{ (tension)}$$

Now $\qquad e_1 = \dfrac{p}{E} - \dfrac{p}{mE} = \dfrac{p}{E}\left(1 - \dfrac{1}{m}\right) = \dfrac{77.34}{2 \times 10^5}(1 - 0.304) = 2.691 \times 10^{-4}$

$$\therefore \qquad \delta d_1 = d_1 . e = 150 \times 2.691 \times 10^{-4} = \mathbf{0.0404\,mm}$$

24.12. THICK SPHERICAL SHELLS

Let us now take the case of thick spherical shell, of internal radius r and external radius R, subjected to internal pressure p, as shown in Fig. 24.10.

Consider an element of radial thickness δx, at any radius x. Let p_x be the radial compressive stress at the radius x, and $p_x + \delta p_x$ be the radial compressive stress at radius $x + \delta x$. Let f_x be the circumferential tensile stress, which is equal in all directions perpendicular to the radius. Let us now consider forces on an elementary spherical shell of radius x and thickness δx.

Bursting force on elementary shell
$$= \pi x^2 p_x - \pi\,(x + \delta x)^2\,(p_x + \delta p_x)$$

Resisting force $= f_x \times 2\,\pi x . \delta x$

Equating the two, we get
$$\pi x^2 . p_x - \pi\,(x + \delta x)^2\,(p_x + \delta p_x) = 2\,\pi x\,\delta x\,f_x$$

$$\therefore \qquad 2 f_x\,\delta x = -2\,p_x . \delta x - x\,\delta p_x$$

(neglecting small quantities of the second and higher order)

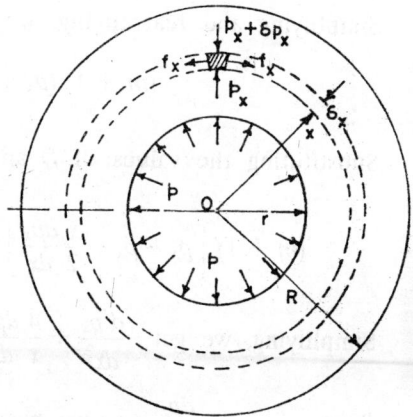

FIG. 24.10

or $\qquad 2 f_x = -2\,p_x - x\,\dfrac{\delta p_x}{\delta x}$ or $\quad f_x = -p_x - \dfrac{x}{2}\dfrac{dp_x}{dx}$ $\qquad \qquad ...(1a)$

Differentiating, $\dfrac{df_x}{dx} = -\dfrac{dp_x}{dx} - \dfrac{1}{2}\left[x\dfrac{d^2p_x}{dx^2} + \dfrac{dp_x}{dx}\right]$ $\qquad \qquad ...(1)$

The elementary spherical shell is subjected to three principal stresses at any point:

(i) The radial pressure p_x (compressive)
(ii) The hoop stress f_x (tensile)
(iii) The hoop stress $f_y = f_x$ (tensile), on a plane at right angles

The radial strain at any point is, $e_x = \dfrac{p_x}{E} + \dfrac{2f_x}{mE}$ (compressive)   ...(2)

The circumferential strain at any point is, $e_y = \dfrac{f_x}{E} + \dfrac{p_x}{mE} - \dfrac{f_x}{mE}$ (tensile)   ...(3)

Owing to pure radial displacement of points, let the radius x increase to $(x + u)$

$\therefore$ Radial strain, $\qquad e_x = \dfrac{\delta(x + u) - \delta x}{\delta x} = \dfrac{\delta u}{\delta x}$ ...(4)

Circumferential strain, $\qquad e_y = \dfrac{(x + u)\,\delta\theta - x\,\delta\theta}{x\,\delta\theta} = \dfrac{u}{x}$ ...(5)

From (4) and (5), $\qquad e_x = \dfrac{\delta u}{\delta x} = \dfrac{\delta}{\delta x}(x\,e_y) = e_y + x\dfrac{\delta e_y}{\delta x}$

Substituting the value of e_x and e_y from (2) and (3), we get

$$-\left(\frac{p_x}{E} + \frac{2f_x}{mE}\right) = \left(\frac{f_x}{E} + \frac{p_x}{mE} - \frac{f_x}{mE}\right) + x\frac{\delta}{\delta x}\left[\frac{f_x}{E} + \frac{p_x}{mE} - \frac{f_x}{mE}\right]$$

or $\qquad -\dfrac{1}{E}\left(p_x + \dfrac{2f_x}{m}\right) = \dfrac{1}{E}\left(\dfrac{m-1}{m}f_x - \dfrac{p_x}{m}\right) + \dfrac{x}{E}\left(\dfrac{m-1}{m}\dfrac{\delta f_x}{\delta x} + \dfrac{1}{m}\dfrac{\delta p_x}{\delta x}\right)$

Simplifying and rearranging, we get

$$(m + 1)(p_x + f_x) + (m - 1)x\frac{df_x}{dx} + x\frac{dp_x}{dx} = 0$$

Substituting the values of f_x and $\dfrac{df_x}{dx}$ from 1(a) and 1 respectively, we get

$$(m + 1)\left[p_x - p_x - \frac{x}{2}\frac{dp_x}{dx}\right] + (m - 1)x\left[-\frac{dp_x}{dx} - \frac{1}{2}\left(x\frac{d^2p_x}{dx^2} + \frac{dp_x}{dx}\right)\right] + x\frac{dp_x}{dx} = 0$$

Simplifying, we get $\dfrac{d^2p_x}{dx^2} + \dfrac{4}{x}\dfrac{dp_x}{dx} = 0$ ...(6)

Putting $\qquad \dfrac{dp_x}{dx} = v$, we have: $\dfrac{dv}{dx} + \dfrac{4}{x}v = 0$

or $\qquad \dfrac{dv}{v} + \dfrac{4dx}{x} = 0$

or $\qquad \log_e v = -4\log_e x + \log_e C_1$, where C_1 is constant of integration.

$\therefore \qquad v = \dfrac{C_1}{x^4} \qquad$ or $\qquad \dfrac{dp_x}{dx} = \dfrac{C_1}{x^4}$

Integrating, we get $\qquad p_x = -\dfrac{C_1}{3x^2} + C_2,$ ...(a) where C_2 is constant of integration.

Since $\qquad f_x = -p_x - \dfrac{x}{2}\dfrac{dp_x}{dx}$ (from 1a), we have

$$f_x = \frac{C_1}{3x^3} - C_2 - \frac{C_1}{2x^3}$$

or $$f_x = -\frac{C_1}{6x^3} - C_2 \qquad \qquad ...(b)$$

If we put $C_1 = -6B$ and $C_2 = -A$, we get the following expressions for p_x and f_x

$$p_x = \frac{2B}{x^3} - A \quad ...(24.20\ a) \qquad \text{and } f_x = \frac{B}{x^3} + A \qquad \qquad ...(24.20\ b)$$

Boundary conditions

At $x = r$, $\qquad \qquad p_x = p$ and at $x = R$, $p_x = 0$

$\therefore \qquad \qquad p = \frac{2B}{r^3} - A \quad ...(c)$ and $0 = \frac{2B}{R^3} - A \qquad \qquad ...(d)$

Solving (c) and (d), we get $B = \dfrac{p\,r^3\,R^3}{2\,(R^3 - r^3)}$ and $A = p\,\dfrac{r^3}{(R^3 - r^3)} \qquad ...(24.21)$

Example 24.10. *Calculate the thickness of shell required for a vessel of spherical shape, 500 mm inside diameter, to withstand an internal pressure of 25 N/mm², if the maximum permissible tensile stress in the shell is 60 N/mm².*

Solution : Given $\qquad \qquad r = 500/2 = 250$ mm ; $p = 25$ N/mm² ; $f_{max} = 60$ N/mm²

Lame's equations are: $\qquad p_x = \dfrac{2B}{x^3} - A$ and $f_x = \dfrac{B}{x^3} + A$

At $x = r = 250$ mm, $\qquad p_x = 25$ N/mm² and $f_x = f_{max} = 60$ N/mm²

$\therefore \qquad \qquad 25 = \dfrac{2B}{(250)^3} - A \quad ...(1)$ and $60 = \dfrac{B}{(250)^3} + A \qquad \qquad ...(2)$

From (1), $\qquad \qquad A = \dfrac{2B}{(250)^3} - 25 = 1.28 \times 10^{-7} B - 25$

Hence from (2), we get $60 = \dfrac{B}{(250)^3} + (1.28 \times 10^{-7} B - 25) = 1.92 \times 10^{-7} B - 25$

From which, $\qquad \qquad B = 442.7 \times 10^6$ and hence $A = 31.67$

Now $\qquad \qquad \qquad p_x = \dfrac{2B}{x^3} - A$

At $x = R$, $\qquad \qquad p_x = 0$. Hence $\dfrac{2B}{R^3} - A = 0$

$\therefore \qquad \qquad R^3 = \dfrac{2B}{A} = \dfrac{2 \times 442.7 \times 10^6}{31.67} = 27.96 \times 10^6$, from which $R = 303.5$ mm

$\therefore \qquad$ Thickness of metal $= R - r = 303.5 - 250 = $ **53.5 mm**

24.13. ADDITIONAL ILLUSTRATIVE EXAMPLES

Example 24.11. *A steel rod of 60 mm diameter is pressed into a steel sleeve so that when assembled, the radial pressure is 16 N/mm² and the circumferential stress at the inside of the sleeve is 24 N/mm². Determine the increase of radial pressure when the bar is subjected to an axial compressive load of 75 kN. Take 1/m = 0.304.*

Solution : Given $\qquad r = 30$ mm ; $p = 16$ N/mm² ; $f = 24$ N/mm² ; $P = 75$ kN

Lame's equations for steel rod

$$p_x = \frac{B}{x^2} - A \text{ (comp.) and } f_x = \frac{B}{x^2} + A \text{ (tensile)}$$

At $x = 0$, p and f are each infinite, unless $B = 0$. Hence $B = 0$.

$$\therefore \qquad\qquad p = -A \text{ or } A = -p \text{ and } f = +A = -p$$

The minus sign shows that f is compressive. This holds for any value of x. Hence the circumferential stress at any point is equal to the radial pressure.

For the sleeve : Initially, $p = 16\ /mm^2$ (comp.) and $f = 24\ N/mm^2$ (tension)

R is unknown. Initially, end load $= 0$

Finally, when $P = 75\ kN$ (comp.), $f_0 = \dfrac{75000}{\dfrac{\pi}{4}(60)^2} = 26.53\ N/mm^2$

Let $\qquad\qquad \Delta f = $ change in hoop stress, when p is applied

and $\qquad\qquad \Delta p = $ change in radial stress, when p is applied

Change in the longitudinal strain of the rod $= \Delta e_0 = \dfrac{26.53}{E}$ (comp.)

Change in the circumferential strain of the sleeve $= \Delta e = \left(\dfrac{\Delta f}{E} + \dfrac{1}{m\,E} \Delta p \right)$ ... expansion ...(1)

For the rod : Change in the circumferential strain for the rod $= \Delta e'$

$$= \frac{\Delta e_0}{m} + \frac{\Delta p}{m\,E} - \frac{\Delta p}{E} = \frac{1}{m}\frac{26.53}{E} + \frac{1}{m}\frac{\Delta p}{E} - \frac{\Delta p}{E} \qquad\qquad ...(2)$$

Since the sleeve and rod are in contact at the common radius, $\Delta e = \Delta e'$

$$\therefore \qquad\qquad \frac{\Delta f}{E} + \frac{\Delta p}{m\,E} = \frac{26.53}{m\,E} + \frac{\Delta p}{m\,E} - \Delta p$$

or $\qquad\qquad\qquad \Delta p = \dfrac{26.53}{m} - \Delta f \qquad\qquad\qquad ...(a)$

This is one relation between Δp and Δf. To get another relation between Δp and Δf, construct Lame's lines for initial and final conditions, as shown in Fig. 24.11. Mark A and A' at distance $1/r^2$ from O, on either side. At A, mark perpendicular AC equal to $p (= 16\ N/mm^2)$. Similarly, at A', mark perpendicular $A'C'$ equal to $f (= 24\ N/mm^2)$. Join C and C', cutting the line AA' at B. Thus, distance $OB = 1/R^2$. The solid line CC' represents initial condition. Again, draw the dotted line EE' representing the final condi-

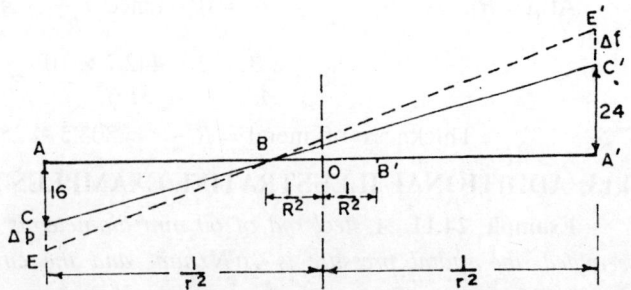

FIG. 24.11

tion, where $CE\ (= \Delta p)$ and $C'E'\ (= \Delta f)$ are the corresponding increases.

By inspection of Fig. 24.11, we have $\dfrac{\Delta f}{\Delta p} = \dfrac{f}{p} = \dfrac{24}{16} = 1.5$ ...(b)

Hence $\Delta f = 1.5 \Delta p$, Substituting in Eq. (a), we get $\Delta p = \dfrac{26.53}{m} - 1.5 \Delta p$

From which $\Delta p = \dfrac{26.53}{m\,(2.5)} = \dfrac{26.53}{0.304 \times 2.5} = \mathbf{34.91\ N/mm^2}$

Example 24.12. *Find the ratio of thickness to internal diameter for a tube subjected to internal pressure when the ratio of pressure to maximum circumferential stress is 0.5.*

Find the alteration of thickness of metal in such a tube 80 mm internal diameter when the pressure is 50 N/mm². E = 200,000 N/mm², μ = 0.304. (U.L.)

Solution : Given $p/f = 0.5$; $r = 80/2 = 40$ mm ; $p = 50\ N/mm^2$.

From Eq. 25.15, we have $f_r = \dfrac{R^2 + r^2}{R^2 - r^2}\,p_r = \dfrac{K^2 + 1}{K^2 - 1}\,p_r$, where $K = \dfrac{R}{r}$

$\therefore$ $(K^2 - 1) = (K^2 + 1)\,0.5$ or $K^2 = 3$

$\therefore$ $K = \dfrac{R}{r} = \sqrt{3}$

Now Ratio $\dfrac{\text{Thickness}}{\text{Internal diameter}} = \dfrac{R - r}{2r} = \dfrac{K - 1}{2} = \dfrac{\sqrt{3} - 1}{2} = \mathbf{0.366}$

Here $r = 40$ mm ; $\therefore$ $R = 40\sqrt{3} = 69.28$ mm

Increase in inside diameter :

$$p_r = 5\ N/mm^2;\ f_r = p/0.5 = 50/0.5 = 100\ N/mm^2$$

$$f_0 = p_r \dfrac{r^2}{R^2 - r^2} = p_r \dfrac{1}{K^2 - 1} = p_r \dfrac{1}{3 - 1} = \dfrac{p_r}{2} = 25\ N/mm^2$$

$\therefore$ Hoop strain $= \left(f_r + \dfrac{p_r}{m} - \dfrac{f_0}{m} \right) \dfrac{1}{E} = (100 + 50 \times 0.304 - 25 \times 0.304) \dfrac{1}{E} = \dfrac{107.6}{E}$

$\therefore$ Increase in internal diameter $= \dfrac{107.6}{E} \times 80 = \dfrac{8608}{E}$ mm ...(1)

Increase in outside diameter:

$$p_R = 0 ; f_R = 50\ N/mm^2 \text{ (since } f_x - p_x = \text{ constant } = 50)$$

$$f_0 = 25\ N/mm^2 \text{ (as before)}$$

$\therefore$ Hoop strain $= \left(f_R + \dfrac{p_R}{m} - \dfrac{f_0}{m} \right) \dfrac{1}{E} = (50 + 0 - 25 \times 0.304) \dfrac{1}{E} = \dfrac{42.4}{E}$

$\therefore$ Increase in the external diameter $= \dfrac{42.4}{E} \times (2 \times 69.28) = \dfrac{5875}{E}$ mm

$\therefore$ Decrease in thickness $= \left(\dfrac{8608 - 5875}{2} \right) \dfrac{1}{200000} = \mathbf{0.00683\ mm}$

Example 24.13. *Two thick steel cylinders A and B, closed at the ends, have the same conditions, the outer diameter of each being 1.6 times the inner diameter. The cylinder A is subject to internal fluid pressure only and B to external fluid pressure only. Find the ratio of the pressures on these cylinders :*

(i) When the greatest circumferential stress has the same numerical value for each cylinder

(ii) When the greatest circumferential strain has the same numerical value for each cylinder.

$$Poisson's\ ratio = 0.304 \qquad\qquad (U.L.)$$

Solution : Given $\qquad R/r = K = 1.6$ for each cylinder.

Let the pressure in cylinder A and B be p_a and p_b respectively.

(a) For cylinder A : Internal pressure $= p_a$; external pressure zero. Due to the internal pressure p_a, the maximum hoop stress will occur at radius r and will be tensile.

From Eq. 24.5, $\qquad f_a = p_a \dfrac{R^2 + r^2}{R^2 - r^2} = \dfrac{K^2 + 1}{K^2 - 1} p_a = \dfrac{(1.6)^2 + 1}{(1.6)^2 - 1} p_a = 2.282\, p_a \qquad ...(1)$

Longitudinal stress, $\qquad f_0 = p_a \dfrac{r^2}{R^2 - r^2} = \dfrac{1}{K^2 - 1} p_a = \dfrac{1}{(1.6)^2 - 1} p_a = 0.641\, p_a$ (tensile)

$\therefore$ Circumferential strain $e_a = \dfrac{f_a}{E} + \dfrac{1}{m}\dfrac{p_a}{E} - \dfrac{0.641\, p_a}{mE} = \dfrac{1}{E}\left(f_a + \dfrac{0.359}{m} p_a\right)$

$$= \frac{1}{E}(2.282\, p_a + 0.359 \times 0.304\, p_a) = \frac{2.391}{E} p_a \qquad ...(2)$$

$$\text{(Expansion)}$$

(b) For cylinder B : External pressure p_b ; Internal pressure zero. Due to external pressure p_b in B, the maximum hoop stress will also be at inner radius r, and will be compressive.

From Eq. 2.47, $\quad f_b = \dfrac{2R^2}{R^2 - r^2} p_b = \dfrac{2K^2}{K^2 - 1} p_b = \dfrac{2(1.6)^2}{(1.6)^2 - 1} p_b = 3.282\, p_b$ (compressive) ...(3)

The longitudinal stress f_0 is given by the equilibrium equation :

$$f_0\, \pi\,(R^2 - r^2) = p_b\, \pi\, R^2$$

or $\qquad\qquad f_0 = \dfrac{R^2}{R^2 - r^2} p_b = \dfrac{K^2}{K^2 - 1} p_b = \dfrac{(1.6)^2}{(1.6)^2 - 1} p_b = 1.641\, p_b$ (compressive)

$\therefore$ Circumferential strain, $\quad e_b = -\dfrac{f_b}{E} + \dfrac{1}{m}\dfrac{f_0}{E} = \dfrac{1}{E}\left(-3.282\, p_b + 0.304 \times 1.641\, p_b\right) = -\dfrac{2.783\, p_b}{E}$ ...(4)

(c) Condition (i). According to this condition, the greatest circumferential stress has the same *numerical value* for each cylinder. Hence from (1) and (3), we have

$$f_a = f_b \text{ or } 2.282\, p_a = 3.282\, p_b$$

$$\therefore \qquad\qquad \frac{p_a}{p_b} = \frac{3.282}{2.282} = \textbf{1.438}$$

(d) Condition (ii). According to this condition, greatest circumferential strain has the same numerical value for each cylinder. Hence from (2) and (4), we have

$$e_a = e_b \text{ or } \frac{2.391}{E}p_a = \frac{2.783\,p_b}{E}$$

or
$$\frac{p_a}{p_b} = \frac{2.783}{2.391} = \mathbf{1.164}$$

Example 24.14. *The maximum stress permitted in a thick cylinder, radii 100 mm and 150 mm is 25 N/mm². The external pressure is 7.5 N/mm². What internal pressure can ·be applied? Plot curves showing the variation of hoop and radial stresses through the material.*

Solution :   Given $R = 150 \text{ mm} ; r = 100 \text{ mm} ; f_{max} = 25 \text{ N/mm}^2 ; p_R = 7.5 \text{ N/mm}^2$

Lame's equations are $p_x = \dfrac{B}{x^2} - A \text{ and } f_x = \dfrac{B}{x^2} + A$

At $x = R = 150 \text{ mm,}$ $p_x = p_R = 7.5 = \dfrac{B}{(150)^2} - A$ ...(1)

Also, at $x = r = 100 \text{ mm,}$ $f_r = f_{max} = 25 = \dfrac{B}{(100)^2} + A$ ...(2)

From (1), $A = \dfrac{B}{22500} - 7.5$; Hence from (2), $25 = \dfrac{B}{10000} + \dfrac{B}{22500} - 7.5$

From which $B = 225000.$ Hence $A = \dfrac{225000}{22500} - 7.5 = 2.5$

$\therefore$
$$f_x - p_x = \left(\frac{B}{x^2} + A\right) - \left(\frac{B}{x^2} - A\right) = 2A = 5$$

Thus, there is a constant difference of 5 N/mm² between the hoop and radial stresses.

At $r = 100 \text{ mm}$

$$p_{100} = \frac{225000}{(100)^2} - 2.5 = 20 \text{ N/mm}^2$$

At $x = 125 \text{ mm}$

$$p_{125} = \frac{225000}{(125)^2} - 2.5 = 11.9 \text{ N/mm}^2$$

$$f_{125} = \frac{225000}{(125)^2} + 2.5 = 16.9 \text{ N/mm}^2$$

At $x = 150 \text{ mm}, p_R = 7.5$

$$f_{150} = \frac{225000}{(150)^2} + 2.5 = 12.5 \text{ N/mm}^2$$

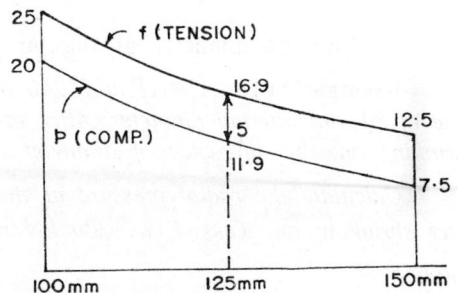

FIG. 24.12

Fig. 24.12 shows the graphical representation of stress variation.

Example 24.15. *A compound cylinder is to be made by shrinking on outer tube of 240 mm external diameter on to an inner tube of 120 mm internal diameter. Determine the common diameter at the junction if the greatest circumferential stress in the inner tube is to be two thirds of the greatest circumferential stress in the outer tube.*

Solution : $R = 240/2 = 120 \text{ mm} ; r = 120/2 = 60 \text{ mm};$

Let us use suffix 1 for the outer tube and suffix 2 for the inner tube. Let r' be the common radius and p' be the radial pressure at the junction. The maximum circumferential stress for the outer tube (f_1) will at $x = r'$ while the maximum circumferential stress for the inner tube (f_2) will be at $x = r$. According to the given condition, $f_2 = \frac{2}{3} f_1$,

For the outer tube : Inner pressure p' acting. Hence from Eq. 24.5 :

$$f_1 = p' \frac{R^2 + r'^2}{R^2 - r'^2} = p' \frac{K_1 + 1}{K_1 - 1}, \text{ where } K_1 = \frac{R^2}{r'^2}$$

For the inner tube: Outer radial pressure p' acting. Hence from eq. 24.7.

$$f_2 = p' \frac{2 r'^2}{r'^2 - r^2} = \frac{2 p'}{1 - K_2} \text{ where } K_2 = \frac{r^2}{r'^2} = \frac{r^2}{R^2} \times \frac{R^2}{r'^2} = \left(\frac{60}{120} \right)^2 K_1 = \frac{K_1}{4}$$

$$= \frac{2 p'}{1 - K_1/4} = \frac{8 p'}{4 - K_1}$$

But, as per given condition, $f_2 = \frac{2}{3} f_1$

$$\therefore \qquad \frac{8 p'}{4 - K_1} = \frac{2}{3} p' \frac{K_1 + 1}{K_1 - 1} \; ; \text{ or } 8 \times 3(K_1 - 1) = 2 (4 - K_1) (K_1 + 1)$$

or $\qquad K_1^2 + 9K_1 - 16 = 0$

which gives $\qquad K_1 = 1.521 = \left(\frac{R}{r'} \right)^2$

or $\qquad \frac{R}{r'} = 1.233$, from which $r' = R/1.233 = 120/1.233 = 97.31$ mm

$\therefore$ Common diameter at the junction $= \mathbf{194.62\ mm}$

Example 24.16. *A steel tube 240 mm external diameter is to be shrunk on another steel tube of 80 mm internal diameter. After shrinking, the diameter at the junction is 100 mm. Before shrinking on, the difference of diameter at the junction was 0.08 mm.*

Calculate the radial pressure at the junction and hoop stress developed in the two tubes after shrinking on. Take E as 200 kN/mm².

Solution :

Given $R = 120$ mm; $r = 40$ mm; $r' = 80$ mm; $\delta r' = 0.04$ mm

(a) For the inner tube, before the fluid is admitted

$$p_x = \frac{B}{x^2} - A$$

At $x = r = 40$ mm, $\qquad p_x = 0 = \frac{B}{(40)^2} - A$, From which $A = \frac{B}{1600}$ ...(1)

At $x = r' = 80$ mm, $\qquad p_x = p' = \frac{B}{(80)^2} - A = \frac{B}{6400} - \frac{B}{1600} = -\frac{3}{6400} B = -4.6875 \times 10^{-4} B$ ...(2)

For the outer tube, before the fluid is admitted: $p_x = \dfrac{B'}{x^2} - A'$

At $x = R = 120$ mm, $\quad p_x = 0 = \dfrac{B'}{(120)^2} - A'$, from which $A' = \dfrac{B'}{14400}$ ...(3)

At $x = r' = 80$ mm, $\quad p_x = p' = \dfrac{B'}{(80)^2} - A' = \dfrac{B'}{6400} - \dfrac{B'}{14400} = 8.68 \times 10^{-5} B'$ ...(4)

Equating (2) and (4), we get $\quad -4.6875 \times 10^{-4} B = 8.68 \times 10^{-5} B'$

From which $\quad\quad\quad\quad B = -0.1852 B'$ ...(a)

Also, from (1), $\quad\quad\quad A = \dfrac{B}{1600} = -1.157 \times 10^{-4} B'$ ...(b)

and from (3) $\quad\quad\quad A' = \dfrac{B'}{14400} = 6.944 \times 10^{-5} B'$ ...(c)

These the values of the three constants A, B and A' are known in terms of B'.

(c) Difference in radii :

From Eq. 14.19, $\quad\quad \dfrac{\delta r'}{r'} = \dfrac{1}{E}\left[\left(\dfrac{B'}{r'^2} + A'\right) - \left(\dfrac{B}{r'^2} + A\right)\right]$

$\therefore \quad \delta r' = 0.04$ mm $= \dfrac{80}{2 \times 10^5}\left[\left\{\dfrac{B'}{(80)^2} + 6.944 \times 10^{-5} B'\right\} - \left\{\dfrac{-0.1852 B'}{(80)^2} - 1.157 \times 10^{-4} B'\right\}\right]$

or $\quad 100 = 1.5625 \times 10^{-4} B' + 6.944 \times 10^{-5} B' + 2.894 \times 10^{-5} B' + 1.157 \times 10^{-4} B'$

From which we get $\quad B' = 270000$. Hence $A' = 18.75$; $A = -31.24$ and $B = -50000$

Thus the values of all the four constants are known.

(d) Radial pressure at the junction

From (4), $\quad p' = 8.68 \times 10^{-5} B' = 8.68 \times 10^{-5} \times 270000 = \mathbf{23.44\ N/mm^2}$ (comp.)

Check: From (2), $\quad p' = -4.6875 \times 10^{-4} B = -4.6875 \times 10^{-4} \times (-50000) = 23.44\ N/mm^2$

(e) Hoop stresses in the tubes : For the inner tube, $f_x = \dfrac{B}{x^2} + A$

At $x = r = 40$ mm; $\quad f_r = \dfrac{-50000}{(40)^2} - 31.24 = -62.49\ N/mm^2 = \mathbf{62.49\ N/mm^2}$ (comp.)

At $x = r' = 80$ mm $\quad f_r' = \dfrac{50000}{(80)^2} - 31.24 = 7.81 - 31.24 = -39.05\ N/mm^2$

$\quad\quad\quad\quad\quad\quad\quad\quad = \mathbf{39.05\ N/mm^2}$ (comp.)

For the outer tube, $\quad f_x = \dfrac{B'}{x^2} + A'$

At $x = r' = 80$ mm $\quad f_r' = \dfrac{270000}{(80)^2} + 18.75 = 42.19 + 18.75 = \mathbf{60.94\ N/mm^2}$ (tensile)

At $x = R = 120$ mm $\quad f_R = \dfrac{270000}{(120)^2} + 18.75 = \mathbf{37.5\ N/mm^2}$ (tensile)

Example 24.17. *Find the ratio of thickness to internal diameter for a tube subjected to internal pressure when the ratio of the internal pressure to the greatest circumferential stress is 0.5. Find the alteration of thickness of metal for such a tube, 250 mm internal diameter when the internal pressure is 60 N/mm². Take 1/m=0.304 and E = 2 × 10⁵ N/mm².*

Solution :

Given $\qquad \dfrac{p}{f} = 0.5$; $p = 60$ N/mm².

Let $r = n.t.$ $\qquad$ But $\quad t = R - r$. Hence $R = r + t = t(n + 1)$

Now $\qquad \dfrac{f}{p} = \dfrac{R^2 + r^2}{R^2 - r^2}$

$\therefore \qquad 2 = \dfrac{[t(n+1)]^2 + (nt)^2}{[t(n+1)]^2 - (nt)^2} = \dfrac{t^2(n^2 + 1 + 2n) + n^2 t^2}{t^2(n^2 + 1 + 2n) - n^2 t^2}$

$\qquad\qquad = \dfrac{2n^2 + 2n + 1}{2n + 1}$

or $\qquad 2(2n + 1) = 2n^2 + 2n + 1$

or $\qquad 2n^2 - 2n - 1 = 0$, from which $n = 1.366$

$\therefore \qquad \dfrac{r}{t} = n = 1.366$ or $\dfrac{t}{r} = \dfrac{1}{1.366} = 0.732$

or $\qquad \dfrac{t}{d} = \mathbf{0.366}$

Change in thickness excluding longitudinal stress

Strain at the inner radius $\qquad e_r = \dfrac{1}{E}\left(f_r + \dfrac{p_r}{m}\right) = \dfrac{1}{E}\left(2p_r + \dfrac{p_r}{m}\right) = \dfrac{p_r}{E}\left(2 + \dfrac{1}{m}\right)$

$\therefore \qquad \delta r = r.. e_r = \dfrac{2.304\, r}{E} p_r$ $\qquad\qquad ...(1)$

Strain at the outer, radius, $\quad e_R = \dfrac{f_R}{E}$ (since $p_R = 0$) $\qquad\qquad ...(2)$

Lame's equations are : $\quad f = \dfrac{B}{x^2} + A$ and $p = \dfrac{B}{x^2} - A$

$\therefore \qquad f_R - p_R = 2A$ or $2p_r - p_r = 2A$. Hence $2A = p_r$ $\qquad ...(3)$

Hence from (2) $\qquad e_R = \dfrac{f_R}{E} = \dfrac{p_r}{E}.$

or $\qquad R.e_R = \dfrac{p_r}{E}.R$

$\therefore$ Change in thickness $= \Delta t = r.e_r - R.e_R = \dfrac{2.304\, r}{E} p_r - R\dfrac{p_r}{E} = \dfrac{p_r}{E}(2.304\, r - R)$

Given $\qquad d = 250$ mm.

Hence $\qquad t = 0.366\,d = 0.366 \times 250 = 91.5$

$\therefore \qquad D = 250 + 2 \times 91.5 = 433\ \text{mm} \quad \text{and} \quad R = 433/2 = 216.5\ \text{mm}$

$d = 250\ \text{mm} \qquad \therefore \qquad r = 250/2 = 125\ \text{mm}$

$\therefore \qquad \Delta t = \dfrac{60}{2 \times 10^5}\,(2.304 \times 125 - 216.5) = 0.02145\ \text{mm}$

Change in thickness due to longitudinal stress

$$f_0 = \frac{\pi\,r^2}{\pi(R^2 - r^2)}\,p_r = \frac{r^2}{R^2 - r^2}\,p_r$$

$$= \frac{(125)^2}{(216.5)^2 - (125)^2} \times 60 = 30\ \text{N/mm}^2$$

$$\Delta t_0 = \text{Change in thickness due to } f_0 = \frac{f_0}{mE}\,t$$

$$= \frac{30 \times 0.304}{2 \times 10^5} \times 91.5 = 0.00417\ \text{mm}$$

Total changes in thickness $= \Delta t + \Delta t_0$

$$= 0.02145 + 0.00417 = \textbf{0.02562 mm}$$

PROBLEMS

1. A thick metallic cylindrical shell of 150 mm internal diameter is required to withstand an internal pressure of 8 N/mm². Find the necessary thickness of the shell if the permissible tensile stress in the section is 20 N/mm². (Cambridge University)

2. A thick spherical shell of 400 mm inside diameter is subjected to an internal pressure of 1.5 N/mm². Determine the necessary thickness of the shell, if the permissible stress in the shell material is 3 N/mm². (U.L.)

3. Find the ratio of thickness to internal diameter of a tube subjected to internal pressure when the pressure is 5/8 of the value of the maximum permissible circumferential stress.

Find the increase in internal diameter of such a tube of 100 mm internal diameter when the internal pressure is 90 N/mm². Take $E = 2.05 \times 10^5$ N/mm² and $1/m = 0.29$. Neglect the longitudinal strain.

4. A thick cylindrical shell is of 200 mm internal diameter and has to withstand an internal pressure of 25 N/mm². Calculate the thickness of metal necessary for the cylinder on the basis of (*i*) the maximum principal stress (*ii*) the maximum principal strain, (*iii*) the maximum shear, and (*iv*) the maximum strain energy. Neglect the longitudinal direct stress. The permissible tensile stress of the shell material is 125 N/mm² and $1/m = 0.3$.

5. A compound cylinder, formed by shrinking one tube on to another, is subjected to an internal pressure of 60 N/mm². Before the fluid is admitted, the internal and external diameters of the compound cylinder are 120 mm and 200 mm and the diameter at the junction is 160 mm. If, after shrinking on, the radial pressure at the common surface is 8 N/mm², calculate the final stress set up by the section.

6. State the formula used in thick cylinder calculations giving the relationships between (a) the hoop stress and the radius, (b) the radial stress, and the radius and from these obtain the relationship in terms of inside and outside diameters between the maximum hoop stress and internal pressure in the case of a cylinder subjected to internal pressure only.

If a cylinder of internal diameter d, wall thickness t and subjected to internal pressure only, is assumed to be a thin shell, what is the greatest value of ratio t/d if the error in the estimated maximum hoop stress is not to exceed 5% ?

7. Make a comparison of the tangential stress distribution caused by the internal pressure p as given by the exact formula with the distribution given by the approximate formula for thin walled cylinder, if (a) $R = 1.1\,r$, and if (b) $R = 4\,r$.

8. A tube 40 mm inside and 60 mm outside diameter is to be reinforced by shrinking on a second tube 80 mm outside diameter. The compound tube is to withstand an internal pressure of 50 N/mm^2 and the shrinkage allowance is to be such that the final maximum stress in each tube is to be the same. Calculate this stress. What is the initial difference of diameters before shrinking on ? Take $E = 207000$ N/mm^2.

ANSWERS

1. 40 mm
2. 52 mm
3. $\dfrac{t}{d} = 0.54$; $\delta d = 0.083$ mm
4. (i) 22.5 mm (ii) 24 mm (iii) 29 mm (iv) 23.5 mm
5. Table below

(+ For tension, − For compression)

Hoop stress (N/mm^2)	Inner tube		Outer tube	
	x=60 mm	x=80 mm	x=80 mm	x=100 mm
(i) Initially	− 36.58	− 28.58	+ 36.44	+ 28.44
(ii) Due to Fluid pressure	+ 127.5	+ 86.48	+ 86.48	+ 67.5
(iii) Final	+ 90.92	+ 57.9	+ 122.92	+ 95.94

6. $f = p\left(\dfrac{D^2 + d^2}{D^2 - d^2}\right)$; $\dfrac{t}{d} = 0.05025$

Analysis of Perfect Frames

25.1. INTRODUCTION : FRAMES

A frame is defined as a structure constructed of several bars which are riveted, bolted or welded together. Such an assemblage of bars is able to resist geometrical distortion under any system of applied loads. The bars, made up of either angle irons, channel sections or T-sections are called the members of the *frame* or frame work. The joints of the frame work may be either flexible, rigid or semi-flexible. In this chapter, we shall assume that the joints are hinged or pin jointed, so that each joint can freely rotate during deformation. Again, such a frame work can be either *statically determinate* or *statically indeterminate*. A statically determinate frame is the one in which the axial forces in the members can be determined by the application of equations of statical equilibrium. For a *plane frame* (*i.e.* a frame in which all the members lie in one plane), there are three such equations, *i.e.* $\Sigma V = 0$, $\Sigma H = 0$ and $\Sigma M = 0$. A statically indeterminate frame is the one in which the axial forces in the members cannot be found by the application of equations of statical equilibrium alone, and additional equations, to be obtained from the deformations of the structure, are required for the analysis. Such frames are also known as *redundant frames*.

25.2. PERFECT FRAMES

Frames may be further classified as (*i*) perfect frame, (*ii*) deficient frame, or (*iii*) redundant frame.

A perfect frame is the one which is composed of members just sufficient to keep it in equilibrium, when loaded. The simplest form of a perfect frame is a triangular frame, consisting of three joints and three members. When such a frame is loaded at its joints, its shape is not distorted. Now, if we want to increase one joint, (or add one more joint D), we would require two additional members AD and CD, as shown in Fig. 25.1(*a ii*). Thus, starting with a three member three jointed frame, every additional joint would require two additional members. Hence the relationship between the number of the mem-

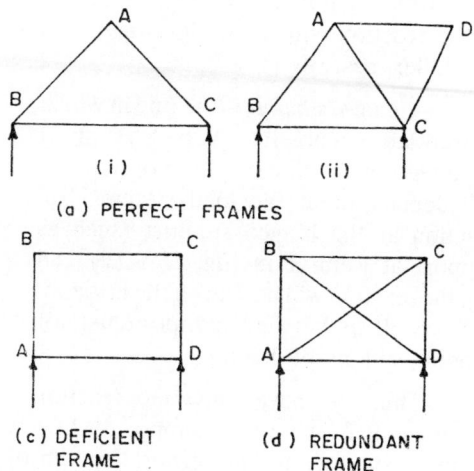

(a) PERFECT FRAMES

(c) DEFICIENT FRAME

(d) REDUNDANT FRAME

FIG. 25.1

bers and number of the joints for a perfect plane frame may be expressed by the formula:

$$n = 2j - 3 \qquad \qquad ...(25.1)$$

where n = number of members and j = number of joints.

If a frame consists of number of members which are less than the one given by Eq. 25.1, the frame is known as the deficient frame, such as the one shown in Fig 25.1(d). Such a frame is unstable. It can be made stable, and thereby converted into a perfect frame by adding either a member AC or the member DB.

If the frame consists of number of members which is greater than the one given by Eq. 25.1, the frame is known as a *redundant frame*, such as the one shown in Fig. 25.1 (c). There are 6 members in the frame having 4 joints, and hence the frame has *one extra member* ; such a frame is statically indeterminate.

To conclude, therefore, we have :

If $n = 2j - 3$, the frame is a *perfect frame*.

If $n < 2j - 3$, the frame is a *deficient frame*.

If $n > 2j - 3$, the frame is a *redundant frame*.

25.3. TYPES OF SUPPORTS AND REACTIONS COMPONENTS

A frame may have two types of supports:

(*a*) Roller support or free support

and   (*b*) Hinged support

A *roller support* is the one in which translation is possible along the *roller base*. At a roller support, the line of action of the reaction will be at right angles to the roller base.

A *hinged support* is the one in which no translation is possible. At such a support the direction and line of action of reaction will depend upon the load system. The reaction at the hinged support (such as support at joint A in Fig. 25.1 (*a*) and (*b*), the reaction will have both the horizontal as well as vertical components, for general system of loading.

Thus, we have only one reaction

FIG.. 25.2. TYPES OF SUPPORTS

component at the roller support, while we have two reaction components (*i.e.* H and V), at a hinged support, for the general system of loading. Since three equations of statical equilibrium (*i.e.* $\Sigma V = 0$ and $\Sigma H = 0$ and $\Sigma M = 0$) are available, the frame is *statically determinate externally*. On the other hand, the frame shown in Fig. 25.3 has hinged support at both the ends A

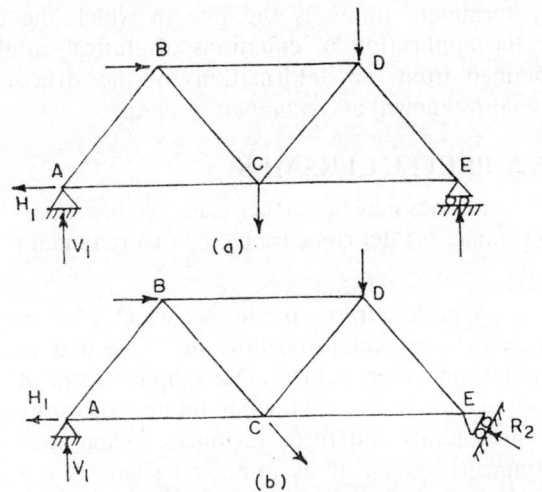

and E, due to which there will be four reaction components (*i.e.* H_1, V_1 and H_2, V_2). Since only three equations of statical equilibrium are available, the frame is *statically indeterminate externally.*

In this chapter, we shall discuss the analysis of only those frames which are statically determinate both externally as well as internally.

25.4. ANALYSIS OF PERFECT FRAMES

The analysis of a perfect frame consists of (*i*) determination of reaction components at the supports, and (*ii*) determination of *force* (usually called *stress*) in individual members. This can be done either by (*a*) analytical methods, or by (*b*) graphical method. In this chapter, we shall discuss only the analytical methods of analysis. For the analysis of statically determinate frames, the principles of statics can be directly applied, keeping in view the following *guiding principles*:

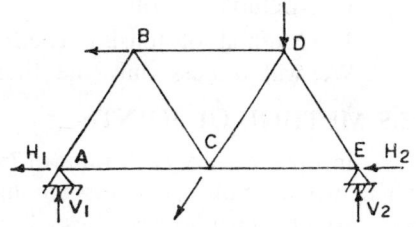

FIG. 25.3

1. The frame as a whole is considered as a rigid body which is in equilibrium under the action of external system of forces and internal system of reactions.

2. Loads are applied only at the joints of the frame work. Due to this, the members carry only the axial forces. The pulls or thrusts of several members meeting at any joint form a system of concurrent forces in equilibrium.

3. Any portion of the frame work may be taken as a rigid body held in equilibrium by the external forces acting upon it together with forces exerted upon it, through members, by the remainder of the frame work.

4. The frame work consists of pinned-joints and it can resist geometrical distortion under the action of external forces.

5. The weight of the members is regarded as negligible in comparison with the external forces.

Stresses and their representation : As stated earlier, loads are applied only at the joints. Hence the members of a frame are subjected to axial forces only. Such axial forces, usually called stresses, can either be *tensile* or *compressive*.

Fig. 25.4 (*ai*) shows a member AB subjected to axial compressive forces P at each end A and B. The internal reactive forces, usually called stresses, will act in opposite direction. Hence the reactive compressive force/stress in AB will be represented by a set of arrows pointing out at A and B shown in Fig. 25.4 (*aii*). Similarly, Fig. 25.4 (*bi*) shows a member CD subjected to axial tensile forces Q at each end C and D. The internal reactive forces, usually called stresses, will act in opposite direction. Hence the reactive tensile force/stress in CD will be represented by a set of arrows pointing inwards at C and D, shown in Fig. 25.4 (*bii*).

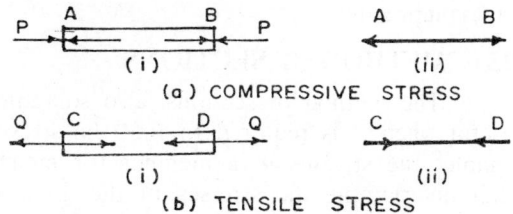

(a) COMPRESSIVE STRESS

(b) TENSILE STRESS

FIG. 25.4. REPRESENTATION OF AXIAL FORCES

Methods of analysis: Following are the main methods of analysis of perfect frames :

    1.   Method of joints;   2. Method of sections

    3.   Method of tension coefficients ; and 4. Graphical method

We will discuss only the first two methods in this chapter.

25.5. METHOD OF JOINTS

In this method, each joint of the frame is treated separately as a free body in equilibrium. When two or more members are meeting at the joint u' r consideration, and if there are only two unknown forces, these forces can be determined by considering the equilibrium of the components of the forces acting at the joint, in two perpendicular directions. The unknown forces are then determined by applying the two equations of static equilibrium, *i.e.* $\Sigma V = 0$ and $\Sigma H = 0$ at the joint. Since the joint is in equilibrium, the sum of the resolved components of the member forces in each direction must be zero. This yields two equations from which the two unknown member forces can be determined.

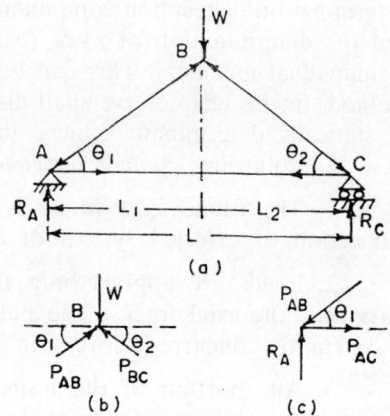

To illustrate the method, let us take the example of a triangular truss shown in Fig. 25.5 (*a*), in which an external load W is acting vertically downwards at apex B. The reactions R_A and R_C can be determined by taking moments of all the forces about point C and A respectively.

FIG. 25.5

    Thus $R_A = \dfrac{1}{L}(WL_2) \uparrow$ and $R_C = \dfrac{1}{L}(WL_1) \uparrow$.

For finding force P_{AB} in the member AB, consider the equilibrium of the joint B, shown in Fig. 25.5 (*c*). Resolving vertically, we get.

$$P_{AB} \sin \theta_1 = R_A \text{ or } P_{AB} = R_A/\sin \theta_1 \text{ (compressive)}$$

Similarly, resolving horizontally, $P_{AC} = P_{AB} \cos \theta_1 = R_A \cot \theta_1$ (tensile)

Alternatively, force in member AB can be found by considering the equilibrium of joint B (Fig. 25.5 *b*). Thus, resolving the forces vertically, we get

$$P_{BA} \sin \theta_1 + P_{BC} . \sin \theta_2 = W \qquad \qquad ...(i)$$
Resolving forces horizontally, we get $P_{BA} \cos \theta_1 = P_{BC} \cos \theta_2$ ...(ii)

Solving (*i*) and (*ii*), we can get the two unknown forces P_{BA} and P_{BC}, both of which are compressive.

25.6. METHOD OF SECTIONS

The method of sections, also sometimes known as the *method of moments*, is specially useful when it is required to find the stresses in a limited number of members. The method enables the stresses in a member (or members) of a simple frame to be calculated without first determining the stresses in the great number of other me-mbers. The method consists of passing a section through the member (or members) in which the stresses are desired, thus dividing the frame into two parts. The equations of static equilibrium can then be applied to *any one part* of the frame.

To illustrate the method, let it be required to find the stresses in members *BC, FC* and *FG*. Pass a section $a - a$ (shown dotted), cutting the three members, and dividing the frame in two parts : Part I and part II. Since the whole frame is in equilibrium each part

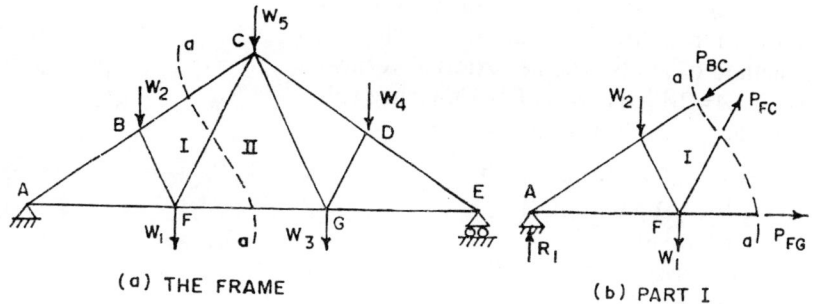

(a) THE FRAME

(b) PART I

FIG. 25.6

will be in equilibrium under the system of external forces and internal reactive forces acting on it. Fig. 25.6(b) shows portion I, which is in equilibrium under the external forces W_1, W_2 and R_1 and under the forces P_{BC}, P_{FC} and P_{FG} exerted by the portion II on portion I at the points where the section $a - a$ cuts the frame. These six forces keep portion I in equilibrium. The following equations of static equilibrium are available.

1. The algebraic sum of resolved parts of the above six forces, in any direction, is zero. and   2. The algebraic sum of the moments of these forces about any point is zero.

To find the force P_{BC}, take moments of the forces about the point F, where the other two forces P_{FC} and P_{FG} meet. Hence the value of the force P_{BC} can be found by the moment equation. The net moment for the two forces R_1 and W_2 about the point F, will be in the clockwise direction; hence the direction of P_{BC} should be the one as shown in Fig. 25.6 (b), so as to provide an anticlockwise moment. Since this direction of P_{BC} *pushes* the portion of the truss to the left of section $a - a$, the force P_{BC} will be compressive.

Similarly, to find the force P_{FC} in the member *FC*, take moments of the forces about the point A, where the other two forces P_{BC} and P_{FG} meet. Hence the magnitude of the force P_{FC} can be found by the moment equation. The sum of the moments of forces W_1 and W_2, about point A, is in the clockwise direction. Hence the direction of P_{FC} should be as marked in Fig. 25.6 (b) so as to yield anticlockwise moment. Since the direction of P_{FC} is away from the section $a - a$, member *FC* will carry a tensile force.

Lastly, to find the force in member *FG*, take moments of all the forces acting on part I, about point C where P_{BC} and P_{FC} meet. The moment equation so obtained will directly yield P_{FG} since there will be only one unknown in the equation. Moreover, the net moment of the forces R_1, W_1 and W_2, about point C, will be in the clockwise direction. Hence the direction of P_{FG} should be as marked in Fig. 25.6 (b), so as to give an anticlockwise moment about C. Since the direction of P_{FG} is pointing away from the section $a - a$, member *FG* will carry tensile force. Thus, the magnitude and direction of force in each of the three members is known. While passing a section, it should be seen that the number of unknown member forces cut by the section do not exceed three. Generally, both the methods are used simultaneously to analyse a frame.

Example 25.1. *Determine the forces in various members of the truss shown in Fig. 25.7.*

Solution : The frame, usually known as a truss, in symmetrical. Hence $R_A = R_B = 2 W (\uparrow)$.

$\sin 30° = 0.5; \cos 30° = 0.866$

(1) Members AB and AF : In order to find P_{AB} and P_{AF}, consider joint A. Since only two unknown forces are there at A, we will use the method of joints. The net external vertical force at $A = 2W - W/2 = 1.5\,W\,(\uparrow)$. Hence resolving the forces vertically, we get

$P_{AB} \sin 30° = 1.5\,W$ from which

$P_{AB} = \dfrac{1.5\,W}{\sin 30°} = \dfrac{1.5\,W}{0.5} = 3W$ (comp.)

Resolving horizontally, $P_{AF} = P_{AB} \cos 30°$
$= 3\,W \times 0.856 = 2.598\,W$ (tension)

(2) Members BC and BF : At joint B, there is one external force (W) and three internal forces, P_{BA}, P_{BC} and P_{BF}. Out of these three internal forces, $P_{BA}\,(= P_{AB})$ is known. We will apply both the method of joints as well as method of sections.

(i) Method of joints (Fig. 25.9 a) : The angles of inclination of various forces can be determined, as marked in Fig. 25.9 (a). Resolving the forces in a direction normal to ABC, we get

$W \cos 30° = P_{BF} \cos 30°$, from which

$P_{BF} = W$ (comp.)

Resolving the forces along the direction ABC,

$P_{BA} = P_{BC} + W \sin 30° + P_{BF} \sin 30°$
∴ $P_{BC} = 3\,W - W\,(0.5) - W\,(0.5) = 2\,W$ (comp.)

(ii) Method of sections (Fig. 25.9 b): Pass a section $a - a$ cutting the three members BC, BF and AF. The left part is shown in Fig. 25.8 (b), along with the reactive forces P_{BC}, P_{BF} and P_{FA}. In order to find P_{BF}, take moments of the forces, about A. Since the lines of action of forces P_{BC} and P_{FA} pass through A, they will have no moments about A.

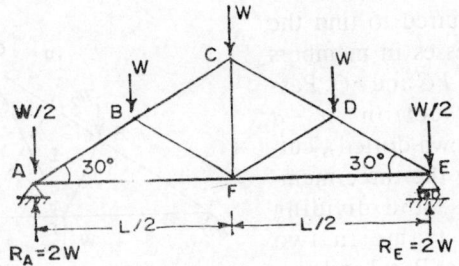

FIG. 25.7

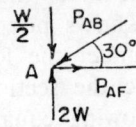

FIG. 25.8

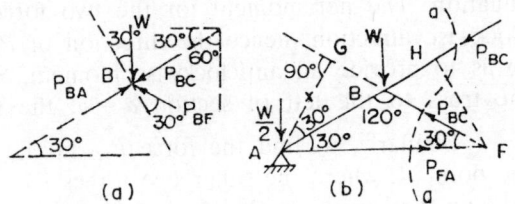

(a)   (b)

FIG. 25.9

Through A, drop a line AG perpendicular to FB (extended). A close inspection, will show that the line AG makes an angle of 30° with AB. Now from the right angled triangle AGF, we get $AG = AF \sin 30° = 0.5\,AF$. Also perpendicular distance of line of action of W from $A = AF/2 = 0.5\,AF$. Now taking moment of all the forces, about A we get

$$P_{BF}\,(AG) = W\left(\frac{AF}{2}\right), \text{ from which } P_{BF} = W\left(\frac{AF}{2\,AG}\right) = W\left(\frac{AF}{2 \times 0.5\,AF}\right) = W$$

The moment of W about A, is in the clockwise direction. Hence the direction of force P_{BF} will be as marked in Fig. 25.9 (b), so as to give an anticlockwise moment. Since the force P_{BF} pushes the section $a - a$, P_{BF} will be compressive.

In order to find force P_{BC}, take moments about point F through which P_{BF} and P_{AF} pass. Draw line FH perpendicular to AB. From right angled triangle AHF, we get $FH = AF \sin 30° = 0.5 AF$. Hence, taking moments of forces about F, we get

$$1.5\, W\, (AF) - W\, (0.5\, (AF) = P_{BC}\, (0.5\, AF)$$

From which $\quad P_{BC} = 2\, (1.5\, W - 0.5) = 2\, W$

The direction of P_{BC} will be as marked in Fig. 25.9 (b). Since it pushes the section $a - a$, P_{BC} will be compressive.

(3) Member CF : In order to find the force in CF, we consider the joint C. Method of sections will not be very useful here, since any section drawn to cut CF will cut three more members.

Hence $\quad P_{CB} = P_{CD} = P_{BC} = 2\, W$ (comp.)

Resolving the forces vertically, we get

$$W + P_{CF} = 2\, P_{CB} \sin 30°$$
$$P_{CF} = 2\, (2\, W)\, 0.5 - W = W \text{ (tensile)}$$

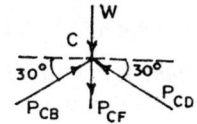

FIG. 25.10

Thus, the forces (stresses) in all the members are known. Fig. 25.11 shows the magnitude and nature of stresses in all the members of the truss/frame. The stresses are also shown tabulated in the stress table (Table 25.1)

TABLE 25.1. STRESS TABLE
(+ FOR COMP. ; – FOR TENSION)

Member	Force
AB(DE)	+3 W
AC(CD)	+2 W
AF(EF)	−2.598 W
BF(DF)	+W
CF	− W

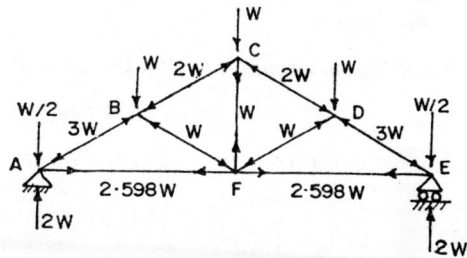

FIG. 25.11

Example 25.2. *A truss is loaded as shown in Fig. 25.12. Determine the forces in all the members of the truss.*

Solution : $\quad \sin 45° = \cos 45° = 0.7071$

(a) Reactions : The reaction at the roller end E will have only the vertical component (V_E) while the reaction at A will have both the horizontal component as well as vertical component (V_A).

Taking moments about A, we get

$$V_E = \frac{1}{2L}\left[2\, W \times \frac{L}{2} + \frac{WL}{2} \right] = 0.75\, W\, (\uparrow)$$

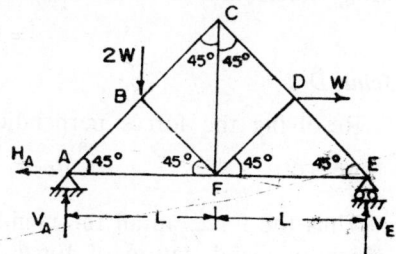

FIG. 25.12

Since $\quad \Sigma V = 0$, we get $V_A = 2\, W - 0.75\, W = 1.25\, W\, (\uparrow)$

Also, since $\Sigma H = 0$, we get $H_A = W\,(\leftarrow)$

(b) Joint A: The forces acting at joint A are shown, in which P_{AB} and P_{AF} are not known.

Resolving vertically : $P_{AB} \sin 45° = V_A = 1.25\,W$

From which $P_{AB} = \dfrac{1.25\,W}{0.7071} = 1.768\,W$ (comp.)

Resolving horizontally : $H_A + P_{AB} \cos 45° = P_{AF},$

From which $P_{AF} = W + 1.768\,W \times 0.7071 = 2.25\,W$ (tension)

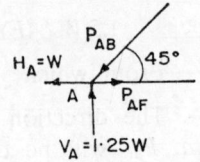

FIG. 25.13

(c) Joint B : Out of four forces acting at B, two forces (*i.e.* P_{BC} and P_{BF}) are unknown.

Resolving the forces perpendicular to the direction AC, we get
$$P_{BF} = 2\,W \sin 45° = 1.414\,W \text{ (comp.)}$$

Resolving along CA,

$P_{BC} + 2\,W \cos 45° = P_{BA},$ from which
$$P_{BC} = 1.768\,W - 2\,W\,(0.7071) = 0.354\,W \text{ (comp.)}$$

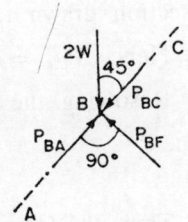

FIG. 25.14

(d) Joint C :

Out of the three forces acting at joint C, there are two unknown forces : P_{CD} and P_{CF}.

Resolving horizontally : $P_{CD} \sin 45° = P_{CB} \sin 45°,$

$\therefore$ $P_{CD} = P_{CB} = 0.354\,W$ (comp.)

Resolving vertically : $P_{CF} = P_{CB} \cdot \cos 45° + P_{CD} \cos 45°$
$$= 2 \times 0.354\,W \times 0.7071$$
$$= 0.5\,W \text{ (tension)}$$

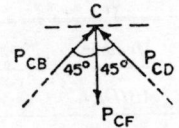

FIG. 25.15

(e) Joint E :

Resolving vertically: $P_{ED} \sin 45° = V_E = 0.75\,W$

$\therefore$ $P_{ED} = \dfrac{0.75\,W}{0.7071} = 1.061\,W$ (comp.)

Resolving horizontally : $P_{EF} = P_{ED} \cos 45° = 1.061\,W \times 0.7071$
$$= 0.75\,W \text{ (tension)}$$

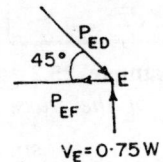

FIG. 25.16

(f) Joint D :

Resolving the forces perpendicular to the direction CE,

we get $P_{DF} = W \sin 45° = 0.7071\,W$ (tension)

Thus the forces in all the members are known. Table 25.2 gives the magnitude and nature of forces in various members while Fig. 25.18 shows the nature of forces in various members.

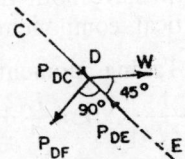

FIG. 25.17

TABLE 25.2. STRESS TABLE

TABLE 25.2. STRESS TABLE
(+ FOR COMP. ; – FOR TENSION)

Member	Force
AB	+ 1.768 W
BC	+ 0.354 W
AF	– 2.25 W
BF	+ 1.414 W
CF	– 0.5 W
CD	+ 0.354 W
DE	+ 1.061 W
EF	– 0.75 W
DF	– 0.7071 W

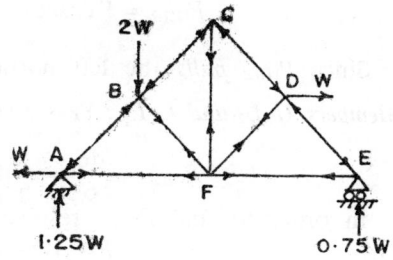

FIG. 25.18

Note : The student, after sufficient practice, can mark the nature of the forces in various members, simply by inspection. The students are advised to find the forces in members BC, BF and AF by method of sections.

25.7. PRATT TRUSS WITH PARALLEL CHORDS

Fig. 25.19 shows a Pratt truss with parallel chords, loaded at the lower nodes. Due to symmetry, reaction R at each support will be equal to 2.5 W.

$$\sin \theta = \frac{6}{\sqrt{(45)^2 + (6)^2}} = 0.8 \;;$$

$$\cos \theta = \frac{4.5}{\sqrt{(4.5)^2 + (6)^2}} = 0.6$$

1. Members $L_0 U_1$, $L_0 L_1$, $U_1 L_2$ and $L_1 L_2$: Consider joint L_0. Resolving vertically,

$$P_{L_0 U_1} \sin\theta = 2.5 \, W$$

$$\therefore \quad P_{L_0 U_1} = (2.5 \, W)/0.8$$

$$= 3.125 \, W \text{ (comp.)}$$

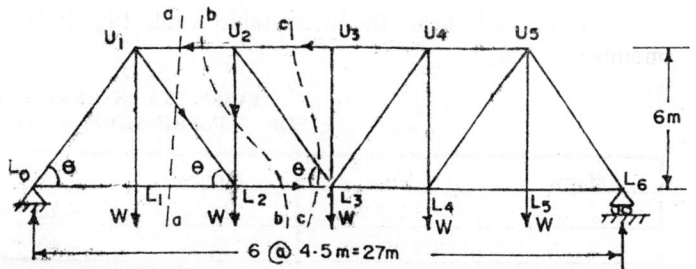

FIG. 25.19

Resolving horizontally,

$$P_{L_0 L_1} = P_{L_0 U_1} \cos \theta = 3.125 \, W (0.6) = 1.875 \, W \text{ (tension)}$$

At joint L_1, we get $P_{L_1 U_1} = W$ (tension). Also, $P_{L_1 L_2} = P_{L_1 L_0} = P_{L_0 L_1} = 1.875 \, W$ (tension)

2. Members $U_1 U_2$ and $U_1 L_2$: Pass a section $a - a$, cutting $U_1 U_2, U_1 L_2$ and $L_1 L_2$. To find the stress in member $U_1 U_2$, take moments about L_2 where the other two members $U_1 L_2$ and $L_1 L_2$ meet. Consider the equilibrium of the portion of the truss to the left of section $a - a$.

Thus, $$P_{U_1 U_2} = \frac{M_{L2}}{6} = \frac{1}{6} [(2.5 \, W \times 9) - (W \times 4.5)] = 3 \, W$$

The direction of $P_{U_1 U_2}$ will be as marked in Fig. 25.19, so as to provide anticlockwise moment. Since $P_{U_1 U_2}$ pushes the portion of the truss to the left of the section $a-a$, $P_{U_1 U_2}$ will be *compressive.*

In order to find the stress in diagonal $U_1 L_2$, resolve the forces vertically.

Thus $\quad P_{U1L2} \sin \theta = R - W = 2.5\,W - W = 1.5\,W = F_{L1L2}$

where F_{L1L2} is the shear force in the panel $L_1 L_2$.

$$\therefore \qquad\qquad P_{U1L2} = F \operatorname{cosec} \theta = \frac{1.5\,W}{0.8} = 1.875\,W$$

Since P_{U1L2} *pulls* the left portion of the truss, it will be *tensile*.

3. **Members $U_2 L_2$ and $L_2 L_3$:** Pass a section $b - b$ and consider the equilibrium of left portion.

$$P_{L2L3} = \frac{M_{U2}}{6} = \frac{1}{6}\,[2.5\,W\,(9) - W\,(4.5)] = 3\,W \text{ (tensile)}$$

In order to find P_{U2L2}, resolve the forces vertically. Thus

$$P_{U2L2} = R - W - W = 2.5\,W - 2\,W = 0.5\,W = F_{L2L3} \text{ (compression)}$$

where F_{L2L3} is the S.F. in the panel $L_2 L_3$.

4. **Members $U_2 U_3$, $U_2 L_3$ and $U_3 L_3$:** Pass a section $c - c$ and consider the equilibrium of the left portion.

Thus, $\qquad\qquad P_{U2U3} = \frac{M_{L3}}{6} = \frac{1}{6}\,[2.5\,W\,(13.5) - W\,(9) - W\,(4.5)] = 3.375\,W \text{ (comp.)}$

For P_{U2L3}, resolve the forces vertically. Thus, $P_{U2L3} \sin \theta = 2.5\,W - W - W = 0.5\,W = F_{L2L3}$
$$\therefore \qquad\qquad P_{U2L3} = F_{L2L3} \operatorname{cosec} \theta = 0.5\,W/0.8 = 0.625\,W \text{ (tension)}$$

For P_{U3L3}, consider joint U_3. Since there is no external load at U_3, we get $P_{U3L3} = 0$

Table 25.3 shows the stress table, while Fig. 25.20 shows the nature of stresses in various members.

TABLE 25.3. STRESS TABLE
(+ FOR COMPRESSION ; − FOR TENSION)

Member	Stress	Member	Stress	Member	Stress
$L_0 U_1$	+ 3.125 W	$L_0 L_1$	− 1.875 W	$U_1 L_2$	− 1.875 W
$U_1 U_2$	+ 3 W	$L_1 L_2$	− 1.875 W	$U_2 L_2$	+ 0.5 W
$U_2 U_3$	+ 3.375 W	$L_2 L_3$	− 3 W	$U_2 L_3$	− 0.625 W
$U_3 U_4$	0	$U_1 L_1$	− W		

Conclusions: From the above discussions, we draw the following conclusions :

1. The force in any *chord member* is given by the bending moment at the opposite joint divided by the height of the truss.

2. The force in any *diagonal* is given by $F \operatorname{cosec} \theta$, where F is the S.F. in the panel and θ is the inclination of the diagonal with the horizontal

3. The force is any *vertical* is equal to the S.F. in the adjoining panel.

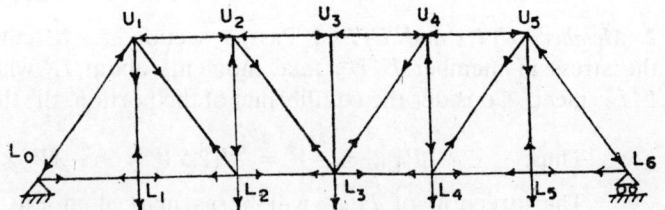

FIG. 25.20

25.8. WARREN GIRDER

Fig. 25.21 shows a three bay Warren girder of equilateral triangles, with loads applied at the lower panel points.

$\sin 60° = 0.866$; $\cos 60° = 0.5$;

Height $h = \dfrac{L \sqrt{3}}{2} = 0.866\,L$

1. Reactions :

$R_1 = \dfrac{1}{3L}\,(1.5\,W \times 2\,L + W \times L)$

$\quad = 1.333\,W$

$R_2 = 1.5\,W + W - 1.333\,W$

$\quad = 1.167\,W$

2. Members of panel $L_0 L_1$

Consider joint L_0.
Resolving vertically, we get

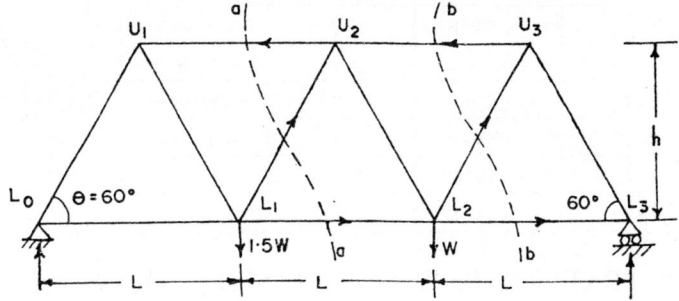

FIG. 25.21

$$P_{L0U1} \cdot \sin 60° = R_1 = 1.333\,W. \quad \text{Hence } P_{L0U1} = \frac{1.333\,W}{0.866} = 1.539\,W \text{ (comp.)}$$

Resolving horizontally, $\quad P_{L0L1} = P_{L0U1} \cos 60° = 1.539 \times 0.5 \approx 0.770\,W$ (tension)

Resolving vertically at U_1, $\quad P_{U1L1} = -P_{U1L0} = -1.539\,W$ (i.e. tension)

3. Members of panel $L_1 L_2$: Pass a section $a - a$.

$$P_{U1U2} = \frac{M_{L1}}{h} = \frac{1}{0.866\,L}\,(1.333\,W \times L) = 1.539\,W \text{ (comp.)}$$

Note that M_{L1} is in the clockwise direction. Hence the direction of arrow for P_{U1U2} will be as marked in Fig. 15.21 so as to provide a balancing moment. Since this direction pushes the section $a - a$, P_{U1U2} will be *compressive*.

Also, $\quad P_{L1L2} = \dfrac{M_{U2}}{h} = \dfrac{1}{0.866\,L}\,[1.333\,W \times 1.5\,L - 1.5\,W \times 0.5\,L] = 1.443\,W$ (tension)

and $\quad P_{U2L1} = F_{L1L2}\,\mathrm{cosec}\,\theta = \dfrac{1.333\,W - 1.5\,W}{0.866} = -0.193\,W$ (i.e. tension)

Resolving vertically at U_2, $P_{U2L2} = -P_{U2L1} = 0.193\,W$ (comp.)

4. Members of panel $L_2 L_3$: Pass a section $b - b$.

$$P_{U2U3} = \frac{M_{L2}}{h} = \frac{1}{0.866\,L}\,[1.333\,W \times 2\,L - 1.5\,W \times L] = 1.346\,W \text{ (comp)}$$

$$P_{L2L3} = \frac{M_{U3}}{h} = \frac{1}{0.866\,L}\,[1.333\,W \times 2.5\,L - 1.5\,W \times 1.5\,L - W \times 0.5\,L] = 0.673\,W \text{ (tension)}$$

$$P_{U3L2} = F_{L2L3}\,\mathrm{cosec}\,60° = \frac{1.333\,W - 1.5\,W - W}{0.866} = -1.348\,W \text{ (i.e. tension)}$$

Resolving vertically at L_3, $P_{L3U3} = \dfrac{R_2}{\sin 60°} = \dfrac{1.167}{0.866} = 1.348\,W$ (comp.)

Check : From joint U_3, $P_{U_3L_3} = -P_{U_3L_2} = 1.348\,W$ (comp.)

The stresses are tabulated in Table 25.4 and marked in Fig. 25.22

TABLE 25.4. STRESS TABLE

(+ FOR COMP. ; – FOR TENSION)

Member	Stress	Member	Stress
L_0U_1	+ 1.539 W	U_2L_2	+ 0.193 W
L_0L_1	– 0.770 W	U_2U_3	+ 1.346 W
U_1L_1	– 1.539 W	L_2U_3	– 1.348 W
U_1U_2	+ 1.539 W	L_2L_3	– 0.673 W
L_1U_2	– 0.193 W	U_3L_3	+ 1.348 W
L_1L_2	– 1.443 W		

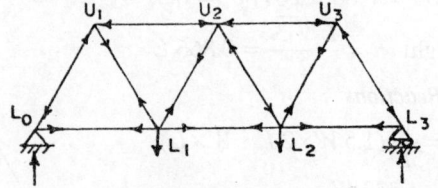

FIG. 25.22

25.9. PRATT TRUSS WITH INCLINED CHORDS

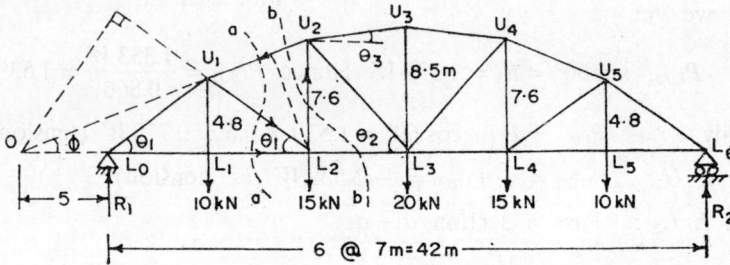

FIG. 25.23

(a) Geometry of the truss : Fig. 25.23 shows a Pratt truss with inclined chords, loaded at lower panel points.

$$\sin\theta_1 = \frac{4.8}{\sqrt{(4.8)^2 + (7)^2}} = 0.5655\,;\ \cos\theta_1 = \frac{7}{\sqrt{(4.8)^2 + (7)^2}} = 0.8247$$

$$\sin\theta_2 = \frac{7.6}{\sqrt{(7.6)^2 + (7)^2}} = \frac{7.6}{10.3325} = 0.7355\,;\ \cos\theta_2 = \frac{7}{10.3325} = 0.6775$$

$$\sin\theta_3 = \frac{8.5 - 7.6}{\sqrt{(8.5 - 7.6)^2 + (7)^2}} = \frac{0.9}{7.0576} = 0.1275\,;\ \cos\theta_3 = \frac{7}{7.0576} = 0.9918$$

Extend U_2U_1 to cut L_1L_0 (extended) at O. Let φ be the inclination of U_2U_1 with horizontal. Then $\tan\varphi = \dfrac{7.6 - 4.8}{7} = 0.4\,;\ \varphi = 21.80°$.

$\therefore\ \sin\varphi = 0.3714\,;\ \cos\varphi = 0.9285\,;\ OL_1 = \dfrac{4.8}{\tan\varphi} = \dfrac{4.8}{0.4} = 12$ m ; $OL_0 = 12 - 7 = 5$ m.

(b) Reactions : Due to symmetry, $R_1 = R_2 = 10 + 15 + 20/2 = 35$ kN

(c) Panel L_0L_1 : Resolving vertically at joint L_0, we get

$$P_{L0U1}\sin\theta_1 = R_1 = 35,\ \text{from which}\ P_{L0U1} = \frac{35}{0.5655} = 61.89 \text{ kN (comp.)}$$

Resolving horizontally, $P_{L0L1} = P_{L0U1} \cos \theta_1 = 61.89 \times 0.8247 = 51.04$ kN (tension)

Resolving vertically at joint L_1, $P_{L1U_1} = 10$ kN (tension)

(d) Panel $L_1 L_2$: Pass a section $a - a$.

$$P_{L1L2} = \frac{M_{U1}}{4.8} = \frac{1}{4.8} (35 \times 7) = 51.04 \text{ kN (tension)}$$

$$P_{U1L2} = \frac{M_0}{O L_2 . \sin \theta_1} = \frac{35 \times 5 - 10 \times 12}{19 \times 0.5655} = 5.12 \text{ kN (tension)}$$

$$P_{U1U2} = \frac{M_{L2}}{O L_2 . \sin \varphi} = \frac{35 \times 14 - 10 \times 7}{19 \times 0.3714} = 59.52 \text{ kN (comp.)}$$

For finding P_{U2L2}, pass a section $b - b$ and take moments about O.

Thus, $$P_{U2L2} = \frac{M_0}{O L_2} = \frac{35 \times 5 - 10 \times 12 - 15 \times 19}{19} = -12.11 \text{ kN } (i.e. \text{ tension})$$

Similarly, the stresses/forces in the other members can be found.

25.10. K-TRUSS

$$\sin \theta = \frac{1.5 L/2}{\sqrt{\left(\frac{1.5L}{2}\right)^2 + L^2}} = \frac{0.75 L}{1.25 L} = 0.6 \text{ ;}$$

$\operatorname{cosec} \theta = \dfrac{1}{0.6} = 1.667;$

$\cos \theta = \dfrac{L}{1.25 L} = 0.8$

$R_1 = R_2$

$= \dfrac{1}{2} (7 \times 2.5W + 5W)$

$= 11.25 W$

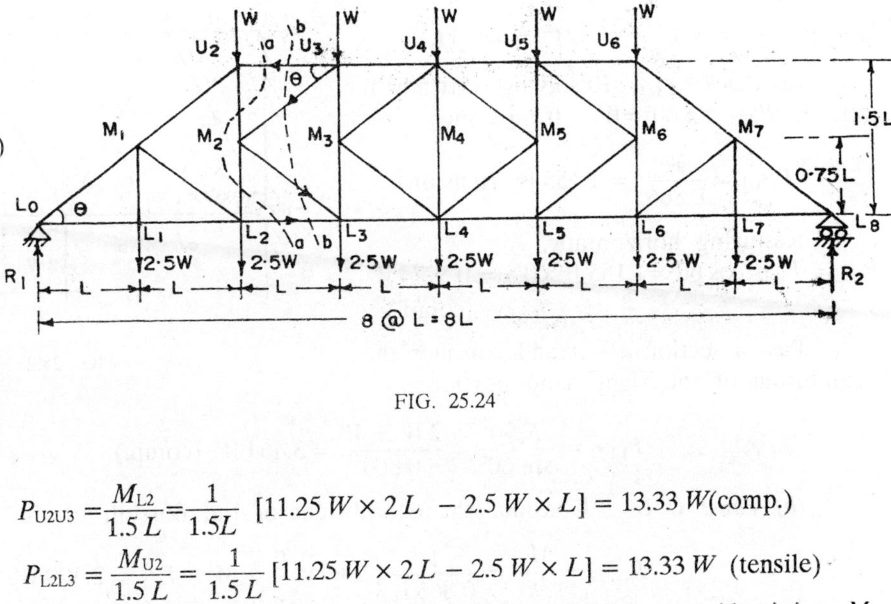

Let us investigate the stresses in panel $L_2 L_3$. Pass a horse shoe section $a - a$ and consider the equilibrium of the portion to the left of $a - a$.

FIG. 25.24

$$P_{U2U3} = \frac{M_{L2}}{1.5 L} = \frac{1}{1.5L} [11.25 W \times 2L - 2.5 W \times L] = 13.33 W \text{(comp.)}$$

Similarly, $$P_{L2L3} = \frac{M_{U2}}{1.5 L} = \frac{1}{1.5 L} [11.25 W \times 2L - 2.5 W \times L] = 13.33 W \text{ (tensile)}$$

In order to find the stresses in the two diagonals $M_2 U_3$ and $M_2 L_3$, consider joint M_2. Since the inclination of both the diagonals is the same, we get $P_{M2U3} = P_{M2L3}$, by resolving the forces in the horizontal direction. Member $M_2 U_3$ will carry a push while member $M_2 L_3$ will carry a pull. Now pass a section $b - b$ and consider the equilibrium of the left portion. Resolving vertically, we get

$$P_{M2U3} \sin \theta + P_{M2L3} \sin \theta = 11.25\,W - 2.5\,W - 2.5\,W - W = 5.25\,W = F_{L2L3}$$

(where F_{L2L3} = S.F. in panel $L_2 L_3 = 5.25\,W$)

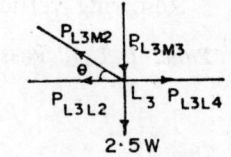

$$\therefore \qquad P_{M2U3} = P_{M2L3} = \frac{1}{2} F_{L2L3} \operatorname{cosec} \theta = \frac{1}{2} \times 5.25\,W \times \frac{1}{0.6} = 4.375\,W$$

Hence $P_{M2U3} = 4.375\,W$ (comp.) and $P_{M2L3} = 4.375\,W$ (tension).

Now consider joint L_3. Resolving the forces *vertically*,

$$P_{L3M3} + 2.5\,W = P_{L3M2} \sin \theta$$

FIG. 25.25 JOINT L_3

$$\therefore \qquad P_{L3M3} = 4.375 \times 0.6 - 2.5\,W = 0.125\,W \text{ (comp.)}$$

Lastly, consider joint U_3. Resolving the forces vertically,

$$P_{U3M3} + W = P_{U3M2} \sin \theta$$

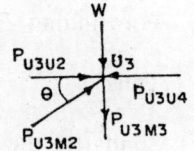

or $\qquad\qquad P_{U3M3} = 4.375\,W \times 0.6 - W = 1.625\,W$ (tension)

Similarly, the forces in the members of other panels can be found.

FIG. 25.26 JOINT U_3

25.11. WARREN TYPE CANTILEVER TRUSS

Fig. 25.27 shows Warren type cantilever truss, having $\theta = 60°$.

Hence $\sin \theta = \dfrac{\sqrt{3}}{2} = 0.866$.

$\operatorname{cosec} \theta = 1.1547$; $\cos \theta = 0.5$

Height $\quad h = \sqrt{L^2 - (L/2)^2} = 0.866\,L$

(a) Panel $L_1 L_2$: Resolving vertically at joint $L_2, P_{L2U2} \sin 60° = W$, from which

$$P_{L2U2} = \frac{W}{0.866} = 1.155\,W \text{ (tension)}$$

Resolving horizontally,

$P_{L2L1} = P_{L2U2} \cos 60° = 1.155\,W \times 0.5 = 0.5774\,W$

(comp.)

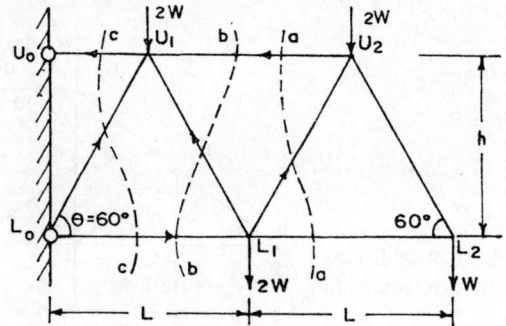

Pass a section $a - a$ and consider the equilibrium of the right hand portion.

FIG. 25.27

$$P_{L1U2} = \frac{F_{L1L2}}{\sin 60°} = \frac{2\,W + W}{0.866} = 3.464\,W \text{ (comp.)}$$

(b) Panel $U_1 U_2$: Consider the equilibrium of the portion to the right of $a - a$.

$$P_{U1U2} = \frac{M_{L1}}{h} = \frac{1}{0.866\,L} \left(2\,W \times \frac{L}{2} + W \times L \right) = 2.309\,W \text{ (tension)}$$

To find P_{U1L1}, pass section $b - b$ and consider the equilibrium of right hand portion.

$$\therefore \qquad P_{U1L1} = \frac{F_{L0L1}}{\sin 60°} = \frac{2\,W + 2\,W + W}{0.866} = 5.774\,W \text{ (tension)}$$

(c) Panel $L_0 L_1$: Consider the equilibrium of the portion to the right of section $b - b$.

$$P_{L0L1} = \frac{M_{U1}}{h} = \frac{1}{0.866\,L}\left(2\,W{\times}L + W{\times}1.5\,L + 2\,W{\times}0.5\,L\right) = 5.196\,W \quad \text{(comp.)}$$

(d) Panel $U_0\,U_1$: Pass a section $c-c$ and consider the equilibrium of the right hand portion.

$$P_{L0U1} = \frac{F_{U0U1}}{\sin 60°} = \frac{2\,W + 2\,W + 2\,W + W}{0.866} = 8.083\,W \quad \text{(comp.)}$$

$$P_{U0U1} = \frac{M_{L0}}{h} = \frac{1}{0.866\,L}\,(2\,W \times 0.5\,L + 2\,W \times L + 2\,W \times 1.5\,L + W \times 2\,L)$$
$$= 9.238\,W \quad \text{(tension)}$$

The results are tabulated in Table 25.5 and stresses are marked in Fig. 25.28.

TABLE 25.5. STRESS TABLE
(+ FOR COMP. ; – FOR TENSION)

Member	Stress	Member	Stress
$U_0\,U_1$	$-9.238\,W$	$U_1\,L_1$	$-5.774\,W$
$U_1\,U_2$	$-2.309\,W$	$U_2\,L_1$	$+3.464\,W$
$U_2\,L_2$	$-1.115\,W$	$L_0\,L_1$	$+5.196\,W$
$U_1\,U_0$	$+8.083\,W$	$L_1\,L_2$	$+0.5774\,W$

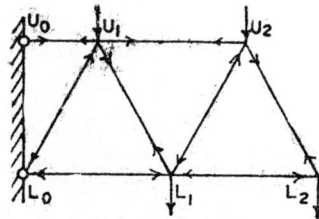

FIG. 25.28

25.12. TRIANGULAR TYPE CANTILEVER TRUSS

(a) Geometry of the truss

$$\tan \theta_1 = \frac{1.2\,L}{3\,L} = 0.4$$

$$\therefore \quad \theta_1 = 21.8° \; ; \sin \theta_1 = 0.3714$$
$$\cos \theta_1 = 0.9285$$

$$U_2\,L_2 = \frac{1.2\,L}{3} = 0.4\,L$$

$$U_1\,L_1 = \frac{1.2\,L}{3} \times 2 = 0.8\,L$$

$$\tan \theta_2 = \frac{U_1\,L_1}{L_0\,L_1} = \frac{0.8\,L}{L} = 0.8$$

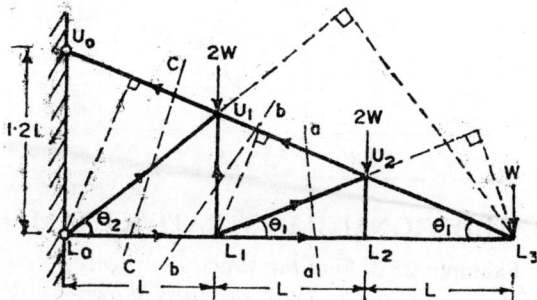

FIG. 25.29

$$\therefore \quad \theta_2 = 38.659° \; ; \sin \theta_2 = 0.6247 \; ; \cos \theta_2 = 0.7809$$

(b) Panel $L_2\,L_3$: Resolving vertically at joint L_3,

$$P_{L3U2} = \frac{W}{\sin \theta_1} = \frac{W}{0.3714} = 2.693\,W \quad \text{(tension)}$$

Resolving horizontally, $P_{L3L2} = P_{L3U2} \cos \theta_1 = 2.693\,W \times 0.9285 = 2.5\,W$ (comp.)

Since there is no load at L_2, $P_{L2U2} = 0$

(c) Panel $L_1\,L_2$: Pass section $a-a$ and consider equilibrium of the R.H. portion.

$$P_{U1U2} = \frac{M_{L1}}{L_1 L_3 \sin \theta_1} = \frac{W(2L) + 2W(L)}{2L(0.3714)} = 5.385 \, W \text{ (tension)}$$

$$P_{L1L2} = \frac{M_{U2}}{U_2 L_2} = \frac{W \times L}{0.4 L} = 2.5 \, W \text{ (comp.)}$$

$$P_{L1U2} = \frac{M_{L3}}{L_1 L_3 \sin \theta_1} = \frac{2W(L)}{2L(0.3714)} = 2.693 \, W \text{ (comp.)}$$

(d) *Panel* $L_0 L_1$: Pass a section $b - b$ and consider the equilibrium of R.H. portion.

$$P_{U1L1} = \frac{M_{L3}}{L_1 L_3} = \frac{2W \times L}{2L} = W \text{ (tension)}$$

$$P_{L0L1} = \frac{M_{U1}}{U_1 L_1} = \frac{2W \times L + W \times 2L}{0.8 L} = 5 \, W \text{ (comp.)}$$

Pass a section $c - c$ and consider the equilibrium of R.H. portion

$$P_{U0U1} = \frac{M_{L0}}{L_0 L_3 \sin \theta_1} = \frac{2W \times L + 2W \times 2L + W \times 3L}{3L(0.3714)} = 8.078 \, W \text{ (tension)}$$

$$P_{L0U1} = \frac{M_{L3}}{L_0 L_3 \sin \theta_2} = \frac{2W \times 2L + 2W \times L}{3L(0.6247)} = 3.202 \, W \text{ (comp.)}$$

The results are tabulated in Table 25.6 and stresses are marked in Fig. 25.30

TABLE 25.6. STRESS TABLE
(+ FOR COMPRESSION ; – FOR TENSION)

Member	Stress	Member	Stress
$U_0 U_1$	$- 8.078 \, W$	$L_2 L_3$	$+ 2.5 \, W$
$U_1 U_2$	$- 5.385 \, W$	$L_0 U_1$	$+ 3.202 \, W$
$U_2 L_3$	$+ 2.693 \, W$	$U_1 L_1$	$- W$
$L_0 L_1$	$+ 5 \, W$	$L_1 U_2$	$+ 2.693 \, W$
$L_1 L_2$	$+ 2.5 \, W$	$U_2 L_2$	0

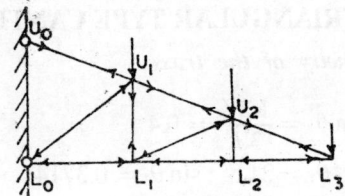

FIG. 25.30

25.13. ADDITIONAL ILLUSTRATIVE EXAMPLES

Example 25.3. *Find the stresses in members* $U_1 U_2$, $U_2 L_2$ *and* $L_2 L_3$ *of the truss shown in Fig. 25.31.*

Solution :

$$R_1 = \frac{1}{16}(W \times 12) = 0.75 \, W$$

$$R_2 = \frac{1}{16}(W \times 4) = 0.25 \, W$$

$$\tan \theta = \frac{9}{12} = 0.75 ; \theta = 36.87°$$

$$\therefore \quad \sin \theta = 0.6 ; \cos \theta = 0.8$$

Pass a section $a - a$ and consider the equilibrium of the right hand portion.

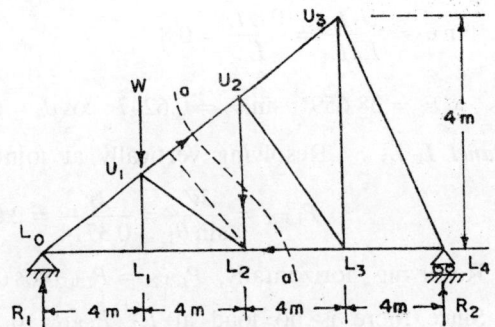

FIG. 25.31

$$P_{U1U2} = \frac{M_{L2}}{L_0 L_2 \sin\theta} = \frac{0.25\,W\,(8)}{8 \times 0.6} = 0.417\,W \quad (\text{comp.})$$

$$P_{L2U2} = \frac{M_{L0}}{L_0 L_2} = \frac{0.25\,W\,(16)}{8} = 0.5\,W \quad (\text{tension})$$

$$P_{L2L3} = \frac{M_{U2}}{U_2 L_2} = \frac{0.25\,W\,(8)}{L_0 L_2 \tan\theta} = \frac{2\,W}{8 \times 0.75} = 0.333\,W \quad (\text{tension})$$

Example 25.4. *Find the forces in members $U_1 U_2$ and $L_1 L_2$ of the roof truss shown in Fig. 25.32.*

(a) Geometry of the truss

The vertical distance between U_2 and $L_1 L_2 = y$
$= 6\tan 30° - 0.9 = 2.564$ m

$L_0 L_1 = \sqrt{(4)^2 + (0.9)^2} = 4.1$ m

$\tan\theta = \dfrac{0.9}{4} = 0.225$

∴ $\theta = 12.68°$. Hence
$\varphi = 30° - 12.68° = 17.32°$

From L_1, drop perpendicular $L_1 N$ on $U_1 U_2$.

∴ $L_1 N = L_0 L_1 \sin\varphi = 4.1 \sin 17.32° = 1.221$ m

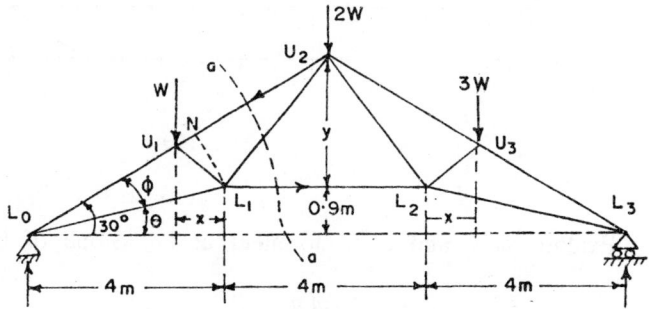

FIG. 25.32

Also, $L_0 U_1 = \dfrac{1}{2} L_0 U_2 = \dfrac{1}{2}\dfrac{6}{\cos 30°} = 3.464$ m

Distance x between the line of action of load at U_1 and the joint L_1
$= x = 4 - L_0 U_1 \cos 30° - 3.464 \cos 30° = 1$ m

(b) Reactions : $R_2 = \dfrac{1}{12}\Big[W\,(4-1) + 2\,W\,(6) + 3\,W\,(8+1) \Big] = 3.5\,W$

$R_1 = \dfrac{1}{12}\Big[W\,(8+1) + 2\,W\,(6) + 3\,W\,(4-1) \Big] = 2.5\,W$

(c) Stresses in $U_1 U_2$ and $L_1 L_2$: Pass a section $a - a$ and consider the equilibrium of L.H. portion.

$$P_{L1L2} = \frac{M_{U2}}{y} = \frac{2.5\,W \times 6 - W\,(2+1)}{2.564} = 4.68\,W \quad (\text{tension})$$

$$P_{U2U1} = \frac{M_{L1}}{L_1 N} = \frac{2.5\,W\,(4) - W\,(1)}{1.221} = 7.371\,W \quad (\text{comp.})$$

Example 25.5. *A pin jointed cantilever frame is hinged to a vertical wall at U_0 and L_0, and is loaded as shown in Fig. 25.33. Determine the forces in members $L_0 L_1$, $U_1 L_1$ and $U_0 U_1$.*

Solution :

(a) Geometry of the truss: $L_0 U_1 = \sqrt{a^2 + (2\,a)^2} = 2.236\,a$; $\tan\theta_1 = a/2\,a = \dfrac{1}{2}$; $\theta_1 = 26.565°$

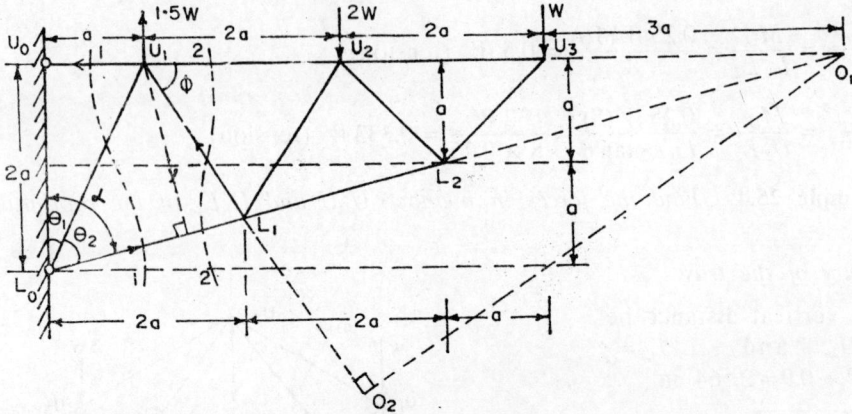

FIG. 25.33

Extend $U_0 U_3$ and $L_0 L_2$ to meet at O_1. Slope of line $L_0 L_2 = \dfrac{2a - a}{4a} = \dfrac{1}{4}$

$\therefore$ $\tan \alpha = \dfrac{4a}{a} = 4 \, ; \alpha = 75.963°$. Hence $\theta_2 = 75.963° - 26.565° = 49.398°$

Also $U_0 O_1 = 2.a \tan \alpha = 2a \times 4 = 8a$. Hence $U_3 O_1 = 3a$

From U_1, drop a perpendicular y on $L_0 L_2$.

Perpendicular $y = L_0 U_1 \sin \theta_2 = 2.236 \, a \times \sin 49.398° = 1.698 \, a$

Extend $U_1 L_1$. From O_1, drop perpendicular $O_1 O_2$ to meet $U_1 L_1$ (extended) in O_2.

Now $\tan \varphi = \dfrac{1.5 \, a}{a} = 1.5$. Hence $\varphi = 56.31°$

$\therefore$ $O_1 O_2 = U_1 O_1 . \sin \varphi = 7 \, a \sin 56.31° = 5.824 \, a$

(b) Stresses in $U_0 U_1$ and $L_0 L_1$:

Pass section $1-1$ and consider the equilibrium of the R.H. portion.

$$P_{\text{U0U1}} = \frac{M_{L0}}{2a} = \frac{(W \times 5a) + (2W \times 3a) - (1.5W \times a)}{2a} = \mathbf{4.75\,W} \ \text{(tension)}$$

and $$P_{\text{L0L1}} = \frac{M_{U1}}{y} = \frac{(W \times 4a) + (2W \times 2a)}{1.698 \, a} = \mathbf{4.711\,W} \ \text{(comp.)}$$

(c) Stress in $U_1 L_1$:

Pass a section $2-2$ and consider the equilibrium of the R.H. portion.

$$P_{\text{U1L1}} = \frac{M_{01}}{O_1 O_2} = \frac{(2W \times 5a) + (W \times 3a)}{5.824 \, a} = \mathbf{2.232\,W} \ \text{(tension)}$$

Example 25.6. *Determine the forces in the members of the frame shown in Fig. 25.34.*

Solution :

(a) Geometry and reactions

$$h = \frac{L}{2} \tan 60° = 0.866\,L$$

$$V_A = \frac{1}{L}\left(W \times \frac{L}{2} - 1.5\,W \times 0.866\,L\right)$$

$$= -0.799\,W \quad (i.e.\ 0.799\,W \downarrow)$$

$$V_B = \frac{1}{L}\left(W \times \frac{L}{2} + 1.5\,W \times 0.866\,L\right)$$

$$= 1.799\,W\,(\uparrow)$$

Since $\Sigma H = 0$, we get $H_A = 1.5\,W\,(\leftarrow)$

(a) Joint B: By inspection, P_{BC} will be compressive and P_{BD} will be tensile.

Hence $P_{BC} \cos 60° = P_{BD} \cos 30°$, from which

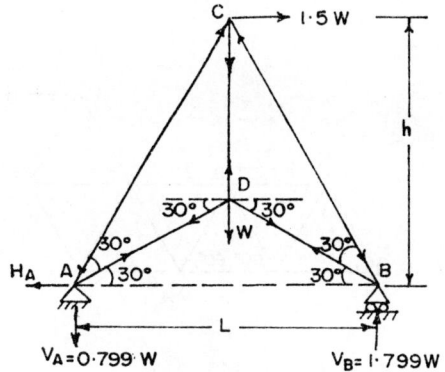

FIG. 25.34

$$P_{BD} = P_{BC} \cdot \frac{\cos 60°}{\cos 30°} = 0.5774\,P_{BC} \qquad \ldots(i)$$

Also, $\qquad P_{BD} \sin 30° + V_B = P_{BC} \sin 60°$

or $(0.5774\,P_{BC}) \times 0.5 + 1.799\,W = 0.866\,P_{BC},$

From which $\qquad P_{BC} = 3.116\,W$ (comp.)

Hence $\qquad P_{BD} = 0.5774 \times 3.116\,W = 1.799\,W$ (tension)

(c) Joint A: By inspection P_{AC} will be compressive while P_{AD} will be tensile.

Resolving vertically, $P_{AC} \sin 60° + V_A = P_{AD} \sin 30°$,

$$\therefore \qquad P_{AD} = \frac{1}{\sin 30°}\,[P_{AC} \sin 60° + V_A]$$

$$= \frac{1}{0.5}\,[0.866\,P_{AC} + 0.799\,W] = 1.732\,P_{AC} + 1.598\,W$$

Resolving horizontally,

$$P_{AC} \cos 60° + H_A = P_{AD} \cos 30°$$

or $\qquad 0.5\,P_{AC} + 1.5\,W = 0.866\,(1.732\,P_{AC} + 1.598\,W)$

From which, $\qquad P_{AC} = 0.116\,W$ (comp.)

and $\qquad P_{AD} = 1.799\,W$ (tension)

(d) Joint D: By inspection, P_{DC} will tensile.

Resolving vertically, $\qquad P_{DC} = P_{DA} \sin 30 + P_{DB} \sin 30° + W$

or $\qquad P_{DC} = 2 \times 1.799\,W \times 0.5 + W = 2.799\,W$ (tension)

PROBLEMS

1. A pin jointed structure, shown in Fig. 25.35, is pinned to an abutment at J and rests on rollers at G. A load W is applied horizontally at D. Determine the forces in all the members   (U.L.)

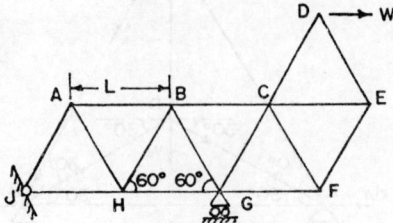

FIG. 25.35

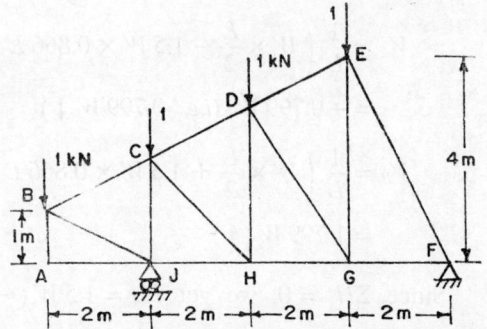

FIG. 25.36

2. A braced frame, shown in Fig. 25.36 is simply supported at J and F. Four 1 kN loads act at B, C, D and E. Determine the forces in CJ, CD, CH and JH.   (U.L.)

3. A cantilever truss is loaded as shown in Fig. 25.37. Find out the value of W, which would produce the force of magnitude 15 kN in the member AB.   (Based on Oxford University)

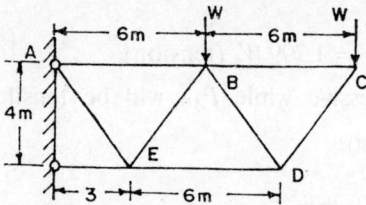

FIG. 25.37

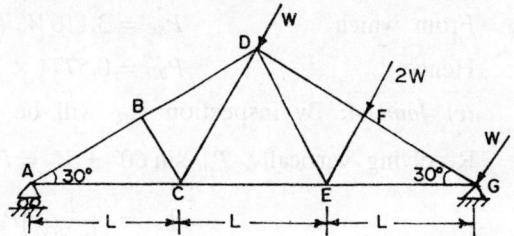

FIG. 25.38

4. A truss of $3L$ span is loaded as shown in Fig. 25.38. Determine the forces in the member BD, CD and CE of the truss.   (Based on Cambridge University)

5. Determine the forces in the members of the frame loaded as shown in Fig. 25.39

(Based on U.L.)

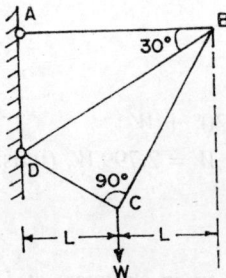

FIG. 25.39

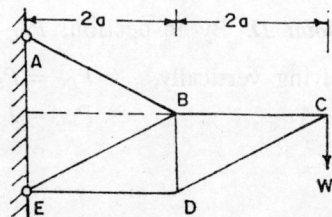

FIG. 25.40

6. Find the forces in all the members of truss, loaded as shown in Fig. 25.40.

7. Determine the forces in the members of the truss shown in Fig. 25.41.

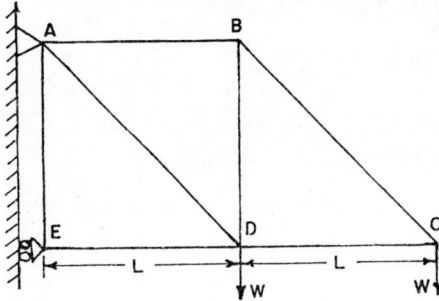

FIG. 25.41

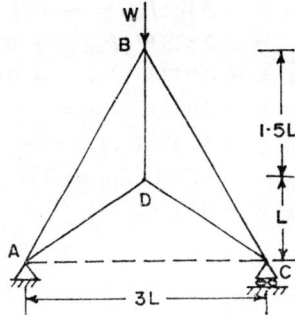

FIG. 25.42

8. Determine the forces in the members of the truss shown in Fig. 25.42.

9. The roof truss shown in Fig. 25.43 and loaded as indicated, is supported on a roller bearing at B and pin jointed at A. Find the forces in DC, EC and EF.

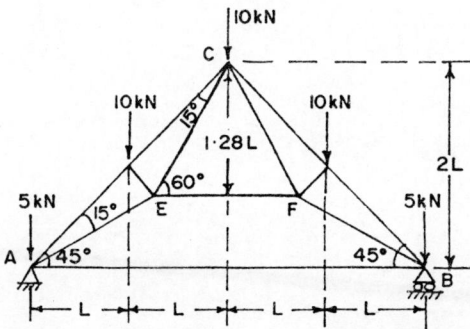

FIG. 25.43

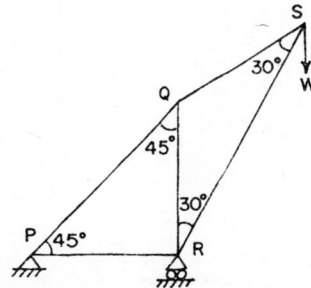

FIG. 25.44

10. Find the forces in all the members of the frame shown in Fig. 25.44.

ANSWERS

1. $P_{AB} = -W$; $P_{BC} = -2W$; $P_{CE} = -W$; $P_{CD} = -W$; $P_{AJ} = -W$; $P_{AH} = +W$

   $P_{BH} = -W$; $P_{BG} = +W$; $P_{CF} = -W$; $P_{EF} = +W$; $P_{JH} = -\dfrac{W}{2}$; $P_{HG} = +\dfrac{W}{2}$

   $P_{DE} = +W$; $P_{CG} = 0$; $P_{GF} = +W$

2. $P_{CJ} = +2.833$; $P_{CD} = +0.248$; $P_{CH} = -1.725$; $P_{JH} = +1$

3. 5 kN

4. $P_{BD} = +2.98W$; $P_{CD} = 0$; $P_{CE} = -2.58W$

5. $P_{AB} = -0.85\,W$; $P_{BC} = -0.85\,W$; $P_{CD} = -0.517\,W$; $P_{DB} = +1.5\,W$

6. $P_{BC} = -2\,W$; $P_{CD} = +2.236\,W$; $P_{BD} = -W$; $P_{ED} = +2\,W$
    $P_{EB} = 0$; $P_{AB} = -2.236\,W$

7. $P_{ED} = +3\,W$; $P_{CD} = +W$; $P_{AB} = -W$; $P_{BC} = -1.414\,W$
    $P_{AD} = -2.828\,W$; $P_{BD} = +W$

8. $P_{AB} = +0.972\,W$; $P_{BC} = +0.972\,W$; $P_{AD} = -0.601\,W$
    $P_{DC} = -0.601\,W$; $P_{BD} = -0.667\,W$

9. $P_{DC} = +42.65$ kN ; $P_{EC} = -29.02$ kN ; $P_{FF} = -15.62$ kN

10. $P_{PQ} = -1.22\,W$; $P_{QS} = -W$; $P_{SR} = +1.725\,W$; $P_{RP} = +0.865\,W$
    $P_{QR} = +0.37\,W$

Riveted Connections

26.1. TYPES OF CONNECTIONS

A structure is an assembly of various elements or components which are fastened together through some type of connection. If connections are not designed properly and fabricated with care, they may be a source of weakness in the finished structure, not only in their structural action but also because they may be the focus of corrosion and aesthetically unpleasing. Where as the design of main members has reached an advanced stage, based upon theories which have been developed and refined, the behaviour of connections is often so complex that theoretical considerations are of little use in practical design. By their very nature, connections are a jumble of *local effects*. Most connections are highly indeterminate, with the distribution of stress depending upon the deformation of fasteners and the detail material. Local restraints may prevent the deformation necessary for desirable stress redistribution.

Following are the *requirements* of a good connection in steelwork:

1. It should be *rigid*, to avoid fluctuating stresses which may cause fatigue failure.

2. It should be such that there is the least possible weakening of the parts to be joined.

3. It should be such that it can be easily installed, inspected and maintained.

The following are the common types of connections used for structural steelwork:

    1.   Riveted connections   2.   Bolted connections.

    3.   Pinned connections   4.   Welded connections.

Rivets, bolts and welds are used extensively, and frequently the economic advantage of one over the other two is so small to be uncertain. However, at one time, riveting prevailed but it has been superseded in importance by welding and high-strength bolting.

26.2. RIVET AND RIVETING

Riveting is a method of joining together structural steel components by inserting ductile metal pins, called *rivets*, into holes of the components to be connected from coming apart. A rivet consists of (*i*) a shank of given length and diameter, and (*ii*) a head known as *manufactured head*. The *size* of the rivet is defined by the diameter of the shank. Riveting is essentially a forging process. Fig. 26.1 shows the essential steps in process of riveting, during which a *hot rivet* is driven in its plastic state, and a head is formed at the other end. The head so formed at the other end of the rivet, with the help of a *riveting hammer* and a *buckling bar*, is known as *driven head*.

Rivets driven in the field during the erection of a structure are known as *field rivets*. Rivets driven in the fabricating shop are known as *shop rivets*. Both these types are known as *hot driven rivets* since the rivets are heated to a temperature ranging between 1000° F to 1950° F before driving. Field rivets are driven by a hand operated pneumatic riveting ham-

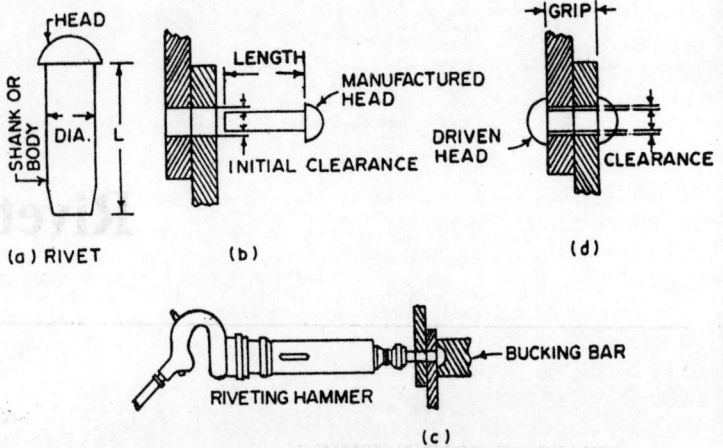

FIG. 26.1. ESSENTIAL STEPS IN RIVETING

mer, while the shop rivets are driven by "bull" riveter. Some rivets are driven at atmospheric temperature. They are known as *cold driven rivets* which are squeezed or driven to fill the holes and to form the heads by application of *large pressure*. However, they are smaller in diameter, ranging from 12 mm to 22 mm. Strength of cold driven rivet is more than hot driven rivets. Rivets driven by hand operated riveting hammer are known as *hand driven rivets* while those driven by power operated equipment are known as *power driven rivets*. Some times, even the field rivets may also be power driven.

26.3. RIVET SIZE, RIVET HOLE AND CONVENTIONAL SYMBOLS

The diameter of unheated rivet, before driving is known as the *nominal diameter*. Rivets are manufactured in nominal diameters of 12, 14, 16, 18, 20, 22, 24, 27, 30, 33, 36, 39, 42 and 48 mm. The diameter of *rivet hole* is made larger than the nominal diameter of the rivet by 1.5 mm for rivets less than or equal to 24 mm and by 2 mm for diameters exceeding 24 mm. The *grip* of the rivets is equal to the total thickness of plates to be joined by the rivet. The *length* of undriven rivet is the sum of (*i*) grip, (*ii*) length required for the head to be formed, and (*iii*) an additional length to fill up the space between the rivet and plate holes.

Several types of heads are used in structural design as shown in Fig. 26.2. The commonly used

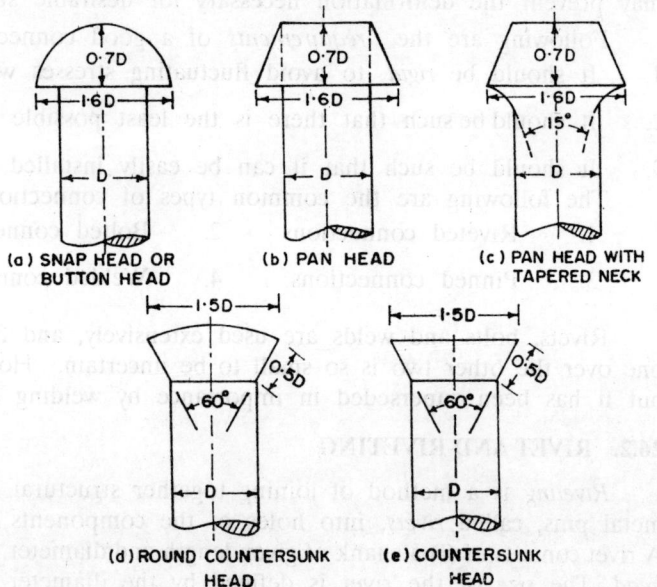

FIG. 26.2. DIFFERENT TYPES OF RIVET HEADS.

head is the *snap head* (Fig. 26.2 *a*) which is also known as *button head* or *round head*. *Counter-sunk* heads are used to provide a flush surface.

Rivet holes are made in the plates to be joined by (*i*) drilling or (*ii*) punching. Drilled holes are always preferred because the holes are perfect. Punched holes damage the plates to be joined.

Rivets are generally made of structural rivet steel conforming to IS 1929-1961 (for diameter between 12 to 48 mm) and IS 2155-1962 (for diameter below 12 mm). *High tensile steel rivets* if used are manufactured from steel conforming to IS: 1149-1982.

Rivets used for various types of structural connections are represented on the drawing through conventional symbols shown in Fig. 26.3.

(1) SHOP SNAP HEAD RIVETS

(2) SHOP COUNTER SUNK (NEAR SIDE) RIVETS

(3) SHOP COUNTER SUNK (FAR SIDE) RIVETS

(4) SHOP COUNTER SUNK (BOTH SIDES) RIVETS

(5) SITE SNAP HEADED RIVETS

(6) SITE COUNTER SUNK (NEAR SIDE) RIVETS

(7) SITE COUNTER SUNK (FAR SIDE) RIVETS

(8) SITE COUNTER SUNK (BOTH SIDES) RIVETS

(9) OPEN HOLE

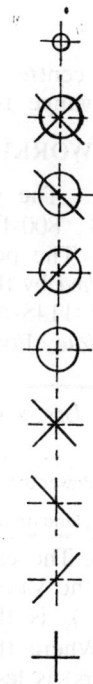

FIG. 26.3. CONVENTIONAL SYMBOLS FOR RIVETING

26.4. COMMON DEFINITIONS (Fig. 26.4)

1. Nominal diameter of Rivet: It is the diameter of unheated rivet. It is the *stated diameter* of the rivet, available in the market.

2. Gross diameter of Rivet: It is the diameter of the rivet in the hole, measured after driving. It is taken equal to the diameter of the hole itself.

3. Gross area of rivet : It is the area calculated on the basis of gross diameter of the rivet.

4. Pitch of rivets (p) : It is the distance between centres of two adjacent rivets in a row.

5. Gauge line: It is the line of rivets which is parallel to the direction of stress.

6. Gauge distance or 'gauge' (g): It is the perpendicular distance between two adjacent gauge lines. This is also known as *back pitch*.

7. Edge distance : It is the distance of the edge of the member or the cover plates from the centre of extreme rivet hole.

8. Lap : It is the distance normal to the joint between edges of the overlapping plates in a lap joint or between the joint and the end of cover plates in a butt joint.

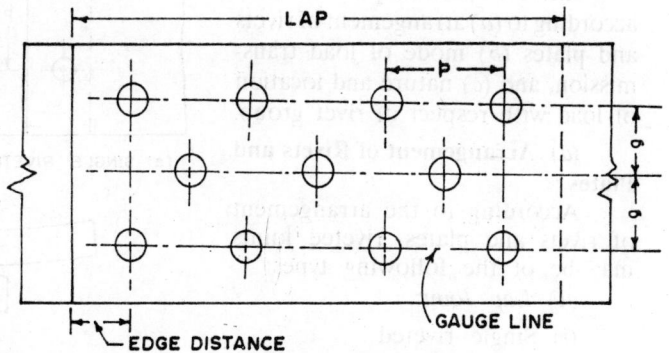

Note : There is a lot of confusion in the available literature about the nomenclatures 'pitch' and 'gauge'. To avoid confusion, *pitch* may be defined

FIG. 26.4. DEFINITION SKETCH.

as the centre to centre distance between rivets *measured along the long direction*s of the joint while gauge is the distance between rivet centres measured along the *short* direction.

26.5. WORKING STRESSES IN RIVETS

1. The working stresses (or maximum permissible stresses) in mild steel shop rivets as per IS : 800-1984 are given in Table 26.1.

2. The permissible stress in a high tensile steel rivet shall be those given in Table 26.1 *multiplied* by the ratio of tensile strength of the rivet material to the tensile strength as specified in IS : 1148-1973.

Note: For field rivets the permissible stresses shall be reduced by 10 percent.

TABLE 26.1. MAXIMUM PERMISSIBLE STRESSES IN RIVETS

Type of Rivet	Axial Tension, σ_{tf} N/mm^2(MPa)	Shear, τ_{vf} N/mm^2 (MPa)	Bearing, σ_{pf} N/mm^2 (MPa)
1. Power driven rivets	100	100	300
2. Hand driven rivets	80	80	250

3. The calculated bearing stress of a rivet on the parts connected by it shall not exceed : (*a*) the value of f_y for hand driven rivets, and (*b*) the value 1.2 f_y for power driven rivets, where f_y is the yield stress of the connected parts.

Where the end distance of a rivet (that is, the edge distance in the direction in which it bears) is less than a limit of twice the effective diameter of the rivet, the permissible bearing stress of that rivet on the connected part shall be reduced in the ratio of the actual and the distance to that limit.

4. Combined shear and tension: Rivets and bolts subjected to both shear and axial tension shall be so proportioned that the calculated shear and axial tension do not exceed the allowable stresses τ_{vf} and σ_{tf} and the expression $\left(\dfrac{\tau_{vf, cal}}{\tau_{vf}} + \dfrac{\sigma_{tf, cal}}{\sigma_{tf}} \right)$ does not exceed 1.4.

26.6. TYPES OF RIVETED JOINTS

A riveted joint may be classified according to (*a*) arrangement of rivets and plates (*b*) mode of load transmission, and (*c*) nature and location of load with respect of rivet group.

(*a*) **Arrangement of Rivets and Plates.**

According to the arrangement of rivets and plates, riveted joints may be of the following types:

(1) *Lap Joint*:

(*i*) Single riveted

(*ii*) double riveted.

(a) SINGLE RIVETED   (b) DOUBLE RIVETED

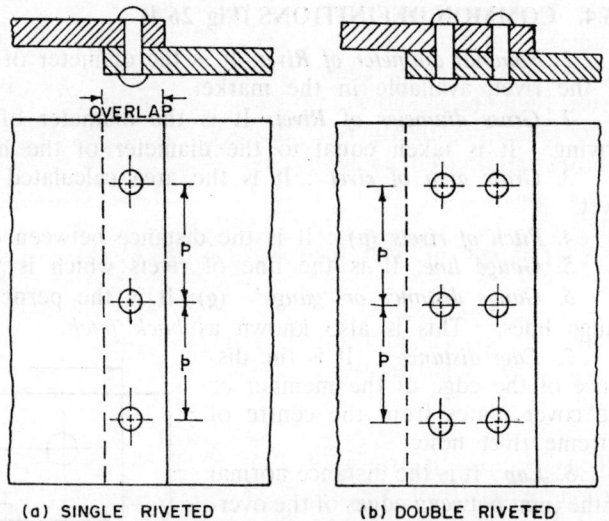

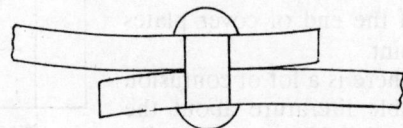

FIG. 26.5. LAP JOINTS

(2) *Butt joint*:

(*i*)   Single riveted butt joint with single cover plate.

(*ii*)   Single riveted butt joint with double cover plate

(*iii*) Doubled riveted butt joint with double cover plate.

Fig. 26.5 (*a*) shows single riveted lap joint, while 26.5 (*b*) shows double riveted lap joint. The two lines of pull in the joined plates are not in alignment, resulting in bending stresses tending to distort the joint, as shown in Fig. 26.5 (*c*).

Fig. 26.6 (*a*) and (*b*) show single riveted butt joint and double riveted butt joint respectively, in which the edges of the plates come flush and the *cover plates* are used to join them. In a single cover butt joint, bending stresses may develop, tending to distort the joint, as shown in Fig. 26.7. This possibility is completely eliminated by using a double cover butt joint.

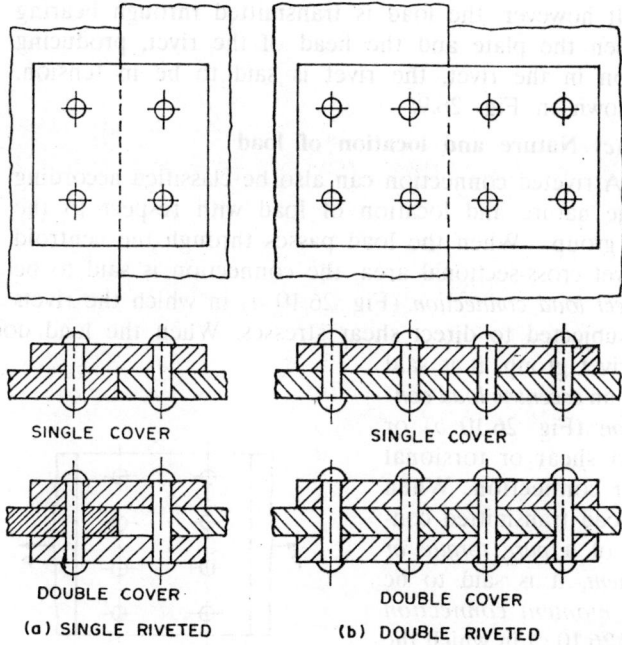

FIG. 26.6. BUTT JOINTS.

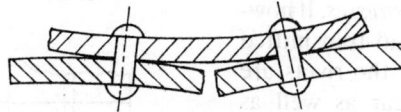

FIG. 26.7. DISTORTION OF BUTT JOINT WITH SINGLE COVER PLATE

(b) Mode of load transmission

Riveted connections can also be classified according to the *mode* of load transmission by the rivets.   If the load is transmitted through *bearing* between the plate and the shank of the rivet producing shear in the rivet (Fig. 26.8), the rivet is said to be in *shear*. When the load is transmitted by shear in only *one section* of the rivet, the rivet is said to be in *single shear* (Fig. 26.8 *a*).   When the loading of the rivet is such as to have the load transmitted in *two shear planes*, the rivet is said to be in *double shear* (Fig. 26.8 *b*). When the load is transmitted by shear in *more than two planes*, the rivet is said to be in *multiple shear* (Fig. 26.8 *c*).

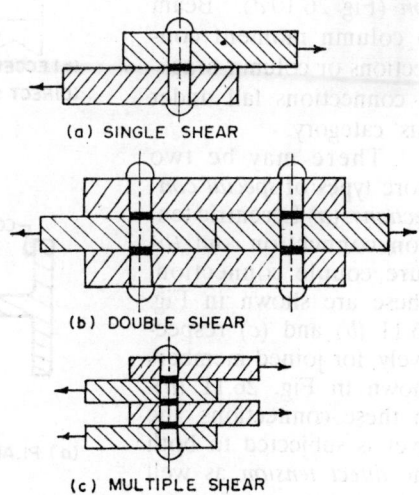

FIG. 26.8. RIVETS IN SHEAR.

If however, the load is transmitted through bearing between the plate and the head of the rivet, producing tension in the rivet, the rivet is said to be in tension, as shown in Fig. 26.9.

(c) Nature and location of load

A riveted connection can also be classified according to the nature and location of load with respect to the rivet group. When the load passes through the centroid of rivet cross-sectional area, the connection is said to be a *direct load connection* (Fig. 26.10 *a*) in which the rivets are subjected to direct shear stresses. When the load does not pass through the centroid of

FIG. 26.9. RIVETS IN TENSION.

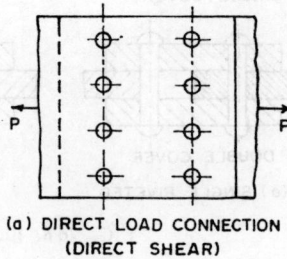

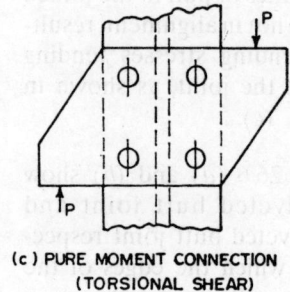

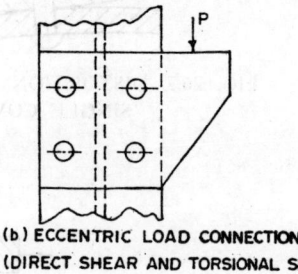

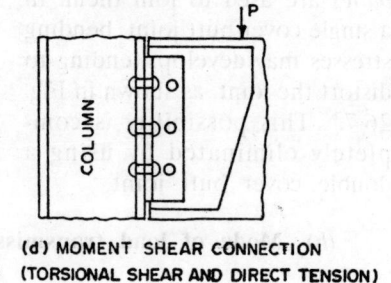

the rivet group, it is said of be an *eccentric load connection* (Fig. 26.10 *b*) or direct shear or torsional shear connection. When the load transmitted consists of a *pure torque or moment*, it is said to be *pure moment connection* (Fig. 26.10 *c*) in which the rivets are subjected to *torsional shear stresses*. If however, the load transmitted is such that the rivets are both in shear as well as in tension, it is said to be *moment-shear connection* or a *tension-shear connection* (Fig. 26.10 *d*). Beam to column moment connections or column-bracket connections fall under this category.

There may be two more types of *special connections*: (*a*) Eccentric tension connection and (*b*) pure couple connection. These are shown in Fig. 26.11 (*b*) and (*c*) respectively, for joined members shown in Fig. 26.11 (*a*). In these connections, the rivet is subjected to both the *direct tension* as well as *bending stress* (compression as well as tension).

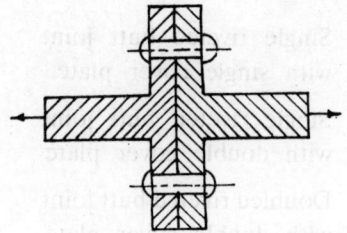

(a) DIRECT LOAD CONNECTION
(DIRECT SHEAR)

(c) PURE MOMENT CONNECTION
(TORSIONAL SHEAR)

(b) ECCENTRIC LOAD CONNECTION
(DIRECT SHEAR AND TORSIONAL SHEAR)

(d) MOMENT SHEAR CONNECTION
(TORSIONAL SHEAR AND DIRECT TENSION)

FIG. 26.10. TYPES OF RIVETED CONNECTIONS.

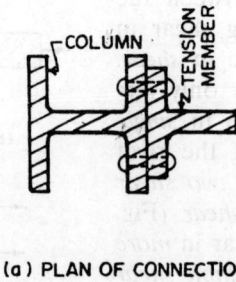

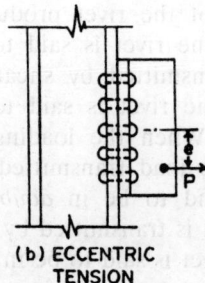

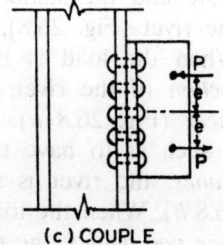

(a) PLAN OF CONNECTION

(b) ECCENTRIC TENSION

(c) COUPLE

FIG. 26.11. SPECIAL CONNECTIONS INDUCING DIRECT TENSION AS WELL AS BENDING STRESSES

26.7. MODES OF FAILURE OF A RIVETED JOINT

A riveted joint may fail in one of the following ways.

1. *Tension failure* in the plate (Fig. 26.12)

2. *Shearing failure* across one or more planes of the rivets (Fig. 26.13)

3. *Bearing failure* between the plates and the rivets (Fig. 26.14)

4. *Plate shear* or *shear out failure* in the plate (Fig. 26.15)

1. Tension failure in the plates

The plate can fail by *tearing off* across the pitch length (Fig. 26.12 *a*) due to lack of tensile strength of the plate on a section along the row of the rivets. The plate may also tear along the diagonal (Fig. 26.12 *b*). However, this type of failure is unlikely to happen if the back pitch is

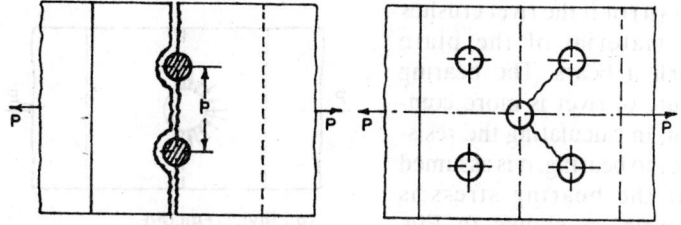

FIG. 26.12. TENSION FAILURE OF PLATES

atleast 13 times the rivet diameter. We will investigate the possibility of failure represented in Fig. 26.12 (*a*) only, as it is assumed that sufficient *back pitch* has been provided.

Let P_{ut} = Pull applied per pitch length, for tension failure

f_t = Ultimate tensile strength of the plate material.

p = pitch of rivets, measured perpendicular to the direction of force.

t = thickness of the plate

d = gross diameter (or formed diameter) of the rivet.

$\therefore$ $P_{ut} = f_t \times$ resisting section

or $P_{ut} = f_t (p - d) t$ ...(26.1)

2. Shearing failue of the rivet

In a riveted joint, the rivets may themselves fail in shear. The tendency is to cut through the rivet across the section lying in the plane between the plates it connects (Fig. 26.13 *a*, *b*). In analysing this possible manner of failure, one must always note whether a rivet acts in *single shear* or *double shear*. In the latter case, two cross-sectional areas of the

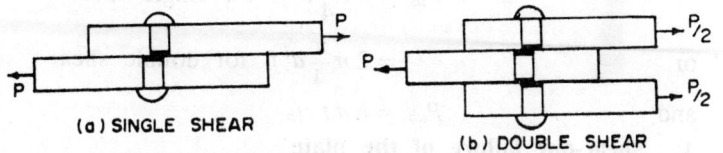

(a) SINGLE SHEAR   (b) DOUBLE SHEAR

FIG. 26.13. SHEAR FAILURE OF RIVET

same rivet resist the applied force. The shearing stress is assumed to be *uniformly distributed* over the cross-section of the rivet.

Let P_{us} = pull required, per pitch length, for shear failure

f_s = ultimate shear strength of the rivet material

d = gross diameter of rivet.

Resisting area of rivet section $= \dfrac{\pi}{4} d^2$ in single shear

and $= 2 \dfrac{\pi}{4} d^2$ in double shear

$$\therefore \qquad P_{us} = \frac{\pi}{4}d^2 f_s \ , \ \text{for single shear}$$

$$\text{and} \qquad P_{us} = 2 \times \frac{\pi}{4}d^2 f_s \ , \ \text{for double shear} \qquad ...(26.2)$$

3. Bearing failure between plates and rivets.

A rivet joint may fail if a rivet itself is deformed by the plate acting on it (Fig. 26.14 *a*) or if the rivet crushes the material of the plate which it bears. The bearing failure of rivet is more common. In calculating the resistance to bearing, it is assumed that the bearing stress is uniform, as shown in Fig. 26.14 (*c*).

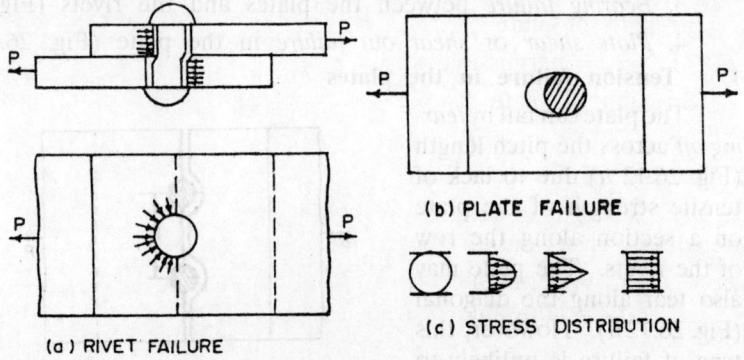

(a) RIVET FAILURE

(b) PLATE FAILURE

(c) STRESS DISTRIBUTION

FIG. 26.14. BEARING FAILURE.

Let $\quad P_{ub}$ = pull required, per pitch length, for bearing failure of rivet.

$\qquad f_b$ = ultimate crushing strength of rivet material.

$\qquad d$ = gross diameter of rivet.

$\qquad t$ = thickness of the plate.

$\qquad P_{ub}$ = (intensity of radial pressure, at failure) × projected area.

$$\therefore \qquad P_{ub} = f_b . d . t \qquad ...(26.3)$$

Equations 26.1, 26.2 and 26.3 are applicable for single riveted joint. If, however there are *n rows of rivets* per pitch length, we have

$$P_{ut} = (p - d) t . f_t \qquad ...(26.1 \ a)$$

$$P_{us} = n . \frac{\pi}{4}d^2 f_s \ \text{for single shear} \qquad ...(26.2 \ a)$$

$$\text{or} \qquad = 2n\frac{\pi}{4}d^2 f_s \ \text{for double shear}$$

$$\text{and} \qquad P_{ub} = n d t . f_b \qquad ...(26.3 \ a)$$

4. Shear-out failure of the plate

Fig. 26.15 (*a*) shows the 'shear-out' failure of plate, which can be prevented by providing a sufficient edge distance beyond the rivet.

Sometimes, *splitting failure* of plate may occur, which can also be prevented by providing a sufficient edge distance. Since the *edge distance* is governed by *code requirements* (see § 26.9), 'shear-out' stresses are not calculated.

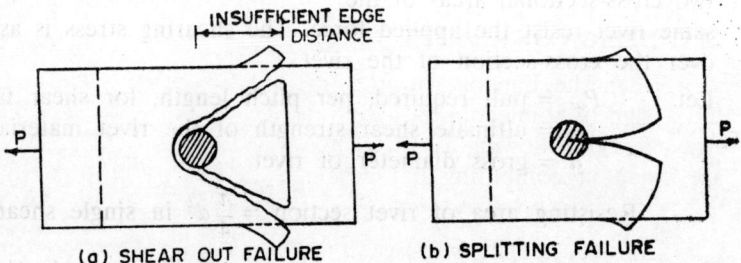

(a) SHEAR OUT FAILURE

(b) SPLITTING FAILURE

FIG. 26.15. SHEAR OUT FAILURE OF PLATE

26.8. STRENGTH OF RIVETED JOINT

In the previous section, we have computed the values of pull required for the failure of a riveted joint, using ultimate strength values for the material. However, same expressions can be used to compute the *strength* of a riveted joint, by using the *permissible values of the stresses in the materials*, as shown below :

1. Strength of plate

Let σ_{at} = permissible stress in plate in axial tension.

Strength of plate P_t, per pitch length is given by

$$P_t = \sigma_{at}\,(p - d)\,t \qquad\qquad ...(26.4)$$

2. Strength of Rivet or Rivet Value

The strength of rivet, commonly known as *rivets value* (R) is the smaller of (i) shearing strength of rivet and (ii) bearing strength of rivet.

Let τ_{vf} = permissible shearing stress in rivet.

σ_{pf} = allowable bearing stress in rivet.

$\therefore$ Shearing strength of rivet, $P_s = \tau_{vf}\,.\,\dfrac{\pi}{4}d^2$ in single shear $...(26.5)$

or $= \tau_{vf}\,.\,2\,\dfrac{\pi}{4}d^2$ in double shear

Bearing strength of rivet, $P_b = \sigma_{pf} \times d \times t$ $...(26.6)$

Strength of riveted joint and efficiency of joint

The strength of a riveted joint will be lesser of values given by Eqs 26.4, 26.5 and 26.6.

Strength of solid plate, $P = \sigma_{at}\,.\,p\,.\,t$ (per pitch length) $...(26.7\ a)$

The efficiency η of joint is defined as the ratio of the strength of the joint to the strength of the plate.

Thus, $\eta = \dfrac{\text{Least of } P_t, P_s \text{ and } P_b}{P}$ $...(26.7\ b)$

It should be noted that Eqs. 26.4, 26.5 and 26.6 give the strength of a single riveted joint. However, if there are n rows of rivets per pitch length, we have

$$P_t = \sigma_{at}\,(p - d)\,t \qquad\qquad ...(26.4\ a)$$

$$P_s = n\,.\,\tau_{vf}\frac{\pi}{4}d^2 \quad \text{in the single shear}$$

or $= n\,\tau_{vf}\,.\,2\dfrac{\pi}{4}d^2$ in the double shear $...(26.5\ a)$

and $P_b = n\,\sigma_{pf}\,.\,d\,.\,t$ $...(26.6\ a)$

26.9. DESIGN OF RIVETED JOINT : AXIAL LOAD

When the line of action of the load coincides with the centre of gravity of rivet areas, the design of connection is based on the *nominal stresses*, which must not exceed the allowable stresses. The following assumptions, which are nearly correct for load approaching the ultimate, are made in computing the nominal stresses.

Assumptions

1. Initial tensile stresses in the rivet is neglected.

2. The frictional resistance to slip between the plates is neglected.

3. The plates are rigid.

4. The rivet fills the hole completely.

5. Deformation of the plates under the load is neglected.

6. Shearing deformation of the rivets is assumed proportional to the shearing stress.

7. Shearing stress in the rivets is assumed to be uniformly distributed over the rivet cross-section.

8. Unit shearing stress in all the rivets of a joint is uniform.

9. Tensile stress concentration due to rivet holes in the plates are neglected.

10. Bearing stress between rivets and plates is assumed to be uniformly distributed over the nominal contact surface between the rivets and plates.

11. Bending of rivets is neglected.

1. Pitch of Rivets

The pitch of rivets in a riveted joint should be such that under a pull P_t, the permissible stress in the rivet for shearing and bearing are not exceeded.

From Eq. 26.4, $P_t = \sigma_{at}(p - d)t$

Strength of rivet = Rivet value $R = P_s$ or P_b which is less.

$\therefore$ $P_t \leq R$

or $\sigma_{at}(p - d)t \leq R$ ...(26.8 a)

From Eq. 26.7, *pitch* (p) can be determined. If Eq. 26.8 a is fulfilled, the strength of joint will be P_t, and will be lesser than (or at the most equal to) P_s or P_b. The efficiency of the joint designed in this manner will be given by

$$\eta = \frac{P_t}{P} = \frac{(p - d)t\,\sigma_{at}}{p\,t\,\sigma_{at}} = \frac{p - d}{p}$$ ...(26.8 b)

IS 800-1984 lays down the following specifications for the pitch of rivets.

(*a*) *Minimum Pitch* : The distance between centres of rivets should be not less than 2.5 times the nominal diameter of rivet.

(*b*) *Maximum Pitch*

(*i*) The distance between centres of any two adjacent rivets (including tacking rivets) shall not exceed $32\,t$ or 300 mm, whichever is less, where t is the thickness of the thinner outside plate.

(*ii*) The distance between centres of two adjacent rivets, in a line lying in the direction of stress, shall not exceed $16\,t$ or 200 mm, whichever is less in tension members, and $12\,t$ or 200 mm, which ever is less in compression members. In the case of compression members in which forces are transferred through butting faces, this distance shall not exceed 4.5 times the diameter of the rivets for a distance from the abutting faces equal to 1.5 times the width of the member.

(*iii*) The distance between centres of any two consecutive rivets in a line adjacent and parallel to an edge of an outside plate shall not exceed (100 mm + $4\,t$) or 200 mm, which ever is less in compression or tension members.

(*iv*) When rivets are staggered at equal intervals and the gauge does not exceed 75 mm, the distances specified in (*ii*) and (*iii*) between centres of rivets, may be increased by 50 percent.

2. Edge Distance

(*a*) The minimum distance from the centre of any hole to the edge of a plate shall not be less than that given in Table 26.2.

(b) Where two or more parts are connected together, a line of rivets shall be provided at a distance of not more than 37 mm + 4 t from the nearest edge, where t is the thickness in mm of the thinner outside plate. In the case of work not exposed to weather, this may be increased to 12 t.

TABLE 26.2. EDGE DISTANCE OF HOLES

Nominal dia. of rivet (mm)	Dia. of hole (mm)	Distance to sheared or hand flame cut hole (mm)	Distance to Rolled, machine flame cut, sawn or planed hole (mm)
(1)	(2)	(3)	(4)
12 or below	13.5 or below	19	17
14	15.5	25	22
16	17.5	29	25
18	19.5	32	29
20	21.5	32	29
22	23.5	38	32
24	25.5	44	38
27	29.0	51	44
30	32.0	57	51
33	35.0	57	51

3. Diameter of Rivet

The diameter of rivet for a given plate thickness is generally chosen from the *Unwin's formula* :

$$d = 6.04\sqrt{t} \qquad\qquad ...(26.9)$$

where t = thickness of plate in mm and d = dia. of rivet in mm.

The diameter of the rivet so found is rounded off to the available size of rivets which are manufactured in nominal diameter of 12, 14, 16, 18, 20, 22, 24, 27, 30, 33, 36, 39, 42 and 48 mm. Commonly used sizes for structural steel works are 16, 18, 20 and 22 mm.

For computation of strength etc, the *formed diameter* (equal of the diameter of hole) is used.

4. Tacking rivets

Tacking rivets are generally used when a structural member consists of two angles (or such other sections), so as the two act as one unit. These rivets are also known as *stitch rivets*. As per IS : 800-1984, when the maximum distance between centres of two adjacent rivets exceeds the specified maximum pitch, taking rivets not subjected to calculated stress shall be used.

The tacking rivets shall have a pitch in line not exceeding 32 times the thickness of outside plate or 300 mm, whichever is less. Where the plates are exposed to the weather, the pitch in line shall not exceed 16 times the thickness of outside plate or 200 mm, whichever is less. In both cases, the lines of rivets shall not be apart at a distance greater than these pitches. All these requirements shall apply to compression members generally, subjected to the stipulation in the code affecting the design and construction of compression members.

In tension members composed of two flats, angles, channels or tees in contact back-to-back or separated back-to-back by a distance not exceeding the aggregate thickness of the connected parts, with solid distance pieces where the parts are separated, shall be provided at pitch in line not exceeding 1000 mm.

For compression members, the tacking rivets shall be at a pitch in line not exceeding 600 mm.

5   Rivets through packings

Number of rivets carrying calculated shear through a packing shall be increased above the number required by normal calculations by 2.5 percent for each 2.0 mm thickness of packing except that, for packing having a thickness of 6 mm or less, no increase need be made. For double shear connections packed on both sides, the number of additional rivets required shall be determined from the thickness of the thicker packing. The additional rivets should preferably be placed in an extension of the packing.

6   Long grip rivets

Where the grip of rivets carrying calculated load exceeds 6 times diameter of the holes, the number of rivets required by normal calculation shall be increased by not less than one percent for each additional 1.5 mm of grip; but the grip shall not exceed 8 times the diameter of the holes.

7.   Countersunk heads of rivets

For countersunk heads, one half of the depth of the counter sinking shall be neglected in calculating the length of rivet in bearing. For rivets in tension with countersunk heads, the tensile value shall be reduced by 33.3 percent. No reduction need be made in shear.

8.   Members meeting at a point

(*i*) For triangulated frames designed on the assumption of pin jointed connections, members meeting at a joint shall, where practicable, have their centroidal axes meeting at a point ; and wherever practicable the centre of resistance of a connection shall be on the line of action of the load so as to avoid an eccentricity or moment on the connections.

(*ii*) Where eccentricity of members or of connection is present, the members and the connections shall provide adequate resistance to the induced bending moments.

(*iii*) Where the design is based on non-intersecting members at a joint, all stresses arising from the eccentricity of the members shall be calculated and stress kept within the limits specified.

26.10.   RIVETED JOINT IN FRAMED STRUCTURES

In the case of a roof truss, bridge truss or other similar framed structure, the load (*P*) to be carried by the member is always known. The number of rivets (*n*) required to connect the member to the other member is given by

$$n = \frac{P}{\text{strength of one rivet}} = \frac{P}{R} \qquad \qquad ...(26.10)$$

where *P* is the pull or push carried by the member.

In the case of tension member carrying pull, the arrangement of rivets found above on each side of joint is of utmost importance, since it will directly determine the width of flat. Rivets in a joint may be arranged in two forms:

(*a*)   Chain Riveting (Fig. 26.16 *a*) and

(*b*)   Diamond Riveting (Fig. 26.16 *b*)

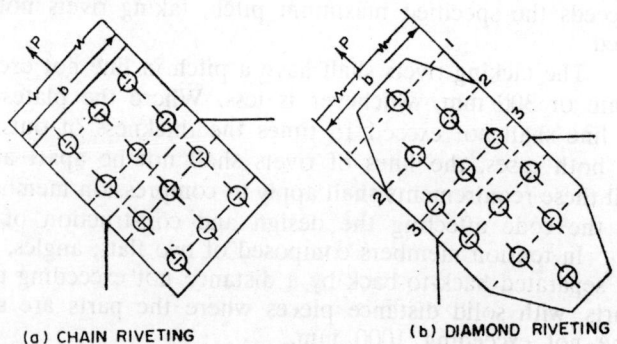

(a) CHAIN RIVETING   (b) DIAMOND RIVETING

FIG. 26.16. ARRANGEMENT OF RIVETS.

In *chain riveting* shown in Fig. 26.16 (*a*) for a case when $n=6$, the flat is weakened by three rivet holes. The width b of the flat in this must be such that

$$P = \sigma_{at} (b - 3d) t \qquad ...(26.11\ a)$$

or $$b = \frac{P}{t \cdot \sigma_{at}} + 3d \qquad ...(26.11)$$

In the case of diamond riveting shown in Fig. 26.16 (*b*), the flat is weakened at the section 1-1 by one rivet hole only and the width of the flat is given by

$$P = \sigma_{at} (b - d) t$$

or $$b = \frac{P}{t \sigma_{at}} + d \qquad ....(26.11\ b)$$

This width is *less* by $2d$ than the previous case. The saving in the width of flat by this amount is of utmost importance in the case of long bridge diagonals. The diamond riveting is, therefore used in preference to chain riveting. It can be shown that the joint get successively stronger at section 2-2, 3-3 etc.

The strength of joint at section 2-2 is

$$P_2 = \sigma_{at} (b - 2d) t + \text{(strength of one rivet in front)}$$

Similarly, the strength of the joint at section 3-3 is

$$P_3 = \sigma_{at} (b - 3d) t + \text{(strength of three rivets in front)}$$

Out of P, P_2 and P_3, usually P is the least. Therefore the efficiency of the joint is given by

$$\eta = \frac{(b - d) t \sigma_{at}}{b t \sigma_{at}} = \frac{b - d}{b} \qquad ...(26.12)$$

26.11. RIVETED JOINTS IN CYLINDRICAL AND SPHERICAL SHELLS

In the case of *cylindrical shells*, hoop stress is $\dfrac{pD}{2t}$, where p is the internal pressure, D is the diameter of the shell and t is the thickness of the plate. If the shell is riveted longitudinally, the efficiency of the joint should also be taken into account while finding its thickness. Similarly, in the case of spherical shells, hoop stress is $\dfrac{pD}{4t}$. Hence

For cylindrical shells, $$t = \frac{pD}{2 \sigma_{at} \eta} \qquad ...(26.13)$$

For spherical shells, $$t = \frac{pD}{4 \sigma_{at} \eta} \qquad ...(26.14)$$

Example 26.1. *Determine the rivet value of 20 mm diameter rivets connecting 12 mm thick plates, if it is in (a) single shear (b) double shear. The permissible stress for rivet in shear and bearing are 80 N/mm² and 250 N/mm² and for plate in bearing is 250 N/mm².*

Solution :

Gross diameter of rivet, $d = 20 + 1.5 = 21.5$ mm

Gross Area of rivet $= \frac{\pi}{4} d^2 = \frac{\pi}{4} (21.5)^2 = 363.05$ mm²

Bearing strength of rivet, $P_b = \sigma_{pf} \times d \times t = 250 \times 21.5 \times 12 = 64500$ N $\qquad ...(i)$

Strength of rivet in single shear, $P_{s_1} = \tau_{vf} \cdot \dfrac{\pi}{4} d^2 = 80 \times 363.05 = 29044$ N   ...(ii)

Strength of rivet in double shear, $P_{s_2} = \tau_{vf} \cdot 2 \times \dfrac{\pi}{4} d^2 = 2 \times 29044 = 58088$ N   ...(iii)

Hence Rivet value in single shear = smaller of P_b and $P_{s_1} = $ **29044 N**.

Rivet value in double shear = smaller of P_b and $P_{s_2} = $ **58088 N**

Example 26.2. *A double riveted double cover butt joint in plates 16 mm thick is made with 20 mm rivets at 80 mm pitch. Calculate the pull per pitch length at which the joint will fail and also its efficiency. Take* $f_t = 480\,N/mm^2$, $f_b = 760\,N/mm^2$ *and* $f_s = 380\,N/mm^2$.

Solution

Gross diameter or formed diameter of rivet = 20 + 1.5 = 21.5 mm. For the tension failure in the plates,

$$P_{ut} = f_t\,(p-d)\,t = 480(80-21.5)16 = 449280\text{ N} = 449.28 \text{ kN}$$

Since there are two rivets in one pitch length, and each rivet is in double shear, we have

$$P_{us} = 2\left(2 \times \dfrac{\pi}{4} d^2\right) f_s = \pi(21.5)^2 \times 380 = 551836 \text{ N} \approx 551.84 \text{ kN}$$

Also, $P_{ub} = 2d.t.f_b = 2 \times 21.5 \times 16 \times 760 = 522880 \text{ N} = 522.88 \text{ kN}$

The joint will thus fail at pull of 449.28 kN, the plates giving way by tearing off.

∴ Strength of the joint = 449.28 kN.

Strength of plate $= P_u = p \cdot t f_t = 80 \times 16 \times 480 = 614400$ N $= 614.4$ kN

∴ $\eta = \dfrac{\text{strength of joint}}{\text{strength of solid plate}} = \dfrac{449.28}{614.4} \times 100 = $ **73.12 %**

Example 26.3. *A single riveted lap joint is used to connect 12 mm thick plates, by providing 20 mm diameter rivets at 50 mm pitch. Determine the strength of the joint and joint efficiency. Take working stress in shear in rivets = 80 N/mm², working stress in bearing in rivets = 250 N/mm² and working stress in axial tension in plates = 0.6 f_y where* $f_y = 260\,N/mm^2$.

Solution : Formed diameter of rivets = 20 + 1.5 = 21.5 mm

$$\sigma_{at} = 0.6 f_y = 0.6 \times 260 = 156 \text{ N/mm}^2$$

Strength of plate in tension, per pitch length;

$$P_t = \sigma_{at}\,(p-d)\,t = 156(50-21.5) \times 12 = 53352 \text{ N}   \text{...(1)}$$

Strength of rivet in single shear:

$$P_s = \tau_{vf} \times \dfrac{\pi}{4} d^2 = 80 \times \dfrac{\pi}{4}(21.5)^2 = 29044 \text{ N}   \text{...(2)}$$

Strength rivet in bearing:

$$P_b = \sigma_{pf} \times d \times t = 250 \times 21.5 \times 12 = 64500 \text{ N}   \text{...(3)}$$

∴   Strength of joint = minimum of the above three values = **29044 N**

Strength of solid plate, $P = \sigma_{at}\,pt = 156 \times 50 \times 12 = 93600$ N   ...(4)

∴   Joint efficiency $= \dfrac{\text{Least of } P_t, P_s \text{ and } P_b}{P} = \dfrac{29044}{93600} \times 100 = $ **31.03%**

Example 26.4. *Determine the load which can be transmitted per pitch length of a double cover butt joint connected by 24 mm diameter shop rivets at 100 mm pitch. The thickness of main plates and cover plates are 16 mm and 12 mm respectively. Take allowable tensile strength of plates equal to 150 N/mm², allowable shear stress in rivets equal to 100 N/mm² and allowable stress in bearing for rivets equal to 300 N/mm². Also, determine the efficiency of the joint.*

Solution   Given : $\sigma_{pf} = 300$ N/mm², $\tau_{vf} = 100$ N/mm² and $\sigma_{at} = 150$ N/mm²

Gross diameter of rivets $= 24 + 1.5 = 25.5$ mm

(*i*) strength of rivet in double shear :

$$P_s = \tau_{vf} \cdot 2 \frac{\pi}{4} d^2 = 100 \times 2 \times \frac{\pi}{4} (25.5)^2 = 102141 \text{ N} \qquad \ldots(i)$$

(*ii*) Strength of rivet in bearing : As the total thickness of cover plates is more than the thickness of the main plate, the strength of the rivet will be found for bearing on main plates.

$$P_b = \sigma_{pf} \times d \times t = 300 \times 25.5 \times 16 = 122400 \text{ N} \qquad \ldots(ii)$$

(*iii*) Strength of plate, per pitch length:

$$P_t = \sigma_{at} (p - d) t = 150(100 - 25.5) 16 = 178800 \qquad \ldots(iii)$$

∴ Strength of joint per pitch length= minimum of (*i*), (*ii*) and (*iii*) = 102141 N

∴ Load which can be transmitted= **102141 N**

Strength of solid plate $= \sigma_{at} \cdot p \cdot t = 150 \times 100 \times 16 = 240000$ N

∴ η of joint $= \dfrac{102141}{240000} \times 100 = $ **42.56%**

Example 26.5. *Fig. 26.17 shows the joint of a boiler shell made of 12 mm thick plates using 20 mm dia. rivets at a pitch of 90 mm. The two cover plates of the butt joint are 8 mm thick, but are of unequal lengths. Determine the strength of the joint per pitch length and its efficiency. Take the following values of permissible stresses:* (i) $\sigma_{at} = 150$ N/mm² (ii) σ_{pf} = 250 N/mm² and (iii) $\tau_{vf} = 80$ N/mm².

Solution :

Here we observe that rivets in row 1 are in single shear, and they bear against 8 mm plate. However, rivets in row 2 are in double shear, and they bear against 12 mm main plate because the total thickness of the two coverplates is more than that of the main plate.

Formed diameter of rivet
    $= 20 + 1.5 = 21.5$ mm

(*a*) **Rivet value in section 1-1**

Strength of rivet in single shear

$$= \tau_{vf} \cdot \frac{\pi}{4} d^2$$

$$= 80 \times \frac{\pi}{4} (21.5)^2 = 29044 \text{ N}$$

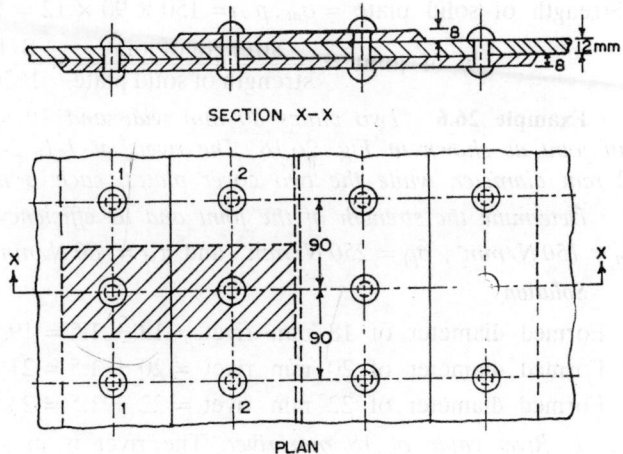

SECTION X-X

PLAN

FIG. 26.17.

Strength of rivet in bearing on 8 mm plate $= \sigma_{pf} \times d \times t$

$$= 250 \times 21.5 \times 8 = 43000 \text{ N}$$

$\therefore$ Rivet value in section 1-1 $= R_1 = 29044$ N

(b) **Rivet value in section 2-2**

Strength of rivet in double shear $= \tau_{vf} \times 2 \frac{\pi}{4} d^2 = 2 \times 29044 = 58088$ N

Strength of rivet in bearing on 12 mm plate $= \sigma_{pf} \times d \times t$

$$= 250 \times 21.5 \times 12 = 64500$$

$\therefore$ Rivet value in section 2-2 $= R_2 = 58088$ N.

(c) **Strength of joint**

Consider one pitch length of the joint, as shown hatched in Fig. 26.17. We will consider three possible chances of failure : (i) failure of rivets at section 1-1 and 2-2 (ii) tearing of main plate at section 1-1 and (iii) tearing of cover plates at section 2-2.

(i) *Strength of joint on the basis of failure of rivets at section 1-1 and 2-2*

$$= R_1 + R_2 = 29044 + 58088 = 87132 \text{ N} \qquad \qquad ...(i)$$

(ii) *Strength of main plate, at section 1-1*

Strength of the joint on the basis of strength of main plate

$$= \sigma_{at}(p - d)\, t = 150(90 - 21.5) \times 12 = 123300 \text{ N} \qquad \qquad ...(ii)$$

(iii) *Strength of cover plates at section 2-2*

Strength of the joint on the basis of strength of cover plates at section 2-2

$$= \sigma_{at}(p - d)\, t = 150(90 - 21.5)2 \times 8 = 164400 \qquad \qquad ...(iii)$$

(iv) *Strength of main plate at section 2-2*

Strength of joint at 2-2 = Strength of main plate at 2-2 + strength of rivet at 1-1

$$= \sigma_{at}(p - d)\, t + R_1 = 150(90 - 21.5)12 + 29044 = 152344 \text{ N} \qquad ...(iv)$$

$\therefore$ Strength of joint per pitch length = least of (i), (ii) (iii) and (iv) = 87132N

Strength of solid plate $= \sigma_{at} \cdot p \cdot t = 150 \times 90 \times 12 = 162000$ N

$\therefore \quad \eta$ of joint $= \dfrac{\text{strength of joint}}{\text{strength of solid plate}} = \dfrac{87132}{162000} \times 100 = \mathbf{53.79\,\%}$

Example 26.6. *Two plates 80 mm wide and 10 mm thick are joined with a triple riveted butt joint as shown in Fig. 26.18. The rivets at 1-1, 2-2 and 3-3 are of 18 mm, 20 mm and 22 mm diameter, while the two cover plates, each 6 mm thick, are of unequal length.*

Determine the strength of the joint and its efficiency, if the allowable values of stresses are: $\sigma_{at} = 150 \, N/mm^2$, $\sigma_{pf} = 250 \, N/mm^2$ *and* $\tau_{vf} = 80 \, N/mm^2$.

Solution

Formed diameter of 18 mm rivet $= 18 + 1.5 = 19.5$ mm

Formed diameter of 20 mm rivet $= 20 + 1.5 = 21.5$ mm

Formed diameter of 22 mm rivet $= 22 + 1.5 = 23.5$ mm.

1. Rivet value of 18 mm rivet: The rivet is in single shear.

Strength of rivet in single shear $= \tau_{vf} \times \dfrac{\pi}{4} d^2 = 80 \times \dfrac{\pi}{4}(19.5)^2 = 23892$ N

Strength of rivet in bearing on 6 mm plate $= \sigma_{pf} . d . t$

$\quad = 250 \times 19.5 \times 6 = 29250$ N

$\therefore$ Rivet value of 18 mm rivet $= R_1 = 23892$ N

2. *Rivet value of 20 mm rivet*: The rivet is in single shear.

Strength of rivet in single shear

$\quad = \tau_{vf} \times \dfrac{\pi}{4} d^2 = 80 \times \dfrac{\pi}{4} (21.5)^2$

$\quad = 29044$ N

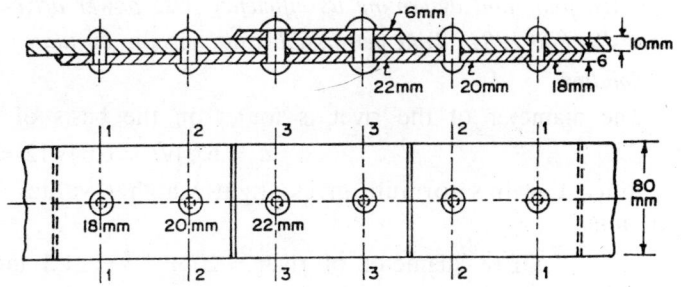

FIG. 26.18.

Strength of rivet in bearing on 6 mm plate $= \sigma_{pf} . d . t$

$$= 250 \times 21.5 \times 6 = 32250 \text{ N}$$

$\therefore$ Rivet value of 20 mm rivet $= R_2 = 29044$ N

3. *Rivet value of 22 mm rivet*: The rivet is in double shear. Also, since the total thickness of cover plates is more than the main plate, the bearing strength of the rivet will be on the basis of 10 mm plate.

$\therefore$ Strength of rivet in double shear $= \tau_{vf} \times 2 \times \dfrac{\pi}{4} d^2$

$$= 80 \times 2 \times \dfrac{\pi}{4} (23.5)^2 \approx 69398 \text{ N}$$

Strength of rivet in bearing on 10 mm plate $= \sigma_{pf} . d . t.$

$$= 250 \times 23.5 \times 10 = 58750 \text{ N}$$

$\therefore$ Rivet value of 22 mm rivet $= R_3 = 58750$ N

(a) strength of joint on the basis of rivet values

$$= R_1 + R_2 + R_3 = 23892 + 29044 + 58750 = 111686 \text{ N} \qquad ...(i)$$

(b) Strength of joint on the basis of failure of main plate at section 1-1

$$= \sigma_{at} (p - d) t = 150(80 - 19.5) \times 10 = 90750 \text{ N} \qquad ...(ii)$$

(c) Strength of joint on the basis of failure of main plate at section 2-2

$$= \text{tearing of main plate at section 2-2} + \text{rivet value of rivet at 1-1}$$
$$= \sigma_{at} (p - d) t + R_1 = 150 (80 - 21.5)10 + 23892 = 111642 \text{ N} \qquad ...(iii)$$

(d) Strength of joint on the basis of failure of main plate at section 3-3.

$$= \text{tearing of main plate at section 3-3} + \text{Rivet value of rivets at 2-2}$$
$$+ \text{rivet value of rivets at 1-1} = \sigma_{at}(p - d)t + R_2 + R_1$$
$$= 150(80 - 23.5)10 + 29044 + 23892 = 137686 \qquad ...(iv)$$

(e) Strength of joint on the basis of failure of cover plates at 3-3

$$= \sigma_{at}(p - d)t = 150(80 - 23.5) (6 + 6) = 101700 \text{ N} \qquad ...(v)$$

$\therefore$ *Strength of joint* = Least of (i), and (ii), (iii), (iv) and (v) = 90750 N

Strength of solid plate $= \sigma_{at} . p . t = 150 \times 80 \times 10 = 120000$ N

$\therefore \qquad \eta$ of joint $= \dfrac{90750}{120000} \times 100 = \mathbf{75.6} \text{ %}$

Example 26.7. *A double cover butt joint is used to connect plates of 12 mm thick. Design the riveted joint and determine its efficiency. Use power driven rivets and take permissible stresses as per IS : 800-1984. Take permissible axial tension in plate = $0.6 f_y$ where $f_y = 250 N/mm^2$.*

Solution

The diameter of the rivet is found on the basis of Unwins formula:
$$d = 6.04\sqrt{t} = 6.04\sqrt{12} = 20.9 \text{ mm}$$

Since Unwin's formula gives slightly higher values, adopt nominal diameter of rivet = 20 mm.

∴   Gross diameter of rivet = 20 + 1.5 = 21.5 mm

The permissible stresses for shop rivets as per IS 800-1984 are as follows :
$$\tau_{vf} = 100 \text{ N/mm}^2; \quad \sigma_{pf} = 300 \text{ N/mm}^2.$$
$$\sigma_{at} = 0.6 f_y = 0.6 \times 250 = 150 \text{ N/mm}^2$$

Let p be the pitch of the rivets.

Strength of rivet in double shear
$$P_s = \tau_{vf} . 2 \frac{\pi}{4} d^2 = 100 \times 2 \times \frac{\pi}{4}(21.5)^2 = 72610 \text{ N}$$

Strength of rivet in bearing on main plate
$$P_b = \sigma_{pf} . d \, t = 300 \times 21.5 \times 12 = 77400 \text{ N}$$

∴   *Rivet value* = 72610 N   ..(*i*)

Strength of plate per pitch length = $\sigma_{at} (p - d)t$
$$= 150(p - 21.5)12 = 1800(p - 21.5) \text{ N} \qquad ...(ii)$$

Equating this to the rivet value, we get
$$1800(p - 21.5) = 72610$$

From which $p = 61.8$ mm

Adopt $p = 60$ mm. Adopt thickness of each cover plates
$$= \frac{5}{8} \times \text{ thickness of main plate}$$
$$= \frac{5}{8} \times 12 = 7.5 \text{ m}$$

Keep thickness = 8 mm

Efficiency of joint = $\dfrac{p - d}{p} \times 100 = \dfrac{60 - 21.5}{60} \times 100 = \mathbf{64.2 \%}$

Example 26.8. *Two plates 12 mm and 10 mm thick are joined by a triple riveted lap joint, in which the pitch of the central row of rivets is half the pitch of rivets in the outer rows. Design the joint and find its efficiency. Take $\sigma_{at} = 150 N/mm^2$, $\tau_{vf} = 80 N/mm^2$ and $\sigma_{pf} = 250 N/mm^2$.*

Solution : Since the Unwin's formula always gives slightly higher value of diameter of the rivet, we will use smaller of the thickness of the two plates.

∴ $d = 6.04\sqrt{t} = 6.04\sqrt{10} = 19.1$ mm.

Use 20 mm rivets.

Gross diameter of rivets = 20 + 1.5 = 21.5 mm.

(i) *Rivet Value*

Strength of rivets in single shear

$$= \tau_{vf} . \frac{\pi}{4} d^2$$

$$= 80 \times \frac{\pi}{4} (21.5)^2 = 29044 \text{ N}$$

Strength of rivets in bearing on 10 mm plate $= \sigma_{pf} . d . t$

$$= 250 \times 21.5 \times 10 = 53750 \text{ N}$$

$\therefore$ Rivet value $R = 29044$ N   ...(i)

(ii) Strength of thinner plate per pitch length, along section 1-1.

$$= \sigma_{at} (p - d)t = 150(p - 21.5)10$$
$$= 1500(p - 21.5)$$
$$= 1500 p - 32250 \quad ...(ii)$$

(iii) Strength of thinner plate per pitch length, along section 2-2

$$= \sigma_{at} (p - 2d)t + R$$
$$= 150(p - 2 \times 21.5)10 + 29044$$
$$= 1500(p - 43) + 29044 \quad ...(iii)$$
$$= 1500 p - 35456$$

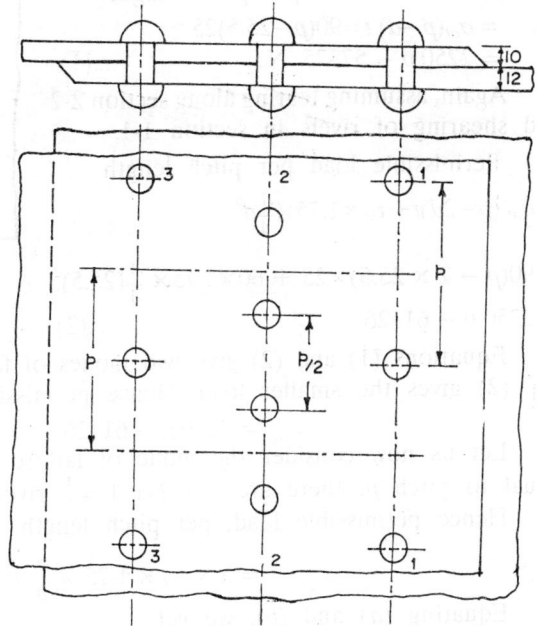

FIG. 26.19.

Hence section 2-2 is weaker, along which the strength of plate is $(1500 p - 35456)$. For maximum joint efficiency, the strength of plate per pitch length should be equal to strength of rivets per pitch length.

$\therefore$ $1500 p - 35456 = 4R = 4 \times 29044$

From which, $p \approx 101$ mm

Minimum permissible pitch $= 2.5 \times 21.5 = 53.8$ mm

Maximum permissible pitch $= 32 t = 32 \times 10 = 320$ mm

Keep pitch equal to 54 mm for the inner row and $2 \times 54 = 108$ mm for the outer rows.

$\therefore$ Strength of joint $= 1500 p - 35456 = 1500 \times 108 - 35456 = 126544$ N

or equal to $4R (= 4 \times 29044 = 116176$ N$)$ whichever is less

$$= 116176.$$

Strength of solid plate $= \sigma_{at} p t = 150 \times 108 \times 10 = 162000$ N

$\therefore$ Efficiency of joint $= \dfrac{116176}{162000} \times 100 = \mathbf{71.7\%}$

Example 26.9. *Plates 25 mm thick are connected by a treble riveted butt joint with two cover straps. The pitch of rivets in the outer row is twice the pitch of those in other rows and the diameter of rivets is 24 mm. Taking the resistance of rivets in double shear equal to 1.75 times their resistance in single shear, determine p for equal tearing and shearing resistance. Also determine the efficiency of the joint. Assume $\sigma_{at} = 90 \, N/mm^2$ and $\tau_{vf} = 60 \, N/mm^2$.*   (U.P.S.C. 1967)

Solution

Formed diameter of rivets $= d = 24 + 1.5 = 25.5$ mm

Consider strip width of joint equal to pitch p.

Let us assume tearing along section 1-1.

Permissible load per pitch length

$$= \sigma_{at}(p-d)\,t = 90(p-25.5)25$$
$$= 2250\,p - 57375 \text{ N} \qquad\qquad ...(1)$$

Again, assuming tearing along section 2-2 and shearing of rivets in section 1-1,

Permissible load per pitch length

$$= \sigma_{at}(p-2d)t + \tau_{vf} \times 1.75 \times \frac{\pi}{4}d^2$$

$$= 90(p - 2 \times 25.5) \times 25 + 60 \times 1.75 \times \frac{\pi}{4}(25.5)^2$$

$$= 2250\,p - 61126 \qquad\qquad ...(2)$$

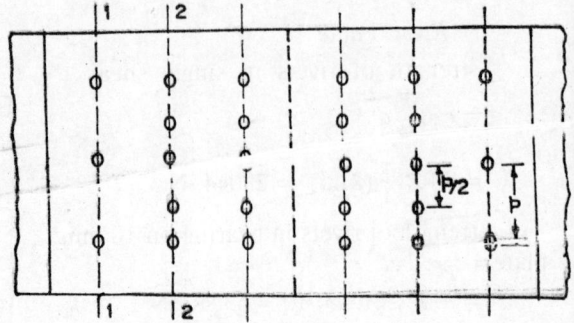

FIG. 26.20.

Equations (1) and (2) give two modes of failure due to tearing of plates, out of which Eq. (2) gives the smaller load. Hence permissible load, per pitch length, in tearing

$$= 2250\,p - 61126 \qquad\qquad\qquad ...(a)$$

Let us now consider the mode of failure due to shearing of rivets. In the strip of joint equal to pitch p, there are $2 + 2 + 1 = 5$ rivets. Each rivet is in double shear.

Hence permissible load, per pitch length,

$$= 5 \times \tau_{vf} \times 1.75 \times \frac{\pi}{4}d^2 = 5 \times 60 \times 1.75 \times \frac{\pi}{4}(25.5)^2 = 268120 \text{ N} \quad ...(b)$$

Equating (a) and (b), we get

$$2250\,p - 61126 = 268120, \quad \text{from which,} \quad p = \textbf{146.3 mm}$$

Permissible load which can be carried by solid plate

$$= \sigma_{at} \cdot p \cdot t = 90 \times 146.3 \times 25 = 329175 \text{ N}$$

$$\therefore \qquad \eta \text{ of the joint} = \frac{268120}{329175} \times 100 = \textbf{81.5\%}$$

Example 26.10. *A butt joint is used to connect two 20 mm thick plates as shown in Fig. 26.21. The diameter of rivets is 18 mm. Determine the efficiency of the joint.*
Take $f_t = 470 \, N/mm^2$, $f_s = 375 \, N/mm^2$ and $f_b = 750 \, N/mm^2$.

Solution

Formed diameter of the rivets $= 18 + 1.5 = 19.5$ mm

Each rivet is in double shear. Strength of each rivet in double shear

$$= P_{us} = 2 \times \frac{\pi}{4}d^2 \times f_s$$

$$= 2 \times \frac{\pi}{4}(19.5)^2 \times 375$$

$$= 223986 \text{ N}$$

Strength of each rivet in bearing $= P_{ub} = f_b \times d \times t$

$$= 750 \times 19.5 \times 20$$

$$= 292500 \text{ N}$$

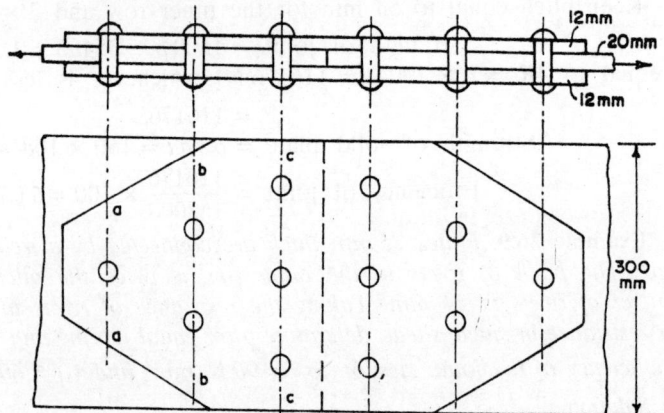

FIG. 26.21

∴ Rivet value $R = 223986$ N

Let us now investigate various modes of failure.

(i) Considering the tearing of main plate at a-a,

$$P_{u1} = (b - d) t.f_t = (300 - 19.5)20 \times 470 = 2.636 \times 10^6 \text{ N} \qquad ...(i)$$

(ii) considering tearing of main plate at b-b and shearing of rivet at a-a,

$$P_{u2} = (b - 2d) t.f_t + P_{us}$$
$$= (300 - 2 \times 19.5)20 \times 470 + 223986 = 2.677 \times 10^6 \text{ N} \qquad ...(ii)$$

(iii) considering tearing of main plate at c-c and shearing of rivets at a and b,

$$P_{u3} = (b - 3d) t f_t + 3P_{us}$$
$$= (300 - 3 \times 19.5)20 \times 470 + 3 \times 223986 = 2.942 \times 10^6 \text{ N} \qquad ...(iii)$$

(iv) Considering failure by shearing of all the rivets,

$$P_{u4} = 6P_{us} = 6 \times 223986 = 1.344 \times 10^6 \text{ N} \qquad ...(iv)$$

(v) Considering failure of bearing surfaces,

$$P_{u5} = 6 P_{ub} = 6 \times 292500 = 1.755 \times 10^6 \text{ N} \qquad ...(v)$$

(vi) Considering tearing of cover plates at c-c,

$$P_{u6} = (b - 3d)2 t'.f_t = (300 - 3 \times 19.5)2 \times 12 \times 470$$
$$= 2.724 \times 10^6 \text{ N} \qquad ...(vi)$$

The most likely mode of failure is (iv) in which the joint fails by shearing of the rivets, the strength of joint being $= 1.344 \times 10^6$ N.

Strength of solid plate $= b.t.f_t = 300 \times 20 \times 470 = 2.82 \times 10^6$ N

∴ η of joint $= \dfrac{1.344 \times 10^6}{2.82 \times 10^6} \times 100 =$ **47.7%**

Example 26.11. *The diagonal of a bridge truss is made of 16 mm thick flat and has to transmit a pull of 600 kN. The diagonal is to be connected to 16 mm thick gusset plate by a double cover butt joint with 20 mm rivets.*

Calculate the number of rivets and width of flat required. Take permissible stresses as follows: $\sigma_{at} = 150 \text{ N/mm}^2$; $\tau_{vf} = 100 \text{ N/mm}^2$ *and* $\sigma_{pf} = 300 \text{ N/mm}^2$. *Sketch the joint and calculate the efficiency of the joint. Also determine (i) the actual stresses induced in the flat and the rivets; and (ii) thickness of cover plates.*

Solution

Formed diameter of rivet $= 20 + 1.5 = 21.5$ mm.

The rivets are in double shear. Strength of rivet in double shear is :

$$P_s = 2 \times 100 \times \frac{\pi}{4} (21.5)^2 = 72610 \text{ N}$$

Strength of rivet in bearing against main plate,

$$P_b = 21.5 \times 16 \times 300 = 103200 \text{ N}$$

∴ Strength of rivet $= R = 72610$ N

∴ Number of rivets required $= \dfrac{600 \times 1000}{72610} = 8.26$

Hence provide 9 rivets to each side, and arrange them in diamond riveting pattern, shown Fig. 26.22.

Let the width of the flat = b. Assuming the section to be weakened by one rivet hole only,

$$P_t = (b - d) t\, \sigma_{at}$$
$$= (b - 21.5)\, 16 \times 150$$

Equating this to external load, we get

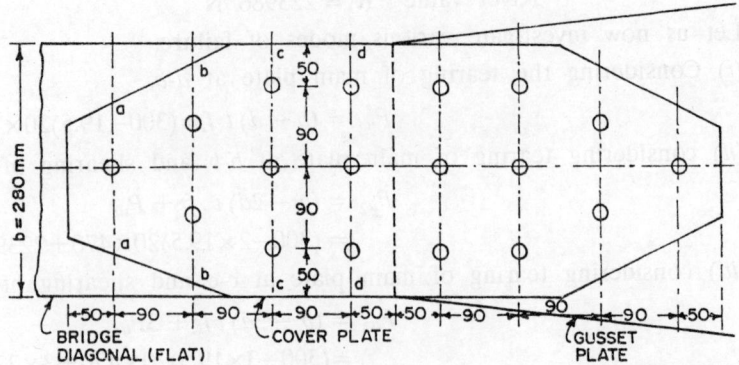

BRIDGE DIAGONAL (FLAT)   COVER PLATE   GUSSET PLATE

FIG. 26.22.

$$(b - 21.5)16 \times 150 = 600 \times 10^3$$

From which, $b = 271.5$ mm

Keep $b = 280$ mm

$$\therefore \qquad \eta = \frac{b - d}{b} = \frac{280 - 21.5}{280} \times 100 = \mathbf{92.3\%}$$

Provide pitch and back pitch = 90 mm. Provide edge distance = 50 mm

Actual stress in rivets

$$f_s = \frac{600 \times 1000}{2 \times \frac{\pi}{4}(21.5)^2 \times 9} = 91.81 \text{ N/mm}^2$$

$$f_b = \frac{600 \times 1000}{21.5 \times 16 \times 9} = 193.8 \text{ N/mm}^2$$

Actual stresses in flat

At section $a - a$, $P = f_1 (b - d) t$

$$\therefore \qquad f_1 = \frac{600000}{(280 - 21.5)\ 16} = 145 \text{ N/mm}^2$$

At section $b - b$, $P = f_2(b - 2d) t + \dfrac{P}{n}$

$$\therefore \qquad 600000 = f_2(280 - 2 \times 21.5) \times 16 + \frac{600000}{9}$$

from which $f_2 = 140.6 \text{ N/mm}^2.$

At section $c-c$, $P = f_3(b - 3d)t + \dfrac{3P}{n}$

$$\therefore \qquad 600000 = f_3\,(280 - 3 \times 21.5)\,16 + \frac{3 \times 600000}{9}$$

$$\therefore \qquad f_3 = 116 \text{ N/mm}^2$$

At section d-d, $P = f_4\,(b - 3d)\, t + \dfrac{6P}{n}$

$$\therefore \qquad 600000 = f_4(280 - 3 \times 21.5)16 + \frac{6 \times 600000}{9}$$

$$\therefore \qquad f_4 = 58 \text{ N/mm}^2$$

Thickness of cover plates

Let the thickness of each cover plate be t'.

$\therefore$ Strength of cover plates at section $d - d$, against tearing

$$= (b - 3d)2t' \, \sigma_{at} = (280 - 3 \times 21.5) \times 2 \, t' \times 150 = 64650 \, t'$$

$\therefore$ Form which
$$64650 \, t' = 600 \times 10^3$$
$$t' = 9.28 \text{ mm} ;$$

Also,
$$t' = \frac{5}{8} t = \frac{5}{8} \times 16 = 10 \text{ mm}$$

Hence keep
$$t' = \textbf{10 mm}.$$

Actual stress in cover plate, at $d - d = \dfrac{600 \times 1000}{(280 - 3 \times 21.5) \times 2 \times 10} = \textbf{139.2 N/mm}^2$

Example 26.12. *A lower chord of truss has a vertical member AB and a diagonal member AC meeting at a point A in it, as shown in Fig. 26.23 along with the axial forces. Design the joint, using hand driven rivets, taking permissible tensile stress in the angles as 0.6 f_y where $f_y = 250 \, N/mm^2$.*

Solution Assume 12 mm thick gusset plate. Minimum thickness of angles = 10 mm. The diameter of the rivet is found on the basis of Unwin's formula:

$$D = 6.04\sqrt{t} = 6.04\sqrt{10} = 19.1 \text{ mm}$$

Use 20 mm rivets. Gross dia. of rivets

$$= 20 + 1.5 = 21.5 \text{ mm}$$

Minimum pitch = $2.5D = 2.5 \times 21.5 = 53.75$ mm.
Provide pitch = 60 mm.

For hand driven rivets, we have

$$\tau_{vf} = 80 \text{ N/mm}^2 ; \ \sigma_{pf} = 250 \text{ N/mm}^2$$
$$\sigma_{at} = 0.6 f_y = 0.6 \times 250 = 150 \text{ N/mm}^2$$

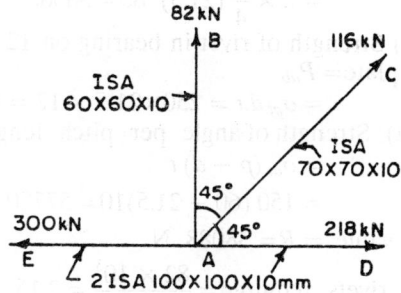

FIG. 26.23.

(a) Member AB

(i) Strength of rivet in single shear $= P_{us} = \dfrac{\pi}{4} d^2 . \tau_{vf}$

$$= \frac{\pi}{4}(21.5)^2 \, 80 = 29044 \text{ N}$$

(ii) Strength of rivets in bearing on 10 mm thick angle

$$= P_{ub} = \sigma_{pf} . d . t = 250 \times 21.5 \times 10 = 53750 \text{ N}$$

(iii) Strength of angle per pitch length $= P_{ut}$

$$= \sigma_{at}(p - d)t = 150(60 - 21.5)10 = 57750 \text{ N}$$

$\therefore$ Rivet value $R = 29044$ N

No. of rivets required $= \dfrac{\text{Force in member } AB}{\text{Rivet Value}} = \dfrac{82 \times 10^3}{29044} = 2.83$

Provide 3 rivets.

(b) Member AC

(i) Strength of rivet in single shear $= P_{us} = \dfrac{\pi}{4} d^2 \tau_{vf}$

$$= \frac{\pi}{4}(21.5)^2 \, 80 = 29044 \text{ N}$$

(*ii*) Strength of rivet in bearing on 10 mm thick angle $= P_{ub}$

$$= \sigma_{pf} d \,.\, t = 250 \times 21.5 \times 10 = 53750 \text{ N}$$

(*iii*) Strength of thinner angle per pitch length

$$= P_{ut} = \sigma_{at}(p - d)t = 150(60 - 21.5)10 = 57750 \text{ N}$$

Rivet value $R = 29044$ N

No. of rivets required $= \dfrac{\text{Force in member } AC}{\text{Rivet Value}} = \dfrac{116 \times 10^3}{29044} = 3.99$

Provide 4 rivets.

(c) Member ED

Net force in member $ED = 300 - 218 = 82$ kN

(*i*) Strength of rivet in double shear $= P_{us}$

$$= 2 \times \frac{\pi}{4} d^2 \tau_{vf}$$

$$= 2 \times \frac{\pi}{4}(21.5)^2 \, 80 = 38088 \text{ N}$$

(*ii*) Strength of rivet in bearing on 12 mm thick gusset plate $= P_{ub}$

$$= \sigma_{pf} d.t = 250 \times 21.5 \times 12 = 64500 \text{ N}$$

(*iii*) Strength of angle per pitch length $= P_{ut}$

$$= \sigma_{at}(p - d)\, t$$

$$= 150(60 - 21.5)10 = 57750 \text{ N}.$$

Rivet value $= R = 38088$ N.

No. of rivets required $= \dfrac{82 \times 10^3}{38088} = 2.15$

Provide 3 rivets.

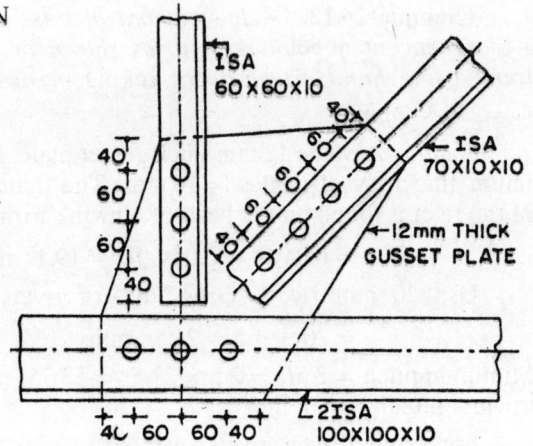

FIG. 26.24.

26.12. RIVETED JOINT SUBJECTED TO MOMENT ACTING IN THE PLANE OF THE JOINT

Sometimes, a riveted joint may be subjected to a load which may not pass through the C.G. of the rivet group. Such a connection is known as *eccentric load connection*. There may be two types of such connections :

1. When the line of action of the load is in the plane of the group of rivets, but is away from the C.G. of rivets (Fig. 26.25 *a*), or when the joint is subjected to a *moment* (Fig. 26.25 *b*) acting in the plane of the joint, and

2. When the line of action of the load does not lie in the plane of the group of rivets (Fig. 26.28).

Fig. 26.25 (*a*) shows a bracket connection in which the load P acts at an eccentricity

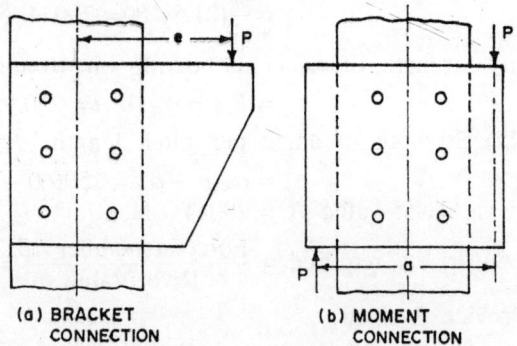

FIG. 26.25. ECCENTRIC LOAD AND MOMENT CONNECTION

e from the C.G. of the rivet group, both being in the same plane. ~~Fig. 26.25~~ (*b*) shows a riveted joint subjected to a pure moment *M* in the plane of the joint.

In the connection of Fig. 26.25 (*a*), the rivets group is subjected to (*i*) a direct load *P* passing through the centroid of the group and (*ii*) a moment *M=P.e*. The two effects are shown separately in Fig. 26.26.

Due to direct load *P*, a shear stress f_1 will be induced in such a way that

$$f_1 = \frac{P}{\Sigma A}$$

where ΣA is the sum of the rivet area. If *A* is the area of cross-section of any particular rivet, the force in the rivet due to direct load is given by

$$F_1 = f_1 . A = \frac{P.A}{\Sigma A} \quad ...(26.15 \ a)$$

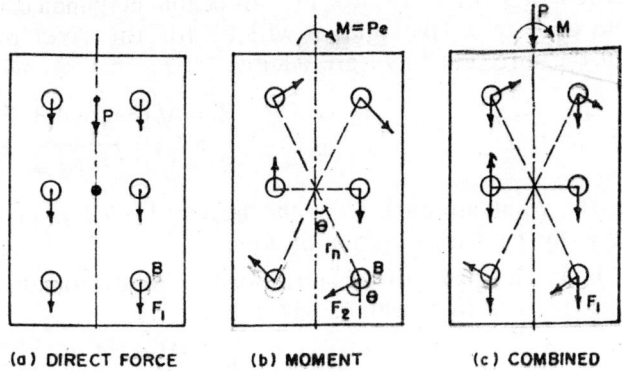

(a) DIRECT FORCE   (b) MOMENT   (c) COMBINED

FIG. 26.26

If all the rivets are of equal area, the above equation reduces to :

$$F_1 = \frac{P.A}{n A} = \frac{P}{n} \qquad ...(26.15)$$

where   *n* = total number of the rivets.

The direction of this force will be vertically downwards, acting through the centre of each rivet, as shown in Fig. 26.26 (*a*).

Due to moment $M(= P.e)$, each rivet will be subjected to torsional shear stress f_2 (Fig. 26.26 *b*). In order to find stress f_2 due to the moment (or couple), it is assumed that (*i*) rivets are perfectly elastic, and (*ii*) the unit stress on each rivet is proportional to its radius vector and acts in a direction perpendicular to the radius vector.

Thus, $f_2 \propto r$ where *r* is the   distance of any rivet from the C.G. of the group.

$$\therefore \qquad\qquad f_2 = k.r \qquad\qquad ...(1)$$

If F_2 is the force in the rivet, we have

$$F_2 = Af_2 = A k r \qquad\qquad ...(2)$$

The moment of resistance of the rivet is$= F_2 . r = A k r^2$

Total moment of resistance of the rivet group$= \Sigma A k r^2 = k \Sigma A r^2$

Equating this to the external moment,

$$k \Sigma A r^2 = P.e$$

or

$$k = \frac{P.e}{\Sigma A . r^2} \qquad\qquad ...(3)$$

Substituting the value of *k* in (1) and (2), we get

$$f_2 = \frac{P.e\,r}{\Sigma A r^2}$$

and

$$F_2 = \frac{P.e.A.r}{\Sigma A.r^2} = \frac{M.A.r}{\Sigma A r^2} \qquad\qquad ...26.16 \ (a)$$

If all the rivets are of equal area,

$$F_2 = \frac{P.e.r}{\Sigma r^2} = \frac{M.r}{\Sigma r^2} \qquad \qquad ...(26.16)$$

In order to find the resultant force R on a rivet, it must be noted that F_1 acts in the direction of P while F_2 acts in a direction perpendicular to the radius vector. The maximum value of R in a rivet group will be for the rivet in which F_1 and the resolved part of F_2 in the direction of F_1 are additive. If F_2 makes angle θ with the direction of F_1, we have

$$R = \sqrt{(F_2 \cos \theta + F_1)^2 + (F_2 \sin \theta)^2}$$

or

$$R = \sqrt{F_1^2 + F_2^2 + 2 F_1 F_2 \cos \theta} \qquad \qquad ...(26.17)$$

The resultant force R in the heavily loaded rivet or any other rivet can also be found graphically by parallelogram of forces.

If, in the place of eccentric load, a pure moment M acts on the rivet group, the load carried by any rivet will be given by

$$R = \frac{M.r.A}{\Sigma A r^2} \text{ in general} \qquad \qquad ...(26.18 \ a)$$

or

$$R = \frac{M.r}{\Sigma r^2} \qquad \qquad ...(26.18)$$

for the particular case when all the rivets have the same area. The direction of R in this case will be perpendicular to the radius vector.

Design of the bracket connection : In the analysis problem, if the number of rivets in a bracket connection (Fig. 26.25 a) are known, then the load P, acting at a given eccentricity, can be easily found by using Eqs. 26.15, 26.16 and 26.17. However, in a design problem, the number of the rivets has to be *assumed*, to start with, for a given load P acting at a given eccentricity, or for a given moment. This can be done as follows, for a connection having large number of rivets.

Let there be l number of rivet lines, with n number of rivets in each line, having pitch p, as shown in Fig. 26.27 (a). Fig. 26.27 (b) shows the stress diagram for one rivet line, wherein the stress in each rivet is proportional to its distance from the neutral axis.

Let f' be the stress in the outermost rivet, and R is the rivet value. We have

$$f' = \frac{R}{p} \qquad \qquad ...(1)$$

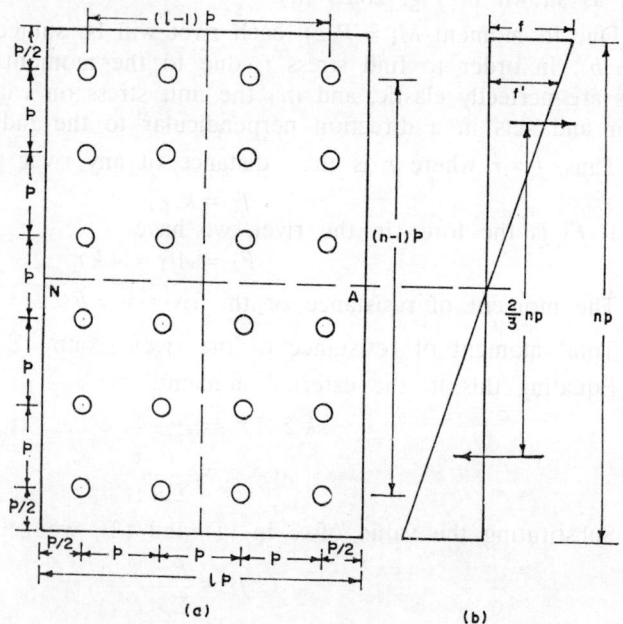

FIG. 26.27.

Hence the maximum stress f of an equivalent rectangular beam is

$$f = f' \cdot \frac{np}{(n-1)p} = \frac{R}{p} \cdot \frac{n}{n-1} \qquad \ldots(2)$$

Let $\qquad\qquad M$ = total moment to be resisted = $P.e$

Moment shared by one rivet line = $\dfrac{M}{l}$

Section modulus = $\dfrac{1}{6}(np)^2$

∴ Fibre stress $\qquad\qquad f = \dfrac{M/l}{\dfrac{1}{6}(np)^2} \qquad\qquad \ldots(3)$

Equating (2) and (3), we get

$$\frac{R}{p} \cdot \frac{n}{n-1} = \frac{M/l}{\dfrac{1}{6}(np)^2}$$

or $\qquad\qquad R = \dfrac{6M.p}{l(np)^2}\left(\dfrac{n-1}{n}\right) \qquad\qquad \ldots(26.19)$

or $\qquad\qquad n = \sqrt{\dfrac{6M}{lpR}\left(\dfrac{n-1}{n}\right)} \qquad\qquad \ldots 26.20~(a)$

If the value of n is large (say more than 6), the factor $\left(\dfrac{n-1}{n}\right)$ can be taken approximately equal to unity. Then

$$n = \sqrt{\frac{6M}{lpR}} \qquad\qquad \ldots(26.20)$$

26.13. RIVETED JOINT SUBJECTED TO MOMENT ACTING PERPENDICULAR TO THE PLANE OF JOINT

Fig. 26.28 (a) shows a bracket connection in which the moment (= eP) is acting in a plane perpendicular to the plane of joint. In such a case, each rivet is subjected to *tension* in addition of *direct shear*. The external load P tries to *rotate* the connection about a *neutral axis*, the location of which depends upon the initial tension, if any, in the rivets.

Case 1 : Initial tension in rivets : If hot driven rivets are used, they will have initial tension when they cool and compress the plates together.

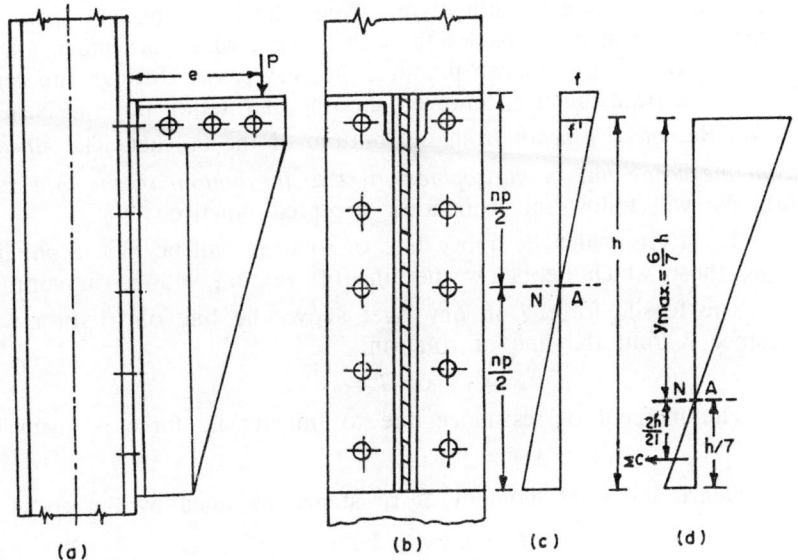

FIG. 26.28.

In that case, the N.A will lie at the mid-height h of the strip, as shown in Fig. 26.28 (c), where $h = np$ for a connection having n number of rivets in each line, provided at a pitch p. Let there be l number of rivets lines.

$$\text{Stress} \quad f = \frac{M}{I} y = \frac{M}{\frac{1}{12}(l \cdot b)(np)^3} \times \frac{np}{2}$$

or

$$f = \frac{6M}{l\, b\, (np)^2} \qquad\qquad\qquad ....(1)$$

Hence effective tensile force T in the extreme rivet is

$$T = f \cdot b \cdot p = \frac{6M \cdot bp}{l \cdot b\, (np)^2}$$

or

$$T = \frac{6M}{l\, p\, n^2} \qquad\qquad ...(2) \qquad\qquad\qquad ...(26.21)$$

The maximum value of T should be equal to rivet value R. Hence from Eq. 26.21, putting $T = R$, we get

$$n = \sqrt{\frac{6M}{l\, p\, R}} \qquad\qquad\qquad\qquad ...(26.22)$$

From the above equation, number of rivets can be computed. Again, calculated tensile stress in the extreme rivet is given by

$$\sigma_{tf,\,cal} = \frac{T}{A} = \frac{6M}{l\, p\, n^2 A} \qquad\qquad\qquad ...(26.23)$$

where A is the effective area of cross section of the extreme rivet. It may be noted that Eq. 26.22 is similar to Eq. 26.20.

Case 2 : No initial tension in rivets: If there is no initial tension in the rivets, as is generally the case in cold driven rivets, the N.A. does not pass through the C.G. of rivet groups. But instead, it passes through a point which lies much *lower* than the C.G of rivet groups. According to British practice, the N.A passes through the centre of bottom most rivet. In the American practice, however, the line of rotation (*i.e.* the N.A.) is assumed at a distance of $\frac{1}{7}$th the *effective depth* from the bottom of the bracket. The *effective depth (h) is the depth from the centre line of the topmost rivet to the bottom of the bracket*, as shown in Fig.. 26.28 (d). We will follow this commonly accepted practice.

The rivets which lie above line of rotation will be in *tension*, in addition to *direct shear*, while those which lie below the line of rotation will be in compression and direct shear.

The tensile force T in any rivet above the line of rotation will be proportional to its distance y from the line of rotation.

$\therefore$

$$T \propto y \quad \text{or} \quad T = ky \qquad\qquad\qquad ...(i)$$

The moment of resistance due to this tensile force is given by

$$\delta M = T \cdot y = k \cdot y^2 \qquad\qquad\qquad ...(ii)$$

Hence the total moment of resistance provided by the rivets in tension is

$$M_t = \Sigma\, k y^2 = k\, \Sigma\, y^2$$

or

$$M_t = \frac{T}{y} \Sigma\, y^2 \qquad\qquad\qquad ...(iii)$$

Hence
$$T = \frac{M_t y}{\Sigma y^2}$$
...(26.24)

Total tensile force $\Sigma T = \dfrac{M_t \Sigma y}{\Sigma y^2}$

For equilibrium, total tensile force must be equal to total compressive force ΣC

∴
$$\Sigma C = \frac{M_t \Sigma y}{\Sigma y^2}$$

This compressive force acts at a distance of $\dfrac{2}{3}\left(\dfrac{h}{7}\right) = \dfrac{2h}{21}$ from the N.A. Hence taking moment about the N.A., we get

External moment = Moment resisted by rivets in tension + moment resisted by rivets and T section in compression

∴
$$M = M_t + \Sigma C \cdot \frac{2h}{21}$$

or
$$M = M_t + \frac{M_t \Sigma y}{\Sigma y^2} \cdot \frac{2h}{21}$$

Hence
$$M_t = \frac{M}{1 + \dfrac{2h}{21} \cdot \dfrac{\Sigma y}{\Sigma y^2}}$$
...(26.25)

Thus, the moment resisted by rivets in tension is known. From this, the tensile force T_{max} in the extreme rivet can be found from Eq. 26.24 :
$$T_{max} = \frac{M_t \cdot y_{max}}{\Sigma y^2}$$
...(26.24 a)

where $y_{max} = \dfrac{6}{7} h$.

Hence the tensile stress in the extreme rivet is given by $\sigma_{tf,cal} = \dfrac{T_{max}}{A} = \dfrac{M_t \cdot y_{max}}{A \Sigma y^2}$ ...(26.26)

Direct shear stress

In both the cases, the direct S.F. in any rivet is given by $F = \dfrac{P}{n}$

Hence direct shear stress in extreme rivet is
$$\tau_{vf,cal} = \frac{F}{A} = \frac{P}{nA}$$
...(26.27)

Interaction Equation

Thus the extreme rivet, in both the cases, is subjected to axial tensile stress $\sigma_{tf,cal}$ and direct shear stress $\tau_{vf,cal}$. Tests have shown that the *strength* of bearing type fasteners subjected to both shear and tension can be approximated by an equation in the form of ellipse. The general form of *interaction equation* can be written as
$$\left(\frac{\sigma_{tf,cal}}{\sigma_{tf}}\right)^2 + \left(\frac{\tau_{vf,cal}}{\tau_{vf}}\right)^2 = 1$$
...(26.28)

According to IS : 800-1984, the rivets subjected to shear and externally applied tensile force should be so proportioned that
$$\left(\frac{\sigma_{tf,cal}}{\sigma_{tf}} + \frac{\tau_{vf,cal}}{\tau_{vf}}\right) \leq 1.4$$
...(26.29)

Design of bracket connection

If the rivets have initial tension, as in the case of hot driven rivets, the number of rivets can be found using Eq. 26.22. If, however, the rivets do not have initial tension, slightly less number of rivets will be required; in such a case, n may be found by modifying Eq. 26.22 as under

$$n = 0.8 \sqrt{\frac{6M}{lpR}} \qquad \qquad ...(26.30)$$

Example 26.13. *A load of 100 kN is carried by a bracket riveted to the flange plate of a stanchion, as shown in Fig. 26.29. Each rivet is of 24 m^r diameter. Calculate the maximum shear stress in any rivet.*

Solution

Formed diameter of rivets

$$= 24 + 1.5 = 25.5 \text{ mm}$$

$$M = P.e = 100 \times 10^3 \times 200 = 20 \times 10^6 \text{ N-mm}$$

Since the area of section of all the rivets is the same,

$$F_1 = \frac{P}{n} = \frac{100000}{8} = 12500 \text{ N}$$

$$\Sigma r^2 = 4(40^2 + 120^2) + 4(40^2 + 40^2)$$

$$= 76800 \text{ mm}^2$$

Rivet B will be the most heavily loaded rivet, for which

$$r = \sqrt{40^2 + 120^2} = 126.5 \text{ mm}$$

$$\therefore \qquad F_2 = \frac{M.r}{\Sigma r^2} = \frac{20 \times 10^6 \times 126.5}{76800} = 32940 \text{ N}$$

$$\cos \alpha = \frac{120}{126.5} = 0.9486 \, ; \quad \sin \alpha = \frac{40}{126.5} = 0.3162$$

$$F_2 \sin \alpha = 32940 \times 0.3162 = 10416 \text{ N} \; ; \qquad F_2 \cos \alpha = 32940 \times 0.9486 = 31248 \text{ N}$$

$$R = \sqrt{(F_1 + F_2 \sin \alpha)^2 + (F_2 \cos \alpha)^2} = \sqrt{(12500 + 10416)^2 + (31248)^2} = 38750 \text{ N}$$

If the rivets are in single shear,

$$f_s = \frac{38750}{\frac{\pi}{4}(25.5)^2} = \textbf{75.9 N/mm}^2$$

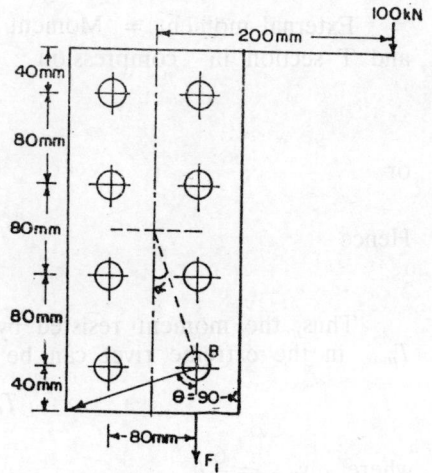

FIG. 26.29.

Example 26.14. *Calculate the shearing stress in the rivets B and C for the connection shown in Fig. 26.30. Rivets A and B have 14 mm diameter while rivet C has a diameter of 22 mm.*

Solution

$$\text{Formed diameter of rivets } A \text{ and } B = 14 + 1.5 = 15.5 \text{ mm}$$

$$\text{Area of cross-section of rivets } A \text{ and } B = \frac{\pi}{4}(15.5)^2 = 188.7 \text{ mm}^2$$

$$\text{Formed diameter of rivet } C = 22 + 1.5 = 23.5 \text{ mm}$$

$$\text{Area of cross-section of rivet } C = \frac{\pi}{4}(23.5)^2 = 433.7 \text{ mm}^2$$

To find the position of C.G. of rivet group, take moments of rivet areas about vertical line passing through C.

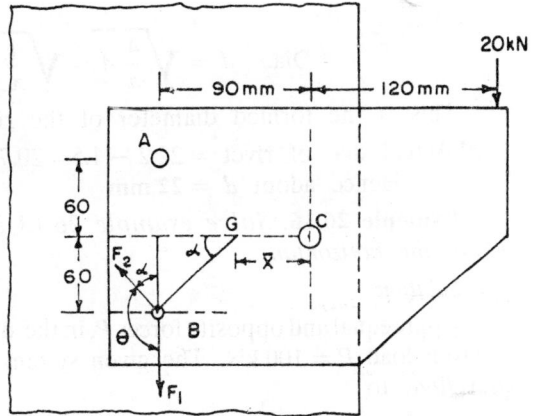

FIG. 26.30.

Thus $\bar{x} = \dfrac{2 \times 188.7 \times 90}{(2 \times 188.7) + 433.7} = 41.9$ mm

$$\Sigma A = (2 \times 188.7) + 433.7 = 811.1 \text{ mm}^2$$

$$M = P.e. = 20000(120 + 41.9)$$
$$= 3238000 \text{ N-mm}$$

In the rivet B,

$$F_{B1} = \frac{PA}{\Sigma A} = \frac{20000 \times 188.7}{811.1} = 4653 \text{ N}$$

Similarly, in the rivet C

$$F_{C1} = \frac{PA}{\Sigma A} = \frac{20000 \times 433.7}{811.1} = 10690 \text{ N}$$

$$\Sigma A r^2 = 2 \times 188.7 (48.1^2 + 60^2) + 433.7 (41.9)^2 = 2993200$$

$$F_{B2} = \frac{M.r.A}{\Sigma A r^2} = \frac{3238000 \times 188.7\sqrt{(48.1)^2 + 60^2}}{2993200} = 15700 \text{ N}$$

and

$$F_{C2} = \frac{M.rA}{\Sigma A r^2} = \frac{3238000 \times 41.9 \times 433.7}{2993200} = 19660 \text{ N}$$

$$R_C = 10690 + 19660 = 30350 \text{ N}$$

$$\alpha = \tan^{-1}\frac{60}{90 - 41.9} = 51.28°,$$

$\therefore$ $$\theta = 180° - 51.28° = 128.72°$$

$$R_B = \sqrt{F_{B1}^2 + F_{B2}^2 + 2 F_{B1}.F_{B2} \cos\theta}$$

$$R_B = \sqrt{(4653)^2 + (15700)^2 + 2 \times 4653 \times 15700 \cos 128.72°} = 13295 \text{ N}$$

$$f_B = \frac{R_B}{188.7} = \frac{13295}{188.7} = 70.45 \text{ N/mm}^2$$

$$f_C = \frac{R_C}{433.7} = \frac{30350}{433.7} = \textbf{69.98 N/mm}^2$$

Example 26.15. *A load of 100 kN is carried by a bracket riveted to the flange plate of a stanchion, as shown in Fig. 26.29. Using 8 rivets, calculate the diameter of the rivets. Each rivet is in single shear. Take $\tau_{vf} = 100 \text{ N/mm}^2$.*

Solution. (Fig. 26.29, Example 26.13). As found in Example 26.13,

$$M = 20 \times 10^6 \text{ ; } F_1 = 12500 \text{ N}$$
$$F_2 = 32940 \text{ N ; } R = 38750 \text{ N}$$

$$\text{Shear stress} = \frac{38750}{A}$$

But this should be equal to permissible shear stress (τ_{vf}).

$\therefore$ $$\frac{38750}{A} = \tau_{vf} = 100.$$

From which $$A = \frac{38750}{100} = 387.50 \text{ mm}^2$$

$\therefore$ Dia. $d = \sqrt{\dfrac{4}{\pi} A} = \sqrt{\dfrac{4}{\pi} \times 387.50} = 22.2$ mm

This is the formed diameter of the rivet.

Actual dia. of rivet $= 22.2 - 1.5 = 20.7$

     Hence adopt $d = \mathbf{22\ mm}$

Example 26.16. *Solve example 26.13 if the load of 100 kN acts at an inclination of 60° to the horizontal.*

Solution

Apply equal and opposite forces P, in the direction of given load $P = 100$ kN. The given system is thus equivalent to

(*i*) A direct load P acting through the C.G. of the rivet group and in the direction of applied load, and

(*ii*) A moment $M = P.e$

F_1 due to direct load $= \dfrac{P}{n} = \dfrac{100000}{8} = 12500$ N, in the direction of P.

F_2 due to moment $= \dfrac{M.r}{\Sigma r^2}$

From Fig. 26.31, $CE = 200 \tan 60° = 346.4$ mm

     $GE = 364.4 - (40 + 80 + 40) = 186.4$ mm

Draw GA perpendicular to DE.

     $GA = e = GE \cos 60° = 186.4 \times \tfrac{1}{2} = 93.2$ mm

     $M = P.e = 100000 \times 93.2 = 93.2 \times 10^5$ N-mm

$\Sigma r^2 = 76800$ mm^2 as found in Example 26.13 and $r = 126.5$ mm

$\therefore$ $F_2 = \dfrac{M.r}{\Sigma r^2} = \dfrac{93.2 \times 10^5 \times 126.5}{76800} = 15350$ N

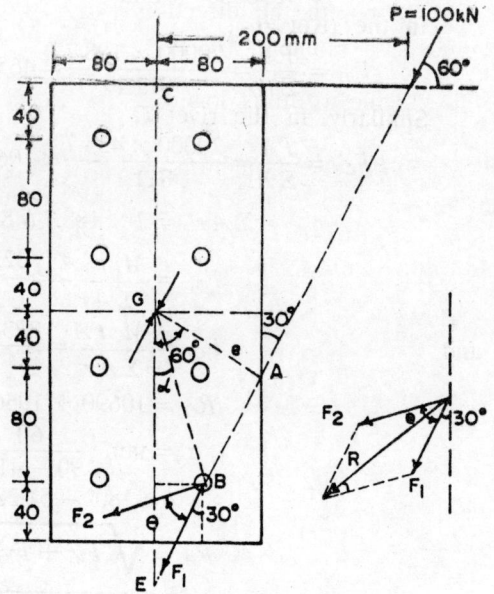

FIG. 26.31.

The maximum F_2 will occur in rivet marked B. The resultant load $R = 26000$ N (found graphically)

       Alternatively, $\alpha = \sin^{-1} \dfrac{40}{126.5} = 18.43°$

$\therefore$ Inclination of F_2 with vertical $= 90° - \alpha = 90° - 18.43° = 71.57°$

    Inclination of F_1 with vertical $= 90° - 60° = 30°$

$\therefore$ Angle θ between F_1 and $F_2 = 71.57° - 30° = 41.57°$

$\therefore$

$$R = \sqrt{F_1^2 + F_2^2 + 2F_1F_2 \cos \theta}$$

$$= \sqrt{(12500)^2 + (15350)^2 + 2(12500 \times 15350) \times \cos 41.57°}$$

$$= 26057 \text{ N}$$

$\therefore$ Maximum shear stress intensity $= \dfrac{26057}{\dfrac{\pi}{4}(25.5)^2} = \mathbf{51.02\ N/mm^2}$

Example 26.17. *A load P kN is to be carried by a bracket riveted to the flange plate of a stanchion as shown in Fig. 26.32. Each rivet is of 22 mm dia. Calculate the maximum value of P which can be allowed so that the maximum stress in any rivet does not exceed the one as prescribed by IS : 800-1984. Use power driven rivets.*

Solution

Apply equal and opposite forces at c.g. of the rivet group, in the direction of the load P. The given system is equivalent to

(*i*) a direct load P acting through the c.g. of the rivet group, in the direction of applied load and

(*ii*) a moment $M = P.e.$

F_1 due to direct load $= \dfrac{P}{n} = \dfrac{P}{6}$ in the direction of P.

F_2 due to moment $= \dfrac{M r}{\Sigma r^2} = \dfrac{P.e.\, r}{\Sigma r^2}$

$AC = 125 + 150 = 275$ mm;

$AO = 150 + 55 = 205$

$\therefore \quad OC = \sqrt{AC^2 + AO^2} = \sqrt{(275)^2 + (205)^2} = 343$ mm

$\beta = \tan^{-1}\dfrac{AO}{AC} = \tan^{-1}\dfrac{205}{275} = 36.7°$

$\alpha = 60° - \beta = 60° - 36.7° = 23.3°$

$e = OC \sin \alpha = 343 \sin 23.3° = 135.66$ mm

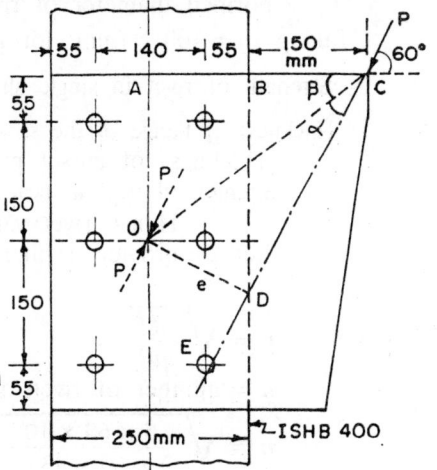

FIG 26.32.

From Fig. 26.33, it is clear by inspection that rivet E is the most heavily loaded.

r of rivet $E = OE = \sqrt{150^2 + 70^2} = 165.53$ mm

$\Sigma r^2 = 4\,(165.53)^2 + 2(70)^2 = 119400$ mm^2

$\therefore \quad F_{E2} = \dfrac{P.e.\, r}{\Sigma r^2} = \dfrac{P \times 135.66 \times 165.53}{119400} = 0.1881P$

$F_{E1} = \dfrac{P}{6} = 0.1667P$

Now $\qquad \gamma = \tan^{-1}\dfrac{70}{150} = 25.02°$

$\therefore \qquad \theta = 60° - \gamma = 60° - 25.02° = 34.98°$

$\therefore \quad R_E = \sqrt{F_1^2 + F_2^2 + 2F_1 F_2 \cos\theta}$

$= \sqrt{(0.1667P)^2 + (0.1881P)^2 + 2 \times 0.1667P \times 0.1881P \times \cos 34.98°}$

$\therefore \qquad R_E = 0.3385P$ kN (where P is in kN)

Max. shear stress in rivet $E = \dfrac{R}{A} = \dfrac{0.3385P \times 1000}{\dfrac{\pi}{4}(23.5)^2}$

$= 0.7804P$ N/mm^2

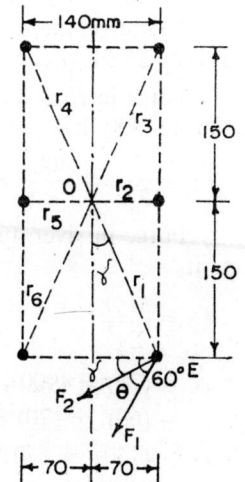

FIG. 26.33

Equating this to permissible stress $\tau_{vf} = 100$ N/mm^2, we get

$P = \dfrac{100}{0.7804} = \mathbf{128.13\ kN}$

Example 26.18. *A double plate bracket is provided using 12 mm thick plates connected to flanges of a steel column having flange thickness of 12.7 mm and transmit a load of 600 kN at an eccentricity of 200 mm. Design the bracket using 22 mm dia. power driven rivets.*

Solution

$$\text{Axial load on one plate} = \frac{1}{2} \times 600 = 300 \text{ kN.}$$

Formed diameter of rivet $= 22 + 1.5 = 23.5$ mm

Taking $\tau_{vf} = 100$ N/mm² for power driven rivets,

Strength of rivet in single shear $= \frac{\pi}{4}(23.5)^2 \times 100 = 43374\,\text{N} = 43.374$ kN   ...(*i*)

Thickness of flange of the section $= 12.7$ mm

Thickness of gusset plate $= 12$ mm. $\therefore\ t = 12$ mm

Strength of rivet in bearings $= d \cdot t \cdot \sigma_{pf} = 23.5 \times 12 \times 300 = 84600$ N   ..(*ii*)

Hence rivet value $= 43.374$ kN

Let us provide a pitch $p = 60$ mm

$$M = P.e = 300 \times 10^3 \times 200 = 60 \times 10^6 \text{ N-mm}$$

Now $n = \sqrt{\dfrac{6M}{lpR}}$.   Here l = number of rivet lines $= 2$ (say)

n = number of rivets in each line.

$\therefore\qquad n = \sqrt{\dfrac{6 \times 60 \times 10^6}{2 \times 60 \times 43374}} = 8.3$

Hence provide $n = 9$.

Total rivets

$= 2n = 2 \times 9 = 18$.

Arrange these as shown in Fig. 26.34 (*a*).

Force in rivet due to axial load of 300 kN:

$$F_1 = \frac{P}{2n} = \frac{300}{2 \times 9} = 16.67 \text{ kN}$$

Force in rivet due to moment:

$$F_2 = \frac{M \cdot r}{\Sigma r^2}$$

$r_1^2 = (70)^2 = 4900$

$r_2^2 = (60)^2 + (70)^2 = 8500$

$r_3^2 = (120)^2 + (70)^2 = 19300$

$r_4^2 = (180)^2 + (70)^2 = 37300$

$r_5^2 = (240)^2 + (70)^2 = 62500$

$\Sigma r^2 = 2r_1^2 + 4(r_2^2 + r_3^2 + r_4^2 + r_5^2)$

$= 520200$.

Also for rivet E,

$r = r_5 = \sqrt{62500} = 250$ mm

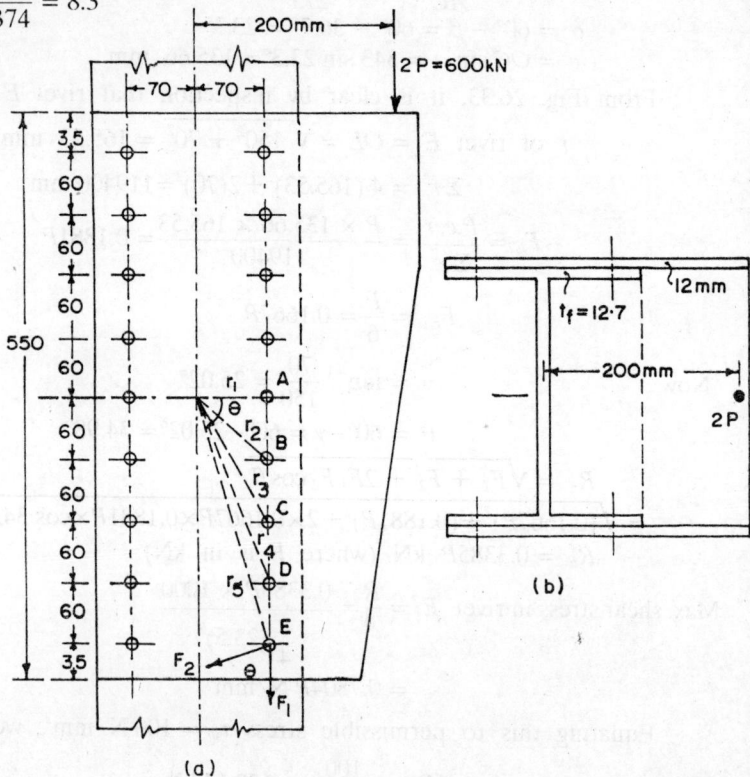

FIG. 26.34.

$$\therefore \qquad F_{2E} = \frac{M.r}{\Sigma r^2} = \frac{60 \times 10^6 \times 250}{520200} = 28835 \text{ N} = 28.835 \text{ kN}$$

Angle $\theta = \tan^{-1} \dfrac{240}{70} = 73.74°; \cos \theta = 0.28$

$$\therefore \qquad R = \sqrt{F_1^2 + F_2^2 + 2F_1 F_2 \cos \theta}$$

$$= \sqrt{(16.67)^2 + (28.835)^2 + 2 \times 16.67 \times 28.835 \times 0.28} = 37.13 \text{ kN}$$

This is less than the rivet value of 43.374 kN. Hence the design is safe.

Example 26.19. *A gantry girder is attached to a steel stanchion, through a bracket connection, as shown in Fig. 26.35. Determine the maximum allowable load, if all the rivets are 16 mm dia and are power driven.*

Solution : For power driven rivets, $\tau_{vf} = 100 \text{ N/mm}^2$.

Formed dia. of rivet = $16 + 1.5 = 17.5$ mm

Strength of rivets in single shear

$$= \frac{\pi}{4}(17.5)^2 \times 100 = 24053 \text{ N}$$

Strength of rivets in double shear
$= 48106$ N

(a) Connection of girder to angles : Rivets A

These rivets connect the web of the girder to two angles, one angle to each side. The rivets are in single shear. There are in all $3 \times 2 = 6$ rivets.

$\therefore \qquad$ Permissible $P = 6 \times 24053$
$$= 144318 \text{ N} \qquad ...(1)$$

(b) Connection of angles to bracket : rivets B

These rivets connect the two angles to the bracket plate. There are 3 rivets and each rivet is in double shear. However, the load P acts at an eccentricity of 40 mm. Hence the maximum force in the outermost rivet of rivet line B

is $$= \sqrt{\left(\frac{P}{3}\right)^2 + \left(\frac{P \times 40 \times 60}{2(60)^2}\right)^2} = 0.4714 P$$

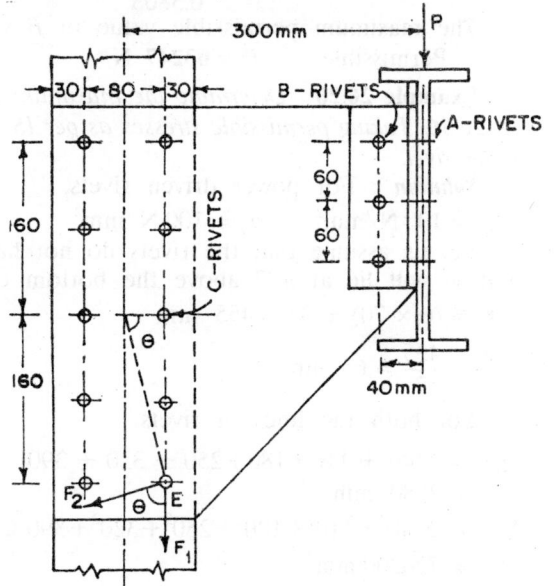

FIG. 26.35.

Equating this to the strength of rivet in double shear, we get

$$0.4714 P = 48106$$

or $$P = 102048 \text{ N} \qquad ...(ii)$$

(c) Connection of bracket to stanchion: Rivets C

The load acts at an eccentricy $e = 300$ mm.

$$M = P.e = 300 P \text{ N-mm.}$$

The maximum force will be induced in the outermost rivet E for which

$$\theta = \tan^{-1} \frac{160}{40} = 75.96° \; ; \; \cos \theta = 0.2426$$

and $$r = \sqrt{(40)^2 + (160)^2} = 164.9 \text{ mm}$$

$$\Sigma r^2 = 4(164.9)^2 + 4[(80)^2 + (40)^2] + 2[(40)^2] = 144000 \text{ mm}^2$$

Now $$F_{E1} = \frac{P}{10} = 0.1 P$$

$$F_{E2} = \frac{P.e.r}{\sum r^2} = \frac{P \times 300 \times 164.9}{144000} = 0.3435\,P$$

Resultant
$$R = \sqrt{F_{E_1}^2 + F_{E_2}^2 + 2\,F_{E_1}.F_{E_2}\cos\theta}$$
$$= \sqrt{(0.1\,P)^2 + (0.3435\,P)^2 + 2\,(0.1\,P)\,(0.3435\,P)\,(0.2426)}$$
$$= 0.3803\,P.$$

The rivet is in single shear.

$\therefore$ $\qquad\qquad 0.3803P = 24053$

or $\qquad\qquad P = \dfrac{24053}{0.3803} = 63247$ N $\qquad\qquad$ ...(iii)

The maximum permissible value of P will be the least of (i), (ii) and (iii).

$\therefore$ $\qquad$ Permissible $\quad P = \mathbf{63247}$ **N**

Example 26.20. *Determine the maximum axial tension in the rivets of the connection shown Fig. 26.36. Taking permissible stresses as per IS : 800 for power driven rivets, determine the diameter of the rivet.*

Solution : For power driven rivets,

$\tau_{vf} = 100\,\text{N/mm}^2$; $\sigma_{tf} = 100\,\text{N/mm}^2$

Let us assume that the rivets do not have initial tension, and that the N.A. or line of rotation will lie at $h/7$ above the bottom edge of bracket.

$h = (6 \times 70) + 35 = 455$ mm

$\therefore \dfrac{h}{7} = \dfrac{455}{7} = 65$ mm

For both the lines of rivets,

$\sum y = 2\,[40 + 110 + 180 + 250 + 320 + 390]$
$\qquad = 2580$ mm

$\sum y^2 = 2\,\left[40^2 + 110^2 + 180^2 + 250^2 + 320^2 + 390^2\right]$
$\qquad = 726200$ mm^2

Moment resisted by rivets which are subjected to tension is

$$M_t = \frac{M}{1 + \dfrac{2h}{21}.\dfrac{\sum y}{\sum y^2}} \qquad\qquad ...(26.25)$$

$$= \frac{150 \times 10^3 \times 200}{1 + \dfrac{2 \times 455}{21} \times \dfrac{2580}{726200}}$$

$$\approx 26 \times 10^6 \text{ N-mm}$$

The maximum tensile force in the top most rivet is

$$T_{max} = \frac{M_t.y_{max}}{\sum y^2} = \frac{26 \times 10^6 \times 390}{726200}$$

$$= \mathbf{13962}\ \textbf{N} \qquad\qquad ...(1)$$

Direct shear stress

$$F_s = \frac{P}{2n} = \frac{150 \times 10^3}{2 \times 7} = 10714 \text{ N} \qquad ...(2)$$

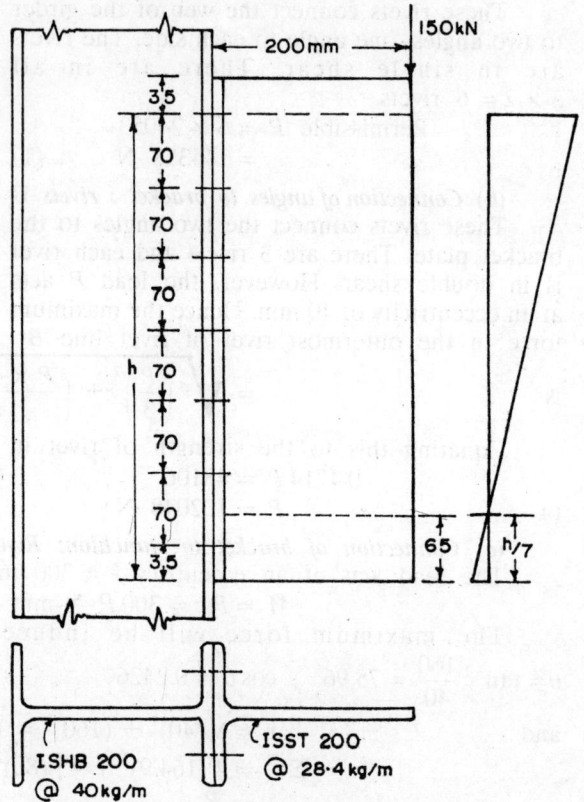

FIG. 26.36.

Let d be the formed diameter of rivet. Hence for the topmost rivets,

$$\sigma_{tf,cal} = \frac{T_{max}}{A} = \frac{13962}{\frac{\pi}{4}d^2} = \frac{17777}{d^2} \qquad \ldots(a)$$

and

$$\tau_{vf,cal} = \frac{F_s}{A} = \frac{10714}{\frac{\pi}{4}d^2} = \frac{13641}{d^2} \qquad \ldots(b)$$

The rivets are subjected to both shear as well as axial tension. Hence the following relationship should be satisfied.

$$\frac{\tau_{vf,cal}}{\tau_{vf}} + \frac{\sigma_{tf,cal}}{\sigma_{tf}} \le 1.4$$

or

$$\frac{13641/d^2}{100} + \frac{17777/d^2}{100} = 1.4$$

from which $d^2 = 224.4$ or $d = 15$ mm

Hence actual dia. of rivet = $15 - 1.5 = 13.5$ mm. $\therefore$ Provide 14 mm dia. rivets.

Example 26.21. *Design a riveted connection joining the bracket angles 2-ISA 100 × 100 × 8 mm using (a) power driven (hot) shop rivets, (b) power driven (cold) shop rivets, as shown in Fig. 26.37.*

Solution

(a) Power driven (hot) shop rivets.

Due to hot rivets, there will be *initial tension* in the rivets, due to which N.A. will lie at the mid-height of the bracket.

Let us use two rows of 20 mm diameter rivets at pitch of 60 mm. The number of rivets per line is given by Eq. 26.22

$$n = \sqrt{\frac{6M}{lpR}}$$

where $M = 200 \times 250 \times 10^3 = 50 \times 10^6$ N-mm

$l = 2$

$p = 60$ mm

$R = \frac{\pi}{4}(21.5)^2 \times 100 = 36305$ N.

$\therefore \quad n = \sqrt{\frac{6 \times 50 \times 10^6}{2 \times 60 \times 36305}} = 8.3$

Provide 9 rivets in each row. Area of each rivet $= \frac{\pi}{4}(21.5)^2 = 363.1$ mm^2.

The calculated tensile stress in extreme rivet is given by Eq. 26.23 :

$$\sigma_{tf,cal} = \frac{6M}{lpn^2A} = \frac{6 \times 50 \times 10^6}{2 \times 60\,(9)^2 \times 363.1} = 85 \text{ N/mm}^2$$

Direct shear load in each rivet

$$= F = \frac{P}{2n} = \frac{200 \times 10^3}{2 \times 9} = 11111.1 \text{N. Hence,}$$

$$\tau_{vf,cal} = \frac{11111.1}{363.1} = 30.6 \text{ N/mm}^2$$

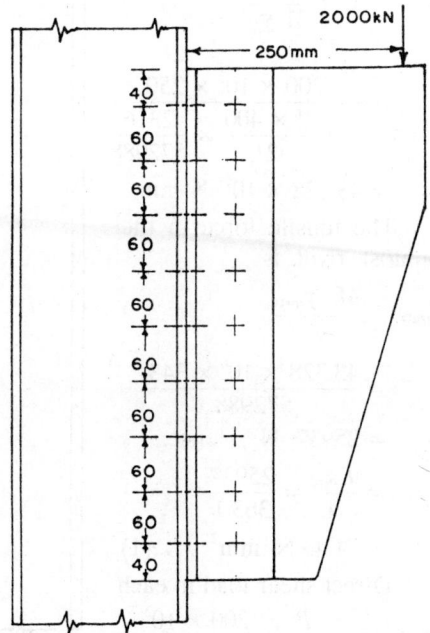

FIG. 26.37.

Now as per Code requirements,

$$\frac{\tau_{vf,cal}}{\tau_{vf}} + \frac{\sigma_{tf,cal}}{\sigma_{tf}} \leq 1.4$$

$\therefore$ $$\frac{30.6}{100} + \frac{85}{100} \leq 1.4$$

or $$1.156 \leq 1.4. \qquad \text{Hence the design is satisfactory.}$$

(b) Power driven (cold) shop rivets

For these rivets, there will be no initial tension. The number of rivets for such a case is given by Eq. 26.30

$$n = 0.8\sqrt{\frac{6M}{lpR}}$$

Providing l = number of rows = 2, $p = 60$ mm and $R = 36305$ N as before, we get

$$n = 0.8\sqrt{\frac{6 \times 50 \times 10^6}{2 \times 60 \times 36305}} = 6.64$$

Hence provide 7 rivets, and arrange these as shown in Fig. 26.38. Keep the edge distance = 40 mm.   Height $h = (60 \times 6) + 40 = 400$ mm

The N.A. will lie at $\frac{h}{7}$ $(= \frac{400}{7} \approx 57 \text{ mm})$ above the bottom edge of the bracket.

For both the lines of rivets,

$$\Sigma y = 2\,[43 + 103 + 163 + 223 + 283 + 343] = 2316 \text{ mm}$$
$$\Sigma y^2 = 2\,[43^2 + 103^2 + 163^2 + 223^2 + 283^2 + 343^2] = 572988$$

$$M_t = \frac{M}{1 + \dfrac{2h}{21}\dfrac{\Sigma y}{\Sigma y^2}}$$

$$= \frac{200 \times 10^3 \times 250}{1 + \dfrac{2 \times 400}{21} \times \dfrac{2316}{572988}}$$

$$= 43.328 \times 10^6 \text{ N-mm}$$

The tensile force in the topmost rivet is

$$T_{max} = \frac{M_t \cdot y_{max}}{y^2}$$

$$= \frac{43.328 \times 10^6 \times 343}{572988}$$

$$= 25937 \text{ N. Hence,}$$

$$\sigma_{tf,cal} = \frac{T_{max}}{A} = \frac{25937}{363.1}$$

$$= 71.43 \text{ N/mm}^2 \qquad ...(1)$$

Direct shear load in each

rivet $= F = \dfrac{P}{2n} = \dfrac{200 \times 10^3}{2 \times 7}$

$$= 14286 \text{ N}$$

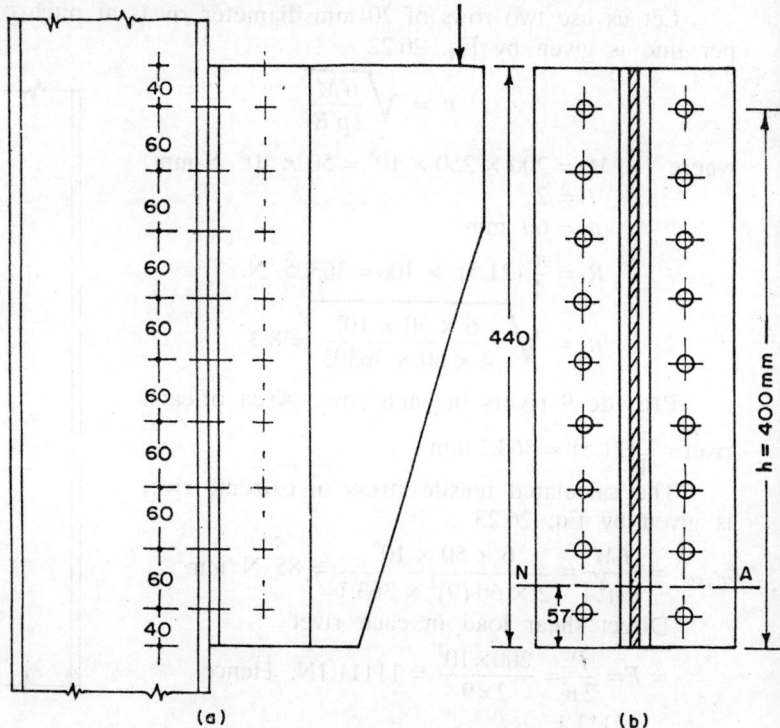

FIG. 26.38.

$$\therefore \qquad \tau_{vf, cal} = \frac{F}{A} = \frac{14286}{363.1} = 39.34 \text{ N/mm}^2 \qquad\qquad ...(2)$$

As per code requirements,

$$\frac{\tau_{vf, cal}}{\tau_{vf}} + \frac{\sigma_{tf, cal}}{\sigma_{tf}} \le 1.4$$

or

$$\frac{39.34}{100} + \frac{71.43}{100} \le 1.4$$

or

$$1.11 \le 1.4. \qquad \text{Hence the design is satisfactory.}$$

PROBLEMS

1. A double riveted lap joint in plates 10 mm thick is made with 16 mm rivets at 60 mm pitch. Estimate how the joint will fail and calculate its efficiency if the tearing strength of the plates is 475 N/mm^2 and shearing and bearing strength of the rivets are 380 N/mm^2 and 750 N/mm^2 respectively. **Ans.** [The joint will fail in shear at a pull of 182700 N; $\eta = 59.2\%$]

2. A double riveted double cover butt joint is used to connect plates 12 mm thick. Determine the diameter of the rivet, rivet value, pitch and efficiency of the joint. Adopt the following working stresses : $\tau_{vf} = 102.5$ N/mm^2 ; $\sigma_{pf} = 236$ N/mm^2 and $\sigma_{at} = 150$ N/mm^2. **Ans.** [22 mm; 66600 N ; 95 mm ; 75.2 %]

3. A bridge truss diagonal carries an axial pull of 500 kN. It is to be connected to a gusset plate 20 mm thick by a double cover butt joint with 22 mm rivets. If the width of the flat tie bar is 250 mm, determine the thickness of the flat. Design an economical joint and determine the efficiency of the joint. Use power driven rivets and take permissible stresses as per IS Code. The permissible stress in plate for axial tension may be taken as $0.6 f_y$ where $f_y = 250$ N/mm^2.

4. A double riveted butt joint, in which the pitch of rivet in the outer rows is twice that in the inner rows, connects two 16 mm thick plates with two cover plates each 12 mm thick. The diameter of rivets is 22 mm. Determine the pitches of the rivets in the two rows if the working stresses are not to exceed the following limits :
Tensile stress in plates : 100 N/mm^2 ; Shear stress in rivets : 75 N/mm^2
Bearing stress in rivets and plates: 150 N/mm^2 ; Make a fully dimensioned sketch of the joint. (Based on U.P.S.C. 1954) **Ans.** [128 mm; 64 mm]

5. A tie bar is attached to a gusset plate by four rivets arranged at the corners as shown in Fig. 26.39, the pitch of the rivets being p. The pull is applied symmetrically. If the rivet D is now removed, the pull being maintained at its former value, calculate by what percentage the load on each of the rivets is increased ? **Ans.** [$A : 17.6$ % ; $B : 21.2\%$; $C : 67.5$ %]

6. Explain the assumptions usually made in estimating the load carried by each rivet in a riveted joint which is subjected to both shear and bending in the plane of the joint. In the arrangement shown in Fig. 26.40, five rivets are sym-

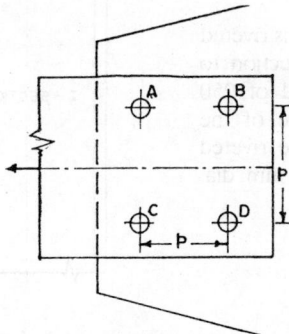

FIG. 26.39.

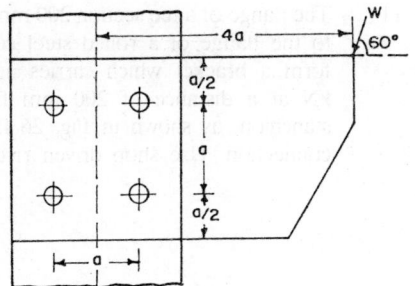

FIG. 26.40.

metrically arranged at the corners and the centre of square of side a. Find in terms of W, the load transmitted by the most heavily loaded rivet. **Ans.** [1.24 W]

7. A riveted steel bracket connection has 22 mm diameter rivets 12 in number arranged as shown in Fig. 26.41. Determine the load P so that allowable stress in the extremely loaded rivet is just reached. Take safe permissible stress in bearing in rivet = 236 N/mm², and safe permissible stress in shearing in rivet = 102.5 N/mm². (J.U. 1965) **Ans.** [186 kN]

8. If the worst rivet in the system shown in Fig. 26.42 may be stressed to 100 N/mm², calculate the safe value for the eccentric load P. The rivets are 24 mm in diameter and are in single shear.

Ans. [140 kN]

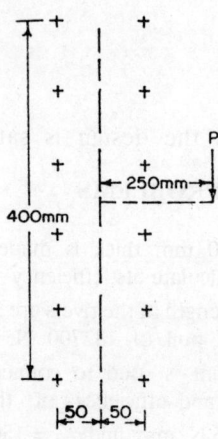

FIG. 26.41.

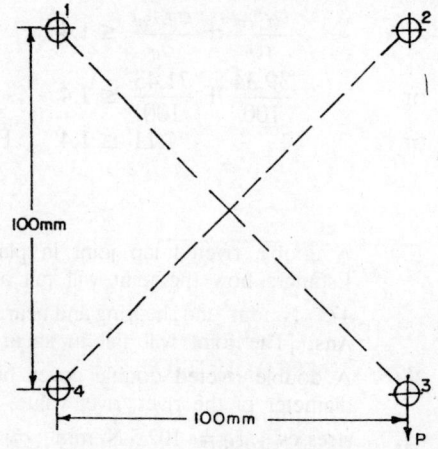

FIG. 26.42.

9. Calculate the maximum load carried by any rivet shown in Fig. 26.43. Rivets A and B are 200 mm² cross-sectional area and rivet C of 400 mm² area.

10. Design a bracket connection shown in Fig. 26.44, if it carries a load of 120 kN at an eccentricity of 350 mm from the centre line. Use power driven rivets. The thickness of bracket is 16 mm and the thickness of flange of the stanchion is 12 mm.

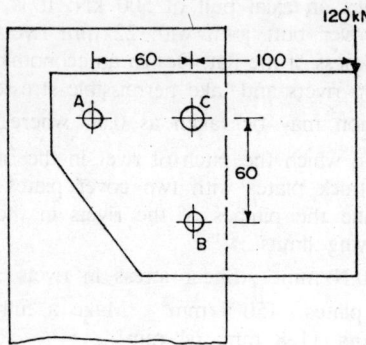

FIG. 26.43.

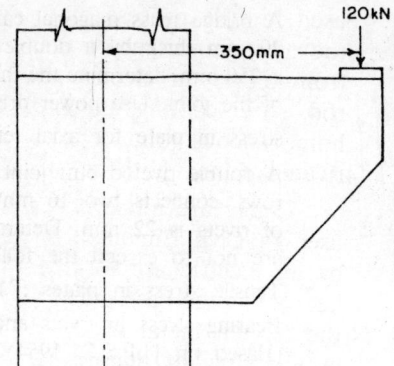

FIG. 26.44.

11. The flange of a tee section 200 mm × 200 mm is riveted to the flange of a rolled steel column of I-section to form a bracket which carries a vertical load of 250 kN at a distance of 200 mm from the face of the stanchion, as shown in Fig. 26.45. Design the riveted connection. Use shop driven rivets, each 20 mm dia.

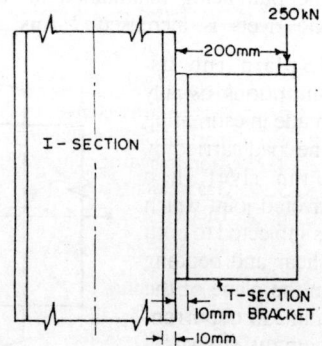

FIG. 26.45.

Welded Connections

27.1. INTRODUCTION

Welding is a process of connecting pieces of metal by application of heat (fusion) with or without pressure. A metallic bond is established between the two pieces. This bond has the same mechanical and physical properties as the parent metal. A number of methods are used for the process of fusion. The oxyacetylene or gas welding and electric arc welding are the most important of these methods. The metal at the joint is melted by the heat generated from either an electric arc or an oxyacetylene flame and fuses with metal from a welding rod. After cooling, the parent metal (base metal) and the weld metal form a continuous and homogeneous joint. The welded connections have become so reliable that they are replacing riveted joints, both in structural as well as machine design.

There are numerous welding processes, shown in Table 27.1, but the one most commonly used in Civil Engineering structures is *electric-arc-welding*. In this process, heat is generated by an electric arc formed between a steel electrode and steel parts to be welded. The arc heat melts the base metal and the electrode simultaneously, and the electromagnetic field carries the molten metal of the welding rod (electrode) towards the base metal. Fusion takes place by the flow of material from the welding rod across the arc. No pressure is applied.

Arc welding process may be of three types: (*i*) shielded (*ii*) unshielded and (*iii*) submerged.

TABLE 27.1 WELDING PROCESS.

(*a*)		*Fusion welding*
	1.	Metal-arc welding : shielded, unshielded, submerged.
	2.	Carbon-arc welding : shielded, unshielded.
	3.	Inert-gas arc welding
	4.	Atomic-hydrogen arc welding
	5.	Gas welding (air or oxyacetelene)
	6.	Thermit welding
(*b*)		*Pressure Welding*
	1.	Forge welding
	2.	Pressure Thermit welding
	3.	Resistance welding (A-C)
	4.	Resistance welding (D-C)—seam and spot welding.

In the *shielded-metal arc welding* or the SMAW process (Fig. 27.1), the electrode is coated with certain mineral compounds which produce a gaseous 'shield' that helps to exclude oxygen and stabilize the arc. A part of the coating melts to form a fluid slag layer which rises to the top, retards the rate of cooling of weld metal, and also protects it from undesirable exposure to atmospheric gases.

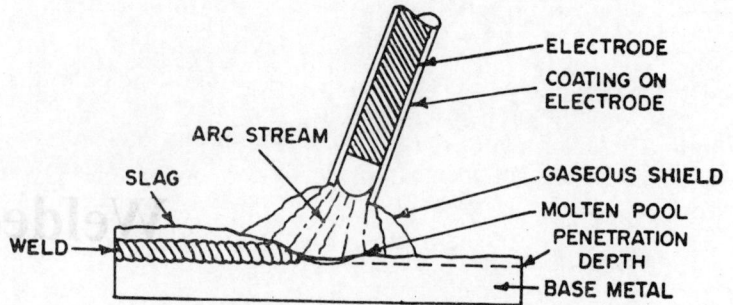

FIG. 27.1. SHIELDED-METAL ARC WELDING PROCESS

In the *non-shielded* metal arc welding, the electrode is uncoated, as shown in Fig. 27.2. Use of coated electrodes results in better quality welds than can be obtained with bare electrodes. Hence modern arc welding is done only with coated electrodes.

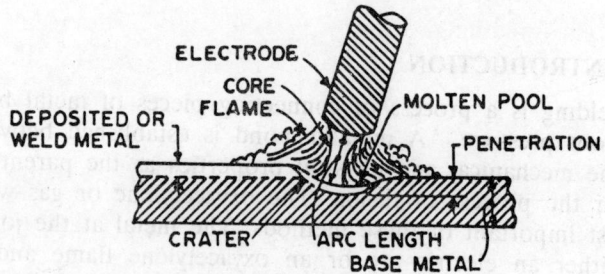

FIG. 27.2. UNSHIELDED METAL ARC WELDING PROCESS

In the *submerged-arc-welding process* or SAW process, the arc is 'submerged' or covered by a mound of fusible powdered flux, and the base electrode wire is fed mechanically from a reel. The arc, at all times, is covered by the flux, as shown in Fig. 27.3. The heat of the arc melts the parent metal, the electrode and part of the flux which forms a slag covering which can be removed later by brushing.

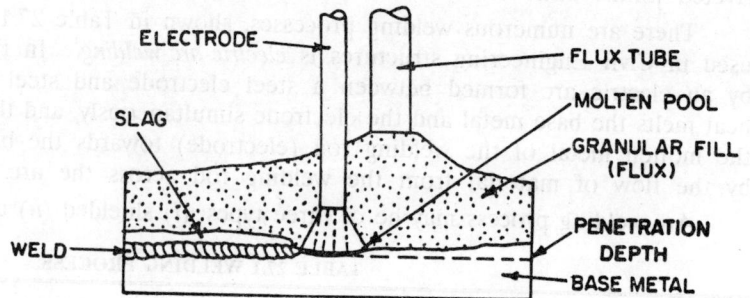

FIG. 27.3. SUBMERGED ARC WELDING PROCESS.

Gas welding is another popular welding process where heat is obtained from combustion of a gas fuel—commonly a mixture of oxygen and acetylene. The process is therefore also known as *oxy-acetelene welding*. The welding rod used for the process may be either shielded or unshielded.

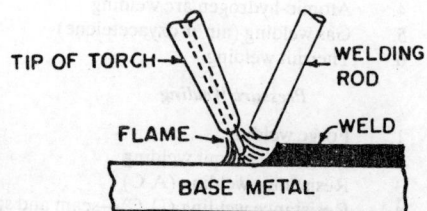

FIG. 27.4. GAS WELDING.

27.2. ADVANTAGES OF WELDING

Welded joints have the following advantages.

1. Welded joints are *economical* from the points of view of cost of labour and materials, both. The filler plates, gusset plates, connecting angles etc. are eliminated in welded joints. The smaller size of members, compared to those which may be used in riveted connections from the practical point of view, may be used here.

2. The *efficiency* of the welded joints is 100% as compared to an efficiency of 75% to 90% in case of riveted joints.

3. The *fabrication* of a complicated structure is *easier* by welded connection as in case of circular steel pipe. The alterations or additions in existing structures are facilitated by it.

4. The welding provides very *rigid joints*. This is in keeping with the modern trend of providing rigid frames.

5. The *noise* associated with the riveting work is a source of a great nuisance. There is *silence* in welding operation.

6. When riveting is done in populated localities, *safety* precautions to protect the public from flying rivets has to be taken. No such precautions are necessary in case of welding operation.

7. The welded structures look more *pleasing* in comparison to riveted one.

8. The welding work is done more *quicker* than the riveting work.

27.3. DISADVANTAGES OF WELDING

Notwithstanding the advantages narrated above, the welded connections have a number of disadvantages in comparison to the riveted connections. The same are narrated below :

1. No provision for expansion and contraction is kept in welded connection and therefore, there is possibility of *cracks* developing in such structures.

2. Due to uneven heating and cooling of the members during welding, the members may *distort* resulting in additional stress.

3. The *inspection* of welding work is more difficult and costlier than the riveting work.

4. The welding work requires a *skilled person* while semi- skilled person can do the riveting work.

5. On account of extreme heat, *fatigue* may take place.

6. There is a greater possibility of *brittle fracture* in welding than in riveting.

27.4. TYPES OF WELDS AND WELDED JOINTS

Welds are classified as follows.

(*a*) *According to their position*: as (*i*) flat, (*ii*) horizontal, (*iii*) vertical and (*iv*) overhead (Fig. 27.5)

(*b*) *According to type of weld* : as (*i*) Butt weld (or groove weld), (*ii*) fillet weld (*iii*) slot weld, and (*iv*) plug weld (Fig. 27.5 and 27.6) and (c) *According to type of joint* : as (i) butt joint (ii) lap joint, (iii) tee joint, (iv) edge joint and (v) corner joint (Fig. 27.7).

Welding is commonly done in four *positions* : flat, horizontal, vertical and overhead, as shown in Fig. 27.5. Vertical and over-head welds are possible be-cause molten metal is carried from the rod to the connected joint by the electromagnetic field of the arc and not by gravity. In the *flat* welding the direction of electromag-netic field is in the direc-tion of gravity.

Butt weld or *grooved weld* is used when the plates or members to be con-nected are in the same plane, or when a T-joint is required, as shown in Fig. 27.6 (a). *Fillet welds* are used for lap joint (Fig. 27.7 b), T-joint (Fig. 27.7 c) or corner joint (Fig. 27.7 e). *Plug weld* (Fig. 27.6 c) and *slot weld* (Fig. 27.6 d) are used wherever sufficient space is not available for providing required length of fillet weld. The slot welds and plug welds are also used for equalizing stress in plates and to prevent buckling in case of wide plates.

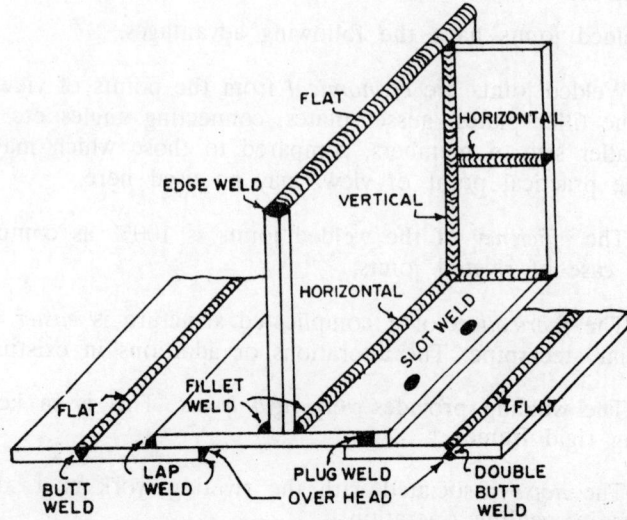

FIG. 27.5. PICTORIAL VIEW SHOWING VARIOUS TYPES OF WELDS.

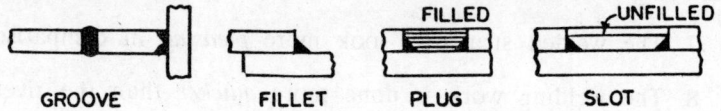

FIG. 27.6. TYPES OF WELDS

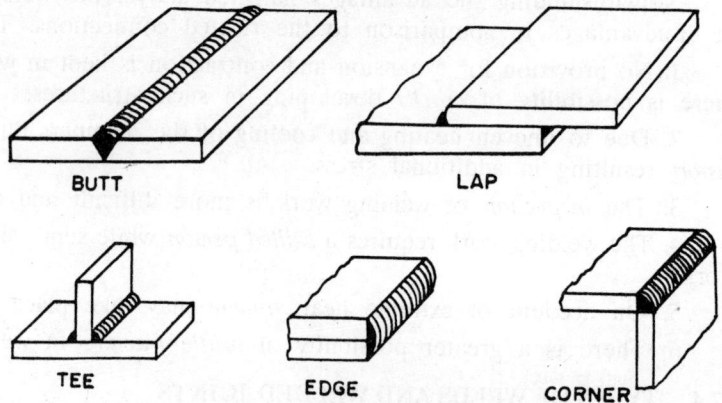

FIG. 27.7. TYPES OF WELDS

27.5. BUTT WELD OR GROOVE WELD

Butt weld or groove weld is used when the plates to be jointed are in the same plane, or when a T-joint is desired, as shown in Fig. 27.6 (a). A butt weld is designated according to the shape of groove made during the preparation of ends of the pieces to be jointed. The common types of butt welds are shown in Fig. 27.8.

A butt weld is specified by the size of the weld. The size of the butt weld is defined by the *effective throat thickness*. Reinforcement is the extra metal deposited proud of the surfaces of the pieces jointed, as shown in Fig. 27.9. The reinforcement may vary between 1 mm to 3 mm and is not included in the throat thickness.

The square butt joints shown in Fig. 27.8 (*a*) and (*b*) are used for thickness less than 8 mm. The *effective thickness* of the weld, called *throat thickness* (Fig. 27.9), is less than the thickness T of the plates jointed. It is taken as $\frac{3}{4}T$. In the single V-built joint (Fig. 27.8 *c*), the throat thickness is taken as $\frac{3}{4}T$. In double V-butt joint, the weld is fully effective and hence the throat thickness is taken equal to T. As a rule, in single U, single V and single J butt welds, where welding is done from one side, full penetration is not possible and hence effective throat thickness is taken equal to $\frac{3}{4}T$. In double-V, double U and double J butt welds, full penetration is possible and the effective thickness of throat is taken equal to the thickness of plates jointed. Whenever two plates of different thickness are jointed, the thickness of thinner plate must be taken into account.

Depending upon the *position*, butt welds may be (*i*) flat, (*ii*) vertical (*iii*) overhead and (*iv*) horizontal, as shown in Fig. 27.10.

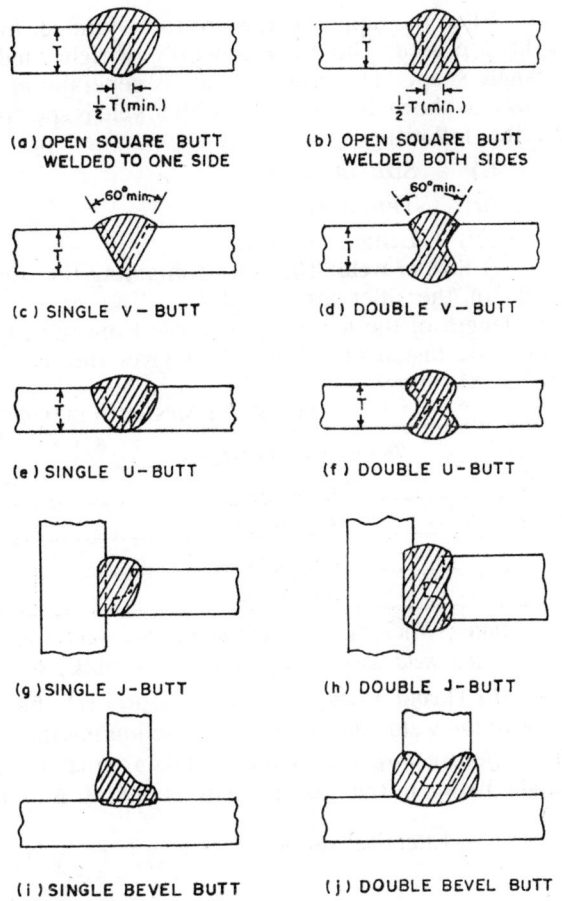

(a) OPEN SQUARE BUTT WELDED TO ONE SIDE

(b) OPEN SQUARE BUTT WELDED BOTH SIDES

(c) SINGLE V – BUTT

(d) DOUBLE V – BUTT

(e) SINGLE U – BUTT

(f) DOUBLE U – BUTT

(g) SINGLE J – BUTT

(h) DOUBLE J – BUTT

(i) SINGLE BEVEL BUTT

(j) DOUBLE BEVEL BUTT

FIG. 27.8. TYPES OF BUTT WELDS.

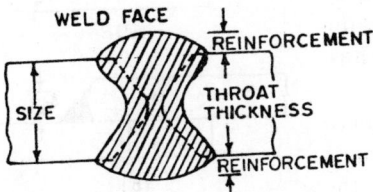

FIG. 27.9. BUTT WELD.

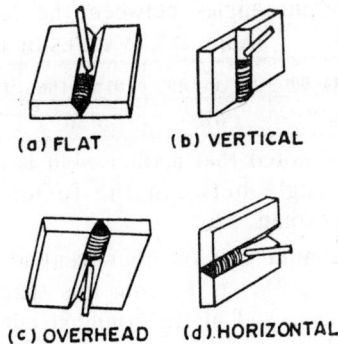

(a) FLAT (b) VERTICAL

(c) OVERHEAD (d) HORIZONTAL

FIG 27.10. POSITIONS FOR WELDING BUTT WELDS

27.6. FILLET WELDS

When the lapped plates are to be jointed, fillet welds are used. These are generally of right angled triangle shape. The outer surface is generally made *convex*, as shown in Fig. 27.11. A fillet weld is specified by the following:

    (*i*)   Size of wled

    (*ii*)   Throat thickness.

    (*iii*)   Length of weld.

    (*i*) **Size of weld**: The sides containing the right

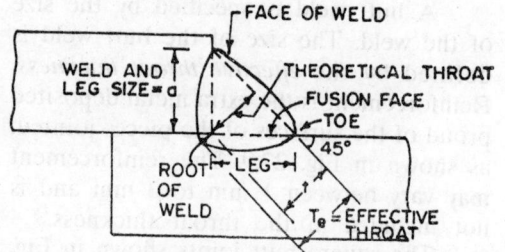

FIG. 27.11. FILLET WELD TERMINOLOGY

angle of the fillet are called *legs*. The *size* of the weld is specified by *minimum leg length*. The length of the leg is the distance from the root of the weld to the toe of the weld, measured along the fusion face. Table 27.1 gives the minimum size of single run fillet weld, as specified by IS : 816–1969.

TABLE 27.2. MINIMUM SIZE OF SINGLE RUN FILLET WELD.

Thickness of thicker part	Min. size
upto 10 mm	3 mm
10 to 20 mm	5 mm
20 to 32 mm	6 mm
32 to 50 mm	8 mm (first run) ; 10 mm (min.)

Note : When the minimum size of the weld is greater than the thickness of thinner part, the minimum size of the weld should be equal to the thickness of thinner part.

(*ii*) Throat thickness: The theoretical throat is the perpendicular distance between the root of the weld, and the hopotenuse joining the two ends of the legs. Reinforcement is neglected. The *effective throat thickness* is taken equal to the theoretical throat thickness, and when the angle between the fusion faces is 90°(as is generally the case), we have :

$$\text{Effective throat thickness } t = \frac{1}{\sqrt{2}} \times \text{ size of weld}$$

or

$$t \approx 0.7 \times \text{ size of weld.} \qquad \qquad ...(27.1)$$

where size of weld = minimum leg length

For angles other than 90° between the fusion faces,

Effective throat thickness = $k \times$ minimum leg length. Table 27.3 gives the values of k for different angles between the fusion faces, as per IS : 816-1969

TABLE 27.3.   VALUES OF k.

Angle	60° to 90°	91° to 100°	101° to 106°	107° to 113°	114° to 120°
k	0.7	0.65	0.60	0.55	0.50

It may be noted that a fillet weld is not used for jointing parts if the angle between the fusion faces is less than 60° or greater than 120°.

The maximum size of fillet weld at the square edge of a plate (Fig. 27.12 *a*) is 1.5 mm less than the plate thickness and in case of a weld at the rounded edges of flanges or the toe of an angle is kept three fourths the thickness of the edge (Fig. 27.12 *b*).

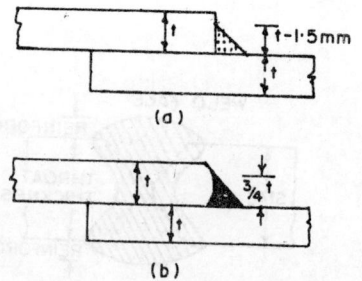

FIG. 27.12. MAXIMUM SIZE OF WELD.

When the fillet weld is placed parallel to the direction of the forces on both the sides of the member, it is called *side fillet weld*. When the weld is placed at the end of the member, such that it is perpendicular to the direction of the force, it is called *end fillet weld*. If the axis of the weld is inclined to the direction of force, it is known as *diagonal fillet weld*.

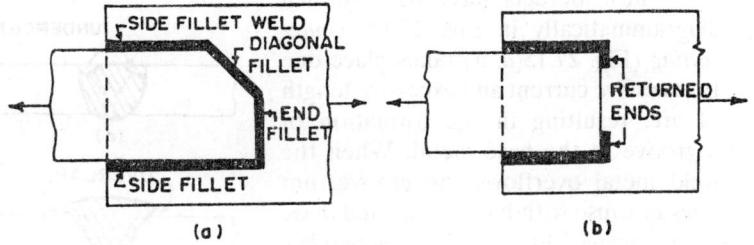

FIG. 27.13.

(*iii*) **Effective length of weld**: The effective length of the weld is taken as overall length minus twice the weld size. The effective length should not be less than four times the size of the weld, otherwise the weld size must be taken as one fourth of its effective length. If only the side welds are used, the length of each side fillet weld must not be less than the perpendicular distance between the two. When the ends are returned, as shown in Fig. 27.13 (*b*), the ends should be carried continuous for a distance not less than twice the size of the weld, specially when the joint is subjected to tensile force. *Only the effective length is shown on the drawing and the additional length (i.e. 2 × weld size) is provided by the welder.*

Special fillet welds may have *unequal* legs. In such a case the diagonal of the weld may make 30° and 60° with the two legs. Similarly, the face of fillet welds may be either *concave* or *mitre* (flat). Such welds are not very common.

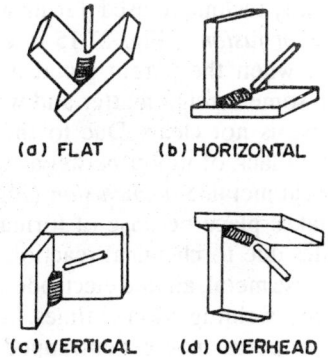

FIG. 27.14. POSITION FOR WELDING : FILLET WELDS.

Depending upon the *position*, fillet welds may be *flat, horizontal, vertical* or *over head*, as shown in Fig. 27.14.

27.7. DEFECTS IN WELDING

Welding is highly specialised technique of jointing, and it should be done carefully so that no *defects* or *imperfections* are left. The most important defects arising from the welding technique are as follows:

1. Undercutting

2. Overlap

3. Incomplete penetration

4. Lack of fusion

5. Slag inclusion

6. Porosity and gas inclusion

7. Edge melting

These defects have been shown diagrammatically in Fig. 27.15. *Under cutting* (Fig. 27.15 *a, b*) takes place due to excessive current and excessive length of arc, resulting in the formation of a groove in the base metal. When the weld metal overflows the groove, but does not fuse with base metal, and *overlap* is formed (Fig. 27.15 *c*). *Incomplete penetration* takes place when the weld metal does not penetrate up to the root of the joint because of faulty groove preparation (Fig. 27.15 *f, g*) or because of faulty technique used during welding. *Lack of fusion* (Fig. 27.15 *d, e*) takes place when the parent metal is coated with some foreign matter and when the groove is not clean. Due to this, there will be lack of union between two runs of weld metal. *Slag inclusion* (Fig. 27.15 *h*) takes place because of formation of oxides due to chemical reaction among the base metal, air and electrode coating, during welding. Some times, a group of *gas pores* may get entrapped in the weld, as shown in Fig. 27.15 (*i*). Such a defect of *gas inclusion* is also called *porosity*. *Edge melting off* occurs in fillet welds (Fig. 27.15 *j*) because of careless welding.

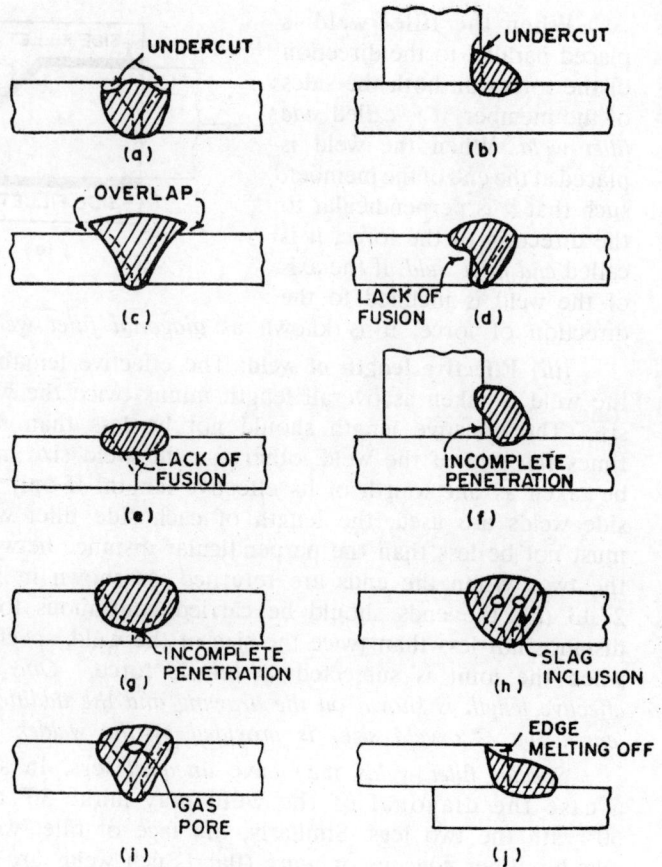

FIG. 27.15. IMPORTANT WELD DEFECTS.

27.8. WORKING STRESSES IN WELDS

Table 27.4 gives the permissible stresses in welds, as per IS : 816-1969, for mild steel conforming to IS : 226-1962 and electrodes conforming to IS : 814-1974.

TABLE 27.4 WORKING STRESSES IN WELDS (IS UNITS)

	Kind of Stress	Max. Permissible Values (Converted into SI units)	
1.	Tension or compression on section through throat of butt weld.	$0.6 f_y$	150 N/mm^2
2.	Bending stress in tension or compression	$0.66 f_y$	165 N/mm^2
3.	Shear on section through throat of butt or fillet weld	$0.44 f_y$	110 N/mm^2
4.	Plug wled.	$0.44 f_y$	110 N/mm^2

Note 1. For welding done at the site (field), the maximum values in shear and tension given above are reduced to 80%.

2. When the effects of wind or earthquake forces are taken in the design, the above values are increased by 25%.

27.9. DESIGN OF FILLET WELDS FOR AXIAL LOADS

Fillet welds are approximately triangular in section, and may be of two types (*i*) standard fillet weld (Fig. 27.16 *a*) and (*ii*) special fillet weld. (Fig. 27.16 *b*). Standard fillet weld consists of isosceles triangle with 45° angles, and has equal legs. Special fillet weld has the side angles 30° and 60°, with unequal leg lengths.

Normally, a fillet weld has convex face, but sometimes, it may have concave face also. In each case, the minimum leg length and throat thickness are shown in Fig. 27.16 (*c*) and 27.16 (*d*) respectively.

Fig. 27.17 shows fillet weld sub-jected to axial load *P*. The strength

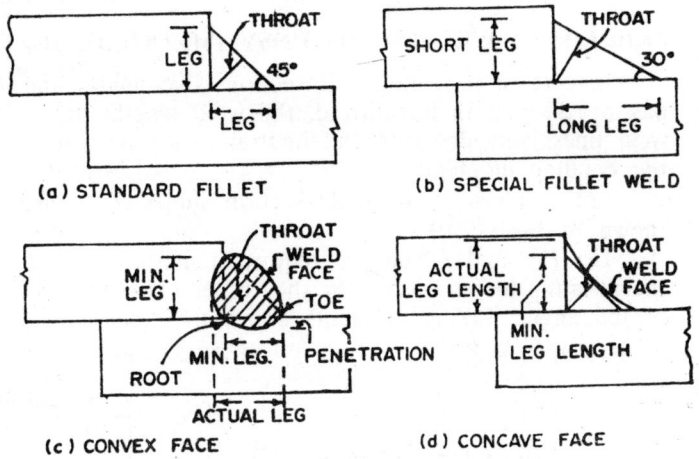

(a) STANDARD FILLET   (b) SPECIAL FILLET WELD

(c) CONVEX FACE   (d) CONCAVE FACE

FIG. 27.16. ELEMENTS OF FILLET WELD.

of fillet weld is determined by its resistance against shear. The maximum stress will develop at the throat and failure will occur by shear along the throat. If we assume a uniform distribution of shear stress, we have:

$$P = \text{stress} \times \text{area.}$$

where   Area = throat thickness × effective length

$$\therefore \qquad P = t \, . \, L \, \tau_{vp} \qquad \qquad ...(27.2)$$

or

$$P = 0.7 \, h \, . \, L \, \tau_{vp} \qquad ...(27.3)$$

where τ_{vp} = permissible maximum shear stress in weld.

   t = effective thickness = $0.7h$

   h = size of the weld.

   L = effective length of the weld.

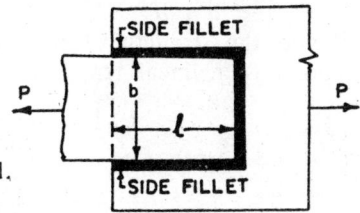

FIG. 27.17.

The specifications for fillet weld have already been given in § 27.6. When only side fillets are used, the effective length in each side is equal to the actual length minus twice the weld size. The effective length should not be less than four times the size of the weld. Also when only the side fillets are used, the length of each side fillet weld must not be less than the perpendicular distance between the two; thus in Fig. 27.17, *l* should not be less than *b*. Also, the perpendicular distance between the two side fillets should not exceed 16 times the thickness of thinner plate jointed. Thus, in Fig. 27.17, *b* should not be greater than 16 *t*. If this distance exceeds 16 *t*, intermediate plug or slot weld should be used so that buckling is prevented.

If *end fillet* is also used, the total length in Eq. 27.3 consists of lengths of side fillet plus the length of end fillet. In case when only end fillets are used, the overlap in a lap joint should not be less than five times the thickness of thinner plate jointed (Fig. 27.18).

Intermittent fillet wleds are used to transfer calculated stress across a joint when the strength required is less than that developed by a continuous weld of even the smallest allowable size for the thickness of parts joined. Any section (or length) of such intermittent fillet weld should not be less than *four times* the weld size, nor less than 40 mm. The clear spacing between the ends of con-secutive effective lengths of intermittent fillet welds carrying

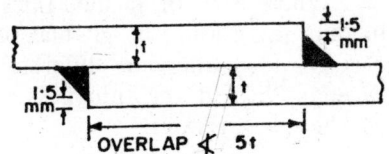

FIG. 27.18.

the calculated stress shall not exceed $12\,t$ for compression and $16\,t$ for tension and shall in no case be more than 200 mm, where t is the thickness of thinner part joined.

27.10. FILLET WELDING OF UNSYMMETRICAL SECTIONS : AXIAL LOAD

In case of unsymmetrical sections like angles and Tee, which are loaded along the axis passing through their centroid, the weld lengths are so arranged that the gravity axis of the weld lines coincides with the neutral axis. This will avoid eccentricity of loading and hence the bending moment.

Let us consider an angle section subjected to axial load P, welded to a gusset plate as shown in Fig. 27.19.

Let L_1 and L_2 be the required lengths of welds on the two faces, and P_1 and P_2 be the resisting forces exerted by the respective welds. These are assumed to act along the edges of the angle. Taking moments about the line of action of P_2, we obtain.

$$(a + b)\,P_1 = P\,a$$

$$\therefore \qquad P_1 = \frac{Pa}{a + b} \qquad \qquad ...(1)$$

Similarly, taking moments about the line of action of P_1

$$(a + b)\,P_2 = Pb$$

$$\text{or} \qquad P_2 = \frac{Pb}{a + b} \qquad \qquad ...(2)$$

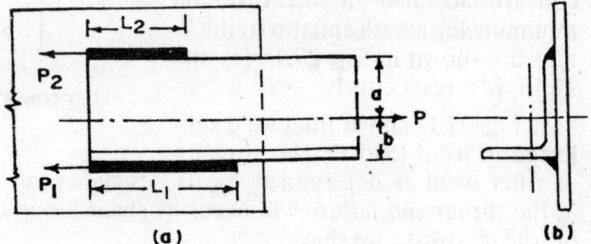

FIG. 27.19.

If s is the strength of the weld per unit length (per lineal length *i.e.* $s = \tau_{vp} \times 1 = \tau_{vp}$ N/mm) we have

$$L_1 = \frac{P_1}{s} = \frac{P \cdot a}{s\,(a + b)} \qquad \qquad ...27.4\ (a)$$

and $$L_2 = \frac{P_2}{s} = \frac{P \cdot b}{s\,(a + b)} \qquad \qquad ...27.4\ (b)$$

Sometimes, it is not possible to accommodate the required length of the weld on the sides of the section. In such cases, end fillets are also provided. The procedure of analysing such a case is similar to the one described above.

27.11. DESIGN OF BUTT WELDS

A butt weld is specified by the effective thickness of its throat, and its strength is taken equal to the strength of parts joined if full penetration of the weld metal is ensured. In the case of double-V, double-U, double-J and double bevel butt joints, full penetration is achieved and hence the *effective throat thickness* is taken equal to the thickness of the thinner parts joined. In the case of single V, U, J, and bevel joints, penetration is generally incomplete, and hence effective throat thickness is taken equal to $\frac{5}{8}$ times the thickness of thinner part connected, as per IS : 816-1969.

Where parts of unequal thickness are joined, the change in thickness should be gradual. A taper not exceeding 1 in 5 is provided when the difference in thickness of the parts exceeds 25% of the thickness of thinner part or 3 mm, whichever is greater.

As per IS : 816-1969, permissible stress in butt weld is taken same as that of parent metal.

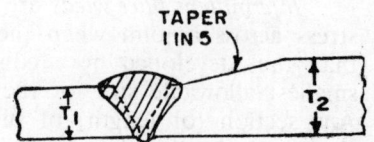

TAPER
1 IN 5

FIG. 27.20.

27.12. DESIGN OF PLUG AND SLOT WELDS

Plug weld (Fig. 27.6 c) and slot weld (Fig. 27.6 d) are used where ever sufficient space is not available for providing required length of the fillet. They are also used for equalising stress in plates and to prevent buckling in case of wide plates. For this purpose, a *slot* is cut in one of the over lapping plates, and the weld metal is filled in it. If the size of the slot is small, and is *filled completely* with weld metal, then it is known as a *plug weld*. However, if the slot is of big size and is fillet welded along its periphery, it is then known as *slot weld*. In either case, the slot may be either of circular or a rectangular shape.

IS : 816-1969 gives the following specifications for plug or slot weld :

1. The width or diameter should not be less than 3 times the thickness of the plate or 25 mm whichever is greater.

2. The corners at the enclosed ends of slots should be rounded with radius not less than $1\frac{1}{2}$ times the thickness or 12 mm whichever is greater.

3. The distance between the edge of the part and the edge of the slot or hole, or between the adjacent slots or holes shall not be less than twice the thickness and not less than 25 mm for holes.

4. The effective area of plug weld shall be considered as the nominal area of the hole in the plane of facing surface. The plug welds shall not be designed to carry stress.

Example 27.1. *Find the safe load that can be transmitted by the fillet welded joint shown in Fig. 27.21. The size of weld is 8 mm. Take the safe stress in the weld equal to 110 N/mm².*

Solution

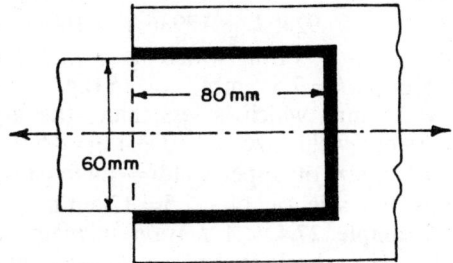

Effective length of weld, $L = 80 + 60 + 80$
$$= 220 \text{ mm}$$

Size of weld $= h = 8$ mm.

$\therefore$ Throat thickness $= t = 0.7h$
$$= 0.7 \times 8 = 5.6 \text{ mm.}$$

$\therefore$ Safe load $P = t . L . \tau_{vp}$
$$= 5.6 \times 220 \times 110$$
$$= 135520 \text{ N} = \textbf{135.52 kN}$$

FIG. 27.21.

Example 27.2. *A 100 mm × 10 mm plate is to be welded to another plate 150 mm × 10 mm by the fillet welding on three sides. The size of the weld is 6 mm. Find out the necessary over lap of the plate, for full strength of the joint. Take allowable tensile stress in plate equal to 150 N/mm² and allowable stress in weld as 110 N/mm².*

Solution

The joint will be designed on the basis of the strength of small plate.

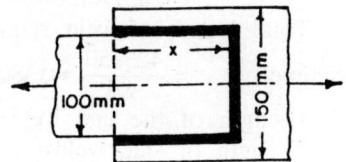

Total load taken by smaller plate $= 100 \times 10 \times 150 = 150000$ N

Throat thickness $= 0.7h = 0.7 \times 6 = 4.2$ mm.

$\therefore$ Allowable load per lineal mm $= 4.2 \times 110 = 462$ N

$\therefore$ Total length of weld required $= \dfrac{150000}{462} \approx 325$ mm.

Effective length of end fillet $= 100$ mm.

$\therefore$ Length to be provided in side fillets
$$= 325 - 100 = 225 \text{ mm}$$

$\therefore$ Overlap $x = \dfrac{225}{2} = 112.5$ mm.

Provide an overlap of 115 mm, as shown in Fig. 27.22. This distance is more than the distance of 100 mm between the two side fillets.

Hence the design is O.K.

Example 27.3. *A tie bar 120 mm × 10 mm is to be connected to other of size 120 mm × 14 mm. If the tie bars are to be loaded by a pull of 160 kN, find out the size of end fillets such that the stresses in both the end fillets are same. Take permissible stress in weld = 110 N/mm².*

Solution

The portion of plates between the welds stretch by the same amount. Therefore, the strain and hence the stress in both the plates are same. The force carried by each plate will be proportional to its thickness. Thus, if the 10 mm thick plate carries a force P_1, the 14 mm thick plate will carry a force $1.4 P_1$. Therefore, to keep the stresses same in both the end welds, we must keep the size of the welds in proportion to the thickness of respective plates.

Let the size of lower weld $A = h$

$\therefore$ Size of the upper weld $B = 1.4 h$

Length of weld in each case = 120 mm.

Strength of lower weld $= 0.7 h \times 120 \times 110$
$= 9240 \, h \, N$

Strength of upper weld $= 0.7 (1.4 h) 120 \times 110$
$= 12936 \, h \, N$

Total load carried by tie bar = 160 kN.

$\therefore \qquad 9240 \, h + 12936 \, h = 160 \times 1000$

From which $h = 7.22$ mm.

Keep $h = 7.5$ mm. $\therefore$ Size of lower weld $= 7.5$ mm, which is less than the maximum permissible weld size of $10 - 1.5 = 8.5$ mm.

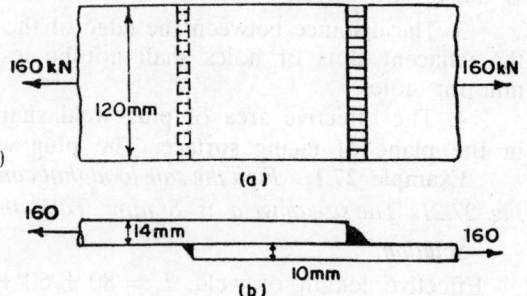
FIG. 27.23.

Also, size of upper weld $= 1.4 h = 1.4 \times 7.5 = \mathbf{10.5 \, mm}$. This is also less than the maximum permissible size of $14 - 1.5 = 12.5$ mm.

Example 27.4. *A tension member consisting of two channels sections 200 mm × 75 mm @ 22.1 kg/m back to back is to be connected to gusset plate. Design the welded joint for the condition that the section is loaded to its full strength. Take A = 2821 sq. mm, thickness of flange = 11.4 mm and the thickness of the web = 6.1 mm, permissible stress in weld equal to 110 N/mm² and permissible stress in the section in axial tension = 150 N/mm².*

Solution

In the case of rolled section, the size of weld is limited to three fourth of the thickness.

$\therefore$ Max. size of weld $= \frac{3}{4} \times 6.1 = 4.6$ mm. We shall provide 4 mm weld.

Strength of weld per linear mm
$= 0.7 \times 4 \times 110 = 308$ N

The load to be carried by each channel
$= 2821 \times 150 = 423150$ N

$\therefore$ Total length of weld required for one channel $= \dfrac{423150}{308} \approx 1380$ mm

Length of the end weld = 200 mm

$\therefore$ Length of side welds
$= 1380 - 200 = 1180$ mm

$\therefore$ Overlap $= \dfrac{1180}{2} = 590$ mm.

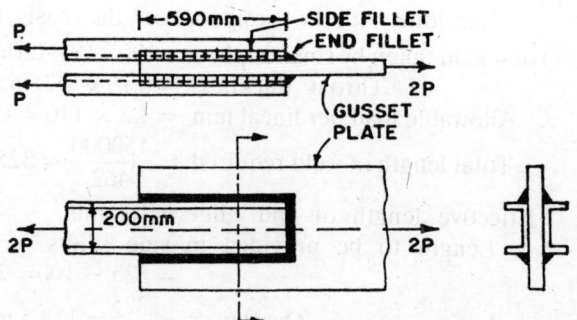
FIG. 27.24.

Example 27.5. *An I-section is built up by welding a 250 mm × 15 mm web plate to two 50 mm × 15 mm flange plates by 8 mm fillet welds. Find out maximum shearing force which may be permitted if the mean shearing stress in the web and the maximum shear stress in weld are not to exceed 100 N/mm².*

Solution

$$I_{xx} = \frac{1}{12}[\,150 \times 280^3 - 135 \times 250^3\,] = 98.62 \times 10^6 \text{ mm}^4$$

Shear stress q at the section passing through welds is given by :

$$q = \frac{F}{I_{xx} \cdot b}(A\bar{y}) \qquad \text{where,}$$

b = effective thickness = 2 × throat thickness = 2 × 8 × 0.7 = 11.2 mm

$A\bar{y}$ = moment of the area about *x-x*

= 150 × 15 (125 + 7.5) = 298125 mm³

q = allowable shear stress = 100 N/mm²

∴ $$100 = \frac{F}{98.62 \times 10^6 \times 11.2}[298125] \qquad\qquad ...(1)$$

From which $F = 370497$ N

Maximum shear force limited on the web = 250 × 15 × 100 = 375000 N   ...(2)

Hence maximum allowable shearing force = lesser of the above two values

= 370497 N ≈ **37.05 kN**

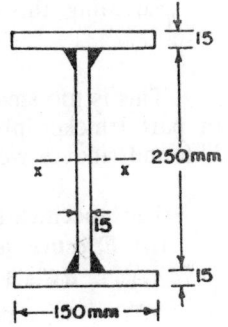

FIG. 27.25.

Example 27.6. *A welded plate girder is to be fabricated using web plates 1600 mm deep and 16 mm thick and flange plates 400 mm wide and 30 mm thick. The girder is to be used over a simply supported span of 20 m, carrying a load of 20 kN/m including its own weight. Design suitable welded connection between the web and the flange, taking permissible stress in weld as 110 N/mm².*

Solution :   S.F. $F = \dfrac{20 \times 10^3 \times 20}{2} = 2 \times 10^5$ N

$$I = \frac{1}{12} \times 16\,(1600)^3 + 2\left[\frac{1}{12} \times 400\,(30)^3 + 400 \times 30\,(815)^2\right] = 2.1405 \times 10^{10} \text{ mm}^4$$

Horizontal shear, per mm length of plate girder, is given by

$$q = \frac{F}{I}(A\bar{y})$$

At the junction of flange and web,

$A\bar{y}$ = (400 × 30) (815) = 9.78 × 10⁶ mm³

∴ $$q = \frac{2 \times 10^5}{2.1405 \times 10^{10}} \times 9.78 \times 10^6$$

$$\approx 91.4 \text{ N/mm}$$

Vertical shear on the compression flange (loaded flange):

w = 20 kN/m = 20 N/mm

∴ Resultant shear

$$q_r = \sqrt{q^2 + w^2} = \sqrt{(91.4)^2 + (20)^2}$$

$$= 93.56 \text{ N/mm}$$

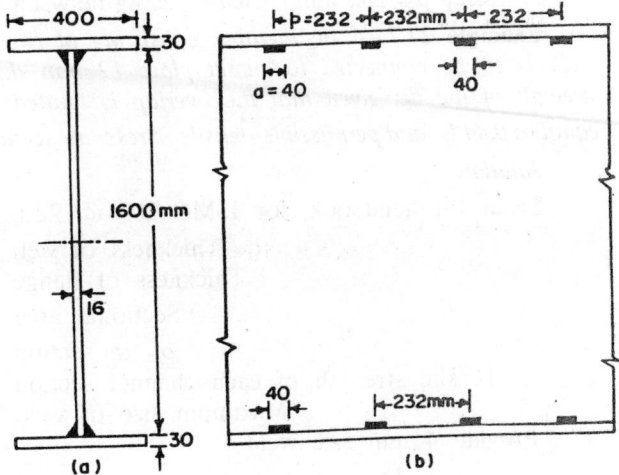

FIG. 27.26.

Let us first try *continuous weld* at each junction, on both sides.

Let h = size of weld.

∴ Strength of weld per lineal mm, $s = 2 \times 0.7h \times 110 = 154\,h$ N/mm.

Equating this to q_r, we get

$$h = \frac{93.56}{154} \approx 0.6 \text{ mm}$$

This is too small. Minimum weld size, as per IS : 816-1969 (Table 27.1), for 30 mm thickness of part (thicker plate) is 6 mm. Since the minimum thickness of weld is much more than h found above, we will use *intermittent weld.*

Let h = 6 mm.

The specifications for intermittent weld are as follows :

(*a*) *Effective length* of each intermittent weld should not be less than the following :

(*i*) $4h = 4 \times 6 = 24$

or   (*ii*)   40 mm.

Hence adopt effective length a = 40 mm.

(*b*) *Pitch* (*p*) *of the intermittent weld*: The clear spacing between intermittent weld should not exceed :

(*i*)   12 × thickness of thinner part = $12 \times 16 = 192$ mm

or   (*ii*)   200 cm

Hence for 192 mm clear spacing between the weld,

$$p = 192 + a = 192 + 40 = 232 \text{ mm} \qquad \qquad ...(i)$$

This is the *maximum spacing*. However, the spacing or pitch (*p*) should be such that the shear in the weld is not more than q_r.

Using 40 mm long intermittent welds on both sides of web plate, weld strength

$$= 2 \times 40 \times 0.7 \times 6 \times 110 = 36960$$

Thus, we have, $p \cdot q_r \leq 36960$

or

$$p \leq \frac{36960}{q_r} \leq \frac{36960}{93.56} \leq 395 \text{ mm.} \qquad \qquad ...(ii)$$

Hence maximum permissible p is lesser of the two given by (*i*) and (*ii*) values

∴ Keep p = 232 mm. Clear spacing between the intermittent welds = $232 - 40 = 192$ mm.

Example 27.7. *A tie member consisting of two channels ISMC 200 @ 22.1 kg/m back to back is to be connected to gusset plate 12 mm thick. Design the welded joint to develop full strength of the tie, given that the overlap is limited to 350 mm. Take permissible stress in weld equal to $0.44\,f_y$ and permissible tensile stress in section equal to $0.6\,f_y$, where $f_y = 250\,N/mm^2$.*

Solution

From ISI handbook, for ISMC 200 @ 22.1 kg/m, we have the following data :

Thickness of web = 6.1 mm

Thickness of flange = 11.4 mm

Sectional area = 28.21 cm^2 = 2821 mm^2

σ_{at} in section = $0.6 \times 250 = 150$ N/mm^2.

∴   Tensile strength of each channel section = $150 \times 2821 = 423150$ N.

Maximum size of weld = $6.1 - 1.5 = 4.6$ mm.

Provide 4 mm size weld.

∴

Permissible stress in weld = $0.44 \times 250 = 110$ N/mm^2

Strength of weld, per mm length = $0.7 \times 4 \times 110 = 308$ N/mm

∴ Length of weld necessary, to connect one channel section.

$$L = \frac{423150}{308} \approx 1374 \text{ mm.} \qquad ...(i)$$

The over lap is limited to 350 mm. Hence available length of weld, even providing end fillets, $= 350 + 350 + 200 = 900$ mm. This falls short of required total length. Hence let us provide additional fillets in two slots, each of length a.

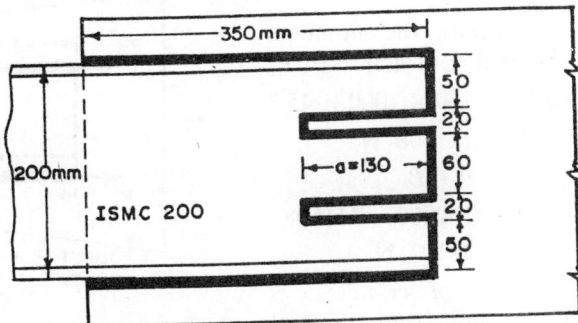

FIG. 27.27.

The width of such a slot should not be less than 3 times the thickness $= 3 \times 6.1 = 18.3$ mm. Hence provide two slots, each of 20 mm width. The edge distance of each slot should not be less than twice the thickness $= 2 \times 6.1 = 12.6$ mm. Hence arrange the slots as shown in Fig. 27.27.

Total length of weld $= (350 \times 2) + 200 + 4a - 2 \times 20 = 860 + 4a$ ...(ii)

Equating this to required value of L we get

$$860 + 4a = L = 1374$$
$$a = 128.5 \text{ mm.}$$

Hence provide 130 mm long slots for fillet welding, as shown in Fig. 27.27.

Example 27.8. *A circular penstock of mild steel, of 1.6 m diameter, is fabricated from 16 mm plate, lapping it and securing it by fillet welds of 12 mm size, provided on the inside and outside of the lapped ends, as shown in Fig. 27.28. Determine the safe internal pressure that can be allowed in the penstock. Take safe stress in weld equal to $110 \, N/mm^2$.*

Solution.

Throat thickness $t = 0.7h = 0.7 \times 12 = 8.4$ mm.

Let $p =$ safe internal pressure (N/mm^2)

$d =$ diameter of penstock (mm) $= 1600$ mm (given)

Internal force per unit length, causing bursting of pipe

$$= p\frac{d}{2} \qquad ...(1)$$

Resistance offered by the weld, per unit length

$$= 2t \cdot \tau_{vp} \qquad ...(2)$$

Equating the two, we get

$$p\frac{d}{2} = 2t \cdot \tau_{vp}.$$

∴
$$p = \frac{4t\,\tau_{vp}}{d} \qquad ...(27.5)$$

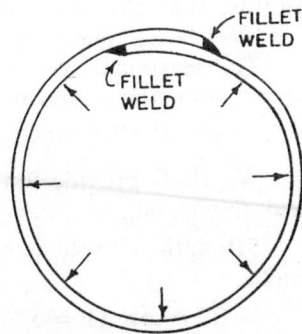

FIG. 27.28.

Substituting the given values, we get

$$p = \frac{4 \times 8.4 \times 110}{1600} = \mathbf{2.31 \, N/mm^2}$$

Example 27.9. *An equal angle 65 mm × 65 mm @ 9.4 kg/m of thickness 10 mm carries a tensile load of 160 kN, applied along its centroidal axis. The angle is to be welded to a gusset plate. Find out the lengths of side fillet welds required at the heel and toe of the angle. Its C.G. is at 19.7 mm from its heel. Take permissible stress in the weld equal to $110 \, N/mm^2$.*

Solution.

Taking the moments about line of action of P_2

$65\,P_1 = 160 \times 1000 \times 45.3$

$\therefore P_1 = 111508$ N

$\therefore P_2 = P - P_1$

$\qquad = 160000 - 111508$

$\qquad = 48492$ N

Size of weld

The maximum size of

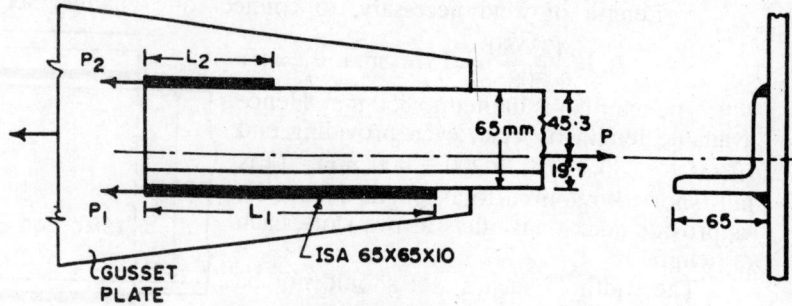

FIG. 27.29.

weld for a rounded edge at the toe of the angle $= \frac{3}{4} \times$ thickness $= \frac{3}{4} \times 10 = 7.5$ mm.

Strength of weld per lineal mm $= 0.7 \times 7.5 \times 110$ N/mm$^2 = 577.5$ N

$\therefore$
$$L_1 = \frac{P_1}{577.5} = \frac{111508}{577.5} = 193 \text{ mm}$$

and
$$L_2 = \frac{P_2}{577.5} = \frac{48492}{577.5} = 84 \text{ mm}$$

These values are *effective* and must be increased by twice the weld size, *i.e.* by $2 \times 7.5 = 15$ mm to get the actual length of the welds.

Example 27.10. *A tie bar consisting of a single angle 60 mm $\times$ 60 mm $\times$ 10 mm is to be welded to a gusset plate. The tie bar carries a load of 150 kN along its centroidal axis. Design the joint if both the side fillets and end fillets are to be provided. The centroidal axis of the angle lies at 18.5 mm from the heel of the angle.*

Solution

The maximum size of fillet weld at the end, along the square edge of the angle will be 1.5 mm less than the thickness of the angle. Therefore, the maximum size of the end fillet $= 10 - 1.5 = 8.5$ mm.

The maximum size of side fillets, along the rounded edge $= \frac{3}{4} \times 10 = 7.5$ mm

We shall provide 7.5 mm weld throughout.

Strength of weld per mm length

$\qquad = 0.7 \times 7.5 \times 110 = 577.5$ N

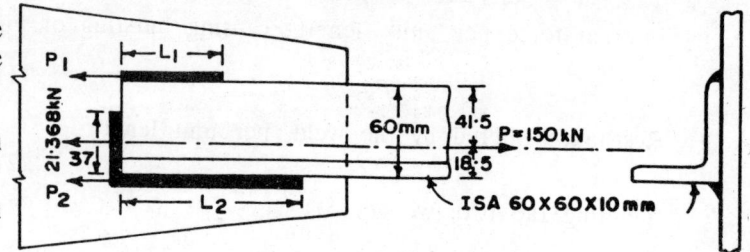

FIG. 27.30.

The end fillet weld will be placed symmetrical about the line of action of the load in order to avoid eccentricity. The maximum length of the end weld is, therefore equal to $2 \times 18.5 = 37$ mm.

$\qquad$ The strength of end weld $= 577.5 \times 37 = 21368$ N $= 21.368$ kN

Taking moments about the line of action of force P_1 we get

$$60\,P_2 = 150 \times 41.5 - 21.368 \times 41.5$$

From which $\qquad P_2 = 88.97$ kN

$\therefore \qquad P_1 = 150 - 88.97 - 21.368 = 39.662$ kN

$$\therefore \qquad \text{Length } L_1 = \frac{P_1}{577.5} = \frac{39.662 \times 1000}{577.5} \approx 69 \quad \text{mm}$$

and $\qquad$ Length $L_2 = \dfrac{P_2}{577.5} = \dfrac{88.97 \times 1000}{577.5} = 154$ mm.

The above values of L_1 and L_2 are *effective lengths*. Twice the size of the weld *i.e.* $2 \times 7.5 = 15$ mm must be added to above lengths to get the actual lengths of side fillets.

Thus, actual $L_1 = 69 + 15 = 84$ mm

and $\qquad$ actual $L_2 = 154 + 15 = 169$ mm

Example 27.11. *Design the welded joint of a truss shown in Fig. 27.31. Take permissible shear stress in weld equal to $110\,N/mm^2$.*

Solution

From ISI hand book, we get the following:

(*i*) For ISA 7550×8 mm, $b = 25.2$ mm; $a = 75 - 25.2 = 49.8$ mm ; $a + b = 75$ mm

(*ii*) For ISA 8050 × 8 mm, $b = 27.3$ mm; $a = 80 - 27.3 = 52.7$ mm ; $a + b = 80$ mm

(a) Member carrying 50 kN compressive load

Min. size of weld = 3 mm.

Max. size of weld $= \frac{3}{4} \times 8 = 6$ mm

Hence provide 6 mm weld.

Strength of weld per mm length,

$$s = 0.7 \times 6 \times 110 = 462 \text{ N}$$

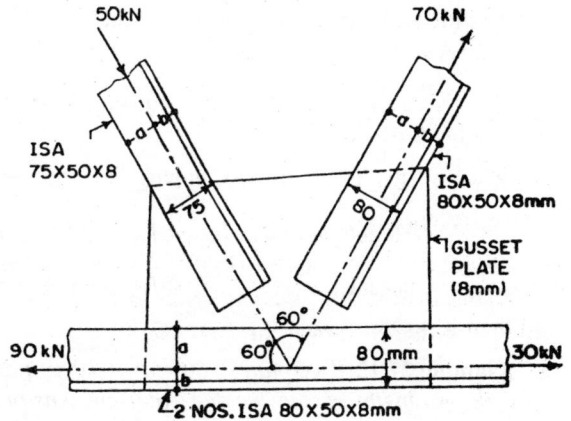

FIG. 27.31.

Provide only side welds of lengths L_1 and L_2. Referring to Fig. 27.19, we get

$$L_1 = \frac{Pa}{s(a+b)} = \frac{50 \times 1000 \times 49.8}{462 \times 75} \approx 72 \text{ mm}$$

and $\qquad L_2 = \dfrac{Pb}{s(a+b)} = \dfrac{50 \times 1000 \times 25.2}{462 \times 75} \approx 37 \text{ mm}$

The above values are effective lengths.

$\therefore \qquad$ Actual $L_1 = 72 + 2 \times 6 = 84$ mm

$\qquad$ Actual $L_2 = 37 + 2 \times 6 = 49$ mm

(b) Member carrying 70 kN tensile load

Keep 6 mm size weld, for which $s = 462$ N as before.

$$\therefore \qquad L_1 = \frac{Pa}{s(a+b)} = \frac{70000 \times 52.7}{462 \times 80} \approx 100 \text{ mm}$$

$$L_2 = \frac{Pb}{s(a+b)} = \frac{70000 \times 27.3}{462 \times 80} \approx 52 \text{ mm}$$

$\therefore \qquad$ Actual $L_1 = 100 + 2 \times 6 = 112$ mm

$\qquad$ Actual $L_2 = 52 + 2 \times 6 = 64$ mm.

(c) Horizontal tie

The horizontal tie is a continuous member carrying a load of 90 kN to one side and 30 kN to the other side. Hence the joint will be designed for a net force $= 90 - 30 = 60$ kN. Since the tie consists of two angles, net force in each angle $= \frac{1}{2} \times 60 = 30$ kN.

Keep 6 mm size weld, for which $s = 462$ N, as before.

$$L_1 = \frac{Pa}{s(a+b)} = \frac{30000 \times 52.7}{462 \times 80} \approx 43 \text{ mm.}$$

Provide this in two halves, so that $\frac{1}{2} L_1 = 21.5 \approx 22$ mm. Also,

$$L_2 = \frac{Pb}{s(a+b)} = \frac{30000 \times 27.3}{462 \times 80} \approx 22 \text{ mm}$$

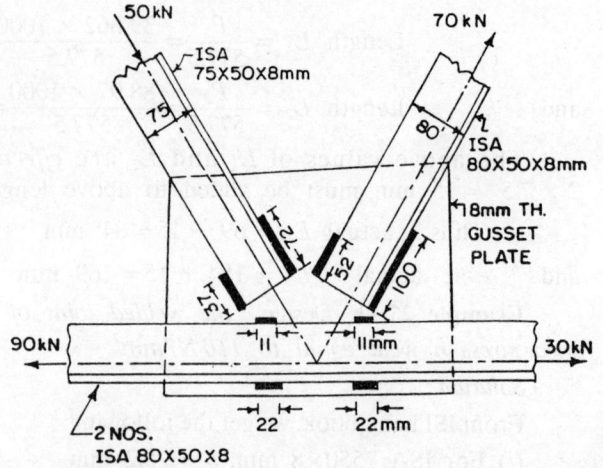

FIG. 27.32.

Provide this also in two halves, so that $\frac{1}{2} L_2 = 11$ mm. These are effective lengths.

Hence actual $\qquad \frac{1}{2} L_1 = 22 + 2 \times 6 = 34$ mm.

and actual $\qquad \frac{1}{2} L_2 = 11 + 2 \times 6 = 23$ mm.

The joint is shown in Fig. 27.32.

Example 27.12. *Two plates 160 mm × 10 mm and 160 mm × 12 mm are to be butt welded. Calculate the strength of the welded joint in tension, if (a) a single-V butt weld, (b) a double-V butt welded is used to connect them. Take permissible stress in weld as 150 N/mm².*

(a) Single-V butt joint

Effective throat thickness $= \frac{5}{8} \times 10 = 6.25$ mm. Hence,

$$P = l \cdot t \cdot \tau_{vp} = 160 \times 6.25 \times 150$$
$$= 150000 \text{ N} = \textbf{150 kN.}$$

(b) Double-V butt joint

In the case of double-V butt joint, complete penetration of weld takes place. Hence effectiven throat thickness = thickness of thinner plate joined = 10 mm.

$\therefore \qquad P = l\,t\,\tau_{vp} = 160 \times 10 \times 150 = 240000$ N = **240 kN.**

The joints are shown in Fig. 27.33.

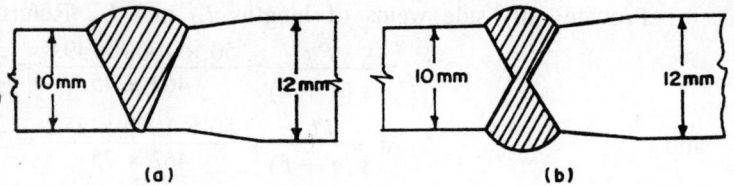

FIG. 27.33.

27.13. ECCENTRICALLY LOADED FILLET WELDED JOINTS

When the line of action of external force does not pass through the centroid of welded joint, the welds are subjected to both the axial load as well as the moment. We shall consider here two cases of fillet welded joints :

1. When the load does not lie in the plane of the welds.

and 2. When the load lies in the plane of the welds.

Case 1 : When the load does not lie in in the plane of welds

This is the usual case when a plate bracket abuts against the flange of a stanchion, and is connected to it by fillet welding applied on both the sides of the plate bracket, as shown in Fig. 27.34.

The fillet weld is subjected to (*i*) vertical shear stress f_a due to axial load P, and (*ii*) horizontal shear stress f_b due to bending moment $M = P \cdot e$.

Let the depth of the bracket be equal to d and fillet welds are applied to both the sides of the plate, for a complete length equal to the depth of plate.
Hence length of weld $L = 2d$.

Vertical shear stress in weld $= f_a = \dfrac{P}{L \cdot t}$

or $\qquad f_a = \dfrac{P}{2 d t} \qquad$ ...(27.6)

where $\qquad t =$ throat thickness of the weld.

Horizontal shear stress due to bending is

$$f_b = \frac{M}{I} \cdot y$$

where $\qquad I = 2 \left(\dfrac{1}{12} t \, d^3 \right) = \dfrac{t d^3}{6} \ $ and $\ y = \dfrac{d}{2}$

$\therefore \qquad f_b = \dfrac{P \cdot e}{t \, d^3/6} \times \dfrac{d}{2}$

or $\qquad f_b = \dfrac{3 \, P \cdot e}{t \, d^2} \qquad$ ...(27.7)

Resultant shear stress f_r is

$\qquad f_r = \sqrt{f_a^2 + f_b^2} \qquad$ ...(27.8)

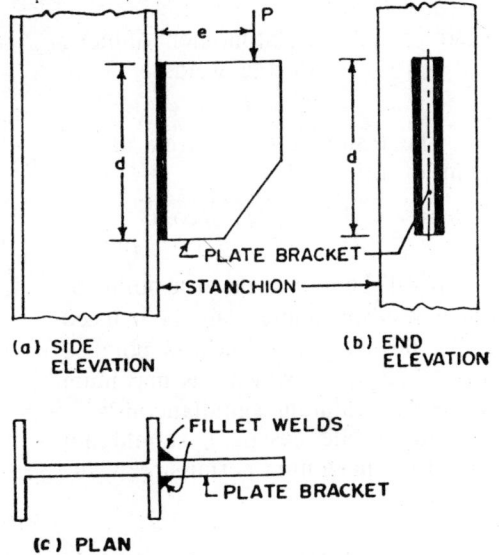

(a) SIDE ELEVATION

(b) END ELEVATION

(c) PLAN

FIG. 27.34.

The resultant shear stress f_r should not exceed the permissible shear stress τ_{vp} in the weld.

For preliminary design, f_b can be assumed to be equal to f_r or τ_{vp}. In that case,

$$f_b = \tau_{vp} = \frac{3Pe}{td^2} \qquad \text{(from Eq. 27.7.)}$$

$\therefore \qquad d = \sqrt{\dfrac{3 P \cdot e}{t \cdot \tau_{vp}}} \qquad$ ...(27.9)

From this, the depth of the bracket can be found.

Case 2. When the load lies in the plane of weld : Torsional stresses

Consider a bracket connection shown in Fig. 27.35 in which a plate bracket is connected to the flange of a stanchion by way of fillet welds applied along the perimeter of the plate. In many cases, two plates are used, one attached to each face. Let P be the load acting on each plate, at an eccentricity e with respect to the centroid of the welds.

The weld element, at any point, will be subjected to two types of stresses : (*i*) vertical shearing stresses f_a due to axial load P and (*ii*) torsional shearing stress f_t due to a torsional moment $T = P \cdot e$. The direction of vertical shear will be *vertical* while the direction of torsional shearing stress will be at right angles to the radius vector joining that point to the centroid of the weld.

Vertical shear stress,

$$f_a = \frac{P}{L\,t} \qquad \qquad ...(27.10)$$

where L = total effective length
of the weld = $(2a + d)$

Torsional shear stress,

$$f_t = \frac{T \cdot r}{J} \qquad \qquad ...(27.11)$$

where J = Polar moment of inertia
of the weld.

$$= I_{xx} + I_{yy}$$

The resultant shear stress at any
point of the weld is

$$f_r = \sqrt{f_a^2 + f_t^2 + 2f_a \cdot f_t \cos\theta}$$

$$...(27.12)$$

f_r will be maximum at a point for
which f_t is maximum. This is induced
at the farthest point such as point A
(Fig. 27.35 c) for which r is maximum
and θ is minimum simultaneously.

For a safe design, f_r should not
exceed the maximum permissible value
τ_{vp}.

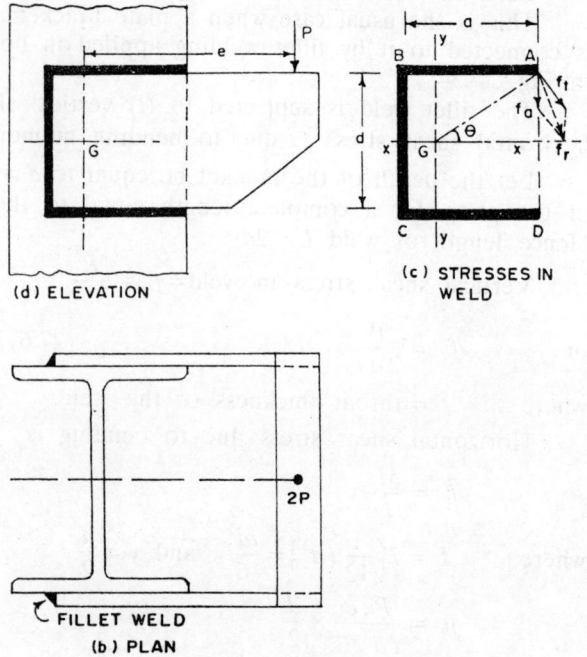

(d) ELEVATION

(c) STRESSES IN WELD

(b) PLAN

FIG. 27.35.

27.14. ECCENTRICALLY LOADED BUTT WELDED JOINTS

In the case of a butt welded joint subjected to eccentric loading, the load will never
lie in the plane of welds. Fig. 27.36 shows a bracket connection in which the plate bracket
has been welded to the flange of steel stanchion by way of a full penetration butt weld. The
length (L) of the butt weld is equal to the height d of the plate bracket.

Let t = thickness of weld throat

Bending moment $M = P \cdot e$.

The weld line will be subjected to two types of stresses : (i) Vertical shear stress f_a due
to load P and (ii) Tensile or compressive stress f_b due to
moment M.

$$f_a = \frac{P}{d \cdot t} \qquad \qquad ...(27.13)$$

and

$$f_b = \frac{M \cdot y}{I_{xx}} = \frac{P \cdot e \cdot d/2}{\dfrac{1}{12} t d^3}$$

or

$$f_b = \frac{6 \cdot P \cdot e}{t d^2} \qquad \qquad ...(27.14)$$

As per IS : 816-1969, for a weld subjected to combined
shear and bending stresses, the *equivalent stress* f_e is given
by

$$f_e = \sqrt{f_b^2 + 3f_a^2} \qquad \qquad ...(27.15)$$

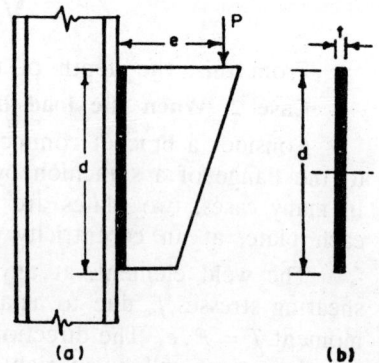

(a)

(b)

FIG. 27.36

As per IS : 800-1984, the equivalent stress f_e should not exceed the max. permissible equivalent stress σ_e.

where $\quad \sigma_e$ = maximum permissible equivalent stress= $0.9 f_y$

$\quad\quad f_y$ = yield stress in parent metal.

For design purposes, the depth of bracket is given by

$$d = \sqrt{\frac{6 . P . e}{t \, \sigma_b}} \qquad\qquad\qquad ...(27.16)$$

where σ_b= permissible bending stress in the butt weld = $0.66 f_y$ = 0.66×250= 165 N/mm^2 for mild steel.

Example 27.13. *A plate bracket, carrying a load of 100 kN at an eccentricity of 120 mm, is connected to the face of a steel stanchion by fillet welds on both the sides of the plate, as shown in Fig. 27.37. Determine the size of the fillet weld.*

(b) If 8 mm fillet weld is used, determine the depth of the bracket.

(c) If 8 mm fillet weld is used with a bracket of 250 mm depth, calculate the resulting stress in the weld.

Solution

(a) Here, d= 300 mm. Let t be the throat thickness.

Vertical shear stress :

$$f_a = \frac{P}{2dt} = \frac{100 \times 1000}{2 \times 300 \, t} = \frac{166.67}{t} \, \text{N/mm}^2 \qquad ...(1)$$

Horizontal shear stress :

$$f_b = \frac{3 \, P . e}{td^2} = \frac{3 \times 100 \times 1000 \times 120}{t \, (300)^2} = \frac{400}{t} \, \text{N/mm}^2 \qquad ...(2)$$

$$\therefore \quad f_r = \sqrt{f_a^2 + f_b^2} = \sqrt{\left(\frac{166.67}{t}\right)^2 + \left(\frac{400}{t}\right)^2} = \frac{433.3}{t} \, \text{N/mm}^2.$$

Equating this to permissible shear stress τ_{vp}= 110 N/mm^2,

we get $\quad\quad\quad t = \dfrac{433.3}{110} = 3.94$ mm

$\therefore \quad\quad$ Size of weld = $\dfrac{t}{0.7} = \dfrac{3.97}{0.7} = 5.6$ mm. Hence provide 6 mm size weld.

(b) If size of weld is 8 mm, we have t= 0.7 × 8= 5.6 mm

Hence from Eq. 27.9,

$$d = \sqrt{\frac{3 \, P . e}{t \, \tau_{vp}}} = \sqrt{\frac{3 \times 100 \times 1000 \times 120}{5.6 \times 110}} \approx \textbf{242 mm}$$

(c) Given: size of weld = 8 mm and d= 250 mm.

$\therefore \quad\quad\quad t = 0.7 \times 8$= 5.6 mm

$$f_a = \frac{P}{2dt} = \frac{100 \times 1000}{2 \times 250 \times 5.6} = 35.71 \, \text{N/mm}^2$$

$$f_b = \frac{3 \, Pe}{td^2} = \frac{3 \times 100 \times 1000 \times 120}{5.6 \, (250)^2} = 102.85 \, \text{N/mm}^2$$

$$\therefore \quad f_r = \sqrt{f_a^2 + f_b^2} = \sqrt{(35.71)^2 + (102.85)^2} = \textbf{108.9 N/mm}^2 < 110 \, \text{N/mm}^2.$$

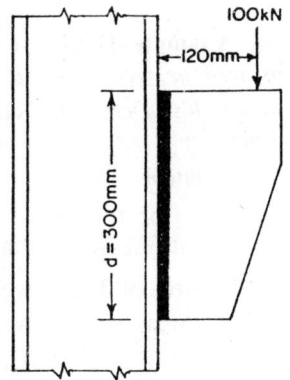

FIG. 27.37.

Example 27.14. *A bracket carrying a load of 120 kN is connected to column by means of two horizontal fillet welds, each of 150 mm effective length and 10 mm thick. The load acts at 80 mm from the face of the column as shown in Fig. 27.38. Find the throat stress.*

Solution

Fig. 27.38 shows the arrangement of the bracket.

$$t = 0.7 \times 10 = 7 \text{ mm}$$

$$f_a = \frac{P}{2Lt} = \frac{120 \times 1000}{2 \times 150 \times 7} = 57.14 \text{ N/mm}^2$$

Moment $= 120000 \times 80 = 96 \times 10^5$ N-mm.

The forces due to bending in the two welds will form a resisting couple $= (150 \times 7 \times f_b) \times 120$.

$$\therefore \qquad 150 \times 7 \times f_b \times 120 = 96 \times 10^5$$

From which $\qquad\qquad f_b = 76.19 \text{ N/mm}^2$

$$\therefore \qquad f_r = \sqrt{(57.14)^2 + (76.19)^2} = \mathbf{95.2 \ N/mm^2}$$

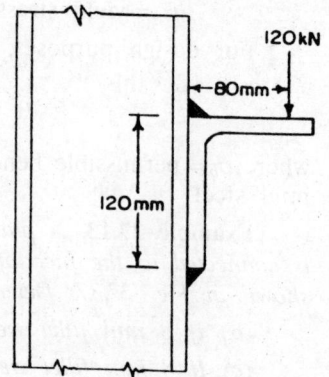

FIG. 27.38.

Example 27.15. *A bracket of I-section is welded to a steel stanchion, by using flange welds as well as web welds as shown in Fig. 27.39. The size of flange welds are double the size of web welds. Determine suitable weld size, taking a permissible shear stress of 110 N/mm² in the welds.*

Solution

Let t be the throat thickness of web welds and $2t$ be the throat thickness of flange welds. Let us also assume that the dimensions marked are *effective lengths* of the welds.

Area of flange welds, at throat $= 2 \times 200 \ (2t) = 800 \ t \text{ mm}^2$

Area of web welds, at throat $= 2 \times 300 \ (t) = 600 \ t \text{ mm}^2$

Total weld area $= 800 \ t + 600 \ t = 1400 \ t$

$$\therefore \text{ Vertical shear stress in the welds } f_a = \frac{300 \times 1000}{1400 \ t} = \frac{214.29}{t} \text{ N/mm}^2 \qquad \qquad ...(i)$$

The bending stress at any point in the weld is given by $f_b = \dfrac{M}{I_{xx}} \cdot y$. Here,

$$I_{xx} = 2 \left[200 \times 2 \ t \times 200^2 + \frac{1}{12} t \ (300)^3 \right]$$

$$= 365 \times 10^5 \ t \text{ mm}^4$$

Hence in the flange weld,

$$f_{bf} = \frac{300 \times 10^3 \times 180}{365 \times 10^5 \ t} \times 200 = \frac{295.89}{t} \text{ N/mm}^2$$

$$...(ii)$$

and in the extreme fibre in web weld,

$$f_{bw} = \frac{300 \times 10^3 \times 180}{365 \times 10^5 \ t} \times 150 = \frac{221.92}{t} \text{ N/mm}^2$$

$$...(iii)$$

Evidently, the horizontal shear stress due to bending, in the flange weld is more than

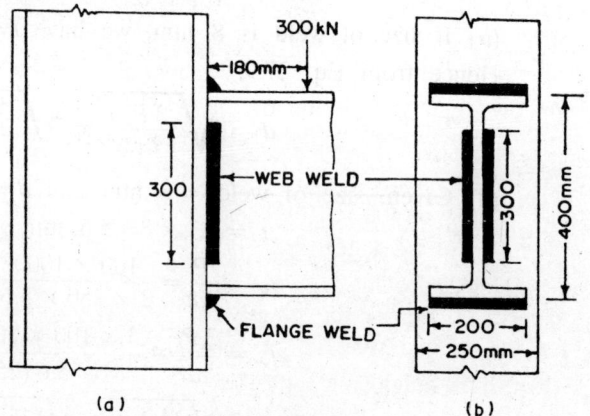

FIG. 27.39.

that in the web weld. Hence the flange weld becomes the governing criterion.

The resultant shear stress in flange weld is

$$f_{rf} = \sqrt{f_a^2 + f_{bf}^2} = \sqrt{\left(\frac{214.29}{t}\right)^2 + \left(\frac{295.89}{t}\right)^2} = \frac{365.34}{t}\,\text{N/mm}^2.$$

Equating this to permissible value $\tau_{vp} = 110\,\text{N/mm}^2$, we get

$$t = \frac{365.34}{110} = 3.32 \text{ mm}$$

$\therefore$ Size of web weld $= \dfrac{3.32}{0.7} = 4.74$ mm

$\therefore$ Provide 5 mm size weld in the webs and 10 mm size weld in the flanges.

Example 27.16. *A 12 mm thick plate bracket, carrying a load of 400 kN at a distance of 500 mm is to be welded to the face of steel stanchion, using intermittent fillet welds applied on both sides of the plate bracket. Design the joint.*

Solution

Let us use 10 mm size weld. The intermittent weld, shown in Fig. 27.40 is analogous to riveted joint subjected to moment when the load is not in the plane of the rivets.

The number of weld lengths, in each line, can be estimated by use of Eq. 26.22 :

$$n = \sqrt{\frac{6M}{lpR}}$$

where l = no. of weld lines = 2 in the present case

   p = pitch of intermittent welds

   R = strength of each portion of intermittent weld.

(*i*) Min. effective length of intermittent weld = 4 × size of weld or 40 mm which ever is greater.

Hence using 10 mm size weld, keep *effective length* = 40 mm and *actual length* = 40 + 2 × 10 = 60 mm.

(*ii*) Clear spacing of the intermittent welds should not be greater than 16 times thickness of plate or 200 mm. Let us use pitch of 150 mm. Hence clear spacing between effective lengths = 150 − 40 = 110 mm, while the actual clear spacing will be = 150 − 60 = 90 mm only.

In the above equation, using $l = 2$, $p = 150$ mm

and R = strength of each weld

   $= 0.7 \times 10 \times 40 \times 110 = 30800$ N,

we get

$$n = \sqrt{\frac{6\,(400 \times 1000 \times 500)}{2 \times 150 \times 30800}} = 11.4, \text{ say } 12$$

Hence provide 12 weld lengths on both sides, each of 60 mm actual length (or 40 mm effective length), at c/c spacing of 150 mm.

Total height of bracket

   $= (11 \times 90) + (12 \times 60) = 1710$ mm.

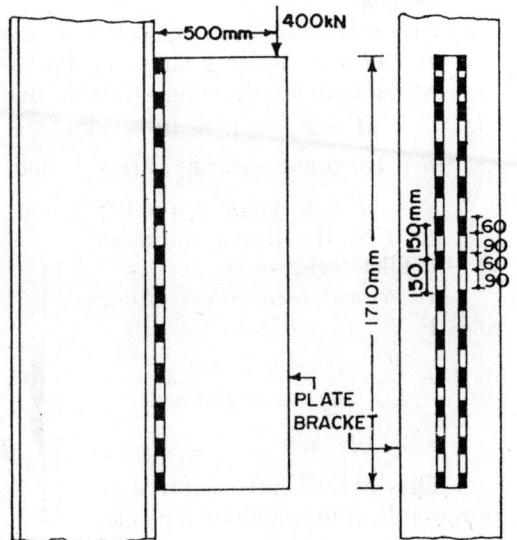

FIG. 27.40.

Example 27.17. *A circular shaft of diameter 120 mm is welded to a rigid plate by a fillet weld of size 6 mm. If a torque of 8 kN-m is applied to the shaft, find the maximum stress in the weld.*

Solution

We shall first derive the relation between the stress developed and the torque applied for such a shaft. Let d be its diameter and h be the size of the weld. Let t be the throat thickness $= 0.7h$. Here $t = 0.7 \times 6 = 4.2$ mm.

Considering a small area δa of the weld as shown in Fig. 27.41,

$$J \approx \Sigma \delta a \times \left(\frac{d}{2}\right)^2$$

$$\therefore \qquad J = \frac{d^2}{4} \Sigma \delta a$$

where $\Sigma \delta a = \pi d . t$

$$\therefore \qquad J = \frac{d^2}{4} . \pi d . t = \frac{\pi d^3}{4} t.$$

Torsional shear stress $f_t = \dfrac{T . r}{J} = T . \dfrac{d}{2} \times \dfrac{4}{\pi d^3 t}$

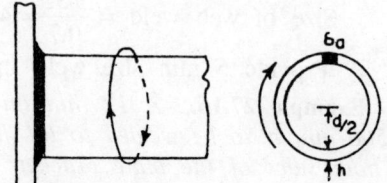

FIG. 27.41.

or $\qquad f_t = \dfrac{2T}{\pi d^2 t}$ ...(27.17)

where $\qquad T = 8$ kN-m $= 8 \times 10^6$ N-mm. Substituting the values, we get

$$f_t = \frac{2 \times 8 \times 10^6}{\pi (120)^2 \times 4.2} = \textbf{84.2 N/mm}^2$$

Example 27.18. *A circular steel pipe 120 mm external diameter and 100 mm internal diameter is welded to a rectangular plate 12 mm thick by fillet weld around the perimeter. The pipe is subjected to a vertical point load of 12 kN acting at 500 mm from the welded end. It is also subjected to a twisting moment of 4 kN-m. Determine the size of the weld, taking permissible shear stress equal to 110 N/mm².*

Solution.

The weld section is subjected to *three* stresses.

(*i*) Vertical shearing stress f_a due to vertical force $P = 12$ kN

(*ii*) Horizontal shearing stress f_b due to moment

$\qquad M = P . e = 12 \times 10^3 \times 500 = 6 \times 10^6$ N-mm.

(*iii*) Torsional shearing stress f_t due to torsional moment

$\qquad T = 4$ kN-m $= 4 \times 10^6$ N-mm.

Let t be the throat thickness of the fillet weld.

(*i*) *Vertical shear stress f_a due to S.F. P*

$$f_a = \frac{P}{Lt} = \frac{P}{\pi d t} = \frac{12000}{\pi \times 120 \times t}$$

$$= \frac{31.8}{t} \text{ N/mm}^2$$

This stress acts vertically downwards, at all sections of the weld.

(*ii*) *Horizontal shear stress f_b due to $M = P . e = 6 \times 10^6$ N-mm*

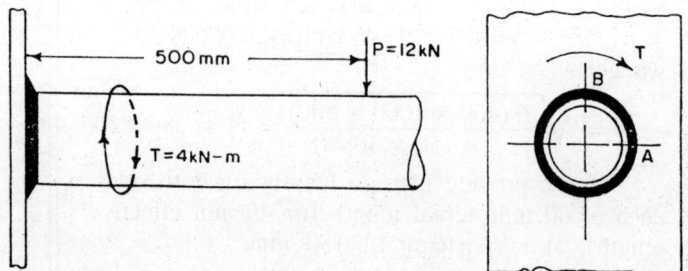

FIG. 27.42.

$$f_b = \frac{M}{I} \cdot y$$

where $\quad I \approx \dfrac{\pi d^3}{8} t = \dfrac{\pi (120)^3}{8} t = 678584\, t$

and $\quad y = \dfrac{d}{2} = 60$ mm

$\therefore \qquad f_b = \dfrac{6 \times 10^6}{678584\, t} \times 60 = \dfrac{530.5}{t}$ N/mm^2

This stress acts perpendicular to the plane of the weld.

(iii) Torsional shear stress f_t due to $T = 4$ kN-m.

$$f_t = \frac{T}{J} \cdot r$$

where $\quad J \approx \dfrac{\pi d^3}{4} t = \dfrac{\pi (120)^3}{4} t = 1357168\, t$

$$r = \frac{d}{2} = 60 \text{ mm}$$

$\therefore \qquad f_t = \dfrac{4 \times 10^6}{1357168\, t} \times 60 = \dfrac{176.8}{t}$ N/mm^2

This stress acts in the plane of weld, along tangent (*i.e.* perpendicular to the radius vector). Let us now consider the combined effect of the three.

At point A: f_b is zero while f_a and f_t are additive since both act vertically downwards. Hence the resultant stress is

$$f_{rA} = f_a + f_t = \frac{31.8}{t} + \frac{176.8}{t} = \frac{208.6}{t} \text{ N/mm}^2 \qquad \qquad ...(i)$$

At point B : f_a and f_t act at right angles to each other, in the same plane (*i.e.* the plane of the weld) while f_b attains its maximum value and acts perpendicular to the plane of the weld. Hence the resultant stress is

$$f_{rB} = \sqrt{f_a^2 + f_t^2 + f_b^2} = \sqrt{\left(\frac{31.8}{t}\right)^2 + \left(\frac{176.8}{t}\right)^2 + \left(\frac{530.5}{t}\right)^2}$$

$$= \frac{560.1}{t} \text{ N/mm}^2 \qquad \qquad ...(ii)$$

Thus maximum stress is induced at point B, which is the critical point. The stress at this point should not exceed permissible stress $\tau_{vp} = 110$ N/mm^2.

$\therefore \qquad \dfrac{560.1}{t} \le 110$

From which $\qquad t \ge \dfrac{560.1}{110} = 5.09$

Hence size of weld $= \dfrac{t}{0.7} = \dfrac{5.09}{0.7} = 7.27$ mm

As per IS 816-1969, for the thickness $= 12$ mm of the thicker part, minimum size of weld is 5 mm. Hence provide **7.5 mm** size fillet weld.

Example 27.19. *A bracket is subjected to a load of 100 kN as shown in Fig. 27.43. The bracket is welded to a stanchion by means of three weld lines as indicated in Fig. 27.43. Find out the size of the welds so that the load is carried safely.*

Solution

Let t be the throat thickness of the weld. If $\bar{x}$ is the distance of centroid of weld area from AB , we have

$$\bar{x} = \frac{2 \times 120\,t \times 60}{2 \times 120\,t + 240\,t} = 30 \text{ mm}$$

∴ Eccentricity of the load $= 100 + 120 - 30 = 190$ mm

$$I_{xx} = \frac{1}{12}\,t\,(240)^3 + 2 \times 120\,t\,(120)^2 = 460.8 \times 10^4\,t\text{ mm}^4$$

$$I_{yy} = 240\,t\,(30)^2 + 2 \times \frac{1}{12}\,t\,(120)^3 + 2 \times 120\,t\,(60 - 30)^2$$

$$= 72 \times 10^4\,t\text{ mm}^4$$

$$J = I_{zz} = I_{xx} + I_{yy}$$

$$= 460.8 \times 10^4\,t + 72 \times 10^4\,t = 532.8 \times 10^4\,t\text{ mm}^4$$

Area $= 2 \times 120\,t + 240\,t = 480\,t\text{ mm}^2$

Vertical shear $f_a = \dfrac{P}{A} = \dfrac{100 \times 1000}{480\,t} = \dfrac{208.3}{t}\,\text{N/mm}^2$ ...(1)

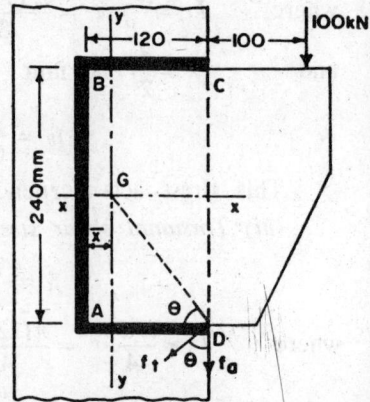

FIG. 27.43.

The maximum stress due to torsion will occur either at C or D.

Length of radius vector for C or $D = \sqrt{(120)^2 + (90)^2} = 150$ mm

Maximum shear stress due to torsion,

$$f_t = \frac{T}{J}\,.\,r = \frac{100000 \times 190}{532.8 \times 10^4\,t} \times 150 = \frac{534.9}{t}\,\text{N/mm}^2$$

Now $\cos \theta = \dfrac{90}{150} = 0.6$

Resultant stress is given by

$$f_r = \sqrt{f_a^2 + f_t^2 + 2 f_a f_t \cos \overline{\theta}}$$

$$= \sqrt{\left(\frac{208.3}{t}\right)^2 + \left(\frac{534.9}{t}\right)^2 + 2\left(\frac{208.3}{t}\right)\left(\frac{534.9}{t}\right) \times 0.6} = \frac{680.6}{t}\,\text{N/mm}^2$$

Equating this to the allowable shear stress of $110\,\text{N/mm}^2$, we get

$$t = \frac{680.6}{110} = 6.19 \text{ mm}$$

∴   Size of weld $= \dfrac{6.19}{0.7} = 8.84$ mm. Hence provide **9 mm** size weld.

Example 27.20. *A plate bracket, made of 10 mm thick plate is butt welded to the flange of a steel stanchion shown in Fig. 27.44. The bracket carries a load of 100 kN at an eccentricity of 110 mm from the face of the stanchion. Design the joint.*

Solution

Let is assume that the butt weld will have complete penetration. In that case the throat thickness will be equal to the thickness of plate of the bracket. Hence $t = 10$ mm

The depth of the bracket can be determined by the approximate expression:

$$d = \sqrt{\frac{6\,.\,P\,.\,e}{t\,\sigma_b}} \qquad\qquad ...(27.16)$$

Here $P = 100$ kN
$e = 110$ mm
$\sigma_b = 165$ N/mm^2.

∴ $d = \sqrt{\dfrac{6 \times 100 \times 10^3 \times 110}{10 \times 165}} = 200$ mm

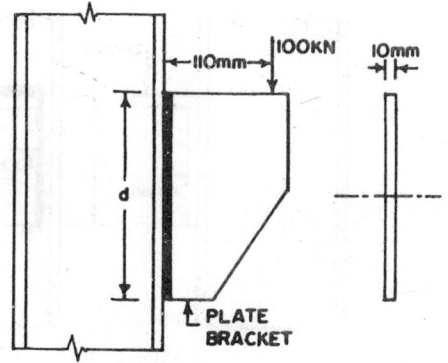

FIG. 27.44.

Let us provide a depth = 200 mm

Check for stresses :

Actual direct shear stress,

$f_a = \dfrac{P}{dt} = \dfrac{100 \times 1000}{200 \times 10} = 50$ N/mm^2

Actual bending stress

$f_b = \dfrac{6\,Pe}{td^2} = \dfrac{6 \times 100 \times 1000 \times 110}{10\,(200)^2} = 165$ N/mm^2

As per IS : 816-1969, the equivalent shear stress is given by

$$f_e = \sqrt{f_b^2 + 3f_a^2} = \sqrt{(165)^2 + 3\,(50)^2} = 186.35 \text{ N/mm}^2$$

As per IS : 800-1984, the equivalent stress f_e should be less than maximum permissible equivalent stress $\sigma_e = 0.9\,f_y$

Taking $f_y = 250$ N/mm^2,

$\sigma_e = 0.9 \times 250 = 225$ N/mm^2.

Since $f_e < \sigma_e$, the design is safe.

PROBLEMS

1. A 150 mm × 16 mm plate is welded to other plate by two side welds 120 mm each and end fillet of 100 mm length. Find the safe axial load to which this joint may be subjected if the size of the weld is 7 mm.

2. A 100 mm × 10 mm plate is welded to other by means of two end fillets and two side fillets of 8 mm as shown in Fig. 27.45. If the plate is loaded to its full strength, find out the required overlap length.

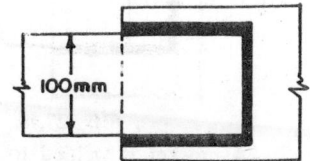

FIG. 27.45.

3. An equal angle 75 mm × 75 mm @ 11.0 kg/m is subjected to a load of 180 kN, whose line of action passes through the centroid of the section, which is at 22.2 mm from the heel. This angle is to be welded to a gusset plate. If the size of the weld is o be 8 mm, find the length of the side fillet welds.

4. An I-section is made up of a 200 mm × 10 mm thick web plate welded to two flange plates 120 mm × 10 mm thick by means of fillet welds to size 6 mm. Calculate the maximum shear force which this section can resist.

5. Fig. 27.46 shows a 10 mm angle bracket 100 mm wide welded to the flange of steel stanchion. It carries a vertical load of 240 kN. The connection consists of continuous 10 mm weld extending along the top and both sides and returned at the bottom of the bracket. Treating the 240 kN load as a vertical shear load (i.e. neglecting bending moment), calculate the depth of bracket making 110 N/mm^2 as the working stress in transverse weld and 79 N/mm^2 in the longitudinal weld

(Based on U.L.)

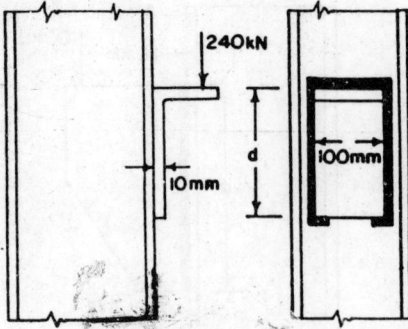

FIG. 27.46.

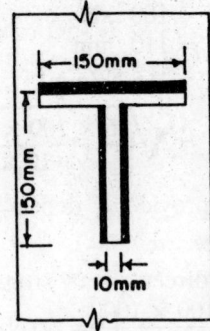

FIG. 27.47.

6. An I-section bracket carrying 120 kN load is connected by a column as shown in Fig. 27.47 by means of two side fillet welds 200 mm deep. The load is eccentric by 70 mm. Calculate the size of the fillet weld.

7. A bracket consisting of T-section 150 mm × 150 mm and 10 mm is connected to a column as shown in Fig. 27.47. The bracket carries 150 kN load at 80 mm eccentricity. If the size of the weld is 6 mm, find out the maximum throat thickness.

8. A bracket shown in Fig. 27.48 is welded to a stanchion by side fillet welds on three sides as indicated by heavy lines. Calculate the maximum force per mm of weld when the bracket carries a load of 200 kN acting as shown.

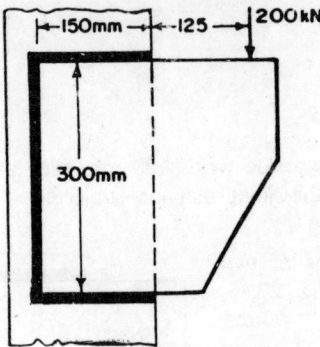

FIG. 27.48.

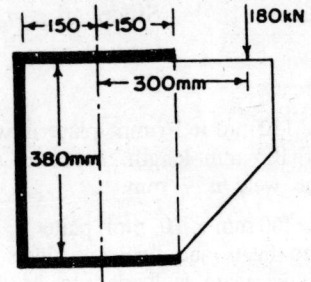

FIG. 27.49.

9. A bracket is welded to a stanchion by fillet welds having a throat thickness of 9 mm and a load of 180 kN is applied in the plane of the bracket, as shown in Fig. 27.49. The weld extends round three sides and has the given dimensions. Determine the maximum stress on the throat of the weld.

10. Determine the size of fillet weld required to join a plate bracket with flange of a stanchion, as shown in Fig. 27.50.

11. Determine the depth of the bracket of Fig. 27.50, if the plate is butt welded, using full penetration butt weld. The thickness of plate is 10 mm.

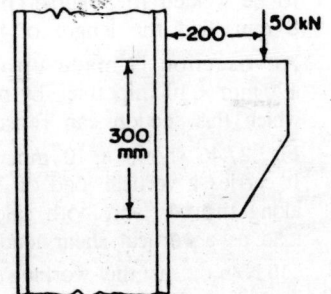

FIG. 27.50.

Subject Index